CHRISTIE JOHN GEANKOPLIS

University of Minnesota

Transport Processes and Separation Process Principles
(Includes Unit Operations)

FOURTH EDITION

PHI Learning Private Limited

New Delhi-110001

2012

This Indian Reprint—₹ 475.00
(Original U.S. Edition—₹ 5290.00)

TRANSPORT PROCESSES AND SEPARATION PROCESS PRINCIPLES
(Includes Unit Operations), 4th ed.
by Christie John Geankoplis

Original edition, entitled *Transport Processes and Separation Process Principles (Includes Unit Operations), 4th ed.* by Christie John Geankoplis, published by Pearson Education, Inc., publishing as Pearson Prentice Hall.

Copyright © 2003 Pearson Education Inc., Upper Saddle River, New Jersey 07458, U.S.A.

ISBN-978-81-203-2614-9

Indian edition published by PHI Learning Private Limited.

This edition is manufactured in India, and is authorized for sale in India, Pakistan, Sri Lanka, Bhutan, Bangladesh, Nepal and the Maldives only.

Published by Asoke K. Ghosh, PHI Learning Private Limited, M-97, Connaught Circus, New Delhi-110001 and Printed by V.K. Batra at Pearl Offset Press Private Limited, New Delhi-110015.

Dedicated to the memory of my beloved mother, Helen,
for her love and encouragement

Contents

Preface

The title of this text has been changed from *Transport Processes and Unit Operations* to *Transport Processes and Separation Process Principles (Includes Unit Operations)*. This was done because the term "unit operations" has been largely superseded by the term "separation processes," which better reflects the modern nomenclature being used.

In this fourth edition, the main objectives and the format of the third edition remain the same. The sections on momentum transfer have been greatly expanded, especially the sections on fluidized beds, flow meters, mixing, and non-Newtonian fluids. Material has been added to the chapters on mass transfer. The chapters on absorption, distillation, and liquid–liquid extraction have also been enlarged. More new material has been added to the sections on ion exchange and crystallization. The chapter on membrane separation processes has been greatly expanded, especially for gas-membrane theory.

The field of chemical engineering involved with physical and physical–chemical changes of inorganic and organic materials and, to some extent, biological materials is overlapping more and more with the other process-engineering fields of ceramic engineering, process metallurgy, agricultural food engineering, wastewater-treatment (civil) engineering, and bioengineering. The principles of momentum, heat, and mass transport and the separation processes are widely used in these processing fields.

The principles of momentum transfer and heat transfer have been taught to all engineers. The study of mass transfer has been limited primarily to chemical engineers. However, engineers in other fields have become more interested in mass transfer in gases, liquids, and solids.

Since chemical and other engineering students must study so many topics today, a more unified introduction to the transport processes of momentum, heat, and mass transfer and to the applications of separation processes is provided. In this text the principles of the transport processes are covered first, and then the separation processes (unit operations). To accomplish this, the text is divided into two main parts.

PART 1: Transport Processes: Momentum, Heat, and Mass

This part, dealing with fundamental principles, includes the following chapters: 1. Introduction to Engineering Principles and Units; 2. Principles of Momentum Transfer and Overall Balances; 3. Principles of Momentum Transfer and Applications; 4. Principles of Steady-State

Heat Transfer; 5. Principles of Unsteady-State Heat Transfer; 6. Principles of Mass Transfer; and 7. Principles of Unsteady-State and Convective Mass Transfer.

PART 2: Separation Process Principles (Includes Unit Operations)

This part, dealing with applications, covers the following separation processes: 8. Evaporation; 9. Drying of Process Materials; 10. Stage and Continuous Gas–Liquid Separation Processes (humidification, absorption); 11. Vapor–Liquid Separation Processes (distillation); 12. Liquid–Liquid and Fluid–Solid Separation Processes (adsorption, ion exchange, extraction, leaching, crystallization); 13. Membrane Separation Processes (dialysis, gas separation, reverse osmosis, ultrafiltration, microfiltration); 14. Mechanical–Physical Separation Processes (filtration, settling, centrifugal separation, mechanical size reduction).

In Chapter 1 elementary principles of mathematical and graphical methods, laws of chemistry and physics, material balances, and heat balances are reviewed. Many readers, especially chemical engineers, may be familiar with most of these principles and may omit all or parts of this chapter.

A few topics, primarily those concerned with the processing of biological materials, may be omitted at the discretion of the reader or instructor; these include Sections 5.5, 6.4, 8.7, 9.11, and 9.12. Over 240 example or sample problems and over 550 homework problems on all topics are included in the text. Some of the homework problems involve biological systems, for those readers who are especially interested in that area.

This text may be used for a course of study following any of the following five suggested plans. In all plans, Chapter 1 may or may not be included.

1. *Study of transport processes of momentum, heat, and mass and separation processes.* In this plan, most of the entire text, covering the principles of the transport processes in Part 1 and the separation processes in Part 2, is covered. This plan would be applicable primarily to chemical engineering as well as to other process-engineering fields in a one-and-one-half-year course of study at the junior and/or senior level.

2. *Study of transport processes of momentum, heat, and mass and selected separation processes.* Only the elementary sections of Part 1 (the principles chapters—2, 3, 4, 5, 6, and 7) are covered, plus selected separation-processes topics in Part 2 applicable to a particular field, in a two-semester or three-quarter course. Students in environmental engineering, food process engineering, and process metallurgy could follow this plan.

3. *Study of transport processes of momentum, heat, and mass.* The purpose of this plan in a two-quarter or two-semester course is to obtain a basic understanding of the transport processes of momentum, heat, and mass transfer. This involves studying sections of the principles chapters—2, 3, 4, 5, 6, and 7 in Part 1—and omitting Part 2, the applied chapters on separation processes.

4. *Study of separations processes.* If the reader has had courses in the transport processes of momentum, heat, and mass, Chapters 2–7 can be omitted and only the separation processes chapters in Part 2 studied in a one-semester or two-quarter course. This plan could be used by chemical and certain other engineers.

5. *Study of mass transfer.* For those such as chemical or mechanical engineers who have had momentum and heat transfer, or those who desire only a background in mass transfer in a one-quarter or one-semester course, Chapters 6, 7, and 10 would be covered. Chapters 9, 11, 12, and 13 might be covered optionally, depending on the needs of the reader.

Different schools and instructors differ on the use of computers in engineering courses. All of the equations and homework problems in this text can be solved by using ordinary hand-held computers. However, more complicated problems involving numerical integration, finite-difference calculations, steady- and unsteady-state two-dimensional diffusion and conduction, and so on, can easily be solved with a computer using spreadsheets. Almost all undergraduate students are proficient in their use.

The SI (Système International d'Unités) system of units has been adopted by the scientific community. Because of this, the SI system of units has been adopted in this text for use in the equations, example problems, and homework problems. However, the most important equations derived in the text are also given in a dual set of units, SI and English, when different. Many example and homework problems are also given using English units.

Christie John Geankoplis

PART 1

Transport Processes: Momentum, Heat, and Mass

CHAPTER 1

Introduction to Engineering Principles and Units

1.1 CLASSIFICATION OF TRANSPORT PROCESSES AND SEPARATION PROCESSES (UNIT OPERATIONS)

1.1A Introduction

In the chemical and other physical processing industries and the food and biological processing industries, many similarities exist in the manner in which the entering feed materials are modified or processed into final materials of chemical and biological products. We can take these seemingly different chemical, physical, or biological processes and break them down into a series of separate and distinct steps that were originally called *unit operations*. However, the term "unit operations" has largely been superseded by the more modern and descriptive term "separation processes." These *separation processes* are common to all types of diverse process industries.

For example, the separation process *distillation* is used to purify or separate alcohol in the beverage industry and hydrocarbons in the petroleum industry. Drying of grain and other foods is similar to drying of lumber, filtered precipitates, and wool. The separation process *absorption* occurs in absorption of oxygen from air in a fermentation process or in a sewage treatment plant and in absorption of hydrogen gas in a process for liquid hydrogenation of oil. Evaporation of salt solutions in the chemical industry is similar to evaporation of sugar solutions in the food industry. Settling and sedimentation of suspended solids in the sewage industry and the mining industry are similar. Flow of liquid hydrocarbons in the petroleum refinery and flow of milk in a dairy plant are carried out in a similar fashion.

Many of these separation processes have certain fundamental and basic principles or mechanisms in common. For example, the mechanism of diffusion or mass transfer occurs in drying, membrane separation, absorption, distillation, and crystallization. Heat transfer occurs in drying, distillation, evaporation, and so on. The following classification of a more fundamental nature is often made, according to transfer or transport processes.

1.1B Fundamental Transport Processes

1. Momentum transfer. This is concerned with the transfer of momentum which occurs in moving media, such as in the separation processes of fluid flow, sedimentation, mixing, and filtration

2. Heat transfer. In this fundamental process, we are concerned with the transfer of heat from one place to another; it occurs in the separation processes of drying, evaporation, distillation, and others.

3. Mass transfer. Here mass is being transferred from one phase to another distinct phase; the basic mechanism is the same whether the phases are gas, solid, or liquid. This includes distillation, absorption, liquid–liquid extraction, membrane separation, adsorption, crystallization, and leaching.

1.1C Classification of Separation Processes

The separation processes deal mainly with the transfer and change of energy and the transfer and change of materials, primarily by physical means but also by physical–chemical means. The important separation processes, which can be combined in various sequences in a process and which are covered in this text, are described next.

1. Evaporation. This refers to the evaporation of a volatile solvent such as water from a nonvolatile solute such as salt or any other material in solution.

2. Drying. In this operation volatile liquids, usually water, are removed from solid materials.

3. Distillation. This is an operation whereby components of a liquid mixture are separated by boiling because of their differences in vapor pressure.

4. Absorption. In this process a component is removed from a gas stream by treatment with a liquid.

5. Membrane separation. This process involves the separation of a solute from a fluid by diffusion of this solute from a liquid or gas through a semipermeable membrane barrier to another fluid.

6. Liquid–liquid extraction. In this case a solute in a liquid solution is removed by contacting with another liquid solvent that is relatively immiscible with the solution.

7. Adsorption. In this process a component of a gas or liquid stream is removed and adsorbed by a solid adsorbent.

8. Ion exchange. Certain ions in solution are removed from a liquid by an ion-exchange solid.

9. Liquid–solid leaching. This involves treating a finely divided solid with a liquid that dissolves out and removes a solute contained in the solid.

10. Crystallization. This concerns the removal of a solute such as a salt from a solution by precipitating the solute from the solution.

11. Mechanical–physical separations. These involve separation of solids, liquids, or gases by mechanical means, such as filtration, settling, centrifugation, and size reduction.

1.1D Arrangement in Parts 1 and 2

This text is arranged in two parts:

Part 1: Transport Processes: Momentum, Heat, and Mass. These fundamental principles are covered extensively in Chapters 1 through 7 in order to provide the basis for study of separation processes in Part 2 of this text.

Part 2: Separation Process Principles (Includes Unit Operations). The various separation processes and their applications to process areas are studied in Part 2 of this text.

There are a number of elementary engineering principles, mathematical techniques, and laws of physics and chemistry that are basic to a study of the principles of momentum, heat, and mass transfer and the separation processes. These are reviewed for the reader in this first chapter. Some readers, especially chemical engineers, agricultural engineers, civil engineers, and chemists, may be familiar with many of these principles and techniques and may wish to omit all or parts of this chapter.

Homework problems at the end of each chapter are arranged in different sections, each corresponding to the number of a given section in the chapter.

1.2 SI SYSTEM OF BASIC UNITS USED IN THIS TEXT AND OTHER SYSTEMS

There are three main systems of basic units employed at present in engineering and science. The first and most important of these is the *SI* (Système International d'Unités) *system,* which has as its three basic units the meter (m), the kilogram (kg), and the second (s). The others are the English foot (ft)–pound (lb)–second (s), or *English system* and the centimeter (cm)–gram (g)–second (s), or *cgs system.*

At present the SI system has been adopted officially for use exclusively in engineering and science, but the older English and cgs systems will still be used for some time. Much of the physical and chemical data and empirical equations are given in these latter two systems. Hence, the engineer not only should be proficient in the SI system but must also be able to use the other two systems to a limited extent.

1.2A SI System of Units

The basic quantities used in the SI system are as follows: the unit of length is the meter (m); the unit of time is the second (s); the unit of mass is the kilogram (kg); the unit of temperature is the kelvin (K); and the unit of an element is the kilogram mole (kg mol). The other standard units are derived from these basic quantities.

The basic unit of force is the newton (N), defined as

$$1 \text{ newton (N)} = 1 \text{ kg} \cdot \text{m/s}^2$$

The basic unit of work, energy, or heat is the newton-meter, or joule (J).

$$1 \text{ joule (J)} = 1 \text{ newton} \cdot \text{m (N} \cdot \text{m)} = 1 \text{ kg} \cdot \text{m}^2/\text{s}^2$$

Power is measured in joules/s or watts (W).

$$1 \text{ joule/s (J/s)} = 1 \text{ watt (W)}$$

The unit of pressure is the newton/m^2 or pascal (Pa).

$$1 \text{ newton/m}^2 \text{ (N/m}^2) = 1 \text{ pascal (Pa)}$$

[Pressure in atmospheres (atm) is not a standard SI unit but is being used during the transition period.] The standard acceleration of gravity is defined as

$$1 \, g = 9.80665 \text{ m/s}^2$$

A few of the standard prefixes for multiples of the basic units are as follows: giga (G) = 10^9, mega (M) = 10^6, kilo (k) = 10^3, centi (c) = 10^{-2}, milli (m) = 10^{-3}, micro (μ) = 10^{-6}, and nano (n) = 10^{-9}. The prefix c is not a preferred prefix.

Temperatures are defined in kelvin (K) as the preferred unit in the SI system. However, in practice, wide use is made of the degree Celsius (°C) scale, which is defined by

$$t°C = T(K) - 273.15$$

Note that 1°C = 1 K and that in the case of temperature difference,

$$\Delta t°C = \Delta T \text{ K}$$

The standard preferred unit of time is the second (s), but time can be in nondecimal units of minutes (min), hours (h), or days (d).

1.2B CGS System of Units

The cgs system is related to the SI system as follows:

$$1 \text{ g mass (g)} = 1 \times 10^{-3} \text{ kg mass (kg)}$$

$$1 \text{ cm} = 1 \times 10^{-2} \text{ m}$$

$$1 \text{ dyne (dyn)} = 1 \text{ g} \cdot \text{cm/s}^2 = 1 \times 10^{-5} \text{ newton (N)}$$

$$1 \text{ erg} = 1 \text{ dyn} \cdot \text{cm} = 1 \times 10^{-7} \text{ joule (J)}$$

The standard acceleration of gravity is

$$g = 980.665 \text{ cm/s}^2$$

1.2C English fps System of Units

The English system is related to the SI system as follows:

$$1 \text{ lb mass (lb}_m) = 0.45359 \text{ kg}$$

$$1 \text{ ft} = 0.30480 \text{ m}$$

$$1 \text{ lb force (lb}_f) = 4.4482 \text{ newton (N)}$$

$$1 \text{ ft} \cdot \text{lb}_f = 1.35582 \text{ newton} \cdot \text{m (N} \cdot \text{m)} = 1.35582 \text{ joules (J)}$$

$$1 \text{ psia} = 6.89476 \times 10^3 \text{ newton/m}^2 \text{ (N/m}^2)$$

$$1.8°F = 1 \text{ K} = 1°C \text{ (centigrade or Celsius)}$$

$$g = 32.174 \text{ ft/s}^2$$

The proportionality factor for Newton's law is

$$g_c = 32.174 \text{ ft} \cdot \text{lb}_m/\text{lb}_f \cdot \text{s}^2$$

The factor g_c in SI units and cgs units is 1.0 and is omitted.

In Appendix A.1, convenient conversion factors for all three systems are tabulated. Further discussions and use of these relationships are given in various sections of the text.

This text uses the SI system as the primary set of units in the equations, sample problems, and homework problems. However, the important equations derived in the text are given in a dual set of units, SI and English, when these equations differ. Some example problems and homework problems are also given using English units. In some cases, intermediate steps and/or answers in example problems are also stated in English units.

1.2D Dimensionally Homogeneous Equations and Consistent Units

A dimensionally homogeneous equation is one in which all the terms have the same units. These units can be the base units or derived ones (for example, $\text{kg/s}^2 \cdot \text{m}$ or Pa). Such an equation can be used with any system of units provided that the same base or derived units are used throughout the equation. No conversion factors are needed when consistent units are used.

The reader should be careful in using any equation and always check it for dimensional homogeneity. To do this, a system of units (SI, English, etc.) is first selected. Then units are substituted for each term in the equation and like units in each term canceled out.

1.3 METHODS OF EXPRESSING TEMPERATURES AND COMPOSITIONS

1.3A Temperature

There are two temperature scales in common use in the chemical and biological industries. These are degrees Fahrenheit (abbreviated °F) and Celsius (°C). It is often necessary to convert from one scale to the other. Both use the freezing point and boiling point of water at 1 atmosphere pressure as base points. Often temperatures are expressed as absolute degrees K (SI standard) or degrees Rankine (°R) instead of °C or °F. Table 1.3-1 shows the equivalences of the four temperature scales.

TABLE 1.3-1. *Temperature Scales and Equivalents*

	Centigrade	Fahrenheit	Kelvin	Rankine	Celsius
Boiling water	100°C	212°F	373.15 K	671.67°R	100°C
Melting ice	0°C	32°F	273.15 K	491.67°R	0°C
Absolute zero	−273.15°C	−459.67°F	0 K	0°R	−273.15°C

The difference between the boiling point of water and melting point of ice at 1 atm is 100°C or 180°F. Thus, a 1.8°F change is equal to a 1°C change. Usually, the value of −273.15°C is rounded to −273.2°C and −459.67°F to −460°F. The following equations can be used to convert from one scale to another:

$$°F = 32 + 1.8(°C) \tag{1.3-1}$$

$$°C = \frac{1}{1.8}(°F - 32) \tag{1.3-2}$$

$$°R = °F + 459.67 \tag{1.3-3}$$

$$K = °C + 273.15 \tag{1.3-4}$$

1.3B Mole Units, and Weight or Mass Units

There are many methods used to express compositions in gases, liquids, and solids. One of the most useful is molar units, since chemical reactions and gas laws are simpler to express in terms of molar units. A mole (mol) of a pure substance is defined as the amount of that substance whose mass is numerically equal to its molecular weight. Hence, 1 kg mol of methane CH_4 contains 16.04 kg. Also, 1.0 lb mol contains 16.04 lb_m.

The mole fraction of a particular substance is simply the moles of this substance divided by the total number of moles. In like manner, the weight or mass fraction is the mass of the substance divided by the total mass. These two compositions, which hold for gases, liquids, and solids, can be expressed as follows for component A in a mixture:

$$x_A \text{ (mole fraction of } A) = \frac{\text{moles of } A}{\text{total moles}} \tag{1.3-5}$$

$$w_A \text{ (mass or wt fraction of } A) = \frac{\text{mass } A}{\text{total mass}} \tag{1.3-6}$$

EXAMPLE 1.3-1. Mole and Mass or Weight Fraction of a Solution
A container holds 50 g of water (B) and 50 g of NaOH (A). Calculate the weight fraction and mole fraction of NaOH. Also, calculate the lb_m of NaOH (A) and H_2O (B).

Solution: Taking as a basis for calculation 50 + 50 or 100 g of solution, the following data are calculated:

Component	G	Wt Fraction	Mol Wt	G Moles	Mole Fraction
H_2O (B)	50.0	$\frac{50}{100} = 0.500$	18.02	$\frac{50.0}{18.02} = 2.78$	$\frac{2.78}{4.03} = 0.690$
NaOH (A)	50.0	$\frac{50}{100} = 0.500$	40.0	$\frac{50.0}{40.0} = 1.25$	$\frac{1.25}{4.03} = 0.310$
Total	100.0	1.000		4.03	1.000

Hence, $x_A = 0.310$ and $x_B = 0.690$ and $x_A + x_B = 0.310 + 0.690 = 1.00$. Also, $w_A + w_B = 0.500 + 0.500 = 1.00$. To calculate the lb_m of each component, Appendix A.1 gives the conversion factor of 453.6 g per 1 lb_m. Using this,

$$\text{lb mass of } A = \frac{50 \, g \, A}{453.6 \, g \, A/\text{lb}_m \, A} = 0.1102 \, \text{lb}_m \, A$$

Note that the g of A in the numerator cancels the g of A in the denominator, leaving lb_m of A in the numerator. The reader is cautioned to put all units down in an equation and cancel those appearing in the numerator and denominator. In a similar manner we obtain $0.1102 \, \text{lb}_m \, B$ ($0.0500 \, \text{kg} \, B$).

The analyses of solids and liquids are usually given as weight or mass fraction or weight percent, and gases as mole fraction or percent. Unless otherwise stated, analyses of solids and liquids will be assumed to be weight (mass) fraction or percent, and of gases to be mole fraction or percent.

1.3C Concentration Units for Liquids

In general, when one liquid is mixed with another miscible liquid, the volumes are not additive. Hence, compositions of liquids are usually not expressed as volume percent of a component but as weight or mole percent. Another convenient way to express concentrations of components in a solution is *molarity*, which is defined as g mol of a component per liter of solution. Other methods used are kg/m^3, g/liter, g/cm^3, lb mol/cu ft, lb_m/cu ft, and lb_m/gallon. All these concentrations depend on temperature, so the temperature must be specified.

The most common method of expressing total concentration per unit volume is density, kg/m^3, g/cm^3, or lb_m/ft^3. For example, the density of water at 277.2 K (4°C) is $1000 \, \text{kg/m}^3$, or $62.43 \, \text{lb}_m/\text{ft}^3$. Sometimes the density of a solution is expressed as *specific gravity*, which is defined as the density of the solution at its given temperature divided by the density of a reference substance at its temperature. If the reference substance is water at 277.2 K, the specific gravity and density of the substance are numerically equal.

1.4 GAS LAWS AND VAPOR PRESSURE

1.4A Pressure

There are numerous ways of expressing the pressure exerted by a fluid or system. An *absolute pressure* of 1.00 atm is equivalent to 760 mm Hg at 0°C, 29.921 in. Hg, 0.760 m Hg, 14.696 lb force per square inch (psia), or 33.90 ft of water at 4°C. *Gage pressure* is the pressure above the absolute pressure. Hence, a pressure of 21.5 lb per square inch gage (*psig*) is 21.5 + 14.7 (rounded off), or 36.2 psia. In SI units, 1 psia = 6.89476×10^3 pascal (Pa) = 6.89476×10^3 newtons/m². Also, 1 atm = 1.01325×10^5 Pa.

In some cases, particularly in evaporation, one may express the pressure as inches of mercury vacuum. This means the pressure as inches of mercury measured "below" the absolute barometric pressure. For example, a reading of 25.4 in. Hg vacuum is 29.92 − 25.4, or 4.52 in. Hg absolute pressure. Pressure conversion units are given in Appendix A.1.

1.4B Ideal Gas Law

An *ideal gas* is defined as one that obeys simple laws. Also, in an ideal gas the gas molecules are considered as rigid spheres which themselves occupy no volume and do not exert forces on one another. No real gases obey these laws exactly, but at ordinary temperatures and pressures of not more than several atmospheres, the ideal laws give answers within a few percent or less of the actual answers. Hence, these laws are sufficiently accurate for engineering calculations.

The *ideal gas law* of Boyle states that the volume of a gas is directly proportional to the absolute temperature and inversely proportional to the absolute pressure. This is expressed as

$$pV = nRT \tag{1.4-1}$$

where p is the absolute pressure in N/m^2, V the volume of the gas in m^3, n the kg mol of the gas, T the absolute temperature in K, and R the gas law constant of $8314.3 \ kg \cdot m^2/kg \ mol \cdot s^2 \cdot K$. When the volume is in ft^3, n in lb moles, and T in °R, R has a value of $0.7302 \ ft^3 \cdot atm/lb \ mol \cdot °R$. For cgs units (see Appendix A.1), $V = cm^3$, $T = K$, $R = 82.057 \ cm^3 \cdot atm/g \ mol \cdot K$, and $n = g$ mol.

In order that amounts of various gases may be compared, *standard conditions of temperature and pressure* (abbreviated STP or SC) are arbitrarily defined as 101.325 kPa (1.0 atm) abs and 273.15 K (0°C). Under these conditions the volumes are as follows:

$$\text{volume of } 1.0 \text{ kg mol (SC)} = 22.414 \ m^3$$

$$\text{volume of } 1.0 \text{ g mol (SC)} = 22.414 \ L \text{ (liter)}$$

$$= 22\,414 \ cm^3$$

$$\text{volume of } 1.0 \text{ lb mol (SC)} = 359.05 \ ft^3$$

EXAMPLE 1.4-1.   Gas-Law Constant

Calculate the value of the gas-law constant R when the pressure is in psia, moles in lb mol, volume in ft^3, and temperature in °R. Repeat for SI units.

Solution: At standard conditions, $p = 14.7$ psia, $V = 359 \ ft^3$, and $T = 460 + 32 = 492°R$ (273.15 K). Substituting into Eq. (1.4-1) for $n = 1.0$ lb mol and solving for R,

$$R = \frac{pV}{nT} = \frac{(14.7 \text{ psia})(359 \ ft^3)}{(1.0 \text{ lb mol})(492°R)} = 10.73 \ \frac{ft^3 \cdot psia}{lb \ mol \cdot °R}$$

$$R = \frac{pV}{nT} = \frac{(1.01325 \times 10^5 \ Pa)(22.414 \ m^3)}{(1.0 \text{ kg mol})(273.15 \ K)} = 8314 \ \frac{m^3 \cdot Pa}{kg \ mol \cdot K}$$

A useful relation can be obtained from Eq. (1.4-1) for n moles of gas at conditions p_1, V_1, T_1, and also at conditions p_2, V_2, T_2. Substituting into Eq. (1.4-1),

$$p_1 V_1 = nRT_1$$

$$p_2 V_2 = nRT_2$$

Combining gives

$$\frac{p_1 V_1}{p_2 V_2} = \frac{T_1}{T_2} \tag{1.4-2}$$

1.4C Ideal Gas Mixtures

Dalton's law for mixtures of ideal gases states that the total pressure of a gas mixture is equal to the sum of the individual partial pressures:

$$P = p_A + p_B + p_C + \cdots \tag{1.4-3}$$

where P is total pressure and $p_A, p_B, p_C, \ldots$ are the partial pressures of the components $A, B, C, \ldots$ in the mixture.

Since the number of moles of a component is proportional to its partial pressure, the mole fraction of a component is

$$x_A = \frac{p_A}{P} = \frac{p_A}{p_A + p_B + p_C + \cdots} \tag{1.4-4}$$

The volume fraction is equal to the mole fraction. Gas mixtures are almost always represented in terms of mole fractions and not weight fractions. For engineering purposes, Dalton's law is sufficiently accurate to use for actual mixtures at total pressures of a few atmospheres or less.

> ### EXAMPLE 1.4-2. Composition of a Gas Mixture
>
> A gas mixture contains the following components and partial pressures: CO_2, 75 mm Hg; CO, 50 mm Hg; N_2, 595 mm Hg; O_2, 26 mm Hg. Calculate the total pressure and the composition in mole fraction.
>
> **Solution:** Substituting into Eq. (1.4-3),
>
> $$P = p_A + p_B + p_C + p_D = 75 + 50 + 595 + 26 = 746 \text{ mm Hg}$$
>
> The mole fraction of CO_2 is obtained by using Eq. (1.4-4).
>
> $$x_A(CO_2) = \frac{p_A}{P} = \frac{75}{746} = 0.101$$
>
> In like manner, the mole fractions of CO, N_2, and O_2 are calculated as 0.067, 0.797, and 0.035, respectively.

1.4D Vapor Pressure and Boiling Point of Liquids

When a liquid is placed in a sealed container, molecules of liquid will evaporate into the space above the liquid and fill it completely. After a time, equilibrium is reached. This vapor will exert a pressure just like a gas and we call this pressure the *vapor pressure* of the liquid. The value of the vapor pressure is independent of the amount of liquid in the container as long as some is present.

If an inert gas such as air is also present in the vapor space, it will have very little effect on the vapor pressure. In general, the effect of total pressure on vapor pressure can be considered as negligible for pressures of a few atmospheres or less.

The vapor pressure of a liquid increases markedly with temperature. For example, from Appendix A.2 for water, the vapor pressure at 50°C is 12.333 kPa (92.51 mm Hg). At 100°C the vapor pressure has increased greatly to 101.325 kPa (760 mm Hg).

The *boiling point* of a liquid is defined as the temperature at which the vapor pressure of a liquid equals the total pressure. Hence, if the atmospheric total pressure is 760 mm Hg, water will boil at 100°C. On top of a high mountain, where the total pressure is considerably less, water will boil at temperatures below 100°C.

A plot of vapor pressure P_A of a liquid versus temperature does not yield a straight line but a curve. However, for moderate temperature ranges, a plot of log P_A versus $1/T$ is a reasonably straight line, as follows:

$$\log P_A = m\left(\frac{1}{T}\right) + b \tag{1.4-5}$$

where m is the slope, b is a constant for the liquid A, and T is the temperature in K.

1.5 CONSERVATION OF MASS AND MATERIAL BALANCES

1.5A Conservation of Mass

One of the basic laws of physical science is the *law of conservation of mass*. This law, stated simply, says that mass cannot be created or destroyed (excluding, of course, nuclear or atomic reactions). Hence, the total mass (or weight) of all materials entering any process must equal the total mass of all materials leaving plus the mass of any materials accumulating or left in the process:

$$\text{input} = \text{output} + \text{accumulation} \tag{1.5-1}$$

In the majority of cases there will be no accumulation of materials in a process, and then the input will simply equal the output. Stated in other words, "what goes in must come out." We call this type of process a *steady-state process:*

$$\text{input} = \text{output (steady state)} \tag{1.5-2}$$

1.5B Simple Material Balances

In this section we do simple material (weight or mass) balances in various processes at steady state with no chemical reaction occurring. We can use units of kg, lb_m, lb mol, g, kg mol, and so on, in our balances. The reader is cautioned to be consistent and not to mix several units in a balance. When chemical reactions occur in the balances (as discussed in Section 1.5D), one should use kg mol units, since chemical equations relate moles reacting. In Section 2.6, overall mass balances will be covered in more detail and in Section 3.6, differential mass balances.

To solve a material-balance problem, it is advisable to proceed by a series of definite steps, as listed below:

1. *Sketch a simple diagram of the process.* This can be a simple box diagram showing each stream entering by an arrow pointing in and each stream leaving by an arrow pointing out. Include on each arrow the compositions, amounts, temperatures, and so on, of that stream. All pertinent data should be on this diagram.
2. *Write the chemical equations involved (if any).*
3. *Select a basis for calculation.* In most cases the problem is concerned with a specific amount of one of the streams in the process, which is selected as the basis.

4. *Make a material balance.* The arrows into the process will be input items and the arrows going out output items. The balance can be a total material balance in Eq. (1.5-2) or a balance on each component present (if no chemical reaction occurs).

Typical processes that do not undergo chemical reactions are drying, evaporation, dilution of solutions, distillation, extraction, and so on. These can be solved by setting up material balances containing unknowns and solving these equations for the unknowns.

EXAMPLE 1.5-1. Concentration of Orange Juice

In the concentration of orange juice, a fresh extracted and strained juice containing 7.08 wt % solids is fed to a vacuum evaporator. In the evaporator, water is removed and the solids content increased to 58 wt % solids. For 1000 kg/h entering, calculate the amounts of the outlet streams of concentrated juice and water.

Solution: Following the four steps outlined, we make a process flow diagram (step 1) in Fig. 1.5-1. Note that the letter W represents the unknown amount of water and C the amount of concentrated juice. No chemical reactions are given (step 2). Basis: 1000 kg/h entering juice (step 3).

To make the material balances (step 4), a total material balance will be made using Eq. (1.5-2):

$$1000 = W + C \qquad \textbf{(1.5-3)}$$

This gives one equation and two unknowns. Hence, a component balance on solids will be made:

$$1000\left(\frac{7.08}{100}\right) = W(0) + C\left(\frac{58}{100}\right) \qquad \textbf{(1.5-4)}$$

To solve these two equations, we solve Eq. (1.5-4) first for C since W drops out. We get $C = 122.1$ kg/h concentrated juice.

Substituting the value of C into Eq. (1.5-3),

$$1000 = W + 122.1$$

and we obtain $W = 877.9$ kg/h water.

FIGURE 1.5-1. *Process flow diagram for Example 1.5-1.*

As a check on our calculations, we can write a balance on the water component:

$$1000\left(\frac{100 - 7.08}{100}\right) = 877.9 + 122.1\left(\frac{100 - 58}{100}\right) \qquad \textbf{(1.5-5)}$$

Solving,

$$929.2 = 877.9 + 51.3 = 929.2$$

In Example 1.5-1 only one unit or separate process was involved. Often, a number of processes in series are involved. Then we have a choice of making a separate balance over each separate process and/or a balance around the complete overall process.

1.5C   Material Balances and Recycle

Processes that have a recycle or feedback of part of the product into the entering feed are sometimes encountered. For example, in a sewage treatment plant, part of the activated sludge from a sedimentation tank is recycled back to the aeration tank where the liquid is treated. In some food-drying operations, the humidity of the entering air is controlled by recirculating part of the hot, wet air that leaves the dryer. In chemical reactions, the material that did not react in the reactor can be separated from the final product and fed back to the reactor.

EXAMPLE 1.5-2.   Crystallization of KNO_3 and Recycle
In a process producing KNO_3 salt, 1000 kg/h of a feed solution containing 20 wt % KNO_3 is fed to an evaporator, which evaporates some water at 422 K to produce a 50 wt % KNO_3 solution. This is then fed to a crystallizer at 311 K, where crystals containing 96 wt % KNO_3 are removed. The saturated solution containing 37.5 wt % KNO_3 is recycled to the evaporator. Calculate the amount of recycle stream R in kg/h and the product stream of crystals P in kg/h.

Solution: Figure 1.5-2 gives the process flow diagram. As a basis we shall use 1000 kg/h of fresh feed. No chemical reactions are occurring. We can make an overall balance on the entire process for KNO_3 and solve for P directly:

FIGURE 1.5-2.   *Process flow diagram for Example 1.5-2.*

$$1000(0.20) = W(0) + P(0.96) \qquad \textbf{(1.5-6)}$$

$$P = 208.3 \text{ kg crystals/h}$$

To calculate the recycle stream, we can make a balance around the evaporator or the crystallizer. Using a balance on the crystallizer, since it now includes only two unknowns, S and R, we get for a total balance,

$$S = R + 208.3 \qquad \textbf{(1.5-7)}$$

For a KNO_3 balance on the crystallizer,

$$S(0.50) = R(0.375) + 208.3(0.96) \qquad \textbf{(1.5-8)}$$

Substituting S from Eq. (1.5-7) into Eq. (1.5-8) and solving, $R = 766.6$ kg recycle/h and $S = 974.9$ kg/h.

1.5D Material Balances and Chemical Reaction

In many cases the materials entering a process undergo chemical reactions in the process, so that the materials leaving are different from those entering. In these cases it is usually convenient to make a molar and not a weight balance on an individual component, such as kg mol H_2 or kg atom H, kg mol CO_3^- ion, kg mol $CaCO_3$, kg atom Na^+, kg mol N_2, and so on. For example, in the combustion of CH_4 with air, balances can be made on kg mol of H_2, C, O_2, or N_2.

EXAMPLE 1.5-3. Combustion of Fuel Gas
A fuel gas containing 3.1 mol % H_2, 27.2% CO, 5.6% CO_2, 0.5% O_2, and 63.6% N_2 is burned with 20% excess air (i.e., the air over and above that necessary for complete combustion to CO_2 and H_2O). The combustion of CO is only 98% complete. For 100 kg mol of fuel gas, calculate the moles of each component in the exit flue gas.

Solution: First, the process flow diagram is drawn (Fig. 1.5-3). On the diagram the components in the flue gas are shown. Let A be moles of air and F be moles of flue gas. Next the chemical reactions are given:

$$CO + \tfrac{1}{2}O_2 \rightarrow CO_2 \qquad \textbf{(1.5-9)}$$

$$H_2 + \tfrac{1}{2}O_2 \rightarrow H_2O \qquad \textbf{(1.5-10)}$$

FIGURE 1.5-3. *Process flow diagram for Example 1.5-3.*

An accounting of the total moles of O_2 in the fuel gas is as follows:

$$\text{mol } O_2 \text{ in fuel gas} = (\tfrac{1}{2})27.2(CO) + 5.6(CO_2) + 0.5(O_2) = 19.7 \text{ mol } O_2$$

For all the H_2 to be completely burned to H_2O, we need, from Eq. (1.5-10), $\tfrac{1}{2}$ mol O_2 for 1 mol H_2, or $3.1(\tfrac{1}{2}) = 1.55$ total mol O_2. For completely burning the CO from Eq. (1.5-9), we need $27.2(\tfrac{1}{2}) = 13.6$ mol O_2. Hence, the amount of O_2 we must add is, theoretically, as follows:

$$\text{mol } O_2 \text{ theoretically needed} = 1.55 + 13.6 - 0.5 \text{ (in fuel gas)}$$

$$= 14.65 \text{ mol } O_2$$

For a 20% excess, we add 1.2(14.65), or 17.58 mol O_2. Since air contains 79 mol % N_2, the amount of N_2 added is (79/21)(17.58), or 66.1 mol N_2.

To calculate the moles in the final flue gas, all the H_2 gives H_2O, or 3.1 mol H_2O. For CO, 2.0% does not react. Hence, 0.02(27.2), or 0.54 mol CO will be unburned.

A total carbon balance is as follows: inlet moles C = 27.2 + 5.6 = 32.8 mol C. In the outlet flue gas, 0.54 mol will be as CO and the remainder of 32.8 − 0.54, or 32.26 mol as CO_2.

For calculating the outlet mol O_2, we make an overall O_2 balance:

$$O_2 \text{ in} = 19.7 \text{ (in fuel gas)} + 17.58 \text{ (in air)} = 37.28 \text{ mol } O_2$$

$$O_2 \text{ out} = (3.1/2) \text{ (in } H_2O) + (0.54/2) \text{ (in CO)} + 32.26 \text{ (in } CO_2) + \text{free } O_2$$

Equating inlet O_2 to outlet, the free remaining O_2 = 3.2 mol O_2. For the N_2 balance, the outlet = 63.6 (in fuel gas) + 66.1 (in air), or 129.70 mol N_2. The outlet flue gas contains 3.10 mol H_2O, 0.54 mol CO, 32.26 mol CO_2, 3.20 mol O_2, and 129.7 mol N_2.

In chemical reactions with several reactants, the limiting reactant component is defined as that compound which is present in an amount less than the amount necessary for it to react stoichiometrically with the other reactants. Then the percent completion of a reaction is the amount of this limiting reactant actually converted, divided by the amount originally present, times 100.

1.6   ENERGY AND HEAT UNITS

1.6A   Joule, Calorie, and Btu

In a manner similar to that used in making material balances on chemical and biological processes, we can also make energy balances on a process. Often a large portion of the energy entering or leaving a system is in the form of heat. Before such energy or heat balances are made, we must understand the various types of energy and heat units.

In the SI system, energy is given in joules (J) or kilojoules (kJ). Energy is also expressed in btu (British thermal units) or cal (calories). The g calorie (abbreviated cal) is defined as the amount of heat needed to heat 1.0 g water 1.0°C (from 14.5°C to 15.5°C). Also, 1 kcal (kilocalorie) = 1000 cal. The btu is defined as the amount of heat needed to raise 1.0 lb water 1°F. Hence, from Appendix A.1,

$$1 \text{ btu} = 252.16 \text{ cal} = 1.05506 \text{ kJ} \qquad (1.6\text{-}1)$$

1.6B Heat Capacity

The *heat capacity* of a substance is defined as the amount of heat necessary to increase the temperature by 1 degree. It can be expressed for 1 g, 1 lb, 1 g mol, 1 kg mol, or 1 lb mol of the substance. For example, a heat capacity is expressed in SI units as J/kg mol · K; in other units as cal/g · °C, cal/g mol · °C, kcal/kg mol · °C, btu/lb$_m$ · °F, or btu/lb mol · °F.

It can be shown that the actual numerical value of a heat capacity is the same in mass units or in molar units. That is,

$$1.0 \text{ cal/g} \cdot °\text{C} = 1.0 \text{ btu/lb}_m \cdot °\text{F} \qquad (1.6\text{-}2)$$

$$1.0 \text{ cal/g mol} \cdot °\text{C} = 1.0 \text{ btu/lb mol} \cdot °\text{F} \qquad (1.6\text{-}3)$$

For example, to prove this, suppose that a substance has a heat capacity of 0.8 btu/lb$_m$ · °F. The conversion is made using 1.8°F for 1°C or 1 K, 252.16 cal for 1 btu, and 453.6 g for 1 lb$_m$, as follows:

$$\text{heat capacity} \left(\frac{\text{cal}}{\text{g} \cdot °\text{C}} \right) = \left(0.8 \frac{\text{btu}}{\text{lb}_m \cdot °\text{F}} \right) \left(252.16 \frac{\text{cal}}{\text{btu}} \right) \left(\frac{1}{453.6 \text{ g/lb}_m} \right) \left(1.8 \frac{°\text{F}}{°\text{C}} \right)$$

$$= 0.8 \frac{\text{cal}}{\text{g} \cdot °\text{C}}$$

The heat capacities of gases (sometimes called *specific heat*) at constant pressure c_p are functions of temperature and for engineering purposes can be assumed to be independent of pressure up to several atmospheres. In most process engineering calculations, one is usually interested in the amount of heat needed to heat a gas from one temperature t_1 to another at t_2. Since the c_p varies with temperature, an integration must be performed or a suitable mean c_{pm} used. These mean values for gases have been obtained for T_1 of 298 K or 25°C (77°F) and various T_2 values, and are tabulated in Table 1.6-1 at 101.325 kPa pressure or less as c_{pm} in kJ/kg mol · K at various values of T_2 in K or °C.

> **EXAMPLE 1.6-1. Heating of N_2 Gas**
> The gas N_2 at 1 atm pressure absolute is being heated in a heat exchanger. Calculate the amount of heat needed in J to heat 3.0 g mol N_2 in the following temperature ranges:
> (a) 298–673 K (25–400°C)
> (b) 298–1123 K (25–850°C)
> (c) 673–1123 K (400–850°C)
>
> **Solution:** For case (a), Table 1.6-1 gives c_{pm} values at 1 atm pressure or less which can be used up to several atm pressures. For N_2 at 673 K, $c_{pm} = 29.68$ kJ/kg mol · K or 29.68 J/g mol · K. This is the mean heat capacity for the range 298–673 K:
>
> $$\text{heat required} = M \text{ g mol} \left(c_{pm} \frac{J}{\text{g mol} \cdot \text{K}} \right) (T_2 - T_1)\text{K} \qquad (1.6\text{-}4)$$

TABLE 1.6-1. *Mean Molar Heat Capacities of Gases Between 298 and TK (25 and T°C) at 101.325 kPa or Less (SI Units: $c_p = kJ/kg\ mol \cdot K$)*

$T(K)$	$T(°C)$	H_2	N_2	CO	Air	O_2	H_2O	CO_2	CH_4	SO_2
298	25	28.86	29.14	29.16	29.19	29.38	33.59	37.20	35.8	39.9
373	100	28.99	29.19	29.24	29.29	29.66	33.85	38.73	37.6	41.2
473	200	29.13	29.29	29.38	29.40	30.07	34.24	40.62	40.3	42.9
573	300	29.18	29.46	29.60	29.61	30.53	34.39	42.32	43.1	44.5
673	400	29.23	29.68	29.88	29.94	31.01	35.21	43.80	45.9	45.8
773	500	29.29	29.97	30.19	30.25	31.46	35.75	45.12	48.8	47.0
873	600	29.35	30.27	30.52	30.56	31.89	36.33	46.28	51.4	47.9
973	700	29.44	30.56	30.84	30.87	32.26	36.91	47.32	54.0	48.8
1073	800	29.56	30.85	31.16	31.18	32.62	37.53	48.27	56.4	49.6
1173	900	29.63	31.16	31.49	31.48	32.97	38.14	49.15	58.8	50.3
1273	1000	29.84	31.43	31.77	31.79	33.25	38.71	49.91	61.0	50.9
1473	1200	30.18	31.97	32.30	32.32	33.78	39.88	51.29	64.9	51.9
1673	1400	30.51	32.40	32.73	32.76	34.19	40.90	52.34		

Mean Molar Heat Capacities of Gases Between 25 and T°C at 1 atm Pressure or Less (English Units: $c_p = btu/lb\ mol \cdot °F$)

$T(°C)$	H_2	N_2	CO	Air	O_2	NO	H_2O	CO_2	HCl	Cl_2	CH_4	SO_2	C_2H_4	SO_3	C_2H_6
25	6.894	6.961	6.965	6.972	7.017	7.134	8.024	8.884	6.96	8.12	8.55	9.54	10.45	12.11	12.63
100	6.924	6.972	6.983	6.996	7.083	7.144	8.084	9.251	6.97	8.24	8.98	9.85	11.35	12.84	13.76
200	6.957	6.996	7.017	7.021	7.181	7.224	8.177	9.701	6.98	8.37	9.62	10.25	12.53	13.74	15.27
300	6.970	7.036	7.070	7.073	7.293	7.252	8.215	10.108	7.00	8.48	10.29	10.62	13.65	14.54	16.72
400	6.982	7.089	7.136	7.152	7.406	7.301	8.409	10.462	7.02	8.55	10.97	10.94	14.67	15.22	18.11
500	6.995	7.159	7.210	7.225	7.515	7.389	8.539	10.776	7.06	8.61	11.65	11.22	15.60	15.82	19.39
600	7.011	7.229	7.289	7.299	7.616	7.470	8.678	11.053	7.10	8.66	12.27	11.45	16.45	16.33	20.58
700	7.032	7.298	7.365	7.374	7.706	7.549	8.816	11.303	7.15	8.70	12.90	11.66	17.22	16.77	21.68
800	7.060	7.369	7.443	7.447	7.792	7.630	8.963	11.53	7.21	8.73	13.48	11.84	17.95	17.17	22.72
900	7.076	7.443	7.521	7.520	7.874	7.708	9.109	11.74	7.27	8.77	14.04	12.01	18.63	17.52	23.69
1000	7.128	7.507	7.587	7.593	7.941	7.773	9.246	11.92	7.33	8.80	14.56	12.15	19.23	17.86	24.56
1100	7.169	7.574	7.653	7.660	8.009	7.839	9.389	12.10	7.39	8.82	15.04	12.28	19.81	18.17	25.40
1200	7.209	7.635	7.714	7.719	8.068	7.898	9.524	12.25	7.45	8.94	15.49	12.39	20.33	18.44	26.15
1300	7.252	7.692	7.772	7.778	8.123	7.952	9.66	12.39							
1400	7.288	7.738	7.818	7.824	8.166	7.994	9.77	12.50							
1500	7.326	7.786	7.866	7.873	8.203	8.039	9.89	12.69							
1600	7.386	7.844	7.922	7.929	8.269	8.092	9.95	12.75							
1700	7.421	7.879	7.958	7.965	8.305	8.124	10.13	12.70							
1800	7.467	7.924	8.001	8.010	8.349	8.164	10.24	12.94							
1900	7.505	7.957	8.033	8.043	8.383	8.192	10.34	13.01							
2000	7.548	7.994	8.069	8.081	8.423	8.225	10.43	13.10							
2100	7.588	8.028	8.101	8.115	8.460	8.255	10.52	13.17							
2200	7.624	8.054	8.127	8.144	8.491	8.277	10.61	13.24							

Source: O. A. Hougen, K. W. Watson, and R. A. Ragatz, *Chemical Process Principles*, Part I, 2nd ed. New York: John Wiley & Sons. Inc.. 1954. With permission.

Chapter 1   Introduction to Engineering Principles and Units

Substituting the known values,

$$\text{heat required} = (3.0)(29.68)(673 - 298) = 33\ 390\ \text{J}$$

For case (b), the c_{pm} at 1123 K (obtained by linear interpolation between 1073 and 1173 K) is 31.00 J/g mol · K:

$$\text{heat required} = (3.0)(31.00)(1123 - 298) = 76\ 725\ \text{J}$$

For case (c), there is no mean heat capacity for the interval 673–1123 K. However, we can use the heat required to heat the gas from 298 to 673 K in case (a) and subtract it from case (b), which includes the heat to go from 298 to 673 K plus 673 to 1123 K:

$$\text{heat required } (673\text{–}1123\ \text{K}) = \text{heat required } (298\text{–}1123\ \text{K})$$

$$- \text{heat required } (298\text{–}673) \qquad \textbf{(1.6-5)}$$

Substituting the proper values into Eq. (1.6-5),

$$\text{heat required} = 76\ 725 - 33\ 390 = 43\ 335\ \text{J}$$

On heating a gas mixture, the total heat required is determined by first calculating the heat required for each individual component and then adding the results to obtain the total.

The heat capacities of solids and liquids are also functions of temperature and independent of pressure. Data are given in Appendix A.2, Physical Properties of Water; A.3, Physical Properties of Inorganic and Organic Compounds; and A.4, Physical Properties of Foods and Biological Materials. More data are available in (P1).

EXAMPLE 1.6-2. *Heating of Milk*
Rich cows' milk (4536 kg/h) at 4.4°C is being heated in a heat exchanger to 54.4°C by hot water. How much heat is needed?

Solution: From Appendix A.4, the average heat capacity of rich cows' milk is 3.85 kJ/kg · K. Temperature rise $\Delta T = (54.4 - 4.4)°C = 50$ K.

$$\text{heat required} = (4536\ \text{kg/h})(3.85\ \text{kJ/kg} \cdot \text{K})(1/3600\ \text{h/s})(50\ \text{K}) = 242.5\ \text{kW}$$

The enthalpy, H, of a substance in J/kg represents the sum of the internal energy plus the pressure–volume term. For no reaction and a constant-pressure process with a change in temperature, the heat change as computed from Eq. (1.6-4) is the difference in enthalpy, ΔH, of the substance relative to a given temperature or base point. In other units, $H = \text{btu/lb}_m$ or cal/g.

1.6C Latent Heat and Steam Tables

Whenever a substance undergoes a change of phase, relatively large amounts of heat change are involved at a constant temperature. For example, ice at 0°C and 1 atm pressure can absorb 6013.4 kJ/kg mol. This enthalpy change is called the *latent heat of fusion*. Data for other compounds are available in various handbooks (P1, W1).

When a liquid phase vaporizes to a vapor phase under its vapor pressure at constant temperature, an amount of heat called the *latent heat of vaporization* must be added. Tabulations of latent heats of vaporization are given in various handbooks. For water at 25°C and a pressure of 23.75 mm Hg, the latent heat is 44 020 kJ/kg mol, and at 25°C and 760 mm Hg, 44 045 kJ/kg mol. Hence, the effect of pressure can be neglected in engineering calculations. However, there is a large effect of temperature on the latent heat of water. Also, the effect of pressure on the heat capacity of liquid water is small and can be neglected.

Since water is a very common chemical, the thermodynamic properties of it have been compiled in steam tables and are given in Appendix A.2 in SI and in English units.

EXAMPLE 1.6-3.   Use of Steam Tables

Find the enthalpy change (i.e., how much heat must be added) for each of the following cases using SI and English units:

  (a) Heating 1 kg (lb_m) water from 21.11°C (70°F) to 60°C (140°F) at 101.325 kPa (1 atm) pressure.
  (b) Heating 1 kg (lb_m) water from 21.11°C (70°F) to 115.6°C (240°F) and vaporizing at 172.2 kPa (24.97 psia).
  (c) Vaporizing 1 kg (lb_m) water at 115.6°C (240°F) and 172.2 kPa (24.97 psia).

Solution: For part (a), the effect of pressure on the enthalpy of liquid water is negligible. From Appendix A.2,

$$H \text{ at } 21.11°C = \ \ 88.60 \text{ kJ/kg} \quad \text{or} \quad \text{at } 70°F = \ \ 38.09 \text{ btu/lb}_m$$

$$H \text{ at } 60°C = 251.13 \text{ kJ/kg} \quad \text{or} \quad \text{at } 140°F = 107.96 \text{ btu/lb}_m$$

$$\text{change in } H = \Delta H = 251.13 - 88.60 = 162.53 \text{ kJ/kg}$$

$$= 107.96 - 38.09 = 69.87 \text{ btu/lb}_m$$

In part (b), the enthalpy at 115.6°C (240°F) and 172.2 kPa (24.97 psia) of the saturated vapor is 2699.9 kJ/kg or 1160.7 btu/lb_m.

$$\text{change in } H = \Delta H = 2699.9 - 88.60 = 2611.3 \text{ kJ/kg}$$

$$= 1160.7 - 38.09 = 1122.6 \text{ btu/lb}_m$$

The latent heat of water at 115.6°C (240°F) in part (c) is

$$2699.9 - 484.9 = 2215.0 \text{ kJ/kg}$$

$$1160.7 - 208.44 = 952.26 \text{ btu/lb}_m$$

1.6D   Heat of Reaction

When chemical reactions occur, heat effects always accompany these reactions. This area where energy changes occur is often called *thermochemistry*. For example, when HCl is neutralized with NaOH, heat is given off and the reaction is exothermic. Heat is absorbed in an endothermic reaction. This heat of reaction is dependent on the chemical nature of each reacting material and product and on their physical states.

For purposes of organizing data, we define a standard heat of reaction ΔH^0 as the change in enthalpy when 1 kg mol reacts under a pressure of 101.325 kPa at a temperature of 298 K (25°C). For example, for the reaction

$$H_2(g) + \tfrac{1}{2}O_2(g) \ \rightarrow \ H_2O(l) \tag{1.6-6}$$

the ΔH^0 is -285.840×10^3 kJ/kg mol or -68.317 kcal/g mol. The reaction is exothermic and the value is negative since the reaction loses enthalpy. In this case, the H_2 gas reacts with the O_2 gas to give liquid water, all at 298 K (25°C).

Special names are given to ΔH^0 depending upon the type of reaction. When the product is formed from the elements, as in Eq. (1.6-6), we call the ΔH^0 the *heat of formation* of the product water, ΔH_f^0. For the combustion of CH_4 to form CO_2 and H_2O, we call it *heat of combustion*, ΔH_c^0. Data are given in Appendix A.3 for various values of ΔH_c^0.

EXAMPLE 1.6-4. Combustion of Carbon

A total of 10.0 g mol of carbon graphite is burned in a calorimeter held at 298 K and 1 atm. The combustion is incomplete, and 90% of the C goes to CO_2 and 10% to CO. What is the total enthalpy change in kJ and kcal?

Solution: From Appendix A.3 the ΔH_c^0 for carbon going to CO_2 is -393.513×10^3 kJ/kg mol or -94.0518 kcal/g mol, and for carbon going to CO it is -110.523×10^3 kJ/kg mol or -26.4157 kcal/g mol. Since 9 mol CO_2 and 1 mol CO are formed,

$$\text{total } \Delta H = 9(-393.513) + 1(-110.523) = -3652 \text{ kJ}$$

$$= 9(-94.0518) + 1(-26.4157) = -872.9 \text{ kcal}$$

If a table of heats of formation, ΔH_f^0, of compounds is available, the standard heat of the reaction, ΔH^0, can be calculated by

$$\Delta H^0 = \sum \Delta H_{f \text{ (products)}}^0 - \sum \Delta H_{f \text{ (reactants)}}^0 \tag{1.6-7}$$

In Appendix A.3, a short table of some values of ΔH_f is given. Other data are also available (H1, P1, S1).

EXAMPLE 1.6-5. Reaction of Methane

For the following reaction of 1 kg mol of CH_4 at 101.32 kPa and 298 K,

$$CH_4(g) + H_2O(l) \rightarrow CO(g) + 3H_2(g)$$

calculate the standard heat of reaction ΔH^0 at 298 K in kJ.

Solution: From Appendix A.3, the following standard heats of formation are obtained at 298 K:

	ΔH_f^0 (kJ/kg mol)
$CH_4(g)$	-74.848×10^3
$H_2O(l)$	-285.840×10^3
$CO(g)$	-110.523×10^3
$H_2(g)$	0

Note that the ΔH_f^0 of all elements is, by definition, zero. Substituting into Eq. (1.6-7),

$$\Delta H^0 = [-110.523 \times 10^3 - 3(0)] - (-74.848 \times 10^3 - 285.840 \times 10^3)$$

$$= +250.165 \times 10^3 \text{ kJ/kg mol} \quad \text{(endothermic)}$$

1.7 CONSERVATION OF ENERGY AND HEAT BALANCES

1.7A Conservation of Energy

In making material balances we used the law of conservation of mass, which states that the mass entering is equal to the mass leaving plus the mass left in the process. In a similar manner, we can state the *law of conservation of energy,* which says that all energy entering a process is equal to that leaving plus that left in the process. In this section elementary heat balances will be made. More elaborate energy balances will be considered in Sections 2.7 and 5.6.

Energy can appear in many forms. Some of the common forms are enthalpy, electrical energy, chemical energy (in terms of ΔH reaction), kinetic energy, potential energy, work, and heat inflow.

In many cases in process engineering, which often takes place at constant pressure, electrical energy, kinetic energy, potential energy, and work either are not present or can be neglected. Then only the enthalpy of the materials (at constant pressure), the standard chemical reaction energy (ΔH^0) at 25°C, and the heat added or removed must be taken into account in the energy balance. This is generally called a *heat balance.*

1.7B Heat Balances

In making a heat balance at steady state we use methods similar to those used in making a material balance. The energy or heat coming into a process in the inlet materials plus any net energy added to the process are equal to the energy leaving in the materials. Expressed mathematically,

$$\sum H_R + (-\Delta H_{298}^0) + q = \sum H_p \tag{1.7-1}$$

where $\sum H_R$ is the sum of enthalpies of all materials entering the reaction process relative to the reference state for the standard heat of reaction at 298 K and 101.32 kPa. If the inlet temperature is above 298 K, this sum will be positive. ΔH_{298}^0 = standard heat of the reaction at 298 K and 101.32 kPa. The reaction contributes heat to the process, so the negative of ΔH_{298}^0 is taken to be positive input heat for an exothermic reaction. Also, q = net energy or heat added to the system. If heat leaves the system, this item will be negative. $\sum H_p$ = sum of enthalpies of all leaving materials referred to the standard reference state at 298 K (25°C).

Note that if the materials coming into a process are below 298 K, $\sum H_R$ will be negative. Care must be taken not to confuse the signs of the items in Eq. (1.7-1). If no chemical reaction occurs, then simple heating, cooling, or phase change is occurring. Use of Eq. (1.7-1) will be illustrated by several examples. For convenience it is common practice to call the terms on the left-hand side of Eq. (1.7-1) input items, and those on the right, output items.

EXAMPLE 1.7-1. Heating of Fermentation Medium

A liquid fermentation medium at 30°C is pumped at a rate of 2000 kg/h through a heater, where it is heated to 70°C under pressure. The waste heat water used to

FIGURE 1.7-1. *Process flow diagram for Example 1.7-1.*

heat this medium enters at 95°C and leaves at 85°C. The average heat capacity of the fermentation medium is 4.06 kJ/kg·K, and that for water is 4.21 kJ/kg·K (Appendix A.2). The fermentation stream and the wastewater stream are separated by a metal surface through which heat is transferred and do not physically mix with each other. Make a complete heat balance on the system. Calculate the water flow and the amount of heat added to the fermentation medium assuming no heat losses. The process flow is given in Fig. 1.7-1.

Solution: It is convenient to use the standard reference state of 298 K (25°C) as the datum to calculate the various enthalpies. From Eq. (1.7-1) the input items are as follows:

Input items. $\sum H_R$ of the enthalpies of the two streams relative to 298 K (25°C) (note that $\Delta t = 30 - 25°C = 5°C = 5$ K):

$$H(\text{liquid}) = (2000 \text{ kg/h})(4.06 \text{ kJ/kg} \cdot \text{K})(5 \text{ K})$$

$$= 4.060 \times 10^4 \text{ kJ/h}$$

$$H(\text{water}) = W(4.21)(95 - 25) = 2.947 \times 10^2 W \text{ kJ/h} \qquad (W = \text{kg/h})$$

$$(-\Delta H^0_{298}) = 0 \qquad \text{(since there is no chemical reaction)}$$

$$q = 0 \qquad \text{(there are no heat losses or additions)}$$

Output items. $\sum H_P$ of the two streams relative to 298 K (25°C):

$$H(\text{liquid}) = 2000(4.06)(70 - 25) = 3.65 \times 10^5 \text{ kJ/h}$$

$$H(\text{water}) = W(4.21)(85 - 25) = 2.526 \times 10^2 W \text{ kJ/h}$$

Equating input to output in Eq. (1.7-1) and solving for W,

$$4.060 \times 10^4 + 2.947 \times 10^2 W = 3.654 \times 10^5 + 2.526 \times 10^2 W$$

$$W = 7720 \text{ kg/h water flow}$$

The amount of heat added to the fermentation medium is simply the difference of the outlet and inlet liquid enthalpies:

$$H(\text{outlet liquid}) - H(\text{inlet liquid}) = 3.654 \times 10^5 - 4.060 \times 10^4$$

$$= 3.248 \times 10^5 \text{ kJ/h (90.25 kW)}$$

Note in this example that since the heat capacities were assumed constant, a simpler balance could have been written as follows:

heat gained by liquid = heat lost by water

$$2000(4.06)(70 - 30) = W(4.21)(95 - 85)$$

Then, solving, $W = 7720$ kg/h. This simple balance works well when c_p is constant. However, when c_p varies with temperature and the material is a gas, c_{pm} values are only available between 298 K (25°C) and t K, and the simple method cannot be used without obtaining new c_{pm} values over different temperature ranges.

EXAMPLE 1.7-2 *Heat and Material Balance in Combustion*

The waste gas from a process of 1000 g mol/h of CO at 473 K is burned at 1 atm pressure in a furnace using air at 373 K. The combustion is complete and 90% excess air is used. The flue gas leaves the furnace at 1273 K. Calculate the heat removed in the furnace.

Solution: First, the process flow diagram is drawn in Fig. 1.7-2, and then a material balance is made:

$$CO(g) + \tfrac{1}{2}O_2(g) \rightarrow CO_2(g)$$

$$\Delta H_{298}^0 = -282.989 \times 10^3 \text{ kJ/kg mol}$$

(from Appendix A.3)

$$\text{mol CO} = 1000 \text{ g mol/h} = \text{moles CO}_2$$

$$= 1.00 \text{ kg mol/h}$$

$$\text{mol O}_2 \text{ theoretically required} = \tfrac{1}{2}(1.00) = 0.500 \text{ kg mol/h}$$

$$\text{mol O}_2 \text{ actually added} = 0.500(1.9) = 0.950 \text{ kg mol/h}$$

$$\text{mol N}_2 \text{ added} = 0.950 \frac{0.79}{0.21} = 3.570 \text{ kg mol/h}$$

$$\text{air added} = 0.950 + 3.570 = 4.520 \text{ kg mol/h} = A$$

$$\text{O}_2 \text{ in outlet flue gas} = \text{added} - \text{used}$$

$$= 0.950 - 0.500 = 0.450 \text{ kg mol/h}$$

$$\text{CO}_2 \text{ in outlet flue gas} = 1.00 \text{ kg mol/h}$$

$$\text{N}_2 \text{ in outlet flue gas} = 3.570 \text{ kg mol/h}$$

FIGURE 1.7-2. *Process flow diagram for Example 1.7-2.*

For the heat balance relative to the standard state at 298 K, we follow Eq. (1.7-1).

Input items

$$H(CO) = 1.00(c_{pm})(473 - 298) = 1.00(29.38)(473 - 298) = 5142 \text{ kJ/h}$$

(The c_{pm} of CO of 29.38 kJ/kg mol · K between 298 and 473 K is obtained from Table 1.6-1.)

$$H(\text{air}) = 4.520(c_{pm})(373 - 298) = 4.520(29.29)(373 - 298) = 9929 \text{ kJ/h}$$

$$q = \text{heat added, kJ/h}$$

(This will give a negative value here, indicating that heat was removed.)

$$-\Delta H_{298}^0 = -(-282.989 \times 10^3 \text{ kJ/kg mol})(1.00 \text{ kg mol/h}) = 282\,990 \text{ kJ/h}$$

Output items

$$H(CO_2) = 1.00(c_{pm})(1273 - 298) = 1.00(49.91)(1273 - 298) = 48\,660 \text{ kJ/h}$$

$$H(O_2) = 0.450(c_{pm})(1273 - 298) = 0.450(33.25)(1273 - 298) = 14\,590 \text{ kJ/h}$$

$$H(N_2) = 3.570(c_{pm})(1273 - 298) = 3.570(31.43)(1273 - 298) = 109\,400 \text{ kJ/h}$$

Equating input to output and solving for q,

$$5142 + 9929 + q + 282\,990 = 48\,660 + 14\,590 + 109\,400$$

$$q = -125\,411 \text{ kJ/h}$$

Hence, heat is removed: $-34\,837$ W.

Often when chemical reactions occur in the process and the heat capacities vary with temperature, the solution in a heat balance can be trial and error if the final temperature is the unknown.

EXAMPLE 1.7-3. *Oxidation of Lactose*
In many biochemical processes, lactose is used as a nutrient, which is oxidized as follows:

$$C_{12}H_{22}O_{11}(s) + 12O_2(g) \rightarrow 12CO_2(g) + 11H_2O(l)$$

The heat of combustion ΔH_c^0 in Appendix A.3 at 25°C is -5648.8×10^3 J/g mol. Calculate the heat of complete oxidation (combustion) at 37°C, which is the temperature of many biochemical reactions. The c_{pm} of solid lactose is 1.20 J/g · K, and the molecular weight is 342.3 g mass/g mol.

Solution: This can be treated as an ordinary heat-balance problem. First, the process flow diagram is drawn in Fig. 1.7-3. Next, the datum temperature of 25°C is selected and the input and output enthalpies calculated. The temperature difference $\Delta t = (37 - 25)$°C = $(37 - 25)$ K.

FIGURE 1.7-3. *Process flow diagram for Example 1.7-3.*

Input items

$$H(\text{lactose}) = (342.3\ \text{g})\left(c_{pm} \frac{J}{g \cdot K} \right)(37 - 25)\ K = 342.3(1.20)(37 - 25)$$

$$= 4929\ J$$

$$H(O_2\ \text{gas}) = (12\ \text{g mol})\left(c_{pm} \frac{J}{g\ \text{mol} \cdot K} \right)(37 - 25)\ K$$

$$= 12(29.38)(37 - 25) = 4230\ J$$

(The c_{pm} of O_2 was obtained from Table 1.6-1.)

$$-\Delta H_{25}^0 = -(-5648.8 \times 10^3)$$

Output items

$$H(H_2O\ \text{liquid}) = 11(18.02\ \text{g})\left(c_{pm} \frac{J}{g \cdot K} \right)(37 - 25)\ K$$

$$= 11(18.02)(4.18)(37 - 25) = 9943\ J$$

(The c_{pm} of liquid water was obtained from Appendix A.2.)

$$H(CO_2\ \text{gas}) = (12\ \text{g mol})\left(c_{pm} \frac{J}{g\ \text{mol} \cdot K} \right)(37 - 25)\ K$$

$$= 12(37.45)(37 - 25) = 5393\ J$$

(The c_{pm} of CO_2 is obtained from Table 1.6-1.)

$\Delta H_{37°C}$:
Setting input = output and solving,

$$4929 + 4230 + 5648.8 \times 10^3 = 9943 + 5393 - \Delta H_{37°c}$$

$$\Delta H_{37°C} = -5642.6 \times 10^3\ J/g\ \text{mol} = \Delta H_{310\ K}$$

1.8 NUMERICAL METHODS FOR INTEGRATION

1.8A Introduction and Graphical Integration

Often the mathematical function $f(x)$ to be integrated is too complex and we are not able to integrate it analytically. Or in some cases the function is one that has been obtained from experimental data, and no mathematical equation is available to represent the data so that they can be integrated analytically. In these cases, we can use either numerical or graphical integration.

Integration of a function $f(x)$ between the limits $x = a$ to $x = b$ can be represented by

$$\int_{x=a}^{x=b} f(x)\, dx \tag{1.8-1}$$

By graphically plotting $f(x)$ versus x, the area under the curve is equal to the value of the integral.

1.8B Numerical Integration and Simpson's Rule

Often it is desirable or necessary to perform a numerical integration by computing the value of a definite integral from a set of numerical values of the integrand $f(x)$. This, of course, can be done graphically, but in most cases numerical methods suitable for the digital computer are desired.

The integral to be evaluated is Eq. (1.8-1), where the interval is $b - a$. The most generally used numerical method is the parabolic rule, often called *Simpson's rule*. This method divides the total interval $b - a$ into an even number of subintervals m, where

$$m = \frac{b - a}{h} \tag{1.8-2}$$

The value of h, a constant, is the spacing in x used. Then, approximating $f(x)$ by a parabola on each subinterval, Simpson's rule is

$$\int_{x=a}^{x=b} f(x)\, dx = \frac{h}{3}\, [f_o + 4(f_1 + f_3 + f_5 + \cdots + f_{m-1})$$
$$+ 2(f_2 + f_4 + f_6 + \cdots + f_{m-2}) + f_m] \tag{1.8-3}$$

where f_0 is the value of $f(x)$ at $x = a$; f_1 the value of $f(x)$ at $x = x_1, \ldots$; f_m the value of $f(x)$ at $x = b$. The reader should note that m must be an even number and the increments evenly spaced. This method is well suited for digital computation with a spreadsheet. Spreadsheets have numerical calculation methods built into their programs. Simpson's rule is a widely used numerical integration method.

In some cases the available experimental data for $f(x)$ are not at equally spaced increments of x. Then the numerical integration can be performed using the sum of the single-interval rectangles (trapezoidal rule) for the value of the interval. This is much less accurate than Simpson's rule. The trapezoidal-rule method becomes more accurate as the interval becomes smaller.

Sometimes the experimental data for $f(x)$ are spaced at large and/or irregular increments of x. These data can be smoothed by fitting a polynomial, exponential, logarithmic, or some other function to the data, which often can be integrated analytically. If the function is relatively complex, then it can be numerically integrated using Simpson's rule. All of this can be done using Excel and a spreadsheet.

PROBLEMS

1.2-1. *Temperature of a Chemical Process.* The temperature of a chemical reaction was found to be 353.2 K. What is the temperature in °F, °C, and °R?

Ans. 176°F, 80°C, 636°R

1.2-2. *Temperature for Smokehouse Processing of Meat.* In smokehouse processing of sausage meat, a final temperature of 155°F inside the sausage is often used. Calculate this temperature in °C, K, and °R.

1.3-1. *Molecular Weight of Air.* For purposes of most engineering calculations, air is assumed to be composed of 21 mol % oxygen and 79 mol % nitrogen. Calculate the average molecular weight.

Ans. 28.9 g mass/g mol, lb mass/lb mol, or kg mass/kg mol

1.3-2. *Oxidation of CO and Mole Units.* The gas CO is being oxidized by O_2 to form CO_2. How many kg of CO_2 will be formed from 56 kg of CO? Also, calculate the kg of O_2 theoretically needed for this reaction. (*Hint:* First write the balanced chemical equation to obtain the mol O_2 needed for 1.0 kg mol CO. Then calculate the kg mol of CO in 56 kg CO.)

Ans. 88.0 kg CO_2, 32.0 kg O_2

1.3-3. *Composition of a Gas Mixture.* A gaseous mixture contains 20 g of N_2, 83 g of O_2, and 45 g of CO_2. Calculate the composition in mole fraction and the average molecular weight of the mixture.

Ans. Average mol wt = 34.2 g mass/g mol, 34.2 kg mass/kg mol

1.3-4. *Composition of a Protein Solution.* A liquid solution contains 1.15 wt % of a protein, 0.27 wt % KCl, and the remainder water. The average molecular weight of the protein by gel permeation is 525 000 g mass/g mol. Calculate the mole fraction of each component in solution.

1.3-5. *Concentration of NaCl Solution.* An aqueous solution of NaCl has a concentration of 24.0 wt % NaCl with a density of 1.178 g/cm^3 at 25°C. Calculate the following.
(a) Mole fraction of NaCl and water.
(b) Concentration of NaCl as g mol/liter, lb_m/ft^3, lb_m/gal, and kg/m^3.

1.4-1. *Conversion of Pressure Measurements in Freeze Drying.* In the experimental measurement of freeze drying of beef, an absolute pressure of 2.4 mm Hg was held in the chamber. Convert this pressure to atm, in. of water at 4°C, μm of Hg, and Pa. (*Hint:* See Appendix A.1 for conversion factors.)

Ans. 3.16×10^{-3} atm, 1.285 in. H_2O, 2400 μm Hg, 320 Pa

1.4-2. *Compression and Cooling of Nitrogen Gas.* A volume of 65.0 ft^3 of N_2 gas at 90°F and 29.0 psig is compressed to 75 psig and cooled to 65°F. Calculate the final volume in ft^3 and the final density in lb_m/ft^3. [*Hint:* Be sure to convert all pressures to psia first and then to atm. Substitute original conditions into Eq. (1.4-1) to obtain n, lb mol.]

1.4-3. *Gas Composition and Volume.* A gas mixture of 0.13 g mol NH_3, 1.27 g mol N_2, and 0.025 g mol H_2O vapor is contained at a total pressure of 830 mm Hg and 323 K. Calculate the following.
(a) Mole fraction of each component.
(b) Partial pressure of each component in mm Hg.
(c) Total volume of mixture in m^3 and ft^3.

1.4-4. *Evaporation of a Heat-Sensitive Organic Liquid.* An organic liquid is being evaporated from a liquid solution containing a few percent nonvolatile dissolved solids. Since it is heat-sensitive and may discolor at high temperatures, it will be evaporated under vacuum. If the lowest absolute pressure that can be obtained in the apparatus is 12.0 mm Hg, what will be the temperature of evaporation in K? It will be assumed that the small amount of solids does not affect the vapor pressure, which is given as follows:

$$\log P_A = -2250\left(\frac{1}{T}\right) + 9.05$$

where P_A is in mm Hg and T in K.

Ans. $T = 282.3$ K or 9.1°C

1.5-1. *Evaporation of Cane Sugar Solutions.* An evaporator is used to concentrate cane sugar solutions. A feed of 10 000 kg/d of a solution containing 38 wt % sugar is evaporated, producing a 74 wt % solution. Calculate the weight of solution produced and amount of water removed.

Ans. 5135 kg/d of 74 wt % solution, 4865 kg/d water

1.5-2. *Processing of Fish Meal.* Fish are processed into fish meal and used as a supplementary protein food. In the processing the oil is first extracted to produce wet fish cake containing 80 wt % water and 20 wt % bone-dry cake. This wet cake feed is dried in rotary-drum dryers to give a "dry" fish cake product containing 40 wt % water. Finally, the product is finely ground and packed. Calculate the kg/h of wet cake feed needed to produce 1000 kg/h of "dry" fish cake product.

Ans. 3000 kg/h wet cake feed

1.5-3. *Drying of Lumber.* A batch of 100 kg of wet lumber containing 11 wt % moisture is dried to a water content of 6.38 kg water/1.0 kg bone-dry lumber. What is the weight of "dried" lumber and the amount of water removed?

1.5-4. *Processing of Paper Pulp.* A wet paper pulp contains 68 wt % water. After the pulp was dried, it was found that 55% of the original water in the wet pulp was removed. Calculate the composition of the "dried" pulp and its weight for a feed of 1000 kg/min of wet pulp.

1.5-5. *Production of Jam from Crushed Fruit in Two Stages.* In a process producing jam (C1), crushed fruit containing 14 wt % soluble solids is mixed in a mixer with sugar (1.22 kg sugar/1.00 kg crushed fruit) and pectin (0.0025 kg pectin/1.00 kg crushed fruit). The resultant mixture is then evaporated in a kettle to produce a jam containing 67 wt % soluble solids. For a feed of 1000 kg crushed fruit, calculate the kg mixture from the mixer, kg water evaporated, and kg jam produced.

Ans. 2222.5 kg mixture, 189 kg water, 2033.5 kg jam

1.5-6. *Drying of Cassava (Tapioca) Root.* Tapioca flour is used in many countries for bread and similar products. The flour is made by drying coarse granules of the cassava root containing 66 wt % moisture to 5% moisture and then grinding to produce a flour. How many kg of granules must be dried and how much water removed to produce 5000 kg/h of flour?

1.5-7. *Processing of Soybeans in Three Stages.* A feed of 10 000 kg of soybeans is processed in a sequence of three stages or steps (E1). The feed contains 35 wt % protein, 27.1 wt % carbohydrate, 9.4 wt % fiber and ash, 10.5 wt % moisture, and 18.0 wt % oil. In the first stage the beans are crushed and pressed to remove oil, giving an expressed-oil stream and a stream of pressed beans containing 6% oil. Assume no loss of other constituents with the oil stream. In the second step the pressed beans are extracted with hexane to produce an extracted-meal stream containing 0.5 wt % oil and a hexane–oil stream. Assume no hexane in the extracted meal. Finally, in the last step the extracted meal is dried to give a dried meal of 8 wt % moisture. Calculate:

(a) Kg of pressed beans from the first stage.
(b) Kg of extracted meal from stage 2.
(c) Kg of final dried meal and the wt % protein in the dried meal.

Ans. (a) 8723 kg; (b) 8241 kg; (c) 7816 kg, 44.8 wt % protein

1.5-8. *Recycle in a Dryer.* A solid material containing 15.0 wt % moisture is dried so that it contains 7.0 wt % water by blowing fresh warm air mixed with recycled air over the solid in the dryer. The inlet fresh air has a humidity of 0.01 kg water/kg dry air, the air from the drier that is recycled has a humidity of 0.1 kg water/kg dry air, and the mixed air to the dryer, 0.03 kg water/kg dry air. For a feed of 100 kg solid/h fed to the dryer, calculate the kg dry air/h in the fresh air, the kg dry air/h in the recycled air, and the kg/h of "dried" product.

Ans. 95.6 kg/h dry air in fresh air, 27.3 kg/h dry air in recycled air, and 91.4 kg/h "dried" product

1.5-9. *Crystallization and Recycle.* It is desired to produce 1000 kg/h of $Na_3PO_4 \cdot 12H_2O$ crystals from a feed solution containing 5.6 wt % Na_3PO_4 and traces of impurity. The original solution is first evaporated in an evaporator to a 35 wt % Na_3PO_4 solution and then cooled to 293 K in a crystallizer, where the hydrated crystals and a mother-liquor solution are removed. One out of every 10 kg of mother liquor is discarded to waste to get rid of the impurities, and the remaining mother liquor is recycled to the evaporator. The solubility of Na_3PO_4 at 293 K is 9.91 wt %. Calculate the kg/h of feed solution and kg/h of water evaporated.

Ans. 7771 kg/h feed, 6739 kg/h water

1.5-10. *Evaporation and Bypass in Orange Juice Concentration.* In a process for concentrating 1000 kg of freshly extracted orange juice (C1) containing 12.5 wt % solids, the juice is strained, yielding 800 kg of strained juice and 200 kg of pulpy juice. The strained juice is concentrated in a vacuum evaporator to give an evaporated juice of 58% solids. The 200 kg of pulpy juice is bypassed around the evaporator and mixed with the evaporated juice in a mixer to improve the flavor. This final concentrated juice contains 42 wt % solids. Calculate the concentration of solids in the strained juice, the kg of final concentrated juice, and the concentration of solids in the pulpy juice bypassed. (*Hint:* First, make a total balance and then a solids balance on the overall process. Next, make a balance on the evaporator. Finally, make a balance on the mixer.)

Ans. 34.2 wt % solids in pulpy juice

1.5-11. *Manufacture of Acetylene.* For the making of 6000 ft³ of acetylene (CHCH) gas at 70°F and 750 mm Hg, solid calcium carbide (CaC_2) which contains 97 wt % CaC_2 and 3 wt % solid inerts is used along with water. The reaction is

$$CaC_2 + 2H_2O \rightarrow CHCH + Ca(OH)_2\downarrow$$

The final lime slurry contains water, solid inerts, and $Ca(OH)_2$ lime. In this slurry the total wt % solids of inerts plus $Ca(OH)_2$ is 20%. How many lb of water must be added and how many lb of final lime slurry is produced? [*Hint:* Use a basis of 6000 ft³ and convert to lb mol. This gives 15.30 lb mol C_2H_2, 15.30 lb mol $Ca(OH)_2$, and 15.30 lb mol CaC_2 added. Convert lb mol CaC_2 feed to lb and calculate lb inerts added. The total lb solids in the slurry is then the sum of the $Ca(OH)_2$ plus inerts. In calculating the water added, remember that some is consumed in the reaction.]

Ans. 5200 lb water added (2359 kg), 5815 lb lime slurry (2638 kg)

1.5-12. *Combustion of Solid Fuel.* A fuel analyzes 74.0 wt % C and 12.0% ash (inert). Air is added to burn the fuel, producing a flue gas of 12.4% CO_2, 1.2% CO, 5.7% O_2, and

80.7% N_2. Calculate the kg of fuel used for 100 kg mol of outlet flue gas and the kg mol of air used. (*Hint:* First calculate the mol O_2 added in the air, using the fact that the N_2 in the flue gas equals the N_2 added in the air. Then make a carbon balance to obtain the total moles of C added.)

1.5-13. *Burning of Coke.* A furnace burns a coke containing 81.0 wt % C, 0.8% H, and the rest inert ash. The furnace uses 60% excess air (air over and above that needed to burn all C to CO_2 and H to H_2O). Calculate the moles of all components in the flue gas if only 95% of the carbon goes to CO_2 and 5% to CO.

1.5-14. *Production of Formaldehyde.* Formaldehyde (CH_2O) is made by the catalytic oxidation of pure methanol vapor and air in a reactor. The moles from this reactor are 63.1 N_2, 13.4 O_2, 5.9 H_2O, 4.1 CH_2O, 12.3 CH_3OH, and 1.2 HCOOH. The reaction is

$$CH_3OH + \tfrac{1}{2}O_2 \rightarrow CH_2O + H_2O$$

A side reaction occurring is

$$CH_2O + \tfrac{1}{2}O_2 \rightarrow HCOOH$$

Calculate the mol methanol feed, mol air feed, and percent conversion of methanol to formaldehyde.

Ans. 17.6 mol CH_3OH, 79.8 mol air, 23.3% conversion

1.6-1. *Heating of CO_2 Gas.* A total of 250 g of CO_2 gas at 373 K is heated to 623 K at 101.32 kPa total pressure. Calculate the amount of heat needed in cal, btu, and kJ.

Ans. 15 050 cal, 59.7 btu, 62.98 kJ

1.6-2. *Heating a Gas Mixture.* A mixture of 25 lb mol N_2 and 75 lb mol CH_4 is being heated from 400°F to 800°F at 1 atm pressure. Calculate the total amount of heat needed in btu.

1.6-3. *Final Temperature in Heating Applesauce.* A mixture of 454 kg of applesauce at 10°C is heated in a heat exchanger by adding 121 300 kJ. Calculate the outlet temperature of the applesauce. (*Hint:* In Appendix A.4 a heat capacity for applesauce is given at 32.8°C. Assume that this is constant and use this as the average c_{pm}.)

Ans. 76.5°C

1.6-4. *Use of Steam Tables.* Using the steam tables, determine the enthalpy change for 1 lb water for each of the following cases:

(a) Heating liquid water from 40°F to 240°F at 30 psia. (Note that the effect of total pressure on the enthalpy of liquid water can be neglected.)

(b) Heating liquid water from 40°F to 240°F and vaporizing at 240°F and 24.97 psia.

(c) Cooling and condensing a saturated vapor at 212°F and 1 atm abs to a liquid at 60°F.

(d) Condensing a saturated vapor at 212°F and 1 atm abs.

Ans. (a) 200.42 btu/lb$_m$; (b) 1152.7 btu/lb$_m$; (c) −1122.4 btu/lb$_m$; (d) −970.3 btu/lb$_m$, −2256.9 kJ/kg

1.6-5. *Heating and Vaporization Using Steam Tables.* A flow rate of 1000 kg/h of water at 21.1°C is heated to 110°C when the total pressure is 244.2 kPa in the first stage of a process. In the second stage at the same pressure the water is heated further, until it is all vaporized at its boiling point. Calculate the total enthalpy change in the first stage and in both stages.

1.6-6. *Combustion of CH_4 and H_2.* For 100 g mol of a gas mixture of 75 mol % CH_4 and 25% H_2, calculate the total heat of combustion of the mixture at 298 K and 101.32 kPa, assuming that combustion is complete.

1.6-7. *Heat of Reaction from Heats of Formation.* For the reaction

$$4NH_3(g) + 5O_2(g) \rightarrow 4NO(g) + 6H_2O(g)$$

calculate the heat of reaction, ΔH, at 298 K and 101.32 kPa for 4 g mol of NH_3 reacting.

Ans. ΔH, heat of reaction = -904.7 kJ

1.7-1. *Heat Balance and Cooling of Milk.* In the processing of rich cows' milk, 4540 kg/h of milk is cooled from 60°C to 4.44°C by a refrigerant. Calculate the heat removed from the milk.

Ans. Heat removed = 269.6 kW

1.7-2. *Heating of Oil by Air.* A flow of 2200 lb_m/h of hydrocarbon oil at 100°F enters a heat exchanger, where it is heated to 150°F by hot air. The hot air enters at 300°F and is to leave at 200°F. Calculate the total lb mol air/h needed. The mean heat capacity of the oil is 0.45 btu/$lb_m \cdot$ °F.

Ans. 70.1 lb mol air/h, 31.8 kg mol/h

1.7-3. *Combustion of Methane in a Furnace.* A gas stream of 10 000 kg mol/h of CH_4 at 101.32 kPa and 373 K is burned in a furnace using air at 313 K. The combustion is complete and 50% excess air is used. The flue gas leaves the furnace at 673 K. Calculate the heat removed in the furnace. (*Hint:* Use a datum of 298 K and liquid water at 298 K. The input items will be the following: the enthalpy of CH_4 at 373 K referred to 298 K; the enthalpy of the air at 313 K referred to 298 K; $-\Delta H_c^0$, the heat of combustion of CH_4 at 298 K, which is referred to liquid water; and q, the heat added. The output items will include: the enthalpies of CO_2, O_2, N_2, and H_2O gases at 673 K referred to 298 K; and the latent heat of H_2O vapor at 298 K and 101.32 kPa from Appendix A.2. It is necessary to include this latent heat since the basis of the calculation and of the ΔH_c^0 is liquid water.)

1.7-4. *Preheating Air by Steam for Use in a Dryer.* An air stream at 32.2°C is to be used in a dryer and is first preheated in a steam heater, where it is heated to 65.5°C. The air flow is 1000 kg mol/h. The steam enters the heater saturated at 148.9°C, is condensed and cooled, and leaves as a liquid at 137.8°C. Calculate the amount of steam used in kg/h.

Ans. 450 kg steam/h

1.7-5. *Cooling of Cans of Potato Soup After Thermal Processing.* A total of 1500 cans of potato soup undergo thermal processing in a retort at 240°F. The cans are then cooled to 100°F in the retort before being removed from the retort by cooling water, which enters at 75°F and leaves at 85°F. Calculate the lb of cooling water needed. Each can of soup contains 1.0 lb of liquid soup, and the empty metal can weighs 0.16 lb. The mean heat capacity of the soup is 0.94 btu/$lb_m \cdot$ °F and that of the metal can is 0.12 btu/$lb_m \cdot$ °F. A metal rack or basket which is used to hold the cans in the retort weighs 350 lb and has a heat capacity of 0.12 btu/$lb_m \cdot$ °F. Assume that the metal rack is cooled from 240°F to 85°F, the temperature of the outlet water. The amount of heat removed from the retort walls in cooling from 240 to 100°F is 10 000 btu. Radiation loss from the retort during cooling is estimated as 5000 btu.

Ans. 21 320 lb water, 9670 kg

1.8-1. *Numerical Integration Using Simpson's Method.* The following experimental data for $y = f(x)$ were obtained:

x	$f(x)$	x	$f(x)$
0	100	0.4	53
0.1	75	0.5	60
0.2	60.5	0.6	72.5
0.3	53.5		

Determine the integral using Simpson's method:

$$A = \int_{x=0}^{x=0.6} f(x)\, dx$$

Ans. $A = 38.45$

1.8-2. *Numerical Integration to Obtain Wastewater Flow.* The rate of flow of wastewater in an open channel has been measured and the following data obtained:

Time (min)	Flow (m^3/min)	Time (min)	Flow (m^3/min)
0	655	70	800
10	705	80	725
20	780	90	670
30	830	100	640
40	870	110	620
50	890	120	610
60	870		

Determine the total flow in m^3 for 120 min by numerical integration.

Ans. 92 350 m^3

REFERENCES

(C1) CHARM, S. E. *The Fundamentals of Food Engineering,* 2nd ed. Westport, Conn.: Avi Publishing Co., Inc., 1971.

(E1) EARLE, R. L. *Unit Operations in Food Processing.* Oxford: Pergamon Press, Inc., 1966.

(H1) HOUGEN, O. A., WATSON, K. M., and RAGATZ, R. A. *Chemical Process Principles,* Part I, 2nd ed. New York: John Wiley & Sons, Inc., 1954.

(O1) OKOS, M. R. M.S. thesis. Ohio State University, Columbus, Ohio, 1972.

(P1) PERRY, R. H., and GREEN, D. *Perry's Chemical Engineers' Handbook*, 6th ed. New York: McGraw-Hill Book Company, 1984.

(S1) SOBER, H. A. *Handbook of Biochemistry, Selected Data for Molecular Biology,* 2nd ed. Boca Raton, Fla.: Chemical Rubber Co., Inc., 1970.

(W1) WEAST, R. C., and SELBY, S. M. *Handbook of Chemistry and Physics,* 48th ed. Boca Raton, Fla.: Chemical Rubber Co., Inc., 1967–1968.

CHAPTER 2

Principles of
Momentum Transfer
and Overall Balances

2.1 INTRODUCTION

The flow and behavior of fluids is important in many of the separation processes in process engineering. A fluid may be defined as a substance that does not permanently resist distortion and, hence, will change its shape. In this text gases, liquids, and vapors are considered to have the characteristics of fluids and to obey many of the same laws.

In the process industries, many of the materials are in fluid form and must be stored, handled, pumped, and processed, so it is necessary that we become familiar with the principles that govern the flow of fluids as well as with the equipment used. Typical fluids encountered include water, air, CO_2, oil, slurries, and thick syrups.

If a fluid is inappreciably affected by changes in pressure, it is said to be *incompressible*. Most liquids are incompressible. Gases are considered to be *compressible* fluids. However, if gases are subjected to small percentage changes in pressure and temperature, their density changes will be small and they can be considered to be incompressible.

Like all physical matter, a fluid is composed of an extremely large number of molecules per unit volume. A theory such as the kinetic theory of gases or statistical mechanics treats the motions of molecules in terms of statistical groups and not in terms of individual molecules. In engineering we are mainly concerned with the bulk or macroscopic behavior of a fluid rather than the individual molecular or microscopic behavior.

In momentum transfer we treat the fluid as a continuous distribution of matter, or a "continuum." This treatment as a continuum is valid when the smallest volume of fluid contains a number of molecules large enough that a statistical average is meaningful and the macroscopic properties of the fluid, such as density, pressure, and so on, vary smoothly or continuously from point to point.

The study of *momentum transfer,* or *fluid mechanics* as it is often called, can be divided into two branches: *fluid statics,* or fluids at rest, and *fluid dynamics,* or fluids in motion. In Section 2.2 we treat fluid statics; in the remaining sections of Chapter 2 and in Chapter 3, fluid dynamics. Since in fluid dynamics momentum is being transferred, the term "momentum transfer" or "transport" is usually used. In Section 2.3 momentum transfer is related to heat and mass transfer.

2.2 FLUID STATICS

2.2A Force, Units, and Dimensions

In a static fluid an important property is the pressure in the fluid. Pressure is familiar as a surface force exerted by a fluid against the walls of its container. Also, pressure exists at any point in a volume of a fluid.

In order to understand *pressure,* which is defined as force exerted per unit area, we must first discuss a basic law of Newton's. This equation for calculation of the force exerted by a mass under the influence of gravity is

$$F = mg \qquad \text{(SI units)}$$

$$F = \frac{mg}{g_c} \qquad \text{(English units)} \tag{2.2-1}$$

where in SI units F is the force exerted in newtons N ($kg \cdot m/s^2$), m the mass in kg, and g the standard acceleration of gravity, 9.80665 m/s^2.

In English units, F is in lb_f, m in lb_m, g is 32.1740 ft/s^2, and g_c (a gravitational conversion factor) is 32.174 $lb_m \cdot ft/lb_f \cdot s^2$. The use of the conversion factor g_c means that g/g_c has a value of 1.0 lb_f/lb_m and that 1 lb_m conveniently gives a force equal to 1 lb_f. Often when units of pressure are given, the word "force" is omitted, as in $lb/in.^2$ (psi) instead of $lb_f/in.^2$. When the mass m is given in g mass, F is g force, $g = 980.665$ cm/s^2, and $g_c = 980.665$ g mass $\cdot$ cm/g force $\cdot s^2$. However, the units g force are seldom used.

Another system of units sometimes used in Eq. (2.2-1) is that where the g_c is omitted and the force ($F = mg$) is given as $lb_m \cdot ft/s^2$, called *poundals.* Then 1 lb_m acted on by gravity will give a force of 32.174 poundals ($lb_m \cdot ft/s^2$). Or if 1 g mass is used, the force ($F = mg$) is expressed in terms of dynes ($g \cdot cm/s^2$). This is the centimeter–gram–second (cgs) system of units.

Conversion factors for different units of force and of force per unit area (pressure) are given in Appendix A.1. Note that always in the SI system, and usually in the cgs system, the term g_c is not used.

EXAMPLE 2.2-1. Units and Dimensions of Force

Calculate the force exerted by 3 lb mass in terms of the following:
  (a) Lb force (English units).
  (b) Dynes (cgs units).
  (c) Newtons (SI units).

Solution: For part (a), using Eq. (2.2-1),

$$F \text{ (force)} = m\frac{g}{g_c} = (3\ lb_m)\left(32.174\ \frac{ft}{s^2}\right)\left(\frac{1}{32.174\ \dfrac{lb_m \cdot ft}{lb_f \cdot s^2}}\right) = 3\ lb\ \text{force}\ (lb_f)$$

For part (b),

$$F = mg = (3\ lb_m)\left(453.59\ \frac{g}{lb_m}\right)\left(980.665\ \frac{cm}{s^2}\right)$$

$$= 1.332 \times 10^6\ \frac{g \cdot cm}{s^2} = 1.332 \times 10^6\ dyn$$

As an alternative method for part (b), from Appendix A.1,

$$1 \text{ dyn} = 2.2481 \times 10^{-6} \text{ lb}_f$$

$$F = (3 \text{ lb}_f) \left(\frac{1}{2.2481 \times 10^{-6} \text{ lb}_f/\text{dyn}} \right) = 1.332 \times 10^6 \text{ dyn}$$

To calculate newtons in part (c),

$$F = mg = \left(3 \text{ lb}_m \times \frac{1 \text{ kg}}{2.2046 \text{ lb}_m} \right) \left(9.80665 \frac{\text{m}}{\text{s}^2} \right)$$

$$= 13.32 \frac{\text{kg} \cdot \text{m}}{\text{s}^2} = 13.32 \text{ N}$$

As an alternative method, using values from Appendix A.1,

$$1 \frac{\text{g} \cdot \text{cm}}{\text{s}^2} (\text{dyn}) = 10^{-5} \frac{\text{kg} \cdot \text{m}}{\text{s}^2} (\text{newton})$$

$$F = (1.332 \times 10^6 \text{ dyn}) \left(10^{-5} \frac{\text{newton}}{\text{dyn}} \right) = 13.32 \text{ N}$$

2.2B Pressure in a Fluid

Since Eq. (2.2-1) gives the force exerted by a mass under the influence of gravity, the force exerted by a mass of fluid on a supporting area, or force/unit area (pressure), also follows from this equation. In Fig. 2.2-1 a stationary column of fluid of height h_2 m and constant cross-sectional area A m^2, where $A = A_0 = A_1 = A_2$, is shown. The pressure above the fluid is P_0 N/m^2; that is, this could be the pressure of the atmosphere above the fluid. The fluid at any point, say h_1, must support all the fluid above it. It can be shown that the forces at any given point in a nonmoving or static fluid must be the same in all directions. Also, for a fluid at rest, the force/unit area, or pressure, is the same at all points with the same elevation. For example, at h_1 m from the top, the pressure is the same at all points shown on the cross-sectional area A_1.

FIGURE 2.2-1. *Pressure in a static fluid.*

The use of Eq. (2.2-1) will be shown in calculating the pressure at different vertical points in Fig. 2.2-1. The total mass of fluid for h_2 m height and density ρ kg/m^3 is

$$\text{total kg fluid} = (h_2 \text{ m})(A \text{ m}^2)\left(\rho \frac{\text{kg}}{\text{m}^3}\right) = h_2 A \rho \text{ kg} \qquad (2.2\text{-}2)$$

Substituting into Eq. (2.2-2), the total force F of the fluid on area A_1 due to the fluid only is

$$F = (h_2 A \rho \text{ kg})(g \text{ m/s}^2) = h_2 A \rho g \frac{\text{kg} \cdot \text{m}}{\text{s}^2} (\text{N}) \qquad (2.2\text{-}3)$$

The pressure P is defined as force/unit area:

$$P = \frac{F}{A} = (h_2 A \rho g)\frac{1}{A} = h_2 \rho g \text{ N/m}^2 \quad \text{or} \quad \text{Pa} \qquad (2.2\text{-}4)$$

This is the pressure on A_2 due to the mass of the fluid above it. However, to get the total pressure P_2 on A_2, the pressure P_0 on the top of the fluid must be added:

$$P_2 = h_2 \rho g + P_0 \text{ N/m}^2 \quad \text{or} \quad \text{Pa} \qquad (2.2\text{-}5)$$

Equation (2.2-5) is the fundamental equation for calculating the pressure in a fluid at any depth. To calculate P_1,

$$P_1 = h_1 \rho g + P_0 \qquad (2.2\text{-}6)$$

The pressure difference between points 2 and 1 is

$$P_2 - P_1 = (h_2 \rho g + P_0) - (h_1 \rho g + P_0) = (h_2 - h_1)\rho g \quad \text{(SI units)}$$

$$P_2 - P_1 = (h_2 - h_1)\rho \frac{g}{g_c} \quad \text{(English units)} \qquad (2.2\text{-}7)$$

Since it is the vertical height of a fluid that determines the pressure in a fluid, the shape of the vessel does not affect the pressure. For example, in Fig. 2.2-2, the pressure P_1 at the bottom of all three vessels is the same and is equal to $h_1 \rho g + P_0$.

EXAMPLE 2.2-2.   Pressure in Storage Tank
A large storage tank contains oil having a density of 917 kg/m^3 (0.917 g/cm^3). The tank is 3.66 m (12.0 ft) tall and is vented (open) to the atmosphere of 1 atm abs at the top. The tank is filled with oil to a depth of 3.05 m (10 ft) and also con-

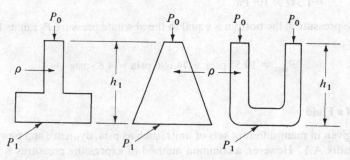

FIGURE 2.2-2.   *Pressure in vessels of various shapes.*

FIGURE 2.2-3. *Storage tank in Example 2.2-2.*

$P_0 = 1$ atm abs

tains 0.61 m (2.0 ft) of water in the bottom of the tank. Calculate the pressure in Pa and psia 3.05 m from the top of the tank and at the bottom. Also calculate the gage pressure at the tank bottom.

Solution: First a sketch is made of the tank, as shown in Fig. 2.2-3. The pressure $P_0 = 1$ atm abs = 14.696 psia (from Appendix A.1). Also,

$$P_0 = 1.01325 \times 10^5 \text{ Pa}$$

From Eq. (2.2-6), using English and then SI units,

$$P_1 = h_1 \rho_{\text{oil}} \frac{g}{g_c} + P_0 = (10 \text{ ft})\left(0.917 \times 62.43 \frac{\text{lb}_m}{\text{ft}^3}\right)\left(1.0 \frac{\text{lb}_f}{\text{lb}_m}\right)\left(\frac{1}{144 \text{ in.}^2/\text{ft}^2}\right)$$
$$+ 14.696 \text{ lb}_f/\text{in.}^2 = 18.68 \text{ psia}$$

$$P_1 = h_1 \rho_{\text{oil}} g + P_0 = (3.05 \text{ m})\left(917 \frac{\text{kg}}{\text{m}^3}\right)\left(9.8066 \frac{\text{m}}{\text{s}^2}\right) + 1.0132 \times 10^5$$
$$= 1.287 \times 10^5 \text{ Pa}$$

To calculate P_2 at the bottom of the tank, $\rho_{\text{water}} = 1.00 \text{ g/cm}^3$ and

$$P_2 = h_2 \rho_{\text{water}} \frac{g}{g_c} + P_1 = (2.0)(1.00 \times 62.43)(1.0)(\tfrac{1}{144}) + 18.68$$
$$= 19.55 \text{ psia}$$
$$= h_2 \rho_{\text{water}} g + P_1 = (0.61)(1000)(9.8066) + 1.287 \times 10^5$$
$$= 1.347 \times 10^5 \text{ Pa}$$

The gage pressure at the bottom is equal to the absolute pressure P_2 minus 1 atm pressure:

$$P_{\text{gage}} = 19.55 \text{ psia} - 14.696 \text{ psia} = 4.85 \text{ psig}$$

2.2C   Head of a Fluid

Pressures are given in many different sets of units, such as psia, dyn/cm², and newtons/m², as given in Appendix A.1. However, a common method of expressing pressures is in terms of head in m or feet of a particular fluid. This height or head in m or feet of the given fluid will exert the same pressure as the pressures it represents. Using Eq. (2.2-4), which relates pressure P and height h of a fluid, and solving for h, which is the head in m,

$$h(\text{head}) = \frac{P}{\rho g} \text{ m} \quad \text{(SI)}$$

$$h = \frac{P g_c}{\rho g} \text{ ft} \quad \text{(English)}$$

(2.2-8)

EXAMPLE 2.2-3. Conversion of Pressure to Head of a Fluid

Given the pressure of 1 standard atm as 101.325 kN/m^2 (Appendix A.1), do as follows:

(a) Convert this pressure to head in m water at 4°C.
(b) Convert this pressure to head in m Hg at 0°C.

Solution: For part (a), the density of water at 4°C in Appendix A.2 is 1.000 g/cm^3. From A.1, a density of 1.000 g/cm^3 equals 1000 kg/m^3. Substituting these values into Eq. (2.2-8),

$$h(\text{head}) = \frac{P}{\rho g} = \frac{101.325 \times 10^3}{(1000)(9.80665)}$$

$$= 10.33 \text{ m of water at } 4°C$$

For part (b), the density of Hg in Appendix A.1 is 13.5955 g/cm^3. For equal pressures P from different fluids, Eq. (2.2-8) can be rewritten as

$$P = \rho_{Hg} h_{Hg} g = \rho_{H_2O} h_{H_2O} g$$

(2.2-9)

Solving for h_{Hg} in Eq. (2.2-9) and substituting known values,

$$h_{Hg}(\text{head}) = \frac{\rho_{H_2O}}{\rho_{Hg}} h_{H_2O} = \left(\frac{1.000}{13.5955}\right)(10.33) = 0.760 \text{ m Hg}$$

2.2D Devices to Measure Pressure and Pressure Differences

In chemical and other industrial processing plants, it is often important to measure and control the pressure in a vessel or process and/or the liquid level in a vessel. Also, since many fluids are flowing in a pipe or conduit, it is necessary to measure the rate at which the fluid is flowing. Many of these flow meters depend upon devices for measuring a pressure or pressure difference. Some common devices are considered in the following paragraphs.

1. Simple U-tube manometer. The U-tube manometer is shown in Fig. 2.2-4a. The pressure p_a N/m^2 is exerted on one arm of the U tube and p_b on the other arm. Both pressures p_a and p_b could be pressure taps from a fluid meter, or p_a could be a pressure tap and p_b the atmospheric pressure. The top of the manometer is filled with liquid B, having a density of ρ_B kg/m^3, and the bottom with a more dense fluid A, having a density of ρ_A kg/m^3. Liquid A is immiscible with B. To derive the relationship between p_a and p_b, p_a is the pressure at point 1 and p_b at point 5. The pressure at point 2 is

$$p_2 = p_a + (Z + R)\rho_B g \text{ N/m}^2$$

(2.2-10)

where R is the reading of the manometer in m. The pressure at point 3 must be equal to that at 2 by the principles of hydrostatics:

$$p_3 = p_2 \tag{2.2-11}$$

The pressure at point 3 also equals the following:

$$p_3 = p_b + Z\rho_B g + R\rho_A g \tag{2.2-12}$$

Equating Eq. (2.2-10) to (2.2-12) and solving,

$$p_a + (Z + R)\rho_B g = p_b + Z\rho_B g + R\rho_A g \tag{2.2-13}$$

$$p_a - p_b = R(\rho_A - \rho_B)g \quad \text{(SI)}$$
$$\tag{2.2-14}$$
$$p_a - p_b = R(\rho_A - \rho_B)\frac{g}{g_c} \quad \text{(English)}$$

The reader should note that the distance Z does not enter into the final result nor do the tube dimensions, provided that p_a and p_b are measured in the same horizontal plane.

EXAMPLE 2.2-4. Pressure Difference in a Manometer

A manometer, as shown in Fig. 2.2-4a, is being used to measure the head or pressure drop across a flow meter. The heavier fluid is mercury, with a density of 13.6 g/cm³, and the top fluid is water, with a density of 1.00 g/cm³. The reading on the manometer is $R = 32.7$ cm. Calculate the pressure difference in N/m² using SI units.

Solution: Converting R to m,

$$R = \frac{32.7}{100} = 0.327 \text{ m}$$

FIGURE 2.2-4. *Manometers to measure pressure differences: (a) U tube; (b) two-fluid U tube.*

Also converting ρ_A and ρ_B to kg/m³ and substituting into Eq. (2.2-14),

$$p_a - p_b = R(\rho_A - \rho_B)g = (0.327 \text{ m})[(13.6 - 1.0)(1000 \text{ kg/m}^3)](9.8066 \text{ m/s}^2)$$
$$= 4.040 \times 10^4 \text{ N/m}^2 \text{ (5.85 psia)}$$

2. Two fluid U tube. In Fig. 2.2-4b a two-fluid U tube is shown, which is a sensitive device for measuring small heads or pressure differences. Let A m² be the cross-sectional area of each of the large reservoirs and a m² be the cross-sectional area of each of the tubes forming the U. Proceeding and making a pressure balance as for the U tube,

$$p_a - p_b = (R - R_0)\left(\rho_A - \rho_B + \frac{a}{A}\rho_B - \frac{a}{A}\rho_C\right)g \qquad \textbf{(2.2-15)}$$

where R_0 is the reading when $p_a = p_b$, R is the actual reading, ρ_A is the density of the heavier fluid, and ρ_B is the density of the lighter fluid. Usually, a/A is made sufficiently small as to be negligible, and also R_0 is often adjusted to zero; then

$$p_a - p_b = R(\rho_A - \rho_B)g \qquad \text{(SI)}$$
$$p_a - p_b = R(\rho_A - \rho_B)\frac{g}{g_c} \qquad \text{(English)} \qquad \textbf{(2.2-16)}$$

If ρ_A and ρ_B are close to each other, the reading R is magnified.

EXAMPLE 2.2-5. Pressure Measurement in a Vessel
The U-tube manometer in Fig. 2.2-5a is used to measure the pressure p_A in a vessel containing a liquid with a density ρ_A. Derive the equation relating the pressure p_A and the reading on the manometer as shown.

Solution: At point 2 the pressure is

$$p_2 = p_{atm} + h_2\rho_B g \text{ N/m}^2 \qquad \textbf{(2.2-17)}$$

FIGURE 2.2-5. *Measurements of pressure in vessels: (a) measurement of pressure in a vessel, (b) measurement of differential pressure.*

At point 1 the pressure is

$$p_1 = p_A + h_1 \rho_A g \qquad (2.2\text{-}18)$$

Equating $p_1 = p_2$ by the principles of hydrostatics and rearranging,

$$p_A = p_{atm} + h_2 \rho_B g - h_1 \rho_A g \qquad (2.2\text{-}19)$$

Another example of a U-tube manometer is shown in Fig. 2.2-5b. In this case the device is used to measure the pressure difference between two vessels.

3. Bourdon pressure gage. Although manometers are used to measure pressures, the most common pressure-measuring device is the mechanical Bourdon-tube pressure gage. A coiled hollow tube in the gage tends to straighten out when subjected to internal pressure, and the degree of straightening depends on the pressure difference between the inside and outside pressures. The tube is connected to a pointer on a calibrated dial.

4. Gravity separator for two immiscible liquids. In Fig. 2.2-6 a continuous gravity separator (decanter) is shown for the separation of two immiscible liquids A (heavy liquid) and B (light liquid). The feed mixture of the two liquids enters at one end of the separator vessel, and the liquids flow slowly to the other end and separate into two distinct layers. Each liquid flows through a separate overflow line as shown. Assuming the frictional resistance to the flow of the liquids is essentially negligible, the principles of fluid statics can be used to analyze the performance.

In Fig. 2.2-6, the depth of the layer of heavy liquid A is h_{A1} m and that of B is h_B. The total depth $h_T = h_{A1} + h_B$ and is fixed by position of the overflow line for B. The heavy liquid A discharges through an overflow leg h_{A2} m above the vessel bottom. The vessel and the overflow lines are vented to the atmosphere. A hydrostatic balance gives

$$h_B \rho_B g + h_{A1} \rho_A g = h_{A2} \rho_A g \qquad (2.2\text{-}20)$$

Substituting $h_B = h_T - h_{A1}$ into Eq. (2.2-20) and solving for h_{A1},

$$h_{A1} = \frac{h_{A2} - h_T \rho_B / \rho_A}{1 - \rho_B / \rho_A} \qquad (2.2\text{-}21)$$

FIGURE 2.2-6. *Continuous atmospheric gravity separator for immiscible liquids.*

This shows that the position of the interface or height h_{A1} depends on the ratio of the densities of the two liquids and on the elevations h_{A2} and h_T of the two overflow lines. Usually, the height h_{A2} is movable so that the interface level can be adjusted.

2.3 GENERAL MOLECULAR TRANSPORT EQUATION FOR MOMENTUM, HEAT, AND MASS TRANSFER

2.3A General Molecular Transport Equation and General Property Balance

1. Introduction to transport processes. In molecular transport processes in general we are concerned with the transfer or movement of a given property or entity by molecular movement through a system or medium which can be a fluid (gas or liquid) or a solid. This property that is being transferred can be mass, thermal energy (heat), or momentum. Each molecule of a system has a given quantity of the property mass, thermal energy, or momentum associated with it. When a difference in concentration of the property exists for any of these properties from one region to an adjacent region, a net transport of this property occurs. In dilute fluids such as gases, where the molecules are relatively far apart, the rate of transport of the property should be relatively fast, since few molecules are present to block the transport or interact. In dense fluids such as liquids, the molecules are close together, and transport or diffusion proceeds more slowly. The molecules in solids are even more closely packed than in liquids and molecular migration is even more restricted.

2. General molecular transport equation. All three of the molecular transport processes of momentum, heat or thermal energy, and mass are characterized in the elementary sense by the same general type of transport equation. First we start by noting the following:

$$\text{rate of transfer process} = \frac{\text{driving force}}{\text{resistance}} \qquad \text{(2.3-1)}$$

This states what is quite obvious—that we need a driving force to overcome a resistance in order to transport a property. This is similar to Ohm's law in electricity, where the rate of flow of electricity is proportional to the voltage drop (driving force) and inversely proportional to the resistance.

We can formalize Eq. (2.3-1) by writing an equation as follows for molecular transport or diffusion of a property:

$$\psi_z = -\delta \frac{d\Gamma}{dz} \qquad \text{(2.3-2)}$$

where ψ_z is defined as the flux of the property as amount of property being transferred per unit time per unit cross-sectional area perpendicular to the z direction of flow in amount of property/s · m^2, δ is a proportionality constant called diffusivity in m^2/s, Γ is concentration of the property in amount of property/m^3, and z is the distance in the direction of flow in m.

If the process is at steady state, then the flux ψ_z is constant. Rearranging Eq. (2.3-2) and integrating,

$$\psi_z \int_{z_1}^{z_2} dz = -\delta \int_{\Gamma_1}^{\Gamma_2} d\Gamma \qquad \text{(2.3-3)}$$

$$\psi_z = \frac{\delta(\Gamma_1 - \Gamma_2)}{z_2 - z_1} \qquad \text{(2.3-4)}$$

FIGURE 2.3-1. *Molecular transport of a property: (a) plot of concentration versus distance for steady state, (b) unsteady-state general property balance.*

A plot of the concentration Γ versus z is shown in Fig. 2.3-1a and is a straight line. Since the flux is in the direction 1 to 2 of decreasing concentration, the slope $d\Gamma/dz$ is negative, and the negative sign in Eq. (2.3-2) gives a positive flux in the direction 1 to 2. In Section 2.3B the specialized equations for momentum, heat, and mass transfer will be shown to be the same as Eq. (2.3-4) for the general property transfer.

EXAMPLE 2.3-1. Molecular Transport of a Property at Steady State

A property is being transported by diffusion through a fluid at steady state. At a given point 1 the concentration is 1.37×10^{-2} amount of property/m^3 and 0.72×10^{-2} at point 2 at a distance $z_2 = 0.40$ m. The diffusivity $\delta = 0.013$ m^2/s and the cross-sectional area is constant.

    (a) Calculate the flux.
    (b) Derive the equation for Γ as a function of distance.
    (c) Calculate Γ at the midpoint of the path.

Solution: For part (a), substituting into Eq. (2.3-4),

$$\psi_z = \frac{\delta(\Gamma_1 - \Gamma_2)}{z_2 - z_1} = \frac{(0.013)(1.37 \times 10^{-2} - 0.72 \times 10^{-2})}{0.40 - 0}$$

$$= 2.113 \times 10^{-4} \text{ amount of property/s} \cdot \text{m}^2$$

For part (b), integrating Eq. (2.3-2) between Γ_1 and Γ and z_1 and z and rearranging,

$$\psi_z \int_{z_1}^{z} dz = -\delta \int_{\Gamma_1}^{\Gamma} d\Gamma \tag{2.3-5}$$

$$\Gamma = \Gamma_1 + \frac{\psi_z}{\delta}(z_1 - z) \tag{2.3-6}$$

For part (c), using the midpoint $z = 0.20$ m and substituting into Eq. (2.3-6),

$$\Gamma = 1.37 \times 10^{-2} + \frac{2.113 \times 10^{-4}}{0.013}(0 - 0.2)$$

$$= 1.045 \times 10^{-2} \text{ amount of property/m}^3$$

3. *General property balance for unsteady state.* In calculating the rates of transport in a system using the molecular transport equation (2.3-2), it is necessary to account for the amount of this property being transported in the entire system. This is done by writing a general property balance or conservation equation for the property (momentum, thermal energy, or mass) at unsteady state. We start by writing an equation for the z direction only, which accounts for all the property entering by molecular transport, leaving, being generated, and accumulating in a system shown in Fig. 2.3-1b, which is an element of volume $\Delta z(1)$ m^3 fixed in space.

$$\begin{pmatrix} \text{rate of} \\ \text{property in} \end{pmatrix} + \begin{pmatrix} \text{rate of generation} \\ \text{of property} \end{pmatrix}$$

$$= \begin{pmatrix} \text{rate of} \\ \text{property out} \end{pmatrix} + \begin{pmatrix} \text{rate of accumulation} \\ \text{of property} \end{pmatrix} \quad \textbf{(2.3-7)}$$

The rate of input is $(\psi_{z|z}) \cdot 1$ amount of property/s and the rate of output is $(\psi_{z|z+\Delta z}) \cdot 1$, where the cross-sectional area is 1.0 m^2. The rate of generation of the property is $R(\Delta z \cdot 1)$, where R is rate of generation of property/s $\cdot$ m^3. The accumulation term is

$$\text{rate of accumulation of property} = \frac{\partial \Gamma}{\partial t}(\Delta z \cdot 1) \quad \textbf{(2.3-8)}$$

Substituting the various terms into Eq. (2.3-7),

$$(\psi_{z|z}) \cdot 1 + R(\Delta z \cdot 1) = (\psi_{z|z+\Delta z}) \cdot 1 + \frac{\partial \Gamma}{\partial t}(\Delta z \cdot 1) \quad \textbf{(2.3-9)}$$

Dividing by Δz and letting Δz go to zero,

$$\frac{\partial \Gamma}{\partial t} + \frac{\partial \psi_z}{\partial z} = R \quad \textbf{(2.3-10)}$$

Substituting Eq. (2.3-2) for ψ_z into (2.3-10) and assuming that δ is constant,

$$\frac{\partial \Gamma}{\partial t} - \delta \frac{\partial^2 \Gamma}{\partial z^2} = R \quad \textbf{(2.3-11)}$$

For the case where no generation is present,

$$\frac{\partial \Gamma}{\partial t} = \delta \frac{\partial^2 \Gamma}{\partial z^2} \quad \textbf{(2.3-12)}$$

This final equation relates the concentration of the property Γ to position z and time t.

Equations (2.3-11) and (2.3-12) are general equations for the conservation of momentum, thermal energy, or mass and will be used in many sections of this text. The equations consider here only molecular transport occurring and not other transport mechanisms such as convection and so on, which will be considered when the specific conservation equations are derived in later sections of this text for momentum, energy, and mass.

2.3B Introduction to Molecular Transport

The kinetic theory of gases gives us a good physical interpretation of the motion of individual molecules in fluids. Because of their kinetic energy the molecules are in rapid random movement, often colliding with each other. Molecular transport or molecular diffusion of a property such as momentum, heat, or mass occurs in a fluid because of these random movements of individual molecules. Each individual molecule containing the property being transferred moves randomly in all directions, and there are fluxes in all directions. Hence, if there is a concentration gradient of the property, there will be a net flux of the property from high to low concentration. This occurs because equal numbers of molecules diffuse in each direction between the high-concentration and low-concentration regions.

1. Momentum transport and Newton's law. When a fluid is flowing in the x direction parallel to a solid surface, a velocity gradient exists where the velocity v_x in the x direction decreases as we approach the surface in the z direction. The fluid has x-directed momentum and its concentration is $v_x \rho$ momentum/m^3, where the momentum has units of kg $\cdot$ m/s. Hence, the units of $v_x \rho$ are (kg $\cdot$ m/s)/m^3. By random diffusion of molecules there is an exchange of molecules in the z direction, an equal number moving in each direction ($+z$ and $-z$ directions) between the faster-moving layer of molecules and the slower adjacent layer. Hence, the x-directed momentum has been transferred in the z direction from the faster- to the slower-moving layer. The equation for this transport of momentum is similar to Eq. (2.3-2) and is Newton's law of viscosity written as follows for constant density ρ:

$$\tau_{zx} = -\nu \frac{d(v_x \rho)}{dz} \tag{2.3-13}$$

where τ_{zx} is flux of x-directed momentum in the z direction, (kg $\cdot$ m/s)/s $\cdot$ m^2; ν is μ/ρ, the momentum diffusivity in m^2/s; z is the distance of transport or diffusion in m; ρ is the density in kg/m^3; and μ is the viscosity in kg/m $\cdot$ s.

2. Heat transport and Fourier's law. Fourier's law for molecular transport of heat or heat conduction in a fluid or solid can be written as follows for constant density ρ and heat capacity c_p:

$$\frac{q_z}{A} = -\alpha \frac{d(\rho c_p T)}{dz} \tag{2.3-14}$$

where q_z/A is the heat flux in J/s $\cdot$ m^2, α is the thermal diffusivity in m^2/s, and $\rho c_p T$ is the concentration of heat or thermal energy in J/m^3. When there is a temperature gradient in a fluid, equal numbers of molecules diffuse in each direction between the hot and the colder region. In this way energy is transferred in the z direction.

3. Mass transport and Fick's law. Fick's law for molecular transport of mass in a fluid or solid for constant total concentration in the fluid is

$$J_{Az}^* = -D_{AB} \frac{dc_A}{dz} \tag{2.3-15}$$

where J_{AZ}^* is the flux of A in kg mol A/s $\cdot$ m^2, D_{AB} is the molecular diffusivity of the molecule A in B in m^2/s, and c_A is the concentration of A in kg mol A/m^3. In a manner similar to momentum and heat transport, when there is a concentration gradient in a fluid, equal numbers of molecules diffuse in each direction between the high- and low-concentration regions and a net flux of mass occurs.

Hence, Eqs. (2.3-13), (2.3-14), and (2.3-15) for momentum, heat, and mass transfer are all similar to each other and to the general molecular transport equation (2.3-2). All equations have a flux on the left-hand side of each equation, a diffusivity in m^2/s, and the derivative of the concentration with respect to distance. All three of the molecular transport equations are mathematically identical. Thus, we state that we have an analogy or similarity among them. It should be emphasized, however, that even though there is a mathematical analogy, the actual physical mechanisms occurring may be totally different. For example, in mass transfer two components are often being transported by relative motion through one another. In heat transport in a solid, the molecules are relatively stationary and the transport is done mainly by the electrons. Transport of momentum can occur by several types of mechanisms. More-detailed considerations of each of the transport processes of momentum, energy, and mass are presented in this and succeeding chapters.

2.4 VISCOSITY OF FLUIDS

2.4A Newton's Law and Viscosity

When a fluid is flowing through a closed channel such as a pipe or between two flat plates, either of two types of flow may occur, depending on the velocity of this fluid. At low velocities the fluid tends to flow without lateral mixing, and adjacent layers slide past one another like playing cards. There are no cross currents perpendicular to the direction of flow, nor eddies or swirls of fluid. This regime or type of flow is called *laminar flow*. At higher velocities eddies form, which leads to lateral mixing. This is called *turbulent flow*. The discussion in this section is limited to laminar flow.

A fluid can be distinguished from a solid in this discussion of viscosity by its behavior when subjected to a stress (force per unit area) or applied force. An elastic solid deforms by an amount proportional to the applied stress. However, a fluid, when subjected to a similar applied stress, will continue to deform, that is, to flow at a velocity that increases with increasing stress. A fluid exhibits resistance to this stress. Viscosity is that property of a fluid which gives rise to forces that resist the relative movement of adjacent layers in the fluid. These *viscous forces* arise from forces existing between the molecules in the fluid and are similar in character to the *shear forces* in solids.

The ideas above can be clarified by a more quantitative discussion of viscosity. In Fig. 2.4-1 a fluid is contained between two infinite (very long and very wide) parallel plates. Suppose that the bottom plate is moving parallel to the top plate and at a constant velocity Δv_z m/s faster relative to the top plate because of a steady force F newtons being applied. This force is called the *viscous drag,* and it arises from the viscous forces in the fluid. The plates are Δy m apart. Each layer of liquid moves in the z direction. The layer immediately adjacent to the bottom plate is carried along at the velocity of this plate. The layer just above is at a

FIGURE 2.4-1. *Fluid shear between two parallel plates.*

slightly slower velocity, each layer moving at a slower velocity as we go up in the y dire' n. This velocity profile is linear, with y direction as shown in Fig. 2.4-1. An analogy to a fluɪᴅ is a deck of playing cards, where, if the bottom card is moved, all the other cards above will slide to some extent.

It has been found experimentally for many fluids that the force F in newtons is directly proportional to the velocity Δv_z in m/s and to the area A in m^2 of the plate used, and inversely proportional to the distance Δy in m. Or, as given by Newton's law of viscosity when the flow is laminar,

$$\frac{F}{A} = -\mu \frac{\Delta v_z}{\Delta y} \qquad (2.4\text{-}1)$$

where μ is a proportionality constant called the *viscosity* of the fluid, in Pa · s or kg/m · s. If we let Δy approach zero, then, using the definition of the derivative,

$$\tau_{yz} = -\mu \frac{dv_z}{dy} \qquad \text{(SI units)} \qquad (2.4\text{-}2)$$

where $\tau_{yz} = F/A$ and is the shear stress or force per unit area in newtons/m^2 (N/m^2). In the cgs system, F is in dynes, μ in g/cm · s, v_z in cm/s, and y in cm. We can also write Eq. (2.2-2) as

$$\tau_{yz} g_c = -\mu \frac{dv_z}{dy} \qquad \text{(English units)} \qquad (2.4\text{-}3)$$

where τ_{yz} is in units of lb$_f$/ft^2.

The units of viscosity in the cgs system are g/cm · s, called *poise* or centipoise (cp). In the SI system, viscosity is given in Pa · s (N · s/m^2 or kg/m · s):

$$1 \text{ cp} = 1 \times 10^{-3} \text{ kg/m} \cdot \text{s} = 1 \times 10^{-3} \text{ Pa} \cdot \text{s} = 1 \times 10^{-3} \text{ N} \cdot \text{s/m}^2 \qquad \text{(SI)}$$

$$1 \text{ cp} = 0.01 \text{ poise} = 0.01 \text{ g/cm} \cdot \text{s}$$

$$1 \text{ cp} = 6.7197 \times 10^{-4} \text{ lb}_m/\text{ft} \cdot \text{s}$$

Other conversion factors for viscosity are given in Appendix A.1. Sometimes the viscosity is given as μ/ρ, kinematic viscosity, in m^2/s or cm^2/s, where ρ is the density of the fluid.

EXAMPLE 2.4-1. Calculation of Shear Stress in a Liquid
Referring to Fig. 2.4-1, the distance between plates is $\Delta y = 0.5$ cm, $\Delta v_z = 10$ cm/s, and the fluid is ethyl alcohol at 273 K having a viscosity of 1.77 cp (0.0177 g/cm · s).
(a) Calculate the shear stress τ_{yz} and the velocity gradient or shear rate dv_z/dy using cgs units.
(b) Repeat, using lb force, s, and ft units (English units).
(c) Repeat, using SI units.

Solution: We can substitute directly into Eq. (2.4-1) or we can integrate Eq. (2.4-2). Using the latter method, rearranging Eq. (2.4-2), calling the bottom plate point 1, and integrating,

$$\tau_{yz} \int_{y_1=0}^{y_2=0.5} dy = -\mu \int_{v_1=10}^{v_2=0} dv_z \qquad (2.4\text{-}4)$$

$$\tau_{yz} = \mu \frac{v_1 - v_2}{y_2 - y_1} \tag{2.4-5}$$

Substituting the known values,

$$\tau_{yz} = \mu \frac{v_1 - v_2}{y_2 - y_1} = \left(0.0177 \frac{g}{cm \cdot s}\right) \frac{(10 - 0)\ cm/s}{(0.5 - 0)\ cm}$$

$$= 0.354 \frac{g \cdot cm/s^2}{cm^2} = 0.354 \frac{dyn}{cm^2} \tag{2.4-6}$$

To calculate the shear rate dv_z/dy, since the velocity change is linear with y,

$$\text{shear rate} = \frac{dv_z}{dy} = \frac{\Delta v_z}{\Delta y} = \frac{(10 - 0)\ cm/s}{(0.5 - 0)\ cm} = 20.0\ s^{-1} \tag{2.4-7}$$

For part (b), using lb force units and the viscosity conversion factor from Appendix A.1,

$$\mu = 1.77\ cp(6.7197 \times 10^{-4}\ lb_m/ft \cdot s)/cp$$

$$= 1.77(6.7197 \times 10^{-4})\ lb_m/ft \cdot s$$

Integrating Eq. (2.4-3),

$$\tau_{yz} = \frac{\mu\ lb_m/ft \cdot s}{g_c \dfrac{lb_m \cdot ft}{lb_f \cdot s^2}} \frac{(v_1 - v_2)ft/s}{(y_2 - y_1)\ ft} \tag{2.4-8}$$

Substituting known values into Eq. (2.4-8) and converting Δv_z to ft/s and Δy to ft, $\tau_{yz} = 7.39 \times 10^{-4}\ lb_f/ft^2$. Also, $dv_z/dy = 20\ s^{-1}$.

For part (c), $\Delta y = 0.5/100 = 0.005$ m, $\Delta v_z = 10/100 = 0.1$ m/s, and $\mu = 1.77 \times 10^{-3}$ kg/m $\cdot$ s $= 1.77 \times 10^{-3}$ Pa $\cdot$ s. Substituting into Eq. (2.4-5),

$$\tau_{yz} = (1.77 \times 10^{-3})(0.10)/0.005 = 0.0354\ N/m^2$$

The shear rate will be the same at $20.0\ s^{-1}$.

2.4B Momentum Transfer in a Fluid

The shear stress τ_{yz} in Eqs. (2.4-1)–(2.4-3) can also be interpreted as a *flux of z-directed momentum in the y direction,* which is the rate of flow of momentum per unit area. The units of momentum are mass times velocity in kg $\cdot$ m/s. The shear stress can be written

$$\tau_{yz} = \frac{kg \cdot m/s}{m^2 \cdot s} = \frac{momentum}{m^2 \cdot s} \tag{2.4-9}$$

This gives an amount of momentum transferred per second per unit area.

This can be shown by considering the interaction between two adjacent layers of a fluid in Fig. 2.4-1 which have different velocities, and hence different momentum, in the z direction. The random motions of the molecules in the faster-moving layer send some of the molecules into the slower-moving layer, where they collide with the slower-moving molecules and tend to speed them up or increase their momentum in the z direction. Also, in the same fashion, molecules in the slower layer tend to retard those in the faster layer. This exchange of molecules between layers produces a transfer or flux of z-directed momentum from high-velocity to low-velocity layers. The negative sign in Eq. (2.4-2) indicates that momentum is transferred down the gradient from high- to low-velocity regions. This is similar to the transfer of heat from high- to low-temperature regions.

2.4C Viscosities of Newtonian Fluids

Fluids that follow Newton's law of viscosity, Eqs. (2.4-1)–(2.4-3), are called *Newtonian fluids*. For a Newtonian fluid, there is a linear relation between the shear stress τ_{yz} and the velocity gradient dv_z/dy (rate of shear). This means that the viscosity μ is a constant and is independent of the rate of shear. For non-Newtonian fluids, the relation between τ_{yz} and dv_z/dy is not linear; that is, the viscosity μ does not remain constant but is a function of shear rate. Certain liquids do not obey this simple law of Newton's. These are primarily pastes, slurries, high polymers, and emulsions. The science of the flow and deformation of fluids is often called *rheology*. A discussion of non-Newtonian fluids will not be given here but will be included in Section 3.5.

The viscosity of gases, which are Newtonian fluids, increases with temperature and is approximately independent of pressure up to a pressure of about 1000 kPa. At higher pressures, the viscosity of gases increases with increase in pressure. For example, the viscosity of N_2 gas at 298 K approximately doubles in going from 100 kPa to about 5×10^4 kPa (R1). In liquids, the viscosity decreases with increasing temperature. Since liquids are essentially incompressible, the viscosity is not affected by pressure.

In Table 2.4-1 some experimental viscosity data are given for some typical pure fluids at 101.32 kPa. The viscosities for gases are the lowest and do not differ markedly from gas to gas, being about 5×10^{-6} to 3×10^{-5} Pa · s. The viscosities for liquids are much greater. The value for water at 293 K is about 1×10^{-3} and for glycerol 1.069 Pa · s. Hence, there are great differences between viscosities of liquids. More complete tables of viscosities are given for water in Appendix A.2, for inorganic and organic liquids and gases in Appendix A.3, and for biological and food liquids in Appendix A.4. Extensive data are available in other references (P1, R1, W1, L1). Methods of estimating viscosities of gases and liquids when experimental

TABLE 2.4-1. *Viscosities of Some Gases and Liquids at 101.32 kPa Pressure*

	Gases				Liquids		
Substance	Temp., K	Viscosity (Pa · s) 10^3 or (kg/m · s) 10^3	Ref.	Substance	Temp., K	Viscosity (Pa · s) 10^3 or (kg/m · s) 10^3	Ref.
Air	293	0.01813	N1	Water	293	1.0019	S1
CO_2	273	0.01370	R1		373	0.2821	S1
	373	0.01828	R1	Benzene	278	0.826	R1
CH_4	293	0.01089	R1				
				Glycerol	293	1069	L1
SO_2	373	0.01630	R1	Hg	293	1.55	R2
				Olive oil	303	84	E1

data are not available are summarized elsewhere (R1). These estimation methods for gases at pressures below 100 kPa are reasonably accurate, with an error within about ±5%, but the methods for liquids are often quite inaccurate.

2.5 TYPES OF FLUID FLOW AND REYNOLDS NUMBER

2.5A Introduction and Types of Fluid Flow

The principles of the statics of fluids, treated in Section 2.2, are almost an exact science. On the other hand, the principles of the motions of fluids are quite complex. The basic relations describing the motions of a fluid are the equations for the overall balances of mass, energy, and momentum, which will be covered in the following sections.

These overall or macroscopic balances will be applied to a finite enclosure or control volume fixed in space. We use the term "overall" because we wish to describe these balances from outside the enclosure. The changes inside the enclosure are determined in terms of the properties of the streams entering and leaving and the exchanges of energy between the enclosure and its surroundings.

When making overall balances on mass, energy, and momentum we are not interested in the details of what occurs inside the enclosure. For example, in an overall balance, average inlet and outlet velocities are considered. However, in a differential balance, the velocity distribution inside an enclosure can be obtained by the use of Newton's law of viscosity.

In this section we first discuss the two types of fluid flow that can occur: laminar flow and turbulent flow. Also, the Reynolds number used to characterize the regimes of flow is considered. Then in Sections 2.6, 2.7, and 2.8, the overall mass balance, energy balance, and momentum balance are covered together with a number of applications. Finally, a discussion is given in Section 2.9 on the methods of making a shell balance on an element to obtain the velocity distribution in the element and the pressure drop.

2.5B Laminar and Turbulent Flow

The type of flow occurring in a fluid in a channel is important in fluid dynamics problems. When fluids move through a closed channel of any cross section, either of two distinct types of flow can be observed, according to the conditions present. These two types of flow can commonly be seen in a flowing open stream or river. When the velocity of flow is slow, the flow patterns are smooth. However, when the velocity is quite high, an unstable pattern is observed, in which eddies or small packets of fluid particles are present, moving in all directions and at all angles to the normal line of flow.

The first type of flow, at low velocities, where the layers of fluid seem to slide by one another without eddies or swirls being present, is called *laminar flow,* and Newton's law of viscosity holds, as discussed in Section 2.4A. The second type of flow, at higher velocities, where eddies are present giving the fluid a fluctuating nature, is called *turbulent flow.*

The existence of laminar and turbulent flow is most easily visualized by the experiments of Reynolds. His experiments are shown in Fig. 2.5-1. Water was allowed to flow at steady state through a transparent pipe with the flow rate controlled by a valve at the end of the pipe. A fine, steady stream of dyed water was introduced from a fine jet as shown and its flow pattern observed. At low rates of water flow, the dye pattern was regular and formed a single line or stream similar to a thread, as shown in Fig. 2.5-1a. There was no lateral mixing of the fluid, and it flowed in streamlines down the tube. By putting in additional jets at other points in the

FIGURE 2:5-1. *Reynolds' experiment for different types of flow:*
(a) laminar flow; (b) turbulent flow.

pipe cross section, it was shown that there was no mixing in any parts of the tube and the fluid flowed in straight parallel lines. This type of flow is called laminar or *viscous flow*.

As the velocity was increased, it was found that at a definite velocity the thread of dye became dispersed and the pattern was very erratic, as shown in Fig. 2.5-1b. This type of flow is known as turbulent flow. The velocity at which the flow changes is known as the *critical velocity*.

2.5C   Reynolds Number

Studies have shown that the transition from laminar to turbulent flow in tubes is not only a function of velocity but also of density and viscosity of the fluid and the tube diameter. These variables are combined into the Reynolds number, which is dimensionless:

$$N_{Re} = \frac{D v \rho}{\mu} \tag{2.5-1}$$

where N_{Re} is the Reynolds number, D the diameter in m, ρ the fluid density in kg/m^3, μ the fluid viscosity in Pa · s, and v the average velocity of the fluid in m/s (where average velocity is defined as the volumetric rate of flow divided by the cross-sectional area of the pipe). Units in the cgs system are D in cm, ρ in g/cm^3, μ in g/cm · s, and v in cm/s. In the English system D is in ft, ρ in lb$_m$/ft^3, μ in lb$_m$/ft · s, and v in ft/s.

The instability of the flow that leads to disturbed or turbulent flow is determined by the ratio of the kinetic or inertial forces to the viscous forces in the fluid stream. The inertial forces are proportional to ρv^2 and the viscous forces to $\mu v/D$, and the ratio $\rho v^2/(\mu v/D)$ is the Reynolds number $D v \rho/\mu$. Further explanation and derivation of dimensionless numbers are given in Section 3.11.

For a straight circular pipe, when the value of the Reynolds number is less than 2100, the flow is always laminar. When the value is over 4000, the flow will be turbulent, except in very special cases. In between—called the *transition region*—the flow can be viscous or turbulent, depending upon the apparatus details, which cannot be predicted.

EXAMPLE 2.5-1 Reynolds Number in a Pipe

Water at 303 K is flowing at the rate of 10 gal/min in a pipe having an inside diameter (ID) of 2.067 in. Calculate the Reynolds number using both English units and SI units.

Solution: From Appendix A.1, 7.481 gal = 1 ft³. The flow rate is calculated as

$$\text{flow rate} = \left(10.0 \frac{\text{gal}}{\text{min}}\right)\left(\frac{1 \text{ ft}^3}{7.481 \text{ gal}}\right)\left(\frac{1 \text{ min}}{60 \text{ s}}\right)$$

$$= 0.0223 \text{ ft}^3/\text{s}$$

$$\text{pipe diameter, } D = \frac{2.067}{12} = 0.172 \text{ ft}$$

$$\text{cross-sectional area of pipe} = \frac{\pi D^2}{4} = \frac{\pi (0.172)^2}{4} = 0.0233 \text{ ft}^2$$

$$\text{velocity in pipe, } v = \left(0.0223 \frac{\text{ft}^3}{s}\right)\left(\frac{1}{0.0233 \text{ ft}^2}\right) = 0.957 \text{ ft/s}$$

From Appendix A.2, for water at 303 K (30°C),

$$\text{density, } \rho = 0.996(62.43) \text{ lb}_m/\text{ft}^3$$

$$\text{viscosity, } \mu = (0.8007 \text{ cp})\left(6.7197 \times 10^{-4}\frac{\text{lb}_m/\text{ft}\cdot\text{s}}{\text{cp}}\right)$$

$$= 5.38 \times 10^{-4} \text{ lb}_m/\text{ft}\cdot\text{s}$$

Substituting into Eq. (2.5-1).

$$N_{\text{Re}} = \frac{Dv\rho}{\mu} = \frac{(0.172 \text{ ft})(0.957 \text{ ft/s})(0.996 \times 62.43 \text{ lb}_m/\text{ft}^3)}{5.38 \times 10^{-4} \text{ lb}_m/\text{ft}\cdot\text{s}}$$

$$= 1.905 \times 10^4$$

Hence, the flow is turbulent. Using SI units,

$$\rho = (0.996)(1000 \text{ kg/m}^3) = 996 \text{ kg/m}^3$$

$$D = (2.067 \text{ in.})(1 \text{ ft/12 in.})(1 \text{ m/3.2808 ft}) = 0.0525 \text{ m}$$

$$v = \left(0.957 \frac{\text{ft}}{s}\right)(1 \text{ m/3.2808 ft}) = 0.2917 \text{ m/s}$$

$$\mu = (0.8007 \text{ cp})\left(1 \times 10^{-3}\frac{\text{kg/m}\cdot\text{s}}{\text{cp}}\right) = 8.007 \times 10^{-4}\frac{\text{kg}}{\text{m}\cdot\text{s}}$$

$$= 8.007 \times 10^{-4} \text{ Pa}\cdot\text{s}$$

$$N_{\text{Re}} = \frac{Dv\rho}{\mu} = \frac{(0.0525 \text{ m})(0.2917 \text{ m/s})(996 \text{ kg/m}^3)}{8.007 \times 10^{-4} \text{ kg/m}\cdot\text{s}} = 1.905 \times 10^4$$

2.6 OVERALL MASS BALANCE AND CONTINUITY EQUATION

2.6A Introduction and Simple Mass Balances

In fluid dynamics fluids are in motion. Generally, they are moved from place to place by means of mechanical devices such as pumps or blowers, by gravity head, or by pressure, and flow through systems of piping and/or process equipment. The first step in the solution of flow problems is generally to apply the principles of the conservation of mass to the whole system or to any part of the system. First, we will consider an elementary balance on a simple geometry, and later we shall derive the general mass-balance equation.

Simple mass or material balances were introduced in Section 1.5, where

$$\text{input} = \text{output} + \text{accumulation} \tag{1.5-1}$$

Since, in fluid flow, we are usually working with rates of flow and usually at steady state, the rate of accumulation is zero and we obtain

$$\text{rate of input} = \text{rate of output (steady state)} \tag{2.6-1}$$

In Fig. 2.6-1 a simple flow system is shown, where fluid enters section 1 with an average velocity v_1 m/s and density ρ_1 kg/m^3. The cross-sectional area is A_1 m^2. The fluid leaves section 2 with average velocity v_2. The mass balance, Eq. (2.6-1), becomes

$$m = \rho_1 A_1 v_1 = \rho_2 A_2 v_2 \tag{2.6-2}$$

where m = kg/s. Often, $v\rho$ is expressed as $G = v\rho$, where G is mass velocity or mass flux in kg/s $\cdot$ m^2. In English units, v is in ft/s, ρ in lb$_m$/ft^3, A in ft^2, m in lb$_m$/s, and G in lb$_m$/s $\cdot$ ft^2.

EXAMPLE 2.6-1. *Flow of Crude Oil and Mass Balance*

A petroleum crude oil having a density of 892 kg/m^3 is flowing through the piping arrangement shown in Fig. 2.6-2 at a total rate of 1.388×10^{-3} m^3/s entering pipe 1.

The flow divides equally in each of pipes 3. The steel pipes are schedule 40 pipe (see Appendix A.5 for actual dimensions). Calculate the following, using SI units:

(a) The total mass flow rate m in pipe 1 and pipes 3.
(b) The average velocity v in 1 and 3.
(c) The mass velocity G in 1.

Solution: From Appendix A.5, the dimensions of the pipes are as follows: 2-in. pipe: D_1 (ID) = 2.067 in.; cross-sectional area

$$A_1 = 0.02330 \text{ ft}^2 = 0.02330(0.0929) = 2.165 \times 10^{-3} \text{ m}^2$$

FIGURE 2.6-1. *Mass balance on flow system.*

FIGURE 2.6-2. *Piping arrangement for Example 2.6-1.*

$1\frac{1}{2}$-in. pipe: D_3 (ID) = 1.610 in.; cross-sectional area

$$A_3 = 0.01414 \text{ ft}^2 = 0.01414(0.0929) = 1.313 \times 10^{-3} \text{ m}^2$$

The total mass flow rate is the same through pipes 1 and 2 and is

$$m_1 = (1.388 \times 10^{-3} \text{ m}^3/\text{s})(892 \text{ kg/m}^3) = 1.238 \text{ kg/s}$$

Since the flow divides equally in each of pipes 3,

$$m_3 = \frac{m_1}{2} = \frac{1.238}{2} = 0.619 \text{ kg/s}$$

For part (b), using Eq. (2.6-2) and solving for v,

$$v_1 = \frac{m_1}{\rho_1 A_1} = \frac{1.238 \text{ kg/s}}{(892 \text{ kg/m}^3)(2.165 \times 10^{-3} \text{ m}^2)} = 0.641 \text{ m/s}$$

$$v_3 = \frac{m_3}{\rho_3 A_3} = \frac{0.619}{(892)(1.313 \times 10^{-3})} = 0.528 \text{ m/s}$$

For part (c),

$$G_1 = v_1\rho_1 = \frac{m_1}{A_1} = \frac{1.238}{2.165 \times 10^{-3}} = 572 \frac{\text{kg}}{\text{s} \cdot \text{m}^2}$$

2.6B Control Volume for Balances

The laws for the conservation of mass, energy, and momentum are all stated in terms of a system; these laws give the interaction of a system with its surroundings. A *system* is defined as a collection of fluid of fixed identity. However, in flow of fluids, individual particles are not easily identifiable. As a result, attention is focused on a given space through which the fluid flows rather than on a given mass of fluid. The method used, which is more convenient, is to select a control volume, which is a region fixed in space through which the fluid flows.

In Fig. 2.6-3 the case of a fluid flowing through a conduit is shown. The control surface shown as a dashed line is the surface surrounding the control volume. In most problems part of the control surface will coincide with some boundary, such as the wall of the conduit. The remaining part of the control surface is a hypothetical surface through which the fluid can

FIGURE 2.6-3. *Control volume for flow through a conduit.*

flow, shown as point 1 and point 2 in Fig. 2.6-3. The control-volume representation is analogous to the open system of thermodynamics.

2.6C   Overall Mass-Balance Equation

In deriving the general equation for the overall balance of the property mass, the law of conservation of mass may be stated as follows for a control volume where no mass is being generated.

$$\begin{pmatrix} \text{rate of mass output} \\ \text{from control volume} \end{pmatrix} - \begin{pmatrix} \text{rate of mass input} \\ \text{from control volume} \end{pmatrix}$$

$$+ \begin{pmatrix} \text{rate of mass accumulation} \\ \text{in control volume} \end{pmatrix} = 0 \quad \text{(rate of mass generation)} \quad \textbf{(2.6-3)}$$

We now consider the general control volume fixed in space and located in a fluid flow field, as shown in Fig. 2.6-4. For a small element of area dA m^2 on the control surface, the rate of mass efflux from this element = $(\rho v)(dA \cos \alpha)$, where $(dA \cos \alpha)$ is the area dA projected in a direction normal to the velocity vector v, α is the angle between the velocity vector v and the outward-directed unit normal vector n to dA, and ρ is the density in kg/m^3. The quantity ρv has units of kg/s $\cdot$ m^2 and is called *a flux* or *mass velocity G*.

FIGURE 2.6-4. *Flow through a differential area dA on a control surface.*

From vector algebra we recognize that $(\rho v)(dA \cos \alpha)$ is the scalar or dot product $\rho(\boldsymbol{v \cdot n}) \, dA$. If we now integrate this quantity over the entire control surface A, we have the net outflow of mass across the control surface, or the net mass efflux in kg/s from the entire control volume V:

$$\left(\begin{array}{c} \text{net mass efflux} \\ \text{from control volume} \end{array} \right) = \iint_A v\rho \cos \alpha \, dA = \iint_A \rho(\boldsymbol{v \cdot n}) \, dA \qquad \textbf{(2.6-4)}$$

We should note that if mass is entering the control volume, that is, flowing inward across the control surface, the next efflux of mass in Eq. (2.6-4) is negative, since $\alpha > 90°$ and $\cos \alpha$ is negative. Hence, there is a net influx of mass. If $\alpha < 90°$, there is a net efflux of mass.

The rate of accumulation of mass within the control volume V can be expressed as follows:

$$\left(\begin{array}{c} \text{rate of mass accumulation} \\ \text{in control volume} \end{array} \right) = \frac{\partial}{\partial t} \iiint_V \rho \, dV = \frac{dM}{dt} \qquad \textbf{(2.6-5)}$$

where M is the mass of fluid in the volume in kg. Substituting Eqs. (2.6-4) and (2.6-5) into (2.6-3), we obtain the general form of the overall mass balance:

$$\iint_A \rho(\boldsymbol{v \cdot n}) \, dA + \frac{\partial}{\partial t} \iiint_V \rho \, dV = 0 \qquad \textbf{(2.6-6)}$$

The use of Eq. (2.6-6) can be shown for a common situation of steady-state one-dimensional flow, where all the flow inward is normal to A_1 and outward normal to A_2, as shown in Fig. 2.6-3. When the velocity v_2 leaving (Fig. 2.6-3) is normal to A_2, the angle α_2 between the normal to the control surface and the direction of the velocity is 0°, and $\cos \alpha_2 = 1.0$. Where v_1 is directed inward, $\alpha_1 > \pi/2$, and for the case in Fig. 2.6-3, α_1 is 180° ($\cos \alpha_1 = -1.0$). Since α_2 is 0° and α_1 is 180°, using Eq. (2.6-4),

$$\iint_A v\rho \cos \alpha \, dA = \iint_{A_2} v\rho \cos \alpha_2 \, dA + \iint_{A_1} v\rho \cos \alpha_1 \, dA \qquad \textbf{(2.6-7)}$$

$$= v_2\rho_2 A_2 - v_1\rho_1 A_1$$

For steady state, $dM/dt = 0$ in Eq. (2.6-5), and Eq. (2.6-6) becomes

$$m = \rho_1 v_1 A_1 = \rho_2 v_2 A_2 \qquad \textbf{(2.6-2)}$$

which is Eq. (2.6-2), derived earlier.

In Fig. 2.6-3 and Eqs. (2.6-3)–(2.6-7) we were not concerned with the composition of any of the streams. These equations can easily be extended to represent an overall mass balance for component i in a multicomponent system. For the case shown in Fig. 2.6-3, we combine Eqs. (2.6-5), (2.6-6), and (2.6-7), add a generation term, and obtain

$$m_{i2} - m_{i1} + \frac{dM_i}{dt} = R_i \qquad \textbf{(2.6-8)}$$

where m_{i2} is the mass flow rate of component i leaving the control volume and R_i is the rate of generation of component i in the control volume in kg per unit time. (Diffusion fluxes are neglected here or are assumed negligible.) In some cases, of course, $R_i = 0$ for no generation. Often it is more convenient to use Eq. (2.6-8) written in molar units.

initial 500 kg salt
solution ($t = 0$, 10% salt)

(1)
10 kg/h
(20% salt)

control
volume

(2)

5 kg/h

FIGURE 2.6-5.   *Control volume for flow in a stirred tank for Example 2.6-2.*

EXAMPLE 2.6-2.   *Overall Mass Balance in Stirred Tank*

Initially, a tank holds 500 kg of salt solution containing 10% salt. At point (1) in the control volume in Fig. 2.6-5, a stream enters at a constant flow rate of 10 kg/h containing 20% salt. A stream leaves at point (2) at a constant rate of 5 kg/h. The tank is well stirred. Derive an equation relating the weight fraction w_A of the salt in the tank at any time t in hours.

Solution: First we make a total mass balance using Eq. (2.6-7) for the net total mass efflux from the control volume:

$$\iint_A v\rho \cos \alpha \, dA = m_2 - m_1 = 5 - 10 = -5 \text{ kg solution/h} \qquad (2.6\text{-}9)$$

From Eq. (2.6-5), where M is total kg of solution in control volume at time t,

$$\frac{\partial}{\partial t} \iiint_V \rho \, dV = \frac{dM}{dt} \qquad (2.6\text{-}5)$$

Substituting Eqs. (2.6-5) and (2.6-9) into (2.6-6), and then integrating,

$$-5 + \frac{dM}{dt} = 0$$

$$\int_{M=500}^{M} dM = 5 \int_{t=0}^{t} dt \qquad (2.6\text{-}10)$$

$$M = 5t + 500 \qquad (2.6\text{-}11)$$

Equation (2.6-11) relates the total mass M in the tank at any time to t.

Next, making a component A salt balance, let w_A = weight fraction of salt in tank at time t and also the concentration in the stream m_2 leaving at time t. Again using Eq. (2.6-7) but for a salt balance,

$$\iint_A v\rho \cos \alpha \, dA = (5)w_A - 10(0.20) = 5w_A - 2 \text{ kg salt/h} \qquad (2.6\text{-}12)$$

Using Eq. (2.6-5) for a salt balance,

$$\frac{\partial}{\partial t} \iiint_V \rho \, dV = \frac{d}{dt}(Mw_A) = \frac{M \, dw_A}{dt} + w_A \frac{dM}{dt} \text{ kg salt/h} \qquad (2.6\text{-}13)$$

Substituting Eqs. (2.6-12) and (2.6-13) into (2.6-6),

$$5w_A - 2 + M\frac{dw_A}{dt} + w_A\frac{dM}{dt} = 0 \qquad \text{(2.6-14)}$$

Substituting the value for M from Eq. (2.6-11) into (2.6-14), separating variables, integrating, and solving for w_A,

$$5w_A - 2 + (500 + 5t)\frac{dw_A}{dt} + w_A\frac{d(500 + 5t)}{dt} = 0$$

$$5w_A - 2 + (500 + 5t)\frac{dw_A}{dt} + 5w_A = 0$$

$$\int_{w_A=0.10}^{w_A}\frac{dw_A}{2 - 10w_A} = \int_{t=0}^{t}\frac{dt}{500 + 5t}$$

$$-\frac{1}{10}\ln\left(\frac{2 - 10w_A}{1}\right) = \frac{1}{5}\ln\left(\frac{500 + 5t}{500}\right)$$

$$\qquad \text{(2.6-15)}$$

$$w_A = -0.1\left(\frac{100}{100 + t}\right)^2 + 0.20$$

$$\qquad \text{(2.6-16)}$$

Note that Eq. (2.6-8) for component i could have been used for the salt balance with $R_i = 0$ (no generation).

2.6D   Average Velocity to Use in Overall Mass Balance

In solving the case in Eq. (2.6-7), we assumed a constant velocity v_1 at section 1 and constant v_2 at section 2. If the velocity is not constant but varies across the surface area, an average or bulk velocity is defined by

$$v_{av} = \frac{1}{A}\iint_A v\, dA \qquad \text{(2.6-17)}$$

for a surface over which v is normal to A and the density ρ is assumed constant.

EXAMPLE 2.6-3.   Variation of Velocity Across Control Surface and Average Velocity

For the case of incompressible flow (ρ is constant) through a circular pipe of radius R, the velocity profile is parabolic for laminar flow as follows:

$$v = v_{max}\left[1 - \left(\frac{r}{R}\right)^2\right] \qquad \text{(2.6-18)}$$

where v_{max} is the maximum velocity at the center where $r = 0$ and v is the velocity at a radial distance r from the center. Derive an expression for the average or bulk velocity v_{av} to use in the overall mass-balance equation.

Solution: The average velocity is represented by Eq. (2.6-17). In Cartesian coordinates dA is $dx\,dy$. However, using polar coordinates, which are more appropriate for a pipe, $dA = r\,dr\,d\theta$, where θ is the angle in polar coordinates. Substituting Eq. (2.6-18), $dA = r\,dr\,d\theta$, and $A = \pi R^2$ into Eq. (2.6-17) and integrating,

$$v_{av} = \frac{1}{\pi R^2} \int_0^{2\pi} \int_0^R v_{max}\left[1 - \left(\frac{r}{R}\right)^2\right] r\,dr\,d\theta$$

$$= \frac{v_{max}}{\pi R^4} \int_0^{2\pi} \int_0^R (R^2 - r^2)r\,dr\,d\theta$$

$$= \frac{v_{max}}{\pi R^4}(2\pi - 0)\left(\frac{R^4}{2} - \frac{R^4}{4}\right) \tag{2.6-19}$$

$$v_{av} = \frac{v_{max}}{2} \tag{2.6-20}$$

In this discussion overall or macroscopic mass balances were made because we wish to describe these balances from outside the enclosure. In this section on overall mass balances, some of the equations presented may have seemed quite obvious. However, the purpose was to develop the methods which should be helpful in the next sections. Overall balances will also be made on energy and momentum in the next sections. These overall balances do not tell us the details of what happens inside. However, in Section 2.9 a shell momentum balance will be made in order to obtain these details, which will give us the velocity distribution and pressure drop. To further study these details of the processes occurring inside the enclosure, differential balances rather than shell balances can be written; these are discussed later in Sections 3.6–3.9 on differential equations of continuity and momentum transfer, Sections 5.6 and 5.7 on differential equations of energy change and boundary-layer flow, and Section 7.5B on differential equations of continuity for a binary mixture.

2.7 OVERALL ENERGY BALANCE

2.7A Introduction

The second property to be considered in the overall balances on a control volume is energy. We shall apply the principle of the conservation of energy to a control volume fixed in space in much the same manner as the principle of conservation of mass was used to obtain the overall mass balance. The energy-conservation equation will then be combined with the first law of thermodynamics to obtain the final overall energy-balance equation.

We can write the first law of thermodynamics as

$$\Delta E = Q - W \tag{2.7-1}$$

where E is the total energy per unit mass of fluid, Q is the heat *absorbed* per unit mass of fluid, and W is the work of all kinds done per unit mass of fluid *upon* the surroundings. In the calculations, each term in the equation must be expressed in the same type of units, such as J/kg (SI), btu/lb$_m$, or ft·lb$_f$/lb$_m$ (English).

Since mass carries with it associated energy due to its position, motion, or physical state, we will find that each of these types of energy will appear in the energy balance. In addition, we can also transport energy across the boundary of the system without transferring mass.

2.7B Derivation of Overall Energy-Balance Equation

The entity balance for a conserved quantity such as energy is similar to Eq. (2.6-3) and is as follows for a control volume:

$$\text{rate of entity output} - \text{rate of entity input}$$
$$+ \text{ rate of entity accumulation} = 0 \qquad (2.7\text{-}2)$$

The energy E present within a system can be classified in three ways:

1. *Potential energy* zg of a unit mass of fluid is the energy present because of the position of the mass in a gravitational field g, where z is the relative height in meters from a reference plane. The units for zg in the SI system are m $\cdot$ m/s^2. Multiplying and dividing by kg mass, the units can be expressed as $(kg \cdot m/s^2) \cdot (m/kg)$, or J/kg. In English units the potential energy is zg/g_c in ft $\cdot$ lb$_f$/lb$_m$.

2. *Kinetic energy* $v^2/2$ of a unit mass of fluid is the energy present because of translational or rotational motion of the mass, where v is the velocity in m/s relative to the boundary of the system at a given point. Again, in the SI system the units of $v^2/2$ are J/kg. In the English system the kinetic energy is $v^2/2g_c$ in ft $\cdot$ lb$_f$/lb$_m$.

3. *Internal energy* U of a unit mass of a fluid is all of the other energy present, such as rotational and vibrational energy in chemical bonds. Again the units are in J/kg or ft $\cdot$ lb$_f$/lb$_m$.

The total energy of the fluid per unit mass is then

$$E = U + \frac{v^2}{2} + zg \qquad \text{(SI)}$$

$$\qquad\qquad\qquad\qquad\qquad\qquad\qquad (2.7\text{-}3)$$

$$E = U + \frac{v^2}{2g_c} + \frac{zg}{g_c} \qquad \text{(English)}$$

The rate of accumulation of energy within the control volume V in Fig. 2.6-4 is

$$\begin{pmatrix} \text{rate of energy accumulation} \\ \text{in control volume} \end{pmatrix} = \frac{\partial}{\partial t} \iiint_V \left(U + \frac{v^2}{2} + zg \right) \rho \, dV \qquad (2.7\text{-}4)$$

Next we consider the rate of energy input and output associated with mass in the control volume. The mass added or removed from the system carries internal, kinetic, and potential energy. In addition, energy is transferred when mass flows into and out of the control volume. Net work is done by the fluid as it flows into and out of the control volume. This pressure–volume work per unit mass fluid is pV. The contribution of shear work is usually neglected. The pV term and U term are combined using the definition of enthalpy, H:

$$H = U + pV \qquad (2.7\text{-}5)$$

Hence, the total energy carried with a unit mass is $(H + v^2/2 + zg)$.

For a small area dA on the control surface in Fig. 2.6-4, the rate of energy efflux is $(H + v^2/2 + zg)(\rho v)(dA \cos \alpha)$, where $(dA \cos \alpha)$ is the area dA projected in a direction normal to the velocity vector v and α is the angle between the velocity vector v and the outward-directed unit normal vector $\boldsymbol{n}$. We now integrate this quantity over the entire control surface to obtain

$$\left(\begin{array}{c}\text{net energy efflux} \\ \text{from control volume}\end{array}\right) = \iint\limits_{A} \left(H + \frac{v^2}{2} + zg\right)(\rho v)\cos\alpha\, dA \qquad \text{(2.7-6)}$$

Now we have accounted for all energy associated with mass in the system and moving across the boundary in the entity balance, Eq. (2.7-2). Next we take into account heat and work energy which transfers across the boundary and is not associated with mass. The term q is the heat transferred per unit time across the boundary to the fluid because of a temperature gradient. Heat absorbed by the system is positive by convention.

The work $\dot{W}$, which is energy per unit time, can be divided into $\dot{W}_S$, purely mechanical shaft work identified with a rotating shaft crossing the control surface, and the pressure–volume work, which has been included in the enthalpy term H in Eq. (2.7-6). By convention, work done by the fluid upon the surroundings, that is, work out of the system, is positive.

To obtain the overall energy balance, we substitute Eqs. (2.7-4) and (2.7-6) into the entity balance Eq. (2.7-2) and equate the resulting equation to $q - \dot{W}_S$:

$$\iint\limits_{A}\left(H + \frac{v^2}{2} + zg\right)(\rho v)\cos\alpha\, dA + \frac{\partial}{\partial t}\iiint\limits_{V}\left(U + \frac{v^2}{2} + zg\right)\rho\, dV = q - \dot{W}_S \qquad \text{(2.7-7)}$$

2.7C Overall Energy Balance for Steady-State Flow System

A common special case of the overall or macroscopic energy balance is that of a steady-state system with one-dimensional flow across the boundaries, a single inlet, a single outlet, and negligible variation of height z, density ρ, and enthalpy H across either inlet or outlet area. This is shown in Fig. 2.7-1. Setting the accumulation term in Eq. (2.7-7) equal to zero and integrating,

FIGURE 2.7-1. *Steady-state flow system for a fluid.*

$$H_2 m_2 - H_1 m_1 + \frac{m_2 (v_2^3)_{av}}{2v_{2av}} - \frac{m_1 (v_1^3)_{av}}{2v_{1av}} + gm_2 z_2 - gm_1 z_1 = q - \dot{W}_S \qquad (2.7\text{-}8)$$

For steady state, $m_1 = \rho_1 v_{1\,av} A_1 = m_2 = m$. Dividing through by m so that the equation is on a unit mass basis,

$$H_2 - H_1 + \frac{1}{2}\left[\frac{(v_2^3)_{av}}{v_{2av}} - \frac{(v_1^3)_{av}}{v_{1av}} \right] + g(z_2 - z_1) = Q - W_S \qquad \text{(SI)} \qquad (2.7\text{-}9)$$

The term $(v^3)_{av}/(2v_{av})$ can be replaced by $v_{av}^2/2\alpha$, where α is the kinetic-energy velocity correction factor and is equal to $v_{av}^3/(v^3)_{av}$. The term α has been evaluated for various flows in pipes and is $\frac{1}{2}$ for laminar flow and close to 1.0 for turbulent flow. (See Section 2.7D.) Hence, Eq. (2.7-9) becomes

$$H_2 - H_1 + \frac{1}{2\alpha}(v_{2av}^2 - v_{1av}^2) + g(z_2 - z_1) = Q - W_S \qquad \text{(SI)}$$

$$(2.7\text{-}10)$$

$$H_2 - H_1 + \frac{1}{2\alpha g_c}(v_{2av}^2 - v_{1av}^2) + \frac{g}{g_c}(z_2 - z_1) = Q - W_S \qquad \text{(English)}$$

Some useful conversion factors from Appendix A.1 are as follows:

$$1 \text{ btu} = 778.17 \text{ ft} \cdot \text{lb}_f = 1055.06 \text{ J} = 1.05506 \text{ kJ}$$

$$1 \text{ hp} = 550 \text{ ft} \cdot \text{lb}_f/\text{s} = 0.7457 \text{ kW}$$

$$1 \text{ ft} \cdot \text{lb}_f/\text{lb}_m = 2.9890 \text{ J/kg}$$

$$1 \text{ J} = 1 \text{ N} \cdot \text{m} = 1 \text{ kg} \cdot \text{m}^2/\text{s}^2$$

2.7D Kinetic-Energy Velocity Correction Factor α

1. Introduction. In obtaining Eq (2.7-8) it was necessary to integrate the kinetic-energy term,

$$\text{kinetic energy} = \iint_A \left(\frac{v^2}{2} \right)(\rho v)\cos \alpha \, dA \qquad (2.7\text{-}11)$$

which appeared in Eq. (2.7-7). To do this we first take ρ as a constant and $\cos \alpha = 1.0$. Then multiplying the numerator and denominator by $v_{av} A$, where v_{av} is the bulk or average velocity, and noting that $m = \rho v_{av} A$, Eq. (2.7-11) becomes

$$\frac{\rho}{2} \iint_A (v^3) dA = \frac{\rho v_{av} A}{2 v_{av} A} \iint_A (v^3) \, dA = \frac{m}{2 v_{av}} \frac{1}{A} \iint_A (v^3) \, dA \qquad (2.7\text{-}12)$$

Dividing through by m so that Eq. (2.7-12) is on a unit mass basis,

$$\left(\frac{1}{2 v_{av}} \right) \frac{1}{A} \iint_A (v^3) \, dA = \frac{(v^3)_{av}}{2 v_{av}} = \frac{v_{av}^2}{2\alpha} \qquad (2.7\text{-}13)$$

where α is defined as

$$\alpha = \frac{v_{av}^3}{(v^3)_{av}} \qquad (2.7\text{-}14)$$

and $(v^3)_{av}$ is defined as follows:

$$(v^3)_{av} = \frac{1}{A} \iint_A (v^3) \, dA \tag{2.7-15}$$

The local velocity v varies across the cross-sectional area of a pipe. To evaluate $(v^3)_{av}$ and, hence, the value of α, we must have an equation relating v as a function of position in the cross-sectional area.

2. Laminar flow. In order to determine the value of α for laminar flow, we first combine Eqs. (2.6-18) and (2.6-20) for laminar flow to obtain v as a function of position r:

$$v = 2v_{av}\left[1 - \left(\frac{r}{R}\right)^2\right] \tag{2.7-16}$$

Substituting Eq. (2.7-16) into (2.7-15) and noting that $A = \pi R^2$ and $dA = r \, dr \, d\theta$ (see Example 2.6-3), Eq. (2.7-15) becomes

$$(v^3)_{av} = \frac{1}{\pi R^2} \int_0^{2\pi} \int_0^R \left[2v_{av}\left(1 - \frac{r^2}{R^2}\right)\right]^3 r \, dr \, d\theta$$

$$= \frac{(2\pi)2^3 v_{av}^3}{\pi R^2} \int_0^R \frac{(R^2 - r^2)^3}{R^6} r \, dr = \frac{16v_{av}^3}{R^8} \int_0^R (R^2 - r^2)^3 r \, dr \tag{2.7-17}$$

Integrating Eq. (2.7-17) and rearranging,

$$(v^3)_{av} = \frac{16v_{av}^3}{R^8} \int_0^R (R^6 - 3r^2R^4 + 3r^4R^2 - r^6) r \, dr$$

$$= \frac{16v_{av}^3}{R^8}\left(\frac{R^8}{2} - \frac{3}{4}R^8 + \frac{1}{2}R^8 - \frac{1}{8}R^8\right)$$

$$= 2v_{av}^3 \tag{2.7-18}$$

Substituting Eq. (2.7-18) into (2.7-14),

$$\alpha = \frac{v_{av}^3}{(v^3)_{av}} = \frac{v_{av}^3}{2v_{av}^3} = 0.50 \tag{2.7-19}$$

Hence, for laminar flow the value of α to use in the kinetic-energy term of Eq. (2.7-10) is 0.50.

3. Turbulent flow. For turbulent flow a relationship is needed between v and position. This can be approximated by the following expression:

$$v = v_{max}\left(\frac{R - r}{R}\right)^{1/7} \tag{2.7-20}$$

where r is the radial distance from the center. Eq. (2.7-20) is substituted into Eq. (2.7-15) and the resultant integrated to obtain the value of $(v^3)_{av}$. Next, Eq. (2.7-20) is substituted into Eq. (2.6-17) and this equation integrated to obtain v_{av} and $(v_{av})^3$. Combining the results for $(v^3)_{av}$ and $(v_{av})^3$ into Eq. (2.7-14), the value of a α is 0.945. (See Problem 2.7-1 for solution.) The value of α for turbulent flow varies from about 0.90 to 0.99. In most cases (except for precise work) the value of α is taken to be 1.0.

2.7E Applications of Overall Energy-Balance Equation

The total energy balance, Eq. (2.7-10), in the form given is not often used when appreciable enthalpy changes occur or appreciable heat is added (or subtracted), since the kinetic- and potential-energy terms are usually small and can be neglected. As a result, when appreciable heat is added or subtracted or large enthalpy changes occur, the methods for doing heat balances described in Section 1.7 are generally used. Examples will be given to illustrate this and other cases.

EXAMPLE 2.7-1. Energy Balance on Steam Boiler
Water enters a boiler at 18.33°C and 137.9 kPa through a pipe at an average velocity of 1.52 m/s. Exit steam at a height of 15.2 m above the liquid inlet leaves at 137.9 kPa, 148.9°C, and 9.14 m/s in the outlet line. At steady state, how much heat must be added per kg mass of steam? The flow in the two pipes is turbulent.

Solution: The process flow diagram is shown in Fig. 2.7-2. Rearranging Eq. (2.7-10) and setting $\alpha = 1$ for turbulent flow and $W_S = 0$ (no external work),

$$Q = (z_2 - z_1)g + \frac{v_2^2 - v_1^2}{2} + (H_2 - H_1) \qquad (2.7\text{-}21)$$

To solve for the kinetic-energy terms,

$$\frac{v_1^2}{2} = \frac{(1.52)^2}{2} = 1.115 \text{ J/kg}$$

$$\frac{v_2^2}{2} = \frac{(9.14)^2}{2} = 41.77 \text{ J/kg}$$

Taking the datum height z_1 at point 1, $z_2 = 15.2$ m. Then,

$$z_2 g = (15.2)(9.80665) = 149.1 \text{ J/kg}$$

From Appendix A.2, steam tables in SI units, H_1 at 18.33°C = 76.97 kJ/kg, H_2 of superheated steam at 148.9°C = 2771.4 kJ/kg, and

$$H_2 - H_1 = 2771.4 - 76.97 = 2694.4 \text{ kJ/kg} = 2.694 \times 10^6 \text{ J/kg}$$

Substituting these values into Eq. (2.7-21),

$$Q = (149.1 - 0) + (41.77 - 1.115) + 2.694 \times 10^6$$

$$Q = 189.75 + 2.694 \times 10^6 = 2.6942 \times 10^6 \text{ J/kg}$$

Q → water $v_1 = 1.52$ m/s, 18.3°C, 137.9 kPa; steam → 15.2 m, $v_2 = 9.14$ m/s, 148.9°C, 137.9 kPa

FIGURE 2.7-2. *Process flow diagram for Example 2.7-1.*

Hence, the kinetic-energy and potential-energy terms totaling 189.75 J/kg are negligible compared to the enthalpy change of 2.694×10^6 J/kg. This 189.75 J/kg would raise the temperature of liquid water about 0.0453°C, a negligible amount.

EXAMPLE 2.7-2. Energy Balance on a Flow System with a Pump

Water at 85.0°C is being stored in a large, insulated tank at atmospheric pressure, as shown in Fig. 2.7-3. It is being pumped at steady state from this tank at point 1 by a pump at the rate of 0.567 m^3/min. The motor driving the pump supplies energy at the rate of 7.45 kW. The water passes through a heat exchanger, where it gives up 1408 kW of heat. The cooled water is then delivered to a second large open tank at point 2, which is 20 m above the first tank. Calculate the final temperature of the water delivered to the second tank. Neglect any kinetic-energy changes, since the initial and final velocities in the tanks are essentially zero.

Solution: From Appendix A.2, steam tables, $H_1(85°C) = 355.90 \times 10^3$ J/kg and $\rho_1 = 1/0.0010325 = 968.5$ kg/m^3. Then, for steady state,

$$m_1 = m_2 = (0.567)(968.5)(\tfrac{1}{60}) = 9.152 \text{ kg/s}$$

Also, $z_1 = 0$ and $z_2 = 20$ m. The work done by the fluid is W_S, but in this case work is done on the fluid and W_S is negative:

$$W_S = -(7.45 \times 10^3 \text{ J/s})(1/9.152 \text{ kg/s}) = -0.8140 \times 10^3 \text{ J/kg}$$

The heat added to the fluid is also negative since it gives up heat and is

$$Q = -(1408 \times 10^3 \text{ J/s})(1/9.152 \text{ kg/s}) = -153.8 \times 10^3 \text{ J/kg}$$

Setting $(v_1^2 - v_2^2)/2 = 0$ and substituting into Eq. (2.7-10),

$$H_2 - 355.90 \times 10^3 + 0 + 9.80665(20 - 0) = (-153.8 \times 10^3) - (-0.814 \times 10^3)$$

Solving, $H_2 = 202.71 \times 10^3$ J/kg. From the steam tables this corresponds to $t_2 = 48.41°C$. Note that in this example, W_S and $g(z_2 - z_1)$ are very small compared to Q.

EXAMPLE 2.7-3. Energy Balance in Flow Calorimeter

A flow calorimeter is being used to measure the enthalpy of steam. The calorimeter, which is a horizontal insulated pipe, consists of an electric heater immersed in a fluid flowing at steady state. Liquid water at 0°C at a rate of 0.3964 kg/min enters the calorimeter at point 1. The liquid is vaporized completely by the heater, where 19.63 kW is added, and steam leaves point 2 at 250°C and 150 kPa absolute. Calculate the exit enthalpy H_2 of the steam if the liquid enthalpy at 0°C is set arbitrarily as 0. The kinetic-energy changes are small and can be neglected. (It will be assumed that pressure has a negligible effect on the enthalpy of the liquid.)

Solution: For this case, $W_S = 0$ since there is no shaft work between points 1 and 2. Also, $(v_2^2/2\alpha - v_1^2/2\alpha) = 0$ and $g(z_2 - z_1) = 0$. For steady state, $m_1 = m_2 = 0.3964/60 = 6.607 \times 10^{-3}$ kg/s. Since heat is added to the system,

$$Q = + \frac{19.63 \text{ kJ/s}}{6.607 \times 10^{-3} \text{ kg/s}} = 2971 \text{ kJ/kg}$$

The value of $H_1 = 0$. Equation (2.7-10) becomes

$$H_2 - H_1 + 0 + 0 = Q - 0$$

The final equation for the calorimeter is

$$H_2 = Q + H_1 \qquad\qquad\qquad \text{(2.7-22)}$$

Substituting $Q = 2971$ kJ/kg and $H_1 = 0$ into Eq. (2.7-22), $H_2 = 2971$ kJ/kg at 250°C and 150 kPa, which is close to the value from the steam table of 2972.7 kJ/kg.

2.7F Overall Mechanical-Energy Balance

A more useful type of energy balance for flowing fluids, especially liquids, is a modification of the total energy balance to deal with mechanical energy. Engineers are often concerned with this special type of energy, called *mechanical energy*, which includes the work term, kinetic energy, potential energy, and the flow work part of the enthalpy term. Mechanical energy is a form of energy that is either work or a form that can be directly converted into work. The other terms in the energy-balance equation (2.7-10), heat terms and internal energy, do not permit simple conversion into work because of the second law of thermodynamics and the efficiency of conversion, which depends on the temperatures. Mechanical-energy terms have no such limitation and can be converted almost completely into work. Energy converted to heat or internal energy is lost work or a loss in mechanical energy caused by frictional resistance to flow.

It is convenient to write an energy balance in terms of this loss, ΣF, which is the sum of all frictional losses per unit mass. For the case of steady-state flow, when a unit mass of fluid passes from inlet to outlet, the batch work done by the fluid, W', is expressed as

$$W' = \int_{V_1}^{V_2} p\, dV - \Sigma F \qquad \left(\Sigma F > 0\right) \qquad\qquad \text{(2.7-23)}$$

This work W' differs from the W of Eq. (2.7-1), which also includes kinetic- and potential-energy effects. Writing the first law of thermodynamics for this case, where ΔE becomes ΔU,

$$\Delta U = Q - W' \tag{2.7-24}$$

The equation defining enthalpy, Eq. (2.7-5), can be written as

$$\Delta H = \Delta U + \Delta pV = \Delta U + \int_{V_1}^{V_2} p\, dV + \int_{p_1}^{p_2} V\, dp \tag{2.7-25}$$

Substituting Eq. (2.7-23) into (2.7-24) and then combining the resultant with Eq. (2.7-25), we obtain

$$\Delta H = Q + \sum F + \int_{p_1}^{p_2} V\, dp \tag{2.7-26}$$

Finally, we substitute Eq. (2.7-26) into (2.7-10) and $1/\rho$ for V, to obtain the overall mechanical-energy-balance equation:

$$\frac{1}{2\alpha}[v_{2av}^2 - v_{1av}^2] + g(z_2 - z_1) + \int_{p_1}^{p_2} \frac{dp}{\rho} + \sum F + W_S = 0 \tag{2.7-27}$$

For English units the kinetic- and potential-energy terms of Eq. (2.7-27) are divided by g_c.

The value of the integral in Eq. (2.7-27) depends on the equation of state of the fluid and the path of the process. If the fluid is an incompressible liquid, the integral becomes $(p_2 - p_1)/\rho$ and Eq. (2.7-27) becomes

$$\frac{1}{2\alpha}(v_{2av}^2 - v_{1av}^2) + g(z_2 - z_1) + \frac{p_2 - p_1}{\rho} + \sum F + W_S = 0 \tag{2.7-28}$$

EXAMPLE 2.7-4. Mechanical-Energy Balance on Pumping System

Water with a density of 998 kg/m³ is flowing at a steady mass flow rate through a uniform-diameter pipe. The entrance pressure of the fluid is 68.9 kN/m² abs in the pipe, which connects to a pump that actually supplies 155.4 J/kg of fluid flowing in the pipe. The exit pipe from the pump is the same diameter as the inlet pipe. The exit section of the pipe is 3.05 m higher than the entrance, and the exit pressure is 137.8 kN/m² abs. The Reynolds number in the pipe is above 4000 in the system. Calculate the frictional loss $\sum F$ in the pipe system.

Solution: First a flow diagram of the system is drawn (Fig. 2.7-4), with 155.4 J/kg mechanical energy added to the fluid. Hence, $W_S = -155.4$, since the work done by the fluid is positive.

Setting the datum height $z_1 = 0$, $z_2 = 3.05$ m. Since the pipe is of constant diameter, $v_1 = v_2$. Also, for turbulent flow $\alpha = 1.0$ and

$$\frac{1}{2(1)}(v_2^2 - v_1^2) = 0$$

$$z_2 g = (3.05 \text{ m})(9.806 \text{ m/s}^2) = 29.9 \text{ J/kg}$$

FIGURE 2.7-4. *Process flow diagram for Example 2.7-4.*

Since the liquid can be considered incompressible, Eq. (2.7-28) is used:

$$\frac{p_1}{\rho} = \frac{68.9 \times 1000}{998} = 69.0 \text{ J/kg}$$

$$\frac{p_2}{\rho} = \frac{137.8 \times 1000}{998} = 138.0 \text{ J/kg}$$

Using Eq. (2.7-28) and solving for $\sum F$, the frictional losses,

$$\sum F = -W_S + \frac{1}{2\alpha}(v_1^2 - v_2^2) + g(z_1 - z_2) + \frac{p_1 - p_2}{\rho} \qquad \textbf{(2.7-29)}$$

Substituting the known values, and solving for the frictional losses,

$$\sum F = -(-155.4) + 0 - 29.9 + 69.0 - 138.0$$

$$= 56.5 \text{ J/kg} \left(18.9 \frac{\text{ft} \cdot \text{lb}_f}{\text{lb}_m}\right)$$

EXAMPLE 2.7-5.   *Pump Horsepower in Flow System*

A pump draws 69.1 gal/min of a liquid solution having a density of 114.8 lb_m/ft^3 from an open storage feed tank of large cross-sectional area through a 3.068-in.-ID suction line. The pump discharges its flow through a 2.067-in.-ID line to an open overhead tank. The end of the discharge line is 50 ft above the level of the liquid in the feed tank. The friction losses in the piping system are $\sum F = 10.0$ ft-lb force/lb mass. What pressure must the pump develop and what is the horse-power of the pump if its efficiency is 65% ($\eta = 0.65$)? The flow is turbulent.

Solution: First, a flow diagram of the system is drawn (Fig. 2.7-5). Equation (2.7-28) will be used. The term W_S in Eq. (2.7-28) becomes

$$W_S = -\eta W_p \qquad \textbf{(2.7-30)}$$

FIGURE 2.7-5. *Process flow diagram for Example 2.7-5.*

where $-W_S$ = mechanical energy actually delivered to the fluid by the pump or net mechanical work, η = fractional efficiency, and W_p is the energy or shaft work delivered to the pump.

From Appendix A.5, the cross-sectional area of the 3.068-in. pipe is 0.05134 ft^2 and of the 2.067-in. pipe, 0.0233 ft^2. The flow rate is

$$\text{flow rate} = \left(69.1 \frac{\text{gal}}{\text{min}} \right) \left(\frac{1 \text{ min}}{60 \text{ s}} \right) \left(\frac{1 \text{ ft}^3}{7.481 \text{ gal}} \right) = 0.1539 \text{ ft}^3/\text{s}$$

$$v_2 = \left(0.1539 \frac{\text{ft}^3}{\text{s}} \right) \left(\frac{1}{0.0233 \text{ ft}^2} \right) = 6.61 \text{ ft/s}$$

$v_1 = 0$, since the tank is very large. Then $v_1^2/2g_c = 0$. The pressure $p_1 = 1$ atm and $p_2 = 1$ atm. Also, $\alpha = 1.0$ since the flow is turbulent. Hence,

$$\frac{p_1}{\rho} - \frac{p_2}{\rho} = 0$$

$$\frac{v_2^2}{2g_c} = \frac{(6.61)^2}{2(32.174)} = 0.678 \frac{\text{ft} \cdot \text{lb}_f}{\text{lb}_m}$$

Using the datum of $z_1 = 0$, we have

$$z_2 \frac{g}{g_c} = (50.0) \frac{32.174}{32.174} = 50.0 \frac{\text{ft} \cdot \text{lb}_f}{\text{lb}_m}$$

Using Eq. (2.4-28), solving for W_S, and substituting the known values,

$$W_S = z_1 \frac{g}{g_c} - z_2 \frac{g}{g_c} + \frac{v_1^2}{2g_c} - \frac{v_2^2}{2g_c} + \frac{p_1 - p_2}{\rho} - \sum F$$

$$= 0 - 50.0 + 0 - 0.678 + 0 - 10 = -60.678 \frac{\text{ft} \cdot \text{lb}_f}{\text{lb}_m}$$

Using Eq. (2.7-30) and solving for W_p,

$$W_p = -\frac{W_S}{\eta} = \frac{60.678}{0.65} \frac{\text{ft} \cdot \text{lb}_f}{\text{lb}_m} = 93.3 \frac{\text{ft} \cdot \text{lb}_f}{\text{lb}_m}$$

$$\text{mass flow rate} = \left(0.1539 \frac{\text{ft}^3}{\text{s}} \right) \left(114.8 \frac{\text{lb}_m}{\text{ft}^3} \right) = 17.65 \frac{\text{lb}_m}{\text{s}}$$

$$\text{pump horsepower} = \left(17.65 \frac{\text{lb}_m}{\text{s}} \right) \left(93.3 \frac{\text{ft} \cdot \text{lb}_f}{\text{lb}_m} \right) \left(\frac{1 \text{ hp}}{550 \text{ ft} \cdot \text{lb}_f/\text{s}} \right)$$

$$= 3.00 \text{ hp}$$

To calculate the pressure the pump must develop, Eq. (2.7-28) must be written over the pump itself between points 3 and 4 as shown on the diagram:

$$v_3 = \left(0.1539 \frac{\text{ft}^3}{\text{s}} \right) \left(\frac{1}{0.05134 \text{ ft}^2} \right) = 3.00 \text{ ft/s}$$

$$v_4 = v_2 = 6.61 \text{ ft/s}$$

Since the difference in level between z_3 and z_4 of the pump itself is negligible, it will be neglected. Rewriting Eq. (2.7-28) between points 3 and 4 and substituting known values ($\Sigma F = 0$, since this is for the piping system),

$$\frac{p_4 - p_3}{\rho} = z_3 \frac{g}{g_c} - z_4 \frac{g}{g_c} + \frac{v_3^2}{2g_c} - \frac{v_4^2}{2g_c} - W_S - \sum F$$

(2.7-31)

$$= 0 - 0 + \frac{(3.00)^2}{2(32.174)} - \frac{(6.61)^2}{2(32.174)} + 60.678 - 0$$

$$= 0 - 0 + 0.140 - 0.678 + 60.678 = 60.14 \frac{\text{ft} \cdot \text{lb}_f}{\text{lb}_m}$$

$$p_4 - p_3 = \left(60.14 \frac{\text{ft} \cdot \text{lb}_f}{\text{lb}_m} \right) \left(114.8 \frac{\text{lb}_m}{\text{ft}^3} \right) \left(\frac{1}{144 \text{ in.}^2/\text{ft}^2} \right)$$

$$= 48.0 \text{ lb force/in.}^2 \text{ (psia pressure developed by pump) (331 kPa)}$$

2.7G Bernoulli Equation for Mechanical-Energy Balance

In the special case where no mechanical energy is added ($W_S = 0$) and for no friction ($\Sigma F = 0$), then Eq. (2.7-28) becomes the Bernoulli equation, Eq. (2.7-32), for turbulent flow, which is of sufficient importance to deserve further discussion:

$$z_1 g + \frac{v_1^2}{2} + \frac{p_1}{\rho} = z_2 g + \frac{v_2^2}{2} + \frac{p_2}{\rho}$$

(2.7-32)

This equation covers many situations of practical importance and is often used in conjunction with the mass-balance equation (2.6-2) for steady state:

$$m = \rho_1 A_1 v_1 = \rho_2 A_2 v_2$$

(2.6-2)

Several examples of its use will be given.

FIGURE 2.7-6. *Process flow diagram for Example 2.7-6.*

EXAMPLE 2.7-6.   *Rate of Flow from Pressure Measurements*

A liquid with a constant density ρ kg/m^3 is flowing at an unknown velocity v_1 m/s through a horizontal pipe of cross-sectional area A_1 m^2 at a pressure p_1 N/m^2, and then it passes to a section of the pipe in which the area is reduced gradually to A_2 m^2 and the pressure is p_2. Assuming no friction losses, calculate the velocities v_1 and v_2 if the pressure difference $(p_1 - p_2)$ is measured.

Solution: In Fig. 2.7-6, the flow diagram is shown with pressure taps to measure p_1 and p_2. From the mass-balance continuity equation (2.6-2), for constant ρ where $\rho_1 = \rho_2 = \rho$,

$$v_2 = \frac{v_1 A_1}{A_2} \tag{2.7-33}$$

For the items in the Bernoulli equation (2.7-32), for a horizontal pipe,

$$z_1 = z_2 = 0$$

Then Eq. (2.7-32) becomes, after substituting Eq. (2.7-33) for v_2,

$$0 + \frac{v_1^2}{2} + \frac{p_1}{\rho} = 0 + \frac{v_1^2 A_1^2 / A_2^2}{2} + \frac{p_2}{\rho} \tag{2.7-34}$$

Rearranging,

$$p_1 - p_2 = \frac{\rho v_1^2 [(A_1/A_2)^2 - 1]}{2} \tag{2.7-35}$$

$$v_1 = \sqrt{\frac{p_1 - p_2}{\rho} \frac{2}{[(A_1/A_2)^2 - 1]}} \quad \text{(SI)}$$

$$v_1 = \sqrt{\frac{p_1 - p_2}{\rho} \frac{2g_c}{[(A_1/A_2)^2 - 1]}} \quad \text{(English)} \tag{2.7-36}$$

Performing the same derivation but in terms of v_2,

$$v_2 = \sqrt{\frac{p_1 - p_2}{\rho} \frac{2}{[1 - (A_2/A_1)^2]}} \tag{2.7-37}$$

Chapter 2   Principles of Momentum Transfer and Overall Balances

FIGURE 2.7-7. *Nozzle flow diagram for Example 2.7-7.*

EXAMPLE 2.7-7.   *Rate of Flow from a Nozzle in a Tank*

A nozzle of cross-sectional area A_2 is discharging to the atmosphere and is located in the side of a large tank, in which the open surface of the liquid in the tank is H m above the center line of the nozzle. Calculate the velocity v_2 in the nozzle and the volumetric rate of discharge if no friction losses are assumed.

Solution: The process flow is shown in Fig. 2.7-7, with point 1 taken in the liquid at the entrance to the nozzle and point 2 at the exit of the nozzle.

Since A_1 is very large compared to A_2, $v_1 \cong 0$. The pressure p_1 is greater than 1 atm (101.3 kN/m^2) by the head of fluid of H m. The pressure p_2, which is at the nozzle exit, is at 1 atm. Using point 2 as a datum, $z_2 = 0$ and $z_1 = 0$ m. Rearranging Eq. (2.7-32),

$$z_1 g + \frac{v_1^2}{2} + \frac{p_1 - p_2}{\rho} = z_2 g + \frac{v_2^2}{2} \qquad (2.7\text{-}38)$$

Substituting the known values,

$$0 + 0 + \frac{p_1 - p_2}{\rho} = 0 + \frac{v_2^2}{2} \qquad (2.7\text{-}39)$$

Solving for v_2,

$$v_2 = \sqrt{\frac{2(p_1 - p_2)}{\rho}} \quad \text{m/s} \qquad (2.7\text{-}40)$$

Since $p_1 - p_3 = H \rho g$ and $p_3 = p_2$ (both at 1 atm),

$$H = \frac{p_1 - p_2}{\rho g} \quad \text{m} \qquad (2.7\text{-}41)$$

where H is the head of liquid with density ρ. Then Eq. (2.4-40) becomes

$$v_2 = \sqrt{2gH} \qquad (2.7\text{-}42)$$

The volumetric flow rate is

$$\text{flow rate} = v_2 A_2 \quad \text{m}^3/\text{s} \qquad (2.7\text{-}43)$$

To illustrate the fact that different points can be used in the balance, points 3 and 2 will be used. Writing Eq. (2.7-32),

$$z_2 g + \frac{v_2^2}{2} + \frac{p_2 - p_3}{\rho} = z_3 g + \frac{v_3^2}{2} \qquad (2.7\text{-}44)$$

Since $p_2 = p_3 = 1$ atm, $v_3 = 0$, and $z_2 = 0$,

$$v_2 = \sqrt{2gz_3} = \sqrt{2gH} \qquad (2.7\text{-}45)$$

2.8 OVERALL MOMENTUM BALANCE

2.8A Derivation of General Equation

A momentum balance can be written for the control volume shown in Fig. 2.6-3 which is somewhat similar to the overall mass-balance equation. Momentum, in contrast to mass and energy, is a vector quantity. The total linear momentum vector P of the total mass M of a moving fluid having a velocity of v is

$$P = Mv \qquad (2.8\text{-}1)$$

The term Mv is the momentum of this moving mass M enclosed at a particular instant in the control volume shown in Fig. 2.6-4. The units of Mv are kg · m/s in the SI system.

Starting with Newton's second law, we will develop the integral momentum-balance equation for linear momentum. Angular momentum will not be considered here. *Newton's law* may be stated: The time rate of change of momentum of a system is equal to the summation of all forces acting on the system and takes place in the direction of the net force:

$$\sum F = \frac{dP}{dt} \qquad (2.8\text{-}2)$$

where F is force. In the SI system F is in newtons (N) and $1\,\text{N} = 1\,\text{kg} \cdot \text{m/s}^2$. Note that in the SI system g_c is not needed, but it is needed in the English system.

The equation for the conservation of momentum with respect to a control volume can be written as follows:

$$\begin{pmatrix} \text{sum of forces acting} \\ \text{on control volume} \end{pmatrix} = \begin{pmatrix} \text{rate of momentum} \\ \text{out of control volume} \end{pmatrix} - \begin{pmatrix} \text{rate of momentum} \\ \text{into control volume} \end{pmatrix}$$

$$+ \begin{pmatrix} \text{rate of accumulation of momentum} \\ \text{in control volume} \end{pmatrix} \qquad (2.8\text{-}3)$$

This is in the same form as the general mass-balance equation (2.6-3), with the sum of the forces as the generation rate term. Hence, momentum is not conserved, since it is generated by external forces on the system. If external forces are absent, momentum is conserved.

Using the general control volume shown in Fig. 2.6-4, we shall evaluate the various terms in Eq. (2.8-3), using methods very similar to the development of the general mass balance. For a small element of area dA on the control surface, we write

$$\text{rate of momentum efflux} = v(\rho v)(dA \cos \alpha) \qquad (2.8\text{-}4)$$

Note that the rate of mass efflux is $(\rho v)(dA \cos \alpha)$. Also, note that $(dA \cos \alpha)$ is the area dA projected in a direction normal to the velocity vector v, and α is the angle between the velocity vector v and the outward-directed-normal vector n. From vector algebra the product in Eq. (2.8-4) becomes

$$v(\rho v)(dA \cos \alpha) = \rho v(v \cdot n)\, dA \qquad (2.8\text{-}5)$$

Integrating over the entire control surface A,

$$\begin{pmatrix} \text{net momentum efflux} \\ \text{from control volume} \end{pmatrix} = \iint_A v(\rho v)\cos\alpha\, dA = \iint_A \rho v(v \cdot n)\, dA \qquad (2.8\text{-}6)$$

The net efflux represents the first two terms on the right-hand side of Eq. (2.8-3).

Similarly to Eq. (2.6-5), the rate of accumulation of linear momentum within the control volume V is

$$\begin{pmatrix} \text{rate of accumulation of momentum} \\ \text{in control volume} \end{pmatrix} = \frac{\partial}{\partial t}\iiint_V \rho v\, dV \qquad (2.8\text{-}7)$$

Substituting Equations (2.8-2), (2.8-6), and (2.8-7) into (2.8-3), the overall linear momentum balance for a control volume becomes

$$\sum F = \iint_A \rho v(v \cdot n)\, dA + \frac{\partial}{\partial t}\iiint_V \rho v\, dV \qquad (2.8\text{-}8)$$

We should note that $\sum F$ in general may have a component in any direction, and that F is the force the surroundings exert on the control-volume fluid. Since Eq. (2.8-8) is a vector equation, we may write the component scalar equations for the x, y, and z directions:

$$\sum F_x = \iint_A v_x \rho v \cos\alpha\, dA + \frac{\partial}{\partial t}\iiint_V \rho v_x\, dV \qquad \text{(SI)}$$

$$\sum F_x = \iint_A v_x \frac{\rho}{g_c} v \cos\alpha\, dA + \frac{\partial}{\partial t}\iiint_V \frac{\rho}{g_c} v_x\, dV \qquad \text{(English)} \qquad (2.8\text{-}9)$$

$$\sum F_y = \iint_A v_y \rho v \cos\alpha\, dA + \frac{\partial}{\partial t}\iiint_V \rho v_y\, dV \qquad (2.8\text{-}10)$$

$$\sum F_z = \iint_A v_z \rho v \cos\alpha\, dA + \frac{\partial}{\partial t}\iiint_V \rho v_z\, dV \qquad (2.8\text{-}11)$$

The force term $\sum F_x$ in Eq. (2.8-9) is composed of the sum of several forces. These are given as follows:

1. *Body force.* The body force F_{xg} is the x-directed force caused by gravity acting on the total mass M in the control volume. This force, F_{xg}, is Mg_x. It is zero if the x direction is horizontal.
2. *Pressure force.* The force F_{xp} is the x-directed force caused by the pressure forces acting on the surface of the fluid system. When the control surface cuts through the fluid, the pressure is taken to be directed inward and perpendicular to the surface. In some cases part of the control surface may be a solid, and this wall is included inside the control surface. Then there is a contribution to F_{xp} from the pressure on the outside of this wall, which typically is atmospheric pressure. If gage pressure is used, the integral of the constant external pressure over the entire outer surface can be automatically ignored.
3. *Friction force.* When the fluid is flowing, an x-directed shear or friction force F_{xs} is present, which is exerted on the fluid by a solid wall when the control surface cuts between the

fluid and the solid wall. In some or many cases, this frictional force may be negligible compared to the other forces and is neglected.

4. *Solid surface force.* In cases where the control surface cuts through a solid, there is present force R_x, which is the x component of the resultant of the forces acting on the control volume at these points. This occurs typically when the control volume includes a section of pipe and the fluid it contains. This is the force exerted by the solid surface on the fluid.

The force terms of Eq. (2.8-9) can then be represented as

$$\sum F_x = F_{xg} + F_{xp} + F_{xs} + R_x \tag{2.8-12}$$

Similar equations can be written for the y and z directions. Then Eq. (2.8-9) becomes, for the x direction,

$$\sum F_x = F_{xg} + F_{xp} + F_{xs} + R_x$$

$$= \iint_A v_x \rho v \cos \alpha \, dA + \frac{\partial}{\partial t} \iiint_v \rho v_x \, dV \tag{2.8-13}$$

2.8B Overall Momentum Balance in Flow System in One Direction

A quite common application of the overall momentum-balance equation is the case of a section of a conduit with its axis in the x direction. The fluid will be assumed to be flowing at steady state in the control volume shown in Fig. 2.6-3 and in Fig. 2.8-1. Since $v = v_x$, Eq. (2.8-13) for the x direction becomes as follows:

$$\sum F_x = F_{xg} + F_{xp} + F_{xs} + R_x = \iint_A v_x \rho v_x \cos \alpha \, dA \tag{2.8-14}$$

Integrating, with $\cos \alpha = \pm 1.0$ and $\rho A = m/v_{av}$,

$$F_{xg} + F_{xp} + F_{xs} + R_x = m \frac{(v_{x2}^2)_{av}}{v_{x\,2av}} - m \frac{(v_{x1}^2)_{av}}{v_{x1av}} \tag{2.8-15}$$

where, if the velocity is not constant and varies across the surface area,

$$(v_x^2)_{av} = \frac{1}{A} \iint_A v_x^2 \, dA \tag{2.8-16}$$

FIGURE 2.8-1. *Flow through a horizontal nozzle in the x direction only.*

The ratio $(v_x^2)_{av}/v_{x\,av}$ is replaced by $v_{x\,av}/\beta$ where β, which is the momentum velocity correction factor, has a value of 0.95 to 0.99 for turbulent flow and $\frac{3}{4}$ for laminar flow. For most applications in turbulent flow, $(v_x)_{av}^2/v_{x\,av}$ is replaced by $v_{x\,av}$, the average bulk velocity. Note that the subscript x on v_x and F_x can be dropped, since $v_x = v$ and $F_x = F$ for one-directional flow.

The term F_{xp}, which is the force caused by the pressures acting on the surface of the control volume, is

$$F_{xp} = p_1 A_1 - p_2 A_2 \qquad (2.8\text{-}17)$$

The friction force will be neglected in Eq. (2.8-15), so $F_{xs} = 0$. The body force $F_{xg} = 0$ since gravity is acting only in the y direction. Substituting F_{xp} from Eq. (2.8-17) into (2.8-15), replacing $(v_x^2)_{av}/v_{x\,av}$ by v/β (where $v_{x\,av} = v$), setting $\beta = 1.0$, and solving for R_x in Eq. (2.8-15),

$$R_x = mv_2 - mv_1 + p_2 A_2 - p_1 A_1 \qquad (2.8\text{-}18)$$

where R_x is the force exerted by the solid on the fluid. The force of the fluid on the solid (reaction force) is the negative of this, or $-R_x$.

EXAMPLE 2.8-1. Momentum Velocity Correction Factor β for Laminar Flow

The momentum velocity correction factor β is defined as follows for flow in one direction, where the subscript x is dropped:

$$\frac{(v^2)_{av}}{v_{av}} = \frac{v_{av}}{\beta} \qquad (2.8\text{-}19)$$

$$\beta = \frac{(v_{av})^2}{(v^2)_{av}} \qquad (2.8\text{-}20)$$

Determine β for laminar flow in a tube.

Solution: Using Eq. (2.8-16),

$$(v^2)_{av} = \frac{1}{A} \iint_A v^2 \, dA \qquad (2.8\text{-}21)$$

Substituting Eq. (2.7-16) for laminar flow into Eq. (2.8-21) and noting that $A = \pi R^2$ and $dA = r \, dr \, d\theta$, we obtain (see Example 2.6-3)

$$(v^2)_{av} = \frac{1}{\pi R^2} \int_0^{2\pi} \int_0^R \left[2v_{av} \left(1 - \frac{r^2}{R^2} \right) \right]^2 r \, dr \, d\theta$$

$$= \frac{(2\pi) 2^2 v_{av}^2}{\pi R^2} \int_0^R \frac{(R^2 - r^2)^2}{R^4} r \, dr \qquad (2.8\text{-}22)$$

Integrating Eq. (2.8-22) and rearranging,

$$(v^2)_{av} = \frac{8 v_{av}^2}{R^6} \left(\frac{R^6}{2} - \frac{R^6}{2} + \frac{R^6}{6} \right) = \tfrac{4}{3} v_{av}^2 \qquad (2.8\text{-}23)$$

Substituting Eq. (2.8-23) into (2.8-20), $\beta = \frac{3}{4}$.

EXAMPLE 2.8-2. Momentum Balance for Horizontal Nozzle

Water is flowing at a rate of 0.03154 m³/s through a horizontal nozzle shown in Fig. 2.8-1 and discharges to the atmosphere at point 2. The nozzle is attached at the upstream end at point 1 and frictional forces are considered negligible. The upstream ID is 0.0635 m and the downstream 0.0286 m. Calculate the resultant force on the nozzle. The density of the water is 1000 kg/m³.

Solution: First, the mass flow and average or bulk velocities at points 1 and 2 are calculated. The area at point 1 is $A_1 = (\pi/4)(0.0635)^2 = 3.167 \times 10^{-3}$ m² and $A_2 = (\pi/4)(0.0286)^2 = 6.424 \times 10^{-4}$ m². Then,

$$m_1 = m_2 = m = (0.03154)(1000) = 31.54 \text{ kg/s}$$

The velocity at point 1 is $v_1 = 0.03154/(3.167 \times 10^{-3}) = 9.96$ m/s, and $v_2 = 0.03154/(6.424 \times 10^{-4}) = 49.1$ m/s.

To evaluate the upstream pressure p_1 we use the mechanical-energy-balance equation (2.7-28) assuming no frictional losses and turbulent flow. (This can be checked by calculating the Reynolds number.) This equation then becomes, for $\alpha = 1.0$,

$$\frac{v_1^2}{2} + \frac{p_1}{\rho} = \frac{v_2^2}{2} + \frac{p_2}{\rho} \qquad (2.8\text{-}24)$$

Setting $p_2 = 0$ gage pressure, $\rho = 1000$ kg/m³, $v_1 = 9.96$ m/s, $v_2 = 49.1$ m/s, and solving for p_1,

$$p_1 = \frac{(1000)(49.1^2 - 9.96^2)}{2} = 1.156 \times 10^6 \text{ N/m}^2 \qquad \text{(gage pressure)}$$

For the x direction, the momentum-balance equation (2.8-18) is used. Substituting the known values and solving for R_x,

$$R_x = 31.54(49.10 - 9.96) + 0 - (1.156 \times 10^6)(3.167 \times 10^{-3})$$

$$= -2427 \text{ N } (-546 \text{ lb}_f)$$

Since the force is negative, it is acting in the negative x direction, or to the left. This is the force of the nozzle on the fluid. The force of the fluid on the solid is $-R_x$, or $+2427$ N.

2.8C Overall Momentum Balance in Two Directions

Another application of the overall momentum balance is shown in Fig. 2.8-2 for a flow system with fluid entering a conduit at point 1 inclined at an angle of α_1 relative to the horizontal x direction and leaving a conduit at point 2 at an angle α_2. The fluid will be assumed to be flowing at steady state and the frictional force F_{xs} will be neglected. Then Eq. (2.8-13) for the x direction becomes as follows for no accumulation:

$$F_{xg} + F_{xp} + R_x = \iint_A v_x \rho v \cos \alpha \, dA \qquad (2.8\text{-}25)$$

FIGURE 2.8-2. *Overall momentum balance for flow system with fluid entering at point 1 and leaving at 2.*

Integrating the surface (area) integral,

$$F_{xg} + F_{xp} + R_x = m \frac{(v_2^2)_{av}}{v_{2av}} \cos \alpha_2 - m \frac{(v_1^2)_{av}}{v_{1av}} \cos \alpha_1 \qquad \textbf{(2.8-26)}$$

The term $(v^2)_{av}/v_{av}$ can again be replaced by v_{av}/β, with β being set at 1.0. From Fig. 2.8-2, the term F_{xp} is

$$F_{xp} = p_1 A_1 \cos \alpha_1 - p_2 A_2 \cos \alpha_2 \qquad \textbf{(2.8-27)}$$

Then Eq. (2.8-26) becomes as follows after solving for R_x:

$$R_x = mv_2 \cos \alpha_2 - mv_1 \cos \alpha_1 + p_2 A_2 \cos \alpha_2 - p_1 A_1 \cos \alpha_1 \qquad \textbf{(2.8-28)}$$

The term $F_{xg} \neq 0$ in this case.

For R_y the body force F_{yg} is in the negative y direction and $F_{yg} = -m_t g$, where m_t is the total mass fluid in the control volume. Replacing $\cos \alpha$ by $\sin \alpha$, the equation for the y direction becomes

$$R_y = mv_2 \sin \alpha_2 - mv_1 \sin \alpha_1 + p_2 A_2 \sin \alpha_2 - p_1 A_1 \sin \alpha_1 + m_t g \qquad \textbf{(2.8-29)}$$

EXAMPLE 2.8-3. Momentum Balance in a Pipe Bend

Fluid is flowing at steady state through a reducing pipe bend, as shown in Fig. 2.8-3. Turbulent flow will be assumed with frictional forces negligible. The volumetric flow rate of the liquid and the pressure p_2 at point 2 are known, as are the pipe diameters at both ends. Derive the equations to calculate the forces on the bend. Assume that the density ρ is constant.

Solution: The velocities v_1 and v_2 can be obtained from the volumetric flow rate and the areas. Also, $m = \rho_1 v_1 A_1 = \rho_2 v_2 A_2$. As in Example 2.8-2, the mechanical-energy-balance equation (2.8-24) is used to obtain the upstream pres-

FIGURE 2.8-3. *Flow through a reducing bend in Example 2.8-3.*

sure, p_1. For the x direction, Eq. (2.8-28) is used for the momentum balance. Since $\alpha_1 = 0°$, $\cos \alpha_1 = 1.0$. Equation (2.8-28) becomes

$$R_x = mv_2 \cos \alpha_2 - mv_1 + p_2 A_2 \cos \alpha_2 - p_1 A_1 \quad \text{(SI)}$$

$$R_x = \frac{m}{g_c} v_2 \cos \alpha_2 - \frac{m}{g_c} v_1 + p_2 A_2 \cos \alpha_2 - p_1 A_1 \quad \text{(English)}$$

(2.8-30)

For the y direction, the momentum-balance equation (2.8-29) is used, where $\sin \alpha_1 = 0$:

$$R_y = mv_2 \sin \alpha_2 + p_2 A_2 \sin \alpha_2 + m_t g \quad \text{(SI)} \qquad \textbf{(2.8-31)}$$

where m_t is total mass fluid in the pipe bend. The pressures at points 1 and 2 are gage pressures since the atmospheric pressures acting on all surfaces cancel. The magnitude of the resultant force of the bend acting on the control volume fluid is

$$|R| = \sqrt{R_x^2 + R_y^2} \qquad \textbf{(2.8-32)}$$

The angle this makes with the vertical is $\theta = \arctan(R_x/R_y)$. Often the gravity force F_{yg} is small compared to the other terms in Eq. (2.8-31) and is neglected.

EXAMPLE 2.8-4. *Friction Loss in a Sudden Enlargement*

A mechanical-energy loss occurs when a fluid flows from a small pipe to a large pipe through an abrupt expansion, as shown in Fig. 2.8-4. Use the momentum balance and mechanical-energy balance to obtain an expression for the loss for a liquid. (*Hint:* Assume that $p_0 = p_1$ and $v_0 = v_1$. Make a mechanical-energy balance between points 0 and 2 and a momentum balance between points 1 and 2. It will be assumed that p_1 and p_2 are uniform over the cross-sectional area.)

Solution: The control volume is selected so that it does not include the pipe wall and R_x drops out. The boundaries selected are points 1 and 2. The flow through plane 1 occurs only through an area A_0. The frictional drag force will be neglected, and all the loss is assumed to be from eddies in this volume. Making a momentum balance between points 1 and 2 using Eq. (2.8-18) and noting that $p_0 = p_1$, $v_1 = v_0$, and $A_1 = A_2$,

$$p_1 A_2 - p_2 A_2 = mv_2 - mv_1 \qquad \textbf{(2.8-33)}$$

FIGURE 2.8-4. *Losses in expansion flow.*

The mass flow rate is $m = v_0 \rho A_0$ and $v_2 = (A_0/A_2)v_0$. Substituting these terms into Eq. (2.8-33) and rearranging gives us

$$v_0^2 \frac{A_0}{A_2}\left(1 - \frac{A_0}{A_2}\right) = \frac{p_2 - p_1}{\rho} \tag{2.8-34}$$

Applying the mechanical-energy-balance equation (2.7-28) to points 1 and 2,

$$\frac{v_0^2 - v_2^2}{2} - \sum F = \frac{p_2 - p_1}{\rho} \tag{2.8-35}$$

Finally, combining Eqs. (2.8-34) and (2.8-35),

$$\sum F = \frac{v_0^2}{2}\left(1 - \frac{A_0}{A_2}\right)^2 \tag{2.8-36}$$

2.8D   Overall Momentum Balance for Free Jet Striking a Fixed Vane

When a free jet impinges on a fixed vane as in Fig. 2.8-5, the overall momentum balance can be applied to determine the force on the smooth vane. Since there are no changes in elevation or pressure before and after impact, there is no loss in energy, and application of the Bernoulli equation shows that the magnitude of the velocity is unchanged. Losses due to impact are neglected. The frictional resistance between the jet and the smooth vane is also neglected. The velocity is assumed to be uniform throughout the jet upstream and downstream. Since the jet is open to the atmosphere, the pressure is the same at all ends of the vane.

In making a momentum balance for the control volume shown for the curved vane in Fig. 2.8-5a, Eq. (2.8-28) is written as follows for steady state, where the pressure terms are zero, $v_1 = v_2$, $A_1 = A_2$, and $m = v_1 A_1 \rho_1 = v_2 A_2 \rho_2$:

$$R_x = mv_2 \cos \alpha_2 - mv_1 + 0 = mv_1(\cos \alpha_2 - 1) \tag{2.8-37}$$

Using Eq. (2.8-29) for the y direction and neglecting the body force,

$$R_y = mv_2 \sin \alpha_2 - 0 = mv_1 \sin \alpha_2 \tag{2.8-38}$$

Hence, R_x and R_y are the force components of the vane on the control volume fluid. The force components on the vane are $-R_x$ and $-R_y$.

FIGURE 2.8-5.   *Free jet impinging on a fixed vane: (a) smooth, curved vane, (b) smooth, flat vane.*

EXAMPLE 2.8-5.   *Force of Free Jet on a Curved, Fixed Vane*
A jet of water having a velocity of 30.5 m/s and a diameter of 2.54×10^{-2} m is deflected by a smooth, curved vane as shown in Fig. 2.8-5a, where $\alpha_2 = 60°$. What is the force of the jet on the vane? Assume that $\rho = 1000$ kg/m^3.

Solution: The cross-sectional area of the jet is $A_1 = \pi(2.54 \times 10^{-2})^2/4 = 5.067 \times 10^{-4}$ m^2. Then, $m = v_1 A_1 \rho_1 = 30.5 \times 5.067 \times 10^{-4} \times 1000 = 15.45$ kg/s. Substituting into Eqs. (2.8-37) and (2.8-38),

$$R_x = 15.45 \times 30.5(\cos 60° - 1) = -235.6 \text{ N } (-52.97 \text{ lb}_f)$$

$$R_y = 15.45 \times 30.5 \sin 60° = 408.1 \text{ N } (91.74 \text{ lb}_f)$$

The force on the vane is $-R_x = +235.6$ N and $-R_y = -408.1$ N. The resultant force is calculated using Eq. (2.8-32).

In Fig. 2.8-5b a free jet at velocity v_1 strikes a smooth, inclined flat plate and the flow divides into two separate streams whose velocities are all equal ($v_1 = v_2 = v_3$) since there is no loss in energy. It is convenient to make a momentum balance in the p direction parallel to the plate. No force is exerted on the fluid by the flat plate in this direction; that is, there is no tangential force. Then, the initial momentum component in the p direction must equal the final momentum component in this direction. This means $\sum F_p = 0$. Writing an equation similar to Eq. (2.8-26), where m_1 is kg/s entering at 1 and m_2 leaves at 2 and m_3 at 3,

$$\sum F_p = 0 = m_2 v_2 - m_1 v_1 \cos \alpha_2 - m_3 v_3$$

$$0 = m_2 v_1 - m_1 v_1 \cos \alpha_2 - m_3 v_1 \qquad \text{(2.8-39)}$$

By the continuity equation,

$$m_1 = m_2 + m_3 \qquad \text{(2.8-40)}$$

Combining and solving,

$$m_2 = \frac{m_1}{2}(1 + \cos \alpha_2), \qquad m_3 = \frac{m_1}{2}(1 - \cos \alpha_2) \qquad \text{(2.8-41)}$$

The resultant force exerted by the plate on the fluid must be normal to it. This means the resultant force is simply $m_1 v_1 \sin \alpha_2$. Alternatively, the resultant force on the fluid can be calculated by determining R_x and R_y from Eqs. (2.8-28) and (2.8-29) and then using Eq. (2.8-32). The force on the bend is the opposite of this.

2.9 SHELL MOMENTUM BALANCE AND VELOCITY PROFILE IN LAMINAR FLOW

2.9A   Introduction

In Section 2.8 we analyzed momentum balances using an overall, macroscopic control volume. From this we obtained the total or overall changes in momentum crossing the control surface. This overall momentum balance did not tell us the details of what happens inside the control volume. In the present section we analyze a small control volume and then shrink this control volume to differential size. In doing this we make a shell momentum balance using the momentum-balance concepts of the preceding section, and then, using the equation for the definition of viscosity, we obtain an expression for the velocity profile inside the enclosure and the pressure drop. The equations are derived for flow systems of simple geometry in laminar flow at steady state.

In many engineering problems a knowledge of the complete velocity profile is not needed, but a knowledge of the maximum velocity, the average velocity, or the shear stress on a surface is needed. In this section we show how to obtain these quantities from the velocity profiles.

2.9B   Shell Momentum Balance Inside a Pipe

Engineers often deal with the flow of fluids inside a circular conduit or pipe. In Fig. 2.9-1 we have a horizontal section of pipe in which an incompressible Newtonian fluid is flowing in

FIGURE 2.9-1.   *Control volume for shell momentum balance on a fluid flowing in a circular tube.*

one-dimensional, steady-state, laminar flow. The flow is fully developed; that is, it is not influenced by entrance effects and the velocity profile does not vary along the axis of flow in the x direction.

The cylindrical control volume is a shell with an inside radius r, thickness Δr, and length Δx. At steady state the conservation of momentum, Eq. (2.8-3), becomes as follows: sum of forces acting on control volume = rate of momentum out − rate of momentum into volume. The pressure forces become, from Eq. (2.8-17),

$$\text{pressure forces} = pA|_x - pA|_{x+\Delta x} = p(2\pi r\,\Delta r)|_x - p(2\pi r\,\Delta r)|_{x+\Delta x} \qquad (2.9\text{-}1)$$

The shear force or drag force acting on the cylindrical surface at the radius r is the shear stress τ_{rx} times the area $2\pi r\,\Delta x$. However, this can also be considered as the rate of momentum flow into the cylindrical surface of the shell as described by Eq. (2.4-9). Hence, the net rate of momentum efflux is the rate of momentum out − rate of momentum in and is

$$\text{net efflux} = (\tau_{rx}\,2\pi r\,\Delta x)|_{r+\Delta r} - (\tau_{rx}\,2\pi r\,\Delta x)|_r \qquad (2.9\text{-}2)$$

The net convective momentum flux across the annular surface at x and $x + \Delta x$ is zero, since the flow is fully developed and the terms are independent of x. This is true since v_x at x is equal to v_x at $x + \Delta x$.

Equating Eq. (2.9-1) to (2.9-2) and rearranging,

$$\frac{(r\tau_{rx})|_{r+\Delta r} - (r\tau_{rx})|_r}{\Delta r} = \frac{r(p|_x - p|_{x+\Delta r})}{\Delta x} \qquad (2.9\text{-}3)$$

In fully developed flow, the pressure gradient $(\Delta p/\Delta x)$ is constant and becomes $(\Delta p/L)$, where Δp is the pressure drop for a pipe of length L. Letting Δr approach zero, we obtain

$$\frac{d(r\tau_{rx})}{dr} = \left(\frac{\Delta p}{L}\right)r \qquad (2.9\text{-}4)$$

Separating variables and integrating,

$$\tau_{rx} = \left(\frac{\Delta p}{L}\right)\frac{r}{2} + \frac{C_1}{r} \qquad (2.9\text{-}5)$$

The constant of integration C_1 must be zero if the momentum flux is not infinite at $r = 0$. Hence,

$$\tau_{rx} = \left(\frac{\Delta p}{2L}\right)r = \frac{p_0 - p_L}{2L}\,r \qquad (2.9\text{-}6)$$

This means that the momentum flux varies linearly with the radius, as shown in Fig. 2.9-2, and the maximum value occurs at $r = R$ at the wall.

Substituting Newton's law of viscosity,

$$\tau_{rx} = -\mu\frac{dv_x}{dr} \qquad (2.9\text{-}7)$$

into Eq. (2.9-6), we obtain the following differential equation for the velocity:

$$\frac{dv_x}{dr} = -\frac{p_0 - p_L}{2\mu L}\,r \qquad (2.9\text{-}8)$$

Integrating using the boundary condition that at the wall, $v_x = 0$ at $r = R$, we obtain the equation for the velocity distribution:

$$v_x = \frac{p_0 - p_L}{4\mu L} R^2 \left[1 - \left(\frac{r}{R} \right)^2 \right] \tag{2.9-9}$$

This result shows us that the velocity distribution is parabolic, as shown in Fig. 2.9-2.

The average velocity $v_{x\,av}$ for a cross section is found by summing up all the velocities over the cross section and dividing by the cross-sectional area, as in Eq. (2.6-17). Following the procedure given in Example 2.6-3, where $dA = r\,dr\,d\theta$ and $A = \pi R^2$,

$$v_{x\,av} = \frac{1}{A} \iint_A v_x \, dA = \frac{1}{\pi R^2} \int_0^{2\pi} \int_0^R v_x r \, dr \, d\theta = \frac{1}{\pi R^2} \int_0^R v_x 2\pi r \, dr \tag{2.9-10}$$

Combining Eqs. (2.9-9) and (2.9-10) and integrating,

$$v_{x\,av} = \frac{(p_0 - p_L)R^2}{8\mu L} = \frac{(p_0 - p_L)D^2}{32\mu L} \tag{2.9-11}$$

where diameter $D = 2R$. Hence, Eq. (2.9-11), which is the *Hagen–Poiseuille equation,* relates the pressure drop and average velocity for laminar flow in a horizontal pipe.

The maximum velocity for a pipe is found from Eq. (2.9-9) and occurs at $r = 0$:

$$v_{x\,max} = \frac{p_0 - p_L}{4\mu L} R^2 \tag{2.9-12}$$

Combining Eqs. (2.9-11) and (2.9-12), we find that

$$v_{x\,av} = \frac{v_{x\,max}}{2} \tag{2.9-13}$$

Also, dividing Eq. (2.9-9) by (2.9-11),

$$\frac{v_x}{v_{x\,av}} = 2 \left[1 - \left(\frac{r}{R} \right)^2 \right] \tag{2.9-14}$$

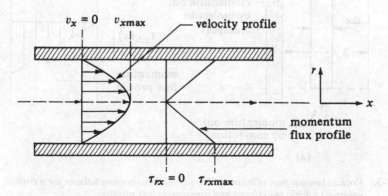

FIGURE 2.9-2. *Velocity and momentum flux profiles for laminar flow in a pipe.*

2.9C Shell Momentum Balance for Falling Film

We now use an approach similar to that used for laminar flow inside a pipe for the case of flow of a fluid as a film in laminar flow down a vertical surface. Falling films have been used to study various phenomena in mass transfer, coatings on surfaces, and so on. The control volume for the falling film is shown in Fig. 2.9-3a, where the shell of fluid considered is Δx thick and has a length of L in the vertical z direction. This region is sufficiently far from the entrance and exit regions so that the flow is not affected by these regions. This means the velocity $v_z(x)$ does not depend on position z.

To start we set up a momentum balance in the z direction over a system Δx thick, bounded in the z direction by the planes $z = 0$ and $z = L$, and extending a distance W in the y direction. First, we consider the momentum flux due to molecular transport. The rate of momentum out − rate of momentum in is the momentum flux at point $x + \Delta x$ minus that at x times the area LW:

$$\text{net efflux} = LW(\tau_{xz})|_{x+\Delta x} - LW(\tau_{xz})|_x \qquad (2.9\text{-}15)$$

The net convective momentum flux is the rate of momentum entering the area $\Delta x W$ at $z = L$ minus that leaving at $z = 0$. This net efflux is equal to 0, since v_z at $z = 0$ is equal to v_z at $z = L$ for each value of x:

$$\text{net efflux} = \Delta x W v_z(\rho v_z)|_{z=L} - \Delta x W v_z(\rho v_z)|_{z=0} = 0 \qquad (2.9\text{-}16)$$

FIGURE 2.9-3. *Vertical laminar flow of a liquid film: (a) shell momentum balance for a control volume Δx thick; (b) velocity and momentum flux profiles.*

The gravity force acting on the fluid is

$$\text{gravity force} = \Delta x W L (\rho g) \tag{2.9-17}$$

Then, using Eq. (2.8-3) for the conservation of momentum at steady state,

$$\Delta x W L (\rho g) = L W (\tau_{xz})|_{x+\Delta x} - L W (\tau_{xz})|_x + 0 \tag{2.9-18}$$

Rearranging Eq. (2.9-18) and letting $\Delta x \to 0$,

$$\frac{\tau_{xz}|_{x+\Delta x} - \tau_{xz}|_x}{\Delta x} = \rho g \tag{2.9-19}$$

$$\frac{d}{dx} \tau_{xz} = \rho g \tag{2.9-20}$$

Integrating using the boundary conditions at $x = 0$, $\tau_{xz} = 0$ at the free liquid surface and at $x = x$, $\tau_{xz} = \tau_{xz}$,

$$\tau_{xz} = \rho g x \tag{2.9-21}$$

This means the momentum-flux profile is linear, as shown in Fig. 2.9-3b, and the maximum value is at the wall. For a Newtonian fluid using Newton's law of viscosity,

$$\tau_{xz} = -\mu \frac{dv_z}{dx} \tag{2.9-22}$$

Combining Eqs. (2.9-21) and (2.9-22) we obtain the following differential equation for the velocity:

$$\frac{dv_z}{dx} = -\left(\frac{\rho g}{\mu}\right) x \tag{2.9-23}$$

Separating variables and integrating gives

$$v_z = -\left(\frac{\rho g}{2\mu}\right) x^2 + C_1 \tag{2.9-24}$$

Using the boundary condition that $v_z = 0$ at $x = \delta$, $C_1 = (\rho g/2\mu)\delta^2$. Hence, the velocity-distribution equation becomes

$$v_z = \frac{\rho g \delta^2}{2\mu} \left[1 - \left(\frac{x}{\delta}\right)^2\right] \tag{2.9-25}$$

This means the velocity profile is parabolic, as shown in Fig. 2.9-3b. The maximum velocity occurs at $x = 0$ in Eq. (2.9-25) and is

$$v_{z\,max} = \frac{\rho g \delta^2}{2\mu} \tag{2.9-26}$$

The average velocity can be found by using Eq. (2.6-17):

$$v_{z\,av} = \frac{1}{A} \iint_A v_z \, dA = \frac{1}{W\delta} \int_0^W \int_0^\delta v_z \, dx \, dy = \frac{W}{W\delta} \int_0^\delta v_z \, dx \tag{2.9-27}$$

Substituting Eq. (2.9-25) into (2.9-27) and integrating,

$$v_{z\,av} = \frac{\rho g \delta^2}{3\mu}$$ (2.9-28)

Combining Eqs. (2.9-26) and (2.9-28), we obtain $v_{z\,av} = \frac{2}{3}v_{z\,max}$. The volumetric flow rate q is obtained by multiplying the average velocity $v_{z\,av}$ times the cross-sectional area δW:

$$q = \frac{\rho g \delta^3 W}{3\mu} \text{ m}^3/\text{s}$$ (2.9-29)

Often in falling films, the mass rate of flow per unit width of wall Γ in kg/s·m is defined as $\Gamma = \rho \delta v_{z\,av}$ and a Reynolds number is defined as

$$N_{Re} = \frac{4\Gamma}{\mu} = \frac{4\rho \delta v_{z\,av}}{\mu}$$ (2.9-30)

Laminar flow occurs for $N_{Re} < 1200$. Laminar flow with rippling present occurs above a N_{Re} of 25.

EXAMPLE 2.9-1. Falling Film Velocity and Thickness

An oil is flowing down a vertical wall as a film 1.7 mm thick. The oil density is 820 kg/m³ and the viscosity is 0.20 Pa·s. Calculate the mass flow rate per unit width of wall, Γ, needed and the Reynolds number. Also calculate the average velocity.

Solution: The film thickness is $\delta = 0.0017$ m. Substituting Eq. (2.9-28) into the definition of Γ,

$$\Gamma = \rho \delta v_{z\,av} = \frac{(\rho \delta)\rho g \delta^2}{3\mu} = \frac{\rho^2 \delta^3 g}{3\mu}$$

$$= \frac{(820)^2(1.7 \times 10^{-3})^3(9.806)}{3 \times 0.20} = 0.05399 \text{ kg/s·m}$$ (2.9-31)

Using Eq. (2.9-30),

$$N_{Re} = \frac{4\Gamma}{\mu} = \frac{4(0.05399)}{0.20} = 1.080$$

Hence, the film is in laminar flow. Using Eq. (2.9-28),

$$v_{z\,av} = \frac{\rho g \delta^2}{3\mu} = \frac{820(9.806)(1.7 \times 10^{-3})^2}{3(0.20)} = 0.03873 \text{ m/s}$$

2.10 DESIGN EQUATIONS FOR LAMINAR AND TURBULENT FLOW IN PIPES

2.10A Velocity Profiles in Pipes

One of the most important applications of fluid flow is flow inside circular conduits, pipes, and tubes. Appendix A.5 gives sizes of commercial standard steel pipe. Schedule 40 pipe in the different sizes is the standard usually used. Schedule 80 has a thicker wall and will withstand about twice the pressure of schedule 40 pipe. Both have the same outside diameter so

FIGURE 2.10-1. *Velocity distribution of a fluid across a pipe.*

FIGURE 2.10-2. *Ratio v_{av}/v_{max} as a function of Reynolds number for pipes.*

that they will fit the same fittings. Pipes of other metals have the same outside diameters as steel pipe to permit interchanging parts of a piping system. Sizes of tubing are generally given by the outside diameter and wall thickness. Perry and Green (P1) give detailed tables of various types of tubing and pipes.

When fluid is flowing in a circular pipe and the velocities are measured at different distances from the pipe wall to the center of the pipe, it has been shown that in both laminar and turbulent flow, the fluid in the center of the pipe is moving faster than the fluid near the walls. These measurements are made at a reasonable distance from the entrance to the pipe. Figure 2.10-1 is a plot of the relative distance from the center of the pipe versus the fraction of maximum velocity v'/v_{max}, where v' is local velocity at the given position and v_{max} the maximum velocity at the center of the pipe. For viscous or laminar flow, the velocity profile is a true parabola, as derived in Eq. (2.9-9). The velocity at the wall is zero.

In many engineering applications the relation between the average velocity v_{av} in a pipe and the maximum velocity v_{max} is useful, since in some cases only the v_{max} at the center point of the tube is measured. Hence, from only one point measurement this relationship between v_{max} and v_{av} can be used to determine v_{av}. In Fig. 2.10-2 experimentally measured values of v_{av}/v_{max} are plotted as a function of the Reynolds numbers $Dv_{av}\rho/\mu$ and $Dv_{max}\rho/\mu$.

The average velocity over the whole cross section of the pipe is precisely 0.5 times the maximum velocity at the center as given by the shell momentum balance in Eq. (2.9-13) for laminar flow. On the other hand, for turbulent flow, the curve is somewhat flattened in the center (see Fig. 2.10-1) and the average velocity is about 0.8 times the maximum. This value of 0.8 varies slightly, depending upon the Reynolds number, as shown in the correlation in Fig. 2.10-2. (*Note:* See Problem 2.6-3, where a value of 0.817 is derived using the $\frac{1}{7}$-power law.)

2.10B Pressure Drop and Friction Loss in Laminar Flow

1. Pressure drop and loss due to friction. When the fluid is in steady-state laminar flow in a pipe, then for a Newtonian fluid the shear stress is given by Eq. (2.4-2), which is rewritten for change in radius dr rather than distance dy, as follows:

$$\tau_{rz} = -\mu \frac{dv_z}{dr} \tag{2.10-1}$$

Using this relationship and making a shell momentum balance on the fluid over a cylindrical shell, the Hagen–Poiseuille equation (2.9-11) for laminar flow of a liquid in circular tubes is obtained. This can be written as

$$\Delta p_f = (p_1 - p_2)_f = \frac{32\mu v(L_2 - L_1)}{D^2} \tag{2.10-2}$$

where p_1 is upstream pressure at point 1, N/m^2; p_2 is pressure at point 2; v is average velocity in tube, m/s; D is inside diameter, m; and $(L_2 - L_1)$ or ΔL is length of straight tube, m. For English units, the right-hand side of Eq. (2.10-2) is divided by g_c.

The quantity $(p_1 - p_2)_f$ or Δp_f is the pressure loss due to skin friction. Then, for constant ρ, the friction loss F_f is

$$F_f = \frac{(p_1 - p_2)_f}{\rho} = \frac{\text{N} \cdot \text{m}}{\text{kg}} \quad \text{or} \quad \frac{\text{J}}{\text{kg}} \quad \text{(SI)}$$

$$F_f = \frac{\text{ft} \cdot \text{lb}_f}{\text{lb}_m} \quad \text{(English)} \tag{2.10-3}$$

This is the mechanical-energy loss due to skin friction for the pipe in N $\cdot$ m/kg of fluid and is part of the $\sum F$ term for frictional losses in the mechanical-energy-balance equation (2.7-28). This term $(p_1 - p_2)_f$ for skin-friction loss is different from the $(p_1 - p_2)$ term, owing to velocity head or potential head changes in Eq. (2.7-28). That part of $\sum F$ which arises from friction within the channel itself by laminar or turbulent flow is discussed in Sections 2.10B and 2.10C. The part of friction loss due to fittings (valves, elbows, etc.), bends, and the like, which sometimes constitute a large part of the friction, is discussed in Section 2.10F. Note that if Eq. (2.7-28) is applied to steady flow in a straight, horizontal tube, we obtain $(p_1 - p_2)/\rho = \sum F$.

One of the uses of Eq. (2.10-2) is in the experimental measurement of the viscosity of a fluid by measuring the pressure drop and volumetric flow rate through a tube of known length and diameter. Slight corrections for kinetic energy and entrance effects are usually necessary in practice. Also, Eq. (2.10-2) is often used in the metering of small liquid flows.

EXAMPLE 2.10-1. Metering of Small Liquid Flows

A small capillary with an inside diameter of 2.22×10^{-3} m and a length 0.317 m is being used to continuously measure the flow rate of a liquid having a density of 875 kg/m^3 and $\mu = 1.13 \times 10^{-3}$ Pa$\cdot$s. The pressure-drop reading across the capillary during flow is 0.0655 m water (density 996 kg/m^3). What is the flow rate in m^3/s if end-effect corrections are neglected?

Solution: Assuming that the flow is laminar, Eq. (2.10-2) will be used. First, to convert the height h of 0.0655 m water to a pressure drop using Eq. (2.2-4),

$$\Delta p_f = h\rho g = (0.0655 \text{ m}) \left(996 \, \frac{\text{kg}}{\text{m}^3}\right) \left(9.80665 \, \frac{\text{m}}{\text{s}^2}\right)$$

$$= 640 \text{ kg} \cdot \text{m/s}^2 \cdot \text{m}^2 = 640 \text{ N/m}^2$$

Substituting into Eq. (2.10-2) the values $\mu = 1.13 \times 10^{-3}$ Pa$\cdot$s, $L_2 - L_1 = 0.317$ m, $D = 2.22 \times 10^{-3}$ m, and $\Delta p_f = 640$ N/m^2, and solving for v,

$$\Delta p_f = \frac{32\mu v(L_2 - L_1)}{D^2} \tag{2.10-2}$$

$$640 = \frac{32(1.13 \times 10^{-3})(v)(0.317)}{(2.22 \times 10^{-3})^2}$$

$$v = 0.275 \text{ m/s}$$

The volumetric rate is then

$$\text{volumetric flow rate} = v\pi \frac{D^2}{4} = \frac{0.275(\pi)(2.22 \times 10^{-3})^2}{4}$$

$$= 1.066 \times 10^{-6} \text{ m}^3/\text{s}$$

Since it was assumed that laminar flow is occurring, the Reynolds number will be calculated to check this:

$$N_{Re} = \frac{Dv\rho}{\mu} = \frac{(2.22 \times 10^{-3})(0.275)(875)}{1.13 \times 10^{-3}} = 473$$

Hence, the flow is laminar as assumed.

2. *Use of friction factor for friction loss in laminar flow.* A common parameter used in laminar and especially in turbulent flow is the *Fanning friction factor, f,* which is defined as the drag force per wetted surface unit area (shear stress τ_s at the surface) divided by the product of density times velocity head, or $\frac{1}{2}\rho v^2$. The force is Δp_f times the cross-sectional area πR^2 and the wetted surface area is $2\pi R \, \Delta L$. Hence, the relation between the pressure drop due to friction and f is as follows for laminar and turbulent flow:

$$f = \frac{\tau_s}{\rho v^2/2} = \frac{\Delta p_f \pi R^2}{2\pi R \, \Delta L} \bigg/ \frac{\rho v^2}{2} \tag{2.10-4}$$

Rearranging, this becomes

$$\Delta p_f = 4f\rho \frac{\Delta L}{D} \frac{v^2}{2} \qquad \text{(SI)}$$

$$\Delta p_f = 4f\rho \frac{\Delta L}{D} \frac{v^2}{2g_c} \qquad \text{(English)}$$

(2.10-5)

$$F_f = \frac{\Delta p_f}{\rho} = 4f \frac{\Delta L}{D} \frac{v^2}{2} \qquad \text{(SI)}$$

$$F_f = 4f \frac{\Delta L}{D} \frac{v^2}{2g_c} \qquad \text{(English)}$$

(2.10-6)

For laminar flow only, combining Eqs. (2.10-2) and (2.10-5),

$$f = \frac{16}{N_{Re}} = \frac{16}{Dv\rho/\mu} \qquad \qquad \text{(2.10-7)}$$

Equations (2.10-2), (2.10-5), (2.10-6), and (2.10-7) for laminar flow hold up to a Reynolds number of 2100. Beyond that, at a N_{Re} value above 2100, Eqs. (2.10-2) and (2.10-7) do not hold for turbulent flow. For turbulent flow, Eqs. (2.10-5) and (2.10-6), however, are used extensively along with empirical methods for predicting the friction factor f, as discussed in the next section.

EXAMPLE 2.10-2. Use of Friction Factor in Laminar Flow

Assume the same known conditions as in Example 2.10-1 except that the velocity of 0.275 m/s is known and the pressure drop Δp_f is to be predicted. Use the Fanning friction factor method.

Solution: The Reynolds number is, as before,

$$N_{Re} = \frac{Dv\rho}{\mu} = \frac{(22.2 \times 10^{-3} \text{ m})(0.275 \text{ m/s})(875 \text{ kg/m}^3)}{1.13 \times 10^{-3} \text{ kg/m} \cdot \text{s}} = 473$$

From Eq. (2.10-7) the friction factor f is

$$f = \frac{16}{N_{Re}} = \frac{16}{473} = 0.0338 \qquad \text{(dimensionless)}$$

Using Eq. (2.10-5) with $\Delta L = 0.317$ m, $v = 0.275$ m/s, $D = 2.22 \times 10^{-3}$ m, and $\rho = 875$ kg/m^3,

$$\Delta p_f = 4f\rho \frac{\Delta L}{D} \frac{v^2}{2} = \frac{4(0.0338)(875)(0.317)(0.275)^2}{(22.2 \times 10^{-3})(2)} = 640 \text{ N/m}^2$$

This, of course, agrees with the value in Example 2.10-1.

When the fluid is a gas and not a liquid, the Hagen–Poiseuille equation (2.10-2) can be written as follows for laminar flow:

$$m = \frac{\pi D^4 M(p_1^2 - p_2^2)}{128(2RT)\mu(L_2 - L_1)} \qquad \text{(SI)}$$

$$m = \frac{\pi D^4 g_c M(p_1^2 - p_2^2)}{128(2RT)\mu(L_2 - L_1)} \qquad \text{(English)}$$

(2.10-8)

Chapter 2   *Principles of Momentum Transfer and Overall Balances* where m = kg/s, M = molecular weight in kg/kg mol, T = absolute temperature in K, and R = 8314.3 N · m/kg mol · K. In English units, R = 1545.3 ft · lb$_f$/lb mol · °R.

2.10C Pressure Drop and Friction Factor in Turbulent Flow

In turbulent flow, as in laminar flow, the friction factor also depends on the Reynolds number. However, it is not possible to predict theoretically the Fanning friction factor f for turbulent flow as was done for laminar flow. The friction factor must be determined empirically (experimentally), and it not only depends upon the Reynolds number but also on surface roughness of the pipe. In laminar flow the roughness has essentially no effect.

Dimensional analysis also shows the dependence of the friction factor on these factors. In Sections 3.11 and 4.14, methods of obtaining the dimensionless numbers and their importance are discussed.

A large number of experimental data on friction factors for smooth pipe and pipes of varying degrees of equivalent roughness have been obtained and the data correlated. For design purposes, to predict the friction factor f and, hence, the frictional pressure drop for round pipe, the friction-factor chart in Fig. 2.10-3 can be used. It is a log–log plot of f versus N_{Re}. This friction factor f is then used in Eqs. (2.10-5) and (2.10-6) to predict the friction loss Δp_f or F_f:

$$\Delta p_f = 4f\rho \frac{\Delta L}{D} \frac{v^2}{2} \quad \text{(SI)}$$

$$\Delta p_f = 4f\rho \frac{\Delta L}{D} \frac{v^2}{2g_c} \quad \text{(English)}$$

(2.10-5)

$$F_f = \frac{\Delta p_f}{\rho} = 4f \frac{\Delta L}{D} \frac{v^2}{2} \quad \text{(SI)}$$

$$F_f = 4f \frac{\Delta L}{D} \frac{v^2}{2g_c} \quad \text{(English)}$$

(2.10-6)

For the region with a Reynolds number below 2100, the line is the same as Eq. (2.10-7). For a Reynolds number above 4000 for turbulent flow, the lowest line in Fig. 2.10-3 represents the friction-factor line for smooth pipes and tubes, such as glass tubes and drawn copper and brass tubes. The other lines, for higher friction factors, represent lines for different relative roughness factors, ε/D, where D is the inside pipe diameter in m and ε is a roughness parameter, which represents the average height in m of roughness projections from the wall (M1). In Fig. 2.10-3, values for the equivalent roughness of new pipes are given (M1). The most common pipe, commercial steel, has a roughness of $\varepsilon = 4.6 \times 10^{-5}$ m (1.5×10^{-4} ft).

The reader should be cautioned about using friction factors f from other sources. The Fanning friction factor f in Eq. (2.10-6) is the one used here. Others use a friction factor that may be four times larger.

> **EXAMPLE 2.10-3. Use of Friction Factor in Turbulent Flow**
> A liquid is flowing through a horizontal straight pipe at 4.57 m/s. The pipe used is commercial steel, schedule 40, 2-in. nominal diameter. The viscosity of the liquid is 4.46 cp and the density 801 kg/m³. Calculate the mechanical-energy friction loss F_f in J/kg for a 36.6-m section of pipe.

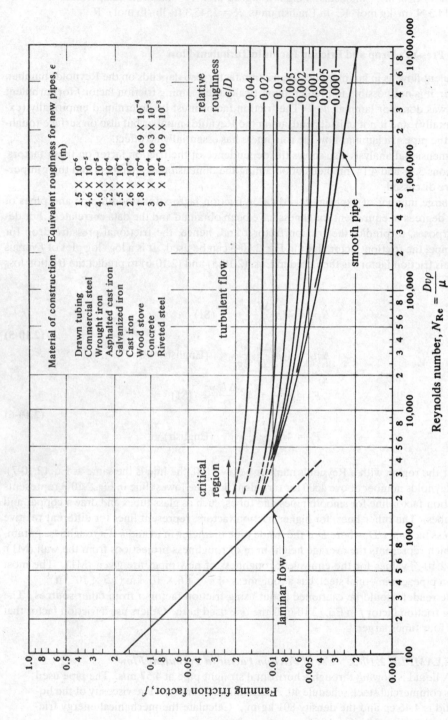

FIGURE 2.10-3. *Friction factors for fluids inside pipes.* [*Based on L. F. Moody, Trans. A.S.M.E.,* **66**, 671 (1944): Mech. Eng. **69**, 1005 (1947). *With permission.*]

The chart shows the following axes and labels:

- Vertical axis: Fanning friction factor, f, ranging from 0.001 to 1.0
- Horizontal axis: Reynolds number, $N_{Re} = \dfrac{Dv\rho}{\mu}$, ranging from 100 to 10,000,000

Regions labeled: laminar flow, critical region, turbulent flow, smooth pipe

Material of construction	Equivalent roughness for new pipes, ϵ (m)
Drawn tubing	1.5×10^{-6}
Commercial steel	4.6×10^{-5}
Wrought iron	4.6×10^{-5}
Asphalted cast iron	1.2×10^{-4}
Galvanized iron	1.5×10^{-4}
Cast iron	2.6×10^{-4}
Wood stove	1.8×10^{-4} to 9×10^{-4}
Concrete	3×10^{-4} to 3×10^{-3}
Riveted steel	9×10^{-4} to 9×10^{-3}

relative roughness ϵ/D curves: 0.04, 0.02, 0.01, 0.005, 0.002, 0.001, 0.0005, 0.0001

Solution: The following data are given: From Appendix A.5, $D = 0.0525$ m, $v = 4.57$ m/s, $\rho = 801$ kg/m³, $\Delta L = 36.6$ m, and

$$\mu = (4.46 \text{ cp})(1 \times 10^{-3}) = 4.46 \times 10^{-3} \text{ kg/m} \cdot \text{s}$$

The Reynolds number is calculated as

$$N_{Re} = \frac{Dv\rho}{\mu} = \frac{0.0525(4.57)(801)}{4.46 \times 10^{-3}} = 4.310 \times 10^{4}$$

Hence, the flow is turbulent. For commercial steel pipe from the table in Fig. 2.10-3, the equivalent roughness is 4.6×10^{-5} m:

$$\frac{\varepsilon}{D} = \frac{4.6 \times 10^{-5} \text{ m}}{0.0525 \text{ m}} = 0.00088$$

For a N_{Re} of 4.310×10^{4}, the friction factor from Fig. 2.10-3 is $f = 0.0060$. Substituting into Eq. (2.10-6), the friction loss is

$$F_f = 4f \frac{\Delta L}{D} \frac{v^2}{2} = \frac{4(0.0060)(36.6)(4.57)^2}{(0.0525)(2)} = 174.8 \frac{J}{kg} \left(58.5 \frac{ft \cdot lb_f}{lb_m} \right)$$

In problems involving the friction loss F_f in pipes, F_f is usually the unknown, with the diameter D, velocity v, and pipe length ΔL known. Then a direct solution is possible, as in Example 2.10-3. However, in some cases, the friction loss F_f is already set by the available head of liquid. Then if the volumetric flow rate and pipe length are set, the unknown to be calculated is the diameter. This solution must be by trial and error, since the velocity v appears in both N_{Re} and f, which are unknown. In another case, with F_f again being already set, the diameter and pipe length are specified. This solution is also by trial and error, to calculate the velocity. Example 2.10-4 indicates the method to be used to calculate the pipe diameter with F_f set. Others (M2) give a convenient chart to aid in these types of calculations.

EXAMPLE 2.10-4. Trial-and-Error Solution to Calculate Pipe Diameter

Water at 4.4°C is to flow through a horizontal commercial steel pipe having a length of 305 m at the rate of 150 gal/min. A head of water of 6.1 m is available to overcome the friction loss F_f. Calculate the pipe diameter.

Solution: From Appendix A.2, the density $\rho = 1000$ kg/m³ and the viscosity μ is

$$\mu = (1.55 \text{ cp})(1 \times 10^{-3}) = 1.55 \times 10^{-3} \text{ kg/m} \cdot \text{s}$$

$$\text{friction loss } F_f = (6.1 \text{ m})g = (6.1)(9.80665) = 59.82 \text{ J/kg}$$

$$\text{flow rate} = \left(150 \frac{\text{gal}}{\text{min}} \right) \left(\frac{1 \text{ ft}^3}{7.481 \text{ gal}} \right) \left(\frac{1 \text{ min}}{60 \text{ s}} \right) (0.028317 \text{ m}^3/\text{ft}^3)$$

$$= 9.46 \times 10^{-3} \text{ m}^3/\text{s}$$

$$\text{area of pipe} = \frac{\pi D^2}{4} \text{ m}^2 \quad (D \text{ is unknown})$$

$$\text{velocity } v = (9.46 \times 10^{-3} \text{ m}^3/\text{s}) \left(\frac{1}{\pi D^2/4 \text{ m}^2} \right) = \frac{0.01204}{D^2} \text{ m/s}$$

The solution is by trial and error since v appears in N_{Re} and f. Assume that $D = 0.089$ m for the first trial.

$$N_{Re} = \frac{Dv\rho}{\mu} = (0.089)\frac{0.01204(1000)}{(0.089)^2(1.55 \times 10^{-3})} = 8.730 \times 10^4$$

For commercial steel pipe and using Fig. 2.10-3, $\varepsilon = 4.6 \times 10^{-5}$ m. Then,

$$\frac{\varepsilon}{D} = \frac{4.6 \times 10^{-5} \text{ m}}{0.089 \text{ m}} = 0.00052$$

From Fig. 2.10-3 for $N_{Re} = 8.730 \times 10^4$ and $\varepsilon/D = 0.00052$, $f = 0.0051$. Substituting into Eq. (2.10-6),

$$F_f = 59.82 = 4f\frac{\Delta L}{D}\frac{v^2}{2} = \frac{4(0.0051)(305)}{D(2)}\frac{(0.01204)^2}{D^4}$$

Solving for D, $D = 0.0945$ m. This does not agree with the assumed value of 0.089 m.

For the second trial, D will be assumed to be 0.0945 m.

$$N_{Re} = (0.0945)\frac{0.01204}{(0.0945)^2}\frac{1000}{1.55 \times 10^{-3}} = 8.220 \times 10^4$$

$$\frac{\varepsilon}{D} = \frac{4.6 \times 10^{-5}}{0.0945} = 0.00049$$

From Fig. 2.10-3, $f = 0.0052$. It can be seen that f does not change much with N_{Re} in the turbulent region:

$$F_f = 59.82 = \frac{4(0.0052)(305)}{D(2)}\frac{(0.01204)^2}{D^4}$$

Solving, $D = 0.0954$ m or 3.75 in. Hence, the solution agrees closely with the assumed value of D.

2.10D Pressure Drop and Friction Factor in Flow of Gases

The equations and methods discussed in this section for turbulent flow in pipes hold for incompressible liquids. They also hold for a gas if the density (or the pressure) changes by less than 10%. Then an average density, ρ_{av} in kg/m^3, should be used and the errors involved will be less than the uncertainty limits in the friction factor f. For gases, Eq. (2.10-5) can be rewritten as follows for laminar and turbulent flow:

$$(p_1 - p_2)_f = \frac{4f\,\Delta LG^2}{D2\rho_{av}} \tag{2.10-9}$$

where ρ_{av} is the density at $p_{av} = (p_1 + p_2)/2$. Also, the N_{Re} used is DG/μ, where G is kg/m$^2 \cdot$ s and is a constant independent of the density and velocity variations for the gas. Equation (2.10-5) can also be written for gases as

$$p_1^2 - p_2^2 = \frac{4f\,\Delta LG^2RT}{DM} \quad \text{(SI)}$$

$$p_1^2 - p_2^2 = \frac{4f\,\Delta LG^2 RT}{g_c DM} \qquad \text{(English)}$$

where R is 8314.3 J/kg mol $\cdot$ K or 1545.3 ft $\cdot$ lb$_f$/lb mol $\cdot$ °R and M is molecular weight.

The derivation of Eqs. (2.10-9) and (2.10-10) applies only to cases with gases where the relative pressure change is small enough that large changes in velocity do not occur. If the exit velocity becomes large, the kinetic-energy term, which has been omitted, becomes important. For pressure changes above about 10%, compressible flow is occurring, and the reader should refer to Section 2.11. In adiabatic flow in a uniform pipe, the velocity in the pipe cannot exceed the velocity of sound.

EXAMPLE 2.10-5. Flow of Gas in Line and Pressure Drop

Nitrogen gas at 25°C is flowing in a smooth tube having an inside diameter of 0.010 m at the rate of 9.0 kg/s $\cdot$ m^2. The tube is 200 m long and the flow can be assumed to be isothermal. The pressure at the entrance to the tube is 2.0265×10^5 Pa. Calculate the outlet pressure.

Solution: The viscosity of the gas from Appendix A.3 is $\mu = 1.77 \times 10^{-5}$ Pa $\cdot$ s at $T = 298.15$ K. Inlet gas pressure $p_1 = 2.0265 \times 10^5$ Pa, $G = 9.0$ kg/s $\cdot$ m^2, $D = 0.010$ m, $M = 28.02$ kg/kg mol, $\Delta L = 200$ m, and $R = 8314.3$ J/kg mol $\cdot$ K. Assuming that Eq. (2.10-10) holds for this case and that the pressure drop is less than 10%, the Reynolds number is

$$N_{Re} = \frac{DG}{\mu} = \frac{0.010(9.0)}{1.77 \times 10^{-5}} = 5085$$

Hence, the flow is turbulent. Using Fig. 2.10-3, $f = 0.0090$ for a smooth tube. Substituting into Eq. (2.10-10),

$$p_1^2 - p_2^2 = \frac{4f\,\Delta LG^2 RT}{DM}$$

$$(2.0265 \times 10^5)^2 - p_2^2 = \frac{4(0.0090)(200)(9.0)^2(8314.3)(298.15)}{0.010(28.02)}$$

$$4.1067 \times 10^{10} - p_2^2 = 0.5160 \times 10^{10}$$

Solving, $p_2 = 1.895 \times 10^5$ Pa. Hence, Eq. (2.10-10) can be used, since the pressure drop is less than 10%.

2.10E Effect of Heat Transfer on Friction Factor

The friction factor f in Fig. 2.10-3 is given for isothermal flow, that is, no heat transfer. When a fluid is being heated or cooled, the temperature gradient will cause a change in physical properties of the fluid, especially the viscosity. For engineering practice the following method of Sieder and Tate (P1, S3) can be used to predict the friction factor for nonisothermal flow for liquids and gases:

1. Calculate the mean bulk temperature t_a as the average of the inlet and outlet bulk fluid temperatures.
2. Calculate the N_{Re} using the viscosity μ_a at t_a and use Fig. 2.10-3 to obtain f.

3. Using the tube wall temperature t_w, determine μ_w at t_w.

4. Calculate ψ for the appropriate case:

$$\psi = \left(\frac{\mu_a}{\mu_w}\right)^{0.17} \qquad \text{(heating)} N_{Re} > 2100 \qquad \text{(2.10-11)}$$

$$\psi = \left(\frac{\mu_a}{\mu_w}\right)^{0.11} \qquad \text{(cooling)} N_{Re} > 2100 \qquad \text{(2.10-12)}$$

$$\psi = \left(\frac{\mu_a}{\mu_w}\right)^{0.38} \qquad \text{(heating)} N_{Re} < 2100 \qquad \text{(2.10-13)}$$

$$\psi = \left(\frac{\mu_a}{\mu_w}\right)^{0.23} \qquad \text{(cooling)} N_{Re} < 2100 \qquad \text{(2.10-14)}$$

5. The final friction factor is obtained by dividing f from step 2 by ψ from step 4.

Hence, when the liquid is being heated, ψ is greater than 1.0 and the final f decreases. The reverse occurs on cooling the liquid.

2.10F Friction Losses in Expansion, Contraction, and Pipe Fittings

Skin-friction losses in flow through straight pipe are calculated by using the Fanning friction factor. However, if the velocity of the fluid is changed in direction or magnitude, additional friction losses occur. This results from additional turbulence which develops because of vortices and other factors. Methods for estimating these losses are discussed below.

1. Sudden enlargement losses. If the cross section of a pipe enlarges very gradually, very little or no extra losses are incurred. If the change is sudden, it results in additional losses due to eddies formed by the jet expanding in the enlarged section. This friction loss can be calculated by the following for turbulent flow in both sections. The following equation was derived in Example 2.8-4 as Eq. (2.8-3.6):

$$h_{ex} = \frac{(v_1 - v_2)^2}{2\alpha} = \left(1 - \frac{A_1}{A_2}\right)^2 \frac{v_1^2}{2\alpha} = K_{ex} \frac{v_1^2}{2\alpha} \frac{J}{kg} \qquad \text{(2.10-15)}$$

where h_{ex} is the friction loss in J/kg, K_{ex} is the expansion-loss coefficent and equals $(1 - A_1/A_2)^2$, v_1 is the upstream velocity in the smaller area in m/s, v_2 is the downstream velocity, and $\alpha = 1.0$. If the flow is laminar in both sections, the factor α in the equation becomes $\frac{1}{2}$. For English units the right-hand side of Eq. (2.10-15) is divided by g_c. Also, $h = ft \cdot lb_f/lb_m$.

2. Sudden contraction losses. When the cross section of the pipe is suddenly reduced, the stream cannot follow around the sharp corner, and additional frictional losses due to eddies occur. For turbulent flow, this is given by

$$h_c = 0.55\left(1 - \frac{A_2}{A_1}\right)\frac{v_2^2}{2\alpha} = K_c \frac{v_2^2}{2\alpha} \frac{J}{kg} \qquad \text{(2.10-16)}$$

where h_c is the friction loss, $\alpha = 1.0$ for turbulent flow, v_2 is the average velocity in the smaller or downstream section, and K_c is the contraction-loss coefficient (P1) and approximately equals 0.55 $(1 - A_2/A_1)$. For laminar flow, the same equation can be used with $\alpha = \frac{1}{2}$ (S2). For English units the right side is divided by g_c.

3. Losses in fittings and valves. Pipe fittings and valves also disturb the normal flow lines in a pipe and cause additional friction losses. In a short pipe with many fittings, the friction loss from these fittings could be greater than in the straight pipe. The friction loss for fittings and valves is given by the following equation:

$$h_f = K_f \frac{v_1^2}{2} \tag{2.10-17}$$

where K_f is the loss factor for the fitting or valve and v_1 is the average velocity in the pipe leading to the fitting. Experimental values for K_f are given in Table 2.10-1 for turbulent flow (P1) and in Table 2.10-2 for laminar flow.

As an alternative method, some texts and references (B1) give data for losses in fittings as an equivalent pipe length in pipe diameters. These data, also given in Table 2.10-1, are presented as L_e/D, where L_e is the equivalent length of straight pipe in m having the same frictional loss as the fitting, and D is the inside pipe diameter in m. The K values in Eqs. (2.10-15) and (2.10-16) can be converted to L_e/D values by multiplying the K by 50 (P1). The L_e values for the fittings are simply added to the length of the straight pipe to get the total length of equivalent straight pipe to use in Eq. (2.10-6).

TABLE 2.10-1. *Friction Loss for Turbulent Flow Through Valves and Fittings*

Type of Fitting or Valve	Frictional Loss, Number of Velocity Heads, K_f	Frictional Loss, Equivalent Length of Straight Pipe in Pipe Diameters, L_e/D
Elbow, 45°	0.35	17
Elbow, 90°	0.75	35
Tee	1	50
Return bend	1.5	75
Coupling	0.04	2
Union	0.04	2
Gate valve		
Wide open	0.17	9
Half open	4.5	225
Globe valve		
Wide open	6.0	300
Half open	9.5	475
Angle valve, wide open	2.0	100
Check valve		
Ball	70.0	3500
Swing	2.0	100
Water meter, disk	7.0	350

Source: R. H. Perry and C. H. Chilton, *Chemical Engineers' Handbook*, 5th ed. New York: McGraw-Hill Book Company, 1973. With permission.

TABLE 2.10-2. *Friction Loss for Laminar Flow Through Valves and Fittings (K1)*

Type of Fitting or Valve	Frictional Loss, Number of Velocity Heads, K_f Reynolds Number					
	50	100	200	400	1000	Turbulent
Elbow, 90°	17	7	2.5	1.2	0.85	0.75
Tee	9	4.8	3.0	2.0	1.4	1.0
Globe valve	28	22	17	14	10	6.0
Check valve, swing	55	17	9	5.8	3.2	2.0

4. Frictional losses in mechanical-energy-balance equation. The frictional losses from the friction in the straight pipe (Fanning friction), enlargement losses, contraction losses, and losses in fittings and valves are all incorporated in the $\sum F$ term of Eq. (2.7-28) for the mechanical-energy balance, so that

$$\sum F = 4f \frac{\Delta L}{D} \frac{v^2}{2} + K_{ex} \frac{v_1^2}{2} + K_c \frac{v_2^2}{2} + K_f \frac{v_1^2}{2} \qquad \textbf{(2.10-18)}$$

If all the velocities, v, v_1, and v_2, are the same, then by factoring, Eq. (2.10-18) becomes, for this special case,

$$\sum F = \left(4f \frac{\Delta L}{D} + K_{ex} + K_c + K_f \right) \frac{v^2}{2} \qquad \textbf{(2.10-19)}$$

The use of the mechanical-energy-balance equation (2.7-28) along with Eq. (2.10-18) will be shown in the following examples.

EXAMPLE 2.10-6. *Friction Losses and Mechanical-Energy Balance*
An elevated storage tank contains water at 82.2°C, as shown in Fig. 2.10-4. It is desired to have a discharge rate at point 2 of 0.223 ft³/s. What must be the height H in ft of the surface of the water in the tank relative to the discharge point? The pipe used is commercial steel pipe, schedule 40, and the lengths of the straight portions of pipe are shown.

Solution: The mechanical-energy-balance equation (2.7-28) is written between points 1 and 2.

$$z_1 \frac{g}{g_c} + \frac{v_1^2}{2\alpha g_c} + \left(\frac{p_1}{\rho_1} - \frac{p_2}{\rho_2} \right) - W_S = z_2 \frac{g}{g_c} + \frac{v_2^2}{2\alpha g_c} + \sum F \qquad \textbf{(2.10-20)}$$

From Appendix A.2, for water, $\rho = 0.970(62.43) = 60.52 \ \text{lb}_m/\text{ft}^3$ and $\mu = 0.347$ cp $= 0.347(6.7197 \times 10^{-4}) = 2.33 \times 10^{-4} \ \text{lb}_m/\text{ft} \cdot \text{s}$. The diameters of the pipes are

For 4-in. pipe: $\quad D_3 = \dfrac{4.026}{12} = 0.3353 \ \text{ft}; \qquad A_3 = 0.0884 \ \text{ft}^2$

For 2-in. pipe: $\quad D_4 = \dfrac{2.067}{12} = 0.1722 \ \text{ft}; \qquad A_4 = 0.02330 \ \text{ft}^2$

FIGURE 2.10-4. *Process flow diagram for Example 2.10-6.*

The velocities in the 4-in. and 2-in. pipe are

$$v_3 = \frac{0.223 \text{ ft}^3/\text{s}}{0.0884 \text{ ft}^2} = 2.523 \text{ ft/s} \quad \text{(4-in. pipe)}$$

$$v_4 = \frac{0.223}{0.02330} = 9.57 \text{ ft/s} \quad \text{(2-in. pipe)}$$

The ΣF term for frictional losses in the system includes the following: (1) contraction loss at tank exit, (2) friction in the 4-in. straight pipe, (3) friction in 4-in. elbow, (4) contraction loss from 4-in. to 2-in. pipe, (5) friction in the 2-in. straight pipe, and (6) friction in the two 2-in. elbows. Calculations for the six items are as follows:

1. Contraction loss at tank exit. From Eq. (2.10-16), for contraction from A_1 to A_3 cross-sectional area, since A_1 of the tank is very large compared to A_3,

$$K_c = 0.55\left(1 - \frac{A_3}{A_1}\right) = 0.55(1 - 0) = 0.55$$

$$h_c = K_c \frac{v_3^2}{2g_c} = 0.55 \frac{(2.523)^2}{2(32.174)} = 0.054 \text{ ft} \cdot \text{lb}_f/\text{lb}_m$$

2. Friction in the 4-in. pipe. The Reynolds number is

$$N_{Re} = \frac{D_3 v_3 \rho}{\mu} = \frac{0.3353(2.523)(60.52)}{2.33 \times 10^{-4}} = 2.193 \times 10^5$$

Hence, the flow is turbulent. From Fig. 2.10-3, $\varepsilon = 4.6 \times 10^{-5}$ m (1.5×10^{-4} ft).

$$\frac{\varepsilon}{D_3} = \frac{0.00015}{0.3353} = 0.000448$$

Then, for $N_{Re} = 219\,300$, the Fanning friction factor $f = 0.0047$. Substituting into Eq. (2.10-6) for $\Delta L = 20.0$ ft of 4-in. pipe,

$$F_f = 4f\frac{\Delta L}{D}\frac{v^2}{2g_c} = 4(0.0047)\frac{20.0}{0.3353}\frac{(2.523)^2}{2(32.174)} = 0.111\frac{\text{ft}\cdot\text{lb}_f}{\text{lb}_m}$$

3. *Friction in 4-in. elbow.* From Table 2.10-1, $K_f = 0.75$. Then, substituting into Eq. (2.10-17),

$$h_f = K_f\frac{v^2}{2g_c} = 0.75\frac{(2.523)^2}{2(32.174)} = 0.074\frac{\text{ft}\cdot\text{lb}_f}{\text{lb}_m}$$

4. *Contraction loss from 4- to 2-in. pipe.* Using Eq. (2.10-16) again for contraction from A_3 to A_4 cross-sectional area,

$$K_c = 0.55\left(1 - \frac{A_4}{A_3}\right) = 0.55\left(1 - \frac{0.02330}{0.0884}\right) = 0.405$$

$$h_c = K_c\frac{v_4^2}{2g_c} = 0.405\frac{(9.57)^2}{2(32.174)} = 0.575\frac{\text{ft}\cdot\text{lb}_f}{\text{lb}_m}$$

5. *Friction in the 2-in pipe.* The Reynolds number is

$$N_{Re} = \frac{D_4 v_4 \rho}{\mu} = \frac{0.1722(9.57)(60.52)}{2.33\times10^{-4}} = 4.280\times10^5$$

$$\frac{\varepsilon}{D} = \frac{0.00015}{0.1722} = 0.00087$$

The Fanning friction factor from Fig. 2.10-3 is $f = 0.0048$. The total length $\Delta L = 125 + 10 + 50 = 185$ ft. Substituting into Eq. (2.10-6),

$$F_f = 4f\frac{\Delta L}{D}\frac{v^2}{2g_c} = 4(0.0048)\frac{185(9.57)^2}{(0.1722)(2)(32.174)} = 29.4\frac{\text{ft}\cdot\text{lb}_f}{\text{lb}_m}$$

6. *Friction in the two 2-in. elbows.* For a $K_f = 0.75$ and two elbows,

$$h_f = 2K_f\frac{v^2}{2g_c} = \frac{2(0.75)(9.57)^2}{2(32.174)} = 2.136\frac{\text{ft}\cdot\text{lb}_f}{\text{lb}_m}$$

The total frictional loss ΣF is the sum of items (1) through (6):

$$\Sigma F = 0.054 + 0.111 + 0.074 + 0.575 + 29.4 + 2.136$$

$$= 32.35 \text{ ft}\cdot\text{lb}_f/\text{lb}_m$$

Using as a datum level z_2, $z_1 = H$ ft, $z_2 = 0$. Since turbulent flow exists, $\alpha = 1.0$. Also, $v_1 = 0$ and $v_2 = v_4 = 9.57$ ft/s. Since p_1 and p_2 are both at 1 atm abs pressure and $\rho_1 = \rho_2$,

$$\frac{p_1}{\rho} - \frac{p_2}{\rho} = 0$$

Also, since no pump is used, $W_S = 0$. Substituting these values into Eq. (2.10-20),

$$H\frac{g}{g_c} + 0 + 0 - 0 = 0 + \frac{1(9.57)^2}{2(32.174)} + 32.35$$

Solving, $H(g/g_c) = 33.77$ ft $\cdot$ lb$_f$/lb$_m$ (100.9 J/kg) and H is 33.77 ft (10.3 m) height of water level above the discharge outlet.

EXAMPLE 2.10-7. Friction Losses with Pump in Mechanical-Energy Balance

Water at 20°C is being pumped from a tank to an elevated tank at the rate of 5.0×10^{-3} m³/s. All of the piping in Fig. 2.10-5 is 4-in. schedule 40 pipe. The pump has an efficiency of 65%. Calculate the kW power needed for the pump.

Solution: The mechanical-energy-balance equation (2.7-28) is written between points 1 and 2, with point 1 being the reference plane:

$$\frac{1}{2\alpha}(v_{2av}^2 - v_{1av}^2) + g(z_2 - z_1) + \frac{p_2 - p_1}{\rho} + \sum F + W_S = 0 \quad \textbf{(2.7-28)}$$

From Appendix A.2, for water, $\rho = 998.2$ kg/m³ and $\mu = 1.005 \times 10^{-3}$ Pa·s. For 4-in. pipe, from Appendix A.5, $D = 0.1023$ m and $A = 8.219 \times 10^{-3}$ m². The velocity in the pipe is $v = 5.0 \times 10^{-3}/(8.219 \times 10^{-3}) = 0.6083$ m/s. The Reynolds number is

$$N_{Re} = \frac{Dv\rho}{\mu} = \frac{0.1023(0.6083)(998.2)}{1.005 \times 10^{-3}} = 6.181 \times 10^4$$

Hence, the flow is turbulent.

The $\sum F$ term for frictional losses includes the following: (1) contraction loss at tank exit, (2) friction in the straight pipe, (3) friction in the two elbows, and (4) expansion loss at the tank entrance.

FIGURE 2.10-5. *Process flow diagram for Example 2.10-7.*

1. Contraction loss at tank exit. From Eq. (2.10-16), for contraction from a large A_1 to a small A_2,

$$k_c = 0.55\left(1 - \frac{A_2}{A_1}\right) = 0.55(1 - 0) = 0.55$$

$$h_c = K_c \frac{v^2}{2\alpha} = (0.55)\frac{(0.6083)^2}{2(1.0)} = 0.102 \text{ J/kg}$$

2. Friction in the straight pipe. From Fig. 2.10-3, $\varepsilon = 4.6 \times 10^{-5}$ m and $\varepsilon/D = 4.6 \times 10^{-5}/0.1023 = 0.00045$. Then for $N_{Re} = 6.181 \times 10^4$, $f = 0.0051$. Substituting into Eq. (2.10-6) for $\Delta L = 5 + 50 + 15 + 100 = 170$ m,

$$F_f = 4f\frac{\Delta L}{D}\frac{v^2}{2} = 4(0.0051)\frac{170}{0.1023}\frac{(0.6083)^2}{2} = 6.272 \text{ J/kg}$$

3. Friction in the two elbows. From Table 2.10-1, $K_f = 0.75$. Then, substituting into Eq. (2.10-7) for two elbows,

$$h_f = 2K_f\frac{v^2}{2} = 2(0.75)\frac{(0.6083)^2}{2} = 0.278 \text{ J/kg}$$

4. Expansion loss at the tank entrance. Using Eq. (2.10-15),

$$K_{ex} = \left(1 - \frac{A_1}{A_2}\right)^2 = (1 - 0)^2 = 1.0$$

$$h_{ex} = K_{ex}\frac{v^2}{2} = 1.0\frac{(0.6083)^2}{2} = 0.185 \text{ J/kg}$$

The total frictional loss is ΣF:

$$\Sigma F = 0.102 + 6.272 + 0.278 + 0.185 = 6.837 \text{ J/kg}$$

Substituting into Eq. (2.7-28), where $(v_1^2 - v_2^2) = 0$ and $(p_2 - p_1) = 0$,

$$0 + 9.806(15.0 - 0) + 0 + 6.837 + W_S = 0$$

Solving, $W_S = -153.93$ J/kg. The mass flow rate is $m = 5.0 \times 10^{-3}(998.2) = 4.991$ kg/s. Using Eq. (2.7-30),

$$W_S = -\eta W_p$$

$$-153.93 = 0.65W_p$$

Solving, $W_p = 236.8$ J/kg. The pump kW power is

$$\text{pump kW} = mW_p = \frac{4.991(236.8)}{1000} = 1.182 \text{ kW}$$

2.10G   Friction Loss in Noncircular Conduits

The friction loss in long, straight channels or conduits of noncircular cross section can be estimated by using the same equations employed for circular pipes if the diameter in the

Reynolds number and in the friction-factor equation (2.10-6) is taken as the equivalent diameter. The equivalent diameter D is defined as four times the hydraulic radius r_H. The hydraulic radius is defined as the ratio of the cross-sectional area of the channel to the wetted perimeter of the channel for turbulent flow only. Hence,

$$D = 4r_H = 4 \frac{\text{cross-sectional area of channel}}{\text{wetted perimeter of channel}} \qquad (2.10\text{-}21)$$

For example, for a circular tube,

$$D = \frac{4(\pi D^2/4)}{\pi D} = D$$

For an annular space with outside diameter D_1 and inside D_2,

$$D = \frac{4(\pi D_1^2/4 - \pi D_2^2/4)}{\pi D_1 + \pi D_2} = D_1 - D_2 \qquad (2.10\text{-}22)$$

For a rectangular duct of sides a and b ft,

$$D = \frac{4(ab)}{2a + 2b} = \frac{2ab}{a + b} \qquad (2.10\text{-}23)$$

For open channels and partly filled ducts in turbulent flow, the equivalent diameter and Eq. (2.10-6) are also used (P1). For a rectangle with depth of liquid y and width b,

$$D = \frac{4(by)}{b + 2y} \qquad (2.10\text{-}24)$$

For a wide, shallow stream of depth y,

$$D = 4y \qquad (2.10\text{-}25)$$

For laminar flow in ducts running full and in open channels with various cross-sectional shapes other than circular, equations are given elsewhere (P1).

2.10H Entrance Section of a Pipe

If the velocity profile at the entrance region of a tube is flat, a certain length of tube is necessary for the velocity profile to be fully established. This length for the establishment of fully developed flow is called the transition length or entry length. This is shown in Fig. 2.10-6 for laminar flow. At the entrance the velocity profile is flat; that is, the velocity is the same at all positions. As the fluid progresses down the tube, the thickness of the boundary layers in-

velocity profile   boundary layer

FIGURE 2.10-6.   *Velocity profiles near a pipe entrance for laminar flow.*

creases until finally they meet at the center of the pipe and the parabolic velocity profile is fully established.

The approximate entry length L_e of a pipe of diameter D for a fully developed velocity profile to be formed in laminar flow is (L2)

$$\frac{L_e}{D} = 0.0575 \, N_{Re} \tag{2.10-26}$$

For turbulent flow, no relation is available to predict the entry length for a fully developed turbulent velocity profile to form. As an approximation, the entry length is nearly independent of the Reynolds number and is fully developed after 50 diameters downstream.

EXAMPLE 2.10-8. *Entry Length for a Fluid in a Pipe*
Water at 20°C is flowing through a tube of diameter 0.010 m at a velocity of 0.10 m/s.
    (a) Calculate the entry length.
    (b) Calculate the entry length for turbulent flow.

Solution: For part (a), from Appendix A.2, $\rho = 998.2$ kg/m^3, $\mu = 1.005 \times 10^{-3}$ Pa·s. The Reynolds number is

$$N_{Re} = \frac{Dv\rho}{\mu} = \frac{0.010(0.10)(998.2)}{1.005 \times 10^{-3}} = 993.2$$

Using Eq. (2.10-26) for laminar flow,

$$\frac{L_e}{D} = \frac{L_e}{0.01} = 0.0575(993.2) = 57.1$$

Hence, $L_e = 0.571$ m.
    For turbulent flow in part (b), $L_e = 50(0.01) = 0.50$ m.

The pressure drop or friction factor in the entry length is greater than in fully developed flow. For laminar flow the friction factor is highest at the entrance (L2) and then decreases smoothly to the fully developed flow value. For turbulent flow there will be some portion of the entrance over which the boundary layer is laminar and the friction-factor profile is difficult to express. As an approximation, the friction factor for the entry length can be taken as two to three times the value of the friction factor in fully developed flow.

2.10I Selection of Pipe Sizes

In large or complex process piping systems, the optimum size of pipe to use for a specific situation depends upon the relative costs of capital investment, power, maintenance, and so on. Charts are available for determining these optimum sizes (P1). However, for small installations, approximations are usually sufficiently accurate. Representative values for ranges of velocity in pipes are shown in Table 2.10-3. For stainless-steel pipes, recent data (D1) show that the velocities in Table 2.10-3 for process lines or pump discharge should be increased by 70%.

TABLE 2.10-3. *Representative Ranges of Velocities in Steel Pipes*

Type of Fluid	Type of Flow	Velocity	
		ft/s	*m/s*
Nonviscous liquid	Inlet to pump	2–3	0.6–0.9
	Process line or pump discharge	5.7	1.7
Viscous liquid	Inlet to pump	0.2–0.8	0.06–0.25
	Process line or pump discharge	3	0.9
Gas air	Process line	53	16
Steam 100 psig	Process line	38	11.6

2.11 COMPRESSIBLE FLOW OF GASES

2.11A Introduction and Basic Equation for Flow in Pipes

When pressure changes in gases occur which are greater than about 10%, the friction-loss equations (2.10-9) and (2.10-10) may be in error since compressible flow is occurring. Then the solution of the energy balance is more complicated because of the variation of the density or specific volume with changes in pressure. The field of compressible flow is very large and covers a very wide range of variation in geometry, pressure, velocity, and temperature. In this section we restrict our discussion to isothermal and adiabatic flow in uniform, straight pipes and do not cover flow in nozzles, which is discussed in some detail in other references (M2, P1).

The general mechanical-energy-balance equation (2.7-27) can be used as a starting point. Assuming turbulent flow, so that $\alpha = 1.0$, and no shaft work, so that $W_S = 0$, and writing the equation for a differential length dL, Eq. (2.7-27) becomes

$$v \, dv + g \, dz + \frac{dp}{\rho} + dF = 0 \qquad (2.11\text{-}1)$$

For a horizontal duct, $dz = 0$. Using only the wall shear frictional term for dF and writing Eq. (2.10-6) in differential form,

$$v \, dv + V \, dp + \frac{4fv^2 \, dL}{2D} = 0 \qquad (2.11\text{-}2)$$

where $V = 1/\rho$. Assuming steady-state flow and a uniform pipe diameter, G is constant and

$$G = v\rho = \frac{v}{V} \qquad (2.11\text{-}3)$$

$$dv = G \, dV \qquad (2.11\text{-}4)$$

Substituting Eqs. (2.11-3) and (2.11-4) into (2.11-2) and rearranging,

$$G^2 \frac{dV}{V} + \frac{dp}{V} + \frac{2fG^2}{D} \, dL = 0 \qquad (2.11\text{-}5)$$

This is the basic differential equation that is to be integrated. To do this the relation between V and p must be known so that the integral of dp/V can be evaluated. This integral depends upon the nature of the flow, and two important conditions used are isothermal and adiabatic flow in pipes.

2.11B Isothermal Compressible Flow

To integrate Eq. (2.11-5) for isothermal flow, an ideal gas will be assumed, where

$$pV = \frac{1}{M} RT \tag{2.11-6}$$

Solving for V in Eq. (2.11-6), and substituting it into Eq. (2.11-5) and integrating, assuming f is constant,

$$G^2 \int_1^2 \frac{dV}{V} + \frac{M}{RT} \int_1^2 p \, dp + 2f \frac{G^2}{D} \int_1^2 dL = 0 \tag{2.11-7}$$

$$G^2 \ln \frac{V_2}{V_1} + \frac{M}{2RT} (p_2^2 - p_1^2) + 2f \frac{G^2}{D} \Delta L = 0 \tag{2.11-8}$$

Substituting p_1/p_2 for V_2/V_1 and rearranging,

$$p_1^2 - p_2^2 = \frac{4f \, \Delta L G^2 RT}{DM} + \frac{2G^2 RT}{M} \ln \frac{p_1}{p_2} \tag{2.11-9}$$

where M = molecular weight in kg mass/kg mol, $R = 8314.34$ N $\cdot$ m/kg mol $\cdot$ K, and T = temperature K. The quantity $RT/M = p_{av}/\rho_{av}$, where $p_{av} = (p_1 + p_2)/2$ and ρ_{av} is the average density at T and p_{av}. In English units, $R = 1545.3$ ft $\cdot$ lb$_f$/lb mol $\cdot$ °R and the right-hand terms are divided by g_c. Equation (2.11-9) then becomes

$$(p_1 - p_2)_f = \frac{4f \, \Delta L G^2}{2D \rho_{av}} + \frac{G^2}{\rho_{av}} \ln \frac{p_1}{p_2} \tag{2.11-10}$$

The first term on the right in Eqs. (2.11-9) and (2.11-10) represents the frictional loss as given by Eqs. (2.10-9) and (2.10-10). The last term in both equations is generally negligible in ducts of appreciable length unless the pressure drop is very large.

EXAMPLE 2.11-1.   Compressible Flow of a Gas in a Pipe Line
Natural gas, which is essentially methane, is being pumped through a 1.016-m-ID pipeline for a distance of 1.609×10^5 m (D1) at a rate of 2.077 kg mol/s. It can be assumed that the line is isothermal at 288.8 K. The pressure p_2 at the discharge end of the line is 170.3×10^3 Pa absolute. Calculate the pressure p_1 at the inlet of the line. The viscosity of methane at 288.8 K is 1.04×10^{-5} Pa $\cdot$ s.

Solution: $D = 1.016$ m, $A = \pi D^2/4 = \pi(1.016)^2/4 = 0.8107$ m^2. Then,

$$G = \left(2.077 \, \frac{\text{kg mol}}{\text{s}} \right) \left(16.0 \, \frac{\text{kg}}{\text{kg mol}} \right) \left(\frac{1}{0.8107 \, \text{m}^2} \right) = 41.00 \, \frac{\text{kg}}{\text{s} \cdot \text{m}^2}$$

$$N_{\text{Re}} = \frac{DG}{\mu} = \frac{1.016(41.00)}{1.04 \times 10^{-5}} = 4.005 \times 10^6$$

From Fig. 2.10-3, $\varepsilon = 4.6 \times 10^5$ m.

$$\frac{\varepsilon}{D} = \frac{4.6 \times 10^{-5}}{1.016} = 0.0000453$$

The friction factor $f = 0.0027$.

In order to solve for p_1 in Eq. (2.11-9), trial and error must be used. Estimating p_1 at 620.5×10^3 Pa, $R = 8314.34$ N $\cdot$ m/kg mol $\cdot$ K, and $\Delta L = 1.609 \times 10^5$ m. Substituting into Eq. (2.11-9),

$$p_1^2 - p_2^2 = \frac{4(0.0027)(1.609 \times 10^5)(41.00)^2(8314.34)(288.8)}{1.016(16.0)}$$

$$+ \frac{2(41.00)^2(8314.34)(288.8)}{(16.0)} \ln \frac{620.5 \times 10^3}{170.3 \times 10^3}$$

$$= 4.375 \times 10^{11} + 0.00652 \times 10^{11} = 4.382 \times 10^{11} (\text{Pa})^2$$

Now, $P_2 = 170.3 \times 10^3$ Pa. Substituting this into the above and solving for p_1, $p_1 = 683.5 \times 10^3$ Pa. Substituting this new value of p_1 into Eq. (2.11-9) again and solving for p_1, the final result is $p_1 = 683.5 \times 10^3$ Pa. Note that the last term in Eq. (2.11-9) in this case is almost negligible.

When the upstream pressure p_1 remains constant, the mass flow rate G changes as the downstream pressure p_2 is varied. From Eq. (2.11-9), when $p_1 = p_2$, $G = 0$, and when $p_2 = 0$, $G = 0$. This indicates that at some intermediate value of p_2, the flow G must be a maximum. This means that the flow is a maximum when $dG/dp_2 = 0$. Performing this differentiation on Eq. (2.11-9) for constant p_1 and f and solving for G,

$$G_{\max} = \sqrt{\frac{Mp_2^2}{RT}} \tag{2.11-11}$$

Using Eqs. (2.11-3) and (2.11-6),

$$v_{\max} = \sqrt{\frac{RT}{M}} = \sqrt{p_2 V_2} \tag{2.11-12}$$

This is the equation for the velocity of sound in the fluid at the conditions for isothermal flow. Thus, for isothermal compressible flow there is a maximum flow for a given upstream p_1, and further reduction of p_2 will not give any further increase in flow. Further details as to the length of pipe and the pressure at maximum flow conditions are discussed elsewhere (D1, M2, P1).

EXAMPLE 2.11-2. Maximum Flow for Compressible Flow of a Gas
For the conditions of Example 2.11-1, calculate the maximum velocity that can be obtained and the velocity of sound at these conditions. Compare with Example 2.11-1.

Solution: Using Eq. (2.11-12) and the conditions in Example 2.11-1,

$$v_{\max} = \sqrt{\frac{RT}{M}} = \sqrt{\frac{8314(288.8)}{16.0}} = 387.4 \text{ m/s}$$

This is the maximum velocity obtainable if p_2 is decreased. This is also the velocity of sound in the fluid at the conditions for isothermal flow. To compare with Example 2.11-1, the actual velocity at the exit pressure p_2 is obtained by combining Eqs. (2.11-3) and (2.11-6) to give

$$v_2 = \frac{RTG}{p_2 M} \tag{2.11-13}$$

$$= \frac{8314.34(288.8)(41.00)}{(170.3 \times 10^3)16.0} = 36.13 \text{ m/s}$$

2.11C   Adiabatic Compressible Flow

When heat transfer through the wall of the pipe is negligible, the flow of gas in compressible flow in a straight pipe of constant cross section is adiabatic. Equation (2.11-5) has been integrated for adiabatic flow and details are given elsewhere (D1, M1, P1). Convenient charts for solving this case are also available (P1). The results for adiabatic flow often deviate very little from isothermal flow, especially in long lines. For very short pipes and relatively large pressure drops, the adiabatic flow rate is greater than the isothermal, but the maximum possible difference is about 20% (D1). For pipes of length about 1000 diameters or longer, the difference is generally less than 5%. Equation (2.11-8) can also be used when the temperature change over the conduit is small by using an arithmetic-average temperature.

Using the same procedures for finding maximum flow that were used in the isothermal case, maximum flow occurs when the velocity at the downstream end of the pipe is the sonic velocity for adiabatic flow. This is

$$v_{max} = \sqrt{\gamma p_2 V_2} = \sqrt{\frac{\gamma RT}{M}} \tag{2.11-14}$$

where, $\gamma = c_p/c_v$, the ratio of heat capacities. For air, $\gamma = 1.4$. Hence, the maximum velocity for adiabatic flow is about 20% greater than for isothermal flow. The rate of flow may not be limited by the flow conditions in the pipe, in practice, but by the development of sonic velocity in a fitting or valve in the pipe. Hence, care should be used in the selection of fittings in such pipes for compressible flow. Further details as to the length of pipe and pressure at maximum flow conditions are given elsewhere (D1, M2, P1).

A convenient parameter often used in compressible-flow equations is the Mach number, N_{Ma}, which is defined as the ratio of v, the speed of the fluid in the conduit, to v_{max}, the speed of sound in the fluid at the actual flow conditions:

$$N_{Ma} = \frac{v}{v_{max}} \tag{2.11-15}$$

At a Mach number of 1.0, the flow is sonic. At a value less than 1.0, the flow is subsonic, and supersonic at a number above 1.0.

PROBLEMS

2.2-1. *Pressure in a Spherical Tank.* Calculate the pressure in psia and kN/m^2 at the bottom of a spherical tank filled with oil having a diameter of 8.0 ft. The top of the tank is vented to the atmosphere having a pressure of 14.72 psia. The density of the oil is 0.922 g/cm^3.

Ans. 17.92 lb$_f$/in.^{2} (psia), 123.5 kN/m^2

2.2-2. Pressure with Two Liquids, Hg and Water. An open test tube at 293 K is filled at the bottom with 12.1 cm of Hg, and 5.6 cm of water is placed above the Hg. Calculate the pressure at the bottom of the test tube if the atmospheric pressure is 756 mm Hg. Use a density of 13.55 g/cm^3 for Hg and 0.998 g/cm^3 for water. Give the answer in terms of dyn/cm^2, psia, and kN/m^2. See Appendix A.1 for conversion factors.

Ans. 1.175×10^6 dyn/cm^2, 17.0 psia, 2.3 psig, 117.5 kN/m^2

2.2-3. Head of a Fluid of Jet Fuel and Pressure. The pressure at the top of a tank of jet fuel is 180.6 kN/m^2. The depth of liquid in the tank is 6.4 m. The density of the fuel is 825 kg/m^3. Calculate the head of the liquid in m that corresponds to the absolute pressure at the bottom of the tank.

2.2-4. Measurement of Pressure. An open U-tube manometer similar to Fig. 2.2-4a is being used to measure the absolute pressure p_a in a vessel containing air. The pressure p_b is atmospheric pressure, which is 754 mm Hg. The liquid in the manometer is water having a density of 1000 kg/m^3. Assume that the density ρ_B is 1.30 kg/m^3 and that the distance Z is very small. The reading R is 0.415 m. Calculate p_a in psia and kPa.

Ans. p_a = 15.17 psia, 104.6 kPa

2.2-5. Measurement of Small Pressure Differences. The two-fluid U-tube manometer is being used to measure the difference in pressure at two points in a line containing air at 1 atm abs pressure. The value of $R_0 = 0$ for equal pressures. The lighter fluid is a hydrocarbon with a density of 812 kg/m^3 and the heavier water has a density of 998 kg/m^3. The inside diameters of the U tube and reservoir are 3.2 mm and 54.2 mm, respectively. The reading R of the manometer is 117.2 mm. Calculate the pressure difference in mm Hg and pascal.

2.2-6. Pressure in a Sea Lab. A sea lab 5.0 m high is to be designed to withstand submersion to 150 m, measured from sea level to the top of the sea lab. Calculate the pressure on top of the sea lab and also the pressure variation on the side of the container measured as the distance x in m from the top of the sea lab downward. The density of seawater is 1020 kg/m^3.

Ans. $p = 10.00(150 + x)$ kN/m^2

2.2-7. Measurement of Pressure Difference in Vessels. In Fig. 2.2-5b the differential manometer is used to measure the pressure difference between two vessels. Derive the equation for the pressure difference $p_A - p_B$ in terms of the liquid heights and densities.

2.2-8. Design of Settler and Separator for Immiscible Liquids. A vertical cylindrical settler–separator is to be designed for separating a mixture flowing at 20.0 m^3/h and containing equal volumes of a light petroleum liquid ($\rho_B = 875$ kg/m^3) and a dilute solution of wash water ($\rho_A = 1050$ kg/m^3). Laboratory experiments indicate a settling time of 15 min is needed to adequately separate the two phases. For design purposes use a 25-min settling time and calculate the size of the vessel needed, the liquid levels of the light and heavy liquids in the vessel, and the height h_{A2} of the heavy-liquid overflow. Assume that the ends of the vessel are approximately flat, that the vessel diameter equals its height, and that one-third of the volume is vapor space vented to the atmosphere. Use the nomenclature given in Fig. 2.2-6.

Ans. $h_{A2} = 1.537$ m

2.3-1. Molecular Transport of a Property with a Variable Diffusivity. A property is being transported through a fluid at steady state through a constant cross-sectional area. At point 1 the concentration Γ_1 is 2.78×10^{-2} amount of property/m^3 and 1.50×10^{-2} at point 2 at a distance of 2.0 m away. The diffusivity depends on concentration Γ as follows:

$$\delta = A + B\Gamma = 0.150 + 1.65\Gamma$$

(a) Derive the integrated equation for the flux in terms of Γ_1 and Γ_2. Then calculate the flux.

(b) Calculate Γ at $z = 1.0$ m and plot Γ versus z for the three points.

Ans. (a) $\psi_z = [A(\Gamma_1 - \Gamma_2) + (B/2)(\Gamma_1^2 - \Gamma_2^2)]/(z_2 - z_1)$

2.3-2. Integration of General-Property Equation for Steady State. Integrate the general-property equation (2.3-11) for steady state and no generation between the points Γ_1 at z_1 and Γ_2 at z_2. The final equation should relate Γ to z.

Ans. $\Gamma = (\Gamma_2 - \Gamma_1)(z - z_1)/(z_2 - z_1) + \Gamma_1$

2.4-1. Shear Stress in Soybean Oil. Using Fig. 2.4-1, the distance between the two parallel plates is 0.00914 m, and the lower plate is being pulled at a relative velocity of 0.366 m/s greater than the top plate. The fluid used is soybean oil with viscosity 4×10^{-2} Pa·s at 303 K (Appendix A.4).

(a) Calculate the shear stress τ and the shear rate using lb force, ft, and s units.

(b) Repeat, using SI untis.

(c) If glycerol at 293 K having a viscosity of 1.069 kg/m·s is used instead of soybean oil, what relative velocity in m/s is needed using the same distance between plates so that the same shear stress is obtained as in part (a)? Also, what is the new shear rate?

Ans. (a) Shear stress = 3.34×10^{-2} lb$_f$/ft^2, shear rate = 40.0 s^{-1}; (b) 1.60 N/m^2; (c) relative velocity = 0.01369 m/s, shear rate = 1.50 s^{-1}

2.4.-2 Shear Stress and Shear Rate in Fluids. Using Fig. 2.4-1, the lower plate is being pulled at a relative velocity of 0.40 m/s greater than the top plate. The fluid used is water at 24°C.

(a) How far apart should the two plates be placed so that the shear stress τ is 0.30 N/m^2? Also, calculate the shear rate.

(b) If oil with a viscosity of 2.0×10^{-2} Pa·s is used instead at the same plate spacing and velocity as in part (a), what are the shear stress and the shear rate?

2.5-1. Reynolds Number for Milk Flow. Whole milk at 293 K having a density of 1030 kg/m^3 and viscosity of 2.12 cp is flowing at the rate of 0.605 kg/s in a glass pipe having a diameter of 63.5 mm.

(a) Calculate the Reynolds number. Is this turbulent flow?

(b) Calculate the flow rate needed in m^3/s for a Reynolds number of 2100 and velocity in m/s.

Ans. (a) $N_{Re} = 5723$, turbulent flow

2.5-2. Pipe Diameter and Reynolds Number. An oil is being pumped inside a 10.0-mm-diameter pipe at a Reynolds number of 2100. The oil density is 855 kg/m^3 and the viscosity is 2.1×10^{-2} Pa·s.

(a) What is the velocity in the pipe?

(b) It is desired to maintain the same Reynolds number of 2100 and the same velocity as in part (a) using a second fluid with a density of 925 kg/m³ and a viscosity of 1.5×10^{-2} Pa · s. What pipe diameter should be used?

2.6-1. *Average Velocity for Mass Balance in Flow Down Vertical Plate.* For a layer of liquid flowing in laminar flow in the z direction down a vertical plate or surface, the velocity profile is

$$v_z = \frac{\rho g \delta^2}{2\mu}\left[1 - \left(\frac{x}{\delta}\right)^2\right]$$

where δ is the thickness of the layer, x is the distance from the free surface of the liquid toward the plate, and v_z is the velocity at a distance x from the free surface.
(a) What is the maximum velocity $v_{z\,max}$?
(b) Derive the expression for the average velocity $v_{z\,av}$ and also relate it to $v_{z\,max}$.

Ans. (a) $v_{z\,max} = \rho g \delta^2/2\mu$, (b) $v_{z\,av} = \frac{2}{3}v_{z\,max}$

2.6-2. *Flow of Liquid in a Pipe and Mass Balance.* A hydrocarbon liquid enters a simple flow system shown in Fig. 2.6-1 at an average velocity of 1.282 m/s, where $A_1 = 4.33 \times 10^{-3}$ m² and $\rho_1 = 902$ kg/m³. The liquid is heated in the process and the exit density is 875 kg/m³. The cross-sectional area at point 2 is 5.26×10^{-3} m². The process is steady state.
(a) Calculate the mass flow rate m at the entrance and exit.
(b) Calculate the average velocity v in 2 and the mass velocity G in 1.

Ans. (a) $m_1 = m_2 = 5.007$ kg/s, (b) $G_1 = 1156$ kg/s · m²

2.6-3. *Average Velocity for Mass Balance in Turbulent Flow.* For turbulent flow in a smooth, circular tube with a radius R, the velocity profile varies according to the following expression at a Reynolds number of about 10^5:

$$v = v_{max}\left(\frac{R - r}{R}\right)^{1/7}$$

where r is the radial distance from the center and v_{max} the maximum velocity at the center. Derive the equation relating the average velocity (bulk velocity) v_{av} to v_{max} for an incompressible fluid. (*Hint:* The integration can be simplified by substituting z for $R - r$.)

Ans. $v_{av} = \left(\frac{49}{60}\right)v_{max} = 0.817v_{max}$

2.6-4. *Bulk Velocity for Flow Between Parallel Plates.* A fluid flowing in laminar flow in the x direction between two parallel plates has a velocity profile given by the following:

$$v_x = v_{x\,max}\left[1 - \left(\frac{y}{y_0}\right)^2\right]$$

where $2y_0$ is the distance between the plates, y is the distance from the center line, and v_x is the velocity in the x direction at position y. Derive an equation relating $v_{x\,av}$ (bulk or average velocity) to $v_{x\,max}$.

Ans. $v_{x\,av} = \frac{2}{3}v_{x\,max}$

2.6-5. *Overall Mass Balance for Dilution Process.* A well-stirred storage vessel contains 10 000 kg of solution of a dilute methanol solution ($w_A = 0.05$ mass fraction alcohol).

A constant flow of 500 kg/min of pure water is suddenly introduced into the tank and a constant rate of withdrawal of 500 kg/min of solution is started. These two flows are continued and remain constant. Assuming that the densities of the solutions are the same and that the total contents of the tank remain constant at 10000 kg of solution, calculate the time for the alcohol content to drop to 1.0 wt%.

Ans. 32.2 min

2.6-6. *Overall Mass Balance for Unsteady-State Process.* A storage vessel is well stirred and contains 500 kg of total solution with a concentration of 5.0% salt. A constant flow rate of 900 kg/h of salt solution containing 16.67% salt is suddenly introduced into the tank and a constant withdrawal rate of 600 kg/h is also started. These two flows remain constant thereafter. Derive an equation relating the outlet withdrawal concentration as a function of time. Also, calculate the concentration after 2.0 h.

2.6-7 *Mass Balance for Flow of Sucrose Solution.* A 20 wt % sucrose (sugar) solution having a density of 1074 kg/m^3 is flowing through the same piping system as in Example 2.6-1 (Fig. 2.6-2). The flow rate entering pipe 1 is 1.892 m^3/h. The flow divides equally in each of pipes 3. Calculate the following:
(a) The velocity in m/s in pipes 2 and 3.
(b) The mass velocity G kg/m$^2 \cdot$ s in pipes 2 and 3.

2.7-1. *Kinetic-Energy Velocity Correction Factor for Turbulent Flow.* Derive the equation to determine the value of α, the kinetic-energy velocity correction factor, for turbulent flow. Use Eq. (2.7-20) to approximate the velocity profile and substitute this into Eq. (2.7-15) to obtain $(v^3)_{av}$. Then use Eqs. (2.7-20), (2.6-17), and (2.7-14) to obtain α.

Ans. $\alpha = 0.9448$

2.7-2. *Flow Between Parallel Plates and Kinetic-Energy Correction Factor.* The equation for the velocity profile of a fluid flowing in laminar flow between two parallel plates is given in Problem 2.6-4. Derive the equation to determine the value of the kinetic-energy velocity correction factor α. [*Hint:* First derive an equation relating v to v_{av}. Then derive the equation for $(v^3)_{av}$ and, finally, relate these results to α.]

2.7-3. *Temperature Drop in Throttling Valve and Energy Balance.* Steam is flowing through an adiabatic throttling valve (no heat loss or external work). Steam enters point 1 upstream of the valve at 689 kPa abs and 171.1°C and leaves the valve (point 2) at 359 kPa. Calculate the temperature t_2 at the outlet. [*Hint:* Use Eq. (2.7-21) for the energy balance and neglect the kinetic-energy and potential-energy terms as shown in Example 2.7-1. Obtain the enthalpy H_1 from Appendix A.2, steam tables. For H_2, linear interpolation of the values in the table will have to be done to obtain t_2.] Use SI units.

Ans. $t_2 = 160.6$°C

2.7-4. *Energy Balance on a Heat Exchanger and a Pump.* Water at 93.3°C is being pumped from a large storage tank at 1 atm abs at a rate of 0.189 m^3/min by a pump. The motor that drives the pump supplies energy to the pump at the rate of 1.49 kW. The water is pumped through a heat exchanger, where it gives up 704 kW of heat and is then delivered to a large open storage tank at an elevation of 15.24 m above the first tank. What is the final temperature of the water to the second tank? Also, what is the gain in enthalpy of the water due to the work input? (*Hint:* Be sure to use the steam tables for the enthalpy of the water. Neglect any kinetic-energy changes but not potential-energy changes.)

Ans. $t_2 = 38.2$°C, work input gain = 0.491 kJ/kg

2.7-5. *Steam Boiler and Overall Energy Balance.* Liquid water under pressure at 150 kPa enters a boiler at 24°C through a pipe at an average velocity of 3.5 m/s in turbulent flow. The exit steam leaves at a height of 25 m above the liquid inlet at 150°C and 150 kPa absolute, and the velocity in the outlet line is 12.5 m/s in turbulent flow. The process is steady state. How much heat must be added per kg of steam?

2.7-6. Energy Balance on a Flow System with a Pump and Heat Exchanger. Water stored in a large, well-insulated storage tank at 21.0°C and atmospheric pressure is being pumped at steady state from this tank by a pump at the rate of 40 m^3/h. The motor driving the pump supplies energy at the rate of 8.5 kW. The water is used as a cooling medium and passes through a heat exchanger, where 255 kW of heat is added to the water. The heated water then flows to a second large, vented tank, which is 25 m above the first tank. Determine the final temperature of the water delivered to the second tank.

2.7-7. Mechanical-Energy Balance in Pumping Soybean Oil. Soybean oil is being pumped through a uniform-diameter pipe at a steady mass-flow rate. A pump supplies 209.2 J/kg mass of fluid flowing. The entrance abs pressure in the inlet pipe to the pump is 103.4 kN/m^2. The exit section of the pipe downstream from the pump is 3.35 m above the entrance and the exit pressure is 172.4 kN/m^2. Exit and entrance pipes are the same diameter. The fluid is in turbulent flow. Calculate the friction loss in the system. See Appendix A.4 for the physical properties of soybean oil. The temperature is 303 K.

Ans. $\sum F = 101.3$ J/kg

2.7-8. Pump Horsepower in Brine System. A pump pumps 0.200 ft^3/s of brine solution having a density of 1.15 g/cm^3 from an open feed tank having a large cross-sectional area. The suction line has an inside diameter of 3.548 in. and the discharge line from the pump a diameter of 2.067 in. The discharge flow goes to an open overhead tank, and the open end of this line is 75 ft above the liquid level in the feed tank. If the friction losses in the piping system are 18.0 ft·lb_f/lb_m, what pressure must the pump develop and what is the horsepower of the pump if the efficiency is 70%? The flow is turbulent.

2.7-9. Pressure Measurements from Flows. Water having a density of 998 kg/m^3 is flowing at the rate of 1.676 m/s in a 3.068-in.-diameter horizontal pipe at a pressure p_1 of 68.9 kPa abs. It then passes to a pipe having an inside diameter of 2.067 in.
(a) Calculate the new pressure p_2 in the 2.067-in. pipe. Assume no friction losses.
(b) If the piping is vertical and the flow is upward, calculate the new pressure p_2. The pressure tap for p_2 is 0.457 m above the tap for p_1.

Ans. (a) $p_2 = 63.5$ kPa; (b) $p_2 = 59.1$ kPa

2.7-10. Draining Cottonseed Oil from a Tank. A cylindrical tank 1.52 m in diameter and 7.62 m high contains cottonseed oil having a density of 917 kg/m^3. The tank is open to the atmosphere. A discharge nozzle of inside diameter 15.8 mm and cross-sectional area A_2 is located near the bottom of the tank. The surface of the liquid is located at $H = 6.1$ m above the center line of the nozzle. The discharge nozzle is opened, draining the liquid level from $H = 6.1$ m to $H = 4.57$ m. Calculate the time in seconds to do this. [Hint: The velocity on the surface of the reservoir is small and can be neglected. The velocity v_2 m/s in the nozzle can be calculated for a given H by Eq. (2.7-36). However, H, and hence v_2, are varying. Set up an unsteady-state mass balance as follows: The volumetric flow rate in the tank is $(A_t \, dH)/dt$, where A_t is the tank cross section in m^2 and $A_t \, dH$ is the m^3 liquid flowing in dt s. This rate must equal the negative of the volumetric rate in the nozzle, or $-A_2 v_2$ m^3/s. The negative sign is present since dH is the negative of v_2. Rearrange this equation and integrate between $H = 6.1$ m at $t = 0$ and $H = 4.57$ m at $t = t_F$.]

Ans. $t_F = 1388$ s.

2.7-11. Friction Loss in Turbine Water Power System. Water is stored in an elevated reservoir. To generate power, water flows from this reservoir down through a large conduit to a turbine and then through a similar-sized conduit. At a point in the conduit 89.5 m above the turbine, the pressure is 172.4 kPa, and at a level 5 m below the turbine, the pressure is 89.6 kPa. The water flow rate is 0.800 m^3/s. The output of the shaft of the turbine is 658 kW. The water density is 1000 kg/m^3. If the efficiency of the turbine in converting the mechanical energy given up by the fluid to the turbine shaft is 89% ($\eta_t = 0.89$), calculate the friction loss in the turbine in J/kg. Note that in the mechanical-energy-balance equation, the W_s is equal to the output of the shaft of the turbine over η_t.

Ans. $\sum F = 85.3$ J/kg

2.7-12. Pipeline Pumping of Oil. A pipeline laid cross-country carries oil at the rate of 795 m^3/d. The pressure of the oil is 1793 kPa gage leaving pumping station 1. The pressure is 862 kPa gage at the inlet to the next pumping station, 2. The second station is 17.4 m higher than the first station. Calculate the lost work ($\sum F$ friction loss) in J/kg mass oil. The oil density is 769 kg/m^3.

2.7-13. Test of Centrifugal Pump and Mechanical-Energy Balance. A centrifugal pump is being tested for performance, and during the test the pressure reading in the 0.305-m-diameter suction line just adjacent to the pump casing is -20.7 kPa (vacuum below atmospheric pressure). In the discharge line with a diameter of 0.254 m at a point 2.53 m above the suction line, the pressure is 289.6 kPa gage. The flow of water from the pump is measured as 0.1133 m^3/s. (The density can be assumed as 1000 kg/m^3.) Calculate the kW input of the pump.

Ans. 38.11 kW

2.7-14. Friction Loss in Pump and Flow System. Water at 20°C is pumped from the bottom of a large storage tank where the pressure is 310.3 kPa gage to a nozzle which is 15.25 m above the tank bottom and discharges to the atmosphere with a velocity in the nozzle of 19.81 m/s. The water flow rate is 45.4 kg/s. The efficiency of the pump is 80% and 7.5 kW are furnished to the pump shaft. Calculate the following:
(a) The friction loss in the pump.
(b) The friction loss in the rest of the process.

2.7-15. Power for Pumping in Flow System. Water is being pumped from an open water reservoir at the rate of 2.0 kg/s at 10°C to an open storage tank 1500 m away. The pipe used is schedule 40 $3\frac{1}{2}$-in. pipe and the frictional losses in the system are 625 J/kg. The surface of the water reservoir is 20 m above the level of the storage tank. The pump has an efficiency of 75%.
(a) What is the kW power required for the pump?
(b) If the pump is not present in the system, will there be a flow?

Ans. (a) 1.143 kW

2.8-1. Momentum Balance in a Reducing Bend. Water is flowing at steady state through the reducing bend in Fig. 2.8-3. The angle $\alpha_2 = 90°$ (a right-angle bend). The pressure at point 2 is 1.0 atm abs. The flow rate is 0.020 m^3/s and the diameters at points 1 and 2 are 0.050 m and 0.030 m, respectively. Neglect frictional and gravitational forces. Calculate the resultant forces on the bend in newtons and lb force. Use $\rho = 1000$ kg/m^3.

Ans. $-R_x = +450.0$ N, $-R_y = -565.8$ N.

2.8-2. Forces on Reducing Bend. Water is flowing at steady state and 363 K at a rate of 0.0566 m^3/s through a 60° reducing bend ($\alpha_2 = 60°$) in Fig. 2.8-3. The inlet pipe diameter is 0.1016 m and the outlet 0.0762 m. The friction loss in the pipe bend can be estimated as $v_2^2/5$. Neglect gravity forces. The exit pressure $p_2 = 111.5$ kN/m^2 gage. Calculate the forces on the bend in newtons.

Ans. $-R_x = +1344$ N, $-R_y = -1026$ N

2.8-3. *Force of Water Stream on a Wall.* Water at 298 K discharges from a nozzle and travels horizontally, hitting a flat, vertical wall. The nozzle has a diameter of 12 mm and the water leaves the nozzle with a flat velocity profile at a velocity of 6.0 m/s. Neglecting frictional resistance of the air on the jet, calculate the force in newtons on the wall.

Ans. $-R_x = 4.059$ N

2.8-4. *Flow Through an Expanding Bend.* Water at a steady-state rate of 0.050 m^3/s is flowing through an expanding bend that changes direction by 120°. The upstream diameter is 0.0762 and the downstream is 0.2112 m. The upstream pressure is 68.94 kPa gage. Neglect energy losses within the elbow and calculate the downstream pressure at 298 K. Also calculate R_x and R_y.

2.8-5. *Force of Stream on a Wall.* Repeat Problem 2.8-3 for the same conditions except that the wall is inclined 45° to the vertical. The flow is frictionless. Assume no loss in energy. The amount of fluid splitting in each direction along the plate can be determined by using the continuity equation and a momentum balance. Calculate this flow division and the force on the wall.

Ans. $m_2 = 0.5774$ kg/s, $m_3 = 0.09907$ kg/s, $-R_x = 2.030$ N, $-R_y = -2.030$ N (force on wall).

2.8-6. *Momentum Balance for Free Jet on a Curved, Fixed Vane.* A free jet having a velocity of 30.5 m/s and a diameter of 5.08×10^{-2} m is deflected by a curved, fixed vane as in Fig. 2.8-5a. However, the vane is curved downward at an angle of 60° instead of upward. Calculate the force of the jet on the vane. The density is 1000 kg/m^3.

Ans. $-R_x = 942.8$ N, $-R_y = 1633$ N

2.8-7. *Momentum Balance for Free Jet on a U-Type, Fixed Vane.* A free jet having a velocity of 30.5 m/s and a diameter of 1.0×10^{-2} m is deflected by a smooth, fixed vane as in Fig. 2.8-5a. However, the vane is in the form of a U so that the exit jet travels in a direction exactly opposite to the entering jet. Calculate the force of the jet on the vane. Use $\rho = 1000$ kg/m^3.

Ans. $-R_x = 146.1$ N, $-R_y = 0$

2.8-8. *Momentum Balance on Reducing Elbow and Friction Losses.* Water at 20°C is flowing through a reducing bend, where α_2 (see Fig. 2.8-3) is 120°. The inlet pipe diameter is 1.829 m, the outlet is 1.219 m, and the flow rate is 8.50 m^3/s. The exit point z_2 is 3.05 m above the inlet and the inlet pressure is 276 kPa gage. Friction losses are estimated as $0.5v_2^2/2$ and the mass of water in the elbow is 8500 kg. Calculate the forces R_x and R_y and the resultant force on the control-volume fluid.

2.8-9. *Momentum Velocity Correction Factor β for Turbulent Flow.* Determine the momentum velocity correction factor β for turbulent flow in a tube. Use Eq. (2.7-20) for the relationship between v and position.

2.9-1. *Film of Water on Wetted-Wall Tower.* Pure water at 20°C is flowing down a vertical wetted-wall column at a rate of 0.124 kg/s · m. Calculate the film thickness and the average velocity.

Ans. $\delta = 3.370 \times 10^{-4}$ m, $v_{z\,av} = 0.3687$ m/s

2.9-2. *Shell Momentum Balance for Flow Between Parallel Plates.* A fluid of constant density is flowing in laminar flow at steady state in the horizontal x direction between two flat and parallel plates. The distance between the two plates in the vertical y direction is $2y_0$. Using a shell momentum balance, derive the equation for the velocity profile within this fluid and the maximum velocity for a distance L m in the x direction. [*Hint:* See the method used in Section 2.9B to derive Eq. (2.9-9). One boundary condition used is $dv_x/dy = 0$ at $y = 0$.]

$$\textbf{Ans.} \quad v_x = \frac{p_0 - p_L}{2\mu L} y_0^2 \left[1 - \left(\frac{y}{y_0} \right)^2 \right]$$

2.9-3. Velocity Profile for Non-Newtonian Fluid. The stress rate of shear for a non-Newtonian fluid is given by

$$\tau_{rx} = K \left(-\frac{dv_x}{dr} \right)^n$$

where K and n are constants. Find the relation between velocity and radial position r for this incompressible fluid at steady state. [*Hint:* Combine the equation given here with Eq. (2.9-6). Then raise both sides of the resulting equation to the $1/n$ power and integrate.]

$$\textbf{Ans.} \quad v_x = \frac{n}{n+1} \left(\frac{p_0 - p_L}{2KL} \right)^{1/n} (R_0)^{(n+1)/n} \left[1 - \left(\frac{r}{R_0} \right)^{(n+1)/n} \right]$$

2.9-4. Shell Momentum Balance for Flow Down an Inclined Plane. Consider the case of a Newtonian fluid in steady-state laminar flow down an inclined plane surface that makes an angle θ with the horizontal. Using a shell momentum balance, find the equation for the velocity profile within the liquid layer having a thickness L and the maximum velocity of the free surface. (*Hint:* The convective-momentum terms cancel for fully developed flow and the pressure-force terms also cancel, because of the presence of a free surface. Note that there is a gravity force on the fluid.)

$$\textbf{Ans.} \quad v_{x\,max} = \rho g L^2 \sin \theta / 2\mu$$

2.10-1. Viscosity Measurement of a Liquid. One use of the Hagen–Poiseuille equation (2.10-2) is in determining the viscosity of a liquid by measuring the pressure drop and velocity of the liquid in a capillary of known dimensions. The liquid used has a density of 912 kg/m^3, and the capillary has a diameter of 2.222 mm and a length of 0.1585 m. The measured flow rate is 5.33×10^{-7} m^3/s of liquid and the pressure drop 131 mm of water (density 996 kg/m^3). Neglecting end effects, calculate the viscosity of the liquid in Pa·s.

$$\textbf{Ans.} \quad \mu = 9.06 \times 10^{-3} \text{ Pa·s}$$

2.10-2. Frictional Pressure Drop in Flow of Olive Oil. Calculate the frictional pressure drop in pascal for olive oil at 293 K flowing through a commercial pipe having an inside diameter of 0.0525 m and a length of 76.2 m. The velocity of the fluid is 1.22 m/s. Use the friction factor method. Is the flow laminar or turbulent? Use physical data from Appendix A.4.

2.10-3. Frictional Loss in Straight Pipe and Effect of Type of Pipe. A liquid having a density of 801 kg/m^3 and a viscosity of 1.49×10^{-3} Pa·s is flowing through a horizontal straight pipe at a velocity of 4.57 m/s. The commercial steel pipe is $1\frac{1}{2}$-in. nominal pipe size, schedule 40. For a length of pipe of 61 m, do as follows:
(a) Calculate the friction loss F_f.
(b) For a smooth tube of the same inside diameter, calculate the friction loss.
   What is the percent reduction of F_f for the smooth tube?

$$\textbf{Ans.} \quad \text{(a) 348.9 J/kg; (b) 274.2 J/kg (91.7 ft·lb}_f\text{/lb}_m\text{), 21.4\% reduction}$$

2.10-4. Trial-and-Error Solution for Hydraulic Drainage. In a hydraulic project a cast-iron pipe having an inside diameter of 0.156 m and a 305-m length is used to drain wastewater at 293 K. The available head is 4.57 m of water. Neglecting any losses in fittings and joints in the pipe, calculate the flow rate in m^3/s. (*Hint:* Assume the physical properties of pure water. The solution is trial and error, since the velocity appears in N_{Re}, which is needed to determine the friction factor. As a first trial, assume that $v = 1.7$ m/s.)

2.10-5. *Mechanical-Energy Balance and Friction Losses.* Hot water is being discharged from a storage tank at the rate of 0.223 ft^3/s. The process flow diagram and conditions are the same as given in Example 2.10-6, except for different nominal pipe sizes of schedule 40 steel pipe as follows. The 20-ft-long outlet pipe from the storage tank is $1\frac{1}{2}$-in. pipe instead of 4-in. pipe. The other piping, which was 2-in. pipe, is now 2.5-in. pipe. Note that now a sudden expansion occurs after the elbow in the $1\frac{1}{2}$-in. pipe to a $2\frac{1}{2}$-in pipe.

2.10-6. *Friction Losses and Pump Horsepower.* Hot water in an open storage tank at 82.2°C is being pumped at the rate of 0.379 m^3/min from the tank. The line from the storage tank to the pump suction is 6.1 m of 2-in. schedule 40 steel pipe and it contains three elbows. The discharge line after the pump is 61 m of 2-in. pipe and contains two elbows. The water discharges to the atmosphere at a height of 6.1 m above the water level in the storage tank.
(a) Calculate all frictional losses ΣF.
(b) Make a mechanical-energy balance and calculate W_S of the pump in J/kg.
(c) What is the kW power of the pump if its efficiency is 75%?

  Ans.   (a) $\Sigma F = 122.8$ J/kg; (b) $W_S = -186.9$ J/kg; (c) 1.527 kW

2.10-7. *Pressure Drop of a Flowing Gas.* Nitrogen gas is flowing through a 4-in. schedule 40 commercial steel pipe at 298 K. The total flow rate is 7.40×10^{-2} kg/s and the flow can be assumed as isothermal. The pipe is 3000 m long and the inlet pressure is 200 kPa. Calculate the outlet pressure.

  Ans. $p_2 = 188.5$ kPa

2.10-8. *Entry Length for Flow in a Pipe.* Air at 10°C and 1.0 atm abs pressure is flowing at a velocity of 2.0 m/s inside a tube having a diameter of 0.012 m.
(a) Calculate the entry length.
(b) Calculate the entry length for water at 10°C and the same velocity.

2.10-9. *Friction Loss in Pumping Oil to Pressurized Tank.* An oil having a density of 833 kg/m^3 and a viscosity of 3.3×10^{-3} Pa · s is pumped from an open tank to a pressurized tank held at 345 kPa gage. The oil is pumped from an inlet at the side of the open tank through a line of commercial steel pipe having an inside diameter of 0.07792 m at the rate of 3.494×10^{-3} m^3/s. The length of straight pipe is 122 m, and the pipe contains two elbows (90°) and a globe valve half open. The level of the liquid in the open tank is 20 m above the liquid level in the pressurized tank. The pump efficiency is 65%. Calculate the kW power of the pump.

2.10-10. *Flow in an Annulus and Pressure Drop.* Water flows in the annulus of a horizontal, concentric-pipe heat exchanger and is being heated from 40°C to 50°C in the exchanger, which has a length of 30 m of equivalent straight pipe. The flow rate of the water is 2.90×10^{-3} m^3/s. The inner pipe is 1-in. schedule 40 and the outer is 2-in. schedule 40. What is the pressure drop? Use an average temperature of 45°C for bulk physical properties. Assume that the wall temperature is an average of 4°C higher than the average bulk temperature so that a correction can be made for the effect of heat transfer on the friction factor.

2.11-1. *Derivation of Maximum Velocity for Isothermal Compressible Flow.* Starting with Eq. (2.11-9), derive Eqs. (2.11-11) and (2.11-12) for the maximum velocity in isothermal compressible flow.

2.11-2. *Pressure Drop in Compressible Flow.* Methane gas is being pumped through a 305-m length of 52.5-mm-ID steel pipe at the rate of 41.0 kg/m$^2 \cdot$ s. The inlet pressure is $p_1 = 345$ kPa abs. Assume isothermal flow at 288.8 K.

(a) Calculate the pressure p_2 at the end of the pipe. The viscosity is 1.04×10^{-5} Pa $\cdot$ s.

(b) Calculate the maximum velocity that can be attained at these conditions and compare with the velocity in part (a).

  Ans.   (a) $p_2 = 298.4$ kPa; (b) $v_{max} = 387.4$ m/s, $v_2 = 20.62$ m/s

2.11-3. *Pressure Drop in Isothermal Compressible Flow.* Air at 288 K and 275 kPa abs enters a pipe and is flowing in isothermal compressible flow in a commercial pipe having an ID of 0.080 m. The length of the pipe is 60 m. The mass velocity at the entrance to the pipe is 165.5 kg/m$^2 \cdot$ s. Assume 29 for the molecular weight of air. Calculate the pressure at the exit. Also, calculate the maximum allowable velocity that can be attained and compare with the actual.

REFERENCES

(B1) BENNETT, C. O., and MEYERS, J. E. *Momentum, Heat and Mass Transfer,* 3rd ed. New York: McGraw-Hill Book Company, 1982.

(D1) DODGE, B. F. *Chemical Engineering Thermodynamics.* New York: McGraw-Hill Book Company, 1944.

(D2) DURAND, A. A., et al. *Chem. Eng.,* **106** (May), 153 (1999).

(E1) EARLE, R. L. *Unit Operations in Food Processing.* Oxford: Pergamon Press, Inc., 1966.

(K1) KITTRIDGE, C. P., and ROWLEY, D. S. *Trans. A.S.M.E.,* **79,** 1759 (1957).

(L1) LANGE, N. A. *Handbook of Chemistry,* 10th ed. New York: McGraw-Hill Book Company, 1967.

(L2) LANGHAAR, H. L. *Trans. A.S.M.E,* **64,** A-55 (1942).

(M1) MOODY, L. F. *Trans. A.S.M.E.,* **66,** 671 (1944); *Mech. Eng.,* **69,** 1005 (1947).

(M2) MCCABE, W. L., SMITH, J. C., and HARRIOTT, P. *Unit Operations of Chemical Engineering,* 4th ed. New York: McGraw-Hill Book Company, 1985.

(N1) National Bureau of Standards. *Tables of Thermal Properties of Gases,* Circular 464 (1955).

(P1) PERRY, R. H., and GREEN, D. *Perry's Chemical Engineers' Handbook,* 6th ed. New York: McGraw-Hill Book Company, 1984.

(R1) REID, R. C., PRAUSNITZ, J. M., and SHERWOOD, T. K. *The Properties of Gases and Liquids,* 3rd ed. New York: McGraw-Hill Book Company, 1977.

(R2) *Reactor Handbook,* vol. 2, AECD-3646. Washington D.C.: Atomic Energy Commission, May 1955.

(S1) SWINDELLS, J. F., COE, J. R., Jr., and GODFREY, T. B. *J. Res. Nat. Bur. Standards,* **48,** 1 (1952).

(S2) SKELLAND, A. H. P. *Non-Newtonian Flow and Heat Transfer.* New York: John Wiley & Sons, Inc., 1967.

(S3) SIEDER, E. N., and TATE, G. E. *Ind. Eng. Chem.,* **28,** 1429 (1936).

(W1) WEAST, R. C. *Handbook of Chemistry and Physics,* 48th ed. Boca Raton, Fla.: Chemical Rubber Co., Inc., 1967–1968.

CHAPTER 3

Principles of Momentum Transfer and Applications

3.1 FLOW PAST IMMERSED OBJECTS AND PACKED AND FLUIDIZED BEDS

3.1A Definition of Drag Coefficient for Flow Past Immersed Objects

1. Introduction and types of drag. In Chapter 2 we were concerned primarily with the momentum transfer and frictional losses for flow of fluids inside conduits or pipes. In this section we consider in some detail the flow of fluids around solid, immersed objects.

The flow of fluids outside immersed bodies appears in many chemical engineering applications and other processing applications. These occur, for example, in flow past spheres in settling, flow through packed beds in drying and filtration, flow past tubes in heat exchangers, and so on. It is useful to be able to predict the frictional losses and/or the force on the submerged objects in these various applications.

In the examples of fluid friction inside conduits that we considered in Chapter 2, the transfer of momentum perpendicular to the surface resulted in a tangential shear stress or drag on the smooth surface parallel to the direction of flow. This force exerted by the fluid on the solid in the direction of flow is called *skin* or *wall drag*. For any surface in contact with a flowing fluid, skin friction will exist. In addition to skin friction, if the fluid is not flowing parallel to the surface but must change direction to pass around a solid body such as a sphere, significant additional frictional losses will occur; this is called *form drag*.

In Fig. 3.1-1a the flow of fluid is parallel to the smooth surface of the flat, solid plate, and the force F in newtons on an element of area dA m^2 of the plate is the wall shear stress τ_w times the area dA, or $\tau_w \, dA$. The total force is the sum of the integrals of these quantities evaluated over the entire area of the plate. Here the transfer of momentum to the surface results in a tangential stress or skin drag on the surface.

In many cases, however, the immersed body is a blunt-shaped solid which presents various angles to the direction of the fluid flow. As shown in Fig. 3.1-1b, the free-stream velocity is v_0 and is uniform on approaching the blunt-shaped body suspended in a very large duct. Lines called *streamlines* represent the path of fluid elements around the suspended body. The thin boundary layer adjacent to the solid surface is shown as a dashed line; at the edge of this

FIGURE 3.1-1. *Flow past immersed objects: (a) flat plate, (b) sphere, (c) streamlined object.*

layer the velocity is essentially the same as the bulk fluid velocity adjacent to it. At the front center of the body, called the *stagnation point,* the fluid velocity will be zero; boundary-layer growth begins at this point and continues over the surface until the layer separates. The tangential stress on the body because of the velocity gradient in the boundary layer is the skin friction. Outside the boundary layer the fluid changes direction to pass around the solid and also accelerates near the front and then decelerates. Because of these effects, an additional force is exerted by the fluid on the body. This phenomenon, called *form drag,* is in addition to the skin drag in the boundary layer.

In Fig. 3.1-1b, as shown, separation of the boundary layer occurs and a wake, covering the entire rear of the object, occurs where large eddies are present and contribute to the form drag. The point of separation depends on the shape of the particle, Reynolds number, and so on, and is discussed in detail elsewhere (S3).

Form drag for bluff bodies can be minimized by streamlining the body (Fig. 3.1-1c), which forces the separation point toward the rear of the body, greatly reducing the size of the wake. Additional discussion of turbulence and boundary layers is given in Section 3.10.

2. Drag coefficient.   From the preceding discussion it is evident that the geometry of the immersed solid is a major factor in determining the amount of total drag force exerted on the body. Correlations of the geometry and flow characteristics for solid objects suspended or held in a free stream (immersed objects) are similar in concept and form to the friction factor–Reynolds number correlation given for flow inside conduits. In flow through conduits, the friction factor was defined as the ratio of the drag force per unit area (shear stress) to the product of density times velocity head, as given in Eq. (2.10-4).

In a similar manner, for flow past immersed objects the drag coefficient C_D is defined as the ratio of the total drag force per unit area to $\rho v_0^2/2$:

$$C_D = \frac{F_D/A_p}{\rho v_0^2/2} \quad \text{(SI)}$$

$$C_D = \frac{F_D/A_p}{\rho v_0^2/2g_c} \quad \text{(English)}$$

(3.1-1)

where F_D is the total drag force in N, A_p is an area in m^2, C_D is dimensionless, v_0 is free-stream velocity in m/s, and ρ is density of fluid in kg/m^3. In English units, F_D is in lb$_f$, v_0 is in ft/s, ρ is in lb$_m$/ft^3, and A_p is in ft^2. The area A_p used is the area obtained by projecting the body on a plane perpendicular to the line of flow. For a sphere, $A_p = \pi D_p^2/4$, where D_p is sphere diameter; for a cylinder whose axis is perpendicular to the flow direction, $A_p = LD_p$, where $L =$ cylinder length. Solving Eq. (3.1-1) for the total drag force,

$$F_D = C_D \frac{v_0^2}{2} \rho A_p$$

(3.1-2)

The Reynolds number for a given solid immersed in a flowing liquid is

$$N_{Re} = \frac{D_p v_0 \rho}{\mu} = \frac{D_p G_0}{\mu}$$

(3.1-3)

where $G_0 = v_0 \rho$.

3.1B Flow Past Sphere, Long Cylinder, and Disk

For each particular shape of object and orientation of the object with respect to the direction of flow, a different relation of C_D versus N_{Re} exists. Correlations of drag coefficient versus Reynolds number are shown in Fig. 3.1-2 for spheres, long cylinders, and disks. The face of

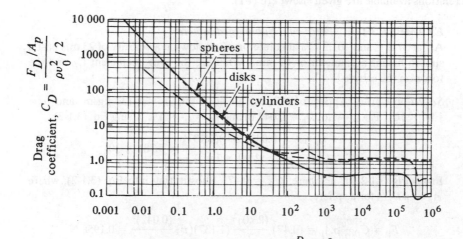

FIGURE 3.1-2. *Drag coefficients for flow past immersed spheres, long cylinders, and disks. (Reprinted with permission from C. E. Lapple and C. B. Shepherd, Ind. Eng. Chem., 32, 606 (1940). Copyright by the American Chemical Society.)*

the disk and the axis of the cylinder are perpendicular to the direction of flow. These curves have been determined experimentally. However, in the laminar region for low Reynolds numbers, less than about 1.0, the experimental drag force for a sphere is the same as the theoretical Stokes' law equation as follows:

$$F_D = 3\pi\mu D_p v_0 \tag{3.1-4}$$

Combining Eqs. (3.1-2) and (3.1-4) and solving for C_D, the drag coefficient predicted by Stokes' law is

$$C_D = \frac{24}{D_p v_0 \rho/\mu} = \frac{24}{N_{Re}} \tag{3.1-5}$$

The variation of C_D with N_{Re} (Fig. 3.1-2) is quite complicated because of the interaction of the factors that control skin drag and form drag. For a sphere, as the Reynolds number is increased beyond the Stokes' law range, separation occurs and a wake is formed. Further increases in N_{Re} cause shifts in the separation point. At about $N_{Re} = 3 \times 10^5$ the sudden drop in C_D is the result of the boundary layer becoming completely turbulent and the point of separation moving downstream. In the region of N_{Re} about 1×10^3 to 2×10^5, the drag coefficient is approximately constant for each shape and $C_D = 0.44$ for a sphere. Above N_{Re} about 5×10^5, the drag coefficients are again approximately constant, with C_D being 0.13 for a sphere, 0.33 for a cylinder, and 1.12 for a disk. Additional discussions and theory concerning flow past spheres are given in Section 3.9E.

For derivations of theory and detailed discussions of the drag force for flow parallel to a flat plate, Section 3.10 on boundary-layer flow and turbulence should be consulted. The flow of fluids normal to banks of cylinders or tubes occurs in heat exchangers and other processing applications. The banks of tubes can be arranged in a number of different geometries. Because of the many possible geometric tube configurations and spacings, it is not possible to have one correlation for the data on pressure drop and friction factors. Details of the many correlations available are given elsewhere (P1).

EXAMPLE 3.1-1. Force on a Submerged Sphere
Air at 37.8°C and 101.3 kPa absolute pressure flows at a velocity of 23 m/s past a sphere having a diameter of 42 mm. What are the drag coefficient C_D and the force on the sphere?

Solution: From Appendix A.3, for air at 37.8°C, $\rho = 1.137$ kg/m^3 and $\mu = 1.90 \times 10^{-5}$ Pa·s. Also, $D_p = 0.042$ m and $v_0 = 23.0$ m/s. Using Eq. (3.1-3),

$$N_{Re} = \frac{D_p v_0 \rho}{\mu} = \frac{0.042(23.0)(1.137)}{1.90 \times 10^{-5}} = 5.781 \times 10^4$$

From Fig. 3.1-2 for a sphere, $C_D = 0.47$. Substituting into Eq. (3.1-2), where $A_p = \pi D_p^2/4$ for a sphere,

$$F_D = C_D \frac{v_0^2}{2}\rho A_p = (0.47)\frac{(23.0)^2}{2}(1.137)(\pi)\frac{(0.042)^2}{4} = 0.1958 \text{ N}$$

EXAMPLE 3.1-2. Force on a Cylinder in a Tunnel
Water at 24°C is flowing past a long cylinder at a velocity of 1.0 m/s in a large tunnel. The axis of the cylinder is perpendicular to the direction of flow. The di-

ameter of the cylinder is 0.090 m. What is the force per meter length on the cylinder?

Solution: From Appendix A.2, for water at 24°C, $\rho = 997.2$ kg/m^3 and $\mu = 0.9142 \times 10^{-3}$ Pa·s. Also, $D_p = 0.090$ m, $L = 1.0$ m, and $v_0 = 1.0$ m/s. Using Eq. (3.1-3),

$$N_{Re} = \frac{D_p v_0 \rho}{\mu} = \frac{0.090(1.0)(997.2)}{0.9142 \times 10^{-3}} = 9.817 \times 10^4$$

From Fig. 3.1-2 for a long cylinder, $C_D = 1.4$. Substituting into Eq. (3.1-2), where $A_p = LD_p = 1.0(0.090) = 0.090$ m^2,

$$F_D = C_D \frac{v_0^2}{2} \rho A_p = (1.4)\frac{(1.0)^2}{2}(997.2)(0.09) = 62.82 \text{ N}$$

3.1C Flow in Packed Beds

1. Introduction. A system of considerable importance in chemical and other process engineering fields is the packed bed or packed column, which is used for a fixed-bed catalytic reactor, adsorption of a solute, absorption, filter bed, and so on. The packing material in the bed may be spheres, irregular particles, cylinders, or various kinds of commercial packings. In the discussion to follow it is assumed that the packing is everywhere uniform and that little or no channeling occurs. The ratio of diameter of the tower to packing diameter should be a minimum of 8:1 to 10:1 for wall effects to be small. In the theoretical approach used, the packed column is regarded as a bundle of crooked tubes of varying cross-sectional area. The theory developed in Chapter 2 for single straight tubes is used to develop the results for the bundle of crooked tubes.

2. Laminar flow in packed beds. Certain geometric relations for particles in packed beds are used in the derivations for flow. The void fraction ε in a packed bed is defined as

$$\varepsilon = \frac{\text{volume of voids in bed}}{\text{total volume of bed (voids plus solids)}} \tag{3.1-6}$$

The specific surface of a particle a_v in m^{-1} is defined as

$$a_v = \frac{S_p}{v_p} \tag{3.1-7}$$

where S_p is the surface area of a particle in m^2 and v_p the volume of a particle in m^3. For a spherical particle,

$$a_v = \frac{6}{D_p} \tag{3.1-8}$$

where D_p is diameter in m. For a packed bed of nonspherical particles, the effective particle diameter D_p is defined as

$$D_P = \frac{6}{a_v} \tag{3.1-9}$$

Since $(1 - \varepsilon)$ is the volume fraction of particles in the bed,

$$a = a_v(1 - \varepsilon) = \frac{6}{D_p}(1 - \varepsilon) \qquad (3.1\text{-}10)$$

where a is the ratio of total surface area in the bed to total volume of bed (void volume plus particle volume) in m^{-1}.

EXAMPLE 3.1-3. Surface Area in Packed Bed of Cylinders

A packed bed is composed of cylinders having a diameter $D = 0.02$ m and a length $h = D$. The bulk density of the overall packed bed is 962 kg/m^3 and the density of the solid cylinders is 1600 kg/m^3.

(a) Calculate the void fraction ε.
(b) Calculate the effective diameter D_p of the particles.
(c) Calculate the value of a in Eq. (3.1-10).

Solution: For part (a), taking 1.00 m^3 of packed bed as a basis, the total mass of the bed is $(962 \text{ kg/m}^3)(1.00 \text{ m}^3) = 962$ kg. This mass of 962 kg is also the mass of the solid cylinders. Hence, volume of cylinders = 962 kg/(1600 kg/m^3) = 0.601 m^3. Using Eq. (3.1-6),

$$\varepsilon = \frac{\text{volume of voids in bed}}{\text{total volume of bed}} = \frac{1.000 - 0.601}{1.000} = 0.399$$

For the effective particle diameter D_p in part (b), for a cylinder where $h = D$, the surface area of a particle is

$$S_p = (2)\frac{\pi D^2}{4} \text{ (ends)} + \pi D(D) \text{ (sides)} = \tfrac{3}{2}\pi D^2$$

The volume v_p of a particle is

$$v_p = \frac{\pi}{4}D^2(D) = \frac{\pi D^3}{4}$$

Substituting into Eq. (3.1-7),

$$a_v = \frac{S_p}{v_p} = \frac{\tfrac{3}{2}\pi D^2}{\tfrac{1}{4}\pi D^3} = \frac{6}{D}$$

Finally, substituting into Eq. (3.1-9),

$$D_p = \frac{6}{a_v} = \frac{6}{6/D} = D = 0.02 \text{ m}$$

Hence, the effective diameter to use is $D_p = D = 0.02$ m. For part (c), using Eq. (3.1-10),

$$a = \frac{6}{D_p}(1 - \varepsilon) = \frac{6}{0.02}(1 - 0.399) = 180.3 \text{ m}^{-1}$$

The average interstitial velocity in the bed is v m/s and is related to the superficial velocity v' based on the cross section of the empty container by

$$v' = \varepsilon v \qquad (3.1\text{-}11)$$

The hydraulic radius r_H for flow defined in Eq. (2.10-21) is modified as follows (B2):

$$r_H = \frac{\left(\begin{array}{c}\text{cross-sectional area} \\ \text{available for flow}\end{array}\right)}{\text{(wetted perimeter)}}$$

$$= \frac{\text{void volume available for flow}}{\text{total wetted surface of solids}}$$

$$= \frac{\text{volume of voids/volume of bed}}{\text{wetted surface/volume of bed}} = \frac{\varepsilon}{a} \qquad \text{(3.1-12)}$$

Combining Eqs. (3.1-10) and (3.1-12),

$$r_H = \frac{\varepsilon}{6(1-\varepsilon)}D_p \qquad \text{(3.1-13)}$$

Since the equivalent diameter D for a channel is $D = 4r_H$, the Reynolds number for a packed bed is as follows, using Eq. (3.1-13) and $v' = \varepsilon v$:

$$N_{Re} = \frac{(4r_H)v\rho}{\mu} = \frac{4\varepsilon}{6(1-\varepsilon)}D_p\frac{v'}{\varepsilon}\frac{\rho}{\mu} = \frac{4}{6(1-\varepsilon)}\frac{D_p v'\rho}{\mu} \qquad \text{(3.1-14)}$$

For packed beds Ergun (E1) defined the Reynolds number as above but without the 4/6 term:

$$N_{Re,p} = \frac{D_p \dot{v}'\rho}{(1-\varepsilon)\mu} = \frac{D_p G'}{(1-\varepsilon)\mu} \qquad \text{(3.1-15)}$$

where $G' = v'\rho$.

For laminar flow, the Hagen–Poiseuille equation (2.10-2) can be combined with Eq. (3.1-13) for r_H and Eq. (3.1-11) to give

$$\Delta p = \frac{32\mu v \, \Delta L}{D^2} = \frac{32\mu(v'/\varepsilon) \, \Delta L}{(4r_H)^2} = \frac{(72)\mu v' \, \Delta L(1-\varepsilon)^2}{\varepsilon^3 D_p^2} \qquad \text{(3.1-16)}$$

The true ΔL is larger because of the tortuous path, and use of the hydraulic radius predicts too large a v'. Experimental data show that the constant should be 150, which gives the Blake–Kozeny equation for laminar flow, void fractions less than 0.5, effective particle diameter D_p, and $N_{Re,p} < 10$:

$$\Delta p = \frac{150\mu v' \, \Delta L}{D_p^2} \frac{(1-\varepsilon)^2}{\varepsilon^3} \qquad \text{(3.1-17)}$$

3. *Turbulent flow in packed beds.* For turbulent flow we use the same procedure by starting with Eq. (2.10-5) and substituting Eqs. (3.1-11) and (3.1-13) into this equation to obtain

$$\Delta p = \frac{3f\rho(v')^2 \, \Delta L}{D_p} \frac{1-\varepsilon}{\varepsilon^3} \qquad \text{(3.1-18)}$$

For highly turbulent flow the friction factor should approach a constant value. Also, it is assumed that all packed beds should have the same relative roughness. Experimental data indicate that $3f = 1.75$. Hence, the final equation for turbulent flow for $N_{Re,p} > 1000$, which is called the Burke–Plummer equation, becomes

$$\Delta p = \frac{1.75\rho(v')^2 \, \Delta L}{D_p} \frac{1 - \varepsilon}{\varepsilon^3} \qquad \text{(3.1-19)}$$

Adding Eq. (3.1-17) for laminar flow and Eq. (3.1-19) for turbulent flow, Ergun (E1) proposed the following general equation for low, intermediate, and high Reynolds numbers, which has been tested experimentally:

$$\Delta p = \frac{150\mu v' \, \Delta L}{D_p^2} \frac{(1 - \varepsilon)^2}{\varepsilon^3} + \frac{1.75\rho(v')^2 \, \Delta L}{D_p} \frac{1 - \varepsilon}{\varepsilon^3} \qquad \text{(3.1-20)}$$

Rewriting Eq. (3.1-20) in terms of dimensionless groups,

$$\frac{\Delta p \rho}{(G')^2} \frac{D_p}{\Delta L} \frac{\varepsilon^3}{1 - \varepsilon} = \frac{150}{N_{Re,p}} + 1.75 \qquad \text{(3.1-21)}$$

See also Eq. (3.1-33) for another form of Eq. (3.1-21). The Ergun equation (3.1-21) can be used for gases by taking the density ρ of the gas as the arithmetic average of the inlet and outlet pressures. The velocity v' changes throughout the bed for a compressible fluid, but G' is a constant. At high values of $N_{Re,p}$, Eqs. (3.1-20) and (3.1-21) reduce to Eq. (3.1-19), and to Eq. (3.1-17) for low values. For large pressure drops with gases, Eq. (3.1-20) can be written in differential form (P1).

EXAMPLE 3.1-4. *Pressure Drop and Flow of Gases in Packed Bed*
Air at 311 K is flowing through a packed bed of spheres having a diameter of 12.7 mm. The void fraction ε of the bed is 0.38 and the bed has a diameter of 0.61 m and a height of 2.44 m. The air enters the bed at 1.10 atm abs at the rate of 0.358 kg/s. Calculate the pressure drop of the air in the packed bed. The average molecular weight of air is 28.97.

Solution: From Appendix A.3, for air at 311 K, $\mu = 1.90 \times 10^{-5}$ Pa·s. The cross-sectional area of the bed is $A = (\pi/4)D^2 = (\pi/4)(0.61)^2 = 0.2922$ m^2. Hence, $G' = 0.358/0.2922 = 1.225$ kg/m^2·s (based on empty cross section of container or bed). $D_p = 0.0127$ m, $\Delta L = 2.44$ m, and inlet pressure $p_1 = 1.1(1.01325 \times 10^5) = 1.115 \times 10^5$ Pa.

From Eq. (3.1-15),

$$N_{Re,p} = \frac{D_p G'}{(1 - \varepsilon)\mu} = \frac{0.0127(1.225)}{(1 - 0.38)(1.90 \times 10^{-5})} = 1321$$

To use Eq. (3.1-21) for gases, the density ρ to use is the average at the inlet p_1 and outlet p_2 pressures, or at $(p_1 + p_2)/2$. This is trial and error since p_2 is unknown. Assuming that $\Delta p = 0.05 \times 10^5$ Pa, $p_2 = 1.115 \times 10^5 - 0.05 \times 10^5 = 1.065 \times 10^5$ Pa. The average pressure is $p_{av} = (1.115 \times 10^5 + 1.065 \times 10^5)/2 = 1.090 \times 10^5$ Pa. The average density to use is

$$\rho_{av} = \frac{M}{RT} p_{av} \qquad \text{(3.1-22)}$$

$$= \frac{28.97(1.090 \times 10^5)}{8314.34(311)} = 1.221 \text{ kg/m}^3$$

Substituting into Eq. (3.1-21) and solving for Δp,

$$\frac{\Delta p(1.221)}{(1.225)^2}\frac{0.0127}{2.44}\frac{(0.38)^3}{1-0.38} = \frac{150}{1321} + 1.75$$

Solving, $\Delta p = 0.0497 \times 10^5$ Pa. This is close enough to the assumed value, so a second trial is not needed.

4. Shape factors. Many particles in packed beds are often irregular in shape. The equivalent diameter of a particle is defined as the diameter of a sphere having the same volume as this particle. The sphericity shape factor ϕ_S of a particle is the ratio of the surface area of this sphere having the same volume as the particle to the actual surface area of the particle. For a sphere, the surface area $S_p = \pi D_p^2$ and the volume $v_p = \pi D_p^3/6$. Hence, for any particle, $\phi_S = \pi D_p^2/S_p$, where S_p is the actual surface area of the particle and D_p is the diameter (equivalent diameter) of the sphere having the same volume as the particle. Then

$$\frac{S_p}{v_p} = \frac{\pi D_p^2/\phi_S}{\pi D_p^3/6} = \frac{6}{\phi_S D_p} \tag{3.1-23}$$

From Eq. (3.1-7),

$$a_v = \frac{S_p}{v_p} = \frac{6}{\phi_S D_p} \tag{3.1-24}$$

Then Eq. (3.1-10) becomes

$$a = \frac{6}{\phi_S D_p}(1 - \varepsilon) \tag{3.1-25}$$

For a sphere, $\phi_S = 1.0$. For a cylinder where diameter = length, ϕ_S is calculated to be 0.874, and for a cube, ϕ_S is calculated to be 0.806. For granular materials it is difficult to measure the actual volume and surface area to obtain the equivalent diameter. Hence, D_p is usually taken to be the nominal size from a screen analysis or visual length measurements. The surface area is determined by adsorption measurements or measurement of the pressure drop in a bed of particles. Then Eq. (3.1-23) is used to calculate ϕ_S (Table 3.1-1). Typical values for many crushed materials are between 0.6 and 0.7. For convenience, for the cylinder and the cube, the nominal diameter is sometimes used (instead of the equivalent diameter), which then gives a shape factor of 1.0.

5. Mixtures of particles. For mixtures of particles of various sizes we can define a mean specific surface a_{vm} as

$$a_{vm} = \sum x_i a_{vi} \tag{3.1-26}$$

where x_i is volume fraction. Combining Eqs. (3.1-24) and (3.1-26),

$$D_{pm} = \frac{6}{a_{vm}} = \frac{6}{\sum x_i(6/\phi_S D_{pi})} = \frac{1}{\sum x_i/(\phi_S D_{pi})} \tag{3.1-27}$$

where D_{pm} is the effective mean diameter for the mixture.

TABLE 3.1-1.   *Shape Factors (Sphericity) of Some Materials*

Material	Shape Factor, ϕ_S	Reference
Spheres	1.0	
Cubes	0.81	
Cylinders, $D_p = h$ (length)	0.87	
Berl saddles	0.3	(B4)
Raschig rings	0.3	(C2)
Coal dust, pulverized	0.73	(C2)
Sand, average	0.75	(C2)
Crushed glass	0.65	(C2)

EXAMPLE 3.1-5.   *Mean Diameter for a Particle Mixture*
A mixture contains three sizes of particles: 25% by volume of 25 mm size, 40%
of 50 mm, and 35% of 75 mm. The sphericity is 0.68. Calculate the effective
mean diameter.

Solution: The following data are given: $x_1 = 0.25$, $D_{p1} = 25$ mm; $x_2 = 0.40$,
$D_{p2} = 50$; $x_3 = 0.35$, $D_{p3} = 75$; $\phi_S = 0.68$. Substituting into Eq. (3.1-27),

$$D_{pm} = \frac{1}{0.25/(0.68 \times 25) + 0.40/(0.68 \times 50) + 0.35/(0.68 \times 75)}$$

$$= 30.0 \text{ mm}$$

6. Darcy's empirical law for laminar flow.   Equation (3.1-17) for laminar flow in packed beds
shows that the flow rate is proportional to Δp and inversely proportional to the viscosity μ
and length ΔL. This is the basis for Darcy's law, as follows, for purely viscous flow in consoli-
dated porous media:

$$v' = \frac{q'}{A} = -\frac{k}{\mu}\frac{\Delta p}{\Delta L} \tag{3.1-28}$$

where v' is superficial velocity based on the empty cross section in cm/s, q' is flow rate in
cm³/s, A is empty cross section in cm², μ is viscosity in cp, Δp is pressure drop in atm, ΔL is
length in cm, and k is permeability in (cm³ flow/s) · (cp) · (cm length)/(cm² area) · (atm pressure drop). The units used for k of cm² · cp/s · atm are often given in darcy or in millidarcy
(1/1000 darcy). Hence, if a porous medium has a permeability of 1 darcy, a fluid of 1 cp viscosity will flow at 1 cm³/s per 1 cm² cross section with a Δp of 1 atm per cm length. This equation is often used in measuring permeabilities of underground oil reservoirs.

3.1D   Flow in Fluidized Beds

1. Types of fluidization in beds.   In a packed bed of small particles, when a fluid enters at
sufficient velocity from the bottom and passes up through the particles, the particles are

pushed upward and the bed expands and becomes fluidized. Two general types of fluidization, *particulate fluidization* and *bubbling fluidization,* can occur.

In *particulate fluidization,* as the fluid velocity is increased the bed continues to expand and remains homogeneous for a time. The particles move farther apart and their motion becomes more rapid. The average bed density at a given velocity is the same in all regions of the bed. An example is catalytic cracking catalysts fluidized by gases. This type of fluidization is very desirable in promoting intimate contact between the gas and solids. Liquids often give particulate fluidization.

In *bubbling fluidization,* the gas passes through the bed as voids or bubbles which contain few particles, and only a small percentage of the gas passes in the spaces between individual particles. The expansion of the bed is small as gas velocity is increased. Sand and glass beads provide examples of this behavior. Since most of the gas is in bubbles, little contact occurs between the individual particles and the bubbles.

Particles which behave as above have been classified by Geldart (G2) into classes. Those called Type A, which exhibit particulate fluidization in gases, fall into the following approximate ranges: For $\Delta\rho = (\rho_p - \rho) = 2000$ kg/m^3, $D_p = 20$–125 μm; $\Delta\rho = 1000$, $D_p = 25$–250; $\Delta\rho = 500$, $D_p = 40$–450; $\Delta\rho = 200$, $D_p = 100$–1000. For those called Type B, which exhibit bubbling fluidization, approximate ranges are as follows: $\Delta\rho = 2000$, $D_p = 125$–700 μm; $\Delta\rho = 1000$, $D_p = 250$–1000; $\Delta\rho = 500$, $D_p = 450$–1500; $\Delta\rho = 200$, $D_p = 1000$–2000.

Another type of behavior, called *slugging,* can occur in bubbling since the bubbles tend to coalesce and grow as they rise in the bed. If the column is small in diameter with a deep bed, bubbles can become large and fill the entire cross section and travel up the tower separated by slugs of solids.

2. Minimum velocity and porosity for particulate fluidization. When a fluid flows upward through a packed bed of particles at low velocities, the particles remain stationary. As the fluid velocity is increased, the pressure drop increases according to the Ergun equation (3.1-20). Upon further increases in velocity, conditions finally occur where the force of the pressure drop times the cross-sectional area equals the gravitational force on the mass of particles. Then the particles begin to move, and this is the onset of fluidization or minimum fluidization. The fluid velocity at which fluidization begins is the minimum fluidization velocity v'_{mf} in m/s based on the empty cross section of the tower (superficial velocity).

The porosity of the bed when true fluidization occurs is the minimum porosity for fluidization, ε_{mf}. Some typical values of ε_{mf} for various materials are given in Table 3.1-2. The bed expands to this voidage or porosity before particle motion appears. This minimum voidage can be determined experimentally by subjecting the bed to a rising gas stream and measuring the height of the bed L_{mf} in m. Generally, it appears best to use gas as the fluid rather than a liquid, since liquids give somewhat higher values of ε_{mf}.

As stated earlier, the pressure drop increases as the gas velocity is increased until the onset of minimum fluidization. Then, as the velocity is further increased, the pressure drop decreases very slightly, and then it remains practically unchanged as the bed continues to expand or increase in porosity with increases in velocity. The bed resembles a boiling liquid. As the bed expands with increase in velocity, it continues to retain its top horizontal surface. Eventually, as the velocity is increased much further, entrainment of particles from the actual fluidized bed becomes appreciable.

TABLE 3.1-2. *Void Fraction, ε_{mf}, at Minimum Fluidization Conditions (L2)*

Type of Particles	Particle Size, D_P (mm)			
	0.06	0.10	0.20	0.40
	Void fraction, ε_{mf}			
Sharp sand ($\phi_S = 0.67$)	0.60	0.58	0.53	0.49
Round sand ($\phi_S = 0.86$)	0.53	0.48	0.43	(0.42)
Anthracite coal ($\phi_S = 0.63$)	0.61	0.60	0.56	0.52
Absorption carbon	0.71	0.69		
Fischer Tropsch catalyst ($\phi_S = 0.58$)		0.58	0.56	(0.54)

The relation between bed height L and porosity ε is as follows for a bed having a uniform cross-sectional area A. Since the volume $LA(1 - \varepsilon)$ is equal to the total volume of solids if they existed as one piece,

$$L_1 A(1 - \varepsilon_1) = L_2 A(1 - \varepsilon_2) \tag{3.1-29}$$

$$\frac{L_1}{L_2} = \frac{1 - \varepsilon_2}{1 - \varepsilon_1} \tag{3.1-30}$$

where L_1 is height of bed with porosity ε_1 and L_2 is height with porosity ε_2.

3. Pressure drop and minimum fluidizing velocity. As a first approximation, the pressure drop at the start of fluidization can be determined as follows. The force obtained from the pressure drop times the cross-sectional area must equal the gravitational force exerted by the mass of the particles minus the buoyant force of the displaced fluid:

$$\Delta p A = L_{mf} A(1 - \varepsilon_{mf})(\rho_p - \rho)g \tag{3.1-31}$$

Hence,

$$\frac{\Delta p}{L_{mf}} = (1 - \varepsilon_{mf})(\rho_p - \rho)g \quad \text{(SI)}$$

$$\tag{3.1-32}$$

$$\frac{\Delta p}{L_{mf}} = (1 - \varepsilon_{mf})(\rho_p - \rho)\frac{g}{g_c} \quad \text{(English)}$$

Often we have irregular-shaped particles in the bed, and it is more convenient to use the particle size and shape factor in the equations. First we substitute for the effective mean diameter D_p the term $\phi_S D_P$, where D_P now represents the particle size of a sphere having the same volume as the particle and ϕ_S the shape factor. Often, the value of D_P is approximated by using the nominal size from a sieve analysis. Then Eq. (3.1-20) for pressure drop in a packed bed becomes

$$\frac{\Delta p}{L} = \frac{150 \mu v'}{\phi_S^2 D_P^2} \frac{(1 - \varepsilon)^2}{\varepsilon^3} + \frac{1.75 \rho (v')^2}{\phi_S D_P} \frac{1 - \varepsilon}{\varepsilon^3} \tag{3.1-33}$$

where $\Delta L = L$, bed length in m.

Equation (3.1-33) can now be used by a small extrapolation for packed beds to calculate the minimum fluid velocity v'_{mf} at which fluidization begins by substituting v'_{mf} for v', ε_{mf} for ε, and L_{mf} for L, and combining the result with Eq. (3.1-32) to give

$$\frac{1.75 D_P^2 (v'_{mf})^2 \rho^2}{\phi_S \varepsilon_{mf}^3 \mu^2} + \frac{150(1 - \varepsilon_{mf}) D_P v'_{mf} \rho}{\phi_S^2 \varepsilon_{mf}^3 \mu} - \frac{D_P^3 \rho(\rho_p - \rho)g}{\mu^2} = 0 \qquad (3.1\text{-}34)$$

Defining a Reynolds number as

$$N_{Re,mf} = \frac{D_P v'_{mf} \rho}{\mu} \qquad (3.1\text{-}35)$$

Eq. (3.1-34) becomes

$$\frac{1.75(N_{Re,mf})^2}{\phi_S \varepsilon_{mf}^3} + \frac{150(1 - \varepsilon_{mf})(N_{Re,mf})}{\phi_S^2 \varepsilon_{mf}^3} - \frac{D_P^3 \rho(\rho_p - \rho)g}{\mu^2} = 0 \qquad (3.1\text{-}36)$$

When $N_{Re,mf} < 20$ (small particles), the first term of Eq. (3.1-36) can be dropped, and when $N_{Re,mf} > 1000$ (large particles), the second term drops out.

If the terms ε_{mf} and/or ϕ_S are not known, Wen and Yu (W4) found for a variety of systems that

$$\phi_S \varepsilon_{mf}^3 \cong \frac{1}{14}, \qquad \frac{1 - \varepsilon_{mf}}{\phi_S^2 \varepsilon_{mf}^3} \cong 11 \qquad (3.1\text{-}37)$$

Substituting into Eq. (3.1-36), the following simplified equation is obtained:

$$N_{Re,mf} - \left[(33.7)^2 + 0.0408 \frac{D_P^3 \rho(\rho_p - \rho)g}{\mu^2} \right]^{1/2} - 33.7 \qquad (3.1\text{-}38)$$

This equation holds for a Reynolds-number range of 0.001 to 4000, with an average deviation of ±25%. Alternative equations are available in the literature (K1, W4).

EXAMPLE 3.1-6. Minimum Velocity for Fluidization

Solid particles having a size of 0.12 mm, a shape factor ϕ_S of 0.88, and a density of 1000 kg/m³ are to be fluidized using air at 2.0 atm abs and 25°C. The voidage at minimum fluidizing conditions is 0.42.

(a) If the cross section of the empty bed is 0.30 m² and the bed contains 300 kg of solid, calculate the minimum height of the fluidized bed.

(b) Calculate the pressure drop at minimum fluidizing conditions.

(c) Calculate the minimum velocity for fluidization.

(d) Use Eq. (3.1-38) to calculate v'_{mf} assuming that data for ϕ_S and ε_{mf} are not available.

Solution: For part (a), the volume of solids = 300 kg/(1000 kg/m³) = 0.300 m³. The height the solids would occupy in the bed if $\varepsilon_1 = 0$ is $L_1 = 0.300$ m³/(0.30 m² cross section) = 1.00 m. Using Eq. (3.1-30) and calling $L_{mf} = L_2$ and $\varepsilon_{mf} = \varepsilon_2$,

$$\frac{L_1}{L_{mf}} = \frac{1 - \varepsilon_{mf}}{1 - \varepsilon_1}$$

$$\frac{1.00}{L_{mf}} = \frac{1 - 0.42}{1 - 0}$$

Solving, $L_{mf} = 1.724$ m.

The physical properties of air at 2.0 atm and 25°C (Appendix A.3) are $\mu = 1.845 \times 10^{-5}$ Pa·s, $\rho = 1.187 \times 2 = 2.374$ kg/m³, and $p = 2.0265 \times 10^5$ Pa. For the particle, $D_P = 0.00012$ m, $\rho_P = 1000$ kg/m³, $\phi_S = 0.88$, and $\varepsilon_{mf} = 0.42$.

For part (b), using Eq. (3.1-32) to calculate Δp,

$$\Delta p = L_{mf}(1 - \varepsilon_{mf})(\rho_p - \rho)g$$

$$= 1.724(1 - 0.42)(1000 - 2.374)(9.80665) = 0.0978 \times 10^5 \text{ Pa}$$

To calculate v'_{mf} for part (c), Eq. (3.1-36) is used:

$$\frac{1.75(N_{Re,mf})^2}{(0.88)(0.42)^3} + \frac{150(1 - 0.42)(N_{Re,mf})}{(0.88)^2(0.42)^3}$$

$$- (0.00012)^3 \frac{2.374(1000 - 2.374)(9.80665)}{(1.845 \times 10^{-5})^2} = 0$$

Solving,

$$N_{Re,mf} = 0.07764 = \frac{D_P v'_{mf} \rho}{\mu} = \frac{0.00012(v'_{mf})(2.374)}{1.845 \times 10^{-5}}$$

$$v'_{mf} = 0.005029 \text{ m/s}$$

Using the simplified Eq. (3.1-38) for part (d),

$$N_{Re,mf} = \left[(33.7)^2 + \frac{0.0408(0.00012)^3(2.374)(1000 - 2.374)(9.80665)}{(1.845 \times 10^{-5})^2} \right]^{1/2} - 33.7$$

$$= 0.07129$$

Solving, $v'_{mf} = 0.004618$ m/s.

4. Expansion of fluidized beds. For the case of small particles and where $N_{Re,f} = D_P v' \rho/\mu < 20$, we can estimate the variation of porosity or bed height L as follows. We assume that Eq. (3.1-36) applies over the whole range of fluid velocities, with the first term being neglected. Then, solving for v',

$$v' = \frac{D_P^2(\rho_p - \rho)g\phi_S^2}{150\mu} \frac{\varepsilon^3}{1 - \varepsilon} = K_1 \frac{\varepsilon^3}{1 - \varepsilon} \tag{3.1-39}$$

We find that all terms except ε are constant for the particular system, and ε depends upon v'. This equation can be used with liquids to estimate ε with $\varepsilon < 0.80$. However, because of clumping and other factors, errors can occur when used for gases.

The flow rate in a fluidized bed is limited on the one hand by the minimum v'_{mf} and on the other by entrainment of solids from the bed proper. This maximum allowable velocity is approximated as the terminal settling velocity v'_t of the particles. (See Section 13.3 for methods for calculating this settling velocity.) Approximate equations for calculating the operating range are as follows (P2). For fine solids and $N_{Re,f} < 0.4$,

$$\frac{v'_t}{v'_{mf}} \cong \frac{90}{1} \tag{3.1-40}$$

For large solids and $N_{Re,f} > 1000$,

$$\frac{v'_t}{v'_{mf}} \cong \frac{9}{1} \tag{3.1-41}$$

EXAMPLE 3.1-7. Expansion of Fluidized Bed

Using the data from Example 3.1-6, estimate the maximum allowable velocity v'_t. Using an operating velocity of 3.0 times the minimum, estimate the voidage of the bed.

Solution: From Example 3.1-6, $N_{Re,mf} = 0.07764$, $v'_{mf} = 0.005029$ m/s, and $\varepsilon_{mf} = 0.42$. Using Eq. (3.1-40), the maximum allowable velocity is

$$v'_t \cong 90(v'_{mf}) = 90(0.005029) = 0.4526 \text{ m/s}$$

Using an operating velocity v' of 2.0 times the minimum,

$$v' = 2.0(v'_{mf}) = 2.0(0.005029) = 0.01006 \text{ m/s}$$

To determine the voidage at this new velocity, we substitute into Eq. (3.1-39) using the known values at minimum fluidizing conditions to determine K_1:

$$0.005029 = K_1 \frac{(0.42)^3}{1 - 0.42}$$

Solving $K_1 = 0.03938$. Then using the operating velocity in Eq. (3.1-39),

$$0.01006 = (0.03938) \frac{\varepsilon^3}{1 - \varepsilon}$$

Solving, the voidage of the bed $\varepsilon = 0.503$ at the operating velocity.

5. *Minimum bubbling velocity.*   The fluidization velocity at which bubbles are first observed is called the *minimum bubbling velocity*, v'_{mb}. For Group B particles, which exhibit bubbling fluidization, v'_{mb} is reasonably close to v'_{mf}. For Group A particles, v'_{mb} is substantially greater than v'_{mf}. The following equation (G3) can be used to calculate v'_{mb}:

$$v'_{mb} = 33 D_p (\mu/\rho)^{-0.1} \tag{3.1-42}$$

where v'_{mb} is minimum bubbling velocity in m/s, μ is viscosity in Pa · s, and ρ is gas density in kg/m^3. If the calculated v'_{mf} is greater than the calculated v'_{mb} by Eq. (3.1-42), then the v'_{mf} should be used as the minimum bubbling velocity (G4).

EXAMPLE 3.1-8. Minimum Bubbling Velocity

Using data from Example 3.1-6, calculate the v'_{mb}.

Solution: Substituting into Eq. (3.1-42),

$$v'_{mb} = 33(0.00012)(1.845 \times 10^{-5}/2.374)^{-0.1} = 0.01284 \text{ m/s}$$

This is substantially greater than the v'_{mf} of 0.005029 m/s.

3.2 MEASUREMENT OF FLOW OF FLUIDS

It is important to be able to measure and control the amount of material entering and leaving a chemical or other processing plant. Since many of the materials are in the form of fluids, they are flowing in pipes or conduits. Many different types of devices are used to measure the flow of fluids. The simplest are those that measure directly the volume of the fluids, such as ordinary gas and water meters and positive-displacement pumps. Current meters make use of an element, such as a propeller or cups on a rotating arm, which rotates at a speed determined by the velocity of the fluid passing through it. Very widely used for fluid metering are the pitot tube, venturi meter, orifice meter, and open-channel weirs.

3.2A Pitot Tube

The pitot tube is used to measure the local velocity at a given point in the flow stream and not the average velocity in the pipe or conduit. In Fig. 3.2-1a, a sketch of this simple device is shown. One tube, the impact tube, has its opening normal to the direction of flow, while the static tube has its opening parallel to the direction of flow.

The fluid flows into the opening at point 2; pressure builds up and then remains stationary at this point, called the *stagnation point*. The difference in the stagnation pressure at point 2 and the static pressure measured by the static tube represents the pressure rise associated with deceleration of the fluid. The manometer measures this small pressure rise. If the fluid is incompressible, we can write the Bernoulli equation (2.7-32) between point 1, where the velocity v_1 is undisturbed before the fluid decelerates, and point 2, where the velocity v_2 is zero:

$$\frac{v_1^2}{2} - \frac{v_2^2}{2} + \frac{p_1 - p_2}{\rho} = 0 \qquad (3.2\text{-}1)$$

Setting $v_2 = 0$ and solving for v_1,

$$v = C_p \sqrt{\frac{2(p_2 - p_1)}{\rho}} \qquad (3.2\text{-}2)$$

FIGURE 3.2-1. *Diagram of pitot tube: (a) simple tube, (b) tube with static pressure holes.*

Chapter 3   Principles of Momentum Transfer and Applications

where v is the velocity v_1 in the tube at point 1 in m/s, p_2 is the stagnation pressure, ρ is the density of the flowing fluid at the static pressure p_1, and C_p is a dimensionless coefficient to take into account deviations from Eq. (3.2-1) that generally varies between about 0.98 and 1.0. For accurate use, the coefficient should be determined by calibration of the pitot tube. This equation applies to incompressible fluids but can be used to approximate the flow of gases at moderate velocities and pressure changes of about 10% or less of the total pressure. For gases the pressure change is often quite low and, hence, accurate measurement of velocities is difficult.

The value of the pressure drop $p_2 - p_1$ or Δp in Pa is related to Δh, the reading on the manometer, by Eq. (2.2-14) as follows:

$$\Delta p = \Delta h(\rho_A - \rho)g \tag{3.2-3}$$

where ρ_A is the density of the fluid in the manometer in kg/m^3 and Δh is the manometer reading in m. In Fig. 3.2-1b, a more compact design is shown with concentric tubes. In the outer tube, static pressure holes are parallel to the direction of flow. Further details are given elsewhere (P1).

Since the pitot tube measures velocity at only one point in the flow, several methods can be used to obtain the average velocity in the pipe. In the first method the velocity is measured at the exact center of the tube to obtain v_{max}. Then by using Fig. 2.10-2, the v_{av} can be obtained. Care should be taken to have the pitot tube at least 100 diameters downstream from any pipe obstruction. In the second method, readings are taken at several known positions in the pipe cross section and then, using Eq. (2.6-17), a graphical or numerical integration is performed to obtain v_{av}.

EXAMPLE 3.2-1. Flow Measurement Using a Pitot Tube

A pitot tube similar to Fig. 3.2-1a is used to measure the airflow in a circular duct 600 mm in diameter. The flowing air temperature is 65.6°C. The pitot tube is placed at the center of the duct and the reading Δh on the manometer is 10.7 mm of water. A static-pressure measurement obtained at the pitot tube position is 205 mm of water above atmospheric. The pitot-tube coefficient $C_p = 0.98$.

(a) Calculate the velocity at the center and the average velocity.
(b) Calculate the volumetric flow rate of the flowing air in the duct.

Solution: For part (a), the properties of air at 65.6°C. from Appendix A.3 are $\mu = 2.03 \times 10^{-5}$ Pa$\cdot$s, $\rho = 1.043$ kg/m^3 (at 101.325 kPa). To calculate the absolute static pressure, the manometer reading $\Delta h = 0.205$ m of water indicates the pressure above 1 atm abs. Using Eq. (2.2-14), the water density as 1000 kg/m^3, and assuming 1.043 kg/m^3 as the air density,

$$\Delta p = 0.205(1000 - 1.043)9.80665 = 2008 \text{ Pa}$$

Then the absolute static pressure $p_1 = 1.01325 \times 10^5 + 0.02008 \times 10^5 = 1.0333 \times 10^5$ Pa. The correct air density in the flowing air is $(1.0333 \times 10^5/1.01325 \times 10^5)(1.043) = 1.063$ kg/m^3. This correct value, when used instead of 1.043, would have a negligible effect on the recalculation of p_1.

To calculate Δp for the pitot tube, Eq. (3.2-3) is used:

$$\Delta p = \Delta h(\rho_A - \rho)g = \frac{10.7}{1000}(1000 - 1.063)(9.80665) = 104.8 \text{ Pa}$$

Using Eq. (3.2-2), the maximum velocity at the center is

$$v = 0.98 \sqrt{\frac{2(104.8)}{1.063}} = 13.76 \text{ m/s}$$

The Reynolds number, using the maximum velocity, is

$$N_{\text{Re}} = \frac{D v_{\max}\rho}{\mu} = \frac{0.600(13.76)(1.063)}{2.03 \times 10^{-5}} = 4.323 \times 10^5$$

From Fig. 2.10-2, $v_{\text{av}}/v_{\max} = 0.85$. Then, $v_{\text{av}} = 0.85(13.76) = 11.70$ m/s.

To calculate the flow rate for part (b), the cross-sectional area of the duct, $A = (\pi/4)(0.600)^2 = 0.2827 \text{ m}^2$. The flow rate = $0.2827(11.70) = 3.308 \text{ m}^3/\text{s}$.

3.2B Venturi Meter

A *venturi meter,* shown in Fig. 3.2-2, is usually inserted directly into a pipeline. A manometer or other device is connected to the two pressure taps shown and measures the pressure difference $p_1 - p_2$ between points 1 and 2. The average velocity at point 1 where the diameter is D_1 m is v_1 m/s, and at point 2 or the throat the velocity is v_2 and the diameter D_2. Since the narrowing down from D_1 to D_2 and the expansion from D_2 back to D_1 is gradual, little frictional loss due to contraction and expansion is incurred.

To derive the equation for the venturi meter, friction is neglected and the pipe is assumed horizontal. Assuming turbulent flow and writing the mechanical-energy-balance equation (2.7-28) between points 1 and 2 for an incompressible fluid,

$$\frac{v_1^2}{2} + \frac{p_1}{\rho} = \frac{v_2^2}{2} + \frac{p_2}{\rho} \tag{3.2-4}$$

The continuity equation for constant p is

$$v_1 \frac{\pi D_1^2}{4} = v_2 \frac{\pi D_2^2}{4} \tag{3.2-5}$$

Combining Eqs. (3.2-4) and (3.2-5) and eliminating v_1,

$$v_2 = \frac{1}{\sqrt{1 - (D_2/D_1)^4}} \sqrt{\frac{2(p_1 - p_2)}{\rho}} \tag{3.2-6}$$

To account for the small friction loss, an experimental coefficient C_v is introduced to give

$$v_2 = \frac{C_v}{\sqrt{1 - (D_2/D_1)^4}} \sqrt{\frac{2(p_1 - p_2)}{\rho}} \quad \text{(SI)}$$

$$v_2 = \frac{C_v}{\sqrt{1 - (D_2/D_1)^4}} \sqrt{\frac{2g_c(p_1 - p_2)}{\rho}} \quad \text{(English)} \tag{3.2-7}$$

FIGURE 3.2-2. *Venturi flow meter.*

FIGURE 3.2-3. *Expansion factor for air in venturi, flow nozzle, and orifice. [Calculated from equations and data in references (A2, M2, S3).]*

This holds for liquids and very small pressure drops in gases of less than 1%. For many meters and a Reynolds number $>10^4$ at point 1, C_v is about 0.98 for pipe diameters below 0.2 m and 0.99 for larger sizes. However, these coefficients can vary, and individual calibration is recommended if the manufacturer's calibration is not available.

To calculate the volumetric flow rate, the velocity v_2 is multiplied by the area A_2:

$$\text{flow rate} = v_2 \frac{\pi D_2^2}{4} \quad \text{m}^3/\text{s} \tag{3.2-8}$$

For the measurement of compressible flow of gases, the adiabatic expansion from p_1 to p_2 pressure must be allowed for in Eq. (3.2-7). A similar equation and the same coefficient C_v are used along with the dimensionless expansion correction factor Y (shown in Fig. 3.2-3 for air) as follows:

$$m = \frac{C_v A_2 Y}{\sqrt{1 - (D_2/D_1)^4}} \sqrt{2(p_1 - p_2)\rho_1} \tag{3.2-9}$$

where m is flow rate in kg/s, ρ_1 is density of the fluid upstream at point 1 in kg/m³, and A_2 is cross-sectional area at point 2 in m².

The pressure difference $p_1 - p_2$ occurs because the velocity is increased from v_1 to v_2. However, farther down the tube the velocity returns to its original value of v_1 for liquids. Because of frictional losses, some of the difference $p_1 - p_2$ is not fully recovered downstream to the original p_1. In a properly designed venturi meter, the permanent loss is about 10% of the differential $p_1 - p_2$, and this represents power loss. A venturi meter is often used to measure flows in large lines, such as city water systems.

3.2C   Orifice Meter

For ordinary installations in a process plant the venturi meter has several disadvantages. It occupies a lot of space and is expensive. Also, the throat diameter is fixed, so that if the flow-rate range is changed considerably, inaccurate pressure differences may result. The *orifice meter* overcomes these objections but at the price of a much larger permanent head or power loss.

FIGURE 3.2-4. *Orifice flow meter.*

A typical sharp-edged orifice is shown in Fig. 3.2-4. A machined and drilled plate having a hole of diameter D_0 is mounted between two flanges in a pipe of diameter D_1. Pressure taps at points 1 upstream and 2 downstream measure $p_1 - p_2$. The exact positions of the two taps are somewhat arbitrary: in one type of meter the taps are installed about 1 pipe diameter upstream and 0.3 to 0.8 pipe diameter downstream. The fluid stream, once past the orifice plate, forms a vena contracta or free-flowing jet.

The equation for the orifice is similar to Eq. (3.2-7):

$$v_0 = \frac{C_0}{\sqrt{1 - (D_0/D_1)^4}} \sqrt{\frac{2(p_1 - p_2)}{\rho}} \tag{3.2-10}$$

where v_0 is the velocity in the orifice in m/s, D_0 is the orifice diameter in m, and C_0 is the dimensionless orifice coefficient. The orifice coefficient C_0 is always determined experimentally. If the N_{Re} at the orifice is above 20000 and D_0/D_1 is less than about 0.5, the value of C_0 is approximately constant and has the value 0.61, which is adequate for design for liquids or gases (M2, P1). Below 20000 the coefficient rises sharply and then drops, and a correlation for C_0 is given elsewhere (P1).

As in the case of the venturi, for the measurement of compressible flow of gases in an orifice, a correction factor Y given in Fig. 3.2-3 for air is used as follows:

$$m = \frac{C_0 A_0 Y}{\sqrt{1 - (D_0/D_1)^4}} \sqrt{2(p_1 - p_2)\rho_1} \tag{3.2-11}$$

where m is flow rate in kg/s, ρ_1 is upstream density in kg/m^3, and A_0 is the cross-sectional area of the orifice. For liquids, Y is 1.0.

The permanent pressure loss is much higher than for a venturi because of the eddies formed when the jet expands below the vena contracta. This loss depends on D_0/D_1 and is as follows:

$$(p_1 - p_4) = (1 - \beta^2)(p_1 - p_2) \tag{3.2-12}$$

where $\beta = D_0/D_1$ (P1) and p_4 is the fully recovered pressure 4–8 pipe diameters downstream. For $\beta = \frac{1}{2}$, this power loss is 75% of $p_1 - p_2$.

EXAMPLE 3.2-2. *Metering Oil Flow by an Orifice*

A sharp-edged orifice having a diameter of 0.0566 m is installed in a 0.1541-m pipe through which oil having a density of 878 kg/m^3 and a viscosity of 4.1 cp is

Chapter 3   Principles of Momentum Transfer and Applications

flowing. The measured pressure difference across the orifice is 93.2 kN/m^2. Calculate the volumetric flow rate in m^3/s. Assume that $C_0 = 0.61$.

Solution:

$$p_1 - p_2 = 93.2 \text{ kN/m}^2 = 9.32 \times 10^4 \text{ N/m}^2$$

$$D_1 = 0.1541 \text{ m} \qquad D_0 = 0.0566 \text{ m} \qquad \frac{D_0}{D_1} = \frac{0.0566}{0.1541} = 0.368$$

Substituting into Eq. (3.2-10),

$$v_0 = \frac{C_0}{\sqrt{1 - (D_0/D_1)^4}}\sqrt{\frac{2(p_1 - p_2)}{\rho}}$$

$$= \frac{0.61}{\sqrt{1 - (0.368)^4}}\sqrt{\frac{2(9.32 \times 10^4)}{878}}$$

$$v_0 = 8.97 \text{ m/s}$$

$$\text{volumetric flow rate} = v_0 \frac{\pi D_0^2}{4} = (8.97)\frac{(\pi)(0.0566)^2}{4}$$

$$= 0.02257 \text{ m}^3/\text{s} \ (0.797 \text{ ft}^3/\text{s})$$

The N_{Re} is calculated see if it is greater than 2×10^4 for $C_0 = 0.61$:

$$\mu = 4.1 \times 1 \times 10^{-3} = 4.1 \times 10^{-3} \text{ kg/m} \cdot \text{s} = 4.1 \times 10^{-3} \text{ Pa} \cdot \text{s}$$

$$N_{\text{Re}} = \frac{D_0 v_0 \rho}{\mu} = \frac{0.0566(8.97)(878)}{4.1 \times 10^{-3}} = 1.087 \times 10^5$$

Hence, the Reynolds number is above 2×10^4.

3.2D Flow-Nozzle Meter

A typical *flow nozzle* is shown in Fig. 3.2-5. It is essentially a short cylinder with the approach being elliptical in shape. This meter has characteristics similar to those of the venturi meter but is shorter and much less expensive. The length of the straight portion of the throat is about one-half the diameter of the throat, D_2. The upstream pressure tap p_1 is 1 pipe diame-

FIGURE 3.2-5. *Flow-nozzle meter.*

ter from the inlet-nozzle face, and the downstream tap p_2 is $\frac{1}{2}$ pipe diameter from the inlet-nozzle face.

The equation for flow for liquids is the same as Eq. (3.2-7) for the venturi, with the coefficient C_n for the flow nozzle replacing C_v for the venturi. Also, the equation for compressible flow of gases for the flow nozzle is the same as Eq. (3.2-9) for the venturi, with the coefficient C_n. The expansion factor Y is the same for the flow nozzle and the venturi.

For the flow nozzle the coefficient C_n ranges from 0.95 at a pipe Reynolds number of 10^4, 0.98 at 10^5, and 0.99 at 10^6 or above (P1, S3). The permanent pressure loss $(p_1 - p_4)$ is as follows, where p_4 is the final, fully recovered downstream pressure:

$$(p_1 - p_4) = \frac{1 - \beta^2}{1 + \beta^2}(p_1 - p_2) \tag{3.2-13}$$

where $\beta = D_2/D_1$. This loss is greater than that for venturi meters and less than that for orifice meters. For $\beta = \frac{1}{2}$, this power loss is 60% of $p_1 - p_2$.

3.2E Variable-Area Flow Meters (Rotameters)

In Fig. 3.2-6 a variable-area flow meter is shown. The fluid enters at the bottom of the tapered glass tube, flows through the annular area around the tube, and exits at the top. The float remains stationary. The differential head or pressure drop is held constant. At a higher flow rate the float rises and the annular area increases to keep a constant pressure drop. The height of rise in the tube is calibrated with the flow rate, and the relation between the meter reading and the flow rate is approximately linear.

For a given float of density p_f and a fluid density ρ_A, the mass flow rate m_A is given by

$$m_A = q_A \rho_A = K\sqrt{\frac{(\rho_f - \rho_A)\rho_A}{\rho_f}} \tag{3.2-14}$$

where q_A, volumetric flow rate, is the reading on the rotameter, and K is a constant which is determined experimentally. If a fluid ρ_B is used instead of ρ_A, at the same height or reading of

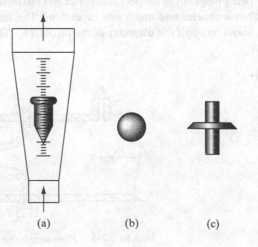

FIGURE 3.2-6. *Rotameter: (a) flow diagram with glass tube, (b) spherical float, (c) viscosity-insensitive float.*

(a)   (b)   (c)

q_A on the rotameter and assuming K does not vary appreciably, the following approximation can be used:

$$\frac{m_A}{m_B} = \frac{q_A \rho_A}{q_B \rho_B} = \sqrt{\frac{(\rho_f - \rho_A)\rho_A}{(\rho_f - \rho_B)\rho_B}} \tag{3.2-15}$$

For gases where $\rho_f \gg \rho_A$ and ρ_B, $q_B = q_A\sqrt{\rho_A/\rho_B}$. Note that the reading on the rotameter is taken at the highest and widest point of the float.

3.2F Other Types of Flow Meters

Many other types of flow meters are available; the more important ones are discussed briefly as follows:

1. Turbine- and paddle-wheel meters. A turbine wheel or a paddle wheel is placed inside a pipe, and the rotary speed depends on the flow rate of the fluid. Residential and industrial gas and water meters are often of the rotary wheel type.

2. Thermal-gas mass flow meters. Gas flowing in a tube is divided into a constant ratio because of laminar flow into a main stream and a small stream in a sensor tube. A small but constant amount of heat is added to the sensor tube flow. By measuring the temperature rise, the output temperature rise can be related to the gas mass flow rate. These meters are mass flow meters and are unaffected by temperature and pressure.

3. Magnetic flow meters. A magnetic field is generated across the conductive fluid flowing in a pipe. Using Faraday's law of electromagnetic inductance, the induced voltage is directly proportional to the flow velocity (D3). The meter is insensitive to changes in density and viscosity. The meter cannot be used with most hydrocarbons because of their low conductivity.

4. Coriolis mass flow meter. This meter is insensitive to operating conditions of viscosity, density, type of fluid, and slurries. Fluid from the main flow enters two U-tube side channels (D3). The fluid induces a Coriolis force according to Newton's second law. The tubes then twist slightly, and the measured twist angle is proportional to the mass flow rate.

5. Vortex-shedding flow meter. When a fluid flows past a blunt object, the fluid forms vortices or eddies (D3). The vortices are counted and the signal is proportional to the flow rate.

3.2G Flow in Open Channels and Weirs

In many instances in process engineering and in agriculture, liquids are flowing in open channels rather than closed conduits. To measure the flow rates, weir devices are often used. A *weir* is a dam over which the liquid flows. The two main types of weirs are the rectangular weir and the triangular weir shown in Fig. 3.2-7. The liquid flows over the weir, and the height h_0 (weir head) in m is measured above the flat base or the notch as shown. This head should be measured at a distance of about $3h_0$ m upstream of the weir by a level or float gage.

The equation for the volumetric flow rate q in m^3/s for a rectangular weir is given by

$$q = 0.415(L - 0.2h_0)h_0^{1.5}\sqrt{2g} \tag{3.2-16}$$

FIGURE 3.2-7. *Types of weirs: (a) rectangular, (b) triangular.*

where L = crest length in m, g = 9.80665 m/s^2, and h_0 = weir head in m. This is called the *modified Francis weir formula* and it agrees with experimental values within 3% if $L > 2h_0$, velocity upstream < 0.6 m/s, $h_0 > 0.09$ m, and the height of the crest above the bottom of the channel > $3h_0$. In English units L and h are in ft, q in ft^3/s, and g = 32.174 ft/s^2.

For the triangular notch weir,

$$q = \frac{0.31 h_0^{2.5}}{\tan \phi} \sqrt{2g} \qquad (3.2\text{-}17)$$

Both Eqs. (3.2-16) and (3.2-17) apply only to water. For other liquids, see data given elsewhere (P1).

3.3 PUMPS AND GAS-MOVING EQUIPMENT

3.3A Introduction

In order to make a fluid flow from one point to another in a closed conduit or pipe, it is necessary to have a driving force. Sometimes this force is supplied by gravity, where differences in elevation occur. Usually, the energy or driving force is supplied by a mechanical device such as a pump or blower, which increases the mechanical energy of the fluid. This energy may be used to increase the velocity (move the fluid), the pressure, or the elevation of the fluid, as seen in the mechanical-energy-balance equation (2.7-28), which relates v, p, ρ, and work. The most common methods of adding energy are by positive displacement or centrifugal action.

Generally, the word "pump" designates a machine or device for moving an incompressible liquid. Fans, blowers, and compressors are devices for moving gas (usually air). Fans discharge large volumes of gas at low pressures on the order of several hundred mm of water. Blowers and compressors discharge gases at higher pressures. In pumps and fans the density of the fluid does not change appreciably, and incompressible flow can be assumed. Compressible flow theory is used for blowers and compressors.

3.3B Pumps

1. Power and work required. Using the total mechanical-energy-balance equation (2.7-28) on a pump and piping system, the actual or theoretical mechanical energy W_S J/kg added to the fluid by the pump can be calculated. Example 2.7-5 shows such a case. If η is the fractional efficiency and W_p the shaft work delivered to the pump, Eq. (2.7-30) gives

$$W_p = -\frac{W_S}{\eta} \qquad (3.3\text{-}1)$$

The actual or brake power of a pump is as follows:

$$\text{brake kW} = \frac{W_p m}{1000} = -\frac{W_S m}{\eta \times 1000} \quad \text{(SI)}$$

$$\text{brake hp} = \frac{W_p m}{550} = -\frac{W_S m}{\eta \times 550} \quad \text{(English)}$$

(3.3-2)

where W_p is J/kg, m is the flow rate in kg/s, and 1000 is the conversion factor W/kW. In English units, W_S is in ft · lb$_f$/lb$_m$ and m in lb$_m$/s. The theoretical or fluid power is

$$\text{theoretical power} = (\text{brake kW})(\eta)$$

(3.3-3)

The mechanical energy W_S in J/kg added to the fluid is often expressed as the developed head H of the pump in m of fluid being pumped, where

$$-W_S = Hg \quad \text{(SI)}$$

$$-W_S = H\frac{g}{g_c} \quad \text{(English)}$$

(3.3-4)

To calculate the power of a fan where the pressure difference is on the order of a few hundred mm of water, a linear average density of the gas between the inlet and outlet of the fan is used to calculate W_S and brake kW or horsepower.

2. *Electric motor efficiency.* Since most pumps are driven by electric motors, the efficiency of the electric motor must be taken into account to determine the total electric power to the motor. Typical efficiencies η_e of electric motors are as follows: 77% for $\frac{1}{2}$-kW motors, 82% for 2 kW, 85% for 5 kW, 88% for 20 kW, 90% for 50 kW, 91% for 100 kW, and 93% for 500 kW and larger. Hence, the total electric power input equals the brake power divided by the electric motor drive efficiency η_e:

$$\text{electric power input (kW)} = \frac{\text{brake kW}}{\eta_e} = \frac{-W_S m}{\eta \eta_e \cdot 1000}$$

(3.3-5)

3. *Suction lift of pumps* (NPSH). The power calculated by Eq. (3.3-4) depends on the differences in pressures and not on the actual pressures being above or below atmospheric pressure. However, the lower limit of the absolute pressure in the suction (inlet) line to the pump is fixed by the vapor pressure of the liquid at the temperature of the liquid in the suction line. If the pressure on the liquid in the suction line drops below the vapor pressure, some of the liquid flashes into vapor (*cavitation*). Then no liquid can be drawn into the pump, and vibration can occur.

To avoid flashes of vapor or cavitation, the pressure at the inlet of the pump must be greater than this vapor pressure and exceed it by a value termed the *net positive suction head required,* or (NPSH)$_R$. Pump manufacturers measure these values experimentally and include them with the pumps furnished.

For water below 100°C at 1750 rpm and centrifugal pumps, typical values of (NPSH)$_R$ are as follows (P4): For pressures 3500 kPa (500 psig) or below: up to 200 gpm, 1.5 m (5 ft); 500 gpm, 2.1 m (7 ft); 1000 gpm, 3 m (10 ft); 2000 gpm, 5.5 m (18 ft). At pressures of 7000 kPa (1000 psig) the values are doubled at 200 gpm or less and at 2000 gpm increased by 20%. At an rpm of 3550, the (NPSH)$_R$ increases by about a factor of 2.2.

FIGURE 3.3-1. *Diagram for (NPSH)$_A$ available in a pumping system.*

To calculate the net positive suction head that will be available (NPSH)$_A$ at the pump suction for the system shown in Fig. 3.3-1, Eq. (3.3-6) can be used:

$$g(\text{NPSH})_A = \frac{p_1}{\rho} - \frac{p_{vp}}{\rho} + gz_1 - \frac{v^2}{2} - \sum F \qquad \text{(SI)}$$

$$\text{(NPSH)}_A = \frac{p_1}{\rho} - \frac{p_{vp}}{\rho} + \frac{g}{g_c}z_1 - \frac{v^2}{2g_c} - \sum F \qquad \text{(English)}$$

(3.3-6)

where (NPSH)$_A$ is in m (ft), ρ is density of liquid in kg/m^3 (lb$_m$/ft^3), p_1 is pressure above liquid surface in N/m^2 (lb$_f$/ft^2), p_{vp} is vapor pressure of fluid at the given temperature in N/m^2 (lb$_f$/ft^2), z_1 is height of open surface of liquid above pump centerline in m (ft), $\sum F$ is friction loss in suction line to pump from Eq. (2.10-18) in J/kg (ft lb$_f$/lb$_m$), and $v^2/2$ is velocity head in J/kg ($v^2/2g_c$ is ft lb$_f$/lb$_m$). Note that in Eq. (3.3-6) for SI units, the (NPSH)$_A$ in m is multiplied by g to give J/kg.

For cold water and the case where all the terms in Eq. (3.3-6) are small except p_1, at atmospheric pressure the (NPSH)$_A$ is 10.3 m (33.9 ft). However, a practical limit is about 7.5 m (24.6 ft). The available NPSH for a given pump should be at least 1 m (3 ft) more than that required by the manufacturer.

EXAMPLE 3.3-1. (NPSH)$_A$ *Available for Pump*

Water at 50°C is in an open tank at atmospheric pressure. The pump is 3.0 m above the open tank level. The velocity in the pipe is 0.9 m/s. The friction head loss in the pipe has been calculated as 1.0 m. The required (NPSH)$_R$ for this pump is 2.0 m. Calculate the available (NPSH)$_A$.

Solution: From Appendix A.2-3, $\rho = 988.07$ kg/m^3. Also, the vapor pressure $p_{vp} = 12.349$ kPa from A.2-9 and $p_1 = 1.01325 \times 10^5$ Pa. Substituting into Eq. (3.3-6) and noting that z_1 is negative and that the friction loss head of 1.0 m is multiplied by g,

$$9.80665(\text{NPSH})_A = \frac{1.01325 \times 10^5}{988.07} - \frac{12.349 \times 10^3}{988.07}$$

$$-9.80665(3.0) - \frac{0.9^2}{2} - 9.80665(1.0)$$

Solving, (NPSH)$_A$ = 5.14 m

Hence, the available (NPSH)$_A$ of 5.14 m is sufficiently greater than that required of 2.0 m.

FIGURE 3.3-2. *Simple centrifugal pump.*

4. Centrifugal pumps.   Process industries commonly use centrifugal pumps. They are available in sizes of about 0.004 to 380 m³/min (1 to 100000 gal/min) and for discharge pressures from a few m of head to 5000 kPa or so. A centrifugal pump in its simplest form consists of an impeller rotating inside a casing. Figure 3.3-2 shows a schematic diagram of a simple centrifugal pump.

The liquid enters the pump axially at point 1 in the suction line and then enters the rotating eye of the impeller, where it spreads out radially. On spreading radially it enters the channels between the vanes at point 2 and flows through these channels to point 3 at the periphery of the impeller. From here it is collected in the volute chamber 4 and flows out the pump discharge at 5. The rotation of the impeller imparts a high-velocity head to the fluid, which is changed to a pressure head as the liquid passes into the volute chamber and out the discharge. Some pumps are also made as two-stage or even multistage pumps.

Many complicating factors determine the actual efficiency and performance characteristics of a pump. Hence, the actual experimental performance of the pump is usually employed. The performance is usually expressed by the pump manufacturer in terms of curves called *characteristic curves*, which are usually for water. The head H in m produced will be the same for any liquid of the same viscosity. The pressure produced, $p = H\rho g$, will be in proportion to the density. Viscosities of less than 0.05 Pa·s (50 cp) have little effect on the head produced. The brake kW varies directly as the density.

Pump efficiencies typical of centrifugal pumps at rated capacities are as follows: 50% for 0.075 m³/min (20 gal/min), 62% for 0.19 m³/min (50 gal/min), 68% for 0.38 m³/min (100 gal/min), 75% for 0.76 m³/min (200 gal/min), 82% for 1.89 m³/min (500 gal/min), and 85% for 3.8 m³/min (1000 gal/min).

As rough approximations, the following relationships, called *affinity laws,* can be used for a given pump. The *capacity* q_1 in m³/s is directly proportional to the rpm N_1 or

$$\frac{q_1}{q_2} = \frac{N_1}{N_2} \tag{3.3-7}$$

The *head* H_1 is proportional to q_1^2, or

$$\frac{H_1}{H_2} = \frac{q_1^2}{q_2^2} = \frac{N_1^2}{N_2^2} \tag{3.3-8}$$

The *power consumed* W_1 is proportional to the product of H_1q_1, or

$$\frac{W_1}{W_2} = \frac{H_1 q_1}{H_2 q_2} = \frac{N_1^3}{N_2^3} \qquad (3.3\text{-}9)$$

A given pump can be modified when needed for a different capacity by changing the impeller size. Then the *affinity laws* for a constant-rpm N are as follows: The capacity q is proportional to the diameter D, the head H is proportional to D^2, and the brake horsepower W is proportional to D^3.

In most pumps, the speed is generally not varied. Characteristic curves for a typical single-stage centrifugal pump operating at a constant speed are given in Fig. 3.3-3 Most pumps are usually rated on the basis of head and capacity at the point of peak efficiency. The efficiency reaches a peak at about 50 gal/min flow rate. As the discharge rate in gal/min increases, the developed head drops. The brake hp increases, as expected, with flow rate.

EXAMPLE 3.3-2. Calculation of Brake Horsepower of a Pump
In order to see how the brake-hp curve is determined, calculate the brake hp at 40 gal/min flow rate for the pump in Fig. 3.3-3.

Solution: At 40 gal/min, the efficiency η from the curve is about 60% and the head H is 38.5 ft. A flow rate of 40 gal/min of water with a density of 62.4 lb mass/ft^3 is

$$m = \left(\frac{40 \text{ gal/min}}{60 \text{ s/min}}\right)\left(\frac{1 \text{ ft}^3}{7.481 \text{ gal}}\right)\left(62.4 \frac{\text{lb}_m}{\text{ft}^3}\right) = 5.56 \frac{\text{lb}_m}{\text{s}}$$

The work W_S is as follows, from Eq. (3.3-4):

$$W_S = -H\frac{g}{g_c} = -38.5 \frac{\text{ft} \cdot \text{lb}_f}{\text{lb}_m}$$

FIGURE 3.3-3. *Characteristic curves for a single-stage centrifugal pump with water. (From W. L. Badger and J. T. Banchero, Introduction to Chemical Engineering. New York: McGraw-Hill Book Company, 1955. With permission.)*

The brake hp from Eq. (3.3-2) is

$$\text{brake hp} = \frac{-W_S m}{\eta \cdot 550} = \frac{38.5(5.56)}{0.60(550)} = 0.65 \text{ hp } (0.48 \text{ kW})$$

This value agrees with the value on the curve in Fig. 3.3-3.

5. Positive-displacement pumps. In this class of pumps, a definite volume of liquid is drawn into a chamber and then forced out of the chamber at a higher pressure. There are two main types of positive-displacement pumps. In the *reciprocating pump* the chamber is a stationary cylinder, and liquid is drawn into the cylinder by withdrawal of a piston in the cylinder. Then the liquid is forced out by the piston on the return stroke. In the *rotary pump* the chamber moves from inlet to discharge and back again. In a gear rotary pump two intermeshing gears rotate, and liquid is trapped in the spaces between the teeth and forced out the discharge.

Reciprocating and rotary pumps can be used to very high pressures, whereas centrifugal pumps are limited in their head and are used for lower pressures. Centrifugal pumps deliver liquid at uniform pressure without shocks or pulsations and can handle liquids with large amounts of suspended solids. In general, in chemical and biological processing plants, centrifugal pumps are primarily used.

Equations (3.3-1) through (3.3-5) hold for calculation of the power of positive-displacement pumps. At a constant speed, the flow capacity will remain constant with different liquids. In general, the discharge rate will be directly dependent upon the speed. The power increases directly as the head, and the discharge rate remains nearly constant as the head increases.

Pump efficiencies η of reciprocating pumps used to calculate brake horsepower are as follows: 55% at 2.2 kW (3 hp), 70% at 7.5 kW (10 hp), 77% at 14.9 kW (20 hp), 85% at 37 kW (50 hp), and 90% at 373 kW (500 hp).

3.3C Gas-Moving Machinery

Gas-moving machinery comprises mechanical devices used for compressing and moving gases. They are often classified or considered from the standpoint of the pressure heads produced and include fans for low pressures, blowers for intermediate pressures, and compressors for high pressures.

1. Fans. The commonest method for moving small volumes of gas at low pressures is by means of a *fan*. Large fans are usually centrifugal and their operating principle is similar to that of centrifugal pumps. The discharge heads are low, from about 0.1 m to 1.5 m H_2O. However, in some cases much of the added energy of the fan is converted to velocity energy and a small amount to pressure head.

In a centrifugal fan, the centrifugal force produced by the rotor causes a compression of the gas, called the *static pressure head*. Also, since the velocity of the gas is increased, a velocity head is produced. Both the static-pressure-head increase and velocity-head increase must be included in estimating efficiency and power. Operating efficiencies are in the range 40–70%. The operating pressure of a fan is generally given as inches of water gage and is the sum of the velocity head and the static pressure of the gas leaving the fan. Incompressible flow theory can be used to calculate the power of fans.

When the rpm or speed of centrifugal fans varies, the performance equations are similar to Eqs. (3.3-7)–(3.3-9) for centrifugal pumps.

EXAMPLE 3.3-3. Brake-kW Power of a Centrifugal Fan

It is desired to use 28.32 m^3/min of air (metered at a pressure of 101.3 kPa and 294.1 K) in a process. This amount of air, which is at rest, enters the fan suction at a pressure of 741.7 mm Hg and a temperature of 366.3 K and is discharged at a pressure of 769.6 mm Hg and a velocity of 45.7 m/s. A centrifugal fan having a fan efficiency of 60% is to be used. Calculate the brake-kW power needed.

Solution: Incompressible flow can be assumed, since the pressure drop is only (27.9/741.7)100, or 3.8% of the upstream pressure. The average density of the flowing gas can be used in the mechanical-energy-balance equation.

The density at the suction, point 1, is

$$\rho_1 = \left(28.97 \frac{\text{kg air}}{\text{kg mol}}\right)\left(\frac{1 \text{ kg mol}}{22.414 \text{ m}^3}\right)\left(\frac{273.2}{366.3}\right)\left(\frac{741.7}{760}\right)$$

$$= 0.940 \text{ kg/m}^3$$

(The molecular weight of 28.97 for air, the volume of 22.414 m^3/kg mol at 101.3 kPa, and 273.2 K were obtained from Appendix A.1.) The density at the discharge, point 2, is

$$\rho_2 = (0.940)\frac{769.6}{741.7} = 0.975 \text{ kg/m}^3$$

The average density of the gas is

$$\rho_{av} = \frac{\rho_1 + \rho_2}{2} = \frac{0.940 + 0.975}{2} = 0.958 \text{ kg/m}^3$$

The mass flow rate of the gas is

$$m = \left(28.32 \frac{\text{m}^3}{\text{min}}\right)\left(\frac{1 \text{ min}}{60 \text{ s}}\right)\left(\frac{1 \text{ kg mol}}{22.414 \text{ m}^3}\right)\left(\frac{273.2}{294.1}\right)\left(28.97 \frac{\text{kg}}{\text{kg mol}}\right)$$

$$= 0.5663 \text{ kg/s}$$

The developed pressure head is

$$\frac{p_2 - p_1}{\rho_{av}} = \frac{(769.6 - 741.7) \text{ mm Hg}}{760 \text{ mm/atm}}\left(1.01325 \times 10^5 \frac{\text{N/m}^2}{\text{atm}}\right)\left(\frac{1}{0.958 \text{ kg/m}^3}\right)$$

$$= 3883 \text{ J/kg}$$

The developed velocity head for $v_1 = 0$ is

$$\frac{v_2^2}{2} = \frac{(45.7)^2}{2} = 1044 \text{ J/kg}$$

Writing the mechanical-energy-balance equation (2.7-28),

$$z_1 g + \frac{v_1^2}{2} + \frac{p_1}{\rho} - W_S = z_2 g + \frac{v_2^2}{2} + \frac{p_2}{\rho} + \sum F$$

Setting $z_1 = 0$, $z_2 = 0$, $v_1 = 0$, and $\Sigma F = 0$, and solving for W_S,

$$-W_S = \frac{p_2 - p_1}{\rho_{av}} + \frac{v_2^2}{2} = 3883 + 1044 = 4927 \text{ J/kg}$$

Substituting into Eq. (3.3-2),

$$\text{brake kW} = \frac{-W_S m}{\eta \cdot 1000} = \frac{4927(0.5663)}{0.60(1000)} = 4.65 \text{ kW (6.23 hp)}$$

2. Blowers and compressors. For handling gas volumes at higher pressure rises than fans, several distinct types of equipment are used. *Turboblowers* or *centrifugal compressors* are widely used to move large volumes of gas for pressure rises from about 5 kPa to several thousand kPa. The principles of operation for a turboblower are the same as for a centrifugal pump. The turboblower resembles the centrifugal pump in appearance, the main difference being that the gas in the blower is compressible. The head of the turboblower, as in a centrifugal pump, is independent of the fluid handled. Multistage turboblowers are often used to go to the higher pressures.

Rotary blowers and compressors are machines of the positive-displacement type and are essentially constant-volume flow-rate machines with variable discharge pressure. Changing the speed will change the volume flow rate. Details of construction of the various types (P1) vary considerably, and pressures up to about 1000 kPa can be obtained, depending on the type.

Reciprocating compressers which are of the positive displacement type using pistons are available for higher pressures. Multistage machines are also available for pressures up to 10 000 kPa or more.

3.3D Equations for Compression of Gases

In blowers and compressors, pressure changes are large and compressible flow occurs. Since the density changes markedly, the mechanical-energy-balance equation must be written in differential form and then integrated to obtain the work of compression. In compression of gases the static-head terms, velocity-head terms, and friction terms are dropped and only the work term dW and the dp/ρ term remain in the differential form of the mechanical-energy equation; or,

$$dW = \frac{dp}{\rho} \tag{3.3-10}$$

Integration between the suction pressure p_1 and discharge pressure p_2 gives the work of compression:

$$W = \int_{p_1}^{p_2} \frac{dp}{\rho} \tag{3.3-11}$$

1. Isothermal compression. To integrate Eq. (3.3-11) for a perfect gas, either isothermal or adiabatic compression is assumed. For isothermal compression, where the gas is cooled on compression, p/ρ is a constant equal to RT/M, where $R = 8314.3$ J/kg mol $\cdot$ K in SI units and 1545.3 ft $\cdot$ lb$_f$/lb mol $\cdot$ °R in English units. Then,

$$\frac{p_1}{\rho_1} = \frac{p}{\rho} \tag{3.3-12}$$

Solving for ρ in Eq. (3.3-12) and substituting it in Eq. (3.3-11), the work for isothermal compression is

$$-W_S = \frac{p_1}{\rho_1} \int_{p_1}^{p_2} \frac{dp}{p} = \frac{p_1}{\rho_1} \ln \frac{p_2}{p_1} = \frac{2.3026 RT_1}{M} \log \frac{p_2}{p_1} \tag{3.3-13}$$

Also, $T_1 = T_2$, since the process is isothermal.

2. Adiabatic compression. For adiabatic compression, the fluid follows an isentropic path and

$$\frac{p_1}{p} = \left(\frac{\rho_1}{\rho}\right)^\gamma \tag{3.3-14}$$

where $\gamma = c_p/c_v$, the ratio of heat capacities. By combining Eqs. (3.3-11) and (3.3-14) and integrating,

$$-W_S = \frac{\gamma}{\gamma - 1} \frac{RT_1}{M} \left[\left(\frac{p_2}{p_1}\right)^{(\gamma-1)/\gamma} - 1\right] \tag{3.3-15}$$

The adiabatic temperatures are related by

$$\frac{T_2}{T_1} = \left(\frac{p_2}{p_1}\right)^{(\gamma-1)/\gamma} \tag{3.3-16}$$

To calculate the brake power when the efficiency is η,

$$\text{brake kW} = \frac{-W_S m}{(\eta)(1000)} \tag{3.3-17}$$

where m = kg gas/s and W_S = J/kg.

The values of γ are approximately 1.40 for air, 1.31 for methane, 1.29 for SO_2, 1.20 for ethane, and 1.40 for N_2 (P1). For a given compression ratio, the work for isothermal compression in Eq. (3.3-13) is less than the work for adiabatic compression in Eq. (3.3-15). Hence, cooling is sometimes used in compressors.

EXAMPLE 3.3-4 Compression of Methane
A single-stage compressor is to compress 7.56×10^{-3} kg mol/s of methane gas at 26.7°C and 137.9 kPa abs to 551.6 kPa abs.
    (a) Calculate the power required if the mechanical efficiency is 80% and the compression is adiabatic.
    (b) Repeat, but for isothermal compression.

Solution: For part (a), $p_1 = 137.9$ kPa, $p_2 = 551.6$ kPa, $M = 16.0$ kg mass/kg mol, and $T_1 = 273.2 + 26.7 = 299.9$ K. The mass flow rate per sec is

$$m = (7.56 \times 10^{-3} \text{ kg mol/s})(16.0 \text{ kg/kg mol}) = 0.121 \frac{\text{kg}}{\text{s}}$$

Substituting into Eq. (3.3-15) for $\gamma = 1.31$ for methane and $p_2/p_1 = 551.6/137.9 = 4.0/1$,

$$-W_S = \frac{\gamma}{\gamma - 1} \frac{RT_1}{M}\left[\left(\frac{p_2}{p_1}\right)^{(\gamma-1)/\gamma} - 1\right]$$

$$= \left(\frac{1.31}{1.31 - 1}\right) \frac{8314.3(299.9)}{16.0}\left[\left(\frac{4}{1}\right)^{(1.31-1)/1.31} - 1\right]$$

$$= 256\,300 \text{ J/kg}$$

Using Eq. (3.3-17),

$$\text{brake kW} = \frac{-W_S m}{\eta \cdot 1000} = \frac{(256\,300)0.121}{0.80(1000)} = 38.74 \text{ kW (52.0 hp)}$$

For part (b), using Eq. (3.3-13) for isothermal compression,

$$-W_S = \frac{2.3026 RT_1}{M} \log \frac{p_2}{p_1} = \frac{2.3026(8314.3)(299.9)}{16.0} \log \frac{4}{1}$$

$$= 216\,000 \text{ J/kg}$$

$$\text{brake kW} = \frac{-W_S m}{\eta \cdot 1000} = \frac{(216\,000)0.121}{0.80(1000)} = 32.67 \text{ kW (43.8 hp)}$$

Hence, isothermal compression uses 15.8% less power.

3. *Polytropic compression.* In large compressors neither isothermal nor adiabatic compression is achieved. This polytropic path is

$$\frac{p_1}{p} = \left(\frac{\rho_1}{\rho}\right)^n \tag{3.3-18}$$

For isothermal compression $n = 1.0$ and for adiabatic, $n = \gamma$. The value of n is found by measuring the pressure p_1 and density ρ_1 at the inlet and p_2 and ρ_2 at the discharge and substituting these values into Eq. (3.3-18).

4. *Multistage compression ratios.* Water cooling is used between each stage in multistage compressors to reduce the outlet temperature to near the inlet temperature for minimum power requirement. The compression ratios should be the same for each stage so that the total power is a minimum. This gives the same power in each stage. Hence, for n stages, the compression ratio (p_b/p_a) for each stage is

$$\frac{p_b}{p_a} = \left(\frac{p_n}{p_1}\right)^{1/n} \tag{3.3-19}$$

where p_1 is the inlet pressure and p_n the outlet pressure from n stages. For two stages, the compression ratio is $\sqrt{p_n/p_1}$.

3.4 AGITATION AND MIXING OF FLUIDS AND POWER REQUIREMENTS

3.4A Purposes of Agitation

In the chemical and other processing industries, many operations are dependent to a great extent on effective agitation and mixing of fluids. Generally, *agitation* refers to forcing a fluid by mechanical means to flow in a circulatory or other pattern inside a vessel. *Mixing* usually implies the taking of two or more separate phases, such as a fluid and a powdered solid or two fluids, and causing them to be randomly distributed through one another.

There are a number of purposes for agitating fluids, some of which are briefly summarized:

1. Blending of two miscible liquids, such as ethyl alcohol and water.
2. Dissolving solids in liquids, such as salt in water.
3. Dispersing a gas in a liquid as fine bubbles, such as oxygen from air in a suspension of microorganisms for fermentation or for the activated sludge process in waste treatment.
4. Suspending of fine solid particles in a liquid, as in the catalytic hydrogenation of a liquid, where solid catalyst particles and hydrogen bubbles are dispersed in the liquid.
5. Agitation of the fluid to increase heat transfer between the fluid and a coil or jacket in the vessel wall.

3.4B Equipment for Agitation

Generally, liquids are agitated in a cylindrical vessel which can be closed or open to the air. The height of liquid is approximately equal to the tank diameter. An impeller mounted on a shaft is driven by an electric motor. A typical agitator assembly is shown in Fig. 3.4-1.

1. Three-blade propeller agitator. There are several types of agitators that are widely used. A common type, shown in Fig. 3.4-1, is a three-bladed marine-type propeller similar to the propeller blade used in driving boats. The propeller can be a side-entering type in a tank or be clamped on the side of an open vessel in an off-center position. These propellers turn at high speeds of 400 to 1750 rpm (revolutions per minute) and are used for liquids of low viscosity. The flow pattern in a baffled tank with a propeller positioned on the center of the tank is shown in Fig. 3.4-1. This type of flow pattern is called *axial flow* since the fluid flows axially down the center axis or propeller shaft and up on the sides of the tank as shown.

(a)   (b)

FIGURE 3.4-1.   *Baffled tank and three-blade propeller agitator with axial-flow pattern: (a) side view, (b) bottom view.*

(a)   (b)   (c)   (d)

FIGURE 3.4-2. *Various types of agitators: (a) four-blade paddle, (b) gate or anchor paddle, (c) six-blade open turbine, (d) pitched-blade (45°) turbine.*

2. Paddle agitators. Various types of paddle agitators are often used at low speeds, between about 20 and 200 rpm. Two-bladed and four-bladed flat paddles are often used, as shown in Fig. 3.4-2a. The total length of the paddle impeller is usually 60–80% of the tank diameter and the width of the blade $\frac{1}{6}$ to $\frac{1}{10}$ of its length. At low speeds mild agitation is obtained in an unbaffled vessel. At higher speeds baffles are used, since, without baffles, the liquid is simply swirled around with little actual mixing. The paddle agitator is ineffective for suspending solids, since good radial flow is present but little vertical or axial flow. An anchor or gate paddle, shown in Fig. 3.4-2b, is often used. It sweeps or scrapes the tank walls and sometimes the tank bottom. It is used with viscous liquids where deposits on walls can occur and to improve heat transfer to the walls. However, it is a poor mixer. Paddle agitators are often used to process starch pastes, paints, adhesives, and cosmetics.

3. Turbine agitators. Turbines that resemble multibladed paddle agitators with shorter blades are used at high speeds for liquids with a very wide range of viscosities. The diameter of a turbine is normally between 30 and 50% of the tank diameter. The turbines usually have four or six blades. Figure 3.4-3 shows a flat six-blade turbine agitator with disk. In Fig. 3.4-2c a flat six-blade open turbine is shown. The turbines with flat blades give radial flow, as shown in Fig. 3.4-3. They are also useful for good gas dispersion; the gas is introduced just below the impeller at its axis and is drawn up to the blades and chopped into fine bubbles. In the pitched-blade turbine shown in Fig. 3.4-2d, with the blades at 45°, some axial flow is imparted so that a combination of axial and radial flow is present. This type is useful in suspending solids since the currents flow downward and then sweep up the solids.

Often a pitched-blade turbine with only four blades is used in suspension of solids. A high-efficiency, three-blade impeller (B6, F2) shown in Fig. 3.4-4a is similar to a four-blade pitched turbine; however, it features a larger pitch angle of 30–60° at the hub and a smaller angle of 10–30° at the tip. This axial-flow impeller produces more fluid motion and mixing per unit of power and is very useful in suspension of solids.

FIGURE 3.4-3. *Baffled tank with six-blade turbine agitator with disk showing flow patterns: (a) side view, (b) bottom view, (c) dimensions of turbine and tank.*

4. Helical-ribbon agitators. This type of agitator is used in highly viscous solutions and operates at a low RPM in the laminar region. The ribbon is formed in a helical path and is attached to a central shaft. The liquid moves in a tortuous flow path down the center and up along the sides in a twisting motion. Similar types are the double-helical-ribbon agitator shown in Fig. 3.4-4b and the helical-screw impeller shown in Fig. 3.4-4c.

5. Agitator selection and viscosity ranges. The viscosity of the fluid is one of several factors affecting the selection of the type of agitator. Indications of the viscosity ranges of these agitators are as follows. Propellers are used for fluid viscosities below about 3 Pa · s (3000 cp); turbines can be used below about 100 Pa · s (100 000 cp); modified paddles such as anchor agitators can be used above 50 Pa · s to about 500 Pa · s (500 000 cp); helical and ribbon-type agitators are often used above this range to about 1000 Pa · s and have been used up to 25 000

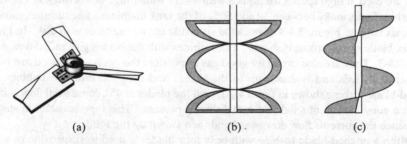

FIGURE 3.4-4. *Other types of agitators: (a) high-efficiency, three-blade impeller, (b) double-helical-ribbon, (c) helical-screw. [Reprinted with permission from André Bakker and Lewis E. Gates, Chem. Eng. Progr., 91 (Dec.), 25 (1995). Copyright by the American Institute of Chemical Engineers.]*

Pa·s. For viscosities greater than about 2.5 to 5 Pa·s (5000 cp) and above, baffles are not needed since little swirling is present above these viscosities.

3.4C Flow Patterns in Agitation

The flow patterns in an agitated tank depend upon the fluid properties, the geometry of the tank, the types of baffles in the tank, and the agitator itself. If a propeller or other agitator is mounted vertically in the center of a tank with no baffles, a swirling flow pattern usually develops. Generally, this is undesirable, because of excessive air entrainment, development of a large vortex, surging, and the like, especially at high speeds. To prevent this, an angular off-center position can be used with propellors with small horsepower. However, for vigorous agitation at higher power, unbalanced forces can become severe and limit the use of higher power.

For vigorous agitation with vertical agitators, baffles are generally used to reduce swirling and still promote good mixing. Baffles installed vertically on the walls of the tank are shown in Fig. 3.4-3. Usually four baffles are sufficient, with their width being about $\frac{1}{12}$ of the tank diameter for turbines and propellers. The turbine impeller drives the liquid radially against the wall, where it divides with one portion flowing upward near the surface and back to the impeller from above and the other flowing downward. Sometimes, in tanks with large liquid depths much greater than the tank diameter, two or three impellers are mounted on the same shaft, each acting as a separate mixer. The bottom impeller is about 1.0 impeller diameter above the tank bottom.

In an agitation system, the volume flow rate of fluid moved by the impeller, or circulation rate, is important in sweeping out the whole volume of the mixer in a reasonable time. Also, turbulence in the moving stream is important for mixing, since it entrains the material from the bulk liquid in the tank into the flowing stream. Some agitation systems require high turbulence with low circulation rates, others low turbulence with high circulation rates. This often depends on the types of fluids being mixed and on the amount of mixing needed.

3.4D Typical "Standard" Design of Turbine

The turbine agitator shown in Fig. 3.4-3 is the most commonly used agitator in the process industries. For design of an ordinary agitation system, this type of agitator is often used in the initial design. The geometric proportions of the agitation system which are considered as a typical "standard" design are given in Table 3.4-1. These relative proportions are the basis for the major correlations of agitator performance in numerous publications. (See Fig. 3.4-3c for nomenclature.)

In some cases $W/D_a = \frac{1}{8}$ for agitator correlations. The number of baffles is four in most uses. The clearance or gap between the baffles and the wall is usually $0.10-0.15\,J$ to ensure that liquid does not form stagnant pockets next to the baffle and wall. In a few correlations the ratio of baffle to tank diameter is $J/D_t = \frac{1}{10}$ instead of $\frac{1}{12}$.

3.4E Power Used in Agitated Vessels

In the design of an agitated vessel, an important factor is the power required to drive the impeller. Since the power required for a given system cannot be predicted theoretically, empir-

TABLE 3.4-1. *Geometric Proportions for a "Standard" Agitation System*

$$\frac{D_a}{D_t} = 0.3 \text{ to } 0.5 \qquad\qquad \frac{H}{D_t} = 1 \qquad\qquad \frac{C}{D_t} = \frac{1}{3}$$

$$\frac{W}{D_a} = \frac{1}{5} \qquad \frac{D_d}{D_a} = \frac{2}{3} \qquad \frac{L}{D_a} = \frac{1}{4} \qquad \frac{J}{D_t} = \frac{1}{12}$$

ical correlations have been developed to predict the power required. The presence or absence of turbulence can be correlated with the impeller Reynolds number N'_{Re}, defined as

$$N'_{Re} = \frac{D_a^2 N \rho}{\mu} \tag{3.4-1}$$

where D_a is the impeller (agitator) diameter in m, N is rotational speed in rev/s, ρ is fluid density in kg/m^3, and μ is viscosity in kg/m·s. The flow is laminar in the tank for $N'_{Re} < 10$, turbulent for $N'_{Re} > 10^4$, and for a range between 10 and 10^4, the flow is transitional, being turbulent at the impeller and laminar in remote parts of the vessel.

Power consumption is related to fluid density ρ, fluid viscosity μ, rotational speed N, and impeller diameter D_a by plots of power number N_p versus N'_{Re}. The power number is

$$N_p = \frac{P}{\rho N^3 D_a^5} \quad \text{(SI)}$$

$$N_p = \frac{P g_c}{\rho N^3 D_a^5} \quad \text{(English)} \tag{3.4-2}$$

where P = power in J/s or W. In English units, $P = \text{ft} \cdot \text{lb}_f/\text{s}$.

Figure 3.4-5 is a correlation (B3, R1) for frequently used impellers with Newtonian liquids contained in baffled, cylindrical vessels. Dimensional measurements of baffle, tank, and impeller sizes are given in Fig. 3.4-3c. These curves may also be used for the same impellers in unbaffled tanks when N'_{Re} is 300 or less (B3, R1). When N'_{Re} is above 300, the power consumption for an unbaffled vessel is considerably less than for a baffled vessel. Curves for other impellers are also available (B3, R1).

The power-number curve for N_p for the high-efficiency, three-blade impeller is shown as curve 6 in Fig. 3-4-5.

Example 3.4-1. Power Consumption in an Agitator

A flat-blade turbine agitator with disk having six blades is installed in a tank similar to Fig. 3.4-3. The tank diameter D_t is 1.83 m, the turbine diameter D_a is 0.61 m, $D_t = H$, and the width W is 0.122 m. The tank contains four baffles, each having a width J of 0.15 m. The turbine is operated at 90 rpm and the liquid in the tank has a viscosity of 10 cp and a density of 929 kg/m^3.

  (a) Calculate the required kW of the mixer.
  (b) For the same conditions, except for the solution having a viscosity of 100 000 cp, calculate the required kW.

$$N'_{Re} = \frac{D_a^2 N \rho}{\mu}$$

FIGURE 3.4-5. *Power correlations for various impellers and baffles (see Fig. 3.4-3c for dimension D_a, D_t, J, and W).*

Curve 1. Flat six-blade turbine with disk (like Fig. 3.4-3 but six blades); $D_a/W = 5$; four baffles each $D_t/J = 12$.

Curve 2. Flat six-blade open turbine (like Fig. 3.4-2c); $D_a/W = 8$; four baffles each $D_t/J = 12$.

Curve 3. Six-blade open turbine (pitched-blade) but blades at 45° (like Fig. 3.4-2d); $D_a/W = 8$; four baffles each $D_t/J = 12$.

Curve 4. Propeller (like Fig. 3.4-1); pitch $= 2D_a$; four baffles each $D_t/J = 10$; also holds for same propeller in angular off-center position with no baffles.

Curve 5. Propeller; pitch $= D_a$; four baffles each $D_t/J = 10$; also holds for same propeller in angular off-center position with no baffles.

Curve 6. High-efficiency impeller (like Fig. 3-4-4a); four baffles each $D_t/J = 12$.

[Curves 1, 2, and 3 reprinted with permission from R. L. Bates. P. L. Fondy, and R. R. Corpstein, Ind. Eng. Chem. Proc. Des. Dev., 2, 310 (1963). Copyright by the American Chemical Society. Curves 4 and 5 from J. H. Rushton, E. W. Costich, and H. J. Everett, Chem. Eng. Progr., 46, 395, 467 (1950). With permission.]

Solution: For part (a) the following data are given: $D_a = 0.61$ m, $W = 0.122$ m, $D_t = 1.83$ m, $J = 0.15$ m, $N = 90/60 = 1.50$ rev/s, $\rho = 929$ kg/m³, and

$$\mu = (10.0\ cp)(1 \times 10^{-3}) = 0.01\ \frac{kg}{m \cdot s} = 0.01\ Pa \cdot s$$

Using Eq. (3.4-1), the Reynolds number is

$$N'_{Re} = \frac{D_a^2 N \rho}{\mu} = \frac{(0.61)^2(1.50)929}{0.01} = 5.185 \times 10^4$$

Using curve 1 in Fig. 3.4-5, since $D_a/W = 5$ and $D_t/J = 12$, $N_P = 5$ for $N'_{Re} = 5.185 \times 10^4$. Solving for P in Eq. (3.4-2) and substituting known values,

$$P = N_P \rho N^3 D_a^5 = 5(929)(1.50)^3(0.61)^5$$

$$= 1324\ J/s = 1.324\ kW\ (1.77\ hp)$$

For part (b),

$$\mu = 100\,000(1 \times 10^{-3}) = 100 \frac{\text{kg}}{\text{m} \cdot \text{s}}$$

$$N'_{\text{Re}} = \frac{(0.61)^2(1.50)929}{100} = 5.185$$

This is in the laminar flow region. From Fig. 3.4-5, $N_P = 14$.

$$P = 14(929)(1.50)^3(0.61)^5 = 3707 \text{ J/s} = 3.71 \text{ kW } (4.98 \text{ hp})$$

Hence, a 10 000-fold increase in viscosity only increases the power from 1.324 to 3.71 kW.

Variations of various geometric ratios from the "standard" design can have different effects on the power number N_P in the turbulent region of the various turbine agitators as follows (B3):

1. For the flat six-blade open turbine, $N_P \propto (W/D_a)^{1.0}$.
2. For the flat six-blade open turbine, varying D_a/D_t from 0.25 to 0.50 has practically no effect on N_P.
3. With two six-blade open turbines installed on the same shaft and the spacing between the two impellers (vertical distance between the bottom edges of the two turbines) being at least equal to D_a, the total power is 1.9 times a single flat-blade impeller. For two six-blade pitched-blade (45°) turbines, the power is also about 1.9 times that of a single pitched-blade impeller.
4. A baffled, vertical square tank or a horizontal cylindrical tank has the same power number as a vertical cylindrical tank. However, marked changes in the flow patterns occur.

The power number for a plain anchor-type agitator similar to Fig. 3.4-2b but without the two horizontal crossbars is as follows for $N'_{\text{Re}} < 100$ (H2):

$$N_P = 215(N'_{\text{Re}})^{-0.955} \tag{3.4-3}$$

where $D_a/D_t = 0.90$, $W/D_t = 0.10$, and $C/D_t = 0.05$.

The power number for a helical-ribbon agitator for very viscous liquids for $N'_{\text{Re}} < 20$ is as follows (H2, P3):

$$N_p = 186(N'_{\text{Re}})^{-1} \qquad \text{(agitator pitch/tank diameter} = 1.0) \tag{3.4-4}$$

$$N_p = 290(N'_{\text{Re}})^{-1} \qquad \text{(agitator pitch/tank diameter} = 0.5) \tag{3.4-5}$$

The typical dimensional ratios used are $D_a/D_t = 0.95$, with some ratios as low as 0.75, and $W/D_t = 0.095$. The agitator pitch is the vertical distance of a single flight of the helix in a 360° rotation (B6).

3.4F   Agitator Scale-Up

1. Introduction.   In the process industries, experimental data are often available for a laboratory-size or pilot-unit-size agitation system, and it is desired to scale up the results to design a full-scale unit. Since the processes to be scaled up are very diverse, no single method can handle all types of scale-up problems, and many approaches to scale-up exist. Geometric similarity is, of course, important and simplest to achieve. Kinematic similarity can be defined in terms of ratios of velocities or of times (R2). Dynamic similarity requires fixed ratios of viscous, inertial, or gravitational forces. Even if geometric similarity is achieved, dynamic and kinematic similarity often cannot be obtained at the same time. Hence, it is frequently up to the designer to rely on judgment and experience in the scale-up.

In many cases, the main objectives usually present in an agitation process are as follows: *equal liquid motion,* such as in liquid blending, where the liquid motion or corresponding velocities are approximately the same in both cases; *equal suspension of solids,* where the levels of suspension are the same; and *equal rates of mass transfer,* where mass transfer is occurring between a liquid and a solid phase, liquid–liquid phases, and so on, and the rates are the same.

2. Scale-up procedure. A suggested step-by-step procedure to follow in the scale-up is detailed as follows for scaling up from the initial conditions, where the geometric sizes given in Table 3.4-1 are D_{a1}, D_{T1}, H_1, W_1, and so on, to the final conditions of D_{a2}, D_{T2}, and so on.

1. Calculate the scale-up ratio R. Assuming that the original vessel is a standard cylinder with $D_{T1} = H_1$, the volume V_1 is

$$V_1 = \left(\frac{\pi D_{T1}^2}{4}\right)(H_1) = \left(\frac{\pi D_{T1}^3}{4}\right) \tag{3.4-6}$$

Then the ratio of the volumes is

$$\frac{V_2}{V_1} = \frac{\pi D_{T2}^3/4}{\pi D_{T1}^3/4} = \frac{D_{T2}^3}{D_{T1}^3} \tag{3.4-7}$$

The scale-up ratio is then

$$R = \left(\frac{V_2}{V_1}\right)^{1/3} = \frac{D_{T2}}{D_{T1}} \tag{3.4-8}$$

2. Using this value of R, apply it to all of the dimensions in Table 3.4-1 to calculate the new dimensions. For example,

$$D_{a2} = RD_{a1}, \qquad J_2 = RJ_1, \ldots \tag{3.4-9}$$

3. Then a scale-up rule must be selected and applied to determine the agitator speed N_2 to be used to duplicate the small-scale results using N_1. This equation is as follows (R2):

$$N_2 = N_1\left(\frac{1}{R}\right)^n = N_1\left(\frac{D_{T1}}{D_{T2}}\right)^n \tag{3.4-10}$$

where $n = 1$ for equal liquid motion, $n = \frac{3}{4}$ for equal suspension of solids, and $n = \frac{2}{3}$ for equal rates of mass transfer (which is equivalent to equal power per unit volume). This value of n is based on empirical and theoretical considerations.

4. Knowing N_2, the power required can be determined using Eq. (3.4-2) and Fig. 3.4-5.

EXAMPLE 3.4-2. Derivation of Scale-Up Rule Exponent

For the scale-up-rule exponent n in Eq. (3.4-10), show the following for turbulent agitation:

(a) That when $n = \frac{2}{3}$, the power per unit volume is constant in the scale-up.

(b) That when $n = 1.0$, the tip speed is constant in the scale-up.

Solution: For part (a), from Fig. 3.4-5, N_P is constant for the turbulent region. From Eq. (3.4-2),

$$P_1 = N_P \rho N_1^3 D_{a1}^5 \qquad (3.4\text{-}11)$$

Then for equal power per unit volume, $P_1/V_1 = P_2/V_2$, or, using Eq. (3.4-6),

$$\frac{P_1}{V_1} = \frac{P_1}{\pi D_{T1}^3/4} = \frac{P_2}{V_2} = \frac{P_2}{\pi D_{T2}^3/4} \qquad (3.4\text{-}12)$$

Substituting P_1 from Eq. (3.4-11) together with a similar equation for P_2 into Eq. (3.4-12) and combining with Eq. (3.4-8).

$$N_2 = N_1 \left(\frac{1}{R} \right)^{2/3} \qquad (3.4\text{-}13)$$

For part (b), using Eq. (3.4-10) with $n = 1.0$, rearranging, and multiplying by π,

$$N_2 = N_1 \left(\frac{D_{T1}}{D_{T2}} \right)^{1.0} \qquad (3.4\text{-}14)$$

$$\pi D_{T2} N_2 = \pi D_{T1} N_1 \qquad (3.4\text{-}15)$$

where $\pi D_{T2} N_2$ is the tip speed in m/s.

To aid the designer of new agitation systems as well as serve as a guide for evaluating existing systems, some approximate guidelines are given as follows for liquids of normal viscosities (M2): for mild agitation and blending, 0.1 to 0.2 kW/m³ of fluid (0.0005 to 0.001 hp/gal); for vigorous agitation, 0.4 to 0.6 kW/m³ (0.002 to 0.003 hp/gal); for intense agitation or where mass transfer is important, 0.8 to 2.0 kW/m³ (0.004 to 0.010 hp/gal). This power in kW is the actual power delivered to the fluid as given in Fig. 3.4-5 and Eq. (3.4-2). This does not include the power used in the gear boxes and bearings. Typical efficiencies of electric motors are given in Section 3.3B. As an approximation, the power lost in the gear boxes and bearings and in inefficiency of the electric motor is about 30 to 40% of P, the actual power input to the fluid.

EXAMPLE 3.4-3. Scale-Up of Turbine Agitation System

An existing agitation system is the same as given in Example 3.4-1a for a flat-blade turbine with a disk and six blades. The given conditions and sizes are $D_{T1} = 1.83$ m, $D_{a1} = 0.61$ m, $W_1 = 0.122$ m, $J_1 = 0.15$ m, $N_1 = 90/60 = 1.50$ rev/s, $\rho = 929$ kg/m³, and $\mu = 0.01$ Pa·s. It is desired to scale up these results for a vessel whose volume is 3.0 times as large. Do this for the following two process objectives:

(a) Where equal rate of mass transfer is desired.

(b) Where equal liquid motion is needed.

Solution: Since $H_1 = D_{T1} = 1.83$ m, the original tank volume $V_1 = (\pi D_{T1}^2/4)(H_1) = \pi(1.83)^3/4 = 4.813$ m³. Volume $V_2 = 3.0(4.813) = 14.44$ m³. Following the steps in the scale-up procedure, and using Eq. (3.4-8),

$$R = \left(\frac{V_2}{V_1}\right)^{1/3} = \left(\frac{14.44}{4.813}\right)^{1/3} = 1.442$$

The dimensions of the larger agitation system are as follows: $D_{T2} = RD_{T1} = 1.442(1.83) = 2.64$ m, $D_{a2} = 1.442(0.61) = 0.880$ m, $W_2 = 1.442(0.122) = 0.176$ m, and $J_2 = 1.442(0.15) = 0.216$ m.

For part (a), for equal mass transfer, $n = \frac{2}{3}$ in Eq. (3.4-10).

$$N_2 = N_1\left(\frac{1}{R}\right)^{2/3} = (1.50)\left(\frac{1}{1.442}\right)^{2/3} = 1.175 \text{ rev/s (70.5 rpm)}$$

Using Eq. (3.4-1),

$$N'_{Re} = \frac{D_a^2 N\rho}{\mu} = \frac{(0.880)^2(1.175)929}{0.01} = 8.453 \times 10^4$$

Using $N_P = 5.0$ in Eq. (3.4-2),

$$P_2 = N_P\rho N_2^3 D_{a2}^5 = 5.0(9.29)(1.175)^3(0.880)^5 = 3977 \text{ J/s} = 3.977 \text{ kW}$$

The power per unit volume is

$$\frac{P_1}{V_1} = \frac{1.324}{4.813} = 0.2752 \text{ kW/m}^3$$

$$\frac{P_2}{V_2} = \frac{3.977}{14.44} = 0.2752 \text{ kW/m}^3$$

The value of 0.2752 kW/m^3 is somewhat lower than the approximate guidelines of 0.8 to 2.0 for mass transfer.

For part (b), for equal liquid motion, $n = 1.0$.

$$N_2 = (1.50)\left(\frac{1}{1.442}\right)^{1.0} = 1.040 \text{ rev/s}$$

$$P_2 = 5.0(929)(1.040)^3(0.880)^5 = 2757 \text{ J/s} = 2.757 \text{ kW}$$

$$\frac{P_2}{V_2} = \frac{2.757}{14.44} = 0.1909 \text{ kW/m}^3$$

3.4G Mixing Times of Miscible Liquids

In one method used to study the blending or mixing time for two miscible liquids, an amount of HCl acid is added to an equivalent of NaOH and the time required for the indicator to change color is noted. This is a measure of molecule–molecule mixing. Other experimental methods are also used. Rapid mixing takes place near the impeller, with slower mixing, which depends on the pumping circulation rate, in the outer zones.

In Fig. 3.4-6, a correlation of mixing time is given for a turbine agitator (B5, M5, N1). The dimensionless mixing factor f_t is defined as

$$f_t = t_T \frac{(ND_a^2)^{2/3} g^{1/6} D_a^{1/2}}{H^{1/2} D_t^{3/2}} \tag{3.4-16}$$

FIGURE 3.4-6. *Correlation of mixing time for miscible liquids using a turbine in a baffled tank (for a plain turbine, turbine with disk, and pitched-blade turbine). [From "Flow Patterns and Mixing Rates in Agitated Vessels" by K. W. Norwood and A. B. Metzner, A.I.Ch.E. J., **6**, 432 (1960). Reproduced by permission of the American Institute of Chemical Engineers, 1960.]*

where t_T is the mixing time in seconds. For $N'_{Re} > 1000$, since f_t is approximately constant, then $t_T N^{2/3}$ is constant. For some other mixers it has been shown that $t_T N$ is approximately constant. For scaling up from vessel 1 to another size vessel 2 with similar geometry and with the same power/unit volume in the turbulent region, the mixing times are related by

$$\frac{t_{T_2}}{t_{T_1}} = \left(\frac{D_{a_2}}{D_{a_1}}\right)^{11/18} \tag{3.4-17}$$

Hence, the mixing time increases for the larger vessel. For scaling up while keeping the same mixing time, the power/unit volume P/V increases markedly:

$$\frac{(P_2/V_2)}{(P_1/V_1)} = \left(\frac{D_{a_2}}{D_{a_1}}\right)^{11/4} \tag{3.4-18}$$

Usually, in scaling up to large-size vessels, a somewhat larger mixing time is used so that the power/unit volume does not increase markedly.

The mixing time for a helical-ribbon agitator is as follows for $N'_{Re} < 20$ (H2):

$$N t_T = 126 \qquad \text{(agitator pitch/tank diameter} = 1.0) \tag{3.4-19}$$

$$N t_T = 90 \qquad \text{(agitator pitch/tank diameter} = 0.5) \tag{3.4-20}$$

For very viscous liquids the helical-ribbon mixer gives a much smaller mixing time than a turbine for the same power/unit volume (M5). For nonviscous liquids, however, it gives longer times.

For a propellor agitator in a baffled tank, a mixing-time correlation is given by Biggs (B5), and that for an unbaffled tank by Fox and Gex (F1).

For a high-efficiency impeller in a baffled tank, mixing-time correlations are given by reference (F2), which shows that mixing times are lower than for pitched-blade agitators.

EXAMPLE 3.4-4. Scale-Up of Mixing Time in a Turbine Agitation System.
Using the existing conditions for the turbine with a disk as in Example 3.4-1,
part (a), do as follows:

- (a) Calculate the mixing time.
- (b) Calculate the mixing time for a smaller vessel with a similar geometric
  ratio, where D_t is 0.30 m instead of 1.83 m. Do this for the same power
  per unit volume as used in part (a).
- (c) Using the same mixing time calculated for the smaller vessel in part (b),
  calculate the new power per unit volume for the larger vessel in part (a).

Solution: In part (a), $D_t = 1.83$ m, $D_a = 0.61$ m, $D_t = H$, $N = 90/60 = 1.50$ rev/s,
$\rho = 929$ kg/m^3, $\mu = 10$ cp $= 0.01$ Pa·s. From Example 3.4-1, $N'_{Re} = 5.185 \times 10^4$,
$N_p = 5$, $P_1 = 1.324$ kW. For the tank volume,

$$V_1 = \frac{\pi(1.83)^2(1.83)}{4} = 4.813 \text{ m}^3$$

The power per unit volume is

$$\frac{P_1}{V_1} = \frac{1.324}{4.813} = 0.2751 \text{ kW/m}^3$$

From Fig. 3.4-6 for $N'_{Re} = 5.185 \times 10^4$, $f_t = 4.0$. Substituting into Eq. (3.4-16),

$$f_t = 4.0 = \frac{t_T(N_1 D_{a1}^2)^{2/3} g^{1/6} D_{a1}^{1/2}}{H_1^{1/2} D_{t1}^{3/2}}$$

$$= \frac{t_T(1.5 \times 0.61^2)^{2/3}(9.80665)^{1/6}(0.61)^{1/2}}{(1.83^{1/2})(1.83)^{3/2}}$$

$$t_T = 17.30 \text{ s}$$

For part (b), the scale-down ratio R from Eq. (3.4-8) is

$$R = D_{T2}/D_{T1} = 0.30/1.83 = 0.1639$$

$$D_{a2} = RD_{a1} = 0.1639(0.61) = 0.1000 \text{ m}$$

Also, $H_2 = D_{T2} = 0.300$ m. Using the same $P_1/V_1 = P_2/V_2 = 0.2751$ kW/m^3 in the
turbulent region, and Eq. (3.4-17),

$$\frac{t_{T2}}{t_{T1}} = \left(\frac{D_{a2}}{D_{a1}}\right)^{11/18}$$

$$t_{T2} = 17.30\left(\frac{0.100}{0.61}\right)^{11/18}$$

Hence, $t_{T2} = 5.73$ s. This shows that the larger vessel has a marked increase in
mixing time from 5.73 to 17.30 s for equal power per unit volume.

For part (c), using the same mixing time of 5.73 s for the smaller vessel, the
power per unit volume of the larger vessel is calculated from Eq. (3.4-18) for
equal mixing times:

$$\frac{P_2/V_2}{P_1/V_1} = \left(\frac{D_{a2}}{D_{a1}}\right)^{11/4}$$

$$\frac{0.2751}{P_1/V_1} = \left(\frac{0.1000}{0.6100}\right)^{11/4}$$

Solving, $P_1/V_1 = 39.73$ kW/m^3. This, of course, is a very large and impractical increase.

3.4H Flow Number and Circulation Rate in Agitation

An agitator acts like a centrifugal pump impeller without a casing and gives a flow at a certain pressure head. This circulation rate Q in m^3/s from the edge of the impeller is the flow rate perpendicular to the impeller discharge area. Fluid velocities have been measured in mixers and have been used to calculate the circulation rates. Data for baffled vessels have been correlated using the dimensionless flow number N_Q (U1):

$$N_Q = \frac{Q}{ND_a^3} \tag{3.4-21}$$

$N_Q = 0.5$ marine propeller (pitch = diameter)

$N_Q = 0.75$ six-blade turbine with disk ($W/D_a = \frac{1}{5}$)

$N_Q = 0.5$ six-blade turbine with disk ($W/D_a = \frac{1}{8}$)

$N_Q = 0.75$ pitched-blade turbine ($W/D_a = \frac{1}{5}$)

3.4I Special Agitation Systems

1. Suspension of solids. In some agitation systems a solid is suspended in the agitated liquid. Examples are when a finely dispersed solid is to be dissolved in the liquid, microorganisms are suspended in fermentation, a homogeneous liquid–solid mixture is to be produced for feed to a process, and a suspended solid is used as a catalyst to speed up a reaction. The suspension of solids is somewhat similar to a fluidized bed. In the agitated system, circulation currents of the liquid keep the particles in suspension. The amount and type of agitation needed depend mainly on the terminal settling velocity of the particles, which can be calculated using the equations in Section 14.3. Empirical equations for predicting the power required to suspend particles are given in references (M2, W1). Equations for pitched-blade turbines and high-efficiency impellers are given by Corpstein et al. (C4).

2. Dispersion of gases and liquids in liquids. In gas–liquid dispersion processes, the gas is introduced below the impeller, which chops the gas into very fine bubbles. The type and degree of agitation affect the size of the bubbles and the total interfacial area. Typical of such processes are aeration in sewage treatment plants, hydrogenation of liquids by hydrogen gas in the presence of a catalyst, absorption of a solute from the gas by the liquid, and fermentation. Correlations are available for predicting the bubble size, holdup, and kW power needed (C3, L1, Z1). For liquids dispersed in immiscible liquids, see reference (T1). The power required for the agitator in gas–liquid dispersion systems can be as much as 10 to 50% less than that required when no gas is present (C3, T2).

FIGURE 3.4-7. *Two-element helical motionless mixer with element length L and pipe diameter D (M2, M6).*

3. Motionless mixers. Mixing of two fluids can be accomplished in motionless mixers in a pipe with no moving parts. In such commercial devices, stationary elements inside a pipe successively divide portions of the stream and then recombine these portions.

Laminar-flow mixers are used to mix highly viscous mixtures. One type of static mixer has a series of fixed helical elements as shown in Fig. 3.4-7. (Note that most mixers have from six to 20 elements.) In the first element, the flow is split into two semicircular channels and the helical shape gives the streams a 180° twist. The next and successive elements are placed at 90° relative to each other and split the flows into two for each element. Each split in flow creates more interfacial area between layers. When these layers become sufficiently thin, molecular diffusion will eliminate concentration differences remaining. When each element divides the flow into two flow channels (M6),

$$\frac{d}{D} - \frac{1}{2^n} \qquad (3.4\text{-}22)$$

where n is the number of elements in series, d is the maximum striation thickness, and D is pipe diameter. When $n = 20$, then about 10^6 divisions occur and d is a very small thickness, which enhances the rate of diffusion.

In another commercial type of static mixer (K3), the stream is divided four times for each element. Each element has interacting bars or corrugated sheets placed lengthwise in the pipe and at a 45° angle to the pipe axis. The lengths L of the various types of elements vary from about 1.0 to 1.5 times the pipe diameter. These mixers are also used in turbulent-flow mixing.

In laminar flow with helical mixers the pressure drop (and, hence, power required) is approximately six times as large as that in the empty pipe. In turbulent flow, because of energy losses due to changes of direction, the pressure drop can be up to several hundred times as large (M6, P1). The power loss is typically about 10% of the power of a dynamic mixer (K3). Motionless mixers are also used for heat transfer, chemical reactions, and dispersion of gases in liquids.

3.4J   Mixing of Powders, Viscous Materials, and Pastes

1. Powders. In mixing of solid particles or powders it is necessary to displace parts of the powder mixture with respect to other parts. The simplest class of devices suitable for gentle blending is the tumbler. However, it is not usually used for breaking up agglomerates. A common type of tumbler is the *double-cone blender*, in which two cones are mounted with their open ends fastened together and rotated, as shown in Fig. 3.4-8a. Baffles can also be used internally. If an internal rotating device is also used in the double cone, agglomerates can also be broken up. Other geometries used are a cylindrical drum with internal baffles or twin-shell V type. Tumblers used specifically for breaking up agglomerates are rotating cylindrical or conical shells charged with metal or porcelain steel balls or rods.

Another class of devices for blending solids is the *stationary shell device,* in which the container is stationary and the material displacement is accomplished by single or multiple rotating inner devices. In the ribbon mixer in Fig. 3.4-8b, a shaft with two open helical screws numbers 1 and 2 attached to it rotates. One screw is left-handed and one right-handed. As the shaft rotates, sections of powder move in opposite directions and mixing occurs. Other types of internal rotating devices are available for special situations (P1). Also, in some devices both the shell and the internal device rotate.

2. Dough, pastes, and viscous materials. In the mixing of dough, pastes, and viscous materials, large amounts of powder are required as the material is divided, folded, or recombined, and as different parts of the material are displaced relative to each other so that fresh surfaces recombine as often as possible. Some machines may require jacketed cooling to remove the heat generated.

The first type of device for this purpose is somewhat similar to those for agitating fluids, with an impeller slowly rotating in a tank. The impeller can be a close-fitting anchor agitator as in Fig. 3.4-2b, where the outer sweep assembly may have scraper blades. A gate impeller can also be used which has horizontal and vertical bars that cut the paste at various levels and

(a)

(b)

(c)

FIGURE 3.4-8. *Mixers for powders and pastes: (a) double-cone powder mixer, (b) ribbon powder mixer with two ribbons, (c) kneader mixer for pastes.*

at the wall, which may have stationary bars. A modified gate mixer is the shear-bar mixer, which contains vertical rotating bars or paddles passing between vertical stationary fingers. Other modifications of these types are those where the can or container will rotate as well as the bars and scrapers. These are called *change-can mixers*.

The most commonly used mixer for heavy pastes and dough is the *double-arm kneader mixer*. The mixing action is bulk movement, smearing, stretching, dividing, folding, and re-combining. The most widely used design employs two contrarotating arms of sigmoid shape which may rotate at different speeds, as shown in Fig. 3.4-8c.

3.5   NON-NEWTONIAN FLUIDS

3.5A   Types of Non-Newtonian Fluids

As discussed in Section 2.4, Newtonian fluids are those which follow Newton's law, Eq. (3.5-1):

$$\tau = -\mu \frac{dv}{dr} \quad \text{(SI)}$$

$$\tau = -\frac{\mu}{g_c} \frac{dv}{dr} \quad \text{(English)}$$

(3.5-1)

where μ is the viscosity and is a constant independent of shear rate. In Fig. 3.5-1 a plot is shown of shear stress τ versus shear rate $-dv/dr$. The line for a Newtonian fluid is straight, the slope being μ.

If a fluid does not follow Eq. (3.5-1), it is a non-Newtonian fluid. Then a plot of τ versus $-dv/dr$ is not linear through the origin for these fluids. Non-Newtonian fluids can be divided into two broad categories on the basis of their shear stress/shear-rate behavior: those whose shear stress is independent of time or duration of shear (time-independent) and those whose shear stress is dependent on time or duration of shear (time-dependent). In addition to un-usual shear-stress behavior, some non-Newtonian fluids also exhibit elastic (rubberlike) be-havior, which is a function of time and results in their being called *viscoelastic fluids*. These fluids exhibit normal stresses perpendicular to the direction of flow in addition to the usual tangential stresses. Most of the emphasis here will be put on the time-independent class, which includes the majority of non-Newtonian fluids.

3.5B   Time-Independent Fluids

1. Bingham plastic fluids. These are the simplest because, as shown in Fig. 3.5-1, they differ from Newtonian only in that the linear relationship does not go through the origin. A finite shear stress τ_C (called *yield stress*) in N/m^2 is needed to initiate flow. Some fluids have a finite yield (shear) stress τ_O, but the plot of τ versus $-dv/dr$ is curved upward or downward. How-ever, this departure from exact Bingham plasticity is often small. Examples of fluids with a yield stress are drilling muds, peat slurries, margarine, chocolate mixtures, greases, soap, grain–water suspensions, toothpaste, paper pulp, and sewage sludge.

2. Pseudoplastic fluids. The majority of non-Newtonian fluids are in this category and in-clude polymer solutions or melts, greases, starch suspensions, mayonnaise, biological fluids, detergent slurries, dispersion media in certain pharmaceuticals, and paints. The shape of the

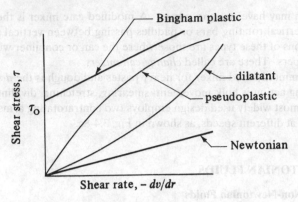

FIGURE 3.5-1. *Shear diagram for Newtonian and time-independent non-Newtonian fluids.*

flow curve is shown in Fig. 3.5-1, and it generally can be represented by a power-law equation (sometimes called the *Ostwald–de Waele equation*):

$$\tau = K\left(-\frac{dv}{dr}\right)^n \quad (n < 1) \tag{3.5-2}$$

where K is consistency index in $N \cdot s^n/m^2$ or $lb_f \cdot s^n/ft^2$, and n is the flow behavior index, dimensionless. The apparent viscosity μ_a in Eq. (3.5-3) is obtained from Eqs. (3.5-1) and (3.5-2) and decreases with increasing shear rate:

$$\mu_a = K\left(-\frac{dv}{dr}\right)^{n-1} \tag{3.5-3}$$

3. Dilatant fluids. These fluids are far less common than pseudoplastic fluids, and their flow behavior (Fig. 3.5-1) shows an increase in apparent viscosity with increasing shear rate. The power-law equation (3.5-2) is often applicable, but with $n > 1$:

$$\tau = K\left(-\frac{dv}{dr}\right)^n \quad (n > 1) \tag{3.5-4}$$

For a Newtonian fluid, $n = 1$. Solutions showing dilatancy are some corn flour–sugar solutions, wet beach sand, starch in water, potassium silicate in water, and some solutions containing high concentrations of powder in water.

3.5C Time-Dependent Fluids

1. Thixotropic fluids. These fluids exhibit a reversible decrease in shear stress with time at a constant rate of shear. This shear stress approaches a limiting value that depends on the shear rate. Examples include some polymer solutions, shortening, some food materials, and paints. At present the theory for time-dependent fluids is still not completely developed.

2. Rheopectic fluids. These fluids are quite rare in occurrence and exhibit a reversible increase in shear stress with time at a constant rate of shear. Examples are bentonite clay suspensions, certain sols, and gypsum suspensions. In design procedures for thixotropic and rheopectic fluids for steady flow in pipes, the limiting flow-property values at a constant rate of shear are sometimes used (S2, W3).

3.5D Viscoelastic Fluids

Viscoelastic fluids exhibit elastic recovery from the deformations that occur during flow. They show both viscous and elastic properties. Part of the deformation is recovered upon removal of the stress. Examples are flour dough, napalm, polymer melts, and bitumens.

3.5E Laminar Flow of Time-Independent Non-Newtonian Fluids

1. Flow properties of a fluid. In determining the flow properties of a time-independent non-Newtonian fluid, a capillary-tube viscometer is often used. The pressure drop ΔP N/m^2 for a given flow rate q m^3/s is measured in a straight tube of length L m and diameter D m. This is repeated for different flow rates or average velocities V m/s. If the fluid is time-independent, these flow data can be used to predict the flow in any other pipe size.

A plot of $D \Delta p/4L$, which is τ_w, the shear stress at the wall in N/m^2, versus $8V/D$, which is proportional to the shear rate at the wall, is shown in Fig. 3.5-2 for a power-law fluid following Eq. (3.5-5):

$$\tau_w = \frac{D \Delta p}{4L} = K' \left(\frac{8V}{D} \right)^{n'} \tag{3.5-5}$$

where n' is the slope of the line when the data are plotted on logarithmic coordinates and K' has units of $N \cdot s^{n'}/m^2$. For $n' = 1$, the fluid is Newtonian; for $n' < 1$, pseudoplastic, or Bingham plastic if the curve does not go through the origin; and for $n' > 1$, dilatant. The K', the consistency index in Eq. (3.5-5), is the value of $D \Delta p/4L$ for $8V/D = 1$. The shear rate at the wall, $(-dv/dr)_w$, is

$$\left(-\frac{dv}{dr} \right)_w = \left(\frac{3n' + 1}{4n'} \right) \left(\frac{8V}{D} \right) \tag{3.5-6}$$

Also, $K' = \mu$ for Newtonian fluids.

Equation (3.5-5) is simply another statement of the power-law model of Eq. (3.5-2) applied to flow in round tubes, and is more convenient to use for pipe-flow situations (D2). Hence, Eq. (3.5-5) defines the flow characteristics just as completely as Eq. (3.5-2). It has

FIGURE 3.5-2. *General flow curve for a power-law fluid in laminar flow in a tube.*

been found experimentally (M3) that for most fluids K' and n' are constant over wide ranges of $8V/D$ or $D\,\Delta p/4L$. For some fluids this is not the case, and K' and n' vary. Then the particular values of K' and n' used must be valid for the actual $8V/D$ or $D\,\Delta p/4L$ with which one is dealing in a design problem. This method using flow in a pipe or tube is often used to determine the flow properties of a non-Newtonian fluid.

In many cases the flow properties of a fluid are determined using a rotational viscometer. The flow properties K and n in Eq. (3.5-2) are determined in this manner. A discussion of the rotational viscometer is given in Section 3.5I.

When the flow properties are constant over a range of shear stresses that occurs for many fluids, the following equations hold (M3):

$$n' = n \tag{3.5-7}$$

$$K' = K\left(\frac{3n'+1}{4n'}\right)^{n'} \tag{3.5-8}$$

Often a generalized viscosity coefficient γ is defined as

$$\gamma = K'8^{n'-1} \quad \text{(SI)}$$
$$\gamma = g_c K'8^{n'-1} \quad \text{(English)} \tag{3.5-9}$$

where γ has units of $\text{N}\cdot\text{s}^{n'}/\text{m}^2$ or $\text{lb}_m/\text{ft}\cdot\text{s}^{2-n'}$

Typical flow-property constants (rheological constants) for some fluids are given in Table 3.5-1. Some data give γ values instead of K' values, but Eq. (3.5-9) can be used to

TABLE 3.5-1. *Flow-Property Constants for Non-Newtonian Fluids*

Fluid	n'	$\gamma\left(\dfrac{N\cdot s^{n'}}{m^2}\right)$	$K\left(\dfrac{N\cdot s^{n'}}{m^2}\right)$	Ref.
		Flow-Property Constants		
1.5% carboxymethylcellulose in water	0.554	1.369		(S1)
3.0% CMC in water	0.566	4.17		(S1)
4% paper pulp in water	0.575	9.12		(A1)
14.3% clay in water	0.350	0.0512		(W2)
10% napalm in kerosene	0.520	1.756		(S1)
25% clay in water	0.185	0.3036		(W2)
Applesauce, brand A (297 K), density = 1.10 g/cm^3	0.645		0.500	(C1)
Banana purée, brand A (297 K), density = 0.977 g/cm^3	0.458		6.51	(C1)
Honey (297 K)	1.00		5.61	(C1)
Cream, 30% fat (276 K)	1.0		0.01379	(M4)
Tomato concentrate, 5.8% total solids (305 K)	0.59		0.2226	(H1)

convert these values if necessary. In some cases in the literature, K or K' values are given as $dyn \cdot s^{n'}/cm^2$ or $lb_f \cdot s^{n'}/ft^2$. From Appendix A.1, the conversion factors are

$$1 \ lb_f \cdot s^{n'}/ft^2 = 47.880 \ N \cdot s^{n'}/m^2$$

$$1 \ dyn \cdot s^{n'}/cm^2 = 2.0886 \times 10^{-3} \ lb_f \cdot s^{n'}/ft^2$$

2. *Equations for flow in a tube.* In order to predict the frictional pressure drop Δp in laminar flow in a tube, Eq. (3.5-5) is solved for Δp ($p_0 - p_L$):

$$\Delta p = \frac{K' 4L}{D} \left(\frac{8V}{D} \right)^{n'} \tag{3.5-10}$$

If the average velocity is desired, Eq. (3.5-5) can be rearranged to give

$$V = \frac{D}{8} \left(\frac{\Delta p \ D}{K' 4L} \right)^{1/n'} \tag{3.5-11}$$

If the equations are desired in terms of K instead of K', Eqs. (3.5-7) and (3.5-8) can be substituted into (3.5-10) and (3.5-11). Substituting Eqs. (3.5-7) and (3.5-8) into Eq. (3.5-11) and noting that $V = v_{x \ av}$,

$$V = v_{xav} = \left(\frac{n}{3n + 1} \right) \left(\frac{p_0 - p_L}{2KL} \right)^{1/n} R_0^{(n+1)/n} \tag{3.5-12}$$

The flow must be laminar. The generalized Reynolds number has been defined as

$$N_{Re,gen} = \frac{D^{n'} V^{2-n'} \rho}{\gamma} = \frac{D^{n'} V^{2-n'} \rho}{K' 8^{n'-1}} = \frac{D^n V^{2-n} \rho}{K 8^{n-1} \left(\dfrac{3n + 1}{4n} \right)^n} \quad \text{(SI)} \tag{3.5-13}$$

3. *Friction factor method.* Alternatively, using the Fanning friction factor method given in Eqs. (2.10-5)–(2.10-7) for Newtonian fluids, but using the generalized Reynolds numbers,

$$f = \frac{16}{N_{Re,gen}} \tag{3.5-14}$$

$$\Delta p = 4f\rho \frac{L}{D} \frac{V^2}{2} \quad \text{(SI)} \tag{3.5-15}$$

$$\Delta p = 4f\rho \frac{L}{D} \frac{V^2}{2g_c} \quad \text{(English)}$$

EXAMPLE 3.5-1. *Pressure Drop of Power-Law Fluid in Laminar Flow*
A power-law fluid having a density of 1041 kg/m^3 is flowing through 14.9 m of a tubing having an inside diameter of 0.0524 m at an average velocity of 0.0728 m/s. The rheological or flow properties of the fluid are $K' = 15.23 \ N \cdot s^{n'}/m^2$ (0.318 $lb_f \cdot s^{n'}/ft^2$) and $n' = 0.40$.

      (a) Calculate the pressure drop and friction loss using Eq. (3.5-10) for laminar flow. Check the generalized Reynolds number to make sure that the flow is laminar.

(b) Repeat part (a) but use the friction factor method.

Solution: The known data are as follows: $K' = 15.23$, $n' = 0.40$, $D = 0.0524$ m, $V = 0.0728$ m/s, $L = 14.9$ m, and $\rho = 1041$ kg/m^3. For part (a), using Eq. (3.5-10),

$$\Delta p = \frac{K'4L}{D}\left(\frac{8V}{D}\right)^{n'} = \frac{15.23(4)(14.9)}{0.0524}\left(\frac{8 \times 0.0728}{0.0524}\right)^{0.4} = 45\,390 \text{ N/m}^2$$

Also, to calculate the friction loss,

$$F_f = \frac{\Delta p}{\rho} = \frac{45\,390}{1041} = 43.60 \text{ J/kg}$$

Using Eq. (3.5-13),

$$N_{\text{Re,gen}} = \frac{D^{n'}V^{2-n'}\rho}{K'g^{n'-1}} = \frac{(0.0524)^{0.40}(0.0728)^{1.60}(1041)}{15.23(8)^{-0.6}} = 1.106$$

Hence, the flow is laminar.

For part (b), using Eq. (3.5-14)

$$f = \frac{16}{N_{\text{Re,gen}}} = \frac{16}{1.106} = 14.44$$

Substituting into Eq. (3.5-15),

$$\Delta p = 4f\rho\frac{L}{D}\frac{V^2}{2} = 4(14.44)(1041)\frac{14.9}{0.0524}\frac{(0.0728)^2}{2}$$

$$= 45.39\,\frac{\text{kN}}{\text{m}^2}\left(946\,\frac{\text{lb}_f}{\text{ft}^2}\right)$$

3.5F Friction Losses in Contractions, Expansions, and Fittings in Laminar Flow

Since non-Newtonian power-law fluids flowing in conduits are often in laminar flow because of their usually high effective viscosity, losses in sudden changes of velocity and fittings are important in laminar flow.

1. Kinetic energy in laminar flow. In application of the total mechanical-energy balance in Eq. (2.7-28), the average kinetic energy per unit mass of fluid is needed. For fluids, this is (S2)

$$\text{average kinetic energy/kg} = \frac{V^2}{2\alpha} \tag{3.5-16}$$

For Newtonian fluids, $\alpha = \frac{1}{2}$ for laminar flow. For power-law non-Newtonian fluids,

$$\alpha = \frac{(2n+1)(5n+3)}{3(3n+1)^2} \tag{3.5-17}$$

For example, if $n = 0.50$, $\alpha = 0.585$. If $n = 1.00$, $\alpha = \frac{1}{2}$. For turbulent flow for Newtonian and non-Newtonian flow, $\alpha = 1.0$(D1).

2. Losses in contractions and fittings. Skelland (S2) and Dodge and Metzner (D2) state that when a fluid leaves a tank and flows through a sudden contraction to a pipe of diameter D_2 or flows from a pipe of diameter D_1 through a sudden contraction to a pipe of D_2, a vena contracta is usually formed downstream from the contraction. General indications are that the frictional pressure losses for pseudoplastic and Bingham plastic fluids are very similar to those for Newtonian fluids at the same generalized Reynolds numbers in laminar and turbulent flow for contractions as well as for fittings and valves.

For contraction losses, Eq. (2.10-16) can be used, where $\alpha = 1.0$ for turbulent flow; and for laminar flow Eq. (3.5-17) can be used to determine α, since n is not 1.00.

For fittings and valves, friction losses should be determined using Eq. (2.10-17) and values from Table 2.10-1.

3. Losses in sudden expansion. For the friction loss for a non-Newtonian fluid in laminar flow through a sudden expansion from D_1 to D_2 diameter, Skelland (S2) gives

$$h_{ex} = \frac{3n + 1}{2n + 1} V_1^2 \left[\frac{n + 3}{2(5n + 3)} \left(\frac{D_1}{D_2} \right)^4 - \left(\frac{D_1}{D_2} \right)^2 + \frac{3(3n + 1)}{2(5n + 3)} \right] \qquad \textbf{(3.5-18)}$$

where h_{ex} is the friction loss in J/kg. In English units Eq. (3.5-18) is divided by g_c and h_{ex} is in ft $\cdot$ lb$_f$/lb$_m$.

Equation (2.10-15) for laminar flow with $\alpha = \frac{1}{2}$ for a Newtonian fluid gives values reasonably close to those of Eq. (3.5-18) for $n = 1$ (Newtonian fluid). For turbulent flow the friction loss can be approximated by Eq. (2.10-15), with $\alpha = 1.0$ for non-Newtonian fluids (S2).

3.5G Turbulent Flow and Generalized Friction Factors

In turbulent flow of time-independent fluids the Reynolds number at which turbulent flow occurs varies with the flow properties of the non-Newtonian fluid. In a comprehensive study Dodge and Metzner (D2) derived a theoretical equation for turbulent flow of non-Newtonian fluids through smooth, round tubes. The final equation is plotted in Fig. 3.5-3, where the Fanning friction factor is plotted versus the generalized Reynolds number, $N_{Re,gen}$, given in Eq. (3.5-13). Power-law fluids with flow-behavior indexes n' between 0.36 and 1.0 were experimentally studied at Reynolds numbers up to 3.5×10^4 and the derivation was confirmed.

The curves for different n' values break off from the laminar line at different Reynolds numbers to enter the transition region. For $n' = 1.0$ (Newtonian), the transition region starts at $N_{Re,gen} = 2100$. Since many non-Newtonian power-law fluids have high effective viscosities, they are often in laminar flow. The correlation for a smooth tube also holds for a rough pipe in laminar flow.

For rough commercial pipes with various values of roughness ε/D, Fig. 3.5-3 cannot be used for turbulent flow, since it is derived for smooth tubes. The functional dependence of the roughness values ε/D on n' requires experimental data which are not yet available. Metzner and Reed (M3, S3) recommend use of the existing relationship, Fig. 2.10-3, for Newtonian fluids in rough tubes using the generalized Reynolds number $N_{Re,gen}$. This is somewhat conservative, since preliminary data indicate that friction factors for pseudoplastic fluids may be slightly smaller than for Newtonian fluids. This is also consistent with Fig. 3.5-3 for smooth tubes, which indicates lower f values for fluids with n' below 1.0 (S2).

EXAMPLE 3.5-2. Turbulent Flow of Power-Law Fluid

A pseudoplastic fluid that follows the power law, having a density of 961 kg/m^3, is flowing through a smooth, circular tube having an inside diameter of 0.0508 m at an average velocity of 6.10 m/s. The flow properties of the fluid are $n' = 0.30$ and

$$N_{Re, gen} = \frac{D^{n'} V^{2-n'} \rho}{\gamma}$$

FIGURE 3.5-3.   *Fanning friction factor versus generalized Reynolds number for time-independent non-Newtonian and Newtonian fluids flowing in smooth tubes. [From D. W. Dodge and A. B. Metzner, A.I.Ch.E. J., 5, 189 (1959). With permission.]*

$K' = 2.744$ N·s$^{n'}$/m^2. Calculate the frictional pressure drop for a tubing 30.5 m long.

Solution: The data are as follows: $K' = 2.744$, $n' = 0.30$, $D = 0.0508$ m, $V = 6.10$ m/s, $\rho = 961$ kg/m^3, and $L = 30.5$ m. Using the general Reynolds-number equation (3.5-13),

$$N_{Re,gen} = \frac{D^{n'} V^{2-n'} \rho}{K' 8^{n'-1}} = \frac{(0.0508)^{0.3}(6.10)^{1.7}(961)}{2.744(8^{-0.7})}$$

$$= 1.328 \times 10^4$$

Hence, the flow is turbulent. Using Fig. 3.5-3 for $N_{Re,gen} = 1.328 \times 10^4$ and $n' = 0.30$, $f = 0.0032$.

Substituting into Eq. (3.5-15),

$$\Delta p = 4f\rho \frac{L}{D} \frac{V^2}{2} = 4(0.0032)(961)\left(\frac{30.5}{0.0508}\right)\frac{(6.10)^2}{2}$$

$$= 137.4 \text{ kN/m}^2 \ (2870 \text{ lb}_f/\text{ft}^2)$$

3.5H   Velocity Profiles for Non-Newtonian Fluids

1. Pseudoplastic and dilatant fluids.   For pipe flow, Eq. (3.5-2) can be written as

$$\tau_{rx} = K\left(\frac{-dv_x}{dr}\right)^n \tag{3.5-19}$$

Equation (2.9-6) holds for all fluids:

$$\tau_{rx} = \frac{(p_0 - p_L)r}{2L} \tag{2.9-6}$$

which relates τ_{rx} with the radial distance r from the center. Equating the above two equations and integrating between $r = r$ and $r = R_0$ where $v_x = 0$,

$$v_x = \frac{n}{n+1}\left(\frac{p_0 - p_L}{2KL}\right)^{1/n} R_0^{(n+1)/n}\left[1 - \left(\frac{r}{R_0}\right)^{(n+1)/n}\right] \tag{3.5-20}$$

At $r = 0$, $v_x = v_{x\,\text{max}}$ and Eq. (3.5-20) becomes

$$v_x = v_{x\,\text{max}}\left[1 - \left(\frac{r}{R_0}\right)^{(n+1)/n}\right] \tag{3.5-21}$$

The average velocity $v_{x\,\text{av}}$ is given by Eq. (3.5-12):

$$v_{x\,\text{av}} = \left(\frac{n}{3n+1}\right)\left(\frac{p_0 - p_L}{2KL}\right)^{1/n} R_0^{(n+1)/n} \tag{3.5-12}$$

Dividing Eq. (3.5-20) by (3.5-12),

$$\frac{v_x}{v_{x\,\text{av}}} = \frac{3n+1}{n+1}\left[1 - \left(\frac{r}{R_0}\right)^{(n+1)/n}\right] \tag{3.5-22}$$

Using Eq. (3.5-22), the velocity profile can be calculated for laminar flow of a Newtonian fluid for $n = 1$ to show the parabolic profile in Fig. 3.5-4. The velocity profiles for pseudoplastic fluids ($n < 1$) show a flatter profile compared to the velocity profile for a Newtonian fluid. For extreme pseudoplastic behavior for $n = 0$, plug flow is obtained across the entire pipe. For dilatant behavior ($n > 1$) the velocity profile is more pointed and narrower. For extreme dilatant fluids ($n = \infty$) the velocity profile is a linear function of the radius.

FIGURE 3.5-4. *Dimensionless velocity profile $v_x/v_{x\,\text{av}}$ for power-law non-Newtonian fluids.*

FIGURE 3.5-5. *Velocity profile and shear diagram for flow of a Bingham
plastic fluid in a pipe.*

2. Bingham plastic fluids. For Bingham plastic fluids a finite yield stress τ_0 in N/m^2 is
needed to initiate flow, as given in Eq. (3.5-23):

$$\tau_{rx} = \tau_0 + \mu\left(-\frac{dv_x}{dr}\right) \qquad (3.5\text{-}23)$$

The velocity profile for this fluid is more complex than that for non-Newtonian fluids. This
velocity profile for Bingham plastic fluids is shown in Fig. 3.5-5. Note the plug-flow region
$r = 0$ to $r = r_0$. In this region $dv_x/dr = 0$ because the momentum flux or shear stress τ_{rx} is less
than the yield value τ_0.

In Table 3.5-2 some typical values for the rheological constants for Bingham plastic fluids
are given.

To derive the equation for pipe flow, note that Eq. (2.9-6) holds for all fluids:

$$\tau_{rx} = \frac{(p_0 - p_L)r}{2L} \qquad (2.9\text{-}6)$$

Substituting Eq. (2.9-6) into (3.5-23),

$$\frac{(p_0 - p_L)r}{2L} = \tau_0 + \mu\left(-\frac{dv_x}{dr}\right) \qquad (3.5\text{-}24)$$

TABLE 3.5-2. *Rheological Constants for Bingham Plastic Fluids*

Fluid	τ_0, N/m^2	μ, Pa·s	Ref.
Coal slurry ($\rho = 1500 \text{ kg/m}^3$)	2.0.	0.03	(D4)
Molten chocolate (100°F)	20	2.0	(D4)
Printing pigment in varnish (10% by wt)	0.4	0.25	(C5)

Rearranging and integrating, where $v_x = v_x$ at $r = r$ and $v_x = 0$ at $r = R$,

$$v_x = \left(\frac{p_0 - p_L}{4\mu L}\right)R^2\left[1 - \left(\frac{r}{R}\right)^2\right] - \frac{\tau_0}{\mu}R\left[1 - \frac{r}{R}\right] \qquad (3.5\text{-}25)$$

The equation holds for the region where $r > r_0$ and up to $r = R$. For the plug-flow region $r \le r_0$, $dv_x/dr = 0$. In this region, using Eq. (2.9-6) and setting $\tau_{rx} = \tau_0$ at r_0,

$$\tau_0 = \frac{(p_0 - p_L)r_0}{2L} \qquad (3.5\text{-}26)$$

Substituting Eq. (3.5-26) into (3.5-25) for $r = r_0$, where plug flow occurs,

$$v_x = \left(\frac{p_0 - p_L}{4\mu L}\right)R^2\left[1 - \frac{r_0}{R}\right]^2 \qquad (3.5\text{-}27)$$

To obtain the flow rate Q in m³/s, the following integral must be evaluated:

$$Q = 2\pi \int_0^{r_0} v_x r\, dr + 2\pi \int_{r_0}^{R} v_x r\, dr \qquad (3.5\text{-}28)$$

Substituting Eq. (3.5-27) into the first part of Eq. (3.5-28) and (3.5-25) into the last part and integrating,

$$Q = \frac{\pi(p_0 - p_L)R^4}{8\mu L}\left[1 - \frac{4}{3}\frac{\tau_0}{\tau_R} + \frac{1}{3}\left(\frac{\tau_0}{\tau_R}\right)^4\right] \qquad (3.5\text{-}29)$$

where $\tau_R = (p_0 - p_L)R/2L$, the momentum flux at the wall. This is the Buckingham–Reiner equation.

When τ_0 is zero, Eq. (3.5-29) reduces to the Hagen–Poiseuille Eq. (2.9-11) for Newtonian fluids.

EXAMPLE 3.5-3.   Flow Rate of a Bingham Plastic Fluid

A printing-pigment solution with properties similar to those in Table 3.5-2 is flowing in a 1.0-cm-diameter pipe which is 10.2 m long. A pressure driving force of 4.35 kN/m² is being used. Calculate the flow rate Q in m³/s.

Solution: From Table 3.5-2, $\tau_0 = 0.4$ N/m² and $\mu = 0.25$ Pa·s. Also, $(p_0 - p) = 4.35$ kN/m² $= 4350$ N/m², $L = 10.2$ m, $R = 1.0/2$ cm $= 0.005$ m. Substituting into Eq. (3.5-26),

$$\tau_0 = 0.4\ \text{N/m}^2 = \frac{(p_0 - p_L)r_0}{2L} = \frac{(4350)r_0}{2(10.2)}$$

Solving,

$$r_0 = \frac{0.400(2)(10.2)}{4350} = 0.001876\ \text{m} = 0.1876\ \text{cm}$$

Substituting into the following for τ_R,

$$\tau_R = \frac{(p_0 - p_L)R}{2L} = \frac{(4350)(0.005)}{2(10.2)} = 1.066\ \text{N/m}^2$$

Finally, substituting into Eq. (3.5-29),

$$Q = \frac{\pi(4350)(0.005)^4}{8(0.25)(10.2)}\left[1 - \frac{4}{3}\frac{0.4}{1.066} + \frac{1}{3}\left(\frac{0.4}{1.066}\right)^4\right]$$

$$Q = 2.120 \times 10^{-7} \text{ m}^3/\text{s}$$

$$v_{x\text{ av}} = \frac{Q}{\pi R^2} = \frac{2.120 \times 10^{-7}}{\pi(0.005)^2} = 2.700 \times 10^{-3} \text{ m/s}$$

3.5I Determination of Flow Properties of Non-Newtonian Fluids Using Rotational Viscometer

The flow-property or rheological constants of non-Newtonian fluids can be measured using pipe flow, as discussed in Section 3.5E. Another, more important method for measuring flow properties is by using a rotating concentric-cylinder viscometer, first described by Couette in 1890. In this device a concentric rotating cylinder (spindle) spins at a constant rotational speed inside another cylinder. Generally, there is a very small gap between the walls. This annulus is filled with the fluid. The torque needed to maintain this constant rotation rate of the inner spindle is measured by means of a torsion wire from which the spindle is suspended. A typical commercial instrument of this type is the Brookfield viscometer. Some types rotate the outer cylinder.

The shear stress at the wall of the bob or spindle is given by

$$\tau_w = \frac{T}{2\pi R_b^2 L} \tag{3.5-30}$$

where τ_w is the shear stress at the wall, N/m² or kg/s² · m; T is the measured torque, kg · m²/s²; R_b is the radius of the spindle, m; and L is the effective length of the spindle, m. Note that Eq. (3.5-30) holds for Newtonian and non-Newtonian fluids.

The shear rate at the surface of the spindle for non-Newtonian fluids is as follows (M6) for $0.5 < R_b/R_c < 0.99$:

$$\left(-\frac{dv}{dr}\right)_w = \frac{2\omega}{n[1 - (R_b/R_c)^{2/n}]} \tag{3.5-31}$$

where R_c is the radius of the outer cylinder or container, m; and ω is the angular velocity of the spindle, rad/s. Also, $\omega = 2\pi N/60$, when N is the RPM. Results calculated using Eq. (3.5-31) give values very close to those using the more complicated equation of Krieger and Maron (K2), also given in (P4, S2).

The power-law equation is given as

$$\tau = K\left(-\frac{dv}{dr}\right)^n \tag{3.5-2}$$

where $K = \text{N} \cdot \text{s}^n/\text{m}^2$, kg · s^{n-2}/m. Substituting Eqs. (3.5-30) and (3.5-31) into (3.5-2) gives

$$T = 2\pi R_b^2 LK\left[\frac{2}{n[1 - (R_b/R_c)^{2/n}]}\right]^n \omega^n \tag{3.5-32}$$

or,

$$T = A\omega^n \tag{3.5-33}$$

Chapter 3   Principles of Momentum Transfer and Applications

where

$$A = 2\pi R_b^2 LK \left[\frac{2}{n[1 - (R_b/R_c)^{2/n}]} \right]^n \tag{3.5-34}$$

Experimental data are obtained by measuring the torque T at different values of ω for a given fluid. The flow-property constants may be evaluated by plotting $\log T$ versus $\log \omega$. The parameter n is the slope of the straight line and the intercept is $\log A$. The consistency factor K is now easily evaluated from Eq. (3.5-34).

Various special cases can be derived for Eq. (3.5-31):

1. *Newtonian fluid.* $(n = 1)$.

$$\left(-\frac{dv}{dr} \right)_w = \frac{2\omega}{1 - (R_b/R_c)^2} \tag{3.5-35}$$

2. *Very large gap* $(R_b/R_c < 0.1)$. This is the case of a spindle immersed in a large beaker of test fluid. Equation (3.5-31) becomes

$$\left(-\frac{dv}{dr} \right)_w = \frac{2\omega}{n} \tag{3.5-36}$$

Substituting Eqs. (3.5-30) and (3.5-36) into (3.5-2),

$$T = 2\pi R_b^2 LK \left(\frac{2}{n} \right)^n \omega^n \tag{3.5-37}$$

Again, as before, the flow-property constants can be evaluated by plotting $\log T$ versus $\log \omega$.

3. *Very narrow gap* $(R_b/R_c > 0.99)$. This is similar to flow between parallel plates. Taking the shear rate at radius $(R_b + R_c)/2$,

$$\left(-\frac{dv}{dr} \right)_w \cong \frac{\Delta v}{\Delta r} = \frac{2\omega}{1 - (R_b/R_c)^2} \tag{3.5-38}$$

This equation, then, is the same as Eq. (3.5-35).

3.5J   Power Requirements in Agitation and Mixing of Non-Newtonian Fluids

For correlating the power requirements in agitation and mixing of non-Newtonian fluids, the power number N_P is defined by Eq. (3.4-2), which is also the equation used for Newtonian fluids. However, the definition of the Reynolds number is much more complicated than for Newtonian fluids, since the apparent viscosity is not constant for non-Newtonian fluids but varies with the shear rates or velocity gradients in the vessel. Several investigators (G1, M1) have used an average apparent viscosity μ_a, which is used in the Reynolds number as follows:

$$N'_{\text{Re},n} = \frac{D_a^2 N \rho}{\mu_a} \tag{3.5-39}$$

The average apparent viscosity can be related to the average shear rate or average velocity gradient by the following method. For a power-law fluid,

$$\tau = K\left(-\frac{dv}{dy}\right)^n_{av} \tag{3.5-40}$$

For a Newtonian fluid,

$$\tau = \mu_a\left(-\frac{dv}{dy}\right)_{av} \tag{3.5-41}$$

Combining Eqs. (3.5-40) and (3.5-41),

$$\mu_a = K\left(-\frac{dv}{dy}\right)^{n-1}_{av} \tag{3.5-42}$$

Metzner and others (G1, M1) found experimentally that the average shear rate $(dv/dy)_{av}$ for pseudoplastic liquids ($n < 1$) varies approximately as follows with the rotational speed:

$$\left(\frac{dv}{dy}\right)_{av} = 11N \tag{3.5-43}$$

Hence, combining Eqs. (3.5-42) and (3.5-43),

$$\mu_a = (11N)^{n-1}K \tag{3.5-44}$$

Substituting into Eq. (3.5-39),

$$N'_{Re,n} = \frac{D_a^2 N^{2-n}\rho}{11^{n-1}K} \tag{3.5-45}$$

Equation (3.5-45) has been used to correlate data for a flat six-blade turbine with disk in pseudoplastic liquids, and the dashed curve in Fig. 3.5-6 shows the correlation (M1). The solid curve applies to Newtonian fluids (R1). Both sets of data were obtained for four baffles with $D_t/J = 10$, $D_a/W = 5$, and $L/W = \frac{5}{4}$. However, since it has been shown that the difference in results for $D_t/J = 10$ and $D_t/J = 12$ is very slight (R1), this Newtonian line can be considered the same as curve 1 in Fig. 3.4-5. The curves in Fig. 3.5-6 show that the results are identical for the Reynolds number range 1–2000, except that they differ only in the Reynolds

FIGURE 3.5-6. *Power correlation in agitation for a flat, six-blade turbine with disk in pseudoplastic non-Newtonian and Newtonian fluids (G1, M1, R1): $D_a/W = 5$, $L/W = 5/4$, $D_t/J = 10$.*

number range 10–100, where the pseudoplastic fluids use less power than the Newtonian fluids. The flow patterns for the pseudoplastic fluids show much greater velocity-gradient changes than do the Newtonian fluids in the agitator. The fluid far from the impeller may be moving in slow laminar flow with a high apparent viscosity. Data for fan turbines and propellers are also available (M1).

3.6 DIFFERENTIAL EQUATIONS OF CONTINUITY

3.6A Introduction

In Sections 2.6, 2.7, and 2.8, overall mass, energy, and momentum balances allowed us to solve many elementary problems in fluid flow. These balances were done on an arbitrary finite volume sometimes called a *control volume*. In these total-energy, mechanical-energy, and momentum balances, we only needed to know the state of the inlet and outlet streams and the exchanges with the surroundings.

These overall balances were powerful tools in solving various flow problems because they did not require knowledge of what goes on inside the finite control volume. Also, in the simple shell-momentum balances made in Section 2.9, expressions were obtained for the velocity distribution and pressure drop. However, to advance in our study of these flow systems, we must investigate in greater detail what goes on inside this finite control volume. To do this, we now use a differential element for a control volume. The differential balances will be somewhat similar to the overall and shell balances, but now we shall make the balance in a single phase and integrate to the phase boundary using the boundary conditions. In the balances done earlier, a balance was made for each new system studied. It is not necessary to formulate new balances for each new flow problem. It is often easier to start with the differential equations for the conservation of mass (equation of continuity) and the conservation of momentum in general form. Then these equations are simplified by discarding unneeded terms for each particular problem.

For nonisothermal systems, a general differential equation for conservation of energy will be considered in Chapter 5. Also, in Chapter 7, a general differential equation of continuity for a binary mixture will be derived. The differential-momentum-balance equation to be derived is based on Newton's second law and allows us to determine the way velocity varies with position and time as well as the pressure drop in laminar flow. The equation of momentum balance can be used for turbulent flow with certain modifications.

Often these conservation equations are called *equations of change,* since they describe the variations in the properties of the fluid with respect to position and time. Before we derive these equations, a brief review of the different types of derivatives with respect to time which occur in these equations and a brief description of vector notation will be given.

3.6B Types of Time Derivatives and Vector Notation

1. Partial time derivative.   Various types of time derivatives are used in the derivations to follow. The most common type of derivative is the partial time derivative. For example, suppose that we are interested in the mass concentration or density ρ in kg/m³ in a flowing stream as a function of position x, y, z and time t. The partial time derivative of ρ is $\partial\rho/\partial t$. This is the local change of density with time at a fixed point x, y, z.

2. *Total time derivative.* Suppose that we want to measure the density in the stream while we are moving about in the stream with velocities in the x, y, and z directions of dx/dt, dy/dt, and dz/dt, respectively. The total derivative $d\rho/dt$ is

$$\frac{d\rho}{dt} = \frac{\partial \rho}{\partial t} + \frac{\partial \rho}{\partial x}\frac{dx}{dt} + \frac{\partial \rho}{\partial y}\frac{dy}{dt} + \frac{\partial \rho}{\partial z}\frac{dz}{dt} \qquad (3.6\text{-}1)$$

This means that the density is a function of t and of the velocity components dx/dt, dy/dt, and dz/dt at which the observer is moving.

3. *Substantial time derivative.* Another useful type of time derivative is obtained if the observer floats along with the velocity v of the flowing stream and notes the change in density with respect to time. This is called the derivative that follows the motion, or the *substantial time derivative, $D\rho/Dt$:*

$$\frac{D\rho}{Dt} = \frac{\partial \rho}{\partial t} + v_x\frac{\partial \rho}{\partial x} + v_y\frac{\partial \rho}{\partial y} + v_z\frac{\partial \rho}{\partial z} = \frac{\partial \rho}{\partial t} + (\boldsymbol{v}\cdot\boldsymbol{\nabla}\rho) \qquad (3.6\text{-}2)$$

where v_x, v_y, and v_z are the velocity components of the stream velocity v, which is a vector. This substantial derivative is applied to both scalar and vector variables. The term $(\boldsymbol{v}\cdot\boldsymbol{\nabla}\rho)$ will be discussed in part 6 of Section 3.6B.

4. *Scalars.* The physical properties encountered in momentum, heat, and mass transfer can be placed in several categories: scalars, vectors, and tensors. Scalars are quantities such as concentration, temperature, length, volume, time, and energy. They have magnitude but no direction and are considered to be zero-order tensors. The common mathematical algebraic laws hold for the algebra of scalars. For example, $bc = cd$, $b(cd) = (bc)d$, and so on.

5. *Vectors.* Velocity, force, momentum, and acceleration are considered vectors since they have magnitude and direction. They are regarded as first-order tensors and are written in boldface letters in this text, such as v for velocity. The addition of two vectors $\boldsymbol{B} + \boldsymbol{C}$ by parallelogram construction and the subtraction of two vectors $\boldsymbol{B} - \boldsymbol{C}$ are shown in Fig. 3.6-1. The vector $\boldsymbol{B}$ is represented by its three projections B_x, B_y, and B_z on the x, y, and z axes, and

$$\boldsymbol{B} = iB_x + jB_y + kB_z \qquad (3.6\text{-}3)$$

where i, j, and k are unit vectors along the axes x, y, and z, respectively.

(a)   (b)

FIGURE 3.6-1. *Addition and subtraction of vectors: (a) addition of vectors, $\boldsymbol{B} + \boldsymbol{C}$; (b) subtraction of vectors, $\boldsymbol{B} - \boldsymbol{C}$.*

In multiplying a scalar quantity r or s by a vector $\mathbf{B}$, the following hold:

$$r\mathbf{B} = \mathbf{B}r \tag{3.6-4}$$

$$(rs)\mathbf{B} = r(s\mathbf{B}) \tag{3.6-5}$$

$$r\mathbf{B} + s\mathbf{B} = (r + s)\mathbf{B} \tag{3.6-6}$$

The following also hold:

$$(\mathbf{B} \cdot \mathbf{C}) = (\mathbf{C} \cdot \mathbf{B}) \tag{3.6-7}$$

$$\mathbf{B} \cdot (\mathbf{C} + \mathbf{D}) = (\mathbf{B} \cdot \mathbf{C}) + (\mathbf{B} \cdot \mathbf{D}) \tag{3.6-8}$$

$$(\mathbf{B} \cdot \mathbf{C})\mathbf{D} \neq \mathbf{B}(\mathbf{C} \cdot \mathbf{D}) \tag{3.6-9}$$

$$(\mathbf{B} \cdot \mathbf{C}) = BC \cos\phi_{BC} \tag{3.6-10}$$

where ϕ_{BC} is the angle between two vectors and is $<180°$.

Second-order tensors τ arise primarily in momentum transfer and have nine components. They are discussed elsewhere (B2).

6. Differential operations with scalars and vectors. The gradient or "grad" of a scalar field is

$$\nabla\rho = i\frac{\partial\rho}{\partial x} + j\frac{\partial\rho}{\partial y} + k\frac{\partial\rho}{\partial z} \tag{3.6-11}$$

where ρ is a scalar such as density.

The divergence or "div" of a vector v is

$$(\nabla \cdot v) = \frac{\partial v_x}{\partial x} + \frac{\partial v_y}{\partial y} + \frac{\partial v_z}{\partial z} \tag{3.6-12}$$

where v is a function of v_x, v_y, and v_z.

The Laplacian of a scalar field is

$$\nabla^2\rho = \frac{\partial^2\rho}{\partial x^2} + \frac{\partial^2\rho}{\partial y^2} + \frac{\partial^2\rho}{\partial z^2} \tag{3.6-13}$$

Other operations that may be useful are

$$\nabla rs = r\nabla s + s\nabla r \tag{3.6-14}$$

$$(\nabla \cdot sv) = (\nabla s \cdot v) + s(\nabla \cdot v) \tag{3.6-15}$$

$$(v \cdot \nabla s) = v_x\frac{\partial s}{\partial x} + v_y\frac{\partial s}{\partial y} + v_z\frac{\partial s}{\partial z} \tag{3.6-16}$$

3.6C   Differential Equation of Continuity

1. Derivation of equation of continuity. A mass balance will be made for a pure fluid flowing through a stationary volume element $\Delta x \, \Delta y \, \Delta z$ which is fixed in space as in Fig. 3.6-2. The mass balance for the fluid with a concentration of ρ kg/m^3 is

$$\text{(rate of mass in)} - \text{(rate of mass out)} = \text{(rate of mass accumulation)} \tag{3.6-17}$$

FIGURE 3.6-2. *Mass balance for a pure fluid flowing through a fixed volume $\Delta x \, \Delta y \, \Delta z$ in space.*

In the x direction the rate of mass entering the face at x having an area of $\Delta y \, \Delta z$ m^2 is $(\rho v_x)_x$ $\Delta y \, \Delta z$ kg/s and that leaving at $x + \Delta x$ is $(\rho v_x)_{x+\Delta x} \, \Delta y \, \Delta z$. The term (ρv_x) is a mass flux in kg/s · m^2. Mass entering and mass leaving in the y and z directions are also shown in Fig. 3.6-2.

The rate of mass accumulation in the volume $\Delta x \, \Delta y \, \Delta z$ is

$$\text{rate of mass accumulation} = \Delta x \, \Delta y \, \Delta z \, \frac{\partial \rho}{\partial t} \qquad \text{(3.6-18)}$$

Substituting all these expressions into Eq. (3.6-17) and dividing both sides by $\Delta x \, \Delta y \, \Delta z$,

$$\frac{[(\rho v_x)_x - (\rho v_x)_{x+\Delta x}]}{\Delta x} + \frac{[(\rho v_y)_y - (\rho v_y)_{y+\Delta y}]}{\Delta y} + \frac{[(\rho v_z)_z - (\rho v_z)_{z+\Delta z}]}{\Delta z} = \frac{\partial \rho}{\partial t} \qquad \text{(3.6-19)}$$

Taking the limit as Δx, Δy, and Δz approach zero, we obtain the equation of continuity or conservation of mass for a pure fluid:

$$\frac{\partial \rho}{\partial t} = -\left[\frac{\partial(\rho v_x)}{\partial x} + \frac{\partial(\rho v_y)}{\partial y} + \frac{\partial(\rho v_z)}{\partial z}\right] = -(\nabla \cdot \rho v) \qquad \text{(3.6-20)}$$

The vector notation on the right side of Eq. (3.6-20) comes from the fact that v is a vector. Equation (3.6-20) tells us how density ρ changes with time at a fixed point resulting from the changes in the mass velocity vector ρv.

We can convert Eq. (3.6-20) into another form by carrying out the actual partial differentiation:

$$\frac{\partial \rho}{\partial t} = -\rho\left(\frac{\partial v_x}{\partial x} + \frac{\partial v_y}{\partial y} + \frac{\partial v_z}{\partial z}\right) - \left(v_x \frac{\partial \rho}{\partial x} + v_y \frac{\partial \rho}{\partial y} + v_z \frac{\partial \rho}{\partial z}\right) \qquad \text{(3.6-21)}$$

Rearranging Eq. (3.6-21),

$$\frac{\partial \rho}{\partial t} + v_x \frac{\partial \rho}{\partial x} + v_y \frac{\partial \rho}{\partial y} + v_z \frac{\partial \rho}{\partial z} = -\rho\left(\frac{\partial v_x}{\partial x} + \frac{\partial v_y}{\partial y} + \frac{\partial v_z}{\partial z}\right) \qquad \text{(3.6-22)}$$

The left-hand side of Eq. (3.6-22) is the same as the substantial derivative in Eq. (3.6-2). Hence, Eq. (3.6-22) becomes

$$\frac{D\rho}{Dt} = -\rho\left(\frac{\partial v_x}{\partial x} + \frac{\partial v_y}{\partial y} + \frac{\partial v_z}{\partial z}\right) = -\rho(\nabla \cdot v) \tag{3.6-23}$$

2. Equation of continuity for constant density. Often in engineering with liquids that are relatively incompressible, the density ρ is essentially constant. Then ρ remains constant for a fluid element as it moves along a path following the fluid motion, or $D\rho/Dt = 0$. Hence, Eq. (3.6-23) becomes, for a fluid of constant density at steady or unsteady state,

$$(\nabla \cdot v) = \frac{\partial v_x}{\partial x} + \frac{\partial v_y}{\partial y} + \frac{\partial v_z}{\partial z} = 0 \tag{3.6-24}$$

At steady state, $\partial\rho/\partial t = 0$ in Eq. (3.6-22).

EXAMPLE 3.6-1. Flow over a Flat Plate

An incompressible fluid flows past one side of a flat plate. The flow in the x direction is parallel to the flat plate. At the leading edge of the plate the flow is uniform at the free stream velocity v_{x0}. There is no velocity in the z direction. The y direction is the perpendicular distance from the plate. Analyze this case using the equation of continuity.

Solution: For this case where ρ is constant, Eq. (3.6-24) holds:

$$\frac{\partial v_x}{\partial x} + \frac{\partial v_y}{\partial y} + \frac{\partial v_z}{\partial z} = 0 \tag{3.6-24}$$

Since there is no velocity in the z direction, we obtain

$$\frac{\partial v_x}{\partial x} = -\frac{\partial v_y}{\partial y} \tag{3.6-25}$$

At a given small value of y close to the plate, the value of v_x must decrease from its free stream velocity v_{x0} as it passes the leading edge in the x direction because of fluid friction. Hence, $\partial v_x/\partial x$ is negative. Then from Eq. (3.6-25), $\partial v_y/\partial y$ is positive and there is a component of velocity away from the plate.

3. Continuity equation in cylindrical and spherical coordinates. It is often convenient to use cylindrical coordinates to solve the equation of continuity if fluid is flowing in a cylinder. The coordinate system as related to rectangular coordinates is shown in Fig. 3.6-3a. The relations between rectangular x, y, z and cylindrical r, θ, z coordinates are

$$x = r\cos\theta \qquad y = r\sin\theta \qquad z = z$$
$$r = +\sqrt{x^2 + y^2} \qquad \theta = \tan^{-1}\frac{y}{x} \tag{3.6-26}$$

Using the relations from Eq. (3.6-26) with Eq. (3.6-20), the equation of continuity in cylindrical coordinates is

$$\frac{\partial\rho}{\partial t} + \frac{1}{r}\frac{\partial(\rho r v_r)}{\partial r} + \frac{1}{r}\frac{\partial(\rho v_\theta)}{\partial\theta} + \frac{\partial(\rho v_z)}{\partial z} = 0 \tag{3.6-27}$$

FIGURE 3.6-3. *Curvilinear coordinate systems: (a) cylindrical coordinates, (b) spherical coordinates.*

For spherical coordinates the variables r, θ, and ϕ are related to x, y, z by the following, as shown in Fig. 3.6-3b:

$$x = r \sin \theta \cos \phi \qquad y = r \sin \theta \sin \phi \qquad z = r \cos \theta$$

$$r = +\sqrt{x^2 + y^2 + z^2} \qquad \theta = \tan^{-1} \frac{\sqrt{x^2 + y^2}}{z} \qquad \phi = \tan^{-1} \frac{y}{x} \tag{3.6-28}$$

The equation of continuity in spherical coordinates becomes

$$\frac{\partial \rho}{\partial t} + \frac{1}{r^2} \frac{\partial(\rho r^2 v_r)}{\partial r} + \frac{1}{r \sin \theta} \frac{\partial(\rho v_\theta \sin \theta)}{\partial \theta} + \frac{1}{r \sin \theta} \frac{\partial(\rho v_\phi)}{\partial \phi} = 0 \tag{3.6-29}$$

3.7 DIFFERENTIAL EQUATIONS OF MOMENTUM TRANSFER OR MOTION

3.7A Derivation of Equations of Momentum Transfer

The *equation of motion* is really the conservation-of-momentum equation (2.8-3), which we can write as

$$\begin{pmatrix} \text{rate of} \\ \text{momentum in} \end{pmatrix} - \begin{pmatrix} \text{rate of} \\ \text{momentum out} \end{pmatrix}$$

$$+ \begin{pmatrix} \text{sum of forces} \\ \text{acting on system} \end{pmatrix} = \begin{pmatrix} \text{rate of momentum} \\ \text{accumulation} \end{pmatrix} \tag{3.7-1}$$

We will make a balance on an element as in Fig. 3.6-2. First we shall consider only the x component of each term in Eq. (3.6-30). The y and z components can be described in an analogous manner.

The rate at which the x component of momentum enters the face at x in the x direction by convection is $(\rho v_x v_x)_x \, \Delta y \, \Delta z$, and the rate at which it leaves at $x + \Delta x$ is $(\rho v_x v_x)_{x + \Delta x} \, \Delta y \, \Delta z$. The quantity (ρv_x) is the concentration in momentum/m³ or (kg · m/s)/m³, and it is multiplied by v_x to give the momentum flux as momentum/s · m².

Chapter 3   Principles of Momentum Transfer and Applications

The x component of momentum entering the face at y is $(\rho v_y v_x)_y \, \Delta x \, \Delta z$, and leaving at $y + \Delta y$ it is $(\rho v_y v_x)_{y+\Delta y} \, \Delta x \, \Delta z$. For the face at z we have $(\rho v_z v_x)_z \, \Delta x \, \Delta y$ entering, and at $z + \Delta z$ we have $(\rho v_z v_x)_{z+\Delta z} \, \Delta x \, \Delta y$ leaving. Hence, the net convective x momentum flow into the volume element $\Delta x \, \Delta y \, \Delta z$ is

$$[(\rho v_x v_x)_x - (\rho v_x v_x)_{x+\Delta x}]\Delta y \, \Delta z + [(\rho v_y v_x)_y - (\rho v_y v_x)_{y+\Delta y}]\Delta x \, \Delta z$$
$$+ [(\rho v_z v_x)_z - (\rho v_z v_x)_{z+\Delta z}]\Delta x \, \Delta y \quad (3.7\text{-}2)$$

Momentum flows in and out of the volume element by the mechanisms of convection or bulk flow as given in Eq. (3.7-2) and also by molecular transfer (by virtue of the velocity gradients in laminar flow). The rate at which the x component of momentum enters the face at x by molecular transfer is $(\tau_{xx})_x \, \Delta y \, \Delta z$, and the rate at which it leaves the surface at $x + \Delta x$ is $(\tau_{xx})_{x+\Delta x} \, \Delta y \, \Delta z$. The rate at which it enters the face at y is $(\tau_{yx})_y \, \Delta x \, \Delta z$, and it leaves at $y + \Delta y$ at a rate of $(\tau_{yx})_{y+\Delta y} \, \Delta x \, \Delta z$. Note that τ_{yx} is the flux of x momentum through the face perpendicular to the y axis. Writing a similar equation for the remaining faces, the net x component of momentum by molecular transfer is

$$[(\tau_{xx})_x - (\tau_{xx})_{x+\Delta x}]\Delta y \, \Delta z + [(\tau_{yx})_y - (\tau_{yx})_{y+\Delta y}]\Delta x \, \Delta z + [(\tau_{zx})_z - (\tau_{zx})_{z+\Delta z}]\Delta x \, \Delta y$$
$$(3.7\text{-}3)$$

These molecular fluxes of momentum may be considered as shear stresses and normal stresses. Hence, τ_{yx} is the x-direction shear stress on the y face and τ_{zx} the shear stress on the z face. Also, τ_{xx} is the normal stress on the x face.

The net fluid-pressure force acting on the element in the x direction is the difference between the forces acting at x and $x + \Delta x$:

$$(p_x - p_{x+\Delta x})\Delta y \, \Delta z \quad (3.7\text{-}4)$$

The gravitational force g_x acting on a unit mass in the x direction is multiplied by the mass of the element to give

$$\rho g_x \, \Delta x \, \Delta y \, \Delta z \quad (3.7\text{-}5)$$

where g_x is the x component of the gravitational vector g.

The rate of accumulation of x momentum in the element is

$$\Delta x \, \Delta y \, \Delta z \, \frac{\partial(\rho v_x)}{\partial t} \quad (3.7\text{-}6)$$

Substituting Eqs. (3.7-2)–(3.7-6) into (3.7-1), dividing by $\Delta x \, \Delta y \, \Delta z$, and taking the limit as Δx, Δy, and Δz approach zero, we obtain the x component of the differential equation of motion:

$$\frac{\partial(\rho v_x)}{\partial t} = -\left[\frac{\partial(\rho v_x v_x)}{\partial x} + \frac{\partial(\rho v_y v_x)}{\partial y} + \frac{\partial(\rho v_z v_x)}{\partial z}\right]$$
$$-\left(\frac{\partial \tau_{xx}}{\partial x} + \frac{\partial \tau_{yx}}{\partial y} + \frac{\partial \tau_{zx}}{\partial z}\right) - \frac{\partial p}{\partial x} + \rho g_x \quad (3.7\text{-}7)$$

The y and z components of the differential equation of motion are, respectively,

$$\frac{\partial(\rho v_y)}{\partial t} = -\left[\frac{\partial(\rho v_x v_y)}{\partial x} + \frac{\partial(\rho v_y v_y)}{\partial y} + \frac{\partial(\rho v_z v_y)}{\partial z}\right]$$
$$-\left(\frac{\partial \tau_{xy}}{\partial x} + \frac{\partial \tau_{yy}}{\partial y} + \frac{\partial \tau_{zy}}{\partial z}\right) - \frac{\partial p}{\partial y} + \rho g_y \quad (3.7\text{-}8)$$

$$\frac{\partial(\rho v_z)}{\partial t} = -\left[\frac{\partial(\rho v_x v_z)}{\partial x} + \frac{\partial(\rho v_y v_z)}{\partial y} + \frac{\partial(\rho v_z v_z)}{\partial z}\right]$$

$$-\left(\frac{\partial \tau_{xz}}{\partial x} + \frac{\partial \tau_{yz}}{\partial y} + \frac{\partial \tau_{zz}}{\partial z}\right) - \frac{\partial p}{\partial z} + \rho g_z \tag{3.7-9}$$

We can use Eq. (3.6-20), which is the continuity equation, and Eq. (3.7-7) to obtain an equation of motion for the x component and also do the same for the y and z components as follows:

$$\rho\left(\frac{\partial v_x}{\partial t} + v_x\frac{\partial v_x}{\partial x} + v_y\frac{\partial v_x}{\partial y} + v_z\frac{\partial v_x}{\partial z}\right) = -\left[\frac{\partial \tau_{xx}}{\partial x} + \frac{\partial \tau_{yx}}{\partial y} + \frac{\partial \tau_{zx}}{\partial z}\right] + \rho g_x - \frac{\partial p}{\partial x} \tag{3.7-10}$$

$$\rho\left(\frac{\partial v_y}{\partial t} + v_x\frac{\partial v_y}{\partial x} + v_y\frac{\partial v_y}{\partial y} + v_z\frac{\partial v_y}{\partial z}\right) = -\left[\frac{\partial \tau_{xy}}{\partial x} + \frac{\partial \tau_{yy}}{\partial y} + \frac{\partial \tau_{zy}}{\partial z}\right] + \rho g_y - \frac{\partial p}{\partial y} \tag{3.7-11}$$

$$\rho\left(\frac{\partial v_z}{\partial t} + v_x\frac{\partial v_z}{\partial x} + v_y\frac{\partial v_z}{\partial y} + v_z\frac{\partial v_z}{\partial z}\right) = -\left[\frac{\partial \tau_{xz}}{\partial x} + \frac{\partial \tau_{yz}}{\partial y} + \frac{\partial \tau_{zz}}{\partial z}\right] + \rho g_z - \frac{\partial p}{\partial z} \tag{3.7-12}$$

Adding vectorially, we obtain an equation of motion for a pure fluid:

$$\rho\frac{Dv}{Dt} = -(\nabla \cdot \tau) - \nabla p + \rho g \tag{3.7-13}$$

We should note that Eqs. (3.7-7)–(3.7-13) are valid for any continuous medium.

3.7B Equations of Motion for Newtonian Fluids with Varying Density and Viscosity

In order to use Eqs. (3.7-7)–(3.7-13) to determine velocity distributions, expressions must be used for the various stresses in terms of velocity gradients and fluid properties. For Newtonian fluids the expressions for the stresses τ_{xx}, τ_{yx}, τ_{zx}, and so on, have been related to the velocity gradients and the fluid viscosity μ (B1, B2, D1) and are as follows:

1. Shear-stress components for Newtonian fluids in rectangular coordinates

$$\tau_{xx} = -2\mu\frac{\partial v_x}{\partial x} + \frac{2}{3}\mu(\nabla \cdot v) \tag{3.7-14}$$

$$\tau_{yy} = -2\mu\frac{\partial v_y}{\partial y} + \frac{2}{3}\mu(\nabla \cdot v) \tag{3.7-15}$$

$$\tau_{zz} = -2\mu\frac{\partial v_z}{\partial z} + \frac{2}{3}\mu(\nabla \cdot v) \tag{3.7-16}$$

$$\tau_{xy} = \tau_{yx} = -\mu\left(\frac{\partial v_x}{\partial y} + \frac{\partial v_y}{\partial x}\right) \tag{3.7-17}$$

$$\tau_{yz} = \tau_{zy} = -\mu\left(\frac{\partial v_y}{\partial z} + \frac{\partial v_z}{\partial y}\right) \tag{3.7-18}$$

$$\tau_{zx} = \tau_{xz} = -\mu\left(\frac{\partial v_z}{\partial x} + \frac{\partial v_x}{\partial z}\right) \tag{3.7-19}$$

$$(\nabla \cdot v) = \left(\frac{\partial v_x}{\partial x} + \frac{\partial v_y}{\partial y} + \frac{\partial v_z}{\partial z} \right) \tag{3.7-20}$$

2. Shear-stress components for Newtonian fluids in cylindrical coordinates

$$\tau_{rr} = -\mu \left[2 \frac{\partial v_r}{\partial r} - \frac{2}{3} (\nabla \cdot v) \right] \tag{3.7-21}$$

$$\tau_{\theta\theta} = -\mu \left[2 \left(\frac{1}{r} \frac{\partial v_\theta}{\partial \theta} + \frac{v_r}{r} \right) - \frac{2}{3} (\nabla \cdot v) \right] \tag{3.7-22}$$

$$\tau_{zz} = -\mu \left[2 \frac{\partial v_z}{\partial z} - \frac{2}{3} (\nabla \cdot v) \right] \tag{3.7-23}$$

$$\tau_{r\theta} = \tau_{\theta r} = -\mu \left[r \frac{\partial (v_\theta/r)}{\partial r} + \frac{1}{r} \frac{\partial v_r}{\partial \theta} \right] \tag{3.7-24}$$

$$\tau_{\theta z} = \tau_{z\theta} = -\mu \left[\frac{\partial v_\theta}{\partial z} + \frac{1}{r} \frac{\partial v_z}{\partial \theta} \right] \tag{3.7-25}$$

$$\tau_{zr} = \tau_{rz} = -\mu \left[\frac{\partial v_z}{\partial r} + \frac{\partial v_r}{\partial z} \right] \tag{3.7-26}$$

$$(\nabla \cdot v) = \frac{1}{r} \frac{\partial (r v_r)}{\partial r} + \frac{1}{r} \frac{\partial v_\theta}{\partial \theta} + \frac{\partial v_z}{\partial z} \tag{3.7-27}$$

3. Shear-stress components for Newtonian fluids in spherical coordinates

$$\tau_{rr} = -\mu \left[2 \frac{\partial v_r}{\partial r} - \frac{2}{3} (\nabla \cdot v) \right] \tag{3.7-28}$$

$$\tau_{\theta\theta} = -\mu \left[2 \left(\frac{1}{r} \frac{\partial v_\theta}{\partial \theta} + \frac{v_r}{r} \right) - \frac{2}{3} (\nabla \cdot v) \right] \tag{3.7-29}$$

$$\tau_{\phi\phi} = -\mu \left[2 \left(\frac{1}{r \sin \theta} \frac{\partial v_\phi}{\partial \phi} + \frac{v_r}{r} + \frac{v_\theta \cot \theta}{r} \right) - \frac{2}{3} (\nabla \cdot v) \right] \tag{3.7-30}$$

$$\tau_{r\theta} = \tau_{\theta r} = -\mu \left[r \frac{\partial (v_\theta/r)}{\partial r} + \frac{1}{r} \frac{\partial v_r}{\partial \theta} \right] \tag{3.7-31}$$

$$\tau_{\theta\phi} = \tau_{\phi\theta} = -\mu \left[\frac{\sin \theta}{r} \frac{\partial (v_\phi/\sin \theta)}{\partial \theta} + \frac{1}{r \sin \theta} \frac{\partial v_\theta}{\partial \phi} \right] \tag{3.7-32}$$

$$\tau_{\phi r} = \tau_{r\phi} = -\mu \left[\frac{1}{r \sin \theta} \frac{\partial v_r}{\partial \phi} + r \frac{\partial (v_\phi/r)}{\partial r} \right] \tag{3.7-33}$$

$$(\nabla \cdot v) = \frac{1}{r^2} \frac{\partial (r^2 v_r)}{\partial r} + \left[\frac{1}{r \sin \theta} \frac{\partial (v_\theta \sin \theta)}{\partial \theta} + \frac{1}{r \sin \theta} \frac{\partial v_\phi}{\partial \phi} \right] \tag{3.7-34}$$

4. Equation of motion for Newtonian fluids with varying density and viscosity.

After Eqs. (3.7-14)–(3.7-20) for shear-stress components are substituted into Eq. (3.7-10) for the x component of momentum, we obtain the general equation of motion for a Newtonian fluid with varying density and viscosity:

$$\rho \frac{Dv_x}{Dt} = \frac{\partial}{\partial x}\left[2\mu \frac{\partial v_x}{\partial x} - \frac{2}{3}\mu(\boldsymbol{\nabla}\cdot\boldsymbol{v})\right] + \frac{\partial}{\partial y}\left[\mu\left(\frac{\partial v_x}{\partial y} + \frac{\partial v_y}{\partial x}\right)\right]$$

$$+ \frac{\partial}{\partial z}\left[\mu\left(\frac{\partial v_z}{\partial x} + \frac{\partial v_x}{\partial z}\right)\right] - \frac{\partial p}{\partial x} + \rho g_x \qquad \text{(3.7-35)}$$

Similar equations are obtained for the y and z components of momentum.

3.7C Equations of Motion for Newtonian Fluids with Constant Density and Viscosity

The equations above are seldom used in their complete forms. When the density ρ and the viscosity μ are constant where $(\boldsymbol{\nabla}\cdot\boldsymbol{v}) = 0$, the equations are simplified and we obtain the equations of motion for Newtonian fluids. These equations are also called the *Navier–Stokes equations*.

1. Equation of motion in rectangular coordinates.   For Newtonian fluids for constant ρ and μ for the x component, y component, and z component we obtain, respectively,

$$\rho\left(\frac{\partial v_x}{\partial t} + v_x \frac{\partial v_x}{\partial x} + v_y \frac{\partial v_x}{\partial y} + v_z \frac{\partial v_x}{\partial z}\right) = \mu\left(\frac{\partial^2 v_x}{\partial x^2} + \frac{\partial^2 v_x}{\partial y^2} + \frac{\partial^2 v_x}{\partial z^2}\right) - \frac{\partial p}{\partial x} + \rho g_x \quad \text{(3.7-36)}$$

$$\rho\left(\frac{\partial v_y}{\partial t} + v_x \frac{\partial v_y}{\partial x} + v_y \frac{\partial v_y}{\partial y} + v_z \frac{\partial v_y}{\partial z}\right) = \mu\left(\frac{\partial^2 v_y}{\partial x^2} + \frac{\partial^2 v_y}{\partial y^2} + \frac{\partial^2 v_y}{\partial z^2}\right) - \frac{\partial p}{\partial y} + \rho g_y \quad \text{(3.7-37)}$$

$$\rho\left(\frac{\partial v_z}{\partial t} + v_x \frac{\partial v_z}{\partial x} + v_y \frac{\partial v_z}{\partial y} + v_z \frac{\partial v_z}{\partial z}\right) = \mu\left(\frac{\partial^2 v_z}{\partial x^2} + \frac{\partial^2 v_z}{\partial y^2} + \frac{\partial^2 v_z}{\partial z^2}\right) - \frac{\partial p}{\partial z} + \rho g_z \quad \text{(3.7-38)}$$

Combining the three equations for the three components, we obtain

$$\rho \frac{Dv}{Dt} = -\boldsymbol{\nabla}p + \rho\boldsymbol{g} + \mu\boldsymbol{\nabla}^2\boldsymbol{v} \qquad \text{(3.7-39)}$$

2. Equation of motion in cylindrical coordinates.   These equations are as follows for Newtonian fluids for constant ρ and μ for the r, θ, and z components, respectively:

$$\rho\left(\frac{\partial v_r}{\partial t} + v_r \frac{\partial v_r}{\partial r} + \frac{v_\theta}{r} \frac{\partial v_r}{\partial \theta} - \frac{v_\theta^2}{r} + v_z \frac{\partial v_r}{\partial z}\right)$$

$$= -\frac{\partial p}{\partial r} + \mu\left[\frac{\partial}{\partial r}\left(\frac{1}{r} \frac{\partial(r v_r)}{\partial r}\right) + \frac{1}{r^2} \frac{\partial^2 v_r}{\partial \theta^2} - \frac{2}{r^2} \frac{\partial v_\theta}{\partial \theta} + \frac{\partial^2 v_r}{\partial z^2}\right] + \rho g_r \quad \text{(3.7-40)}$$

$$\rho\left(\frac{\partial v_\theta}{\partial t} + v_r \frac{\partial v_\theta}{\partial r} + \frac{v_\theta}{r} \frac{\partial v_\theta}{\partial \theta} + \frac{v_r v_\theta}{r} + v_z \frac{\partial v_\theta}{\partial z}\right)$$

$$= -\frac{1}{r} \frac{\partial p}{\partial \theta} + \mu\left[\frac{\partial}{\partial r}\left(\frac{1}{r} \frac{\partial(r v_\theta)}{\partial r}\right) + \frac{1}{r^2} \frac{\partial^2 v_\theta}{\partial \theta^2} + \frac{2}{r^2} \frac{\partial v_r}{\partial \theta} + \frac{\partial^2 v_\theta}{\partial z^2}\right] + \rho g_\theta \quad \text{(3.7-41)}$$

$$\rho\left(\frac{\partial v_z}{\partial t} + v_r \frac{\partial v_z}{\partial r} + \frac{v_\theta}{r} \frac{\partial v_z}{\partial \theta} + v_z \frac{\partial v_z}{\partial z}\right)$$

$$= -\frac{\partial p}{\partial z} + \mu\left[\frac{1}{r} \frac{\partial}{\partial r}\left(r \frac{\partial v_z}{\partial r}\right) + \frac{1}{r^2} \frac{\partial^2 v_z}{\partial \theta^2} + \frac{\partial^2 v_z}{\partial z^2}\right] + \rho g_z \quad \text{(3.7-42)}$$

3. *Equation of motion in spherical coordinates.* The equations for Newtonian fluids are given below for constant ρ and μ for the r, θ, and ϕ components, respectively:

$$\rho\left(\frac{\partial v_r}{\partial t} + v_r \frac{\partial v_r}{\partial r} + \frac{v_\theta}{r} \frac{\partial v_r}{\partial \theta} + \frac{v_\phi}{r \sin \theta} \frac{\partial v_r}{\partial \phi} - \frac{v_\theta^2 + v_\phi^2}{r}\right)$$

$$= -\frac{\partial p}{\partial r} + \mu\left(\nabla^2 v_r - \frac{2}{r^2} v_r - \frac{2}{r^2} \frac{\partial v_\theta}{\partial \theta} - \frac{2}{r^2} v_\theta \cot\theta - \frac{2}{r^2 \sin\theta} \frac{\partial v_\phi}{\partial \phi}\right) + \rho g_r \quad \text{(3.7-43)}$$

$$\rho\left(\frac{\partial v_\theta}{\partial t} + v_r \frac{\partial v_\theta}{\partial r} + \frac{v_\theta}{r} \frac{\partial v_\theta}{\partial \theta} + \frac{v_\phi}{r \sin\theta} \frac{\partial v_\theta}{\partial \phi} + \frac{v_r v_\theta}{r} - \frac{v_\phi^2 \cot\theta}{r}\right)$$

$$= -\frac{1}{r} \frac{\partial p}{\partial \theta} + \mu\left(\nabla^2 v_\theta + \frac{2}{r^2} \frac{\partial v_r}{\partial \theta} - \frac{v_\theta}{r^2 \sin^2 \theta} - \frac{2}{r^2} \frac{\cos\theta}{\sin^2\theta} \frac{\partial v_\phi}{\partial \phi}\right) + \rho g_\theta \quad \text{(3.7-44)}$$

$$\rho\left(\frac{\partial v_\phi}{\partial t} + v_r \frac{\partial v_\phi}{\partial r} + \frac{v_\theta}{r} \frac{\partial v_\phi}{\partial \theta} + \frac{v_\phi}{r \sin\theta} \frac{\partial v_\phi}{\partial \phi} + \frac{v_\phi v_r}{r} + \frac{v_\theta v_\phi}{r} \cot\theta\right)$$

$$= -\frac{1}{r \sin\theta} \frac{\partial p}{\partial \phi} + \mu\left(\nabla^2 v_\phi - \frac{v_\phi}{r^2 \sin^2\theta} + \frac{2}{r^2 \sin\theta} \frac{\partial v_r}{\partial \phi} + \frac{2\cos\theta}{r^2 \sin^2\theta} \frac{\partial v_\theta}{\partial \phi}\right) + \rho g_\phi \quad \text{(3.7-45)}$$

where in the three equations above,

$$\nabla^2 = \frac{1}{r^2} \frac{\partial}{\partial r}\left(r^2 \frac{\partial}{\partial r}\right) + \frac{1}{r^2 \sin\theta} \frac{\partial}{\partial \theta}\left(\sin\theta \frac{\partial}{\partial \theta}\right) + \frac{1}{r^2 \sin^2\theta}\left(\frac{\partial^2}{\partial \phi^2}\right) \quad \text{(3.7-46)}$$

Significant advantages and uses arise in the transformation from rectangular coordinates to cylindrical coordinates. For example, in Eq. (3.7-40) the term $\rho v_\theta^2/r$ is the centrifugal force. This gives the force in the r direction (radial) resulting from the motion of the fluid in the θ direction. Note that this term is obtained automatically from the transformation from rectangular to cylindrical coordinates. It does not have to be added to the equation on physical grounds.

The Coriolis force $\rho v_r v_\theta/r$ also arises automatically in the transformation of coordinates in Eq. (3.7-41). It is the effective force in the θ direction when there is flow in both the r and the θ directions, as in the case of flow near a rotating disk.

3.8 USE OF DIFFERENTIAL EQUATIONS OF CONTINUITY AND MOTION

3.8A Introduction

The purpose and uses of the differential equations of motion and continuity, as mentioned previously, are to apply these equations to any viscous-flow problem. For a given specific problem, the terms that are zero or near zero are simply discarded and the remaining equations used to solve for the velocity, density, and pressure distributions. Of course, it is necessary to know the initial conditions and the boundary conditions to solve the equations. Several examples will be given to illustrate the general methods used.

We will consider cases for flow in specific geometries that can easily be described mathematically, such as flow between parallel plates and in cylinders.

3.8B Differential Equations of Continuity and Motion for Flow between Parallel Plates

Two examples will be considered, one for horizontal plates and one for vertical plates.

EXAMPLE 3.8-1. Laminar Flow Between Horizontal Parallel Plates
Derive the equation giving the velocity distribution at steady state for laminar flow of a constant-density fluid with constant viscosity flowing between two flat and parallel plates. The velocity profile desired is at a point far from the inlet or outlet of the channel. The two plates will be considered to be fixed and of infinite width, with the flow driven by the pressure gradient in the x direction.

Solution: Assuming that the channel is horizontal, Fig. 3.8-1 shows the axes selected, with flow in the x direction and the width in the z direction. The velocities v_y and v_z are then zero. The plates are a distance $2y_0$ apart.

The continuity equation (3.6-24) for constant density is

$$\frac{\partial v_x}{\partial x} + \frac{\partial v_y}{\partial y} + \frac{\partial v_z}{\partial z} = 0 \qquad (3.6\text{-}24)$$

Since v_y and v_z are zero, Eq. (3.6-24) becomes

$$\frac{\partial v_x}{\partial x} = 0 \qquad (3.8\text{-}1)$$

The Navier–Stokes equation for the x component is

$$\rho\left(\frac{\partial v_x}{\partial t} + v_x\frac{\partial v_x}{\partial x} + v_y\frac{\partial v_x}{\partial y} + v_z\frac{\partial v_x}{\partial z}\right) = \mu\left(\frac{\partial^2 v_x}{\partial x^2} + \frac{\partial^2 v_x}{\partial y^2} + \frac{\partial^2 v_x}{\partial z^2}\right) - \frac{\partial p}{\partial x} + \rho g_x$$

$$(3.7\text{-}36)$$

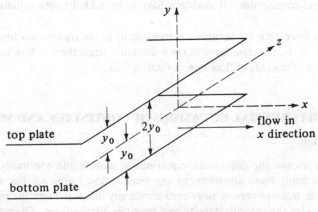

top plate

bottom plate

flow in
x direction

FIGURE 3.8-1. *Flow between two parallel plates in Example 3.8-1.*

Also, $\partial v_x/\partial t = 0$ for steady state, $v_y = 0$, $v_z = 0$, $\partial v_x/\partial x = 0$, $\partial^2 v_x/\partial x^2 = 0$. We can see that $\partial v_x/\partial z = 0$, since there is no change of v_x with z. Then $\partial^2 v_x/\partial z^2 = 0$. Making these substitutions into Eq. (3.7-36), we obtain

$$\frac{\partial p}{\partial x} - \rho g_x = \mu \frac{\partial^2 v_x}{\partial y^2} \tag{3.8-2}$$

In fluid-flow problems we will be concerned with gravitational force only in the vertical direction for g_x, which is g, the gravitational force, in m/s^2. We shall combine the static pressure p and the gravitational force and call them simply p, as follows (note that $g_x = 0$ for the present case of a horizontal pipe but is not zero for the general case of a nonhorizontal pipe):

$$p = p + \rho g h \tag{3.8-3}$$

where h is the distance upward from any chosen reference plane (h is in the direction opposed to gravity). Then Eq. (3.8-2) becomes

$$\frac{\partial p}{\partial x} = \mu \frac{\partial^2 v_x}{\partial y^2} \tag{3.8-4}$$

We can see that p is not a function of z. Also, assuming that $2y_0$ is small, p is not a function of y. (Some references avoid this problem and simply use p as a dynamic pressure, which is rigorously correct since dynamic pressure gradients cause flow. In a fluid at rest, the total pressure gradient is the hydrostatic pressure gradient, and the dynamic pressure gradient is zero.) Also, $\partial p/\partial x$ is a constant in this problem, since v_x is not a function of x. Then Eq. (3.8-4) becomes an ordinary differential equation:

$$\frac{d^2 v_x}{dy^2} = \frac{1}{\mu} \frac{dp}{dx} = \text{const} \tag{3.8-5}$$

Integrating Eq. (3.8-5) once, using the condition $dv_x/dy = 0$ at $y = 0$ for symmetry,

$$\frac{dv_x}{dy} = \left(\frac{1}{\mu} \frac{dp}{dx}\right) y \tag{3.8-6}$$

Integrating again, using $v_x = 0$ at $y = y_0$,

$$v_x = \frac{1}{2\mu} \frac{dp}{dx} (y^2 - y_0^2) \tag{3.8-7}$$

The maximum velocity in Eq. (3.8-7) occurs when $y = 0$, giving

$$v_{x\max} = \frac{1}{2\mu} \frac{dp}{dx} (-y_0^2) \tag{3.8-8}$$

Combining Eqs. (3.8-7) and (3.8-8),

$$v_x = v_{x\max} \left[1 - \left(\frac{y}{y_0}\right)^2 \right] \tag{3.8-9}$$

Hence, a parabolic velocity profile is obtained. This result was also obtained in Eq. (2.9-9) when using a shell-momentum balance.

FIGURE 3.8-2. *Flow between vertical parallel plates in Example 3.8-2.*

The results obtained in Example 3.8-1 could also have been obtained by making a force balance on a differential element of fluid and using the symmetry of the system to omit certain terms.

EXAMPLE 3.8-2. Laminar Flow Between Vertical Plates with One Plate Moving

A Newtonian fluid is confined between two parallel and vertical plates as shown in Fig. 3.8-2 (W6). The surface on the left is stationary and the other is moving vertically at a constant velocity v_0. Assuming that the flow is laminar, solve for the velocity profile.

Solution: The equation to use is the Navier–Stokes equation for the y coordinate, Eq. (3.7-37):

$$\rho\left(\frac{\partial v_y}{\partial t} + v_x\frac{\partial v_y}{\partial x} + v_y\frac{\partial v_y}{\partial y} + v_z\frac{\partial v_y}{\partial z}\right)$$

$$= \mu\left(\frac{\partial^2 v_y}{\partial x^2} + \frac{\partial^2 v_y}{\partial y^2} + \frac{\partial^2 v_y}{\partial z^2}\right) - \frac{\partial p}{\partial y} + \rho g_y \quad \textbf{(3.7-37)}$$

At steady state, $\partial v_y/\partial t = 0$. The velocities v_x and $v_z = 0$. Also, $\partial v_y/\partial y = 0$ from the continuity equation, $\partial v_y/\partial z = 0$, and $\rho g_y = -\rho g$. The partial derivatives become derivatives and Eq. (3.7-37) becomes

$$\mu\frac{d^2 v_y}{dx^2} - \frac{dp}{dy} - \rho g = 0 \quad \textbf{(3.8-10)}$$

This is similar to Eq. (3.8-2) in Example 3.8-1. The pressure gradient dp/dy is constant. Integrating Eq. (3.8-10) once yields

$$\frac{dv_y}{dx} - \frac{x}{\mu}\left(\frac{dp}{dy} + \rho g\right) = C_1 \quad \textbf{(3.8-11)}$$

Integrating again gives

$$v_y - \frac{x^2}{2\mu}\left(\frac{dp}{dy} + \rho g\right) = C_1 x + C_2 \quad \textbf{(3.8-12)}$$

The boundary conditions are at $x = 0$, $v_y = 0$ and at $x = H$, $v_y = v_0$. Solving for the constants, $C_1 = v_0/H - (H/2\mu)(dp/dy + \rho g)$ and $C_2 = 0$. Hence, Eq. (3.8-12) becomes

$$v_y = -\frac{1}{2\mu}\left(\frac{dp}{dy} + \rho g\right)(Hx - x^2) + v_0\frac{x}{H} \tag{3.8-13}$$

3.8C Differential Equations of Continuity and Motion for Flow in Stationary and Rotating Cylinders

Several examples will be given for flow in stationary and rotating cylinders.

EXAMPLE 3.8-3. Laminar Flow in a Circular Tube

Derive the equation for steady-state viscous flow in a horizontal tube of radius r_0, where the fluid is far from the tube inlet. The fluid is incompressible and μ is a constant. The flow is driven in one direction by a constant-pressure gradient.

Solution: The fluid will be assumed to flow in the z direction in the tube, as shown in Fig. 3.8-3. The y direction is vertical and the x direction horizontal. Since v_x and v_y are zero, the continuity equation becomes $\partial v_z/\partial z = 0$. For steady state $\partial v_z/\partial t = 0$. Then substituting into Eq. (3.7-38) for the z component, we obtain

$$\frac{dp}{dz} = \mu\left(\frac{\partial^2 v_z}{\partial x^2} + \frac{\partial^2 v_z}{\partial y^2}\right) \tag{3.8-14}$$

To solve Eq. (3.8-14), we can use cylindrical coordinates from Eq. (3.6-26), giving

$$z = z \qquad x = r\cos\theta \qquad y = r\sin\theta$$

$$r = +\sqrt{x^2 + y^2} \qquad \theta = \tan^{-1}\frac{y}{x} \tag{3.6-26}$$

FIGURE 3.8-3. Horizontal flow in a tube in Example 3.8-3.

Substituting these into Eq. (3.8-14),

$$\frac{1}{\mu}\frac{dp}{dz} = \frac{\partial^2 v_z}{\partial r^2} + \frac{1}{r}\frac{\partial v_z}{\partial r} + \frac{1}{r^2}\frac{\partial^2 v_z}{\partial \theta^2} \tag{3.8-15}$$

The flow is symmetrical about the z axis, so $\partial^2 v_z/\partial\theta^2$ is zero in Eq. (3.8-15). As before, dp/dz is a constant, and Eq. (3.8-15) becomes

$$\frac{1}{\mu}\frac{dp}{dz} = \text{const} = \frac{d^2 v_z}{dr^2} + \frac{1}{r}\frac{dv_z}{dr} = \frac{1}{r}\frac{d}{dr}\left(r\frac{dv_z}{dr}\right) \tag{3.8-16}$$

Alternatively, Eq. (3.7-42) in cylindrical coordinates can be used for the z component and the terms that are zero discarded:

$$\rho\left(\frac{\partial v_z}{\partial t} + v_r\frac{\partial v_z}{\partial r} + \frac{v_\theta}{r}\frac{\partial v_z}{\partial \theta} + v_z\frac{\partial v_z}{\partial z}\right)$$

$$= -\frac{\partial p}{\partial z} + \mu\left[\frac{1}{r}\frac{\partial}{\partial r}\left(r\frac{\partial v_z}{\partial r}\right) + \frac{1}{r^2}\frac{\partial^2 v_z}{\partial \theta^2} + \frac{\partial^2 v_z}{\partial z^2}\right] + \rho g_z \tag{3.7-42}$$

As before, $\partial v_z/\partial t = 0$, $\partial^2 v_z/\partial\theta^2 = 0$, $v_r = 0$, $\partial v_z/\partial\theta = 0$, $\partial v_z/\partial z = 0$. Then Eq. (3.7-42) becomes identical to Eq. (3.8-16).

The boundary conditions for the first integration are $dv_z/dr = 0$ at $r = 0$. For the second integration, $v_z = 0$ at $r = r_0$ (tube radius). The result is

$$v_z = \frac{1}{4\mu}\frac{dp}{dz}(r^2 - r_0^2) \tag{3.8-17}$$

Converting to the maximum velocity as before,

$$v_z = v_{z\max}\left[1 - \left(\frac{r}{r_0}\right)^2\right] \tag{3.8-18}$$

If Eq. (3.8-17) is integrated over the pipe cross section using Eq. (2.9-10) to give the average velocity $v_{z\,av}$,

$$v_{z\,av} = -\frac{r_0^2}{8\mu}\frac{dp}{dz} \tag{3.8-19}$$

Integrating to obtain the pressure drop from $z = 0$ for $p = p_1$ to $z = L$ for $p = p_2$, we obtain

$$p_1 - p_2 = \frac{8\mu v_{z\,av}L}{r_0^2} = \frac{32\mu v_{z\,av}L}{D^2} \tag{3.8-20}$$

where $D = 2r_0$. This is the Hagen–Poiseuille equation, derived previously as Eq. (2.9-11).

EXAMPLE 3.8-4. Laminar Flow in a Cylindrical Annulus
Derive the equation for steady-state laminar flow inside the annulus between two concentric horizontal pipes. This type of flow occurs often in concentric-pipe heat exchangers.

FIGURE 3.8-4. *Flow through a cylindrical annulus.*

Solution: In this case Eq. (3.8-16) also still holds. However, the velocity in the annulus will reach a maximum at some radius $r = r_{max}$ which is between r_1 and r_2, as shown in Fig. 3.8-4. For the first integration of Eq. (3.8-16), the boundary conditions are $dv_z/dr = 0$ at $r = r_{max}$, which gives

$$\frac{r\,dv_z}{dr} = \left(\frac{1}{\mu}\frac{dp}{dz}\right)\left(\frac{r^2}{2} - \frac{r_{max}^2}{2}\right) \quad \text{(3.8-21)}$$

Also, for the second integration of Eq. (3.8-21), $v_z = 0$ at the inner wall where $r = r_1$, giving

$$v_z = \left(\frac{1}{2\mu}\frac{dp}{dz}\right)\left(\frac{r^2}{2} - \frac{r_1^2}{2} - r_{max}^2 \ln\frac{r}{r_1}\right) \quad \text{(3.8-22)}$$

Repeating the second integration but for $v_r = 0$ at the outer wall where $r = r_2$, we obtain

$$v_z = \left(\frac{1}{2\mu}\frac{dp}{dz}\right)\left(\frac{r^2}{2} - \frac{r_2^2}{2} - r_{max}^2 \ln\frac{r}{r_2}\right) \quad \text{(3.8-23)}$$

Combining Eqs. (3.8-22) and (3.8-23) and solving for r_{max},

$$r_{max} = \sqrt{\frac{1}{\ln(r_2/r_1)}(r_2^2 - r_1^2)/2} \quad \text{(3.8-24)}$$

In Fig. 3.8-4 the velocity profile predicted by Eq. (3.8-23) is plotted. For the case where $r_1 = 0$, r_{max} in Eq. (3.8-24) becomes zero and Eq. (3.8-23) reduces to Eq. (3.8-17) for a single circular pipe.

EXAMPLE 3.8-5. *Velocity Distribution for Flow Between Coaxial Cylinders*

Tangential laminar flow of a Newtonian fluid with constant density is occurring between two vertical coaxial cylinders in which the outer one is rotating (S4) with an angular velocity of ω, as shown in Fig. 3.8-5. It can be assumed that end effects can be neglected. Determine the velocity and the shear-stress distributions for this flow.

Solution: On physical grounds the fluid moves in a circular motion; the velocity v_r in the radial direction is zero and v_z in the axial direction is zero. Also,

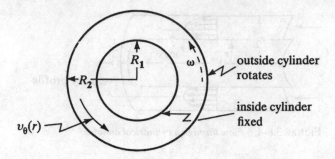

FIGURE 3.8-5. *Laminar flow in the region between two coaxial cylinders in Example 3.8-5.*

$\partial\rho/\partial t = 0$ at steady state. There is no pressure gradient in the θ direction. The equation of continuity in cylindrical coordinates as derived before is

$$\frac{\partial\rho}{\partial t} + \frac{1}{r}\frac{\partial(\rho v_r)}{\partial r} + \frac{1}{r}\frac{\partial(\rho v_\theta)}{\partial\theta} + \frac{\partial(\rho v_z)}{\partial z} = 0 \qquad \text{(3.6-27)}$$

All terms in this equation are zero.

The equations of motion in cylindrical coordinates, Eqs. (3.7-40), (3.7-41), and (3.7-42), reduce to the following, respectively:

$$-\rho\frac{v_\theta^2}{r} = -\frac{\partial p}{\partial r} \qquad (r\text{-component}) \qquad \text{(3.8-25)}$$

$$0 = \frac{d}{dr}\left(\frac{1}{r}\frac{d(rv_\theta)}{dr}\right) \qquad (\theta\text{-component}) \qquad \text{(3.8-26)}$$

$$0 = -\frac{\partial p}{\partial z} + \rho g_z \qquad (z\text{-component}) \qquad \text{(3.8-27)}$$

Integrating Eq. (3.8-26),

$$v_\theta = C_1 r + \frac{C_2}{r} \qquad \text{(3.8-28)}$$

To solve for the integration constants C_1 and C_2, the following boundary conditions are used: at $r = R_1$, $v_\theta = 0$; at $r = R_2$, $v_\theta = \omega R_2$. The final equation is

$$v_\theta = \frac{\omega}{(R_1^2 - R_2^2)/(R_1 R_2^2)}\left[\frac{R_1}{r} - \frac{r}{R_1}\right] \qquad \text{(3.8-29)}$$

Using the shear-stress component for Newtonian fluids in cylindrical coordinates,

$$\tau_{r\theta} = -\mu\left[r\frac{\partial(v_\theta/r)}{\partial r} + \frac{1}{r}\frac{\partial v_r}{\partial\theta}\right] \qquad \text{(3.7-31)}$$

The last term in Eq. (3.7-31) is zero. Substituting Eq. (3.8-29) into (3.7-31) and differentiating gives

$$\tau_{r\theta} = -2\mu\omega R_2^2 \left(\frac{1}{r^2}\right)\left[\frac{R_1^2/R_2^2}{1 - R_1^2/R_2^2}\right] \tag{3.8-30}$$

The torque T that is necessary to rotate the outer cylinder is the product of the force times the lever arm:

$$T = (2\pi R_2 H)(-\tau_{r\theta})|_{r=R_2}(R_2)$$

$$= 4\pi\mu H\omega R_2^2 \left[\frac{R_1^2/R_2^2}{1 - R_1^2/R_2^2}\right] \tag{3.8-31}$$

where H is the length of the cylinder. This type of device has been used to measure fluid viscosities from observations of angular velocities and torque and has also been used as a model for some friction bearings.

EXAMPLE 3.8-6.   Rotating Liquid in a Cylindrical Container

A Newtonian fluid of constant density is in a vertical cylinder of radius R (Fig. 3.8-6) with the cylinder rotating about its axis at angular velocity ω (B2). Find the shape of the free surface at steady state.

Solution: The system can be described in cylindrical coordinates. As in Example 3.8-5, at steady state, $v_r = v_z = 0$ and $g_r = g_\theta = 0$. The final equations in cylindrical coordinates given below are the same as Eqs. (3.8-25)–(3.8-27) for Example 3.8-5, except that $g_z = -g$ in Eq. (3.8-27):

$$\rho\frac{v_\theta^2}{r} - \frac{\partial p}{\partial r} \tag{3.8-32}$$

$$0 = \mu\frac{\partial}{\partial r}\left(\frac{1}{r}\frac{\partial(rv_\theta)}{\partial r}\right) \tag{3.8-33}$$

$$\frac{\partial p}{\partial z} = -\rho g \tag{3.8-34}$$

FIGURE 3.8-6.   *Liquid being rotated in a container with a free surface in Example 3.8-6.*

$$p = p_0 \text{ at surface}$$

$$p = p(r, z)$$

Integration of Eq. (3.8-33) gives the same equation as in Example 3.8-5:

$$v_\theta = C_1 r + \frac{C_2}{r} \qquad \text{(3.8-28)}$$

The constant C_2 must be zero since v_θ cannot be infinite at $r = 0$. At $r = R$, the velocity $v_\theta = R\omega$. Hence, $C_1 = \omega$ and we obtain

$$v_\theta = \omega r \qquad \text{(3.8-35)}$$

Combining Eqs. (3.8-35) and (3.8-32),

$$\frac{\partial p}{\partial r} = \rho \omega^2 r \qquad \text{(3.8-36)}$$

Hence, we see that Eqs. (3.8-36) and (3.8-34) show that pressure depends upon r because of the centrifugal force and upon z because of the gravitational force:

$$\frac{\partial p}{\partial z} = -\rho g \qquad \text{(3.8-34)}$$

Since the term p is a function of position, we can write the total differential of pressure as

$$dp = \frac{\partial p}{\partial r}\, dr + \frac{\partial p}{\partial z}\, dz \qquad \text{(3.8-37)}$$

Combining Eqs. (3.8-34) and (3.8-36) with (3.8-37) and integrating,

$$p = \frac{\rho \omega^2 r^2}{2} - \rho g z + C_3 \qquad \text{(3.8-38)}$$

The constant of integration can be determined, since $p = p_0$ at $r = 0$ and $z = z_0$. The equation becomes

$$p - p_0 = \frac{\rho \omega^2 r^2}{2} + \rho g(z_0 - z) \qquad \text{(3.8-39)}$$

The free surface consists of all points on this surface at $p = p_0$. Hence,

$$z - z_0 = \left(\frac{\omega^2}{2g}\right) r^2 \qquad \text{(3.8-40)}$$

This shows that the free surface is in the shape of a parabola.

3.9 OTHER METHODS FOR SOLUTION OF DIFFERENTIAL EQUATIONS OF MOTION

3.9A Introduction

In Section 3.8 we considered examples where the Navier–Stokes differential equations of motion could be solved analytically. These cases were used where there was only one nonvanishing component of the velocity. To solve these equations for flows in two and three directions is quite complex.

In this section we will consider some approximations that simplify the differential equations to allow us to obtain analytical solutions. Terms will be omitted which are quite small compared to the terms retained.

Three cases will be considered in this section: inviscid flow, potential flow, and creeping flow. The fourth case, for boundary-layer flow, will be considered in Section 3.10. The solution of these equations may be simplified by using a stream function $\psi(x, y)$ and/or a velocity potential $\phi(x, y)$ rather than the terms of the velocity components v_x, v_y, and v_z.

3.9B Stream Function

The stream function $\psi(x, y)$ is a convenient parameter by which we can represent two-dimensional, steady, incompressible flow. This stream function ψ in m^2/s is related to the velocity components v_x and v_y by

$$v_x = \frac{\partial \psi}{\partial y} \qquad v_y = -\frac{\partial \psi}{\partial x} \tag{3.9-1}$$

These definitions of v_x and v_y can then be used in the x and y components of the differential equation of motion, Eqs. (3.7-36) and (3.7-37), together with $v_z = 0$, to obtain a differential equation for ψ that is equivalent to the Navier–Stokes equation. Details are given elsewhere (B2).

The stream function is very useful because of its physical significance, that is, that in steady flow, lines defined by $\psi = constant$ are streamlines, which are the actual curves traced out by the particles of fluid. A stream function exists for all two-dimensional, steady, incompressible flow whether viscous or inviscid and whether rotational or irrotational.

EXAMPLE 3.9-1. Stream Function and Streamlines
The stream function relationship is given as $\psi = xy$. Find the equations for the components of velocity. Also plot the streamlines for a constant $\psi = 4$ and $\psi = 1$.

Solution: Using Eq. (3.9-1),

$$v_x = \frac{\partial \psi}{\partial y} = \frac{\partial(xy)}{\partial y} = x$$

$$v_y = -\frac{\partial \psi}{\partial x} = -\frac{\partial(xy)}{\partial x} = -y$$

To determine the streamline for $\psi = constant = 1 = xy$, assume that $y = 0.5$ and solve for x:

$$\psi = 1 = xy = x(0.5)$$

Hence, $x = 2$. Repeating, for $y = 1$, $x = 1$; for $y = 2$, $x = 0.5$; for $y = 5$, $x = 0.2$, and so on. Doing the same for $\psi = constant = 4$, the streamlines for $\psi = 1$ and $\psi = 4$ are plotted in Fig. 3.9-1. A possible flow model is flow around a corner.

FIGURE 3.9-1. *Plot of streamlines for $\psi = xy$ for Example 3.9-1.*

3.9C Differential Equations of Motion for Ideal Fluids (Inviscid Flow)

Special equations for *ideal or inviscid fluids* can be obtained for a fluid having a constant density and zero viscosity. These are called the *Euler equations*. Equations (3.7-36)–(3.7-38) for the x, y, and z components of momentum become

$$\rho\left(\frac{\partial v_x}{\partial t} + v_x \frac{\partial v_x}{\partial x} + v_y \frac{\partial v_x}{\partial y} + v_z \frac{\partial v_x}{\partial z}\right) = -\frac{\partial p}{\partial x} + \rho g_x \qquad (3.9\text{-}2)$$

$$\rho\left(\frac{\partial v_y}{\partial t} + v_x \frac{\partial v_y}{\partial x} + v_y \frac{\partial v_y}{\partial y} + v_z \frac{\partial v_y}{\partial z}\right) = -\frac{\partial p}{\partial y} + \rho g_y \qquad (3.9\text{-}3)$$

$$\rho\left(\frac{\partial v_z}{\partial t} + v_x \frac{\partial v_z}{\partial x} + v_y \frac{\partial v_z}{\partial y} + v_z \frac{\partial v_z}{\partial z}\right) = -\frac{\partial p}{\partial z} + \rho g_z \qquad (3.9\text{-}4)$$

At very high Reynolds numbers the viscous forces are quite small compared to the inertia forces and the viscosity can be assumed as zero. These equations are useful in calculating pressure distribution at the outer edge of the thin boundary layer in flow past immersed bodies. Away from the surface outside the boundary layer this assumption of an ideal fluid is often valid.

3.9D Potential Flow and Velocity Potential

The velocity potential or potential function $\phi(x, y)$ in m²/s is useful in inviscid flow problems and is defined as

$$v_x = \frac{\partial \phi}{\partial x} \qquad v_y = \frac{\partial \phi}{\partial y} \qquad v_z = \frac{\partial \phi}{\partial z} \qquad (3.9\text{-}5)$$

This potential exists only for a flow with zero angular velocity, or irrotationality. This type of flow of an ideal or inviscid fluid (ρ = constant, $\mu = 0$) is called *potential flow*. Additionally, the velocity potential ϕ exists for three-dimensional flows, whereas the stream function does not.

The vorticity of a fluid is defined as follows:

$$\frac{\partial v_y}{\partial x} - \frac{\partial v_x}{\partial y} = 2\omega_z \qquad (3.9\text{-}6)$$

or,

$$\frac{\partial^2 \psi}{\partial x^2} + \frac{\partial^2 \psi}{\partial y^2} = -2\omega_z \qquad (3.9\text{-}7)$$

where $2\omega_z$ is the vorticity and ω_z in s^{-1} is angular velocity about the z axis. If $2\omega_z = 0$, the flow is irrotational and a potential function exists.

Using Eq. (3.6-24), the conservation-of-mass equation for flows in the x and y directions is as follows for constant density:

$$\frac{\partial v_x}{\partial x} + \frac{\partial v_y}{\partial y} = 0 \qquad (3.9\text{-}8)$$

Differentiating v_x in Eq. (3.9-5) with respect to x and v_y with respect to y and substituting into Eq. (3.9-8),

$$\frac{\partial^2 \phi}{\partial x^2} + \frac{\partial^2 \phi}{\partial y^2} = 0 \qquad (3.9\text{-}9)$$

This is Laplace's equation in rectangular coordinates. If suitable boundary conditions exist or are known, Eq. (3.9-9) can be solved to give $\phi(x, y)$. Then the velocity at any point can be obtained using Eq. (3.9-5). Techniques for solving this equation include using numerical analysis, conformal mapping, and functions of a complex variable, and are given elsewhere (B2, S3). Euler's equations can then be used to find the pressure distribution.

When the flow is inviscid and irrotational, a similar type of Laplace equation is obtained from Eq. (3.9-7) for the stream function:

$$\frac{\partial^2 \psi}{\partial x^2} + \frac{\partial^2 \psi}{\partial y^2} = 0 \qquad (3.9\text{-}10)$$

Lines of constant ϕ are called equal potential lines and for potential flow are everywhere perpendicular (orthogonal) to lines of constant ψ. This can be proved as follows. A line of constant ψ would be such that the change in ψ is zero:

$$d\psi = \frac{\partial \psi}{\partial x} \, dx + \frac{\partial \psi}{\partial y} \, dy = 0 \qquad (3.9\text{-}11)$$

Then, substituting Eq. (3.9-1) into the above,

$$\left(\frac{dy}{dx} \right)_{\psi=\text{constant}} = \frac{v_y}{v_x} \qquad (3.9\text{-}12)$$

Also, for lines of constant ϕ,

$$d\phi = \frac{\partial \phi}{\partial x} \, dx + \frac{\partial \phi}{\partial y} \, dy = 0 \qquad (3.9\text{-}13)$$

$$\left(\frac{dy}{dx} \right)_{\phi=\text{constant}} = -\frac{v_x}{v_y} \qquad (3.9\text{-}14)$$

Hence,

$$\left(\frac{dy}{dx} \right)_{\phi=\text{constant}} = -\frac{1}{(dy/dx)_{\psi=\text{constant}}} \qquad (3.9\text{-}15)$$

An example of the use of the stream function is in obtaining the flow pattern for inviscid, irrotational flow past a cylinder of infinite length. The fluid approaching the cylinder has a steady and uniform velocity of v_∞ in the x direction. Laplace's equation (3.9-10) can be converted to cylindrical coordinates to give

$$\frac{\partial^2 \psi}{\partial r^2} + \frac{1}{r}\frac{\partial \psi}{\partial r} + \frac{1}{r^2}\frac{\partial^2 \psi}{\partial \theta^2} = 0 \qquad (3.9\text{-}16)$$

where the velocity components are given by

$$v_r = \frac{1}{r}\frac{\partial \psi}{\partial \theta} \qquad v_\theta = -\frac{\partial \psi}{\partial r} \qquad (3.9\text{-}17)$$

Using four boundary conditions which are needed and the method of separation of variables, the stream function ψ is obtained. Converting to rectangular coordinates,

$$\psi = v_\infty y \left(1 - \frac{R^2}{x^2 + y^2}\right) \qquad (3.9\text{-}18)$$

where R is the cylinder radius. The streamlines and the constant-velocity-potential lines are plotted in Fig. 3.9-2 as a flow net.

EXAMPLE 3.9-2.   Stream Function for a Flow Field
The velocity components for a flow field are as follows:

$$v_x = a(x^2 - y^2) \qquad v_y = -2axy$$

Prove that it satisfies the conservation of mass and determine ψ.

Solution: First we determine $\partial v_x / \partial x = 2ax$ and $\partial v_y / \partial y = -2ax$. Substituting these values into Eq. (3.6-24), the conservation of mass for two-dimensional flow,

$$\frac{\partial v_x}{\partial x} + \frac{\partial v_y}{\partial y} = 0 \qquad \text{or} \qquad 2ax - 2ax = 0$$

$\psi = $ constant

$\theta = $ constant

FIGURE 3.9-2.   *Streamlines ($\psi = $ constant) and constant velocity potential lines ($\phi = $ constant) for the steady and irrotational flow of an inviscid and incompressible fluid about an infinite circular cylinder.*

Then using Eq. (3.9-1),

$$v_x = \frac{\partial \psi}{\partial y} = ax^2 - ay^2 \qquad v_y = -\frac{\partial \psi}{\partial x} = -2axy \qquad \textbf{(3.9-19)}$$

Integrating Eq. (3.9-19) for v_x,

$$\psi = ax^2 y - \frac{ay^3}{3} + f(x) \qquad \textbf{(3.9-20)}$$

Integrating Eq. (3.9-19) for v_y,

$$-\psi = -\frac{2ax^2 y}{2} + f(y) \qquad \textbf{(3.9-21)}$$

Equating Eq. (3.9-20) to (3.9-21),

$$ax^2 y - \frac{ay^3}{3} + f(x) = ax^2 y - f(y) \qquad \textbf{(3.9-22)}$$

Canceling like terms,

$$-\frac{ay^3}{3} + f(x) = -f(y) \qquad \textbf{(3.9-23)}$$

Hence, $f(x) = 0$ and $f(y) = ay^3/3$. Substituting $f(x) = 0$ into Eq. (3.9-20),

$$\psi = ax^2 y - \frac{ay^3}{3} \qquad \textbf{(3.9-24)}$$

EXAMPLE 3.9-3. Stream Function and Velocities from Potential Function

The potential function for a two-dimensional, irrotational, incompressible flow field is given as $\phi = x^2 - 2y - y^2$. Find the stream function ψ and the velocity components v_x and v_y.

Solution: Using Eqs. (3.9-1) and (3.9-5),

$$v_x = \frac{\partial \psi}{\partial y} \qquad v_y = -\frac{\partial \psi}{\partial x} \qquad v_x = \frac{\partial \phi}{\partial x} \qquad v_y = \frac{\partial \phi}{\partial y}$$

Combining,

$$\frac{\partial \phi}{\partial x} = \frac{\partial \psi}{\partial y} \qquad \frac{\partial \phi}{\partial y} = -\frac{\partial \psi}{\partial x} \qquad \textbf{(3.9-25)}$$

Differentiating the potential function with respect to x and equating the result to $\partial \psi / \partial y$ from Eq. (3.9-25),

$$\frac{\partial \phi}{\partial x} = 2x - 0 - 0 = 2x = -\frac{\partial \psi}{\partial y} \qquad \textbf{(3.9.26)}$$

Differentiating the potential function with respect to y and equating the result to $-\partial \psi / \partial x$ from Eq. (3.9-25),

$$\frac{\partial \phi}{\partial y} = 0 - 2 - 2y = -\frac{\partial \psi}{\partial x} \qquad \textbf{(3.9-27)}$$

Integrating Eq. (3.9-26),

$$\psi = 2xy + f(x) \tag{3.9-28}$$

Integrating Eq. (3.9-27),

$$\psi = 2x + 2xy + f(y) \tag{3.9-29}$$

Equating Eq. (3.9-28) to (3.9-29),

$$\psi = 2xy + f(x) = 2x + 2xy + f(y) \tag{3.9-30}$$

Hence, after canceling $2xy$ from both sides,

$$f(x) = 2x + f(y) \tag{3.9-31}$$

Therefore, $f(x) = 2x$ and $f(y) = 0$. Substituting $f(x) = 2x$ into Eq. (3.9-28),

$$\psi = 2xy + 2x \tag{3.9-32}$$

The velocities are, from Eqs. (3.9-26) and (3.9-27),

$$\frac{\partial \psi}{\partial y} = v_x = 2x \qquad -\frac{\partial \psi}{\partial x} = v_y = 2 - 2y \tag{3.9-33}$$

In potential flow, the stream function and potential function are used to represent the flow in the main body of the fluid. These ideal fluid solutions do not satisfy the condition that $v_x = v_y = 0$ on the wall surface. Near the wall we have viscous drag and we use boundary-layer theory, where we obtain approximate solutions for the velocity profiles in this thin boundary layer taking into account viscosity. This is discussed in Section 3.10. Then we splice this solution onto the ideal flow solution that describes flow outside the boundary layer.

3.9E Differential Equations of Motion for Creeping Flow

At very low Reynolds numbers, below about 1, the term *creeping flow* is used to describe flow at very low velocities. This type of flow applies for the fall or settling of small particles through a fluid. Stokes' law is derived using this type of flow in problems of settling and sedimentation.

In flow around a sphere, for example, the fluid changes velocity and direction in a complex manner. If the inertia effects in this case were important, it would be necessary to keep all the terms in the three Navier–Stokes equations. Experiments show that at a Reynolds number below about 1, the inertia effects are small and can be omitted. Hence, the equations of motion, Eqs. (3.7-36)–(3.7-38) for creeping flow of an incompressible fluid, become

$$\frac{\partial p}{\partial x} = \mu \left(\frac{\partial^2 v_x}{\partial x^2} + \frac{\partial^2 v_x}{\partial y^2} + \frac{\partial^2 v_x}{\partial z^2} \right) \tag{3.9-34}$$

$$\frac{\partial p}{\partial y} = \mu \left(\frac{\partial^2 v_y}{\partial x^2} + \frac{\partial^2 v_y}{\partial y^2} + \frac{\partial^2 v_y}{\partial z^2} \right) \tag{3.9-35}$$

$$\frac{\partial p}{\partial z} = \mu \left(\frac{\partial^2 v_z}{\partial x^2} + \frac{\partial^2 v_z}{\partial y^2} + \frac{\partial^2 v_z}{\partial z^2} \right) \tag{3.9-36}$$

For flow past a sphere the stream function ψ can be used in the Navier–Stokes equation in spherical coordinates to obtain the equation for the stream function and the velocity distribution and pressure distribution over the sphere. Then by integration over the whole sphere, the form drag, caused by the pressure distribution, and the skin friction or viscous drag, caused by the shear stress at the surface, can be summed to give the total drag:

$$F_D = 3\pi\mu D_p v \qquad \text{(SI)}$$

$$F_D = \frac{3\pi\mu D_p v}{g_c} \qquad \text{(English)} \tag{3.9-37}$$

where F_D is total drag force in N, D_p is particle diameter in m, v is free stream velocity of fluid approaching the sphere in m/s, and μ is viscosity in kg/m · s. This is Stokes' equation for the drag force on a sphere.

Often Eq. (3.9-37) is rewritten as follows:

$$F_D = C_D \frac{v^2}{2}\rho A \qquad \text{(SI)}$$

$$F_D = C_D \frac{v^2}{2g_c}\rho A \qquad \text{(English)} \tag{3.9-38}$$

where C_D is a drag coefficient, equal to $24/N_{Re}$ for Stokes' law, and A is the projected area of the sphere, $\pi D_p^2/4$. This is discussed in more detail in Section 3.1 for flow past spheres.

3.10 BOUNDARY-LAYER FLOW AND TURBULENCE

3.10A Boundary-Layer Flow

In Sections 3.8 and 3.9, the Navier–Stokes equations were used to find relations that described laminar flow between flat plates and inside circular tubes, flow of ideal fluids, and creeping flow. In this section the flow of fluids around objects will be considered in more detail, with particular attention being given to the region close to the solid surface, called the *boundary layer*.

In the boundary-layer region near the solid, the fluid motion is greatly affected by this solid surface. In the bulk of the fluid away from the boundary layer, the flow can often be adequately described by the theory of ideal fluids with zero viscosity. However, in the thin boundary layer, viscosity is important. Since the region is thin, simplified solutions can be obtained for the boundary-layer region. Prandtl originally suggested this division of the problem into two parts, which has been used extensively in fluid dynamics.

In order to help explain boundary layers, an example of boundary-layer formation in the steady-state flow of a fluid past a flat plate is given in Fig. 3.10-1. The velocity of the fluid upstream of the leading edge at $x = 0$ of the plate is uniform across the entire fluid stream and has the value v_∞. The velocity of the fluid at the interface is zero and the velocity v_x in the x direction increases as one goes farther from the plate. The velocity v_x approaches asymptotically the velocity v_∞ of the bulk of the stream.

The dashed line L is drawn so that the velocity at that point is 99% of the bulk velocity v_∞. The layer or zone between the plate and the dashed line constitutes the boundary layer. When the flow is laminar, the thickness δ of the boundary layer increases with $\sqrt{x}$ as we move in the x direction. The Reynolds number is defined as $N_{Re,x} = xv_\infty\rho/\mu$, where x is the distance downstream from the leading edge. When the Reynolds number is less than 2×10^5, the flow is laminar, as shown in Fig. 3.10-1.

FIGURE 3.10-1. *Boundary layer for flow past a flat plate.*

The transition from laminar to turbulent flow on a smooth plate occurs in the Reynolds-number range 2×10^5 to 3×10^6, as shown in Fig. 3.10-1. When the boundary layer is turbulent, a thin, viscous sublayer persists next to the plate. The drag caused by the viscous shear in the boundary layers is called *skin friction* and is the only drag present for flow past a flat plate.

The type of drag occurring when fluid flows by a bluff or blunt shape such as a sphere or cylinder, which is mostly caused by a pressure difference, is termed *form drag*. This drag predominates in flow past such objects at all except low values of the Reynolds number, and often a wake is present. Skin friction and form drag both occur in flow past a bluff shape, and the total drag is the sum of the skin friction and the form drag. (See also Section 3.1A.)

3.10B Boundary-Layer Separation and Formation of Wakes

We discussed the growth of the boundary layer at the leading edge of a plate as shown in Fig. 3.10-2. However, some important phenomena also occur at the trailing edge of this plate and other objects. At the trailing edge or rear edge of the flat plate, the boundary layers are present at the top and bottom sides of the plate. On leaving the plate, the boundary layers gradually intermingle and disappear.

If the direction of flow is at right angles to the plate, as shown in Fig. 3.10-2, a boundary layer forms as before in the fluid that is flowing over the upstream face. Once at the edge of

FIGURE 3.10-2. *Flow perpendicular to a flat plate and boundary-layer separation.*

the plate, however, the momentum in the fluid prevents it from making the abrupt turn around the edge of the plate, and it separates from the plate. A zone of decelerated fluid is present behind the plate and large eddies (vortices), called the *wake*, are formed in this area. The eddies consume large amounts of mechanical energy. This separation of boundary layers occurs when the change in velocity of the fluid flowing past an object is too large in direction or magnitude for the fluid to adhere to the surface.

Since formation of a wake causes large losses in mechanical energy, it is often necessary to minimize or prevent boundary-layer separation by streamlining the objects or by other means. This is also discussed in Section 3.1A for flow past immersed objects.

3.10C Laminar Flow and Boundary-Layer Theory

1. Boundary-layer equations. When laminar flow is occurring in a boundary layer, certain terms in the Navier–Stokes equations become negligible and can be neglected. The thickness of the boundary layer δ is arbitrarily taken as the distance away from the surface where the velocity reaches 99% of the free stream velocity. The concept of a relatively thin boundary layer leads to some important simplifications of the Navier–Stokes equations.

For two-dimensional laminar flow in the x and y directions of a fluid having a constant density, Eqs. (3.7-36) and (3.7-37) become as follows for flow at steady state as shown in Figure 3.10-1 when we neglect the body forces g_x and g_y:

$$v_x \frac{\partial v_x}{\partial x} + v_y \frac{\partial v_x}{\partial y} = -\frac{1}{\rho}\frac{\partial p}{\partial x} + \frac{\mu}{\rho}\left(\frac{\partial^2 v_x}{\partial x^2} + \frac{\partial^2 v_x}{\partial y^2}\right) \tag{3.10-1}$$

$$v_x \frac{\partial v_y}{\partial x} + v_y \frac{\partial v_y}{\partial y} = -\frac{1}{\rho}\frac{\partial p}{\partial y} + \frac{\mu}{\rho}\left(\frac{\partial^2 v_y}{\partial x^2} + \frac{\partial^2 v_y}{\partial y^2}\right) \tag{3.10-2}$$

The continuity equation for two-dimensional flow becomes

$$\frac{\partial v_x}{\partial x} + \frac{\partial v_y}{\partial y} = 0 \tag{3.10-3}$$

In Eq. (3.10-1), the term $(\mu/\rho)(\partial^2 v_x/\partial x^2)$ is negligible in comparison with the other terms in the equation. Also, it can be shown that all the terms containing v_y and its derivatives are small. Hence, the final two boundary-layer equations to be solved are Eqs. (3.10-3) and (3.10-4):

$$v_x \frac{\partial v_x}{\partial x} + v_y \frac{\partial v_x}{\partial y} = -\frac{1}{\rho}\frac{dp}{dx} + \frac{\mu}{\rho}\frac{\partial^2 v_x}{\partial y^2} \tag{3.10-4}$$

2. Solution for laminar boundary layer on a flat plate. An important case in which an analytical solution has been obtained for the boundary-layer equations is for the laminar boundary layer on a flat plate in steady flow, as shown in Fig. 3.10-1. A further simplification can be made in Eq. (3.10-4) in that dp/dx is zero since v_∞ is constant.

The final boundary-layer equations reduce to the equation of motion for the x direction and the continuity equation as follows:

$$v_x \frac{\partial v_x}{\partial x} + v_y \frac{\partial v_x}{\partial y} = \frac{\mu}{\rho}\frac{\partial^2 v_x}{\partial y^2} \tag{3.10-5}$$

$$\frac{\partial v_x}{\partial x} + \frac{\partial v_y}{\partial y} = 0 \qquad (3.10\text{-}3)$$

The boundary conditions are $v_x = v_y = 0$ at $y = 0$ (y is distance from plate), and $v_x = v_\infty$ at $y = \infty$.

The solution of this problem for laminar flow over a flat plate giving v_x and v_y as a function of x and y was first obtained by Blasius and later elaborated by Howarth (B1, B2, S3). The mathematical details of the solution are quite tedious and complex and will not be given here. The general procedure will be outlined. Blasius reduced the two equations to a single ordinary differential equation which is nonlinear. The equation could not be solved to give a closed form, but a series solution was obtained.

The results of the work by Blasius are given as follows. The boundary-layer thickness δ, where $v_x \cong 0.99v_\infty$, is given approximately by

$$\delta = \frac{5.0x}{\sqrt{N_{\text{Re},x}}} = 5.0\sqrt{\frac{\mu x}{\rho v_\infty}} \qquad (3.10\text{-}6)$$

where $N_{\text{Re},x} = xv_\infty\rho/\mu$. Hence, the thickness δ varies as $\sqrt{x}$.

The drag in flow past a flat plate consists only of skin friction and is calculated from the shear stress at the surface at $y = 0$ for any x as follows:

$$\tau_0 = \mu\left(\frac{\partial v_x}{\partial y}\right)_{y=0} \qquad (3.10\text{-}7)$$

From the relation of v_x as a function of x and y obtained from the series solution, Eq. (3.10-7) becomes

$$\tau_0 = 0.332\mu v_\infty\sqrt{\frac{\rho v_\infty}{\mu x}} \qquad (3.10\text{-}8)$$

The total drag is given by the following for a plate of length L and width b:

$$F_D = b\int_0^L \tau_0\,dx \qquad (3.10\text{-}9)$$

Substituting Eq. (3.10-8) into (3.10-9) and integrating,

$$F_D = 0.664b\sqrt{\mu\rho v_\infty^3 L} \qquad (3.10\text{-}10)$$

The drag coefficient C_D related to the total drag on one side of the plate having an area $A = bL$ is defined as

$$F_D = C_D\frac{v_\infty^2}{2}\rho A \qquad (3.10\text{-}11)$$

Substituting the value for A and Eq. (3.10-10) into (3.10-11),

$$C_D = 1.328\sqrt{\frac{\mu}{Lv_\infty\rho}} = \frac{1.328}{N_{\text{Re},L}^{1/2}} \qquad (3.10\text{-}12)$$

where $N_{\text{Re},L} = Lv_\infty\rho/\mu$. A form of Eq. (3.10-11) is used in Section 14.3 for particle movement through a fluid. The definition of C_D in Eq. (3.10-12) is similar to the Fanning friction factor f for pipes.

The equation derived for C_D applies to the laminar boundary layer only for $N_{Re,L}$ less than about 5×10^5. Also, the results are valid only for positions where x is sufficiently far from the leading edge so that x or L is much greater than δ. Experimental results on the drag coefficient to a flat plate confirm the validity of Eq. (3.10-12). Boundary-layer flow past many other shapes has been successfully analyzed using similar methods.

3.10D Nature and Intensity of Turbulence

1. Nature of turbulence. Since turbulent flow is important in many areas of engineering, the nature of turbulence has been extensively investigated. Measurements of the velocity fluctuations of the eddies in turbulent flow have helped explain turbulence.

For turbulent flow there are no exact solutions of flow problems as there are in laminar flow, since the approximate equations used depend on many assumptions. However, useful relations have been obtained by combining experimental data and theory. Some of these relations will be discussed.

Turbulence can be generated by contact between two layers of fluid moving at different velocities or by a flowing stream in contact with a solid boundary, such as a wall or sphere. When a jet of fluid from an orifice flows into a mass of fluid, turbulence can arise. In turbulent flow at a given place and time, large eddies are continually being formed which break down into smaller eddies and finally disappear. Eddies can be as small as about 0.1–1 mm and as large as the smallest dimension of the turbulent stream. Flow inside an eddy is laminar because of its large size.

In turbulent flow the velocity is fluctuating in all directions. In Fig. 3.10-3 a typical plot of the variation of the instantaneous velocity v_x in the x direction at a given point in turbulent flow is shown. The velocity v'_x is the deviation of the velocity from the mean velocity $\bar{v}_x$ in the x direction of flow of the stream. Similar relations also hold for the y and z directions:

$$v_x = \bar{v}_x + v'_x, \qquad v_y = \bar{v}_y + v'_y, \qquad v_z = \bar{v}_z + v'_z \tag{3.10-13}$$

$$\bar{v}_x = \frac{1}{t} \int_0^t v_x \, dt \tag{3.10-14}$$

where the mean velocity $\bar{v}_x$ is the time-averaged velocity for time t, v_x the instantaneous total velocity in the x direction, and v'_x the instantaneous deviating or fluctuating velocity in the x

FIGURE 3.10-3. *Velocity fluctuations in turbulent flow.*

direction. These fluctuations can also occur in the y and z directions. The value of v'_x fluctuates about zero as an average and, hence, the time-averaged values $\bar{v}'_x = 0$, $\bar{v}'_y = 0$, $\bar{v}'_z = 0$. However, the values of v'^2_x, v'^2_y, and v'^2_z will not be zero. Similar expressions can also be written for pressure, which also fluctuates.

2. Intensity of turbulence. The time average of the fluctuating components vanishes over a time period of a few seconds. However, the time average of the mean square of the fluctuating components is a positive value. Since the fluctuations are random, the data have been analyzed by statistical methods. The level or intensity of turbulence can be related to the square root of the sum of the mean squares of the fluctuating components. This intensity of turbulence is an important parameter in the testing of models and the theory of boundary layers.

The intensity of turbulence I can be defined mathematically as

$$I = \frac{\sqrt{\frac{1}{3}(\bar{v}'^2_x + \bar{v}'^2_y + \bar{v}'^2_z)}}{\bar{v}_x} \tag{3.10-15}$$

This parameter I is quite important. Such factors as boundary-layer transition, separation, and heat- and mass-transfer coefficients depend upon the intensity of turbulence. Simulation of turbulent flows in testing of models requires that the Reynolds number and the intensity of turbulence be the same. One method used to measure intensity of turbulence is to utilize a hot-wire anemometer.

3.10E   Turbulent Shear or Reynolds Stresses

In a fluid flowing in turbulent flow, shear forces occur wherever there is a velocity gradient across a shear plane, and these are much larger than those occurring in laminar flow. The velocity fluctuations in Eq. (3.10-13) give rise to turbulent shear stresses. The equations of motion and the continuity equation are still valid for turbulent flow. For an incompressible fluid having a constant density ρ and viscosity μ, the continuity equation (3.6-24) holds:

$$\frac{\partial v_x}{\partial x} + \frac{\partial v_y}{\partial y} + \frac{\partial v_z}{\partial z} = 0 \tag{3.6-24}$$

Also, the x component of the equation of motion, Eq. (3.7-36), can be written as follows if Eq. (3.6-24) holds:

$$\frac{\partial(\rho v_x)}{\partial t} + \frac{\partial(\rho v_x v_x)}{\partial x} + \frac{\partial(\rho v_x v_y)}{\partial y} + \frac{\partial(\rho v_x v_z)}{\partial z} = \mu\left(\frac{\partial^2 v_x}{\partial x^2} + \frac{\partial^2 v_x}{\partial y^2} + \frac{\partial^2 v_x}{\partial z^2}\right) - \frac{\partial p}{\partial x} + \rho g_x \tag{3.10-16}$$

We can rewrite the continuity equation (3.6-24) and Eq. (3.10-16) by replacing v_x by $\bar{v}_x + v'_x$, v_y by $\bar{v}_y + v'_y$, v_z by $\bar{v}_z + v'_z$, and p by $\bar{p} + p'$:

$$\frac{\partial(\bar{v}_x + v'_x)}{\partial x} + \frac{\partial(\bar{v}_y + v'_y)}{\partial y} + \frac{\partial(\bar{v}_z + v'_z)}{\partial z} = 0 \tag{3.10-17}$$

$$\frac{\partial[\rho(\bar{v}_x + v'_x)]}{\partial t} + \frac{\partial[\rho(\bar{v}_x + v'_x)(\bar{v}_x + v'_x)]}{\partial x} + \frac{\partial[\rho(\bar{v}_x + v'_x)(\bar{v}_y + v'_y)]}{\partial y}$$

$$+ \frac{\partial[\rho(\bar{v}_x + v'_x)(\bar{v}_z + v'_z)]}{\partial z} = \mu\nabla^2(\bar{v}_x + v'_x) - \frac{\partial(\bar{p} + p')}{\partial x} + \rho g_x \tag{3.10-18}$$

Now we use the fact that the time-averaged value of the fluctuating velocities is zero ($\bar{v}'_x, \bar{v}'_y, \bar{v}'_z$ are zero), and that the time-averaged product $\overline{v'_x v'_y}$ is not zero. Then Eqs. (3.10-17) and (3.10-18) become

$$\frac{\partial \bar{v}_x}{\partial x} + \frac{\partial \bar{v}_y}{\partial y} + \frac{\partial \bar{v}_z}{\partial z} = 0 \qquad (3.10\text{-}19)$$

$$\frac{\partial(\rho \bar{v}_x)}{\partial t} + \frac{\partial(\rho \bar{v}_x \bar{v}_x)}{\partial x} + \frac{\partial(\rho \bar{v}_x \bar{v}_y)}{\partial y} + \frac{\partial(\rho \bar{v}_x \bar{v}_z)}{\partial z}$$

$$+ \left[\frac{\partial(\rho \overline{v'_x v'_x})}{\partial x} + \frac{\partial(\rho \overline{v'_x v'_y})}{\partial y} + \frac{\partial(\rho \overline{v'_x v'_z})}{\partial z} \right] = \mu \nabla^2 \bar{v}_x - \frac{\partial \bar{p}}{\partial x} + \rho g_x \quad (3.10\text{-}20)$$

By comparing these two time-smoothed equations with Eqs. (3.6-24) and (3.10-16), we see that the time-smoothed values everywhere replace the instantaneous values. However, in Eq. (3.10-20) new terms arise in the set of brackets which are related to turbulent velocity fluctuations. For convenience we use the notation

$$\bar{\tau}^t_{xx} = \rho \overline{v'_x v'_x}, \qquad \bar{\tau}^t_{yx} = \rho \overline{v'_x v'_y}, \qquad \bar{\tau}^t_{zx} = \rho \overline{v'_x v'_z} \qquad (3.10\text{-}21)$$

These are the components of the turbulent momentum flux and are called *Reynolds stresses*.

3.10F Prandtl Mixing Length

The equations derived for turbulent flow must be solved to obtain velocity profiles. To do this, more simplifications must be made before the expressions for the Reynolds stresses can be evaluated. A number of semiempirical equations have been used; the eddy-diffusivity model of Boussinesq is one early attempt to evaluate these stresses. By analogy to the equation for shear stress in laminar flow, $\tau_{yx} = -\mu(dv_x/dy)$, the turbulent shear stress can be written as

$$\bar{\tau}^t_{yx} = -\eta_t \frac{d\bar{v}_x}{dy} \qquad (3.10\text{-}22)$$

where η_t is a turbulent or eddy viscosity, which is a strong function of position and flow. This equation can also be written as follows:

$$\bar{\tau}^t_{yx} = -\rho \varepsilon_t \frac{d\bar{v}_x}{dy} \qquad (3.10\text{-}23)$$

where $\varepsilon_t = \eta_t/\rho$ is eddy diffusivity of momentum in m^2/s, by analogy to the momentum diffusivity μ/ρ for laminar flow.

In his mixing-length model Prandtl developed an expression to evaluate these stresses by assuming that eddies move in a fluid in a manner similar to the movement of molecules in a gas. The eddies move a distance called the mixing length L before they lose their identity.

Actually, the moving eddy or "lump" of fluid will gradually lose its identity. However, in the definition of the Prandtl mixing length L, this small packet of fluid is assumed to retain its identity while traveling the entire length L and then lose its identity or be absorbed in the host region.

Prandtl assumed that the velocity fluctuation v'_x is due to a "lump" of fluid moving a distance L in the y direction and retaining its mean velocity. At point L, the lump of fluid will differ in mean velocity from the adjacent fluid by $\bar{v}_{x|y+L} - \bar{v}_{x|y}$. Then the value of $v'_{x|y}$ is

$$v'_{x|y} = \bar{v}_{x|y+L} - \bar{v}_{x|y} \qquad (3.10\text{-}24)$$

The length L is small enough that the velocity difference can be written as

$$v'_{x|y} = \bar{v}_{x|y+L} - \bar{v}_{x|y} = L \frac{d\bar{v}_x}{dy} \qquad \text{(3.10-25)}$$

Hence,

$$v'_x = L \frac{d\bar{v}_x}{dy} \qquad \text{(3.10-26)}$$

Prandtl also assumed $v'_x \simeq v'_y$. Then the time average, $\overline{v'_x x'_y}$, is

$$\overline{v'_x v'_y} = -L^2 \left| \frac{d\bar{v}_x}{dy} \right| \frac{d\bar{v}_x}{dy} \qquad \text{(3.10-27)}$$

The minus sign and the absolute value were used to make the quantity $\overline{v'_x v'_y}$ agree with experimental data. Substituting Eq. (3.10-27) into (3.10-21),

$$\bar{\tau}^t_{yx} = -\rho L^2 \left| \frac{d\bar{v}_x}{dy} \right| \frac{d\bar{v}_x}{dy} \qquad \text{(3.10-28)}$$

Comparing with Eq. (3.10-23),

$$\varepsilon_t = L^2 \left| \frac{d\bar{v}_x}{dy} \right| \qquad \text{(3.10-29)}$$

3.10G   Universal Velocity Distribution in Turbulent Flow

To determine the velocity distribution for turbulent flow at steady state inside a circular tube, we divide the fluid inside the pipe into two regions: a central core where the Reynolds stress approximately equals the shear stress; and a thin, viscous sublayer adjacent to the wall where the shear stress is due only to viscous shear and the turbulence effects are assumed negligible. Later we include a third region, the buffer zone, where both stresses are important.

Dropping the subscripts and superscripts on the shear stresses and velocity, and considering the thin, viscous sublayer, we can write

$$\tau_0 = -\mu \frac{dv}{dy} \qquad \text{(3.10-30)}$$

where τ_0 is assumed constant in this region. On integration,

$$\tau_0 y = \mu v \qquad \text{(3.10-31)}$$

Defining a friction velocity as follows and substituting into Eq. (3.10-31),

$$v^* = \sqrt{\frac{\tau_0}{\rho}} \qquad \text{(3.10-32)}$$

$$\frac{v}{v^*} = \frac{yv^*}{\mu/\rho} \qquad \text{(3.10-33)}$$

The dimensionless velocity ratio on the left can be written as

$$v^+ = v\sqrt{\frac{\rho}{\tau_0}} \quad \text{(SI)}$$

(3.10-34)

$$v^+ = v\sqrt{\frac{\rho}{\tau_0 g_c}} \quad \text{(English)}$$

The dimensionless number on the right can be written as

$$y^+ = \frac{\sqrt{\tau_0 \rho}}{\mu} y \quad \text{(SI)}$$

(3.10-35)

$$y^+ = \frac{\sqrt{\tau_0 g_c \rho}}{\mu} y \quad \text{(English)}$$

where y is the distance from the wall of the tube. For a tube of radius r_0, $y = r_0 - r$, where r is the distance from the center. Hence, for the viscous sublayer, the velocity distribution is

$$v^+ = y^+$$

(3.10-36)

Next, considering the turbulent core where any viscous stresses are neglected, Eq. (3.10-28) becomes

$$\tau = \rho L^2 \left(\frac{dv}{dy}\right)^2$$

(3.10-37)

where dv/dy is always positive and the absolute value sign is dropped. Prandtl assumed that the mixing length is proportional to the distance from the wall, or

$$L = Ky$$

(3.10-38)

and that $\tau = \tau_0 = $ constant. Equation (3.10-37) now becomes

$$\tau_0 = \rho K^2 y^2 \left(\frac{dv}{dy}\right)^2$$

(3.10-39)

Hence,

$$v^* = Ky \frac{dv}{dy}$$

(3.10-40)

Upon integration,

$$v^* \ln y = Kv + K_1$$

(3.10-41)

where K_1 is a constant. The constant K_1 can be found by assuming that v is zero at a small value of y, say y_0:

$$\frac{v}{v^*} = v^+ = \frac{1}{K} \ln \frac{y}{y_0}$$

(3.10-42)

Introducing the variable y^+ by multiplying the numerator and denominator of the term y/y_0 by v^*/ν, where $\nu = \mu/\rho$, we obtain

$$v^+ = \frac{1}{K}\left(\ln \frac{yv^*}{\nu} - \ln \frac{y_0 v^*}{\nu}\right)$$

(3.10-43)

FIGURE 3.10-4. *Universal velocity profile for turbulent flow in smooth circular tubes.*

$$v^+ = \frac{1}{K} \ln y^+ + C_1 \tag{3.10-44}$$

A large amount of velocity distribution data by Nikuradse and others for a range of Reynolds numbers of 4000 to 3.2×10^6 have been obtained, and the data fit Eq. (3.10-36) in the region up to y^+ of 5 and also fit Eq. (3.10-44) above y^+ of 30, with K and C_1 being universal constants. For the region of y^+ from 5 to 30, which is defined as the buffer region, an empirical equation of the form of Eq. (3.10-44) fits the data. In Fig. 3.10-4 the following relations which are valid are plotted to give a universal velocity profile for fluids flowing in smooth, circular tubes:

$$v^+ = y^+ \qquad (0 < y^+ < 5) \tag{3.10-45}$$

$$v^+ = 5.0 \ln y^+ - 3.05 \qquad (5 < y^+ < 30) \tag{3.10-46}$$

$$v^+ = 2.5 \ln y^+ + 5.5 \qquad (30 < y^+) \tag{3.10-47}$$

Three distinct regions are apparent in Fig. 3.10-4. The first region next to the wall is the *viscous sublayer* (historically called "laminar" sublayer), given by Eq. (3.10-45), where the velocity is proportional to the distance from the wall. The second region, called the *buffer layer,* is given by Eq. (3.10-46), and is a region of transition between the viscous sublayer with practically no eddy activity and the violent eddy activity in the *turbulent core region* given by Eq. (3.10-47). These equations can then be used and related to the Fanning friction factor discussed earlier in this chapter. They can also be used in solving turbulent boundary-layer problems.

3.10H Integral Momentum Balance for Boundary-Layer Analysis

1. Introduction and derivation of integral expression.   In the solution for the laminar boundary layer on a flat plate, the Blasius solution is quite restrictive, since it is only for laminar flow over a flat plate. Other, more complex systems cannot be solved by this method. An approx-

FIGURE 3.10-5. *Control volume for integral analysis of the boundary-layer flow.*

imate method developed by von Kármán can be used when the configuration is more complicated or the flow is turbulent. This is an approximate momentum integral analysis of the boundary layer using an empirical or assumed velocity distribution.

In order to derive the basic equation for a laminar or turbulent boundary layer, a small control volume in the boundary layer on a flat plate is used, as shown in Fig. 3.10-5. The depth in the z direction is b. Flow is only through the surfaces A_1 and A_2 and also from the top curved surface at δ. An overall integral momentum balance using Eq. (2.8-8) and overall integral mass balance using Eq. (2.6-6) are applied to the control volume inside the boundary layer at steady state, and the final integral expression by von Kármán is (B2, S3)

$$\frac{\tau_0}{\rho} = \frac{d}{dx} \int_0^\delta v_x (v_\infty - v_x)\, dy \tag{3.10-48}$$

where τ_0 is the shear stress at the surface $y = 0$ at point x along the plate. Also, δ and τ_0 are functions of x.

Equation (3.10-48) is an expression whose solution requires knowledge of the velocity v_x as a function of the distance from the surface, y. The accuracy of the results will, of course, depend on how closely the assumed velocity profile approaches the actual profile.

2. Integral momentum balance for laminar boundary layer. Before we use Eq. (3.10-48) for the turbulent boundary layer, this equation will be applied to the laminar boundary layer over a flat plate so that the results can be compared with the exact Blasius solution in Eqs. (3.10-6)–(3.10-12).

In this analysis certain boundary conditions must be satisfied in the boundary layer:

$$v_x = 0 \quad \text{at } y = 0$$
$$v_x \cong v_\infty \quad \text{at } y = \delta \tag{3.10-49}$$
$$\frac{dv_x}{dy} \cong 0 \quad \text{at } y = \delta$$

The conditions above are fulfilled in the following simple, assumed velocity profile:

$$\frac{v_x}{v_\infty} = \frac{3}{2}\frac{y}{\delta} - \frac{1}{2}\left(\frac{y}{\delta}\right)^3 \tag{3.10-50}$$

The shear stress τ_0 at a given x can be obtained from

$$\tau_0 = \mu \left(\frac{dv_x}{dy} \right)_{y=0} \qquad (3.10\text{-}51)$$

Differentiating Eq. (3.10-50) with respect to y and setting $y = 0$,

$$\left(\frac{dv_x}{dy} \right)_{y=0} = \frac{3v_\infty}{2\delta} \qquad (3.10\text{-}52)$$

Substituting Eq. (3.10-52) into (3.10-51),

$$\tau_0 = \frac{3\mu v_\infty}{2\delta} \qquad (3.10\text{-}53)$$

Substituting Eq. (3.10-50) into Eq. (3.10-48) and integrating between $y = 0$ and $y = \delta$, we obtain

$$\frac{d\delta}{dx} = \frac{280}{39} \frac{\tau_0}{v_\infty^2 \rho} \qquad (3.10\text{-}54)$$

Combining Eqs. (3.10-53) and (3.10-54) and integrating between $\delta = 0$ and $\delta = \delta$, and $x = 0$ and $x = L$,

$$\delta = 4.64 \sqrt{\frac{\mu L}{\rho v_\infty}} \qquad (3.10\text{-}55)$$

where the length of plate is $x = L$. Proceeding in a manner similar to Eqs. (3.10-6)–(3.10-12), the drag coefficient is

$$C_D = 1.292 \sqrt{\frac{\mu}{L v_\infty \rho}} = \frac{1.292}{N_{Re,L}^{1/2}} \qquad (3.10\text{-}56)$$

A comparison of Eq. (3.10-6) with (3.10-55) and (3.10-12) with (3.10-56) shows the success of this method. Only the numerical constants differ slightly. This method can be used with reasonable accuracy for cases where an exact analysis is not feasible.

3. Integral momentum analysis for turbulent boundary layer. The procedures used for the integral momentum analysis for a laminar boundary layer can be applied to the turbulent boundary layer on a flat plate. A simple empirical velocity distribution for pipe flow which is valid up to a Reynolds number of 10^5 can be adapted for the boundary layer on a flat plate, to become

$$\frac{v_x}{v_\infty} = \left(\frac{y}{\delta} \right)^{1/7} \qquad (3.10\text{-}57)$$

This is the Blasius $\frac{1}{7}$-power law, which is often used.

Equation (3.10-57) is substituted into the integral relation equation (3.10-48):

$$\frac{d}{dx} \int_0^\delta v_\infty^2 \left[\left(\frac{y}{\delta} \right)^{1/7} - \left(\frac{y}{\delta} \right)^{2/7} \right] dy = \frac{\tau_0}{\rho} \qquad (3.10\text{-}58)$$

The power-law equation does not hold, as y goes to zero at the wall. Another useful relation is the Blasius correlation for shear stress for pipe flow, which is consistent at the wall for the wall shear stress τ_0. For boundary-layer flow over a flat plate, it becomes

$$\frac{\tau_0}{\rho v_\infty^2} = 0.023 \left(\frac{\delta v_\infty \rho}{\mu} \right)^{-1/4} \tag{3.10-59}$$

Integrating Eq. (3.10-58), combining the result with Eq. (3.10-59), and integrating between $\delta = 0$ and $\delta = \delta$, and $x = 0$ and $x = L$,

$$\delta = 0.376 \left(\frac{L v_\infty \rho}{\mu} \right)^{-1/5} \qquad L = \frac{0.376 L}{N_{\text{Re},L}^{1/5}} \tag{3.10-60}$$

Integration of the drag force as before gives

$$C_D = \frac{0.072}{N_{\text{Re},L}^{1/5}} \tag{3.10-61}$$

In this development the turbulent boundary layer was assumed to extend to $x = 0$. Actually, a certain length at the front has a laminar boundary layer. Experimental data agree with Eq. (3.10-61) reasonably well from a Reynolds number of 5×10^5 to 10^7. More-accurate results at higher Reynolds numbers can be obtained by using a logarithmic velocity distribution, Eqs. (3.10-45)–(3.10-47).

3.11 DIMENSIONAL ANALYSIS IN MOMENTUM TRANSFER

3.11A Dimensional Analysis of Differential Equations

In this chapter we have derived several differential equations describing various flow situations. Dimensional homogeneity requires that every term in a given equation have the same units. Then, the ratio of one term in the equation to another term is dimensionless. Knowing the physical meaning of each term in the equation, we are then able to give a physical interpretation to each of the dimensionless parameters or numbers formed. These dimensionless numbers, such as the Reynolds number and others, are useful in correlating and predicting transport phenomena in laminar and turbulent flow.

Often it is not possible to integrate the differential equation describing a flow situation. However, we can use the equation to find out which dimensionless numbers can be used in correlating experimental data for this physical situation.

An important example of this involves the use of the Navier–Stokes equation, which often cannot be integrated for a given physical situation. To start, we use Eq. (3.7-36) for the x component of the Navier–Stokes equation. At steady state this becomes

$$v_x \frac{\partial v_x}{\partial x} + v_y \frac{\partial v_x}{\partial y} + v_z \frac{\partial v_x}{\partial z} = g_x - \frac{1}{\rho} \frac{\partial p}{\partial x} + \frac{\mu}{\rho} \left(\frac{\partial^2 v_x}{\partial x^2} + \frac{\partial^2 v_x}{\partial y^2} + \frac{\partial^2 v_x}{\partial z^2} \right) \tag{3.11-1}$$

Each term in this equation has the units length/time^2, or L/t^2.

In this equation each term has a physical significance. First we use a single characteristic velocity v and a single characteristic length L for all terms. Then the expression of each term in Eq. (3.11-1) is as follows: The left-hand side can be expressed as v^2/L and the right-hand terms, respectively, as g, $p/\rho L$, and $\mu v/\rho L^2$. We then write

$$\left[\frac{v^2}{L} \right] = [g] - \left[\frac{p}{\rho L} \right] + \left[\frac{\mu v}{\rho L^2} \right] \tag{3.11-2}$$

This expresses a dimensional equality and not a numerical equality. Each term has dimensions L/t^2.

The left-hand term in Eq. (3.11-2) represents the inertia force and the terms on the right-hand side represent, respectively, the gravity force, pressure force, and viscous force. Dividing each of the terms in Eq. (3.11-2) by the inertia force $[v^2/L]$, the following dimensionless groups or their reciprocals are obtained:

$$\frac{[v^2/L]}{[g]} = \frac{\text{inertia force}}{\text{gravity force}} = \frac{v^2}{gL} = N_{Fr} \qquad \text{(Froude number)} \qquad \textbf{(3.11-3)}$$

$$\frac{[p/\rho L]}{[v^2/L]} = \frac{\text{pressure force}}{\text{inertia force}} = \frac{p}{\rho v^2} = N_{Eu} \qquad \text{(Euler number)} \qquad \textbf{(3.11-4)}$$

$$\frac{[v^2/L]}{[\mu v/\rho L^2]} = \frac{\text{inertia force}}{\text{viscous force}} = \frac{Lv\rho}{\mu} = N_{Re} \qquad \text{(Reynolds number)} \qquad \textbf{(3.11-5)}$$

Note that this method not only gives the various dimensionless groups for a differential equation but also gives physical meaning to these dimensionless groups. The length, velocity, and so forth to be used in a given case will be that value which is most significant. For example, the length may be the diameter of a sphere, the length of a flat plate, and so on.

Systems that are geometrically similar are said to be *dynamically similar* if the parameters representing ratios of forces pertinent to the situation are equal. This means that the Reynolds, Euler, or Froude numbers must be equal between the two systems.

This dynamic similarity is an important requirement in obtaining experimental data for a small model and extending these data to scale up to the large prototype. Since experiments with full-scale prototypes would often be difficult and/or expensive, it is customary to study small models. This is done in the scale-up of chemical process equipment and in the design of ships and airplanes.

3.11B Dimensional Analysis Using the Buckingham Method

The method of obtaining the important dimensionless numbers from the basic differential equations is generally the preferred method. In many cases, however, we are not able to formulate a differential equation which clearly applies. Then a more general procedure is required, known as the *Buckingham method*. In this method the listing of the important variables in the particular physical problem is done first. Then we determine the number of dimensionless parameters into which the variables may be combined by using the Buckingham pi theorem.

The *Buckingham theorem* states that the functional relationship among q quantities or variables whose units may be given in terms of u fundamental units or dimensions may be written as $(q - u)$ independent dimensionless groups, often called π's. [This quantity u is actually the maximum number of these variables that will not form a dimensionless group. However, only in a few cases is u not equal to the number of fundamental units (B1).]

Let us consider the following example, to illustrate the use of this method. An incompressible fluid is flowing inside a circular tube of inside diameter D. The significant variables are pressure drop Δp, velocity v, diameter D, tube length L, viscosity μ, and density ρ. The total number of variables is $q = 6$.

The fundamental units or dimensions are $u = 3$ and are mass M, length L, and time t. The units of the variables are as follows: Δp in M/Lt^2, v in L/t, D in L, L in L, μ in M/Lt, and ρ in M/L^3. The number of dimensionless groups or π's is $q - u$, or $6 - 3 = 3$. Thus,

$$\pi_1 = f(\pi_2, \pi_3) \qquad \textbf{(3.11-6)}$$

Next, we must select a core group of u (or 3) variables which will appear in each π group and among them contain all the fundamental dimensions. Also, no two of the variables selected for the core can have the same dimensions. In choosing the core, the variable whose effect one desires to isolate is often excluded (for example, Δp). This leaves us with the variables v, D, μ and ρ to be used. (L and D have the same dimensions.)

We will select D, v, and ρ to be the core variables common to all three groups. Then the three dimensionless groups are

$$\pi_1 = D^a v^b \rho^c \, \Delta p^1 \tag{3.11-7}$$

$$\pi_2 = D^d v^e \rho^f L^1 \tag{3.11-8}$$

$$\pi_3 = D^g v^h \rho^i \mu^1 \tag{3.11-9}$$

To be dimensionless, the variables must be raised to certain exponents a, b, c, and so forth.

First we consider the π_1 group:

$$\pi_1 = D^a v^b \rho^c \, \Delta p^1 \tag{3.11-7}$$

To evaluate these exponents, we write Eq. (3.11-7) dimensionally by substituting the dimensions for each variable:

$$M^0 L^0 t^0 = 1 = L^a \left(\frac{L}{t}\right)^b \left(\frac{M}{L^3}\right)^c \frac{M}{Lt^2} \tag{3.11-10}$$

Next we equate the exponents of L on both sides of this equation, of M, and finally of t:

$$(L) \quad 0 = a + b - 3c - 1$$

$$(M) \quad 0 = c + 1 \tag{3.11-11}$$

$$(t) \quad 0 = -b - 2$$

Solving these equations, $a = 0$, $b = -2$, and $c = -1$.

Substituting these values into Eq. (3.11-7),

$$\pi_1 = \frac{\Delta p}{v^2 \rho} = N_{\text{Eu}} \tag{3.11-12}$$

Repeating this procedure for π_2 and π_3,

$$\pi_2 = \frac{L}{D} \tag{3.11-13}$$

$$\pi_3 = \frac{Dv\rho}{\mu} = N_{\text{Re}} \tag{3.11-14}$$

Finally, substituting π_1, π_2, and π_3 into Eq. (3.11-6),

$$\frac{\Delta p}{v^2 \rho} = f\left(\frac{L}{D}, \frac{Dv\rho}{\mu}\right) \tag{3.11-15}$$

Combining Eq. (2.10-5) with the left-hand side of Eq. (3.11-15), the result obtained shows that the friction factor is a function of the Reynolds number (as was shown before in the empirical correlation of friction factor and Reynolds number) and of the length/diameter ratio. In pipes with $L/D \gg 1$ or pipes with fully developed flow, the friction factor is found to be independent of L/D.

This type of analysis is useful in empirical correlations of data. However, it does not tell us the importance of each dimensionless group, which must be determined by experimentation, nor does it select the variables to be used.

PROBLEMS

3.1-1. *Force on a Cylinder in a Wind Tunnel.* Air at 101.3 kPa absolute and 25°C is flowing at a velocity of 10 m/s in a wind tunnel. A long cylinder having a diameter of 90 mm is placed in the tunnel and the axis of the cylinder is held perpendicular to the air flow. What is the force on the cylinder per meter length?

Ans. $C_D = 1.3$, $F_D = 6.94$ N

3.1-2. *Wind Force on a Steam Boiler Stack.* A cylindrical steam boiler stack has a diameter of 1.0 m and is 30.0 m high. It is exposed to a wind at 25°C having a velocity of 50 miles/h. Calculate the force exerted on the boiler stack.

Ans. $C_D = 0.33$, $F_D = 2935$ N

3.1-3. *Effect of Velocity on Force on a Sphere and Stokes' Law.* A sphere having a diameter of 0.042 m is held in a small wind tunnel, where air at 37.8°C and 1 atm abs and various velocities is forced past it.
   (a) Determine the drag coefficient and force on the sphere for a velocity of 2.30×10^{-4} m/s. Use Stokes' law here if it is applicable.
   (b) Also determine the force for velocities of 2.30×10^{-3}, 2.30×10^{-2}, 2.30×10^{-1}, and 2.30 m/s. Make a plot of F_D versus velocity.

3.1-4. *Drag Force on Bridge Pier in River.* A cylindrical bridge pier 1.0 m in diameter is submerged to a depth of 10 m. Water in the river at 20°C is flowing past at a velocity of 1.2 m/s. Calculate the force on the pier.

3.1-5. *Surface Area in a Packed Bed.* A packed bed is composed of cubes 0.020 m on a side and the bulk density of the packed bed is 980 kg/m³. The density of the solid cubes is 1500 kg/m³.
   (a) Calculate ε, effective diameter D_p, and a.
   (b) Repeat for the same conditions but for cylinders having a diameter of $D = 0.02$ m and a length $h = 1.5D$.

Ans. (a) $\varepsilon = 0.3467$, $D_p = 0.020$ m, $a = 196.0$ m^{-1}

3.1-6. *Derivation for Number of Particles in a Bed of Cylinders.* For a packed bed containing cylinders, where the diameter D of the cylinders is equal to the length h, do as follows for a bed having a void fraction ε:
   (a) Calculate the effective diameter.
   (b) Calculate the number of cylinders, n, in 1 m³ of the bed.

Ans. (a) $D_p = D$

3.1-7. *Derivation of Dimensionless Equation for Packed Bed.* Starting with Eq. (3.1-20), derive the dimensionless equation (3.1-21). Show all steps in the derivation.

3.1-8. *Flow and Pressure Drop of Gases in Packed Bed.* Air at 394.3 K flows through a packed bed of cylinders having a diameter of 0.0127 m and length the same as the diameter. The bed void fraction is 0.40 and the length of the packed bed is 3.66 m. The air enters the bed at 2.20 atm abs at the rate of 2.45 kg/m² · s based on the empty cross section of the bed. Calculate the pressure drop of air in the bed.

Ans. $\Delta p = 0.1547 \times 10^5$ Pa

3.1-9. *Flow of Water in a Filter Bed.* Water at 24°C is flowing by gravity through a filter bed of small particles having an equivalent diameter of 0.0060 m. The void fraction of the bed is measured as 0.42. The packed bed has a depth of 1.50 m. The liquid level of water above the bed is held constant at 0.40 m. What is the water velocity v' based on the empty cross section of the bed?

3.1-10. Mean Diameter of Particles in Packed Bed. A mixture of particles in a packed bed contains the following volume percent of particles and sizes: 15%, 10 mm; 25%, 20 mm; 40%, 40 mm; 20%, 70 mm. Calculate the effective mean diameter, D_{pm}, if the shape factor is 0.74.

Ans. $D_{pm} = 18.34$ mm

3.1-11. Permeability and Darcy's Law. A sample core of porous rock obtained from an oil reservoir is 8 cm long and has a diameter of 2.0 cm. It is placed in a core holder. With a pressure drop of 1.0 atm, the water flow at 20.2°C through the core is measured as 2.60 cm³/s. What is the permeability in darcy?

3.1-12. Minimum Fluidization and Expansion of Fluid Bed. Particles having a size of 0.10 mm, a shape factor of 0.86, and a density of 1200 kg/m³ are to be fluidized using air at 25°C and 202.65 kPa abs pressure. The void fraction at minimum fluidizing conditions is 0.43. The bed diameter is 0.60 m and the bed contains 350 kg of solids.
(a) Calculate the minimum height of the fluidized bed.
(b) Calculate the pressure drop at minimum fluidizing conditions.
(c) Calculate the minimum velocity for fluidization.
(d) Using 4.0 times the minimum velocity, estimate the porosity of the bed.

Ans. (a) $L_{mf} = 1.810$ m; (b) $\Delta p = 0.1212 \times 10^5$ Pa; (c) $v'_{mf} = 0.004374$ m/s; (d) $\varepsilon = 0.604$

3.1-13. Minimum Fluidization Velocity Using a Liquid. A tower having a diameter of 0.1524 m is being fluidized with water at 20.2°C. The uniform spherical beads in the tower bed have a diameter of 4.42 mm and a density of 1603 kg/m³. Estimate the minimum fluidizing velocity and compare with the experimental value of 0.02307 m/s found by Wilhelm and Kwauk (W5).

3.1-14. Fluidization of a Sand-Bed Filter. To clean a sand-bed filter, it is fluidized at minimum conditions using water at 24°C. The round sand particles have a density of 2550 kg/m³ and an average size of 0.40 mm. The sand has the properties given in Table 3.1-2.
(a) The bed diameter is 0.40 m and the desired height of the bed at these minimum fluidizing conditions is 1.75 m. Calculate the amount of solids needed.
(b) Calculate the pressure drop at these conditions and the minimum velocity for fluidization.
(c) Using 4.0 times the minimum velocity, estimate the porosity and height of the expanded bed.

Ans. (a) 325.2 kg solids; (b) 1.546×10^4 Pa

3.2-1. Flow Measurement Using a Pitot Tube. A pitot tube is used to measure the flow rate of water at 20°C in the center of a pipe having an inside diameter of 102.3 mm. The manometer reading is 78 mm of carbon tetrachloride at 20°C. The pitot tube coefficient is 0.98.
(a) Calculate the velocity at the center and the average velocity.
(b) Calculate the volumetric flow rate of the water.

Ans. (a) $v_{max} = 0.9372$ m/s, $v_{av} = 0.773$ m/s; (b) 6.35×10^{-3} m³/s

3.2-2. Gas Flow Rate Using a Pitot Tube. The flow rate of air at 37.8°C is being measured at the center of a duct having a diameter of 800 mm by a pitot tube. The pressure-difference reading on the manometer is 12.4 mm of water. At the pitot-tube position, the static-pressure reading is 275 mm of water above 1 atm abs. The pitot-tube coefficient is 0.97. Calculate the velocity at the center and the volumetric flow rate of the air.

3.2-3. Pitot-Tube Traverse for Flow-Rate Measurement. In a pitot-tube traverse of a pipe having an inside diameter of 155.4 mm in which water at 20°C is flowing, the following data were obtained:

Distance from Wall (mm)	Reading in Manometer (mm of Carbon Tetrachloride)
26.9	122
52.3	142
77.7	157
103.1	137
128.5	112

The pitot-tube coefficient is 0.98.
(a) Calculate the maximum velocity at the center.
(b) Calculate the average velocity. [*Hint:* Use Eq. (2.6-17) and do a numerical or a graphical integration.]

3.2-4. Metering Flow by a Venturi. A venturi meter having a throat diameter of 38.9 mm is installed in a line having an inside diameter of 102.3 mm. It meters water having a density of 999 kg/m^3. The measured pressure drop across the venturi is 156.9 kPa. The venturi coefficient C_v is 0.98. Calculate the gal/min and m^3/s flow rate.

Ans.   330 gal/min, 0.0208 m^3/s

3.2-5. Use of a Venturi to Meter Water Flow. Water at 20°C is flowing in a 2-in. schedule 40 steel pipe. Its flow rate is measured by a venturi meter having a throat diameter of 20 mm. The manometer reading is 214 mm of mercury. The venturi coefficient is 0.98. Calculate the flow rate.

3.2-6. Metering of Oil Flow by an Orifice. A heavy oil at 20°C having a density of 900 kg/m^3 and a viscosity of 6 cp is flowing in a 4-in. schedule 40 steel pipe. When the flow rate is 0.0174 m^3/s, it is desired to have a pressure-drop reading across the manometer equivalent to 0.93×10^5 Pa. What size orifice should be used if the orifice coefficient is assumed as 0.61? What is the permanent pressure loss?

3.2-7. Water Flow Rate in an Irrigation Ditch. Water is flowing in an open channel in an irrigation ditch. A rectangular weir having a crest length $L = 1.75$ ft is used. The weir head is measured as $h_0 = 0.47$ ft. Calculate the flow rate in ft^3/s and m^3/s.

Ans.   Flow rate = 1.776 ft^3/s, 0.0503 m^3/s

3.2-8. Sizing a Flow Nozzle. A flow nozzle is to be sized for use in a pipe having an internal diameter of 1.25 in. to meter 0.60 ft^3/min of water at 25°C. A pressure drop of 10.0 in. of water is to be used. Calculate the size of the flow nozzle and the permanent power loss in hp. Assume the coefficient $C_n = 0.96$.

Ans. $D_2 = 0.506$ in., $p_1 - p_4 = 37.38$ lb$_f$/ft^2 (1.789 kPa)

3.3-1. ***Brake Horsepower of Centrifugal Pump.*** Using Fig. 3.3-2 and a flow rate of 60 gal/min, do as follows:

(a) Calculate the brake hp of the pump using water with a density of 62.4 lb_m/ft^3. Compare with the value from the curve.

(b) Do the same for a nonviscous liquid having a density of 0.85 g/cm³.

Ans. (b) 0.69 brake hp (0.51 kW)

3.3-2. ***kW Power of a Fan.*** A centrifugal fan is to be used to take a flue gas at rest (zero velocity) and at a temperature of 352.6 K and a pressure of 749.3 mm Hg and discharge this gas at a pressure of 800.1 mm Hg and a velocity of 38.1 m/s. The volume flow rate of gas is 56.6 std m³/min of gas (at 294.3 K and 760 mm Hg). Calculate the brake kW of the fan if its efficiency is 65% and the gas has a molecular weight of 30.7. Assume incompressible flow.

3.3-3. ***Adiabatic Compression of Air.*** A compressor operating adiabatically is to compress 2.83 m³/min of air at 29.4°C and 102.7 kN/m² to 311.6 kN/m². Calculate the power required if the efficiency of the compressor is 75%. Also, calculate the outlet temperature.

3.3-4. ***(NPSH)$_R$ for Feed to Distillation Tower.*** A feed rate of 200 gpm of a hydrocarbon mixture at 70°C is being pumped from a tank at 1 atm abs pressure to a distillation tower. The density of the feed is 46.8 lb_m/ft^3 and its vapor pressure is 8.45 psia. The velocity in the inlet line to the pump is 3 ft/s and the friction loss between the tank and pump is 3.5 ft of fluid. The net positive suction head required is 6 ft.

(a) How far below the liquid level in the tank must the pump be to obtain this required (NPSH)$_R$?

(b) If the feed is at the boiling point, calculate the pump position.

Ans. (a) $z_1 = -9.57$ ft $(-2.92$ m)

3.4-1. ***Power for Liquid Agitation.*** It is desired to agitate a liquid having a viscosity of 1.5×10^{-3} Pa·s and a density of 969 kg/m³ in a tank having a diameter of 0.91 m. The agitator will be a six-blade open turbine having a diameter of 0.305 m operating at 180 rpm. The tank has four vertical baffles, each with a width J of 0.076 m. Also, $W = 0.0381$ m. Calculate the required kW. Use curve 2, Fig. 3.4-4.

Ans. $N_P = 2.5$, power = 0.172 kW (0.231 hp)

3.4-2. ***Power for Agitation and Scale-Up.*** A turbine agitator having six flat blades and a disk has a diameter of 0.203 m and is used in a tank having a diameter of 0.61 m and height of 0.61 m. The width $W = 0.0405$ m. Four baffles are used having a width of 0.051 m. The turbine operates at 275 rpm in a liquid having a density of 909 kg/m³ and viscosity of 0.020 Pa·s.

(a) Calculate the kW power of the turbine and kW/m³ of volume.

(b) Scale up this system to a vessel having a volume of 100 times the original for the case of equal mass transfer rates.

Ans. (a) $P = 0.1508$ kW, $P/V = 0.845$ kW/m³;
(b) $P_2 = 15.06$ kW, $P_2/V_2 = 0.845$ kW/m³

3.4-3. ***Scale-down of Process Agitation System.*** An existing agitation process operates using the same agitation system and fluid as described in Example 3.4-1a. It is desired to design a small pilot unit with a vessel volume of 2.0 liters so that effects of various process variables on the system can be studied in the laboratory. The rates of mass transfer appear to be important in this system, so the scale-down should be on this basis. Design the new system specifying sizes, rpm, and kW power.

3.4-4. *Anchor Agitation System.* An anchor-type agitator similar to that described for Eq. (3.4-3) is to be used to agitate a fluid having a viscosity of 100 Pa·s and a density of 980 kg/m³. The vessel size is $D_t = 0.90$ m and $H = 0.90$ m. The rpm is 50. Calculate the power required.

3.4-5. *Design of Agitation System.* An agitation system is to be designed for a fluid having a density of 950 kg/m³ and viscosity of 0.005 Pa·s. The vessel volume is 1.50 m³ and a standard six-blade open turbine with blades at 45°C (curve 3, Fig. 3.4-4) is to be used with $D_a/W = 8$ and $D_a/D_t = 0.35$. For the preliminary design a power of 0.5 kW/m³ volume is to be used. Calculate the dimensions of the agitation system, rpm, and kW power.

3.4-6. *Scale-Up of Mixing Times for a Turbine.* For scaling up a turbine-agitated system, do as follows:
(a) Derive Eq. (3.4-17) for the same power/unit volume.
(b) Derive Eq. (3.4-18) for the same mixing times.

3.4-7. *Mixing Time in a Turbine-Agitated System.* Do as follows:
(a) Predict the time of mixing for the turbine system in Example 3.4-1a.
(b) Using the same system as part (a) but with a tank having a volume of 10.0 m³ and the same power/unit volume, predict the new mixing time.
      Ans. (a) $f_t = 4.0$, $t_T = 17.3$ s

3.4-8. *Effect of Viscosity on Mixing Time.* Using the same conditions for the turbine mixer as in Example 3.4-4, part (a), except for a viscous fluid with a viscosity of 100 Pa·s (100 000 cp), calculate the mixing time. Compare this mixing time with that for the viscosity of 10 cp. Also calculate the power per unit volume.
      Ans. $t_T = 562$ s

3.4-9. *Mixing Time in a Helical Mixer.* A helical mixer with an agitator pitch/tank diameter = 1.0 and with $D_t = 1.83$ m and $D_a/D_t = 0.95$ is being used to agitate a viscous fluid having a viscosity of 200 000 cp and a density of 950 kg/m³. The value of $N = 0.3$ rev/s. Calculate the mixing time and the power per unit volume.
      Ans. $t_T = 420$ s

3.5-1. *Pressure Drop of Power-Law Fluid, Banana Purée.* A power-law biological fluid, banana purée, is flowing at 23.9°C, with a velocity of 1.018 m/s, through a smooth tube 6.10 m long having an inside diameter of 0.01267 m. The flow properties of the fluid are $K = 6.00$ N·s$^{0.454}$/m² and $n = 0.454$. The density of the fluid is 976 kg/m³.
(a) Calculate the generalized Reynolds number and also the pressure drop using Eq. (3.5-9). Be sure to convert K to K' first.
(b) Repeat part (a), but use the friction factor method.
      Ans. (a) $N_{Re,gen} = 63.6$, $\Delta p = 245.2$ kN/m² (5120 lb$_f$/ft²)

3.5-2. *Pressure Drop of Pseudoplastic Fluid.* A pseudoplastic power-law fluid having a density of 63.2 lb$_m$/ft³ is flowing through 100 ft of pipe having an inside diameter of 2.067 in. at an average velocity of 0.500 ft/s. The flow properties of the fluid are $K = 0.280$ lb$_f$·s^n/ft² and $n = 0.50$. Calculate the generalized Reynolds number and also the pressure drop, using the friction factor method.

3.5-3. *Turbulent Flow of Non-Newtonian Fluid, Applesauce.* Applesauce having the flow properties given in Table 3.5-1 is flowing in a smooth tube having an inside diameter of 50.8 mm and a length of 3.05 m at a velocity of 4.57 m/s.
(a) Calculate the friction factor and the pressure drop in the smooth tube.

(b) Repeat, but for a commercial pipe having the same inside diameter with a roughness of $\varepsilon = 4.6 \times 10^{-5}$ m.

Ans. (a) $N_{Re,gen} = 4855, f = 0.0073$; (b) $f = 0.0100$

3.5-4. Agitation of a Non-Newtonian Liquid. A pseudoplastic liquid having the properties $n = 0.53$, $K = 26.49$ N·s^{n}/m^2, and $\rho = 975$ kg/m^3 is being agitated in a system such as in Fig. 3.5-4 where $D_t = 0.304$ m, $D_a = 0.151$ m, and $N = 5$ rev/s. Calculate μ_a, $N'_{Re,n}$, and the kW power for this system.

Ans. $\mu_a = 4.028$ Pa·s, $N'_{Re,n} = 27.60$, $N_P = 3.1$, $P = 0.02966$ kW

3.5-5. Velocity Profile of a Bingham Plastic Fluid. For the conditions of Example 3.5-3, do as follows:

(a) Calculate the velocity for the plug-flow region at $r = r_0$.

(b) Calculate the velocity for values of r of 0.35 cm, 0.45 cm, and 0.50 cm and plot the complete velocity profile versus radial position.

3.5-6 Pressure Drop for Bingham Plastic Fluid. A Bingham plastic fluid has a value of $\tau_0 = 1.2$ N/m^2 and a viscosity $\mu = 0.4$ Pa·s. The fluid is flowing at 5.70×10^{-5} m^3/s in a pipe 2.5 m long with an internal diameter of 3.0 cm. Calculate the pressure drop $(p_0 - p_L)$ in N/m^2 and r_0. (*Hint:* This is a trial-and-error solution. As a first trial, assume $\tau_0 = 0$.)

Ans. $(p_0 - p_L) = 3400$ N/m^2

3.5-7. Flow Properties of a Non-Newtonian Fluid from Rotational Viscometer Data. Following are data obtained on a fluid using a Brookfield rotational viscometer:

RPM	0.5	1	2.5	5	10	20	50
Torque (dyn-cm)	86.2	168.9	402.5	754	1365	2379	4636

The diameter of the inner concentric rotating spindle is 25.15 mm, the outer cylinder diameter is 27.62 mm, and the effective length is 92.39 mm. Determine the flow properties of this non-Newtonian fluid.

Ans. $n = 0.870$

3.6-1. Equation of Continuity in a Cylinder. Fluid having a constant density ρ is flowing in the z direction through a circular pipe with axial symmetry. The radial direction is designated by r.

(a) Using a cylindrical shell balance with dimensions dr and dz, derive the equation of continuity for this system.

(b) Use the equation of continuity in cylindrical coordinates to derive the equation.

3.6-2. Change of Coordinates for Continuity Equation. Using the general equation of continuity given in rectangular coordinates, convert it to Eq. (3.6-27), which is the equation of continuity in cylindrical coordinates. Use the relationships in Eq. (3.6-26) to do this.

3.7-1. Combining Equations of Continuity and Motion. Using the continuity equation and the equations of motion for the x, y, and z components, derive Eq. (3.7-13).

3.8-1. Average Velocity in a Circular Tube. Using Eq. (3.8-17) for the velocity in a circular tube as a function of radius r,

$$v_z = \frac{1}{4\mu} \frac{dp}{dz} (r^2 - r_0^2)$$

(3.8-17)

derive Eq. (3.8-19) for the average velocity:

$$v_{z\,av} = -\frac{r_0^2}{8\mu}\frac{dp}{dz} \qquad (3.8\text{-}19)$$

3.8-2. *Laminar Flow in a Cylindrical Annulus.* Derive all the equations given in Example 3.8-4 showing all the steps. Also, derive the equation for the average velocity $v_{z\,av}$. Finally, integrate to obtain the pressure drop from $z = 0$ for $p = p_0$ to $z = L$ for $p = p_L$.

$$\textbf{Ans.} \quad v_{z\,av} = -\frac{1}{8\mu}\frac{dp}{dz}\left[r_2^2 + r_1^2 - \frac{r_2^2 - r_1^2}{\ln(r_2/r_1)}\right],$$

$$v_{z\,av} = \frac{p_0 - p_L}{8\mu L}\left[r_2^2 + r_1^2 - \frac{r_2^2 - r_1^2}{\ln(r_2/r_1)}\right]$$

3.8-3. *Velocity Profile in Wetted-Wall Tower.* In a vertical wetted-wall tower, the fluid flows down the inside as a thin film δ m thick in laminar flow in the vertical z direction. Derive the equation for the velocity profile v_z, as a function of x, the distance from the liquid surface toward the wall. The fluid is at a large distance from the entrance. Also, derive expressions for $v_{z\,av}$ and $v_{z\,max}$. (*Hint:* At $x = \delta$, which is at the wall, $v_z = 0$. At $x = 0$, the surface of the flowing liquid, $v_z = v_{z\,max}$.) Show all steps.

$$\textbf{Ans.} \quad v_z = (\rho g \delta^2/2\mu)[1 - (x/\delta)^2], \; v_{z\,av} = \rho g \delta^2/3\mu, \; v_{z\,max} = \rho g \delta^2/2\mu$$

3.8-4. *Velocity Profile in Falling Film and Differential Momentum Balance.* A Newtonian liquid is flowing as a falling film on an inclined flat surface. The surface makes an angle β with the vertical. Assume that in this case the section being considered is sufficiently far from both ends that there are no end effects on the velocity profile. The thickness of the film is δ. The apparatus is similar to Fig. 2.9-3 but is not vertical. Do as follows:

(a) Derive the equation for the velocity profile of v_z as a function of x in this film using the differential momentum balance equation.

(b) What are the maximum velocity and the average velocity?

(c) What is the equation for the momentum flux distribution of τ_{xz}? [*Hint:* Can Eq. (3.7-19) be used here?]

$$\textbf{Ans.} \quad \text{(a) } v_z = (\rho g \delta^2 \cos \beta/2\mu)[1 - (x/\delta)^2]; \; \text{(c) } \tau_{xz} = \rho g x \cos \beta$$

3.8-5. *Velocity Profiles for Flow Between Parallel Plates.* In Example 3.8-2 a fluid is flowing between vertical parallel plates with one plate moving. Do as follows:

(a) Determine the average velocity and the maximum velocity.

(b) Make a sketch of the velocity profile for three cases where the surface is moving upward, moving downward, and stationary.

3.8-6. *Conversion of Shear Stresses in Terms of Fluid Motion.* Starting with the x component of motion, Eq. (3.7-10), which is in terms of shear stresses, convert it to the equation of motion, Eq. (3.7-36), in terms of velocity gradients, for a Newtonian fluid with constant ρ and μ. Note that $(\nabla \cdot v) = 0$ in this case. Also, use of Eqs. (3.7-14)–(3.7-20) should be considered.

3.8-7. *Derivation of Equation of Continuity in Cylindrical Coordinates.* By means of a mass balance over a stationary element whose volume is $r\,\Delta r\,\Delta\theta\,\Delta z$, derive the equation of continuity in cylindrical coordinates.

3.8-8. *Flow between Two Rotating Coaxial Cylinders.* The geometry of two coaxial cylinders is the same as in Example 3.8-5. In this case, however, both cylinders are rotating, the inner rotating with an annular velocity of ω_1 and the outer at ω_2. Determine the velocity and the shear-stress distributions using the differential equation of momentum.

$$\text{Ans.} \quad v_\theta = \frac{R_2^2}{R_2^2 - R_1^2}\left[r\left(\omega_2 - \frac{\omega_1 R_1^2}{R_2^2}\right) - \frac{R_1^2}{r}(\omega_2 - \omega_1)\right]$$

3.9-1. *Potential Function.* The potential function ϕ for a given flow situation is $\phi = C(x^2 - y^2)$, where C is a constant. Check to see if it satisfies Laplace's equation. Determine the velocity components v_x and v_y.

$$\text{Ans.} \quad v_x = 2Cx, v_y = -2Cy \; (C = \text{constant})$$

3.9-2. *Determining the Velocities from the Potential Function.* The potential function for flow is given as $\phi = Ax + By$, where A and B are constants. Determine the velocities v_x and v_y.

3.9-3. *Stream Function and Velocity Vector.* Flow of a fluid in two dimensions is given by the stream function $\psi = Bxy$, where $B = 50 \text{ s}^{-1}$ and the units of x and y are in cm. Determine the value of v_x, v_y, and the velocity vector at $x = 1$ cm and $y = 1$ cm.

$$\text{Ans.} \quad v = 70.7 \text{ cm/s}$$

3.9-4. *Stream Function and Potential Function.* A liquid is flowing parallel to the x axis. The flow is uniform and is represented by $v_x = U$ and $v_y = 0$.
(a) Find the stream function ψ for this flow field and plot the streamlines.
(b) Find the potential function and plot the potential lines.

$$\text{Ans.} \quad \text{(a) } \psi = Uy$$

3.9-5. *Velocity Components and Stream Function.* A liquid is flowing in a uniform manner at an angle of β with respect to the x axis. Its velocity components are $v_x = U \cos \beta$ and $v_y = U \sin \beta$. Find the stream function and the potential function.

$$\text{Ans.} \quad \psi = Uy \cos \beta - Ux \sin \beta$$

3.9-6. *Flow Field with Concentric Streamlines.* The flow of a fluid that has concentric streamlines has a stream function represented by $\psi = 1/(x^2 + y^2)$. Find the components of velocity v_x and v_y. Also, determine if the flow is rotational and, if so, determine the vorticity, $2\omega_z$.

3.9-7. *Potential Function and Velocity Field.* In Example 3.9-2 the velocity components were given. Show if a velocity potential exists and, if so, also determine ϕ.

$$\text{Ans.} \quad \phi = ax^3/3 - axy^2$$

3.9-8. *Euler's Equation of Motion for an Ideal Fluid.* Using the Euler equations (3.9-2)–(3.9-4) for ideal fluids with constant density and zero viscosity, obtain the following equation:

$$\rho \frac{Dv}{Dt} = -\nabla p + \rho g$$

3.9-9. *Plot of Streamlines.* For Ex. (3.9-3) plot the streamlines for $\psi = 0$ and $\psi = 2$ when $x > 0$.

3.9-10. *Stream Function for Two-Dimensional Flow.* Find the stream function of the two-dimensional flow with constant density where $v_x = U[(y/L)^2 - (y/L)]$ and $v_y = 0$. The flow is between two parallel plates spaced L distance apart. Also plot the velocity profile of v_x versus y.

$$\text{Ans.} \quad \psi = UL\left[\frac{1}{3}\left(\frac{y}{L}\right)^3 - \frac{1}{2}\left(\frac{y}{L}\right)^2\right]$$

3.9-11. *Stream and Potential Functions and Plots of These Functions.* Determine the stream function ψ when the velocities are $v_x = 2x$ and $v_y = -2y$. Also determine the potential function ϕ. Plot the stream function for $\psi = 1$ and $\psi = 2$. Also plot the equal potential lines for $\phi = 1$ and $\phi = 4$.

$$\text{Ans.} \quad \psi = 2xy, \phi = x^2 - y^2$$

3.9-12. *Velocity Field from Stream Function.* Given the stream function $\psi = 3x^2 + 2y^2$, calculate v_x and v_y and draw the streamlines for $\psi = 1$ and $\psi = 2$.

Ans. $v_x = 4y, v_y = -6x$

3.9-13. *Streamline from Velocities.* The velocity $v_x = x^2$ and $v_y = -2xy$. Determine the stream function ψ.

Ans. $\psi = x^2y$

3.9-14. *Stream Function from Velocity Potential.* Find the stream function ψ from the velocity potential $\phi = UL[(x/L)^3 - (3xy^2)/L^3]$, where U and L are constants. Also, find v_x and v_y.

Ans. $v_x = \dfrac{3U}{L^2}[x^2 - y^2], v_y = -\dfrac{6Uxy}{L^2}$

3.10-1. *Laminar Boundary Layer on Flat Plate.* Water at 20°C is flowing past a flat plate at 0.914 m/s. The plate is 0.305 m wide.

(a) Calculate the Reynolds number 0.305 m from the leading edge to determine if the flow is laminar.

(b) Calculate the boundary-layer thickness at $x = 0.152$ and $x = 0.305$ m from the leading edge.

(c) Calculate the total drag on the 0.305-m-long plate.

Ans. (a) $N_{Re,L} = 2.77 \times 10^5$; (b) $\delta = 0.0029$ m at $x = 0.305$ m

3.10-2. *Air Flow Past a Plate.* Air at 294.3 K and 101.3 kPa is flowing past a flat plate at 6.1 m/s. Calculate the thickness of the boundary layer at a distance of 0.3 m from the leading edge and the total drag for a 0.3-m-wide plate.

3.10-3. *Boundary-Layer Flow Past a Plate.* Water at 293 K is flowing past a flat plate at 0.5 m/s. Do as follows:

(a) Calculate the boundary-layer thickness in m at a point 0.1 m from the leading edge.

(b) At the same point, calculate the point shear stress τ_0. Also calculate the total drag coefficient.

3.10-4. *Transition Point to Turbulent Boundary Layer.* Air at 101.3 kPa and 293 K is flowing past a smooth, flat plate at 100 ft/s. The turbulence in the air stream is such that the transition from a laminar to a turbulent boundary layer occurs at $N_{Re,L} = 5 \times 10^5$.

(a) Calculate the distance from the leading edge where the transition occurs.

(b) Calculate the boundary-layer thickness δ at a distance of 0.5 ft and 3.0 ft from the leading edge. Also calculate the drag coefficient for both distances $L = 0.5$ and 3.0 ft.

3.11-1. *Dimensional Analysis for Flow Past a Body.* A fluid is flowing external to a solid body. The force F exerted on the body is a function of the fluid velocity v, fluid density ρ, fluid viscosity μ, and a dimension of the body L. By dimensional analysis, obtain the dimensionless groups formed from the variables given. (*Note:* Use the M, L, t system of units. The units of F are ML/t^2. Select v, ρ, and L as the core variables.)

Ans. $\pi_1 = (F/L^2)/\rho v^2, \pi_2 = \mu/Lv\rho$

3.11-2. *Dimensional Analysis for Bubble Formation.* Dimensional analysis is to be used to correlate data on bubble size with the properties of the liquid when gas bubbles are formed by a gas issuing from a small orifice below the liquid surface. Assume that the significant variables are bubble diameter D, orifice diameter d, liquid density ρ, surface tension σ in N/m, liquid viscosity μ, and g. Select d, ρ, and g as the core variables.

Ans. $\pi_1 = D/d, \pi_2 = \sigma/\rho d^2 g, \pi_3 = \mu^2/\rho^2 d^3 g$

Chapter 3   Principles of Momentum Transfer and Applications

REFERENCES

(A1) Allis Chalmers Mfg. Co. *Bull. 1659.*

(A2) American Gas Association, "Orifice Metering of Natural Gas," *Gas Measurement Rept. 3,* New York, 1955.

(B1) BENNETT, C. O., and MYERS, J. E. *Momentum, Heat, and Mass Transfer,* 3rd ed. New York: McGraw-Hill Book Company, 1982.

(B2) BIRD, R. B., STEWART, W. E., and LIGHTFOOT, E. N. *Transport Phenomena.* New York: John Wiley & Sons, Inc., 1960.

(B3) BATES, R. L., FONDY, P. L., and CORPSTEIN, R. R. *I.E.C. Proc. Des. Dev.,* **2,** 310 (1963).

(B4) BROWN, G. G., et al. *Unit Operations.* New York: John Wiley & Sons, Inc., 1950.

(B5) BIGGS, R. D. *A.I.Ch.E. J.,* **9,** 636 (1963).

(B6) BAKKER, A., and GATES, L. E. *Chem. Eng. Progr.,* **91** (Dec.), 25 (1995).

(C1) CHARM, S. E. *The Fundamentals of Food Engineering.* 2nd ed. Westport, Conn.: Avi Publishing Co., Inc., 1971.

(C2) CARMAN, P. C. *Trans. Inst. Chem. Eng. (London),* **15,** 150 (1937).

(C3) CALDERBANK, P. H. In *Mixing: Theory and Practice,* Vol. 2, V. W. Uhl and J. B. Gray (eds.). New York: Academic Press, Inc., 1967.

(C4) CORPSTEIN, R. R., FASANO, J. B., and MYERS, K. J. *Chem. Eng.,* **101** (Oct.), 138 (1994).

(C5) CASSON, N. A. *Rheology of Disperse Systems* (C. C. Mill, ed.), New York: Pergamon Press, 1959.

(D1) DREW, T. B., and HOOPES, J. W., JR. *Advances in Chemical Engineering.* New York: Academic Press, Inc., 1956.

(D2) DODGE, D. W., and METZNER, A. B. *A.I.Ch.E. J.,* **5,** 189 (1959).

(D3) DOEBELIN, E. O. *Measurement Systems Application and Design.* 4th ed. New York: McGraw-Hill Book Company, 1990.

(D4) DARBY, R., and MELSON, J. *Chem. Eng.,* **88** (No. 12), 59 (1981).

(E1) ERGUN, S. *Chem. Eng. Progr.,* **48,** 89 (1952).

(F1) FOX, E. A., and GEX, V. E. *A.I.Ch.E. J.,* **2,** 539 (1956).

(F2) FASANO, J. B., BAKKER, A., and PENNEY, W. R. *Chem. Eng.,* **101** (Aug.), 110 (1994).

(G1) GODLESKI, E. S., and SMITH, J. C. *A.I.Ch.E. J.,* **8,** 617 (1962).

(G2) GELDART, D. *Powder Technol.,* **6,** 201 (1972); **7,** 285 (1973).

(G3) GELDART, D., and ABRAHAMSEN, A. R. *Powder Technol.,* **19,** 133 (1978).

(G4) GELDART, D. *Gas Fluidization Technology.* New York: John Wiley & Sons. Inc., 1986.

(H1) HARPER, J. C., and EL SAHRIGI. *J. Food Sci.,* **30,** 470 (1965).

(H2) HO, F. C., and KWONG, A. *Chem. Eng.,* July 23, 94 (1973).

(K1) KUNII, D., and LEVENSPIEL, O. *Fluidization Engineering.* New York: John Wiley & Sons, Inc., 1969.

(K2) KRIEGER, I. M., and MARON, S. H. *J. Appl. Phys.,* **25,** 72 (1954).

(K3) Koch Engineering Co. *Bull. KSM-5* (1986).

(L1) LEAMY, G. H. *Chem. Eng.,* Oct. 15, 115 (1973).

(L2) LEVA, M., WEINTRAUB, M., GRUMMER, M., POLLCHIK, M., and STORCH, H. H. *U.S. Bur. Mines Bull.,* 504 (1951).

(M1) METZNER, A. B., FEEHS, R. H., RAMOS, H. L., OTTO, R. E., and TUTHILL, J. D. *A.I.Ch.E. J.,* **7,** 3 (1961).

(M2) MCCABE, W. L., SMITH, J. C., and HARRIOTT, P. *Unit Operations of Chemical Engineering,* 4th ed. New York: McGraw-Hill Book Company, 1985.

(M3) METZNER, A. B., and REED, J. C. *A.I.Ch.E. J.,* **1,** 434 (1955).

(M4)   MOHSENIN, N. N. *Physical Properties of Plant and Animal Materials,* Vol. 1, Part II. New York: Gordon & Breach, Inc., 1970.

(M5)   MOO-YUNG, TICHAR, M. K., and DULLIEN, F. A. L. *A.I.Ch.E. J.,* **18,** 178 (1972).

(M6)   MEYERS, K. J., BAKKER, A., and RYAN, D. *Chem. Eng. Progr.,* **93** (June), 28 (1997).

(M7)   McKELVEY, J. M. *Polymer Processing.* New York: John Wiley & Sons, Inc., 1962.

(N1)   NORWOOD, K. W., and METZNER, A. B. *A.I.Ch.E. J.,* **6,** 432 (1960).

(P1)   PERRY, R. H., and GREEN, D. *Perry's Chemical Engineers' Handbook,* 6th ed. New York: McGraw-Hill Book Company, 1984.

(P2)   PINCHBECK, P. H., and POPPER, F. *Chem. Eng. Sci.,* **6,** 57 (1956).

(P3)   PATTERSON, W. I., CARREAU, P. J., and YAP, C. Y. *A.I.Ch.E. J.,* **25,** 208 (1979).

(P4)   PERRY, R. H., and CHILTON, C. H. *Chemical Engineers' Handbook,* 5th ed. New York: McGraw-Hill Book Company, 1973.

(R1)   RUSHTON, J. H., COSTICH, D. W., and EVERETT, H. *J. Chem. Eng. Progr.,* **46,** 395, 467 (1950).

(R2)   RAUTZEN, R. R., CORPTSTEIN, R. R., and DICKEY, D. S. *Chem. Eng.,* Oct. 25, 119 (1976).

(S1)   STEVENS, W. E. Ph.D. thesis, University of Utah, 1953.

(S2)   SKELLAND, A. H. P. *Non-Newtonian Flow and Heat Transfer.* New York: John Wiley & Sons, Inc., 1967.

(S3)   STREETER, V. L. *Handbook of Fluid Dynamics.* New York: McGraw-Hill Book Company, 1961.

(S4)   SCHLICHTING, H. *Boundary Layer Theory.* New York: McGraw-Hill Book Company, 1955.

(T1)   TREYBAL, R. E. *Liquid Extraction,* 2nd ed. New York: McGraw-Hill Book Company, 1953.

(T2)   TREYBAL, R. E. *Mass Transfer Operations,* 3rd ed. New York: McGraw-Hill Book Company, 1980.

(U1)   UHL, V. W., and GRAY, J. B. (eds.), *Mixing: Theory and Practice,* Vol. I. New York: Academic, 1969.

(W1)   WEISMAN, J., and EFFERDING, L. E. *A.I.Ch.E. J.,* **6,** 419 (1960).

(W2)   WINNING, M. D. M.Sc. thesis, University of Alberta, 1948.

(W3)   WALTERS, K. *Rheometry.* London: Chapman & Hall Ltd., 1975.

(W4)   WEN, C. Y., and YU, Y. H. *A.I.Ch.E. J.,* **12,** 610 (1966).

(W5)   WILHELM, R. H., and KWAUK, M. *Chem. Eng. Progr.,* **44,** 201 (1948).

(W6)   WELTY, J. R., WICKS, C. E., and WILSON, R. E. *Fundamentals of Momentum, Heat, and Mass Transfer,* 3rd ed. New York: John Wiley & Sons, 1984.

(Z1)   ZLOKARNIK, M., and JUDAT, H. *Chem. Eng. Tech.,* **39,** 1163 (1967).

CHAPTER 4

Principles of
Steady-State
Heat Transfer

4.1 INTRODUCTION AND MECHANISMS OF HEAT TRANSFER

4.1A Introduction to Steady-State Heat Transfer

The transfer of energy in the form of heat occurs in many chemical and other types of processes. Heat transfer often occurs in combination with other separation processes, such as drying of lumber or foods, alcohol distillation, burning of fuel, and evaporation. The heat transfer occurs because of a temperature-difference driving force and heat flows from the high- to the low-temperature region.

In Section 2.3 we derived an equation for a general property balance of momentum, thermal energy, or mass at unsteady state by writing Eq. (2.3-7). Writing a similar equation but specifically for heat transfer,

$$\begin{pmatrix} \text{rate of} \\ \text{heat in} \end{pmatrix} + \begin{pmatrix} \text{rate of} \\ \text{generation of heat} \end{pmatrix}$$

$$= \begin{pmatrix} \text{rate of} \\ \text{heat out} \end{pmatrix} + \begin{pmatrix} \text{rate of} \\ \text{accumulation of heat} \end{pmatrix} \qquad (4.1-1)$$

Assuming the rate of transfer of heat occurs only by conduction, we can rewrite Eq. (2.3-14), which is *Fourier's law,* as

$$\frac{q_x}{A} = -k \frac{dT}{dx} \qquad (4.1-2)$$

Making an unsteady-state heat balance for the x direction only on the element of volume or control volume in Fig. 4.1-1 by using Eqs. (4.1-1) and (4.1-2), with the cross-sectional area being A m^2,

$$q_{x|x} + \dot{q}(\Delta x \cdot A) = q_{x|x+\Delta x} + \rho c_p \frac{\partial T}{\partial t} (\Delta x \cdot A) \qquad (4.1-3)$$

FIGURE 4.1-1. *Unsteady-state balance for heat transfer in control volume.*

where $\dot{q}$ is rate of heat generated per unit volume. Assuming no heat generation and also assuming steady-state heat transfer, where the rate of accumulation is zero, Eq. (4.1-3) becomes

$$q_{x|x} = q_{x|x+\Delta x} \qquad \textbf{(4.1-4)}$$

This means the rate of heat input by conduction = the rate of heat output by conduction; or q_x is a constant with time for steady-state heat transfer.

In this chapter we are concerned with a control volume where the rate of accumulation of heat is zero and we have steady-state heat transfer. The rate of heat transfer is then constant with time, and the temperatures at various points in the system do not change with time. To solve problems in steady-state heat transfer, various mechanistic expressions in the form of differential equations for the different modes of heat transfer such as Fourier's law are integrated. Expressions for the temperature profile and heat flux are then obtained in this chapter.

In Chapter 5 the conservation-of-energy equations (2.7-2) and (4.1-3) will be used again when the rate of accumulation is not zero and unsteady-state heat transfer occurs. The mechanistic expression for Fourier's law in the form of a partial differential equation will be used where the temperature at various points and the rate of heat transfer change with time. In Section 5.6 a general differential equation of energy change will be derived and integrated for various specific cases to determine the temperature profile and heat flux.

4.1B Basic Mechanisms of Heat Transfer

Heat transfer may occur by any one or more of the three basic mechanisms of heat transfer: conduction, convection, and radiation.

1. Conduction. In conduction, heat can be conducted through solids, liquids, and gases. The heat is conducted by the transfer of the energy of motion between adjacent molecules. In a gas the "hotter" molecules, which have greater energy and motions, impart energy to the adjacent molecules at lower energy levels. This type of transfer is present to some extent in all solids, gases, or liquids in which a temperature gradient exists. In conduction, energy can also be transferred by "free" electrons, which is quite important in metallic solids. Examples of heat transfer mainly by conduction are heat transfer through walls of exchangers or a refrigerator, heat treatment of steel forgings, freezing of the ground during the winter, and so on.

2. *Convection.* The transfer of heat by convection implies the transfer of heat by bulk transport and mixing of macroscopic elements of warmer portions with cooler portions of a gas or liquid. It also often refers to the energy exchange between a solid surface and a fluid. A distinction must be made between forced-convection heat transfer, where a fluid is forced to flow past a solid surface by a pump, fan, or other mechanical means, and natural or free convection, where warmer or cooler fluid next to the solid surface causes a circulation because of a density difference resulting from the temperature differences in the fluid. Examples of heat transfer by convection are loss of heat from a car radiator where the air is being circulated by a fan, cooking of foods in a vessel being stirred, cooling of a hot cup of coffee by blowing over the surface, and so on.

3. *Radiation.* Radiation differs from heat transfer by conduction and convection in that no physical medium is needed for its propagation. Radiation is the transfer of energy through space by means of electromagnetic waves in much the same way as electromagnetic light waves transfer light. The same laws that govern the transfer of light govern the radiant transfer of heat. Solids and liquids tend to absorb the radiation being transferred through them, so that radiation is important primarily in transfer through space or gases. The most important example of radiation is the transport of heat to the earth from the sun. Other examples are cooking of food when passed below red-hot electric heaters, heating of fluids in coils of tubing inside a combustion furnace, and so on.

4.1C Fourier's Law of Heat Conduction

As discussed in Section 2.3 for the general molecular transport equation, all three main types of rate-transfer processes—momentum transfer, heat transfer, and mass transfer—are characterized by the same general type of equation. The transfer of electric current can also be included in this category. This basic equation is as follows:

$$\text{rate of a transfer process} = \frac{\text{driving force}}{\text{resistance}} \qquad \text{(2.3-1)}$$

This equation states what we know intuitively: that in order to transfer a property such as heat or mass, we need a driving force to overcome a resistance.

The transfer of heat by conduction also follows this basic equation and is written as Fourier's law for heat conduction in fluids or solids:

$$\frac{q_x}{A} = -k\,\frac{dT}{dx} \qquad \text{(4.1-2)}$$

where q_x is the heat-transfer rate in the x direction in watts (W), A is the cross-sectional area normal to the direction of flow of heat in m^2, T is temperature in K, x is distance in m, and k is the thermal conductivity in $W/m \cdot K$ in the SI system. The quantity q_x/A is called the heat flux in W/m^2. The quantity dT/dx is the temperature gradient in the x direction. The minus sign in Eq. (4.1-2) is required because if the heat flow is positive in a given direction, the temperature decreases in this direction.

The units in Eq. (4.1-2) may also be expressed in the cgs system, with q_x in cal/s, A in cm^2, k in cal/s $\cdot$ °C $\cdot$ cm, T in °C, and x in cm. In the English system, q_x is in btu/h, A in ft^2, T in °F,

x in ft, k in btu/h $\cdot$ °F $\cdot$ ft, and q_x/A in btu/h $\cdot$ ft^2. From Appendix A.1, the conversion factors are, for thermal conductivity,

$$1\ \text{btu/h} \cdot \text{ft} \cdot °\text{F} = 4.1365 \times 10^{-3}\ \text{cal/s} \cdot \text{cm} \cdot °\text{C} \tag{4.1-5}$$

$$1\ \text{btu/h} \cdot \text{ft} \cdot °\text{F} = 1.73073\ \text{W/m} \cdot \text{K} \tag{4.1-6}$$

For heat flux and power,

$$1\ \text{btu/h} \cdot \text{ft}^2 = 3.1546\ \text{W/m}^2 \tag{4.1-7}$$

$$1\ \text{btu/h} = 0.29307\ \text{W} \tag{4.1-8}$$

Fourier's law, Eq. (4.1-2), can be integrated for the case of steady-state heat transfer through a flat wall of constant cross-sectional area A, where the inside temperature is T_1 at point 1 and T_2 at point 2, a distance of $x_2 - x_1$ m away. Rearranging Eq. (4.1-2),

$$\frac{q_x}{A} \int_{x_1}^{x_2} dx = -k \int_{T_1}^{T_2} dT \tag{4.1-9}$$

Integrating, assuming that k is constant and does not vary with temperature and dropping the subscript x on q_x for convenience,

$$\frac{q}{A} = \frac{k}{x_2 - x_1}(T_1 - T_2) \tag{4.1-10}$$

EXAMPLE 4.1-1. Heat Loss Through an Insulating Wall

Calculate the heat loss per m^2 of surface area for an insulating wall composed of 25.4-mm-thick fiber insulating board, where the inside temperature is 352.7 K and the outside temperature is 297.1 K.

Solution: From Appendix A.3, the thermal conductivity of fiber insulating board is 0.048 W/m $\cdot$ K. The thickness $x_2 - x_1 = 0.0254$ m. Substituting into Eq. (4.1-10),

$$\frac{q}{A} = \frac{k}{x_2 - x_1}(T_1 - T_2) = \frac{0.048}{0.0254}(352.7 - 297.1)$$

$$= 105.1\ \text{W/m}^2$$

$$= (105.1\ \text{W/m}^2)\,\frac{1}{(3.1546\ \text{W/m}^2)/(\text{btu/h} \cdot \text{ft}^2)} = 33.30\ \text{btu/h} \cdot \text{ft}^2$$

4.1D Thermal Conductivity

The defining equation for thermal conductivity is given as Eq. (4.1-2), and with this definition, experimental measurements have been made to determine the thermal conductivity of different materials. In Table 4.1-1 thermal conductivities are given for a few materials for the purpose of comparison. More-detailed data are given in Appendix A.3 for inorganic and organic materials and Appendix A.4 for food and biological materials. As seen in Table 4.1-1, gases have quite low values of thermal conductivity, liquids intermediate values, and solid metals very high values.

TABLE 4.1-1. *Thermal Conductivities of Some Materials at 101.325 kPa (1 Atm) Pressure* (k *in W/m · K*)

Substance	Temp. (K)	k	Ref.	Substance	Temp. (K)	k	Ref.
Gases				Solids			
Air	273	0.0242	(K2)	Ice	273	2.25	(C1)
	373	0.0316		Fire claybrick	473	1.00	(P1)
H_2	273	0.167	(K2)	Paper	—	0.130	(M1)
n-Butane	273	0.0135	(P2)	Hard rubber	273	0.151	(M1)
Liquids				Cork board	303	0.043	(M1)
Water	273	0.569	(P1)	Asbestos	311	0.168	(M1)
	366	0.680		Rock wool	266	0.029	(K1)
Benzene	303	0.159	(P1)	Steel	291	45.3	(P1)
	333	0.151			373	45	
Biological				Copper	273	388	(P1)
materials					373	377	
and foods							
Olive oil	293	0.168	(P1)	Aluminum	273	202	(P1)
	373	0.164					
Lean beef	263	1.35	(C1)				
Skim milk	275	0.538	(C1)				
Applesauce	296	0.692	(C1)				
Salmon	277	0.502	(C1)				
	248	1.30					

1. Gases. In gases the mechanism of thermal conduction is relatively simple. The molecules are in continuous random motion, colliding with one another and exchanging energy and momentum. If a molecule moves from a high-temperature region to a region of lower temperature, it transports kinetic energy to this region and gives up this energy through collisions with lower-energy molecules. Since smaller molecules move faster, gases such as hydrogen should have higher thermal conductivities, as shown in Table 4.1-1.

Theories to predict thermal conductivities of gases are reasonably accurate and are given elsewhere (R1). The thermal conductivity increases approximately as the square root of the absolute temperature and is independent of pressure up to a few atmospheres. At very low pressures (vacuum), however, the thermal conductivity approaches zero.

2. Liquids. The physical mechanism of conduction of energy in liquids is somewhat similar to that of gases, where higher-energy molecules collide with lower-energy molecules. However, the molecules are packed so closely together that molecular force fields exert a strong effect on the energy exchange. Since an adequate molecular theory of liquids is not available, most correlations to predict the thermal conductivities are empirical. Reid et al. (R1) discuss these in detail. The thermal conductivity of liquids varies moderately with temperature and often can be expressed as a linear variation.

$$k = a + bT \qquad (4.1\text{-}11)$$

where a and b are empirical constants. Thermal conductivities of liquids are essentially independent of pressure.

Water has a high thermal conductivity compared to organic-type liquids such as benzene. As shown in Table 4.1-1, the thermal conductivities of most unfrozen foodstuffs, such as skim milk and applesauce, which contain large amounts of water have thermal conductivities near that of pure water.

3. Solids. The thermal conductivity of homogeneous solids varies quite widely, as may be seen for some typical values in Table 4.1-1. The metallic solids of copper and aluminum have very high thermal conductivities, while some insulating nonmetallic materials such as rock wool and corkboard have very low conductivities.

Heat or energy is conducted through solids by two mechanisms. In the first, which applies primarily to metallic solids, heat, like electricity, is conducted by free electrons which move through the metal lattice. In the second mechanism, present in all solids, heat is conducted by the transmission of energy of vibration between adjacent atoms.

Thermal conductivities of insulating materials such as rock wool approach that of air since the insulating materials contain large amounts of air trapped in void spaces. Superinsulations to insulate cryogenic materials such as liquid hydrogen are composed of multiple layers of highly reflective materials separated by evacuated insulating spacers. Values of thermal conductivity are considerably lower than for air alone.

Ice has a thermal conductivity much greater than water. Hence, the thermal conductivities of frozen foods such as lean beef and salmon given in Table 4.1-1 are much higher than for unfrozen foods.

4.1E Convective Heat-Transfer Coefficient

It is well known that a hot piece of material will cool faster when air is blown or forced past the object. When the fluid outside the solid surface is in forced or natural convective motion, we express the rate of heat transfer from the solid to the fluid, or vice versa, by the following equation:

$$q = hA(T_w - T_f) \qquad (4.1\text{-}12)$$

where q is the heat-transfer rate in W, A is the area in m^2, T_w is the temperature of the solid surface in K, T_f is the average or bulk temperature of the fluid flowing past in K, and h is the convective heat-transfer coefficient in $W/m^2 \cdot K$. In English units, h is in btu/h $\cdot$ ft$^2 \cdot$ °F.

The coefficient h is a function of the system geometry, fluid properties, flow velocity, and temperature difference. In many cases, empirical correlations are available to predict this coefficient, since it often cannot be predicted theoretically. Since we know that when a fluid flows past a surface there is a thin, almost stationary layer or film of fluid adjacent to the wall which presents most of the resistance to heat transfer, we often call the coefficient h a *film coefficient*.

TABLE 4.1-2. *Approximate Magnitude of Some Heat-Transfer Coefficients*

	Range of Values of h	
Mechanism	$btu/h \cdot ft^2 \cdot °F$	$W/m^2 \cdot K$
Condensing steam	1000–5000	5700–28 000
Condensing organics	200–500	1100–2800
Boiling liquids	300–5000	1700–28 000
Moving water	50–3000	280–17 000
Moving hydrocarbons	10–300	55–1700
Still air	0.5–4	2.8–23
Moving air	2–10	11.3–55

In Table 4.1-2 some order-of-magnitude values of h for different convective mechanisms of free or natural convection, forced convection, boiling, and condensation are given. Water gives the highest values of the heat-transfer coefficients.

To convert the heat-transfer coefficient h from English to SI units,

$$1 \text{ btu/h} \cdot ft^2 \cdot °F = 5.6783 \text{ W/m}^2 \cdot K$$

4.2 CONDUCTION HEAT TRANSFER

4.2A Conduction Through a Flat Slab or Wall

In this section Fourier's equation (4.1-2) will be used to obtain equations for one-dimensional steady-state conduction of heat through some simple geometries. For a flat slab or wall where the cross-sectional area A and k in Eq. (4.1-2) are constant, we obtained Eq. (4.1-10), which we rewrite as

$$\frac{q}{A} = \frac{k}{x_2 - x_1}(T_1 - T_2) = \frac{k}{\Delta x}(T_1 - T_2) \tag{4.2-1}$$

This is shown in Fig. 4.2-1, where $\Delta x = x_2 - x_1$. Equation (4.2-1) indicates that if T is substituted for T_2 and x for x_2, the temperature varies linearly with distance, as shown in Fig. 4.2-1b.

If the thermal conductivity is not constant but varies linearly with temperature, then substituting Eq. (4.1-11) into Eq. (4.1-2) and integrating,

$$\frac{q}{A} = \frac{a + b\dfrac{T_1 + T_2}{2}}{\Delta x}(T_1 - T_2) = \frac{k_m}{\Delta x}(T_1 - T_2) \tag{4.2-2}$$

where

$$k_m = a + b\frac{T_1 + T_2}{2} \tag{4.2-3}$$

FIGURE 4.2-1. *Heat conduction in a flat wall: (a) geometry of wall, (b) temperature plot.*

This means that the mean value of k (i.e., k_m) to use in Eq. (4.2-2) is the value of k evaluated at the linear average of T_1 and T_2.

As stated in the introduction to transport processes in Eq. (2.3-1), the rate of a transfer process equals the driving force over the resistance. Equation (4.2-1) can be rewritten in that form:

$$q = \frac{T_1 - T_2}{\Delta x/kA} = \frac{T_1 - T_2}{R} = \frac{\text{driving force}}{\text{resistance}} \quad \text{(4.2-4)}$$

where $R = \Delta x/kA$ and is the resistance in K/W or h · °F/btu.

4.2B Conduction Through a Hollow Cylinder

In many instances in the process industries, heat is being transferred through the walls of a thick-walled cylinder, such as a pipe that may or may not be insulated. Consider the hollow cylinder in Fig. 4.2-2 with an inside radius of r_1, where the temperature is T_1, an outside radius of r_2 having a temperature of T_2, and a length of L m. Heat is flowing radially from the inside surface to the outside. Rewriting Fourier's law, Eq. (4.1-2), with distance dr instead of dx,

$$\frac{q}{A} = -k \frac{dT}{dr} \quad \text{(4.2-5)}$$

The cross-sectional area normal to the heat flow is

$$A = 2\pi r L \quad \text{(4.2-6)}$$

Substituting Eq. (4.2-6) into (4.2-5), rearranging, and integrating,

$$\frac{q}{2\pi L} \int_{r_1}^{r_2} \frac{dr}{r} = -k \int_{T_1}^{T_2} dT \quad \text{(4.2-7)}$$

$$q = k \frac{2\pi L}{\ln(r_2/r_1)}(T_1 - T_2) \quad \text{(4.2-8)}$$

FIGURE 4.2-2. *Heat conduction in a cylinder.*

Multiplying numerator and denominator by $(r_2 - r_1)$,

$$q = kA_{lm}\frac{T_1 - T_2}{r_2 - r_1} = \frac{T_1 - T_2}{(r_2 - r_1)/(kA_{lm})} = \frac{T_1 - T_2}{R} \qquad (4.2\text{-}9)$$

where

$$A_{lm} = \frac{(2\pi Lr_2) - (2\pi Lr_1)}{\ln(2\pi Lr_2/2\pi Lr_1)} = \frac{A_2 - A_1}{\ln(A_2/A_1)} \qquad (4.2\text{-}10)$$

$$R = \frac{r_2 - r_1}{kA_{lm}} = \frac{\ln(r_2/r_1)}{2\pi kL} \qquad (4.2\text{-}11)$$

The log mean area is A_{lm}. In engineering practice, if $A_2/A_1 < 1.5/1$, the linear mean area of $(A_1 + A_2)/2$ is within 1.5% of the log mean area. From Eq. (4.2-8), if r is substituted for r_2 and T for T_2, the temperature is seen to be a linear function of $\ln r$ instead of r as in the case of a flat wall. If the thermal conductivity varies with temperature as in Eq. (4.1-10), it can be shown that the mean value to use in a cylinder is still k_m of Eq. (4.2-3).

EXAMPLE 4.2-1. *Length of Tubing for Cooling Coil*

A thick-walled cylindrical tubing of hard rubber having an inside radius of 5 mm and an outside radius of 20 mm is being used as a temporary cooling coil in a bath. Ice water is flowing rapidly inside, and the inside wall temperature is 274.9 K. The outside surface temperature is 297.1 K. A total of 14.65 W must be removed from the bath by the cooling coil. How many m of tubing are needed?

Solution: From Appendix A.3, the thermal conductivity at 0°C (273 K) is $k = 0.151$ W/m·K. Since data at other temperatures are not available, this value will be used for the range of 274.9 to 297.1 K.

$$r_1 = \frac{5}{1000} = 0.005 \text{ m} \qquad r_2 = \frac{20}{1000} = 0.02 \text{ m}$$

The calculation will be done first for a length of 1.0 m of tubing. Solving for the areas A_1, A_2, and A_{lm} in Eq. (4.2-10),

$$A_1 = 2\pi Lr_1 = 2\pi(1.0)(0.005) = 0.0314 \text{ m}^2 \qquad A_2 = 0.1257 \text{ m}^2$$

$$A_{lm} = \frac{A_2 - A_1}{\ln(A_2/A_1)} = \frac{0.1257 - 0.0314}{\ln(0.1257/0.0314)} = 0.0680 \text{ m}^2$$

Substituting into Eq. (4.2-9) and solving,

$$q = kA_{lm}\frac{T_1 - T_2}{r_2 - r_1} = 0.151(0.0682)\left(\frac{274.9 - 297.1}{0.02 - 0.005}\right)$$

$$= -15.2 \text{ W (51.9 btu/h)}$$

The negative sign indicates that the heat flow is from r_2 on the outside to r_1 on the inside. Since 15.2 W is removed for a 1-m length, the needed length is

$$\text{length} = \frac{14.65 \text{ W}}{15.2 \text{ W/m}} = 0.964 \text{ m}$$

Note that the thermal conductivity of rubber is quite small. Generally, metal cooling coils are used, since the thermal conductivity of metals is quite high. The liquid film resistances in this case are quite small and are neglected.

4.2C Conduction Through a Hollow Sphere

Heat conduction through a hollow sphere is another case of one-dimensional conduction. Using Fourier's law for constant thermal conductivity with distance dr, where r is the radius of the sphere,

$$\frac{q}{A} = -k\frac{dT}{dr} \tag{4.2-5}$$

The cross-sectional area normal to the heat flow is

$$A = 4\pi r^2 \tag{4.2-12}$$

Substituting Eq. (4.2-12) into (4.2-5), rearranging, and integrating,

$$\frac{q}{4\pi}\int_{r_1}^{r_2}\frac{dr}{r^2} = -k\int_{T_1}^{T_2}dt \tag{4.2-13}$$

$$q = \frac{4\pi k(T_1 - T_2)}{1/r_1 - 1/r_2} = \frac{T_1 - T_2}{(1/r_1 - 1/r_2)/4\pi k} \tag{4.2-14}$$

It can easily be shown that the temperature varies hyperbolically with the radius. (See Problem 4.2-5.)

4.3 CONDUCTION THROUGH SOLIDS IN SERIES

4.3A Plane Walls in Series

In the case where there is a multilayer wall of more than one material present, as shown in Fig. 4.3-1, we proceed as follows. The temperature profiles in the three materials A, B, and C are shown. Since the heat flow q must be the same in each layer, we can write Fourier's equation for each layer as

$$q = \frac{k_A A}{\Delta x_A}(T_1 - T_2) = \frac{k_B A}{\Delta x_B}(T_2 - T_3) = \frac{k_C A}{\Delta x_C}(T_3 - T_4) \tag{4.3-1}$$

FIGURE 4.3-1. *Heat flow through a multilayer wall.*

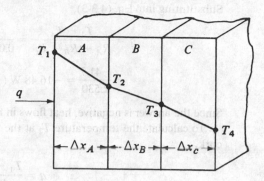

Solving each equation for ΔT,

$$T_1 - T_2 = q\,\frac{\Delta x_A}{k_A A} \qquad T_2 - T_3 = q\,\frac{\Delta x_B}{k_B A} \qquad T_3 - T_4 = q\,\frac{\Delta x_C}{k_C A} \qquad (4.3\text{-}2)$$

Adding the equations for $T_1 - T_2$, $T_2 - T_3$, and $T_3 - T_4$, the internal temperatures T_2 and T_3 drop out and the final rearranged equation is

$$q = \frac{T_1 - T_4}{\Delta x_A/(k_A A) + \Delta x_B/(k_B A) + \Delta x_C/(k_C A)} = \frac{T_1 - T_4}{R_A + R_B + R_C} \qquad (4.3\text{-}3)$$

where the resistance $R_A = \Delta x_A/k_A A$, and so on.

Hence, the final equation is in terms of the overall temperature drop, $T_1 - T_4$, and the total resistance, $R_A + R_B + R_C$.

EXAMPLE 4.3-1. Heat Flow Through an Insulated Wall of a Cold Room

A cold-storage room is constructed of an inner layer of 12.7 mm of pine, a middle layer of 101.6 mm of cork board, and an outer layer of 76.2 mm of concrete. The wall surface temperature is 255.4 K inside the cold room and 297.1 K at the outside surface of the concrete. Use conductivities from Appendix A.3 for pine, 0.151; for cork board, 0.0433; and for concrete, 0.762 W/m · K. Calculate the heat loss in W for 1 m^2 and the temperature at the interface between the wood and cork board.

Solution: Calling $T_1 = 255.4$, $T_4 = 297.1$ K, pine as material A, cork as B, and concrete as C, a tabulation of the properties and dimensions is as follows:

$$k_A = 0.151 \qquad k_B = 0.0433 \qquad k_C = 0.762$$

$$\Delta x_A = 0.0127 \text{ m} \qquad \Delta x_B = 0.1016 \text{ m} \qquad \Delta x_C = 0.0762 \text{ m}$$

The resistances for each material are, from Eq. (4.3-3), for an area of 1 m^2,

$$R_A = \frac{\Delta x_A}{k_A A} = \frac{0.0127}{0.151(1)} = 0.0841 \text{ K/W}$$

$$R_B = \frac{\Delta x_B}{k_B A} = \frac{0.1016}{0.0433(1)} = 2.346 \text{ K/W}$$

$$R_C = \frac{\Delta x_C}{k_C A} = \frac{0.0762}{0.762(1)} = 0.100 \text{ K/W}$$

Substituting into Eq. (4.3-3),

$$q = \frac{T_1 - T_4}{R_A + R_B + R_C} = \frac{255.4 - 297.1}{0.0841 + 2.346 + 0.100}$$

$$= \frac{-41.7}{2.530} = -16.48 \text{ W } (-56.23 \text{ btu/h})$$

Since the answer is negative, heat flows in from the outside.

To calculate the temperature T_2 at the interface between the pine wood and cork,

$$q = \frac{T_1 - T_2}{R_A}$$

Substituting the known values and solving,

$$-16.48 = \frac{255.4 - T_2}{0.0841} \quad \text{and} \quad T_2 = 256.79 \text{ K at the interface}$$

An alternative procedure for calculating T_2 is to use the fact that the temperature drop is proportional to the resistance:

$$T_1 - T_2 = \frac{R_A}{R_A + R_B + R_C}(T_1 - T_4) \tag{4.3-4}$$

Substituting,

$$255.4 - T_2 = \frac{0.0841(255.4 - 297.1)}{2.530} = -1.39 \text{ K}$$

Hence, $T_2 = 256.79$ K, as calculated before.

4.3B Multilayer Cylinders

In the process industries, heat transfer often occurs through multilayers of cylinders, as for example when heat is being transferred through the walls of an insulated pipe. Figure 4.3-2 shows a pipe with two layers of insulation around it, that is, a total of three concentric hollow

FIGURE 4.3-2. *Radial heat flow through multiple cylinders in series.*

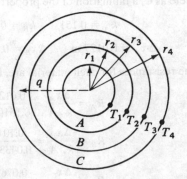

cylinders. The temperature drop is $T_1 - T_2$ across material A, $T_2 - T_3$ across B, and $T_3 - T_4$ across C.

The heat-transfer rate q will, of course, be the same for each layer, since we are at steady state. Writing an equation similar to Eq. (4.2-9) for each concentric cylinder,

$$q = \frac{T_1 - T_2}{(r_2 - r_1)/(k_A A_{A\,\mathrm{lm}})} = \frac{T_2 - T_3}{(r_3 - r_2)/(k_B A_{B\,\mathrm{lm}})} = \frac{T_3 - T_4}{(r_4 - r_3)/(k_C A_{C\,\mathrm{lm}})} \tag{4.3-5}$$

where

$$A_{A\,\mathrm{lm}} = \frac{A_2 - A_1}{\ln(A_2/A_1)} \qquad A_{B\,\mathrm{lm}} = \frac{A_3 - A_2}{\ln(A_3/A_2)} \qquad A_{C\,\mathrm{lm}} = \frac{A_4 - A_3}{\ln(A_4/A_3)} \tag{4.3-6}$$

Using the same method of combining the equations to eliminate T_2 and T_3 as was done for the flat walls in series, the final equations are

$$q = \frac{T_1 - T_4}{(r_2 - r_1)/(k_A A_{A\,\mathrm{lm}}) + (r_3 - r_2)/(k_B A_{B\,\mathrm{lm}}) + (r_4 - r_3)/(k_C A_{C\,\mathrm{lm}})} \tag{4.3-7}$$

$$q = \frac{T_1 - T_4}{R_A + R_B + R_C} = \frac{T_1 - T_4}{\Sigma R} \tag{4.3-8}$$

Hence, the overall resistance is again the sum of the individual resistances in series.

EXAMPLE 4.3-2. Heat Loss from an Insulated Pipe

A thick-walled tube of stainless steel (A) having a $k = 21.63$ W/m·K with dimensions of 0.0254 m ID and 0.0508 m OD is covered with a 0.0254-m-thick layer of an insulation (B), $k = 0.2423$ W/m·K. The inside-wall temperature of the pipe is 811 K and the outside surface of the insulation is at 310.8 K. For a 0.305-m length of pipe, calculate the heat loss and also the temperature at the interface between the metal and the insulation.

Solution: Calling $T_1 = 811$ K, T_2 the interface, and $T_3 = 310.8$ K, the dimensions are

$$r_1 = \frac{0.0254}{2} = 0.0127\text{ m} \qquad r_2 = \frac{0.0508}{2} = 0.0254\text{ m} \qquad r_3 = 0.0508\text{ m}$$

The areas are as follows for $L = 0.305$ m:

$$A_1 = 2\pi L r_1 = 2\pi(0.305)(0.0127) = 0.0243\text{ m}^2$$
$$A_2 = 2\pi L r_2 = 2\pi(0.305)(0.0254) = 0.0487\text{ m}^2$$
$$A_3 = 2\pi L r_3 = 2\pi(0.305)(0.0508) = 0.0974\text{ m}^2$$

From Eq. (4.3-6), the log mean areas for the stainless steel (A) and insulation (B) are

$$A_{A\,\mathrm{lm}} = \frac{A_2 - A_1}{\ln(A_2/A_1)} = \frac{0.0487 - 0.0243}{\ln(0.0487/0.0243)} = 0.0351\text{ m}^2$$

$$A_{B\,\mathrm{lm}} = \frac{A_3 - A_2}{\ln(A_3/A_2)} = \frac{0.0974 - 0.0487}{\ln(0.0974/0.0487)} = 0.0703\text{ m}^2$$

From Eq. (4.3-7) the resistances are

$$R_A = \frac{r_2 - r_1}{k_A A_{A \, lm}} = \frac{0.0127}{21.63(0.0351)} = 0.01673 \text{ K/W}$$

$$R_B = \frac{r_3 - r_2}{k_B A_{B \, lm}} = \frac{0.0254}{0.2423(0.0703)} = 1.491 \text{ K/W}$$

Hence, the heat-transfer rate is

$$q = \frac{T_1 - T_3}{R_A + R_B} = \frac{811 - 310.8}{0.01673 + 1.491} = 331.7 \text{ W (1132 btu/h)}$$

To calculate the temperature T_2,

$$q = \frac{T_1 - T_2}{R_A} \quad \text{or} \quad 331.7 = \frac{811 - T_2}{0.01673}$$

Solving, $811 - T_2 = 5.5$ K and $T_2 = 805.5$ K. Only a small temperature drop occurs across the metal wall because of its high thermal conductivity.

4.3C Conduction Through Materials in Parallel

Suppose that two plane solids A and B are placed side by side in parallel, and the direction of heat flow is perpendicular to the plane of the exposed surface of each solid. Then the total heat flow is the sum of the heat flow through solid A plus that through B. Writing Fourier's equation for each solid and summing,

$$q_T = q_A + q_B = \frac{k_A A_A}{\Delta x_A}(T_1 - T_2) + \frac{k_B A_B}{\Delta x_B}(T_3 - T_4) \tag{4.3-9}$$

where q_T is total heat flow, T_1 and T_2 are the front and rear surface temperatures for solid A, and T_3 and T_4 are those for solid B.

If we assume that $T_1 = T_3$ (front temperatures the same for A and B) and $T_2 = T_4$ (equal rear temperatures),

$$q_T = \frac{T_1 - T_2}{\Delta x_A / k_A A_A} + \frac{T_1 - T_2}{\Delta x_B / k_B A_B} = \left(\frac{1}{R_A} + \frac{1}{R_B} \right)(T_1 - T_2) \tag{4.3-10}$$

An example would be an insulated wall (A) of a brick oven where steel reinforcing members (B) are in parallel and penetrate the wall. Even though the area A_B of the steel would be small compared to the insulated brick area A_A, the higher conductivity of the metal (which could be several hundred times larger than that of the brick) could allow a large portion of the heat lost to be conducted by the steel.

Another example is a method of increasing heat conduction to accelerate the freeze-drying of meat. Spikes of metal in the frozen meat conduct heat more rapidly into the insides of the meat.

It should be mentioned that in some cases some two-dimensional heat flow can occur if the thermal conductivities of the materials in parallel differ markedly. Then the results using Eq. (4.3-10) would be affected somewhat.

4.3D Combined Convection and Conduction and Overall Coefficients

In many practical situations the surface temperatures (or boundary conditions at the surface) are not known, but there is a fluid on both sides of the solid surfaces. Consider the plane wall in Fig. 4.3-3a, with a hot fluid at temperature T_1 on the inside surface and a cold fluid at T_4 on the outside surface. The convective coefficient on the outside is h_o W/m$^2 \cdot$K and h_i on the inside. (Methods for predicting the convective h will be given later, in Section 4.4 of this chapter.)

The heat-transfer rate using Eqs. (4.1-12) and (4.3-1) is given as

$$q = h_i A(T_1 - T_2) = \frac{k_A A}{\Delta x_A}(T_2 - T_3) = h_o A(T_3 - T_4) \qquad \textbf{(4.3-11)}$$

Expressing $1/h_i A$, $\Delta x_A/k_A A$, and $1/h_o A$ as resistances and combining the equations as before,

$$q = \frac{T_1 - T_4}{1/h_i A + \Delta x_A/k_A A + 1/h_o A} = \frac{T_1 - T_4}{\Sigma R} \qquad \textbf{(4.3-12)}$$

The overall heat transfer by combined conduction and convection is often expressed in terms of an overall heat-transfer coefficient U defined by

$$q = UA\,\Delta T_{\text{overall}} \qquad \textbf{(4.3-13)}$$

where $\Delta T_{\text{overall}} = T_1 - T_4$ and U is

$$U = \frac{1}{1/h_i + \Delta x_A/k_A + 1/h_o}\; \frac{\text{W}}{\text{m}^2 \cdot \text{K}} \left(\frac{\text{btu}}{\text{h} \cdot \text{ft}^2 \cdot {}^\circ\text{F}}\right) \qquad \textbf{(4.3-14)}$$

A more important application is heat transfer from a fluid outside a cylinder, through a metal wall, to a fluid inside the tube, as often occurs in heat exchangers. In Fig. 4.3-3b, such a case is shown.

Using the same procedure as before, the overall heat-transfer rate through the cylinder is

$$q = \frac{T_1 - T_4}{1/h_i A_i + (r_o - r_i)/k_A A_{A\,\text{lm}} + 1/h_o A_o} = \frac{T_1 - T_4}{\Sigma R} \qquad \textbf{(4.3-15)}$$

FIGURE 4.3-3. *Heat flow with convective boundaries: (a) plane wall, (b) cylindrical wall.*

where A_i represents $2\pi L r_i$, the inside area of the metal tube; $A_{A\,lm}$ the log mean area of the metal tube; and A_o the outside area.

The overall heat-transfer coefficient U for the cylinder may be based on the inside area A_i or the outside area A_o of the tube. Hence,

$$q = U_i A_i (T_1 - T_4) = U_o A_o (T_1 - T_4) = \frac{T_1 - T_4}{\Sigma R} \qquad (4.3\text{-}16)$$

$$U_i = \frac{1}{1/h_i + (r_o - r_i)A_i/k_A A_{A\,lm} + A_i/A_o h_o} \qquad (4.3\text{-}17)$$

$$U_o = \frac{1}{A_o/A_i h_i + (r_o - r_i)A_o/k_A A_{A\,lm} + 1/h_o} \qquad (4.3\text{-}18)$$

EXAMPLES 4.3-3. Heat Loss by Convection and Conduction and Overall U

Saturated steam at 267°F is flowing inside a $\frac{3}{4}$-in. steel pipe having an ID of 0.824 in. and an OD of 1.050 in. The pipe is insulated with 1.5 in. of insulation on the outside. The convective coefficient for the inside steam surface of the pipe is estimated as $h_i = 1000$ btu/h $\cdot$ ft$^2 \cdot$ °F, and the convective coefficient on the outside of the lagging is estimated as $h_o = 2$ btu/h $\cdot$ ft$^2 \cdot$ °F. The mean thermal conductivity of the metal is 45 W/m $\cdot$ K or 26 btu/h $\cdot$ ft $\cdot$ °F and 0.064 W/m $\cdot$ K or 0.037 btu/h $\cdot$ ft $\cdot$ °F for the insulation.

(a) Calculate the heat loss for 1 ft of pipe using resistances if the surrounding air is at 80°F.
(b) Repeat, using the overall U_i based on the inside area A_i.

Solution: Calling r_i the inside radius of the steel pipe, r_1 the outside radius of the pipe, and r_o the outside radius of the lagging, then

$$r_i = \frac{0.412}{12} \text{ ft} \qquad r_1 = \frac{0.525}{12} \text{ ft} \qquad r_o = \frac{2.025}{12} \text{ ft}$$

For 1 ft of pipe, the areas are as follows:

$$A_i = 2\pi L r_i = 2\pi(1)\left(\frac{0.412}{12}\right) = 0.2157 \text{ ft}^2$$

$$A_1 = 2\pi L r_1 = 2\pi(1)\left(\frac{0.525}{12}\right) = 0.2750 \text{ ft}^2$$

$$A_o = 2\pi L r_o = 2\pi(1)\left(\frac{2.025}{12}\right) = 1.060 \text{ ft}^2$$

From Eq. (4.3-6), the log mean areas for the steel (A) pipe and lagging (B) are

$$A_{A\,lm} = \frac{A_1 - A_i}{\ln(A_1/A_i)} = \frac{0.2750 - 0.2157}{\ln(0.2750/0.2157)} = 0.245$$

$$A_{B\,lm} = \frac{A_o - A_1}{\ln(A_o/A_1)} = \frac{1.060 - 0.2750}{\ln(1.060/0.2750)} = 0.583$$

From Eq. (4.3-15) the various resistances are

$$R_i = \frac{1}{h_i A_i} = \frac{1}{1000(0.2157)} = 0.00464$$

$$R_A = \frac{r_1 - r_i}{k_A A_{A \, lm}} = \frac{(0.525 - 0.412)/12}{26(0.245)} = 0.00148$$

$$R_B = \frac{r_o - r_1}{k_B A_{B \, lm}} = \frac{(2.025 - 0.525)/12}{0.037(0.583)} = 5.80$$

$$R_o = \frac{1}{h_o A_o} = \frac{1}{2(1.060)} = 0.472$$

Using an equation similar to Eq. (4.3-15),

$$q = \frac{T_i - T_o}{R_i + R_A + R_B + R_o} = \frac{267 - 80}{0.00464 + 0.00148 + 5.80 + 0.472} \qquad \text{(4.3-19)}$$

$$= \frac{267 - 80}{6.278} = 29.8 \text{ btu/h}$$

For part (b), the equation relating U_i to q is Eq. (4.3-16), which can be equated to Eq. (4.3-19):

$$q = U_i A_i (T_i - T_o) = \frac{T_i - T_o}{\sum R} \qquad \text{(4.3-20)}$$

Solving for U_i,

$$U_i = \frac{1}{A_i \sum R} \qquad \text{(4.3-21)}$$

Substituting known values,

$$U_i = \frac{1}{0.2157(6.278)} = 0.738 \frac{\text{btu}}{\text{h} \cdot \text{ft}^2 \cdot {}^\circ\text{F}}$$

Then to calculate q,

$$q = U_i A_i (T_i - T_o) = 0.738(0.2157)(267 - 80) = 29.8 \text{ btu/h} \ (8.73 \text{ W})$$

4.3E   Conduction with Internal Heat Generation

In certain systems heat is generated inside the conducting medium; that is, a uniformly distributed heat source is present. Examples of this are electric-resistance heaters and nuclear fuel rods. Also, if a chemical reaction is occurring uniformly in a medium, a heat of reaction is given off. In the agricultural and sanitation fields, compost heaps and trash heaps in which biological activity is occurring will have heat given off.

Other important examples are in food processing, where the heat of respiration of fresh fruits and vegetables is present. These heats of generation can be as high as 0.3 to 0.6 W/kg or 0.5 to 1 btu/h $\cdot$ lb$_m$.

FIGURE 4.3-4. *Plane wall with internal heat generation at steady state.*

1. Heat generation in plane wall. In Fig. 4.3-4 a plane wall is shown with internal heat generation. Heat is conducted only in the x direction. The other walls are assumed to be insulated. The temperature T_w in K at $x = L$ and $x = -L$ is held constant. The volumetric rate of heat generation is $\dot{q}$ W/m^3 and the thermal conductivity of the medium is k W/m·K.

To derive the equation for this case of heat generation at steady state, we start with Eq. (4.1-3) but drop the accumulation term:

$$q_{x|x} + \dot{q}(\Delta x \cdot A) = q_{x|x+\Delta x} + 0 \tag{4.3-22}$$

where A is the cross-sectional area of the plate. Rearranging, dividing by Δx, and letting Δx approach zero,

$$\frac{-dq_x}{dx} + \dot{q} \cdot A = 0 \tag{4.3-23}$$

Substituting Eq. (4.1-2) for q_x,

$$\frac{d^2T}{dx^2} + \frac{\dot{q}}{k} = 0 \tag{4.3-24}$$

Integration gives the following for $\dot{q}$ constant:

$$T = -\frac{\dot{q}}{2k} x^2 + C_1 x + C_2 \tag{4.3-25}$$

where C_1 and C_2 are integration constants. The boundary conditions are at $x = L$ or $-L$, $T = T_w$, and at $x = 0$, $T = T_0$ (center temperature). Then, the temperature profile is

$$T = -\frac{\dot{q}}{2k} x^2 + T_0 \tag{4.3-26}$$

The center temperature is

$$T_0 = \frac{\dot{q}L^2}{2k} + T_w \tag{4.3-27}$$

The total heat lost from the two faces at steady state is equal to the total heat generated, $\dot{q}_T$, in W:

$$\dot{q}_T = \dot{q}(2LA) \tag{4.3-28}$$

where A is the cross-sectional area (surface area at T_w) of the plate.

2. Heat generation in cylinder.   In a similar manner an equation can be derived for a cylinder of radius R with uniformly distributed heat sources and constant thermal conductivity. The heat is assumed to flow only radially, that is, the ends are neglected or insulated. The final equation for the temperature profile is

$$T = \frac{\dot{q}}{4k}(R^2 - r^2) + T_w \tag{4.3-29}$$

where r is distance from the center. The center temperature T_0 is

$$T_0 = \frac{\dot{q}R^2}{4k} + T_w \tag{4.3-30}$$

EXAMPLE 4.3-4.   Heat Generation in a Cylinder

An electric current of 200 A is passed through a stainless-steel wire having a radius R of 0.001268 m. The wire is $L = 0.91$ m long and has a resistance R of 0.126 ohms. The outer surface temperature T_w is held at 422.1 K. The average thermal conductivity is $k = 22.5$ W/m $\cdot$ K. Calculate the center temperature.

Solution: First the value of $\dot{q}$ must be calculated. Since power $= I^2R$, where I is current in amps and R is resistance in ohms,

$$I^2R = \text{watts} = \dot{q}\pi R^2 L \tag{4.3-31}$$

Substituting known values and solving,

$$(200)^2(0.126) = \dot{q}\pi(0.001268)^2(0.91)$$

$$\dot{q} = 1.096 \times 10^9 \text{ W/m}^3$$

Substituting into Eq. (4.3-30) and solving, $T_0 = 441.7$ K.

4.3F   Critical Thickness of Insulation for a Cylinder

In Fig. 4.3-5 a layer of insulation is installed around the outside of a cylinder whose radius r_1 is fixed and with a length L. The cylinder has a high thermal conductivity and the inner temperature T_1 at point r_1 outside the cylinder is fixed. An example is the case where the cylinder is a metal pipe with saturated steam inside. The outer surface of the insulation at T_2 is exposed to an environment at T_0 where convective heat transfer occurs. It is not obvious if adding more insulation with a thermal conductivity of k will decrease the heat-transfer rate.

At steady state the heat-transfer rate q through the cylinder and the insulation equals the rate of convection from the surface:

$$q = h_o A(T_2 - T_0) \tag{4.3-32}$$

FIGURE 4.3-5. *Critical radius for insulation of cylinder or pipe.*

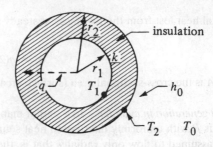

insulation

As insulation is added, the outside area, which is $A = 2\pi r_2 L$, increases, but T_2 decreases. However, it is not apparent whether q increases or decreases. To determine this, an equation similar to Eq. (4.3-15) with the resistance of the insulation represented by Eq. (4.2-11) is written using the two resistances:

$$q = \frac{2\pi L(T_1 - T_0)}{\dfrac{\ln(r_2/r_1)}{k} + \dfrac{1}{r_2 h_o}} \qquad \text{(4.3-33)}$$

To determine the effect of the thickness of insulation on q, we take the derivative of q with respect to r_2, equate this result to zero, and obtain the following for maximum heat flow:

$$\frac{dq}{dr_2} = \frac{-2\pi L(T_1 - T_0)(1/r_2 k - 1/r_2^2 h_o)}{\left[\dfrac{\ln(r_2/r_1)}{k} + \dfrac{1}{r_2 h_o}\right]^2} = 0 \qquad \text{(4.3-34)}$$

Solving,

$$(r_2)_{cr} = \frac{k}{h_o} \qquad \text{(4.3-35)}$$

where $(r_2)_{cr}$ is the value of the critical radius when the heat-transfer rate is a maximum. Hence, if the outer radius r_2 is less than the critical value, adding more insulation will actually increase the heat-transfer rate q. Also, if the outer radius is greater than the critical, adding more insulation will decrease the heat-transfer rate. Using values of k and h_o typically encountered, the critical radius is only a few mm. As a result, adding insulation on small electrical wires could increase the heat loss. Adding insulation to large pipes decreases the heat-transfer rate.

EXAMPLE 4.3-5. *Insulating an Electrical Wire and Critical Radius*
An electric wire having a diameter of 1.5 mm and covered with a plastic insulation (thickness = 2.5 mm) is exposed to air at 300 K and $h_o = 20$ W/m^2·K. The insulation has a k of 0.4 W/m·K. It is assumed that the wire surface temperature is constant at 400 K and is not affected by the covering.
    (a) Calculate the value of the critical radius.
    (b) Calculate the heat loss per m of wire length with no insulation.
    (c) Repeat (b) for insulation being present.

Solution: For part (a), using Eq. (4.3-35),

$$(r_2)_{cr} = \frac{k}{h_o} = \frac{0.4}{20} = 0.020 \text{ m} = 20 \text{ mm}$$

For part (b), $L = 1.0$ m, $r_2 = 1.5/(2 \times 1000) = 0.75 \times 10^{-3}$ m, $A = 2\pi r_2 L$. Substituting into Eq. (4.3-32),

$$q = h_o A(t_2 - T_0) = (20)(2\pi \times 0.75 \times 10^{-3} \times 1)(400 - 300) = 9.42 \text{ W}$$

For part (c) with insulation, $r_1 = 1.5/(2 \times 1000) = 0.75 \times 10^{-3}$ m, $r_2 = (2.5 + 1.5/2)/1000 = 3.25 \times 10^{-3}$ m. Substituting into Eq. (4.3-33),

$$q = \frac{2\pi(1.0)(400 - 300)}{\dfrac{\ln(3.25 \times 10^{-3}/0.75 \times 10^{-3})}{0.4} + \dfrac{1}{(3.25 \times 10^{-3})(20)}} = 32.98 \text{ W}$$

Hence, adding insulation greatly increases the heat loss.

4.3G Contact Resistance at an Interface

In the equations derived in this section for conduction through solids in series (see Fig. 4.3-1), it has been assumed that the adjacent touching surfaces are at the same temperature, that is, that completely perfect contact is made between the surfaces. For many engineering designs in industry, this assumption is reasonably accurate. However, in cases such as in nuclear power plants, where very high heat fluxes are present, a significant drop in temperature may be present at the interface. This interface resistance, called *contact resistance,* occurs when the two solids do not fit tightly together and a thin layer of stagnant fluid is trapped between the two surfaces. At some points the solids touch at peaks in the surfaces and at other points the fluid occupies the open space.

This interface resistance is a complex function of the roughness of the two surfaces, the pressure applied to hold the surfaces in contact, the interface temperature, and the interface fluid. Heat transfer takes place by conduction, radiation, and convection across the trapped fluid and also by conduction through the points of contact of the solids. No completely reliable empirical correlations or theories are available to predict contact resistances for all types of materials. See references (C7, R2) for detailed discussions.

The equation for the contact resistance is often given as follows:

$$q = h_c A \, \Delta T = \frac{\Delta T}{1/h_c A} = \frac{\Delta T}{R_c} \qquad (4.3\text{-}36)$$

where h_c is the contact-resistance coefficient in W/m$^2 \cdot$ K, ΔT the temperature drop across the contact resistance in K, and R_c the contact resistance. The contact resistance R_c can be added to the other resistances in Eq. (4.3-3) to include this effect for solids in series. For contact between two ground-metal surfaces, h_c values on the order of magnitude of about 0.2×10^4 to 1×10^4 W/m$^2 \cdot$ K have been obtained.

An approximation of the maximum contact resistance can be obtained if the maximum gap Δx between the surfaces can be estimated. Then, assuming that the heat transfer across the gap is by conduction only through the stagnant fluid, h_c is estimated as

$$h_c = \frac{k}{\Delta x} \qquad (4.3\text{-}37)$$

If any actual convection, radiation, or point-to-point contact is present, it will reduce this assumed resistance.

4.4 STEADY-STATE CONDUCTION AND SHAPE FACTORS

4.4A Introduction and Graphical Method for Two-Dimensional Conduction

In previous sections of this chapter we discussed steady-state heat conduction in one direction. In many cases, however, steady-state heat conduction is occurring in two directions, that is, two-dimensional conduction is occurring. The two-dimensional solutions are more involved and in most cases analytical solutions are not available. One important approximate method for solving such problems is to use a numerical method discussed in detail in Section 4.15. Another important approximate method is the graphical method, which is a simple method that can provide reasonably accurate answers for the heat-transfer rate. This method is particularly applicable to systems having isothermal boundaries.

In the graphical method we first note that for one-dimensional heat conduction through a flat slab (see Fig. 4.2-1) the direction of the heat flux or flux lines is always perpendicular to the isotherms. The graphical method for two-dimensional conduction is also based on the requirement that the heat-flux lines and isotherm lines intersect each other at right angles while forming a network of curvilinear squares. This means, as shown in Fig. 4.4-1, that we can sketch the isotherms and also the flux lines until they intersect at right angles (are perpendicular to each other). With care and experience we can obtain reasonably accurate results. General steps to use in this graphical method are as follows:

1. Draw a model to scale of the two-dimensional solid. Label the isothermal boundaries. In Fig. 4.4-1, T_1 and T_2 are isothermal boundaries.
2. Select a number N that is the number of equal temperature subdivisions between the isothermal boundaries. In Fig. 4.4-1, $N = 4$ subdivisions between T_1 and T_2. Sketch in the

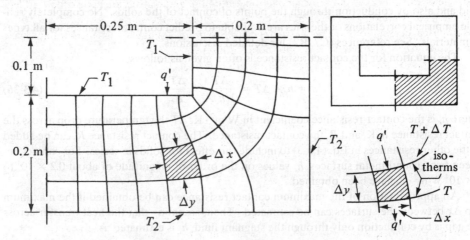

FIGURE 4.4-1. *Graphical curvilinear-square method for two-dimensional heat conduction in a rectangular flue.*

isotherm lines and the heat-flow or -flux lines so that they are perpendicular to each other at the intersections. Note that isotherms are perpendicular to adiabatic (insulated) boundaries and also lines of symmetry.

3. Keep adjusting the isotherm and flux lines until for each curvilinear square the condition $\Delta x = \Delta y$ is satisfied.

In order to calculate the heat flux using the results of the graphical plot, we first assume unit depth of the material. The heat flow q' through the curvilinear section shown in Fig. 4.4-1 is given by Fourier's law:

$$q' = -kA \frac{dT}{dy} = k(\Delta x \cdot 1) \frac{\Delta T}{\Delta y} \tag{4.4-1}$$

This heat flow q' will be the same through each curvilinear square within this heat-flow lane. Since $\Delta x = \Delta y$, each temperature subdivision ΔT is equal. This temperature subdivision can be expressed in terms of the overall temperature difference $T_1 - T_2$ and N, the number of equal subdivisions:

$$\Delta T = \frac{T_1 - T_2}{N} \tag{4.4-2}$$

Also, the heat flow q' through each lane is the same, since $\Delta x = \Delta y$ in the construction and in Eq. (4.4-1). Hence, the total heat transfer q through all of the lanes is

$$q = Mq' = Mk \, \Delta T \tag{4.4-3}$$

where M is the total number of heat-flow lanes as determined by the graphical procedure. Substituting Eq. (4.4-2) into (4.4-3),

$$q = \frac{M}{N} k(T_1 - T_2) \tag{4.4-4}$$

EXAMPLE 4.4-1. *Two-Dimensional Conduction by Graphical Procedure*
Determine the total heat transfer through the walls of the flue shown in Fig. 4.4-1 if $T_1 = 600$ K, $T_2 = 400$ K, $k = 0.90$ W/m $\cdot$ K, and L (length of flue) = 5 m.

Solution: In Fig. 4.4-1, $N = 4$ temperature subdivisions and $M = 9.25$. The total heat-transfer rate through the four identical sections with a depth or length L of 5 m is obtained by using Eq. (4.4-4):

$$q = 4 \left[\frac{M}{N} kL(T_1 - T_2) \right] = 4 \left[\frac{9.25}{4} (0.9)(5.0)(600 - 400) \right]$$

$$= 8325 \text{ W}$$

4.4B Shape Factors in Conduction

In Eq. (4.4-4) the factor M/N is called the conduction shape factor S, where

$$S = \frac{M}{N} \tag{4.4-5}$$

$$q = kS(T_1 - T_2) \tag{4.4-6}$$

TABLE 4.4-1. *Conduction Shape Factors for* $q = kS(T_1 - T_2)$*

Cylinder of length L in a square		$S = \dfrac{2\pi L}{\ln(0.54\, a/r_1)}$
Horizontal buried cylinder of length L		$S = \dfrac{2\pi L}{\ln(2H/r_1)} \quad (H > 3r_1)$
Two parallel cylinders of length L		$S = \dfrac{2\pi L}{\cosh^{-1}\left[\dfrac{H^2 - r_1^2 - r_2^2}{2 r_1 r_2}\right]}$
Sphere buried		$S = \dfrac{4\pi r_1}{1 - r_1/2H}$

*The thermal conductivity of the medium is k.

This shape factor S has units of m and is used in two-dimensional heat conduction where only two temperatures are involved. The shape factors for a number of geometries have been obtained and some are given in Table 4.4-1.

For a three-dimensional geometry such as a furnace, separate shape factors are used to obtain the heat flow through the edge and corner sections. When each of the interior dimensions is greater than one-fifth of the wall thickness, the shape factors are as follows for a uniform wall thickness T_w:

$$S_{\text{wall}} = \frac{A}{T_w} \qquad S_{\text{edge}} = 0.54L \qquad S_{\text{corner}} = 0.15T_w \tag{4.4-7}$$

where A is the inside area of wall and L the length of inside edge. For a completely enclosed geometry, there are six wall sections, 12 edges, and eight corners. Note that for a single flat wall, $q = kS_{wall}(T_1 - T_2) = k(A/T_w)(T_1 - T_2)$, which is the same as Eq. (4.2-1) for conduction through a single flat slab.

For a long, hollow cylinder of length L such as that in Fig. 4.2-2,

$$S = \frac{2\pi L}{\ln(r_2/r_1)} \qquad (4.4\text{-}8)$$

For a hollow sphere, from Eq. (4.2-14),

$$S = \frac{4\pi r_2 r_1}{r_2 - r_1} \qquad (4.4\text{-}9)$$

4.5 FORCED CONVECTION HEAT TRANSFER INSIDE PIPES

4.5A Introduction and Dimensionless Numbers

In most situations involving a liquid or a gas in heat transfer, convective heat transfer usually occurs as well as conduction. In most industrial processes where heat transfer is occurring, heat is being transferred from one fluid through a solid wall to a second fluid. In Fig. 4.5-1 heat is being transferred from the hot flowing fluid to the cold flowing fluid. The temperature profile is shown.

The velocity gradient, when the fluid is in turbulent flow, is very steep next to the wall in the thin viscous sublayer where turbulence is absent. Here the heat transfer is mainly by conduction, with a large temperature difference of $T_2 - T_3$ in the warm fluid. As we move farther away from the wall, we approach the turbulent region, where rapidly moving eddies tend to equalize the temperature. Hence, the temperature gradient is less and the difference $T_1 - T_2$ is small. The average temperature of fluid A is slightly less than the peak value T_1. A similar explanation can be given for the temperature profile in the cold fluid.

The convective coefficient for heat transfer through a fluid is given by

$$q = hA(T - T_w) \qquad (4.5\text{-}1)$$

where h is the convective coefficient in W/m$^2 \cdot$ K, A is the area in m^2, T is the bulk or average temperature of the fluid in K, T_w is the temperature of the wall in contact with the fluid in K,

FIGURE 4.5-1. *Temperature profile for heat transfer by convection from one fluid to another*

and q is the heat-transfer rate in W. In English units, q is in btu/h, h in btu/h · ft^2 · °F, A in ft^2, and T and T_w in °F.

The type of fluid flow, whether laminar or turbulent, of the individual fluid has a great effect on the heat-transfer coefficient h, which is often called a *film coefficient*, since most of the resistance to heat transfer is in a thin film close to the wall. The more turbulent the flow, the greater the heat-transfer coefficient.

There are two main classifications of convective heat transfer. The first is free or *natural convection*, where the motion of the fluid results from the density changes in heat transfer. The buoyant effect produces a natural circulation of the fluid, so it moves past the solid surface. In the second type, *forced convection*, the fluid is forced to flow by pressure differences, a pump, a fan, and so on.

Most of the correlations for predicting film coefficients h are semiempirical in nature and are affected by the physical properties of the fluid, the type and velocity of flow, the temperature difference, and the geometry of the specific physical system. Some approximate values for convective coefficients were presented in Table 4.1-2. In the following correlations, either SI or English units can be used, since the equations are dimensionless.

To correlate these data for heat-transfer coefficients, dimensionless numbers such as the Reynolds and Prandtl numbers are used. The Prandtl number is the ratio of the shear component of diffusivity for momentum μ/ρ to the diffusivity for heat $k/\rho c_p$ and physically relates the relative thicknesses of the hydrodynamic layer and thermal boundary layer:

$$N_{Pr} = \frac{\mu/\rho}{k/\rho c_p} = \frac{c_p \mu}{k} \tag{4.5-2}$$

Values of the N_{Pr} for gases are given in Appendix A.3 and range from about 0.5 to 1.0. Values for liquids range from about 2 to well over 10^4. The dimensionless Nusselt number, N_{Nu}, is used to relate data for the heat-transfer coefficient h to the thermal conductivity k of the fluid and a characteristic dimension D:

$$N_{Nu} = \frac{hD}{k} \tag{4.5-3}$$

For example, for flow inside a pipe, D is the diameter.

4.5B Heat-Transfer Coefficient for Laminar Flow Inside a Pipe

Certainly, the most important convective heat-transfer process industrially is that of cooling or heating a fluid flowing inside a closed circular conduit or pipe. Different types of correlations for the convective coefficient are needed for laminar flow (N_{Re} below 2100), for fully turbulent flow (N_{Re} above 6000), and for the transition region (N_{Re} between 2100 and 6000).

For laminar flow of fluids inside horizontal tubes or pipes, the following equation of Sieder and Tate (S1) can be used for $N_{Re} < 2100$:

$$(N_{Nu})_a = \frac{h_a D}{k} = 1.86 \left(N_{Re} \, N_{Pr} \frac{D}{L} \right)^{1/3} \left(\frac{\mu_b}{\mu_w} \right)^{0.14} \tag{4.5-4}$$

where D = pipe diameter in m, L = pipe length before mixing occurs in the pipe in m, μ_b = fluid viscosity at bulk average temperature in Pa · s, μ_w = viscosity at the wall temperature, c_p = heat capacity in J/kg · K, k = thermal conductivity in W/m · K, h_a = average heat-transfer coefficient in $W/m^2 \cdot K$, and N_{Nu} = dimensionless Nusselt number. All the physical properties are evaluated at the bulk fluid temperature except μ_w. The Reynolds number is

$$N_{Re} = \frac{Dv\rho}{\mu} \tag{4.5-5}$$

and the Prandtl number,

$$N_{Pr} = \frac{c_p\mu}{k} \tag{4.5-6}$$

This equation holds for $(N_{Re}N_{Pr}D/L) > 100$. If used down to $(N_{Re}N_{Pr}D/L) > 10$, it still holds to $\pm 20\%$ (B1). For $(N_{Re}N_{Pr}D/L) < 100$, another expression is available (P1).

In laminar flow the average coefficient h_a depends strongly on heated length. The average (arithmetic mean) temperature drop ΔT_a is used in the equation to calculate the heat-transfer rate q:

$$q = h_a A \, \Delta T_a = h_a A \frac{(T_w - T_{bi}) + (T_w - T_{bo})}{2} \tag{4.5-7}$$

where T_w is the wall temperature in K, T_{bi} the inlet bulk fluid temperature, and T_{bo} the outlet bulk fluid temperature.

For large pipe diameters and large temperature differences ΔT between pipe wall and bulk fluid, natural convection effects can increase h (P1). Equations are also available for laminar flow in vertical tubes.

4.5C Heat-Transfer Coefficient for Turbulent Flow Inside a Pipe

When the Reynolds number is above 6000, the flow is fully turbulent. Since the rate of heat transfer is greater in the turbulent region, many industrial heat-transfer processes are in the turbulent region.

The following equation has been found to hold for tubes but is also used for pipes. It holds for a $N_{Re} > 6000$, a N_{Pr} between 0.7 and 16 000, and $L/D > 60$.

$$N_{Nu} = \frac{h_L D}{k} = 0.027 N_{Re}^{0.8} N_{Pr}^{1/3} \left(\frac{\mu_b}{\mu_w}\right)^{0.14} \tag{4.5-8}$$

where h_L is the heat-transfer coefficient based on the log mean driving force ΔT_{lm} (see Section 4.5H). The fluid properties except for μ_w are evaluated at the mean bulk temperature. If the bulk fluid temperature varies from the inlet to the outlet of the pipe, the mean of the inlet and outlet temperatures is used. For an $L/D < 60$, where the entry is an abrupt contraction, an approximate correction is provided by multiplying the right-hand side of Eq. (4.5-8) by a correction factor given in Section 4.5F.

The use of Eq. (4.5-8) may be trial and error, since the value of h_L must be known in order to evaluate T_w, and hence μ_w, at the wall temperature. Also, if the mean bulk temperature increases or decreases in the tube length L because of heat transfer, the bulk temperature at length L must be estimated in order to have a mean bulk temperature of the entrance and exit to use.

The heat-transfer coefficient for turbulent flow is somewhat greater for a pipe than for a smooth tube. This effect is much less than in fluid friction, and it is usually neglected in calculations. Also, for liquid metals that have Prandtl numbers $\ll 1$, other correlations must be used to predict the heat-transfer coefficient. (See Section 4.5G.) For shapes of tubes other than circular, the equivalent diameter can be used, as discussed in Section 4.5E.

For air at 1 atm total pressure, the following simplified equation holds for turbulent flow in pipes:

$$h_L = \frac{3.52v^{0.8}}{D^{0.2}} \quad \text{(SI)}$$

$$h_L = \frac{0.5v_s^{0.8}}{(D')^{0.2}} \quad \text{(English)}$$

(4.5-9)

where D is in m, v in m/s, and h_L in W/m$^2 \cdot$ K for SI units; and D' is in in., v_s in ft/s, and h_L in btu/h $\cdot$ ft$^2 \cdot$ °F for English units.

Water is often used in heat-transfer equipment. A simplified equation to use for a temperature range of $T = 4$–105°C (40–220°F) is

$$h_L = 1429(1 + 0.0146T°\text{C}) \frac{v^{0.8}}{D^{0.2}} \quad \text{(SI)}$$

$$h_L = 150(1 + 0.011T°\text{F}) \frac{v_s^{0.8}}{(D')^{0.2}} \quad \text{(English)}$$

(4.5-10)

For organic liquids, a very simplified equation to use for approximations is as follows (P3):

$$h_L = 423 \frac{v^{0.8}}{D^{0.2}} \quad \text{(SI)}$$

$$h_L = 60 \frac{v_s^{0.8}}{(D')^{0.2}} \quad \text{(English)}$$

(4.5-11)

For flow inside helical coils and N_{Re} above 10^4, the predicted film coefficient for straight pipes should be increased by the factor $(1 + 3.5D/D_{\text{coil}})$.

EXAMPLE 4.5-1. Heating of Air in Turbulent Flow

Air at 206.8 kPa and an average of 477.6 K is being heated as it flows through a tube of 25.4 mm inside diameter at a velocity of 7.62 m/s. The heating medium is 488.7 K steam condensing on the outside of the tube. Since the heat-transfer coefficient of condensing steam is several thousand W/m$^2 \cdot$ K and the resistance of the metal wall is very small, it will be assumed that the surface wall temperature of the metal in contact with the air is 488.7 K. Calculate the heat-transfer coefficient for an $L/D > 60$ and also the heat-transfer flux q/A.

Solution: From Appendix A.3, for physical properties of air at 477.6 K (204.4°C), $\mu_b = 2.60 \times 10^{-5}$ Pa$\cdot$s, $k = 0.03894$ W/m, $N_{\text{Pr}} = 0.686$. At 488.7 K (215.5°C), $\mu_w = 2.64 \times 10^{-5}$ Pa$\cdot$s.

$$\mu_b = 2.60 \times 10^{-5} \text{ Pa}\cdot\text{s} = 2.60 \times 10^{-5} \text{ kg/m}\cdot\text{s}$$

$$\rho = (28.97)\left(\frac{1}{22.414}\right)\left(\frac{206.8}{101.33}\right)\left(\frac{273.2}{477.6}\right) = 1.509 \text{ kg/m}^3$$

The Reynolds number calculated at the bulk fluid temperature of 477.6 K is

$$N_{Re} = \frac{Dv\rho}{\mu} = \frac{0.0254(7.62)(1.509)}{2.6 \times 10^{-5}} = 1.122 \times 10^4$$

Hence, the flow is turbulent and Eq. (4.5-8) will be used. Substituting into Eq. (4.5-8),

$$N_{Nu} = \frac{h_L D}{k} = 0.027 N_{Re}^{0.8} N_{Pr}^{1/3} \left(\frac{\mu_b}{\mu_w}\right)^{0.14}$$

$$\frac{h_L(0.0254)}{0.03894} = 0.027(1.122 \times 10^4)^{0.8}(0.686)^{1/3}\left(\frac{0.0260}{0.0264}\right)^{0.14}$$

Solving, $h_L = 63.2$ W/m$^2 \cdot$ K (11.13 btu/h $\cdot$ ft$^2 \cdot$ °F).

To solve for the flux q/A,

$$\frac{q}{A} = h_L(T_w - T) = 63.2(488.7 - 477.6)$$

$$= 701.1 \text{ W/m}^2 \ (222.2 \text{ btu/h} \cdot \text{ft}^2)$$

4.5D Heat-Transfer Coefficient for Transition Flow Inside a Pipe

In the transition region for a N_{Re} between 2100 and 6000, the empirical equations are not well defined, just as in the case of fluid friction factors. No simple equation exists for accomplishing a smooth transition from heat transfer in laminar flow to that in turbulent flow, that is, a transition from Eq. (4.5-4) at a $N_{Re} = 2100$ to Eq. (4.5-8) at a $N_{Re} = 6000$.

The plot in Fig. 4.5-2 represents an approximate relationship to use between the various heat-transfer parameters and the Reynolds number between 2100 and 6000. For below a N_{Re} of 2100, the curves represent Eq. (4.5-4), and above 10^4, Eq. (4.5-8). The mean ΔT_a of Eq. (4.5-7) should be used with the h_a in Fig. 4.5-2.

FIGURE 4.5-2.   *Correlation of heat-transfer parameters for transition region for Reynolds numbers between 2100 and 6000. (From
R. H. Perry and C. H. Chilton, Chemical Engineers'
Handbook. 5th ed. New York: McGraw-Hill Book Company, 1973. With permission.)*

4.5E   Heat-Transfer Coefficient for Noncircular Conduits

A heat-transfer system often used is one in which fluids flow at different temperatures in concentric pipes. The heat-transfer coefficient of the fluid in the annular space can be predicted by using the same equations as for circular pipes. However, the equivalent diameter defined in Section 2.10G must be used. For an annular space, D_{eq} is the ID of the outer pipe D_1 minus the OD of the inner pipe D_2. For other geometries, an equivalent diameter can also be used.

> **EXAMPLE 4.5-2.   Water Heated by Steam and Trial-and-Error Solution**
> Water is flowing in a horizontal 1-in. schedule 40 steel pipe at an average temperature of 65.6°C and a velocity of 2.44 m/s. It is being heated by condensing steam at 107.8°C on the outside of the pipe wall. The steam-side coefficient has been estimated as $h_o = 10\,500$ W/m$^2 \cdot$ K.
> (a) Calculate the convective coefficient h_i for water inside the pipe.
> (b) Calculate the overall coefficient U_i based on the inside surface area.
> (c) Calculate the heat-transfer rate q for 0.305 m of pipe with the water at an average temperature of 65.6°C.

Solution: From Appendix A.5, the various dimensions are $D_i = 0.0266$ m and $D_o = 0.0334$ m. For water at a bulk average temperature of 65.6°C, from Appendix A.2, $N_{Pr} = 2.72$, $\rho = 0.980(1000) = 980$ kg/m^3, $k = 0.633$ W/m $\cdot$ K, and $\mu = 4.32 \times 10^{-4}$ Pa $\cdot$ S $= 4.32 \times 10^{-4}$ kg/m $\cdot$ s.

The temperature of the inside metal wall is needed and will be assumed as about one-third the difference between 65.6 and 107.8, or 80°C $= T_w$, for the first trial. Hence, μ_w at 80°C $= 3.56 \times 10^{-4}$ Pa $\cdot$ s.

First, the Reynolds number of the water is calculated at the bulk average temperature:

$$N_{Re} = \frac{D_i v \rho}{\mu} = \frac{0.0266(2.44)(980)}{4.32 \times 10^{-4}} = 1.473 \times 10^5$$

Hence, the flow is turbulent. Using Eq. (4.5-8) and substituting known values,

$$\frac{h_L D}{k} = 0.027 N_{Re}^{0.8} \, N_{Pr}^{1/3} \left(\frac{\mu_b}{\mu_w} \right)^{0.14}$$

$$\frac{h_L(0.0266)}{0.663} = 0.027(1.473 \times 10^5)^{0.8}(2.72)^{1/3}\left(\frac{4.32 \times 10^{-4}}{3.56 \times 10^{-4}} \right)^{0.14}$$

Solving, $h_L = h_i = 13\,324$ W/m$^2 \cdot$ K.

For part (b), the various areas are as follows for 0.305-m pipe:

$$A_i = \pi D_i L = \pi(0.0266)(0.305) = 0.0255 \text{ m}^2$$

$$A_{lm} = \pi \frac{(0.0266 + 0.0334)0.305}{2} = 0.0287 \text{ m}^2$$

$$A_o = \pi (0.0334)(0.305) = 0.0320 \text{ m}^2$$

The k for steel is 45.0 W/m $\cdot$ K. The resistances are

$$R_i = \frac{1}{h_i A_i} = \frac{1}{(13\,324)0.0255} = 0.002943$$

$$R_m = \frac{r_o - r_i}{k A_{\mathrm{lm}}} = \frac{0.0334 - 0.0266}{2}\; \frac{1}{45.0(0.0287)} = 0.002633$$

$$R_o = \frac{1}{h_o A_o} = \frac{1}{(10\,500)(0.0320)} = 0.002976$$

$$\sum R = 0.002943 + 0.002633 + 0.002976 = 0.008552$$

The overall temperature difference is $(107.8 - 65.6)°C = 42.2°C = 42.2$ K.
The temperature drop across the water film is

$$\text{temperature drop} = \frac{R_i}{\sum R}(42.2) = \left(\frac{0.002943}{0.008552}\right)(42.2) = 14.5 \text{ K} = 14.5°C$$

Hence, $T_w = 65.6 + 14.5 = 80.1°C$. This is quite close to the original estimate of 80°C. The only physical property changing in the second estimate would be μ_w. This would have a negligible effect on h_i, and a second trial is not necessary.

For part (b), the overall coefficient is, by Eq. (4.3-16),

$$q = U_i A_i (T_o - T_i) = \frac{T_o - T_i}{\sum R}$$

$$U_i = \frac{1}{A_i \sum R} = \frac{1}{0.0255\,(0.008552)} = 4586 \text{ W/m}^2 \cdot \text{K}.$$

For part (c), with the water at an average temperature of 65.6°C,

$$T_o - T_i = 107.8 - 65.6 = 42.2°C = 42.2 \text{ K}$$

$$q = U_i A_i (T_o - T_i) = 4586(0.0255)(42.2) = 4935 \text{ W}$$

4.5F Entrance-Region Effect on Heat-Transfer Coefficient

Near the entrance of a pipe where the fluid is being heated, the temperature profile is not fully developed and the local coefficient h is greater than the fully developed heat-transfer coefficient h_L for turbulent flow. At the entrance itself, where no temperature gradient has been established, the value of h is infinite. The value of h drops rapidly and is approximately the same as h_L at $L/D \cong 60$, where L is the entrance length. These relations for turbulent flow inside a pipe are as follows where the entrance is an abrupt contraction:

$$\frac{h}{h_L} = 1 + \left(\frac{D}{L}\right)^{0.7} \qquad 2 < \frac{L}{D} < 20 \tag{4.5-12}$$

$$\frac{h}{h_L} = 1 + 6\left(\frac{D}{L}\right) \qquad 20 < \frac{L}{D} < 60 \tag{4.5-13}$$

where h is the average value for a tube of finite length L and h_L is the value for a very long tube.

4.5G Liquid-Metals Heat-Transfer Coefficient

Liquid metals are sometimes used as heat-transfer fluids in cases where a fluid is needed over a wide temperature range at relatively low pressures. Liquid metals are often used in nuclear reactors and have high heat-transfer coefficients as well as a high heat capacity per unit volume. The high heat-transfer coefficients are due to the very high thermal conductivities and, hence, low Prandtl numbers. In liquid metals in pipes, heat transfer by conduction is very important in the entire turbulent core because of the high thermal conductivity and is often more important than the convection effects.

For fully developed turbulent flow in tubes with uniform heat flux, the following equation can be used (L1):

$$N_{Nu} = \frac{h_L D}{k} = 0.625 N_{Pe}^{0.4} \tag{4.5-14}$$

where the Peclet number $N_{Pe} = N_{Re} N_{Pr}$. This holds for $L/D > 60$ and N_{Pe} between 100 and 10^4. For constant wall temperatures,

$$N_{Nu} = \frac{h_L D}{k} = 5.0 + 0.025 N_{Pe}^{0.8} \tag{4.5-15}$$

for $L/D > 60$ and $N_{Pe} > 100$. All physical properties are evaluated at the average bulk temperature.

EXAMPLE 4.5-3. Liquid-Metal Heat Transfer Inside a Tube

A liquid metal flows at a rate of 4.00 kg/s through a tube having an inside diameter of 0.05 m. The liquid enters at 500 K and is heated to 505 K in the tube. The tube wall is maintained at a temperature of 30 K above the fluid bulk temperature and constant heat flux is also maintained. Calculate the required tube length. The average physical properties are as follows: $\mu = 7.1 \times 10^{-4}$ Pa·s, $\rho = 7400$ kg/m^3, $c_p = 120$ J/kg·K, $k = 13$ W/m·K.

Solution: The area is $A = \pi D^2/4 = \pi(0.05)^2/4 = 1.963 \times 10^{-3}$ m^2. Then $G = 4.0/1.963 \times 10^{-3} = 2.038 \times 10^3$ kg/m^2·s. The Reynolds number is

$$N_{Re} = \frac{DG}{\mu} = \frac{0.05(2.038 \times 10^3)}{7.1 \times 10^{-4}} = 1.435 \times 10^5$$

$$N_{Pr} = \frac{c_p \mu}{k} = \frac{120(7.1 \times 10^{-4})}{13} = 0.00655$$

Using Eq. (4.5-14),

$$h_L = \frac{k}{D}(0.625)N_{Pe}^{0.4} = \frac{13}{0.05}(0.625)(1.435 \times 10^5 \times 0.00655)^{0.4}$$

$$= 2512 \text{ W/m}^2 \cdot \text{K}$$

Using a heat balance,

$$q = mc_p \, \Delta T$$

$$= 4.00(120)(505 - 500) = 2400 \text{ W} \tag{4.5-16}$$

Substituting into Eq. (4.5-1),

$$\frac{q}{A} = \frac{2400}{A} = h_L(T_w - T) = 2512(30) = 75\ 360\ \text{W/m}^2$$

Hence, $A = 2400/75\ 360 = 3.185 \times 10^{-2}\ \text{m}^2$. Then,

$$A = 3.185 \times 10^{-2} = \pi DL = \pi(0.05)(L)$$

Solving, $L = 0.203$ m.

4.5H Log Mean Temperature Difference and Varying Temperature Drop

Equations (4.5-1) and (4.3-12) as written apply only when the temperature drop $(T_i - T_o)$ is constant for all parts of the heating surface. Hence, the equation

$$q = U_i A_i(T_i - T_o) = U_o A_o(T_i - T_o) = UA(\Delta T) \tag{4.5-17}$$

only holds at one point in the apparatus when the fluids are being heated or cooled. However, as the fluids travel through the heat exchanger, they become heated or cooled and either T_i or T_o or both vary. Then $(T_i - T_o)$ or ΔT varies with position, and some mean ΔT_m must be used over the whole apparatus.

In a typical heat exchanger, a hot fluid inside a pipe is cooled from T_1' to T_2' by a cold fluid which is flowing on the outside in a double pipe countercurrently (in the reverse direction) and is heated from T_2 to T_1, as shown in Fig. 4.5-3a. The ΔT shown is varying with distance. Hence, ΔT in Eq. (4.5-17) varies as the area A goes from 0 at the inlet to A at the outlet of the exchanger.

For countercurrent flow of the two fluids as in Fig. 4.5-3a, the heat-transfer rate is

$$q = UA\ \Delta T_m \tag{4.5-18}$$

where ΔT_m is a suitable mean temperature difference to be determined. For a dA area, a heat balance on the hot and the cold fluids gives

$$dq = -m'c_p'\ dT' = mc_p\ dT \tag{4.5-19}$$

FIGURE 4.5-3. *Temperature profiles for one-pass double-pipe heat exchangers: (a) countercurrent flow; (b) cocurrent or parallel flow.*

where m is flow rate in kg/s. The values of m, m', c_p, c'_p, and U are assumed constant. Also,

$$dq = U(T' - T) \, dA \qquad (4.5\text{-}20)$$

From Eq. (4.5-19), $dT' = -dq/m'c'_p$ and $dT = dq/mc_p$. Then,

$$dT' - dT = d(T' - T) = -dq \left(\frac{1}{m'c'_p} + \frac{1}{mc_p} \right) \qquad (4.5\text{-}21)$$

Substituting Eq. (4.5-20) into (4.5-21),

$$\frac{d(T' - T)}{T' - T} = -U \left(\frac{1}{m'c'_p} + \frac{1}{mc_p} \right) dA \qquad (4.5\text{-}22)$$

Integrating between points 1 and 2,

$$\ln\left(\frac{T'_2 - T_2}{T'_1 - T_1} \right) = -UA \left(\frac{1}{m'c'_p} + \frac{1}{mc_p} \right) \qquad (4.5\text{-}23)$$

Making a heat balance between the inlet and outlet,

$$q = m'c'_p(T'_1 - T'_2) = mc_p(T_2 - T_1) \qquad (4.5\text{-}24)$$

Solving for $m'c'_p$ and mc_p in Eq. (4.5-24) and substituting into Eq. (4.5-23),

$$q = \frac{UA[(T'_2 - T_2) - (T'_1 - T_1)]}{\ln[(T'_2 - T_2)/(T'_1 - T_1)]} \qquad (4.5\text{-}25)$$

Comparing Eqs. (4.5-18) and (4.5-25), we see that ΔT_m is the log mean temperature difference ΔT_{lm}. Hence, in the case where the overall heat-transfer coefficient U is constant throughout the equipment and the heat capacity of each fluid is constant, the proper temperature driving force to use over the entire apparatus is the log mean driving force,

$$q = UA \, \Delta T_{lm} \qquad (4.5\text{-}26)$$

where

$$\Delta T_{lm} = \frac{\Delta T_2 - \Delta T_1}{\ln(\Delta T_2/\Delta T_1)} \qquad (4.5\text{-}27)$$

It can be also shown that for parallel flow, as pictured in Fig. 4.5-3b, the log mean temperature difference should be used. In some cases, where steam is condensing, T'_1 and T'_2 may be the same. The equations still hold for this case. When U varies with distance or other complicating factors occur, other references should be consulted (B2, P3, W1).

EXAMPLE 4.5-4.   Heat-Transfer Area and Log Mean Temperature Difference

A heavy hydrocarbon oil which has a $c_{pm} = 2.30$ kJ/kg·K is being cooled in a heat exchanger from 371.9 K to 349.7 K and flows inside the tube at a rate of 3630 kg/h. A flow of 1450 kg water/h enters at 288.6 K for cooling and flows outside the tube.

    (a) Calculate the water outlet temperature and heat-transfer area if the overall $U_i = 340$ W/m²·K and the streams are countercurrent.

    (b) Repeat for parallel flow.

Solution: Assume a $c_{pm} = 4.187$ kJ/kg·K for water. The water inlet $T_2 = 288.6$ K, outlet $= T_1$; oil inlet $T_1' = 371.9$, outlet $T_2' = 349.7$ K. Calculating the heat lost by the oil,

$$q = \left(3630\,\frac{kg}{h}\right)\left(2.30\,\frac{kJ}{kg\cdot K}\right)(371.9 - 349.7)\,K$$

$$= 185\,400\text{ kJ/h} \quad \text{or} \quad 51\,490\text{ W} \quad (175\,700\text{ btu/h})$$

By a heat balance, the q must also equal the heat gained by the water:

$$q = 185\,400\text{ kJ/h} = \left(1450\,\frac{kg}{h}\right)\left(4.187\,\frac{kJ}{kg\cdot K}\right)(T_1 - 288.6)\,K$$

Solving, $T_1 = 319.1$ K.

To solve for the log mean temperature difference, $\Delta T_2 = T_2' - T_2 = 349.7 - 288.6 = 61.1$ K, $\Delta T_1 = T_1' - T_1 = 371.9 - 319.1 = 52.8$ K. Substituting into Eq. (4.5-27),

$$\Delta T_{lm} = \frac{\Delta T_2 - \Delta T_1}{\ln(\Delta T_2/\Delta T_1)} = \frac{61.1 - 52.8}{\ln(61.1/52.8)} = 56.9\text{ K}$$

Using Eq. (4.5-26),

$$q = U_i A_i \,\Delta T_{lm}$$

$$51\,490 = 340(A_i)(56.9)$$

Solving, $A_i = 2.66$ m^2.

For part (b), the water outlet is still $T_1 = 319.1$ K. Referring to Fig. 4.5-3b, $\Delta T_2 = 371.9 - 288.6 = 83.3$ K and $\Delta T_1 = 349.7 - 319.1 = 30.6$ K. Again, using Eq. (4.5-27) and solving, $\Delta T_{lm} = 52.7$ K. Substituting into Eq. (4.5-26), $A_i = 2.87$ m^2. This is a larger area than for counterflow. This occurs because counterflow gives larger temperature driving forces, and it is usually preferred over parallel flow for this reason.

EXAMPLE 4.5-5. Laminar Heat Transfer and Trial and Error

A hydrocarbon oil at 150°F enters inside a pipe with an inside diameter of 0.0303 ft and a length of 15 ft with a flow rate of 80 lb$_m$/h. The inside pipe surface is assumed constant at 350°F, since steam is condensing outside the pipe wall, and has a very large heat-transfer coefficient. The properties of the oil are $c_{pm} = 0.50$ btu/lb$_m$·°F and $k_m = 0.083$ btu/h·ft·°F. The viscosity of the oil varies with temperature as follows: 150°F, 6.50 cp; 200°F, 5.05 cp; 250°F, 3.80 cp; 300°F, 2.82 cp; 350°F, 1.95 cp. Predict the heat-transfer coefficient and the oil outlet temperature, T_{bo}.

Solution: This is a trial-and-error solution since the outlet temperature of the oil T_{bo} is unknown. The value of $T_{bo} = 250$°F will be assumed and checked later. The bulk mean temperature of the oil to use for the physical properties is $(150 + 250)/2$ or 200°F. The viscosity at 200°F is

$$\mu_b = 5.05(2.4191) = 12.23\,\frac{lb_m}{ft\cdot h}$$

At the wall temperature of 350°F,

$$\mu_w = 1.95(2.4191) = 4.72 \, \frac{lb_m}{ft \cdot h}$$

The cross-section area of the pipe A is

$$A = \frac{\pi D_i^2}{4} = \frac{\pi(0.0303)^2}{4} = 0.000722 \, ft^2$$

$$G = \frac{m}{A} = \frac{80 \, lb_m/h}{0.000722 \, ft^2} = 111\,000 \, \frac{lb_m}{ft^2 \cdot h}$$

The Reynolds number at the bulk mean temperature is

$$N_{Re} = \frac{D_i v \rho}{\mu} = \frac{D_i G}{\mu} = \frac{0.0303(111\,000)}{12.23} = 275.5$$

The Prandtl number is

$$N_{Pr} = \frac{c_p \mu}{k} = \frac{0.50(12.23)}{0.083} = 73.7$$

Since the N_{Re} is below 2100, the flow is in the laminar region and Eq. (4.5-4) will be used. Even at the outlet temperature of 250°F, the flow is still laminar. Substituting,

$$(N_{Nu})_a = \frac{h_a D}{k} = 1.86 \left(N_{Re} N_{Pr} \frac{D}{L} \right)^{1/3} \left(\frac{\mu_b}{\mu_w} \right)^{0.14}$$

$$\frac{h_a(0.0303)}{0.083} = 1.86 \left[275.5(73.7) \left(\frac{0.0303}{15.0} \right) \right]^{1/3} \left(\frac{12.23}{4.72} \right)^{0.14}$$

Solving, $h_a = 20.1 \, btu/h \cdot ft^2 \cdot °F \, (114 \, W/m^2 \cdot K)$.

Next, making a heat balance on the oil,

$$q = mc_{pm}(T_{bo} - T_{bi}) = 80.0(0.50)(T_{bo} - 150) \qquad \text{(4.5-28)}$$

Using Eq. (4.5-7)

$$q = h_a A \, \Delta T_a \qquad \text{(4.5-7)}$$

For ΔT_a,

$$\Delta T_a = \frac{(T_w - T_{bi}) + (T_w - T_{bo})}{2}$$

$$= \frac{(350 - 150) + (350 - T_{bo})}{2}$$

$$= 275 - 0.5 T_{bo}$$

Equating Eq. (4.5-28) to (4.5-7) and substituting,

$$80.0(0.50)(T_{bo} - 150) = hA \, \Delta T_a$$

$$= 20.1[\pi(0.303)(15)](275 - 0.5 T_{bo})$$

Solving, $T_{bo} = 255°F$.

This is higher than the assumed value of 250°F. For the second trial, the mean bulk temperature of the oil would be $(150 + 255)/2$ or 202.5°F. The new viscosity is 5.0 cp compared with 5.05 for the first estimate. This only affects the $(\mu_b/\mu_w)^{0.14}$ factor in Eq. (4.5-4), since the viscosity effect in the $(N_{Re})(N_{Pr})$ factor cancels out. The heat-transfer coefficient will change by less than 0.2%, which is negligible. Hence, the outlet temperature of $T_1 = 255°F$ (123.9°C) is correct.

4.6 HEAT TRANSFER OUTSIDE VARIOUS GEOMETRIES IN FORCED CONVECTION

4.6A Introduction

In many cases a fluid is flowing over completely immersed bodies such as spheres, tubes, plates, and so on, and heat transfer is occurring between the fluid and the solid only. Many of these shapes are of practical interest in process engineering. The sphere, cylinder, and flat plate are perhaps of greatest importance, with heat transfer between these surfaces and a moving fluid frequently encountered.

When heat transfer occurs during immersed flow, the flux is dependent on the geometry of the body, the position on the body (front, side, back, etc.), the proximity of other bodies, the flow rate, and the fluid properties. The heat-transfer coefficient varies over the body. The average heat-transfer coefficient is given in the empirical relationships to be discussed in the following sections.

In general, the average heat-transfer coefficient on immersed bodies is given by

$$N_{Nu} = CN_{Re}^m N_{Pr}^{1/3} \tag{4.6-1}$$

where C and m are constants that depend on the various configurations. The fluid properties are evaluated at the film temperature $T_f = (T_w + T_b)/2$, where T_w is the surface or wall temperature and T_b the average bulk fluid temperature. The velocity in the N_{Re} is the undisturbed free stream velocity v of the fluid approaching the object.

4.6B Flow Parallel to Flat Plate

When the fluid is flowing parallel to a flat plate and heat transfer is occurring between the whole plate of length L m and the fluid, the N_{Nu} is as follows for a $N_{Re,L}$ below 3×10^5 in the laminar region and a $N_{Pr} > 0.7$:

$$N_{Nu} = 0.664 N_{Re,L}^{0.5} N_{Pr}^{1/3} \tag{4.6-2}$$

where $N_{Re,L} = Lv\rho/\mu$ and $N_{Nu} = hL/k$.

For the completely turbulent region at a $N_{Re,L}$ above 3×10^5 (K1, K3) and $N_{Pr} > 0.7$,

$$N_{Nu} = 0.0366 N_{Re,L}^{0.8} N_{Pr}^{1/3} \tag{4.6-3}$$

However, turbulence can start at a $N_{Re,L}$ below 3×10^5 if the plate is rough (K3), and then Eq. (4.6-3) will hold and give a N_{Nu} greater than that given by Eq. (4.6-2). For a $N_{Re,L}$ below about 2×10^4, Eq. (4.6-2) gives the larger value of N_{Nu}.

EXAMPLE 4.6-1. Cooling a Copper Fin

A smooth, flat, thin fin of copper extending out from a tube is 51 mm by 51 mm square. Its temperature is approximately uniform at 82.2°C. Cooling air at 15.6°C and 1 atm abs flows parallel to the fin at a velocity of 12.2 m/s.

(a) For laminar flow, calculate the heat-transfer coefficient, h.

(b) If the leading edge of the fin is rough so that all of the boundary layer or film next to the fin is completely turbulent, calculate h.

Solution: The fluid properties will be evaluated at the film temperature $T_f = (T_w + T_b)/2$:

$$T_f = \frac{T_w + T_b}{2} = \frac{82.2 + 15.6}{2} = 48.9°C \ (322.1 \ K)$$

The physical properties of air at 48.9°C from Appendix A.3 are $k = 0.0280$ W/m·K, $\rho = 1.097$ kg/m³, $\mu = 1.95 \times 10^{-5}$ Pa·s, $N_{Pr} = 0.704$. The Reynolds number is, for $L = 0.051$ m,

$$N_{Re,L} = \frac{Lv\rho}{\mu} = \frac{(0.051)(12.2)(1.097)}{1.95 \times 10^{-5}} = 3.49 \times 10^4$$

Substituting into Eq. (4.6-2),

$$N_{Nu} = \frac{hL}{k} = 0.664 N_{Re,L}^{0.5} N_{Pr}^{1/3}$$

$$\frac{h(0.051)}{(0.0280)} = 0.664(3.49 \times 10^4)^{0.5}(0.704)^{1/3}$$

Solving, $h = 60.7$ W/m²·K (10.7 btu/h·ft²·°F).

For part (b), substituting into Eq. (4.6-3) and solving, $h = 77.2$ W/m²·K (13.6 btu/h·ft²·°F).

4.6C Cylinder with Axis Perpendicular to Flow

Often a cylinder containing a fluid inside is being heated or cooled by a fluid flowing perpendicular to its axis. The equation for predicting the average heat-transfer coefficient of the outside of the cylinder for gases and liquids is (K3, P3) Eq. (4.6-1), with C and m as given in Table 4.6-1. The $N_{Re} = Dv\rho/\mu$, where D is the outside tube diameter and all physical proper-

TABLE 4.6-1. *Constants for Use in Eq. (4.6-1) for Heat Transfer to Cylinders with Axis Perpendicular to Flow ($N_{Pr} > 0.6$)*

N_{Re}	m	C
1–4	0.330	0.989
4–40	0.385	0.911
$40–4 \times 10^3$	0.466	0.683
$4 \times 10^3–4 \times 10^4$	0.618	0.193
$4 \times 10^4–2.5 \times 10^5$	0.805	0.0266

ties are evaluated at the film temperature T_f. The velocity is the undisturbed free stream velocity approaching the cylinder.

4.6D Flow Past Single Sphere

When a single sphere is being heated or cooled by a fluid flowing past it, the following equation can be used to predict the average heat-transfer coefficient for a $N_{\text{Re}} = Dv\rho/\mu$ of 1 to 70 000 and a N_{Pr} of 0.6 to 400:

$$N_{\text{Nu}} = 2.0 + 0.60 N_{\text{Re}}^{0.5} N_{\text{Pr}}^{1/3} \tag{4.6-4}$$

The fluid properties are evaluated at the film temperature T_f. A somewhat more accurate correlation, which takes into account the effects of natural convection at these lower Reynolds numbers, is available for a N_{Re} range 1–17 000 from other sources (S2).

> **EXAMPLE 4.6-2. Cooling of a Sphere**
> Using the same conditions as Example 4.6-1, where air at 1 atm abs pressure and 15.6°C is flowing at a velocity of 12.2 m/s, predict the average heat-transfer coefficient for air flowing past a sphere having a diameter of 51 mm and an average surface temperature of 82.2°C. Compare this with the value of $h = 77.2$ W/m$^2 \cdot$ K for the flat plate in turbulent flow.
>
> **Solution:** The physical properties at the average film temperature of 48.9°C are the same as for Example 4.6-1. The N_{Re} is
>
> $$N_{\text{Re}} = \frac{Dv\rho}{\mu} = \frac{(0.051)(12.2)(1.097)}{1.95 \times 10^{-5}} = 3.49 \times 10^4$$
>
> Substituting into Eq. (4.6-4) for a sphere,
>
> $$N_{\text{Nu}} = \frac{hD}{k} = \frac{h(0.051)}{0.0280} = 2.0 + 0.60 N_{\text{Re}}^{0.5} N_{\text{Pr}}^{1/3}$$
>
> $$= 2.0 + (0.60)(3.49 \times 10^4)^{0.5}(0.704)^{1/3}$$
>
> Solving, $h = 56.1$ W/m$^2 \cdot$ K (9.88 btu/h $\cdot$ ft$^2 \cdot$ °F). This value is somewhat smaller than the value of $h = 77.2$ W/m$^2 \cdot$ K (13.6 btu/h $\cdot$ ft$^2 \cdot$ °F) for a flat plate.

4.6E Flow Past Banks of Tubes or Cylinders

Many types of commercial heat exchangers are constructed with multiple rows of tubes, where the fluid flows at right angles to the bank of tubes. An example is a gas heater in which a hot fluid inside the tubes heats a gas passing over the outside of the tubes. Another example is a cold liquid stream inside the tubes being heated by a hot fluid on the outside.

Figure 4.6-1 shows the arrangement for banks of tubes in-line and banks of tubes staggered, where D is tube OD in m (ft), S_n is distance m (ft) between the centers of the tubes normal to the flow, and S_p that parallel to the flow. The open area to flow for in-line tubes is $(S_n - D)$ and $(S_p - D)$; for staggered tubes it is $(S_n - D)$ and $(S'_p - D)$. Values of C and m to be used in Eq. (4.6-1) for a Reynolds-number range of 2000 to 40 000 for heat transfer to banks of tubes containing more than 10 transverse rows in the direction of flow are given in Table 4.6-2. For less than 10 rows, Table 4.6-3 gives correction factors.

FIGURE 4.6-1. *Nomenclature for banks of tubes in Table 4.6-2: (a) in-line tube rows, (b) staggered tube rows.*

TABLE 4.6-2. *Values of C and m To Be Used in Eq. (4.6-1) for Heat Transfer to Banks of Tubes Containing More Than 10 Transverse Rows*

Arrangement	$\dfrac{S_n}{D} = \dfrac{S_p}{D} = 1.25$		$\dfrac{S_n}{D} = \dfrac{S_p}{D} = 1.50$		$\dfrac{S_n}{D} = \dfrac{S_p}{D} = 2.0$	
	C	m	C	m	C	m
In-line	0.386	0.592	0.278	0.620	0.254	0.632
Staggered	0.575	0.556	0.511	0.562	0.535	0.556

Source: E. D. Grimison, *Trans. ASME,* **59,** 583 (1937).

TABLE 4.6-3. *Ratio of h for N Transverse Rows Deep to h for 10 Transverse Rows Deep (for Use with Table 4.6-2)*

N	1	2	3	4	5	6	7	8	9	10
Ratio for staggered tubes	0.68	0.75	0.83	0.89	0.92	0.95	0.97	0.98	0.99	1.00
Ratio for in-line tubes	0.64	0.80	0.87	0.90	0.92	0.94	0.96	0.98	0.99	1.00

Source: W. M. Kays and R. K. Lo, *Stanford Univ. Tech. Rept. 15,* Navy Contract N6-ONR-251 T.O.6, 1952.

For cases where S_n/D and S_p/D are not equal to each other, the reader should consult Grimison (G1) for more data. In baffled exchangers where there is normal leakage where all the fluid does not flow normal to the tubes, the average values of h obtained should be multiplied by about 0.6 (P3). The Reynolds number is calculated using the minimum area open to flow for the velocity. All physical properties are evaluated at T_f.

EXAMPLE 4.6-3. Heating Air by a Bank of Tubes

Air at 15.6°C and 1 atm abs flows across a bank of tubes containing four transverse rows in the direction of flow and 10 rows normal to the flow at a velocity of 7.62 m/s as the air approaches the bank of tubes. The tube surfaces are maintained at 57.2°C. The outside diameter of the tubes is 25.4 mm and the tubes are in-line to the flow. The spacing S_n of the tubes normal to the flow is 38.1 mm and S_p is also 38.1 mm parallel to the flow. For a 0.305-m length of the tube bank, calculate the heat-transfer rate.

Solution: Referring to Fig. 4.6-1a,

$$\frac{S_n}{D} = \frac{38.1}{25.4} = \frac{1.5}{1} \qquad \frac{S_p}{D} = \frac{38.1}{25.4} = \frac{1.5}{1}$$

Since the air is heated in passing through the four transverse rows, an outlet bulk temperature of 21.1°C will be assumed. The average bulk temperature is then

$$T_b = \frac{15.6 + 21.1}{2} = 18.3°C$$

The average film temperature is

$$T_f = \frac{T_w + T_b}{2} = \frac{57.2 + 18.3}{2} = 37.7°C$$

From Appendix A.3, for air at 37.7°C,

$$k = 0.02700 \text{ W/m} \cdot \text{K} \qquad N_{Pr} = 0.705$$
$$c_p = 1.0048 \text{ kJ/kg} \cdot \text{K} \qquad \rho = 1.137 \text{ kg/m}^3$$
$$\mu = 1.90 \times 10^{-5} \text{ Pa} \cdot \text{s}$$

The ratio of the minimum-flow area to the total frontal area is $(S_n - D)/S_n$. The maximum velocity in the tube banks is then

$$v_{max} = \frac{vS_n}{S_n - D} = \frac{7.62(0.0381)}{(0.0381 - 0.0254)} = 22.86 \text{ m/s}$$

$$N_{Re} = \frac{Dv_{max}\rho}{\mu} = \frac{0.0254(22.86)(1.137)}{1.90 \times 10^{-5}} = 3.47 \times 10^4$$

For $S_n/D = S_p/D = 1.5/1$, the values of C and m from Table 4.6-2 are 0.278 and 0.620, respectively. Substituting into Eq. (4.6-1) and solving for h,

$$h = \frac{k}{D} C N_{Re}^m N_{Pr}^{1/3} = \left(\frac{0.02700}{0.0254}\right)(0.278)(3.47 \times 10^4)^{0.62}(0.705)^{1/3}$$

$$= 171.8 \text{ W/m}^2 \cdot \text{K}$$

This h is for 10 rows. For only four rows in the transverse direction, the h must be multiplied by 0.90, as given in Table 4.6-3.

Since there are 10×4 or 40 tubes, the total heat-transfer area per 0.305 m length is

$$A = 40\pi DL = 40\pi(0.0254)(0.305) = 0.973 \text{ m}^2$$

The total heat-transfer rate q using an arithmetic average temperature difference between the wall and the bulk fluid is

$$q = hA(T_w - T_b) = (0.90 \times 171.8)(0.973)(57.2 - 18.3) = 5852 \text{ W}$$

Next, a heat balance on the air is made to calculate its temperature rise ΔT using the calculated q. First, the mass flow rate of air m must be calculated. The total frontal area of the tube-bank assembly of 10 rows of tubes each 0.305 m long is

$$A_t = 10S_n(1.0) = 10(0.0381)(0.305) = 0.1162 \text{ m}^2$$

The density of the entering air at 15.6°C is $\rho = 1.224 \text{ kg/m}^3$. The mass flow rate m is

$$m = v\rho A_t(3600) = 7.62(1.224)(0.1162) = 1.084 \text{ kg/s}$$

For the heat balance, the mean c_p of air at 18.3°C is 1.0048 kJ/kg·K, and then

$$q = 5852 = mc_p \, \Delta T = 1.084(1.0048 \times 10^3) \, \Delta T$$

Solving, $\Delta T = 5.37$°C.

Hence, the calculated outlet bulk gas temperature is $15.6 + 5.37 = 20.97$°C, which is close to the assumed value of 21.1°C. If a second trial were to be made, the new average T_b to use would be $(15.6 + 20.97)/2$ or 18.28°C.

4.6F Heat Transfer for Flow in Packed Beds

Correlations for heat-transfer coefficients for packed beds are useful in designing fixed-bed systems such as catalytic reactors, dryers for solids, and pebble-bed heat exchangers. In Section 3.1C the pressure drop in packed beds was considered and discussions of the geometry factors in these beds were given. For determining the rate of heat transfer in packed beds for a differential length dz in m,

$$dq = h(aS \, dz)(T_1 - T_2) \tag{4.6-5}$$

where a is the solid-particle surface area per unit volume of bed in m^{-1}, S the empty cross-sectional area of bed in m^2, T_1 the bulk gas temperature in K. and T_2 the solid surface temperature.

For the heat transfer of gases in beds of spheres (G2, G3) and a Reynolds number range of 10–10 000,

$$\varepsilon J_H = \varepsilon \frac{h}{c_p v' \rho} \left(\frac{c_p \mu}{k} \right)_f^{2/3} = \frac{2.876}{N_{\text{Re}}} + \frac{0.3023}{N_{\text{Re}}^{0.35}} \tag{4.6-6}$$

where v' is the superficial velocity based on the cross section of the empty container in m/s [see Eq. (3.1-11)], ε is the void fraction, $N_{\text{Re}} = D_p G'/\mu_f$, and $G' = v'\rho$ is the superficial mass velocity in $\text{kg/m}^2 \cdot \text{s}$. The subscript f indicates properties evaluated at the film temperature, with others at the bulk temperature. This correlation can also be used for a fluidized bed. An alternate equation to use in place of Eq. (4.6-6) for fixed and fluidized beds is Eq. (7.3-36) for a Reynolds-number range of 10–4000. The term J_H is called the Colburn J factor and is defined as in Eq. (4.6-6) in terms of h.

Equations for heat transfer to noncircular cylinders such as hexagons and so forth are given elsewhere (H1, J1, P3).

4.7 NATURAL CONVECTION HEAT TRANSFER

4.7A Introduction

Natural convection heat transfer occurs when a solid surface is in contact with a gas or liquid which is at a different temperature from the surface. Density differences in the fluid arising from the heating process provide the buoyancy force required to move the fluid. Free or natural convection is observed as a result of the motion of the fluid. An example of heat transfer by natural convection is a hot radiator used for heating a room. Cold air encountering the radiator is heated and rises in natural convection because of buoyancy forces. The theoretical derivation of equations for natural convection heat-transfer coefficients requires the solution of motion and energy equations.

An important heat-transfer system occurring in process engineering is that in which heat is being transferred from a hot vertical plate to a gas or liquid adjacent to it by natural convection. The fluid is not moving by forced convection but only by natural or free convection. In Fig. 4.7-1 the vertical flat plate is heated and the free convection boundary layer is formed. The velocity profile differs from that in a forced convection system in that the velocity at the wall is zero and also is zero at the other edge of the boundary layer, since the free stream velocity is zero for natural convection. The boundary layer initially is laminar as shown, but at some distance from the leading edge it starts to become turbulent. The wall temperature is T_w K and the bulk temperature T_b.

The differential momentum-balance equation is written for the x and y directions for the control volume ($dx\,dy \cdot 1$). The driving force is the buoyancy force in the gravitational field and is due to the density difference of the fluid. The momentum balance becomes

$$\rho\left(v_x\frac{\partial v_x}{\partial x} + v_y\frac{\partial v_x}{\partial y}\right) = g(\rho_b - \rho) + \mu\frac{\partial^2 v_x}{\partial y^2} \tag{4.7-1}$$

where ρ_b is the density at the bulk temperature T_b and ρ the density at T. The density difference can be expressed in terms of the volumetric coefficient of expansion β and substituted back into Eq. (4.7-1):

$$\beta = \frac{\rho_b - \rho}{\rho(T - T_b)} \tag{4.7-2}$$

For gases, $\beta = 1/T$. The energy-balance equation can be expressed as follows:

$$\rho c_p\left(v_x\frac{\partial T}{\partial x} + v_y\frac{\partial T}{\partial y}\right) = k\frac{\partial^2 T}{\partial y^2} \tag{4.7-3}$$

FIGURE 4.7-1. *Boundary-layer velocity profile for natural convection heat transfer from a heated, vertical plate.*

The solutions of these equations have been obtained by using integral methods of analysis discussed in Section 3.10. Results have been obtained for a vertical plate, which is the simplest case and serves to introduce the dimensionless Grashof number discussed below. However, in other physical geometries the relations are too complex and empirical correlations have been obtained. These are discussed in the following sections.

4.7B Natural Convection from Various Geometries

1. Natural convection from vertical planes and cylinders.   For an isothermal vertical surface or plate with height L less than 1 m (P3), the average natural convection heat-transfer coefficient can be expressed by the following general equation:

$$N_{Nu} = \frac{hL}{k} = a\left(\frac{L^3 \rho^2 g \beta \, \Delta T}{\mu^2} \frac{c_p \mu}{k}\right)^m = a(N_{Gr} N_{Pr})^m \tag{4.7-4}$$

where a and m are constants from Table 4.7-1, N_{Gr} the Grashof number, ρ density in kg/m^3, μ viscosity in kg/m·s, ΔT the positive temperature difference between the wall and bulk fluid or vice versa in K, k the thermal conductivity in W/m·K, c_p the heat capacity in J/kg·K, β the volumetric coefficient of expansion of the fluid in 1/K [for gases β is $1/(T_f K)$], and g is 9.80665 m/s^2. All the physical properties are evaluated at the film temperature $T_f = (T_w + T_b)/2$. In general, for a vertical cylinder with length L m, the same equations can be used as for a vertical plate. In English units β is $1/(T_f°F + 460)$ in 1/°R and g is $32.174 \times (3600)^2$ ft/h^2.

TABLE 4.7-1. *Constants for Use with Eq. (4.7-4) for Natural Convection*

Physical Geometry	$N_{Gr}N_{Pr}$	a	m	Ref.
Vertical planes and cylinders [vertical height $L < 1$ m (3 ft)]				
	$<10^4$	1.36	$\frac{1}{5}$	(P3)
	10^4–10^9	0.59	$\frac{1}{4}$	(M1)
	$>10^9$	0.13	$\frac{1}{3}$	(M1)
Horizontal cylinders [diameter D used for L and $D < 0.20$ m (0.66 ft)]				
	$<10^{-5}$	0.49	0	(P3)
	10^{-5}–10^{-3}	0.71	$\frac{1}{25}$	(P3)
	10^{-3}–1	1.09	$\frac{1}{10}$	(P3)
	1–10^4	1.09	$\frac{1}{5}$	(P3)
	10^4–10^9	0.53	$\frac{1}{4}$	(M1)
	$>10^9$	0.13	$\frac{1}{3}$	(P3)
Horizontal plates				
Upper surface of heated plates or lower surface of cooled plates	10^5–2×10^7	0.54	$\frac{1}{4}$	(M1)
	2×10^7–3×10^{10}	0.14	$\frac{1}{3}$	(M1)
Lower surface of heated plates or upper surface of cooled plates	10^5–10^{11}	0.58	$\frac{1}{5}$	(F1)

The Grashof number can be interpreted physically as a dimensionless number that represents the ratio of the buoyancy forces to the viscous forces in free convection and plays a role similar to that of the Reynolds number in forced convection.

EXAMPLE 4.7-1. *Natural Convection from Vertical Wall of an Oven*
A heated vertical wall 1.0 ft (0.305 m) high of an oven for baking food with the surface at 450°F (505.4 K) is in contact with air at 100°F (311 K). Calculate the heat-transfer coefficient and the heat transfer/ft (0.305 m) width of wall. Note that heat transfer for radiation will not be considered. Use English and SI units.

Solution: The film temperature is

$$T_f = \frac{T_w + T_b}{2} = \frac{450 + 100}{2} = 275°F = \frac{505.4 + 311}{2} = 408.2 \text{ K}$$

The physical properties of air at 275°F are $k = 0.0198$ btu/h · ft · °F, 0.0343 W/m · K; $\rho = 0.0541$ lb$_m$/ft^3, 0.867 kg/m^3; $N_{Pr} = 0.690$; $\mu = (0.0232 \text{ cp}) \times (2.4191) = 0.0562$ lb$_m$/ft · h $= 2.32 \times 10^{-5}$ Pa · s; $\beta = 1/408.2 = 2.45 \times 10^{-3}$ K^{-1}, $\beta = 1/(460 + 275) = 1.36 \times 10^{-3}$ °R^{-1}; $\Delta T = T_w - T_b = 450 - 100 = 350°F$ (194.4 K). The Grashof number is, in English units,

$$N_{Gr} = \frac{L^3 \rho^2 g \beta \, \Delta T}{\mu^2} = \frac{(1.0)^3 (0.0541)^2 (32.174)(3600)^2 (1.36 \times 10^{-3})(350)}{(0.0562)^2}$$

$$= 1.84 \times 10^8$$

In SI units,

$$N_{Gr} = \frac{(0.305)^3 (0.867)^2 (9.806)(2.45 \times 10^{-3})(194.4)}{(2.32 \times 10^{-5})^2} = 1.84 \times 10^8$$

The Grashof numbers calculated using English and SI units must, of course, be the same as shown:

$$N_{Gr} N_{Pr} = (1.84 \times 10^8)(0.690) = 1.270 \times 10^8$$

Hence, from Table 4.7-1, $a = 0.59$ and $m = \frac{1}{4}$ for use in Eq. (4.7-4). Solving for h in Eq. (4.7-4) and substituting known values,

$$h = \frac{k}{L} a (N_{Gr} \, N_{Pr})^m = \left(\frac{0.0198}{1.0}\right)(0.59)(1.270 \times 10^8)^{1/4} = 1.24 \text{ btu/h · ft}^2 \cdot °F$$

$$h = \left(\frac{0.0343}{0.305}\right)(0.59)(1.27 \times 10^8)^{1/4} = 7.03 \text{ W/m}^2 \cdot \text{K}$$

For a 1-ft width of wall, $A = 1 \times 1 = 1.0$ ft^2 (0.305 × 0.305 m^2). Then

$$q = hA(T_w - T_b) = (1.24)(1.0)(450 - 100) = 433 \text{ btu/h}$$

$$q = 7.03(0.305 \times 0.305)(194.4) = 127.1 \text{ W}$$

A considerable amount of heat will also be lost by radiation. This will be considered in Section 4.10.

Physical Geometry	$N_{Gr}N_{Pr}$	$h = btu/h \cdot ft^2 \cdot °F$ $L = ft, \Delta T = °F$ $D = ft$	$h = W/m^2 \cdot K$ $L = m, \Delta T = K$ $D = m$	Ref.
		Equation		
		Air at 101.32 kPa (1 atm) abs pressure		
Vertical planes and	10^4–10^9	$h = 0.28(\Delta T/L)^{1/4}$	$h = 1.37(\Delta T/L)^{1/4}$	(P1)
cylinders	$>10^9$	$h = 0.18(\Delta T)^{1/3}$	$h = 1.24\,\Delta T^{1/3}$	(P1)
Horizontal cylinders	10^3–10^9	$h = 0.27(\Delta T/D)^{1/4}$	$h = 1.32(\Delta T/D)^{1/4}$	(M1)
	$>10^9$	$h = 0.18(\Delta T)^{1/3}$	$h = 1.24\,\Delta T^{1/3}$	(M1)
Horizontal plates				
Heated plate facing	10^5–2×10^7	$h = 0.27(\Delta T/L)^{1/4}$	$h = 1.32(\Delta T/L)^{1/4}$	(M1)
upward or cooled	2×10^7–3×10^{10}	$h = 0.22(\Delta T)^{1/3}$	$h = 1.52\,\Delta T^{1/3}$	(M1)
plate facing downward				
Heated plate facing	3×10^5–3×10^{10}	$h = 0.12(\Delta T/L)^{1/4}$	$h = 0.59(\Delta T/L)^{1/4}$	(M1)
downward or cooled plate facing upward				
		Water at 70°F (294 K)		
Vertical planes and cylinders	10^4–10^9	$h = 26(\Delta T/L)^{1/4}$	$h = 127(\Delta T/L)^{1/4}$	(P1)
		Organic liquids at 70°F (294 K)		
Vertical planes and cylinders	10^4–10^9	$h = 12(\Delta T/L)^{1/4}$	$h = 59(\Delta T/L)^{1/4}$	(P1)

Simplified equations for the natural convection heat transfer from air to vertical planes and cylinders at 1 atm abs pressure are given in Table 4.7-2. In SI units the equation for the range of $N_{Gr}N_{Pr}$ of 10^4 to 10^9 is the one usually encountered, and this holds for $(L^3 \Delta T)$ values below about 4.7 $m^3 \cdot K$ and film temperatures between 255 and 533 K. To correct the value of h to pressures other than 1 atm, the values of h in Table 4.7-2 can be multiplied by $(p/101.32)^{1/2}$ for $N_{Gr}N_{Pr}$ 10^4 to 10^9 and by $(p/101.32)^{2/3}$ for $N_{Gr}N_{Pr} > 10^9$, where p = pressure in kN/m^2. In English units the range of $N_{Gr}N_{Pr}$ of 10^4 to 10^9 is encountered when $(L^3 \Delta T)$ is less than about 300 $ft^3 \cdot °F$. The value of h can be corrected to pressures other than 1.0 atm abs by multiplying the h at 1 atm by $p^{1/2}$ for $N_{Gr}N_{Pr}$ of 10^4 to 10^9 and by $p^{2/3}$ for $N_{Gr}N_{Pr}$ above 10^9, where p = atm abs pressure. Simplified equations are also given for water and organic liquids.

EXAMPLE 4.7-2. Natural Convection and Simplified Equation
Repeat Example 4.7-1 but use the simplified equation.

Solution: The film temperature of 408.2 K is in the range 255–533 K. Also,

$$L^3 \Delta T = (0.305)^3 (194.4) = 5.5$$

This is slightly greater than the value of 4.7 given as the approximate maximum for use of the simplified equation. However, in Example 4.7-1 the value of $N_{Gr}N_{Pr}$ is below 10^9, so the simplified equation from Table 4.7-2 will be used:

$$h = 1.37\left(\frac{\Delta T}{L}\right)^{1/4} = 1.37\left(\frac{194.4}{0.305}\right)^{1/4}$$

$$= 6.88 \text{ W/m}^2 \cdot \text{K } (1.21 \text{ btu/h} \cdot \text{ft}^2 \cdot \text{°F})$$

The heat-transfer rate q is

$$q = hA(T_w - T_b) = 6.88(0.305 \times 0.305)(194.4) = 124.4 \text{ W } (424 \text{ btu/h})$$

This value is reasonably close to the value of 127.1 W for Example 4.7-1.

2. Natural convection from horizontal cylinders. For a horizontal cylinder with an outside diameter of D m, Eq. (4.7-4) is used with the constants given in Table 4.7-1. The diameter D is used for L in the equation. Simplified equations are given in Table 4.7-2. The usual case for pipes is for the $N_{Gr}N_{Pr}$ range 10^4 to 10^9 (M1).

3. Natural convection from horizontal plates. For horizontal flat plates Eq. (4.7-4) is also used with the constants given in Table 4.7-1 and simplified equations in Table 4.7-2. The dimension L to be used is the length of a side of a square plate, the linear mean of the two dimensions for a rectangle, and 0.9 times the diameter of a circular disk.

4. Natural convection in enclosed spaces. Free convection in enclosed spaces occurs in a number of processing applications. One example is in an enclosed double window in which two layers of glass are separated by a layer of air for energy conservation. The flow phenomena inside these enclosed spaces are complex, since a number of different types of flow patterns can occur. At low Grashof numbers the heat transfer is mainly by conduction across the fluid layer. As the Grashof number is increased, different flow regimes are encountered.

The system for two vertical plates of height L m containing the fluid with a gap of δ m is shown in Fig. 4.7-2, where the plate surfaces are at temperatures T_1 and T_2. The Grashof number is defined as

$$N_{Gr,\delta} = \frac{\delta^3 \rho^2 g \beta (T_1 - T_2)}{\mu^2} \tag{4.7-5}$$

FIGURE 4.7-2. *Natural convection in enclosed vertical space.*

The Nusselt number is defined as

$$N_{\mathrm{Nu},\delta} = \frac{h\delta}{k} \tag{4.7-6}$$

The heat flux is calculated from

$$\frac{q}{A} = h(T_1 - T_2) \tag{4.7-7}$$

The physical properties are all evaluated at the mean temperature between the two plates.

For gases enclosed between vertical plates and $L/\delta > 3$ (H1, J1, K1, P1),

$$N_{\mathrm{Nu},\delta} = \frac{h\delta}{k} = 1.0 \qquad (N_{\mathrm{Gr},\delta} N_{\mathrm{Pr}} < 2 \times 10^3) \tag{4.7-8}$$

$$N_{\mathrm{Nu},\delta} = 0.20 \frac{(N_{\mathrm{Gr},\delta} N_{\mathrm{Pr}})^{1/4}}{(L/\delta)^{1/9}} \qquad (6 \times 10^3 < N_{\mathrm{Gr},\delta} N_{\mathrm{Pr}} < 2 \times 10^5) \tag{4.7-9}$$

$$N_{\mathrm{Nu},\delta} = 0.073 \frac{(N_{\mathrm{Gr},\delta} N_{\mathrm{Pr}})^{1/3}}{(L/\delta)^{1/9}} \qquad (2 \times 10^5 < N_{\mathrm{Gr},\delta} N_{\mathrm{Pr}} < 2 \times 10^7) \tag{4.7-10}$$

For liquids in vertical plates,

$$N_{\mathrm{Nu},\delta} = \frac{h\delta}{k} = 1.0 \qquad (N_{\mathrm{Gr},\delta} N_{\mathrm{Pr}} < 1 \times 10^3) \tag{4.7-11}$$

$$N_{\mathrm{Nu},\delta} = 0.28 \frac{(N_{\mathrm{Gr},\delta} N_{\mathrm{Pr}})^{1/4}}{(L/\delta)^{1/4}} \qquad (1 \times 10^3 < N_{\mathrm{Gr},\delta} N_{\mathrm{Pr}} < 1 \times 10^7) \tag{4.7-12}$$

For gases or liquids in a vertical annulus, the same equations hold as for vertical plates.

For gases in horizontal plates with the lower plate hotter than the upper,

$$N_{\mathrm{Nu},\delta} = 0.21(N_{\mathrm{Gr},\delta} N_{\mathrm{Pr}})^{1/4} \qquad (7 \times 10^3 < N_{\mathrm{Gr},\delta} N_{\mathrm{Pr}} < 3 \times 10^5) \tag{4.7-13}$$

$$N_{\mathrm{Nu},\delta} = 0.061(N_{\mathrm{Gr},\delta} N_{\mathrm{Pr}})^{1/3} \qquad (N_{\mathrm{Gr},\delta} N_{\mathrm{Pr}} > 3 \times 10^5) \tag{4.7-14}$$

For liquids in horizontal plates with the lower plate hotter than the upper (G5),

$$N_{\mathrm{Nu},\delta} = 0.069(N_{\mathrm{Gr},\delta} N_{\mathrm{Pr}})^{1/3} N_{\mathrm{Pr}}^{0.074} \qquad (1.5 \times 10^5 < N_{\mathrm{Gr},\delta} N_{\mathrm{Pr}} < 1 \times 10^9) \tag{4.7-15}$$

EXAMPLE 4.7-3. Natural Convection in Enclosed Vertical Space

Air at 1 atm abs pressure is enclosed between two vertical plates where $L = 0.6$ m and $\delta = 30$ mm. The plates are 0.4 m wide. The plate temperatures are $T_1 = 394.3$ K and $T_2 = 366.5$ K. Calculate the heat-transfer rate across the air gap.

Solution: The mean temperature between the plates is used to evaluate the physical properties: $T_f = (T_1 + T_2)/2 = (394.3 + 366.5)/2 = 380.4$ K. Also, $\delta = 30/1000 = 0.030$ m. From Appendix A.3, $\rho = 0.9295$ kg/m³, $\mu = 2.21 \times 10^{-5}$ Pa·s, $k = 0.03219$ W/m·K, $N_{\mathrm{Pr}} = 0.693$, $\beta = 1/T_f = 1/380.4 = 2.629 \times 10^{-3}$ K^{-1}.

$$N_{\mathrm{Gr},\delta} = \frac{(0.030)^3(0.9295)^2(9.806)(2.629 \times 10^{-3})(394.3 - 366.5)}{(2.21 \times 10^{-5})^2}$$

$$= 3.423 \times 10^4$$

Also, $N_{Gr,\delta}N_{Pr} = (3.423 \times 10^4)0.693 = 2.372 \times 10^4$. Using Eq. (4.7-9),

$$h = \frac{k}{\delta} \frac{(0.20)(N_{Gr,\delta}N_{Pr})^{1/4}}{(L/\delta)^{1/9}} = \frac{0.03219(0.20)(2.352 \times 10^4)^{1/4}}{0.030(0.6/0.030)^{1/9}}$$

$$= 1.909 \text{ W/m}^2 \cdot \text{K}$$

The area $A = (0.6 \times 0.4) = 0.24 \text{ m}^2$. Substituting into Eq. (4.7-7),

$$q = hA(T_1 - T_2) = 1.909(0.24)(394.3 - 366.5) = 12.74 \text{ W}$$

5. Natural convection from other shapes. For spheres, blocks, and other types of enclosed air spaces, references elsewhere (H1, K1, M1, P1, P3) should be consulted. In some cases when a fluid is forced over a heated surface at low velocity in the laminar region, combined forced convection plus natural convection heat transfer occurs. For further discussion of this, see (H1, K1, M1).

4.8 BOILING AND CONDENSATION

4.8A Boiling

1. Mechanisms of boiling. Heat transfer to a boiling liquid is very important in evaporation and distillation as well as in other kinds of chemical and biological processing, such as petroleum processing, control of the temperature of chemical reactions, evaporation of liquid foods, and so on. The boiling liquid is usually contained in a vessel with a heating surface of tubes or vertical or horizontal plates which supply the heat for boiling. The heating surfaces can be heated electrically or by a hot or condensing fluid on the other side of the heated surface.

In boiling, the temperature of the liquid is the boiling point of this liquid at the pressure in the equipment. The heated surface is, of course, at a temperature above the boiling point. Bubbles of vapor are generated at the heated surface and rise through the mass of liquid. The vapor accumulates in a vapor space above the liquid level and is withdrawn.

Boiling is a complex phenomenon. Suppose we consider a small heated horizontal tube or wire immersed in a vessel containing water boiling at 373.2 K (100°C). The heat flux is q/A W/m^2; $\Delta T = T_w - 373.2$ K, where T_w is the tube or wire wall temperature; and h is the heat-transfer coefficient in W/m$^2 \cdot$ K. Starting with a low ΔT, the q/A and h values are measured. This is repeated at higher values of ΔT and the data obtained are plotted as q/A versus ΔT, as shown in Fig. 4.8-1.

In the first region A of the plot in Fig. 4.8-1, at low temperature drops, the mechanism of boiling is essentially that of heat transfer to a liquid in natural convection. The variation of h with $\Delta T^{0.25}$ is approximately the same as that for natural convection to horizontal plates or cylinders. The very few bubbles formed are released from the surface of the metal and rise without appreciably disturbing the normal natural convection.

In the region B of nucleate boiling for a ΔT of about 5–25 K (9–45°F), the rate of bubble production increases so that the velocity of circulation of the liquid increases. The heat-transfer coefficient h increases rapidly and is proportional to ΔT^2 to ΔT^3 in this region.

In the region C of transition boiling, many bubbles are formed so quickly that they tend to coalesce and form a layer of insulating vapor. Increasing the ΔT increases the thickness of this layer and the heat flux and h drop as ΔT is increased. In the region D of film boiling, bubbles detach themselves regularly and rise upward. At higher ΔT values radiation through the

$$\Delta T \ K = T_w - 373.2 \ K$$

$$\Delta T \ ^\circ F = T_w - 212 ^\circ F$$

FIGURE 4.8-1. *Boiling mechanisms for water at atmospheric pressure, heat flux vs. temperature drop: (A) natural convection, (B) nucleate boiling, (C) transition boiling, (D) film boiling.*

vapor layer next to the surface helps increase the q/A and h. Similar-shaped curves are obtained for other shapes of surfaces (M1).

The curve of h versus ΔT has approximately the same shape as in Fig. 4.8-1. The values of h are quite large. At the beginning of region B in Fig. 4.8-1 for nucleate boiling, h has a value of about 5700–11 400 $W/m^2 \cdot K$, or 1000–2000 $btu/h \cdot ft^2 \cdot °F$, and at the end of this region h has a peak value of almost 57 000 $W/m^2 \cdot K$, or 10 000 $btu/hr \cdot ft^2 \cdot °F$. These values are quite high, and in most cases the percent resistance of the boiling film is only a few percent of the overall resistance to heat transfer.

The regions of commercial interest are the nucleate and film-boiling regions (P3). Nucleate boiling occurs in kettle-type and natural-circulation reboilers.

2. Nucleate boiling. In the nucleate-boiling region, the heat flux is affected by ΔT, pressure, nature and geometry of the surface and system, and physical properties of the vapor and liquid. Equations have been derived by Rohesenow et al. (P1). They apply to single tubes or flat surfaces and are quite complex.

Simplified empirical equations for estimating the boiling heat-transfer coefficients for water boiling on the outside of submerged surfaces at 1.0 atm abs pressure have been developed (J2).

For a horizontal surface (SI and English units),

$$h, \ btu/h \cdot ft^2 \cdot °F = 151(\Delta T \ °F)^{1/3} \qquad q/A, \ btu/h \cdot ft^2, <5000$$
$$h, \ W/m^2 \cdot K = 1043(\Delta T \ K)^{1/3} \qquad q/A, \ kW/m^2, <16 \tag{4.8-1}$$

$$h, \ btu/h \cdot ft^2 \cdot °F = 0.168(\Delta T \ °F)^3 \qquad 5000 < q/A, \ btu/h \cdot ft^2, <75\,000$$
$$h, \ W/m^2 \cdot K = 5.56(\Delta T \ K)^3 \qquad 16 < q/A, \ kW/m^2, <240 \tag{4.8-2}$$

For a vertical surface,

$$h, \text{btu/h} \cdot \text{ft}^2 \cdot {}^\circ\text{F} = 87(\Delta T \ {}^\circ\text{F})^{1/7} \qquad q/A, \text{btu/h} \cdot \text{ft}^2, <1000$$

$$h, \text{W/m}^2 \cdot \text{K} = 537(\Delta T \ \text{K})^{1/7} \qquad q/A, \text{kW/m}^2, <3 \tag{4.8-3}$$

$$h, \text{btu/h} \cdot \text{ft}^2 \cdot {}^\circ\text{F} = 0.240(\Delta T \ {}^\circ\text{F})^3 \qquad 1000 < q/A, \text{btu/h} \cdot \text{ft}^2, <20\ 000$$

$$h, \text{W/m}^2 \cdot \text{K} = 7.95(\Delta T \ \text{K})^3 \qquad 3 < q/A, \text{kW/m}^2, <63 \tag{4.8-4}$$

where $\Delta T = T_w - T_{\text{sat}}$ K or °F.

If the pressure is p atm abs, the values of h at 1 atm given above are multiplied by $(p/1)^{0.4}$. Equations (4.8-1) and (4.8-3) are in the natural convection region.

For forced convection boiling inside tubes, the following simplified relation can be used (J3):

$$h = 2.55(\Delta T \ \text{K})^3 e^{p/1551} \ \text{W/m}^2 \cdot \text{K} \qquad \text{(SI)}$$

$$h = 0.077(\Delta T \ {}^\circ\text{F})^3 e^{p/225} \ \text{btu/h} \cdot \text{ft}^2 \cdot {}^\circ\text{F} \qquad \text{(English)} \tag{4.8-5}$$

where p in this case is in kPa (SI units) and psia (English units).

3. Film boiling. In the film-boiling region, the heat-transfer rate is low in view of the large temperature drop used, which is not utilized effectively. Film boiling has been subjected to considerable theoretical analysis. Bromley (B3) gives the following equation to predict the heat-transfer coefficient in the film-boiling region on a horizontal tube:

$$h = 0.62 \left[\frac{k_v^3 \rho_v (\rho_l - \rho_v) g (h_{fg} + 0.4 c_{pv} \Delta T)}{D \mu_v \Delta T} \right]^{1/4} \tag{4.8-6}$$

where k_v is the thermal conductivity of the vapor in W/m·K, ρ_v the density of the vapor in kg/m³, ρ_l the density of the liquid in kg/m³, h_{fg} the latent heat of vaporization in J/kg, $\Delta T = T_w - T_{\text{sat}}$, T_{sat} the temperature of saturated vapor in K, D the outside tube diameter in m, μ_v the viscosity of the vapor in Pa·s, and g the acceleration of gravity in m/s². The physical properties of the vapor are evaluated at the film temperature of $T_f = (T_w + T_{\text{sat}})/2$, and h_{fg} at the saturation temperature. If the temperature difference is quite high, some additional heat transfer occurs by radiation (H1).

EXAMPLE 4.8-1.   *Rate of Heat Transfer in a Jacketed Kettle*

Water is being boiled at 1 atm abs pressure in a jacketed kettle with steam condensing in the jacket at 115.6°C. The inside diameter of the kettle is 0.656 m and the height is 0.984 m. The bottom is slightly curved but it will be assumed to be flat. Both the bottom and the sides up to a height of 0.656 m are jacketed. The kettle surface for heat transfer is 3.2-mm stainless steel with a k of 16.27 W/m·K. The condensing-steam coefficient h_i inside the jacket has been estimated as 10 200 W/m²·K. Predict the boiling heat-transfer coefficient h_o for the bottom surface of the kettle.

Solution: A diagram of the kettle is shown in Fig. 4.8-2. The simplified equations will be used for the boiling coefficient h_o. The solution is trial and error, since the inside metal surface temperature T_w is unknown. Assuming that $T_w = 110°C$,

$$\Delta T = T_w - T_{\text{sat}} = 110 - 100 = 10°C = 10 \text{ K}$$

FIGURE 4.8-2. *Steam-jacketed kettle and boiling water for Example 4.8-1.*

Substituting into Eq. (4.8-2),

$$h_o = 5.56(\Delta T)^3 = 5.56(10)^3 = 5560 \ \text{W/m}^2 \cdot \text{K}$$

$$\frac{q}{A} = h \ \Delta T = 5560(10) = 55\ 600 \ \text{W/m}^2$$

To check the assumed T_w, the resistance R_i of the condensing steam, R_w of the metal wall, and R_o of the boiling liquid must be calculated. Assuming equal areas of the resistances for $A = 1 \ \text{m}^2$, then by Eq. (4.3-12),

$$R_i = \frac{1}{h_i A} = \frac{1}{10\ 200(1)} = 9.80 \times 10^{-5}$$

$$R_w = \frac{\Delta x}{k A} = \frac{3.2/1000}{16.27(1.0)} = 19.66 \times 10^{-5}$$

$$R_o = \frac{1}{h_o A} = \frac{1}{5560(1)} = 17.98 \times 10^{-5}$$

$$\sum R = 9.80 \times 10^{-5} + 19.66 \times 10^{-5} + 17.98 \times 10^{-5}$$

$$= 47.44 \times 10^{-5}$$

The temperature drop across the boiling film is then

$$\Delta T = \frac{R_o}{\sum R}(115.6 - 100) = \frac{17.98 \times 10^{-5}}{47.44 \times 10^{-5}}(15.6) = 5.9°\text{C}$$

Hence, $T_w = 100 + 5.9 = 105.9°\text{C}$. This is lower than the assumed value of 110°C.

For the second trial, $T_w = 108.3°\text{C}$ will be used. Then, $\Delta T = 108.3 - 100 = 8.3°\text{C}$ and, from Eq. (4.8-2), the new $h_o = 3180$. Calculating the new $R_o = 31.44 \times 10^{-5}$, and

$$\Delta T = \left(\frac{31.44 \times 10^{-5}}{60.90 \times 10^{-5}}\right)(115.6 - 100) = 8.1°\text{C}$$

and

$$T_w = 100 + 8.1 = 108.1°\text{C}$$

This value is reasonably close to the assumed value of 108.3°C, so no further trials will be made.

4.8B Condensation

1. Mechanisms of condensation. Condensation of a vapor to a liquid and vaporization of a liquid to a vapor both involve a change of phase of a fluid with large heat-transfer coefficients. Condensation occurs when a saturated vapor such as steam comes in contact with a solid whose surface temperature is below the saturation temperature, to form a liquid such as water.

Normally, when a vapor condenses on a surface such as a vertical or horizontal tube or other surface, a film of condensate is formed on the surface and flows over the surface by the action of gravity. It is this film of liquid between the surface and the vapor that forms the main resistance to heat transfer. This is called *film-type condensation.*

Another type of condensation, *dropwise condensation,* can occur, where small drops are formed on the surface. These drops grow and coalesce, and the liquid flows from the surface. During this condensation, large areas of tube are devoid of any liquid and are exposed directly to the vapor. Very high rates of heat transfer occur on these bare areas. The average coefficient can be as high as 110 000 W/m$^2 \cdot$ K (20 000 btu/h $\cdot$ ft$^2 \cdot$ °F), which is five to 10 times larger than film-type coefficients. Film-condensation coefficients are normally much greater than those in forced convection and are on the order of magnitude of several thousand W/m$^2 \cdot$ K or more.

Dropwise condensation occurs on contaminated surfaces and when impurities are present. Film-type condensation is more dependable and more common. Hence, for normal design purposes, film-type condensation is assumed.

2. Film-condensation coefficients for vertical surfaces. Film-type condensation on a vertical wall or tube can be analyzed analytically by assuming laminar flow of the condensate film down the wall. The film thickness is zero at the top of the wall or tube and increases in thickness as it flows downward because of condensation. Nusselt (H1, W1) assumed that the heat transfer from the condensing vapor at T_{sat} K, through this liquid film, and to the wall at T_w K was by conduction. Equating this heat transfer by conduction to that from condensation of the vapor, a final expression can be obtained for the average heat-transfer coefficient over the whole surface.

In Fig. 4.8-3a, vapor at T_{sat} is condensing on a wall whose temperature is T_w K. The condensate is flowing downward in laminar flow. Assuming unit thickness, the mass of the element with liquid density ρ_l in Fig. 4.8-3b is $(\delta - y)(dx \cdot 1)\rho_l$. The downward force on this element is the gravitational force minus the buoyancy force, or $(\delta - y)(dx) \times (\rho_l - \rho_v)g$, where ρ_v is the density of the saturated vapor. This force is balanced by the viscous-shear force at the plane y of $\mu_l(dv/dy)$ $(dx \cdot 1)$. Equating these forces,

$$(\delta - y)(dx)(\rho_l - \rho_v)g = \mu_l \left(\frac{dv}{dy}\right)(dx) \tag{4.8-7}$$

Integrating and using the boundary condition that $v = 0$ at $y = 0$,

$$v = \frac{g(\rho_l - \rho_v)}{\mu_l}(\delta y - y^2/2) \tag{4.8-8}$$

FIGURE 4.8-3.   *Film condensation on a vertical plate: (a) increase in film thickness with position, (b) balance on element of condensate.*

The mass flow rate of film condensate at any point x for unit depth is

$$m = \int_0^\delta \rho_l v \, dy = \int_0^\delta \rho_l \frac{g(\rho_l - \rho_v)}{\mu_l}(\delta y - y^2/2) \, dy \qquad \text{(4.8-9)}$$

Integrating,

$$m = \frac{\rho_l g(\rho_l - \rho_v)\delta^3}{3\mu_l} \qquad \text{(4.8-10)}$$

At the wall, for area $(dx \cdot 1)$ m^2, the rate of heat transfer is as follows if a linear temperature distribution is assumed in the liquid between the wall and the vapor:

$$q_x = -k_l(dx \cdot 1) \left.\frac{dT}{dy}\right|_{y=0} = k_l \, dx \, \frac{T_{\text{sat}} - T_w}{\delta} \qquad \text{(4.8-11)}$$

In a dx distance, the rate of heat transfer is q_x. Also, in this dx distance, the increase in mass from condensation is dm. Using Eq. (4.8-10),

$$dm = d\left[\frac{\rho_l g(\rho_l - \rho_v)\delta^3}{3\mu_l}\right] = \frac{\rho_l g(\rho_l - \rho_v)\delta^2 \, d\delta}{\mu_l} \qquad \text{(4.8-12)}$$

Making a heat balance for dx distance, the mass flow rate dm times the latent heat h_{fg} must equal the q_x from Eq. (4.8-11):

$$h_{fg} \frac{\rho_l g(\rho_l - \rho_v)\delta^2 \, d\delta}{\mu_l} = k_l \, dx \, \frac{T_{\text{sat}} - T_w}{\delta} \qquad \text{(4.8-13)}$$

Integrating, with $\delta = 0$ at $x = 0$ and $\delta = \delta$ at $x = x$,

$$\delta = \left[\frac{4\mu_l k_l x(T_{\text{sat}} - T_w)}{g h_{fg} \rho_l(\rho_l - \rho_v)}\right]^{1/4} \qquad \text{(4.8-14)}$$

Using the local heat-transfer coefficient h_x at x, a heat balance gives

$$h_x(dx \cdot 1)(T_{sat} - T_w) = k_l(dx \cdot 1)\frac{T_{sat} - T_w}{\delta} \tag{4.8-15}$$

This gives

$$h_x = \frac{k_l}{\delta} \tag{4.8-16}$$

Combining Eqs. (4.8-14) and (4.8-16),

$$h_x = \left[\frac{\rho_l(\rho_l - \rho_v)gh_{fg}k_l^3}{4\mu_l x(T_{sat} - T_w)}\right]^{1/4} \tag{4.8-17}$$

By integrating over the total length L, the average value of h is obtained as follows:

$$h = \frac{1}{L}\int_0^L h_x\,dx = \tfrac{4}{3}h_{x=L} \tag{4.8-18}$$

$$h = 0.943\left[\frac{\rho_l(\rho_l - \rho_v)gh_{fg}k_l^3}{\mu_l L(T_{sat} - T_w)}\right]^{1/4} \tag{4.8-19}$$

However, for laminar flow, experimental data are about 20% above Eq. (4.8-19).

Hence, the final recommended expression for vertical surfaces in laminar flow is (M1)

$$N_{Nu} = \frac{hL}{k_l} = 1.13\left(\frac{\rho_l(\rho_l - \rho_v)gh_{fg}L^3}{\mu_l k_l \Delta T}\right)^{1/4} \tag{4.8-20}$$

where ρ_l is the density of liquid in kg/m^3 and ρ_v that of the vapor, g is 9.8066 m/s^2, L is the vertical height of the surface or tube in m, μ_l is the viscosity of liquid in Pa · s, k_l is the liquid thermal conductivity in W/m · K, $\Delta T = T_{sat} - T_w$ in K, and h_{fg} is the latent heat of condensation in J/kg at T_{sat}. All physical properties of the liquid except h_{fg} are evaluated at the film temperature $T_f = (T_{sat} + T_w)/2$. For long vertical surfaces the flow at the bottom can be turbulent. The Reynolds number is defined as

$$N_{Re} = \frac{4m}{\pi D\mu_l} = \frac{4\Gamma}{\mu_l} \qquad \text{(vertical tube, diameter D)} \tag{4.8-21}$$

$$N_{Re} = \frac{4m}{W\mu_l} = \frac{4\Gamma}{\mu_l} \qquad \text{(vertical plate, width W)} \tag{4.8-22}$$

where m is total kg mass/s of condensate at tube or plate bottom and $\Gamma = m/\pi D$ or m/W. The N_{Re} should be below about 1800 for Eq. (4.8-20) to hold. The reader should note that some references define N_{Re} as Γ/μ. Then this N_{Re} should be below 450.

For turbulent flow for $N_{Re} > 1800$ (M1),

$$N_{Nu} = \frac{hL}{k_l} = 0.0077\left(\frac{g\rho_l^2 L^3}{\mu_l^2}\right)^{1/3}(N_{Re})^{0.4} \tag{4.8-23}$$

Solution of this equation is by trial and error, since a value of N_{Re} must first be assumed in order to calculate h.

EXAMPLE 4.8-2. Condensation on a Vertical Tube

Steam saturated at 68.9 kPa (10 psia) is condensing on a vertical tube 0.305 m (1.0 ft) long having an OD of 0.0254 m (1.0 in.) and a surface temperature of 86.11°C (187°F). Calculate the average heat-transfer coefficient using English and SI units.

Solution: From Appendix A.2,

$$T_{sat} = 193°F \, (89.44°C) \qquad T_w = 187°F \, (86.11°C)$$

$$T_f = \frac{T_w + T_{sat}}{2} = \frac{187 + 193}{2} = 190°F \, (87.8°C)$$

latent heat $h_{fg} = 1143.3 - 161.0 = 982.3 \, btu/lb_m$

$$= 2657.8 - 374.6 = 2283.2 \, kJ/kg = 2.283 \times 10^6 \, J/kg$$

$$\rho_l = \frac{1}{0.01657} = 60.3 \, lb_m/ft^3 = 60.3(16.018) = 966.7 \, kg/m^3$$

$$\rho_v = \frac{1}{40.95} = 0.0244 \, lb_m/ft^3 = 0.391 \, kg/m^3$$

$$\mu_l = (0.324 \, cp)(2.4191) = 0.784 \, lb_m/ft \cdot h = 3.24 \times 10^{-4} \, Pa \cdot s$$

$$k_l = 0.390 \, btu/ft \cdot h \cdot °F = (0.390)(1.7307) = 0.675 \, W/m \cdot K$$

$$L = 1 \, ft = 0.305 \, m \qquad \Delta T = T_{sat} - T_w = 193 - 187 = 6°F \, (3.33 \, K)$$

Assuming a laminar film, using Eq. (4.8-20) in English as well as SI units, and neglecting ρ_v as compared to ρ_l,

$$N_{Nu} = 1.13 \left(\frac{\rho_l^2 g h_{fg} L^3}{\mu_l k_l \Delta T} \right)^{1/4}$$

$$= 1.13 \left[\frac{(60.3)^2 (32.174)(3600)^2 (982.3)(1.0)^3}{(0.784)(0.390)(6)} \right]^{1/4} = 6040$$

$$N_{Nu} = 1.13 \left[\frac{(966.7)^2 (9.806)(2.283 \times 10^6)(0.305)^3}{(3.24 \times 10^{-4})(0.675)(3.33)} \right]^{1/4} = 6040$$

$$N_{Nu} = \frac{hL}{k_l} = \frac{h(1.0)}{0.390} = 6040 \qquad \text{SI units:} \quad \frac{h(0.305)}{0.675} = 6040$$

Solving, $h = 2350 \, btu/h \cdot ft^2 \cdot °F = 13\,350 \, W/m^2 \cdot K$.

Next, the N_{Re} will be calculated to see if laminar flow occurs as assumed. To calculate the total heat transferred for a tube of area

$$A = \pi DL = \pi(1/12)(1.0) = \pi/12 \, ft^2, \qquad A = \pi(0.0254)(0.305) \, m^2$$

$$q = hA \, \Delta T \tag{4.8-24}$$

However, this q must also equal that obtained by condensation of $m \, lb_m/h$ or kg/s. Hence,

$$q = hA \, \Delta T = h_{fg} m \tag{4.8-25}$$

Substituting the values given and solving for m,

$$2350(\pi/12)(193 - 187) = 982.3(m) \qquad m = 3.77 \text{ lb}_m/\text{h}$$

$$13.350(\pi)(0.0254)(0.305)(3.33) = 2.284 \times 10^6(m) \qquad m = 4.74 \times 10^{-4} \text{ kg/s}$$

Substituting into Eq. (4.8-21),

$$N_{Re} = \frac{4m}{\pi D \mu_l} = \frac{4(3.77)}{\pi(1/12)(0.784)} = 73.5 \qquad N_{Re} = \frac{4(4.74 \times 10^{-4})}{\pi(0.0254)(3.24 \times 10^{-4})} = 73.5$$

Hence, the flow is laminar as assumed.

3. Film-condensation coefficients outside horizontal cylinders. The analysis of Nusselt can also be extended to the practical case of condensation outside a horizontal tube. For a single tube the film starts out with zero thickness at the top of the tube and increases in thickness as it flows around to the bottom and then drips off. If there is a bank of horizontal tubes, the condensate from the top tube drips onto the one below; and so on.

For a vertical tier of N horizontal tubes placed one below the other with outside tube diameter D (M1),

$$N_{Nu} = \frac{hD}{k_l} = 0.725\left(\frac{\rho_l(\rho_l - \rho_v)g h_{fg} D^3}{N \mu_l k_l \, \Delta T}\right)^{1/4} \tag{4.8-26}$$

In most practical applications, the flow is in the laminar region and Eq. (4.8-26) holds (C3, M1).

4.9 HEAT EXCHANGERS

4.9A Types of Exchangers

1. Introduction. In the process industries the transfer of heat between two fluids is generally done in heat exchangers. The most common type is one in which the hot and cold fluids do not come into direct contact with each other but are separated by a tube wall or a flat or curved surface. The transfer of heat from the hot fluid to the wall or tube surface is accomplished by convection, through the tube wall or plate by conduction, and then by convection to the cold fluid. In the preceding sections of this chapter we have discussed the calculation procedures for these various steps. Now we will discuss some of the types of equipment used and overall thermal analyses of exchangers. Complete, detailed design methods have been highly developed and will not be considered here.

2. Double-pipe heat exchanger. The simplest exchanger is the double-pipe or concentric-pipe exchanger. This is shown in Fig. 4.9-1, where one fluid flows inside one pipe and the other fluid flows in the annular space between the two pipes. The fluids can be in cocurrent or countercurrent flow. The exchanger can be made from a pair of single lengths of pipe with fittings at the ends or from a number of pairs interconnected in series. This type of exchanger is useful mainly for small flow rates.

3. Shell-and-tube exchanger. If larger flows are involved, a shell-and-tube exchanger is used, which is the most important type of exchanger in use in the process industries. In these exchangers the flows are continuous. Many tubes in parallel are used, where one fluid flows

FIGURE 4.9-1. *Flow in a double-pipe heat exchanger.*

(a)

(b)

FIGURE 4.9-2. *Shell-and-tube heat exchangers: (a) 1 shell pass and 1 tube pass (1–1 exchanger); (b) 1 shell pass and 2 tube passes (1–2 exchanger).*

inside these tubes. The tubes, arranged in a bundle, are enclosed in a single shell and the other fluid flows outside the tubes in the shell side. The simplest shell-and-tube exchanger is shown in Fig. 4.9-2a for one shell pass and one tube pass, or a 1–1 counterflow exchanger. The cold fluid enters and flows inside through all the tubes in parallel in one pass. The hot fluid enters at the other end and flows counterflow across the outside of the tubes. Cross-baffles are used so that the fluid is forced to flow perpendicular across the tube bank rather than parallel with it. The added turbulence generated by this cross-flow increases the shell-side heat-transfer coefficient.

FIGURE 4.9-3. *Flow patterns of cross-flow heat exchangers: (a) one fluid mixed (gas) and one fluid unmixed; (b) both fluids unmixed.*

In Fig. 4.9-2b a 1–2 parallel–counterflow exchanger is shown. The liquid on the tube side flows in two passes as shown and the shell-side liquid flows in one pass. In the first pass of the tube side, the cold fluid is flowing counterflow to the hot shell-side fluid; in the second pass of the tube side, the cold fluid flows in parallel (cocurrent) with the hot fluid. Another type of exchanger has two shell-side passes and four tube passes. Other combinations of number of passes are also used sometimes, with the 1–2 and 2–4 types being the most common.

4. Cross-flow exchanger. When a gas such as air is being heated or cooled, a common device used is the cross-flow heat exchanger shown in Fig. 4.9-3a. One of the fluids, which is a liquid, flows inside through the tubes, and the exterior gas flows across the tube bundle by forced or sometimes natural convection. The fluid inside the tubes is considered to be unmixed, since it is confined and cannot mix with any other stream. The gas flow outside the tubes is mixed, since it can move about freely between the tubes, and there will be a tendency for the gas temperature to equalize in the direction normal to the flow. For the unmixed fluid inside the tubes, there will be a temperature gradient both parallel and normal to the direction of flow.

A second type of cross-flow heat exchanger shown in Fig. 4.9-3b is typically used in air-conditioning and space-heating applications. In this type the gas flows across a finned-tube bundle and is unmixed, since it is confined in separate flow channels between the fins as it passes over the tubes. The fluid in the tubes is unmixed.

Discussions of other types of specialized heat-transfer equipment will be deferred to Section 4.13. The remainder of this section deals primarily with shell-and-tube and cross-flow heat exchangers.

4.9B Log-Mean-Temperature-Difference Correction Factors

In Section 4.5H it was shown that when the hot and cold fluids in a heat exchanger are in true countercurrent flow or in cocurrent (parallel) flow, the log mean temperature difference should be used:

$$\Delta T_{lm} = \frac{\Delta T_2 - \Delta T_1}{\ln(\Delta T_2/\Delta T_1)} \tag{4.9-1}$$

where ΔT_2 is the temperature difference at one end of the exchanger and ΔT_1 at the other end. This ΔT_{lm} holds for a double-pipe heat exchanger and a 1–1 exchanger with one shell pass and one tube pass in parallel or counterflow.

In cases where a multiple-pass heat exchanger is involved, it is necessary to obtain a different expression for the mean temperature difference, depending on the arrangement of the shell and tube passes. Considering first the one-shell-pass, two-tube-pass exchanger in Fig. 4.9-2b, the cold fluid in the first tube pass is in counterflow with the hot fluid. In the second tube pass, the cold fluid is in parallel flow with the hot fluid. Hence, the log mean temperature difference, which applies either to parallel or to counterflow but not to a mixture of both types, as in a 1–2 exchanger, cannot be used to calculate the true mean temperature drop without a correction.

The mathematical derivation of the equation for the proper mean temperature to use is quite complex. The usual procedure is to use a correction factor F_T which is so defined that when it is multiplied by the ΔT_{lm}, the product is the correct mean temperature drop ΔT_m to use. In using the correction factors F_T, it is immaterial whether the warmer fluid flows through the tubes or the shell (K1). The factor F_T has been calculated (B4) for a 1–2 exchanger and is shown in Fig. 4.9-4a. Two dimensionless ratios are used as follows:

$$Z = \frac{T_{hi} - T_{ho}}{T_{co} - T_{ci}} \tag{4.9-2}$$

$$Y = \frac{T_{co} - T_{ci}}{T_{hi} - T_{ci}} \tag{4.9-3}$$

where T_{hi} = inlet temperature of hot fluid in K (°F), T_{ho} = outlet of hot fluid, T_{ci} inlet of cold fluid, and T_{co} = outlet of cold fluid.

In Fig. 4.9-4b, the factor F_T (B4) for a 2–4 exchanger is shown. In general, it is not recommended to use a heat exchanger for conditions under which $F_T < 0.75$. Another shell-and-tube arrangement should be used. Correction factors for two types of cross-flow exchanger are given in Fig. 4.9-5. Other types are available elsewhere (B4, P1).

Using the nomenclature of Eqs. (4.9-2) and (4.9-3), the ΔT_{lm} of Eq. (4.9-1) can be written as

$$\Delta T_{lm} = \frac{(T_{hi} - T_{co}) - (T_{ho} - T_{ci})}{\ln[(T_{hi} - T_{co})/(T_{ho} - T_{ci})]} \tag{4.9-4}$$

Then the equation for an exchanger is

$$q = U_i A_i \, \Delta T_m = U_o A_o \, \Delta T_m \tag{4.9-5}$$

where

$$\Delta T_m = F_T \, \Delta T_{lm} \tag{4.9-6}$$

EXAMPLE 4.9-1. Temperature Correction Factor for a Heat Exchanger
A 1–2 heat exchanger containing one shell pass and two tube passes heats 2.52 kg/s of water from 21.1 to 54.4°C by using hot water under pressure entering at 115.6 and leaving at 48.9°C. The outside surface area of the tubes in the exchanger is $A_o = 9.30 \text{ m}^2$.

(a) Calculate the mean temperature difference ΔT_m in the exchanger and the overall heat-transfer coefficient U_o.

(a)

(b)

FIGURE 4.9-4. *Correction factor F_T to log mean temperature difference: (a) 1–2 and 1–4 exchangers, (b) 2–4 exchangers. [From R. A. Bowman, A. C. Mueller, and W. M. Nagle, Trans. A.S.M.E., **62**, 284, 285 (1940). With permission.]*

(a)

(b)

FIGURE 4.9-5. *Correction factor F_T to log mean temperature difference for cross-flow exchangers [$Z = (T_{hi} - T_{ho})/(T_{co} - T_{ci})$]: (a) single pass, shell fluid mixed, other fluid unmixed, (b) single pass, both fluids unmixed. [From R. A. Bowman, A. C. Mueller, and W. M. Nagle, Trans. A.S.M.E., **62**, 288, 289 (1940). With permission.]*

(b) For the same temperatures but using a 2–4 exchanger, what would be the ΔT_m?

Solution: The temperatures are as follows:

$$T_{hi} = 115.6°C \qquad T_{ho} = 48.9°C \qquad T_{ci} = 21.1°C \qquad T_{co} = 54.4°C$$

First making a heat balance on the cold water, assuming a c_{pm} of water of 4187 J/kg·K and $T_{co} - T_{ci} = (54.4 - 21.1)°C = 33.3°C = 33.3$ K,

$$q = mc_{pm}(T_{co} - T_{ci}) = (2.52)(4187)(54.4 - 21.1) = 348\ 200 \text{ W}$$

The log mean temperature difference using Eq. (4.9-4) is

$$\Delta T_{lm} = \frac{(115.6 - 54.4) - (48.9 - 21.1)}{\ln[(115.6 - 54.4)/(48.9 - 21.1)]} = 42.3°C = 42.3 \text{ K}$$

Next, substituting into Eqs. (4.9-2) and (4.9-3),

$$Z = \frac{T_{hi} - T_{ho}}{T_{co} - T_{ci}} = \frac{115.6 - 48.9}{54.4 - 21.1} = 2.00 \qquad \textbf{(4.9-2)}$$

$$Y = \frac{T_{co} - T_{ci}}{T_{hi} - T_{ci}} = \frac{54.4 - 21.1}{115.6 - 21.1} = 0.352 \qquad \textbf{(4.9-3)}$$

From Fig. 4.9-4a, $F_T = 0.74$. Then, by Eq. (4.9-6),

$$\Delta T_m = F_T \Delta T_{lm} = 0.74(42.3) = 31.3°C = 31.3 \text{ K} \qquad \textbf{(4.9-6)}$$

Rearranging Eq. (4.9-5) to solve for U_o and substituting the known values, we have

$$U_o = \frac{q}{A_o \Delta T_m} = \frac{348\ 200}{(9.30)(31.3)} = 1196 \text{ W/m}^2 \cdot \text{K (211 bu/h} \cdot \text{ft}^2 \cdot °\text{F)}$$

For part (b), using a 2–4 exchanger and Fig. 4.9-4b, $F_T = 0.94$. Then,

$$\Delta T_m = F_T \Delta T_{lm} = 0.94(42.3) = 39.8°C = 39.8 \text{ K}$$

Hence, in this case the 2–4 exchanger utilizes more of the available temperature driving force.

4.9C Heat-Exchanger Effectiveness

1. Introduction. In the preceding section the log mean temperature difference was used in the equation $q = UA\ \Delta T_{lm}$ in the design of heat exchangers. This form is convenient when the inlet and outlet temperatures of the two fluids are known or can be determined by a heat balance. Then the surface area can be determined if U is known. However, when the temperatures of the fluids leaving the exchanger are not known and a given exchanger is to be used, a tedious trial-and-error procedure is necessary. To solve these cases, a method called the heat-exchanger effectiveness ε is used which does not involve any of the outlet temperatures.

The heat-exchanger effectiveness is defined as the ratio of the actual rate of heat transfer in a given exchanger to the maximum possible amount of heat transfer if an infinite heat-transfer area were available. The temperature profile for a counterflow heat exchanger is shown in Fig. 4.9-6.

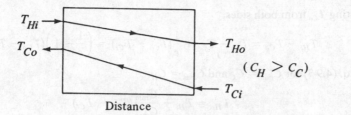

FIGURE 4.9-6. *Temperature profile for countercurrent heat exchanger.*

2. Derivation of effectiveness equation.   The heat balance for the cold (C) and hot (H) fluids is

$$q = (mc_p)_H(T_{Hi} - T_{Ho}) = (mc_p)_C(T_{Co} - T_{Ci}) \qquad \textbf{(4.9-7)}$$

Calling $(mc_p)_H = C_H$ and $(mc_p)_C = C_C$, then in Fig. 4.9-6, $C_H > C_C$, and the cold fluid undergoes a greater temperature change than the hot fluid. Hence, we designate C_C as C_{min} or minimum heat capacity. Then, if there is an infinite area available for heat transfer, $T_{Co} = T_{Hi}$. Then the effectiveness ε is

$$\varepsilon = \frac{C_H(T_{Hi} - T_{Ho})}{C_C(T_{Hi} - T_{Ci})} = \frac{C_{max}(T_{Hi} - T_{Ho})}{C_{min}(T_{Hi} - T_{Ci})} \qquad \textbf{(4.9-8)}$$

If the hot fluid is the minimum fluid, $T_{Ho} = T_{Ci}$, and

$$\varepsilon = \frac{C_C(T_{Co} - T_{Ci})}{C_H(T_{Hi} - T_{Ci})} = \frac{C_{max}(T_{Co} - T_{Ci})}{C_{min}(T_{Hi} - T_{Ci})} \qquad \textbf{(4.9-9)}$$

In both equations the denominators are the same and the numerator gives the actual heat transfer:

$$q = \varepsilon C_{min}(T_{Hi} - T_{Ci}) \qquad \textbf{(4.9-10)}$$

Note that Eq. (4.9-10) uses only inlet temperatures, which is an advantage when inlet temperatures are known and it is desired to predict the outlet temperatures for a given existing exchanger.

For the case of a single-pass, counterflow exchanger, combining Eqs. (4.9-8) and (4.9-9),

$$\varepsilon = \frac{C_H(T_{Hi} - T_{Ho})}{C_{min}(T_{Hi} - T_{Ci})} = \frac{C_C(T_{Co} - T_{Ci})}{C_{min}(T_{Hi} - T_{Ci})} \qquad \textbf{(4.9-11)}$$

We consider first the case when the cold fluid is the minimum fluid. Rewriting Eq. (4.5-25) using the present nomenclature,

$$q = C_C(T_{Co} - T_{Ci}) = UA \frac{(T_{Ho} - T_{Ci}) - (T_{Hi} - T_{Co})}{\ln[(T_{Ho} - T_{Ci})/(T_{Hi} - T_{Co})]} \qquad \textbf{(4.9-12)}$$

Combining Eq. (4.9-7) with the left side of Eq. (4.9-11) and solving for T_{Hi},

$$T_{Hi} = T_{Ci} + \frac{1}{\varepsilon}(T_{Co} - T_{Ci}) \qquad \textbf{(4.9-13)}$$

Subtracting T_{Co} from both sides,

$$T_{Hi} - T_{Co} = T_{Ci} - T_{Co} + \frac{1}{\varepsilon}(T_{Co} - T_{Ci}) = \left(\frac{1}{\varepsilon} - 1\right)(T_{Co} - T_{Ci}) \qquad \textbf{(4.9-14)}$$

From Eq. (4.9-7) for $C_{min} = C_C$ and $C_{max} = C_H$,

$$T_{Ho} = T_{Hi} - \frac{C_{min}}{C_{max}}(T_{Co} - T_{Ci}) \qquad \textbf{(4.9-15)}$$

This can be rearranged to give the following:

$$T_{Ho} - T_{Ci} = T_{Hi} - T_{Ci} - \frac{C_{min}}{C_{max}}(T_{Co} - T_{Ci}) \qquad \textbf{(4.9-16)}$$

Substituting Eq. (4.9-13) into (4.9-16),

$$T_{Ho} - T_{Ci} = \frac{1}{\varepsilon}(T_{Co} - T_{Ci}) - \frac{C_{min}}{C_{max}}(T_{Co} - T_{Ci}) \qquad \textbf{(4.9-17)}$$

Finally, substituting Eqs. (4.9-14) and (4.9-17) into (4.9-12), rearranging, taking the antilog of both sides, and solving for ε,

$$\varepsilon = \frac{1 - \exp\left[-\dfrac{UA}{C_{min}}\left(1 - \dfrac{C_{min}}{C_{max}}\right)\right]}{1 - \dfrac{C_{min}}{C_{max}}\exp\left[-\dfrac{UA}{C_{min}}\left(1 - \dfrac{C_{min}}{C_{max}}\right)\right]} \qquad \textbf{(4.9-18)}$$

We define NTU as the number of transfer units as follows:

$$\text{NTU} = \frac{UA}{C_{min}} \qquad \textbf{(4.9-19)}$$

The same result would have been obtained if $C_H = C_{min}$.

For parallel flow we obtain

$$\varepsilon = \frac{1 - \exp\left[\dfrac{-UA}{C_{min}}\left(1 + \dfrac{C_{min}}{C_{max}}\right)\right]}{1 + \dfrac{C_{min}}{C_{max}}} \qquad \textbf{(4.9-20)}$$

In Fig. 4.9-7, Eqs. (4.9-18) and (4.9-20) have been plotted in convenient graphical form. Additional charts are available for different shell-and-tube and cross-flow arrangements (K1).

EXAMPLE 4.9-2. Effectiveness of Heat Exchanger

Water flowing at a rate of 0.667 kg/s enters a countercurrent heat exchanger at 308 K and is heated by an oil stream entering at 383 K at a rate of 2.85 kg/s ($c_p = 1.89$ kJ/kg·K). The overall $U = 300$ W/m²·K and the area $A = 15.0$ m². Calculate the heat-transfer rate and the exit water temperature.

Solution: Assuming that the exit water temperature is about 370 K, the c_p for water at an average temperature of $(308 + 370)/2 = 339$ K is 4.192 kJ/kg·K (Appendix A.2). Then, $(mc_p)_H = C_H = 2.85(1.89 \times 10^3) = 5387$ W/K and $(mc_p)_C = C_C = 0.667(4.192 \times 10^3) = 2796$ W/K $= C_{min}$. Since C_C is the minimum, $C_{min}/C_{max} = 2796/5387 = 0.519$.

FIGURE 4.9-7. *Heat-exchanger effectiveness ε: (a) counterflow exchanger, (b) parallel flow exchanger.*

Using Eq. (4.9-19), NTU $= UA/C_{min} = 300(15.0)/2796 = 1.607$. Using Fig. (4.9-7a) for a counterflow exchanger, $\varepsilon = 0.71$. Substituting into Eq. (4.9-10),

$$q = \varepsilon C_{min}(T_{Hi} - T_{Ci}) = 0.71(2796)(383 - 308) = 148\ 900\ \text{W}$$

Using Eq. (4.9-7),

$$q = 148\ 900 = 2796(T_{Co} - 308)$$

Solving, $T_{Co} = 361.3$ K.

4.9D Fouling Factors and Typical Overall U Values

In actual practice, heat-transfer surfaces do not remain clean. Dirt, soot, scale, and other deposits form on one or both sides of the tubes of an exchanger and on other heat-transfer surfaces. These deposits offer additional resistance to the flow of heat and reduce the overall heat-transfer coefficient U. In petroleum processes coke and other substances can deposit. Silting and deposits of mud and other materials can occur. Corrosion products which could constitute a serious resistance to heat transfer may form on the surfaces. Biological growth such as algae can occur with cooling water and in the biological industries.

To avoid or lessen these fouling problems, chemical inhibitors are often added to minimize corrosion, salt deposition, and algae growth. Water velocities above 1 m/s are generally used to help reduce fouling. Large temperature differences may cause excessive deposition of solids on surfaces and should be avoided if possible.

The effect of such deposits and fouling is usually taken care of in design by adding a term for the resistance of the fouling on the inside and outside of the tube in Eq. (4.3-17) as follows:

$$U_i = \frac{1}{1/h_i + 1/h_{di} + (r_o - r_i)A_i/k_A A_{A\ \text{lm}} + A_i/A_o h_o + A_i/A_o h_{do}} \qquad (4.9\text{-}21)$$

TABLE 4.9-1. *Typical Fouling Coefficients (P3, N1)*

	h_d $(W/m^2 \cdot K)$	h_d $(btu/h \cdot ft^2 \cdot °F)$
Distilled and seawater	11 350	2000
City water	5680	1000
Muddy water	1990–2840	350–500
Gases	2840	500
Vaporizing liquids	2840	500
Vegetable and gas oils	1990	350

TABLE 4.9-2. *Typical Values of Overall Heat-Transfer Coefficients in Shell-and-Tube Exchangers (H1, P3, W1)*

	U $(W/m^2 \cdot K)$	U $(btu/h \cdot ft^2 \cdot °F)$
Water to water	1140–1700	200–300
Water to brine	570–1140	100–200
Water to organic liquids	570–1140	100–200
Water to condensing steam	1420–2270	250–400
Water to gasoline	340–570	60–100
Water to gas oil	140–340	25–60
Water to vegetable oil	110–285	20–50
Gas oil to gas oil	110–285	20–50
Steam to boiling water	1420–2270	250–400
Water to air (finned tube)	110–230	20–40
Light organics to light organics	230–425	40–75
Heavy organics to heavy organics	55–230	10–40

where h_{di} is the fouling coefficient for the inside and h_{do} the fouling coefficient for the outside of the tube in $W/m^2 \cdot K$. A similar expression can be written for U_o using Eq. (4.3-18).

Fouling coefficients recommended for use in designing heat-transfer equipment are available in many references (P3, N1). A short tabulation of some typical fouling coefficients is given in Table 4.9-1.

In order to perform preliminary estimates of sizes of shell-and-tube heat exchangers, typical values of overall heat-transfer coefficients are given in Table 4.9-2. These values should be useful as a check on the results of the design methods described in this chapter.

4.10   INTRODUCTION TO RADIATION HEAT TRANSFER

4.10A   Introduction and Basic Equation for Radiation

1. Nature of radiant heat transfer.   In the preceding sections of this chapter we have studied conduction and convection heat transfer. In conduction, heat is transferred from one part of a body to another, and the intervening material is heated. In convection, heat is transferred by the actual mixing of materials and by conduction. In radiant heat transfer, the medium through which the heat is transferred usually is not heated. Radiation heat transfer is the transfer of heat by electromagnetic radiation.

Thermal radiation is a form of electromagnetic radiation similar to X rays, light waves, gamma rays, and so on, differing only in wavelength. It obeys the same laws as light: It travels in straight lines, can be transmitted through space and vacuum, and so on. It is an important mode of heat transfer and is especially important where large temperature differences occur, as, for example, in a furnace with boiler tubes, in radiant dryers, or in an oven baking food. Radiation often occurs in combination with conduction and convection. An elementary discussion of radiant heat transfer will be given here, with a more advanced and comprehensive discussion being given in Section 4.11.

In an elementary sense the mechanism of radiant heat transfer is composed of three distinct steps or phases:

1. The thermal energy of a hot source, such as the wall of a furnace at T_1, is converted into energy in the form of electromagnetic-radiation waves.
2. These waves travel through the intervening space in straight lines and strike a cold object at T_2, such as a furnace tube containing water to be heated.
3. The electromagnetic waves that strike the body are absorbed by the body and converted back to thermal energy or heat.

2. Absorptivity and black bodies.   When thermal radiation (such as light waves) falls upon a body, part is absorbed by the body in the form of heat, part is reflected back into space, and part may actually be transmitted through the body. For most cases in process engineering, bodies are opaque to transmission, so this will be neglected. Hence, for opaque bodies,

$$\alpha + \rho = 1.0 \qquad (4.10\text{-}1)$$

where α is absorptivity or fraction absorbed and ρ is reflectivity or fraction reflected.

A *black body* is defined as one that absorbs all radiant energy and reflects none. Hence, $\rho = 0$ and $\alpha = 1.0$ for a black body. Actually, in practice there are no perfect black bodies, but a close approximation is a small hole in a hollow body, as shown in Fig. 4.10-1. The inside surface of the hollow body is blackened by charcoal. The radiation enters the hole and impinges

FIGURE 4.10-1.   *Concept of a perfect black body.*

hole

on the rear wall; part is absorbed there and part is reflected in all directions. The reflected rays impinge again, part is absorbed, and the process continues. Hence, essentially all of the energy entering is absorbed and the area of the hole acts as a perfect black body. The surface of the inside walls is "rough" and rays are scattered in all directions, unlike a mirror, where they are reflected at a definite angle.

As stated previously, a black body absorbs all radiant energy falling on it and reflects none. Such a black body also emits radiation, depending on its temperature, and does not reflect any. The ratio of the emissive power of a surface to that of a black body is called *emissivity* ε and is 1.0 for a black body. Kirchhoff's law states that at the same temperature T_1, α_1 and ε_1 of a given surface are the same, or

$$\alpha_1 = \varepsilon_1 \tag{4.10-2}$$

Equation (4.10-2) holds for any black or nonblack solid surface.

3. Radiation from a body and emissivity. The basic equation for heat transfer by radiation from a perfect black body with an emissivity $\varepsilon = 1.0$ is

$$q = A\sigma T^4 \tag{4.10-3}$$

where q is heat flow in W, A is m^2 surface area of body, σ is a constant 5.676×10^{-8} W/m$^2 \cdot$K^4 (0.1714×10^{-8} btu/h $\cdot$ ft$^2 \cdot$ °R^4), and T is temperature of the black body in K (°R).

For a body that is not a black body and has an emissivity $\varepsilon < 1.0$, the emissive power is reduced by ε, or

$$q = A\varepsilon\sigma T^4 \tag{4.10-4}$$

Substances that have emissivities of less than 1.0 are called *gray bodies* when the emissivity is independent of the wavelength. All real materials have an emissivity $\varepsilon < 1$.

Since the emissivity ε and absorptivity α of a body are equal at the same temperature, the emissivity, like absorptivity, is low for polished metal surfaces and high for oxidized metal surfaces. Typical values are given in Table 4.10-1 but do vary some with temperature. Most non-metallic substances have high values. Additional data are tabulated in Appendix A.3.

TABLE 4.10-1. *Total Emissivity, ε, of Various Surfaces*

Surface	T(K)	T(°F)	Emissivity, ε
Polished aluminum	500	440	0.039
	850	1070	0.057
Polished iron	450	350	0.052
Oxidized iron	373	212	0.74
Polished copper	353	176	0.018
Asbestos board	296	74	0.96
Oil paints, all colors	373	212	0.92–0.96
Water	273	32	0.95

4.10B Radiation to a Small Object from Surroundings

In the case of a small gray object of area A_1 m^2 at temperature T_1 in a large enclosure at a higher temperature T_2, there is a net radiation to the small object. The small body emits an amount of radiation to the enclosure given by Eq. (4.10-4) as $A_1\varepsilon_1\sigma T_1^4$. The emissivity ε_1 of this body is taken at T_1. The small body also absorbs an amount of energy from the surroundings at T_2 given by $A_1\alpha_{12}\sigma T_2^4$. The α_{12} is the absorptivity of body 1 for radiation from the enclosure at T_2. The value of α_{12} is approximately the same as the emissivity of this body at T_2. The net heat of absorption is then, by the Stefan–Boltzmann equation,

$$q = A_1\varepsilon_1\sigma T_1^4 - A_1\alpha_{12}\sigma T_2^4 = A_1\sigma(\varepsilon_1 T_1^4 - \alpha_{12}T_2^4) \qquad \textbf{(4.10-5)}$$

A further simplification of Eq. (4.10-5) is usually made for engineering purposes by using only one emissivity for the small body, at temperature T_2. Thus,

$$q = A_1\varepsilon\sigma(T_1^4 - T_2^4) \qquad \textbf{(4.10-6)}$$

EXAMPLE 4.10-1. Radiation to a Metal Tube

A small oxidized horizontal metal tube with an OD of 0.0254 m (1 in.), 0.61 m (2 ft) long, and with a surface temperature at 588 K (600°F) is in a very large furnace enclosure with fire-brick walls and the surrounding air at 1088 K (1500°F). The emissivity of the metal tube is 0.60 at 1088 K and 0.46 at 588 K. Calculate the heat transfer to the tube by radiation using SI and English units.

Solution: Since the large-furnace surroundings are very large compared to the small enclosed tube, the surroundings, even if gray, when viewed from the position of the small body appear black, and Eq. (4.10-6) is applicable. Substituting given values into Eq. (4.10-6) with an ε of 0.6 at 1088 K,

$$A_1 = \pi DL = \pi(0.0254)(0.61)\ \text{m}^2 = \pi(1/12)(2.0)\ \text{ft}^2$$

$$q = A_1\varepsilon\sigma(T_1^4 - T_2^4) = [\pi(0.0254)(0.61)](0.6)(5.676 \times 10^{-8})[(588)^4 - (1088)^4]$$

$$= -2130\ \text{W}$$

$$= [\pi(1/12)(2)](0.6)(0.1714 \times 10^{-8})[(1060)^4 - (1960)^4] = -7270\ \text{btu/h}$$

Other examples of small objects in large enclosures occurring in the process industries are a loaf of bread in an oven receiving radiation from the walls around it, a package of meat or food radiating heat to the walls of a freezing enclosure, a hot ingot of solid iron cooling and radiating heat in a large room, and a thermometer measuring the temperature in a large duct.

4.10C Combined Radiation and Convection Heat Transfer

When radiation heat transfer occurs from a surface, it is usually accompanied by convective heat transfer, unless the surface is in a vacuum. When the radiating surface is at a uniform temperature, we can calculate the heat transfer for natural or forced convection using the methods described in the previous sections of this chapter. The radiation heat transfer is calculated by the Stefan–Boltzmann equation (4.10-6). Then the total rate of heat transfer is the sum of convection plus radiation.

As discussed before, the heat-transfer rate by convection and the convective coefficient are given by

$$q_{\text{conv}} = h_c A_1 (T_1 - T_2) \qquad (4.10\text{-}7)$$

where q_{conv} is the heat-transfer rate by convection in W, h_c the natural or forced convection coefficient in $\text{W/m}^2 \cdot \text{K}$, T_1 the temperature of the surface, and T_2 the temperature of the air and the enclosure. A radiation heat-transfer coefficient h_r in $\text{W/m}^2 \cdot \text{K}$ can be defined as

$$q_{\text{rad}} = h_r A_1 (T_1 - T_2) \qquad (4.10\text{-}8)$$

where q_{rad} is the heat-transfer rate by radiation in W. The total heat transfer is the sum of Eqs. (4.10-7) and (4.10-8),

$$q = q_{\text{conv}} + q_{\text{rad}} = (h_c + h_r) A_1 (T_1 - T_2) \qquad (4.10\text{-}9)$$

To obtain an expression for h_r, we equate Eq. (4.10-6) to (4.10-8) and solve for h_r:

$$h_r = \frac{\varepsilon \sigma (T_1^4 - T_2^4)}{T_1 - T_2} = \varepsilon(5.676) \frac{(T_1/100)^4 - (T_2/100)^4}{T_1 - T_2} \qquad \text{(SI)}$$

$$\qquad (4.10\text{-}10)$$

$$h_r = \varepsilon(0.1714) \frac{(T_1/100)^4 - (T_2/100)^4}{T_1 - T_2} \qquad \text{(English)}$$

A convenient chart giving values of h_r in English units calculated from Eq. (4.10-10) with $\varepsilon = 1.0$ is given in Fig. 4.10-2. To use values from this figure, the value obtained from the

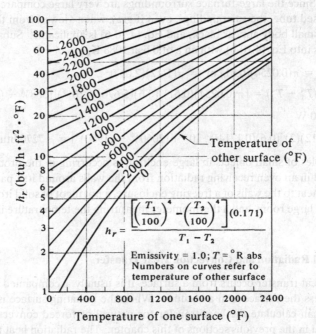

FIGURE 4.10-2. *Radiation heat-transfer coefficient as a function of temperature. (From R. H. Perry and C. H. Chilton, Chemical Engineers' Handbook, 5th ed. New York: McGraw-Hill Book Company, 1973. With permission.)*

Chapter 4   Principles of Steady-State Heat Transfer

figure should be multiplied by ε to give the value of h_r to use in Eq. (4.10-9). If the air temperature is not the same as T_2 of the enclosure, Eqs. (4.10-7) and (4.10-8) must be used separately and not combined together as in (4.10-9).

EXAMPLE 4.10-2. Combined Convection Plus Radiation from a Tube

Recalculate Example 4.10-1 for combined radiation plus natural convection to the horizontal 0.0254-m tube.

Solution: The area A of the tube $= \pi(0.0254)(0.61) = 0.0487 \text{ m}^2$. For the natural convection coefficient to the 0.0254-m horizontal tube, the simplified equation from Table 4.7-2 will be used as an approximation even though the film temperature is quite high:

$$h_c = 1.32\left(\frac{\Delta T}{D}\right)^{1/4}$$

Substituting the known values,

$$h_c = 1.32\left(\frac{1088 - 588}{0.0254}\right)^{1/4} = 15.64 \text{ W/m}^2 \cdot \text{K}$$

Using Eq. (4.10-10) and $\varepsilon = 0.6$,

$$h_r = (0.60)(5.676)\frac{(1088/100)^4 - (588/100)^4}{1088 - 588} = 87.3 \text{ W/m}^2 \cdot \text{K}$$

Substituting into Eq. (4.10-9),

$$q = (h_c + h_r)A_1(T_1 - T_2) = (15.64 + 87.3)(0.0487)(588 - 1088)$$

$$= -2507 \text{ W}$$

Hence, the heat loss of -2130 W for radiation is increased to only -2507 W when natural convection is also considered. In this case, because of the large temperature difference, radiation is the most important factor.

Perry and Green (P3, pp. 10–14) give a convenient table of natural convection plus radiation coefficients $(h_c + h_r)$ from single horizontal oxidized steel pipes as a function of the outside diameter and temperature difference. The coefficients for insulated pipes are about the same as those for a bare pipe (except that lower surface temperatures are involved for the insulated pipes), since the emissivity of cloth insulation wrapping is about that of oxidized steel, approximately 0.8. A more detailed discussion of radiation will be given in Section 4.11.

4.10D Effect of Radiation on Temperature Measurement of a Gas

When a temperature sensor or probe (thermometer, thermocouple, etc.) is used to measure the temperature of a gas flowing in an enclosure, significant errors can occur. Radiation heat exchange will take place between the sensor and the wall and convection heat transfer between the sensor and the gas. The sensor will indicate a temperature between the true gas and wall surface temperatures. This is shown in Fig. 4.10-3, where the wall temperature T_w is less than the true gas temperature T_g.

FIGURE 4.10-3. *Temperature measurement of a gas showing radiation and convection heat transfer for a bare probe and a shielded probe.*

The equations for the heat transfer q_c by convection to the probe and radiation q_r from the probe to the wall are as follows for $T_w < T_g$:

$$q_c = h_c A_p (T_g - T_p) = q_r = \varepsilon A_p (5.676) \left(\frac{T_p}{100} \right)^4 - \left(\frac{T_w}{100} \right)^4 \qquad \textbf{(4.10-11)}$$

where A_p is the area of the tube in m^2 and ε is the emissivity of the probe.

EXAMPLE 4.10-3. Effect of Radiation on Temperature Measurement in a Gas

A thermocouple is measuring the temperature of hot air flowing in a pipe whose walls are at $T_w = 400$ K (260°F). The true gas temperature $T_g = 465$ K (377°F). Calculate the temperature T_p indicated by the thermocouple. The emissivity of the probe is assumed as $\varepsilon = 0.6$ and the convection heat-transfer coefficient $h_c = 40$ W/m$^2 \cdot$ K.

Solution: Substituting into Eq. (4.10-11) for convection, q_c, and for radiation, q_r,

$$q_c = h_c A_p (T_g - T_p) = 40 A_p (465 - T_p)$$

$$q_r = 0.6 A_p (5.676) [(T_p/100)^4 - (400/100)^4]$$

Equating $q_c = q_r$, canceling out the term A_p, and solving by trial and error, $T_p = 451.4$ K. Hence, the thermocouple reading of $T_p = 451.4$ K (352.5°F) is 13.6 K (24.5°F) lower than the true gas temperature of 465 K (377°F).

Probes with a radiation shield as shown in Fig. 4.10-3 are often used to reduce radiation errors. The shield will have a temperature which is closer to the gas temperature than is the wall. Since the probe now radiates heat to a surface which is closer to the gas temperature, the radiation loss is less. It can be shown that with one shield, the radiation heat loss will be halved. Multiple shields can be used to further reduce the error. Using a polished surface on the probe to reduce the emissivity lowers the radiation heat loss. This also reduces the measurement error.

4.11 ADVANCED RADIATION HEAT-TRANSFER PRINCIPLES

4.11A Introduction and Radiation Spectrum

1. Introduction. This section will cover some basic principles together with some advanced topics on radiation that were not covered in Section 4.10. The exchange of radiation between two surfaces depends upon the size, shape, and relative orientation of these two surfaces and also upon their emissivities and absorptivities. In the cases to be considered the surfaces are separated by nonabsorbing media such as air. When gases such as CO_2 and H_2O vapor are present, some absorption by the gases occurs, which is not considered until later in this section.

2. Radiation spectrum and thermal radiation. Energy can be transported in the form of electromagnetic waves, which travel at the speed of light. Bodies may emit many forms of radiant energy, such as gamma rays, thermal energy, radio waves, and so on. In fact, there is a continuous spectrum of electromagnetic radiation. This electromagnetic spectrum is divided into a number of wavelength ranges, such as cosmic rays ($\lambda < 10^{-13}$ m), gamma rays ($\lambda = 10^{-13}$ to 10^{-10} m), thermal radiation ($\lambda = 10^{-7}$ to 10^{-4} m), and so on. The electromagnetic radiation produced solely because of the temperature of the emitter is called thermal radiation and exists between the wavelengths of 10^{-7} and 10^{-4} m. This portion of the electromagnetic spectrum is of importance in radiant thermal heat transfer. Electromagnetic waves having wavelengths between 3.8×10^{-7} and 7.6×10^{-7} m, called *visible radiation,* can be detected by the human eye. This visible radiation lies within the thermal radiation range.

When different surfaces are heated to the same temperature, they do not all emit or absorb the same amount of thermal radiant energy. A body that absorbs and emits the maximum amount of energy at a given temperature is called a *black body.* A black body is a standard to which other bodies can be compared.

3. Planck's law and emissive power. When a black body is heated to a temperature T, photons are emitted from the surface which have a definite distribution of energy. Planck's equation relates the monochromatic emissive power $E_{B\lambda}$ in W/m^3 at a temperature T in K and a wavelength λ in m:

$$E_{B\lambda} = \frac{3.7418 \times 10^{-16}}{\lambda^5 [e^{1.4388 \times 10^{-2}/\lambda T} - 1]} \tag{4.11-1}$$

A plot of Eq. (4.11-1) is given in Fig. 4.11-1 and shows that the energy given off increases with T. Also, for a given T, the emissive power reaches a maximum value at a wavelength that decreases as the temperature T increases. At a given temperature the radiation emitted extends over a spectrum of wavelengths. The visible-light spectrum occurs in the low λ region. The sun has a temperature of about 5800 K and the solar spectrum straddles this visible range.

For a given temperature, the wavelength at which the black-body emissive power is a maximum can be determined by differentiating Eq. (4.11-1) with respect to λ at constant T and setting the result equal to zero. The result is as follows and is known as *Wien's displacement law:*

$$\lambda_{max} T = 2.898 \times 10^{-3} \text{ m} \cdot \text{K} \tag{4.11-2}$$

The locus of the maximum values is shown in Fig. 4.11-1.

FIGURE 4.11-1. *Spectral distribution of total energy emitted by a black body at various temperatures of the black body.*

4. Stefan–Boltzmann law. The total emissive power is the total amount of radiation energy per unit area leaving a surface with temperature T over all wavelengths. For a black body, the total emissive power is given by the integral of Eq. (4.11-1) at a given T over all wavelengths, or the area under the curve in Fig. 4.11-1:

$$E_B = \int_0^\infty E_{B\lambda}\, d\lambda \tag{4.11-3}$$

This gives

$$E_B = \sigma T^4 \tag{4.11-4}$$

The result is the Stefan–Boltzmann law with $\sigma = 5.676 \times 10^{-8}$ W/m$^2 \cdot$ K^4. The units of E_B are W/m^2.

5. Emissivity and Kirchhoff's law. An important property in radiation is the emissivity of a surface. The *emissivity* ε of a surface is defined as the total emitted energy of the surface divided by the total emitted energy of a black body at the same temperature:

$$\varepsilon = \frac{E}{E_B} = \frac{E}{\sigma T^4} \tag{4.11-5}$$

Since a black body emits the maximum amount of radiation, ε is always <1.0.

We can derive a relationship between the absorptivity α_1 and emissivity ε_1 of a material by placing this material in an isothermal enclosure and allowing the body and enclosure to reach the same temperature at thermal equilibrium. If G is the irradiation on the body, the energy absorbed must equal the energy emitted:

$$\alpha_1 G = E_1 \qquad (4.11-6)$$

If this body is removed and replaced by a black body of equal size, then at equilibrium,

$$\alpha_2 G = E_B \qquad (4.11-7)$$

Dividing Eq. (4.11-6) by (4.11-7),

$$\frac{\alpha_1}{\alpha_2} = \frac{E_1}{E_B} \qquad (4.11-8)$$

But $\alpha_2 = 1.0$ for a black body. Hence, since $E_1/E_B = \varepsilon_1$,

$$\alpha_1 = \frac{E_1}{E_B} = \varepsilon_1 \qquad (4.11-9)$$

This is Kirchhoff's law, which states that at thermal equilibrium $\alpha = \varepsilon$ of a body. When a body is not at equilibrium with its surroundings, the result is not valid.

6. *Concept of gray body.* A gray body is defined as a surface for which the monochromatic properties are constant over all wavelengths. For a gray surface,

$$\varepsilon_\lambda = \text{const.}, \qquad \alpha_\lambda = \text{const.} \qquad (4.11-10)$$

Hence, the total absorptivity α and the monochromatic absorptivity α_λ of a gray surface are equal, as are ε and ε_λ:

$$\alpha = \alpha_\lambda, \qquad \varepsilon = \varepsilon_\lambda \qquad (4.11-11)$$

Applying Kirchhoff's law to a gray body, $\alpha_\lambda = \varepsilon_\lambda$ and

$$\alpha = \varepsilon \qquad (4.11-12)$$

As a result, the total absorptivity and emissivity are equal for a gray body even if the body is not in thermal equilibrium with its surroundings.

Gray bodies do not exist in practice; the concept of a gray body is an idealized one. The absorptivity of a surface actually varies with the wavelength of the incident radiation. Engineering calculations can often be based on the assumption of a gray body with reasonable accuracy. The α is assumed constant even with a variation in λ of the incident radiation. Also, in actual systems, various surfaces may be at different temperatures. In these cases, α for a surface is evaluated by determining the emissivity not at the actual surface temperature but at the temperature of the source of the other radiating surface or emitter, since this is the temperature the absorbing surface would reach if the absorber and emitter were at thermal equilibrium. The temperature of the absorber has only a slight effect on the absorptivity.

4.11B Derivation of View Factors in Radiation for Various Geometries

1. *Introduction.* The concepts and definitions presented in Section 4.11A form a sufficient foundation so that the net radiant exchange between surfaces can be determined. If two surfaces are arranged so that radiant energy can be exchanged, a net flow of energy will occur

from the hotter surface to the colder surface. The size, shape, and orientation of two radiating surfaces or a system of surfaces are factors in determining the net heat-flow rate between them. To simplify the discussion we assume that the surfaces are separated by a nonabsorbing medium such as air. This assumption is adequate for many engineering applications. However, in cases such as a furnace, the presence of CO_2 and H_2O vapor make such a simplification impossible because of their high absorptivities.

The simplest geometrical configuration will be considered first, that of radiation exchange between parallel, infinite planes. This assumption implies that there are no edge effects in the case of finite surfaces. First, the simplest case will be treated, in which the surfaces are black bodies, and then more complicated geometries and gray bodies will be treated.

2. View factor for infinite parallel black planes. If two parallel and infinite black planes at T_1 and T_2 are radiating toward each other, plane 1 emits σT_1^4 radiation to plane 2, which is all absorbed. Also, plane 2 emits σT_2^4 radiation to plane 1, which is all absorbed. Then for plane 1, the net radiation is from plane 1 to 2,

$$q_{12} = A_1\sigma(T_1^4 - T_2^4) \tag{4.11-13}$$

In this case all the radiation from 1 to 2 is intercepted by 2; that is, the fraction of radiation leaving 1 that is intercepted by 2 is F_{12}, which is 1.0. The factor F_{12} is called the geometric view factor or simply view factor. Hence,

$$q_{12} = F_{12}A_1\sigma(T_1^4 - T_2^4) \tag{4.11-14}$$

where F_{12} is fraction of radiation leaving surface 1 in all directions which is intercepted by surface 2. Also,

$$q_{21} = F_{21}A_2\sigma(T_1^4 - T_2^4) \tag{4.11-15}$$

In the case of parallel plates, $F_{12} = F_{21} = 1.0$ and the geometric factor is simply omitted.

3. View factor for infinite parallel gray planes. If both of the parallel plates A_1 and A_2 are gray, with emissivities and absorptivities of $\varepsilon_1 = \alpha_1$ and $\varepsilon_2 = \alpha_2$, respectively, we can proceed as follows. Since each surface has an unobstructed view of the other, the view factor is 1.0. In unit time, surface A_1 emits $\varepsilon_1 A_1 \sigma T_1^4$ radiation to A_2. Of this, the fraction ε_2 (where $\alpha_2 = \varepsilon_2$) is absorbed:

$$\text{absorbed by } A_2 = \varepsilon_2(\varepsilon_1 A_1\sigma T_1^4) \tag{4.11-16}$$

Also, the fraction $(1 - \varepsilon_2)$ or the amount $(1 - \varepsilon_2)(\varepsilon_1 A_1\sigma T_1^4)$ is reflected back to A_1. Of this amount A_1 reflects back to A_2 a fraction $(1 - \varepsilon_1)$ or an amount $(1 - \varepsilon_1)(1 - \varepsilon_2)(\varepsilon_1 A_1\sigma T_1^4)$. The surface A_2 absorbs the fraction ε_2, or

$$\text{absorbed by } A_2 = \varepsilon_2(1 - \varepsilon_1)(1 - \varepsilon_2)(\varepsilon_1 A_1\sigma T_1^4) \tag{4.11-17}$$

The amount reflected back to A_1 from A_2 is $(1 - \varepsilon_2)(1 - \varepsilon_1)(1 - \varepsilon_2)(\varepsilon_1 A_1\sigma T_1^4)$. Then A_1 absorbs ε_1 of this and reflects back to A_2 an amount $(1 - \varepsilon_1)(1 - \varepsilon_2)(1 - \varepsilon_1)(1 - \varepsilon_2) \times (\varepsilon_1 A_1\sigma T_1^4)$. The surface A_2 then absorbs

$$\text{absorbed by } A_2 = \varepsilon_2(1 - \varepsilon_1)(1 - \varepsilon_2)(1 - \varepsilon_1)(1 - \varepsilon_2)(\varepsilon_1 A_1\sigma T_1^4) \tag{4.11-18}$$

This continues, and the total amount absorbed at A_2 is the sum of Eqs. (4.11-16), (4.11-17), (4.11-18), and so on:

$$q_{1\to2} = A_1\sigma T_1^4[\varepsilon_1\varepsilon_2 + \varepsilon_1\varepsilon_2(1 - \varepsilon_1)(1 - \varepsilon_2) + \varepsilon_1\varepsilon_2(1 - \varepsilon_1)^2(1 - \varepsilon_2)^2 + \cdots] \quad \text{(4.11-19)}$$

The result is a geometric series (M1):

$$q_{1\to2} = A_1\sigma T_1^4\frac{\varepsilon_1\varepsilon_2}{1 - (1 - \varepsilon_1)(1 - \varepsilon_2)} = A_1\sigma T_1^4\frac{1}{1/\varepsilon_1 + 1/\varepsilon_2 - 1} \quad \text{(4.11-20)}$$

Repeating the above for the amount absorbed at A_1 which comes from A_2,

$$q_{2\to1} = A_1\sigma T_2^4\frac{1}{1/\varepsilon_1 + 1/\varepsilon_2 - 1} \quad \text{(4.11-21)}$$

The net radiation is the difference of Eqs. (4.11-20) and (4.11-21):

$$q_{12} = A_1\sigma(T_1^4 - T_2^4)\frac{1}{1/\varepsilon_1 + 1/\varepsilon_2 - 1} \quad \text{(4.11-22)}$$

If $\varepsilon_1 = \varepsilon_2 = 1.0$ for black bodies, Eq. (4.11-22) becomes Eq. (4.11-13).

EXAMPLE 4.11-1. Radiation Between Parallel Planes

Two parallel gray planes which are very large have emissivities of $\varepsilon_1 = 0.8$ and $\varepsilon_2 = 0.7$; surface 1 is at 1100°F (866.5 K) and surface 2 at 600°F (588.8 K). Use English and SI units for the following:

(a) What is the net radiation from 1 to 2?

(b) If the surfaces are both black, what is the net radiation?

Solution: For part (a), using Eq. (4.11-22) and substituting the known values,

$$\frac{q_{12}}{A_1} = \frac{\sigma(T_1^4 - T_2^4)}{1/\varepsilon_1 + 1/\varepsilon_2 - 1} = (0.1714 \times 10^{-8})\frac{(1100 + 460)^4 - (600 + 460)^4}{1/0.8 + 1/0.7 - 1}$$

$$= 4750 \text{ btu/h} \cdot \text{ft}^2$$

$$\frac{q_{12}}{A_1} = (5.676 \times 10^{-8})\frac{(866.5)^4 - (588.8)^4}{1/0.8 + 1/0.7 - 1} = 15\,010 \text{ W/m}^2$$

For black surfaces in part (b), using Eq. (4.11-13),

$$q = 7960 \text{ btu/h} \cdot \text{ft}^2 \quad \text{or} \quad 25\,110 \text{ W/m}^2$$

Note the large reduction in radiation when surfaces with emissivities less than 1.0 are used.

Example 4.11-1 shows the large influence that emissivities less than 1.0 have on radiation. This fact is used to reduce radiation loss or gain from a surface by using planes as a radiation shield. For example, for two parallel surfaces of emissivity ε at T_1 and T_2, the interchange is, by Eq. (4.11-22),

$$\frac{(q_{12})_0}{A} = \frac{\sigma(T_1^4 - T_2^4)}{2/\varepsilon - 1} \quad \text{(4.11-23)}$$

FIGURE 4.11-2. *Radiation between two black surfaces: (a) two planes alone, (b) two planes connected by refractory reradiating walls.*

(a)   (b)

The subscript 0 indicates that there are no planes in between the two surfaces. Suppose that we now insert one or more radiation planes between the original surfaces. Then it can be shown that

$$\frac{(q_{12})_N}{A} = \frac{1}{N+1} \frac{\sigma(T_1^4 - T_2^4)}{2/\varepsilon - 1}$$ (4.11-24)

where N is the number of radiation planes or shields between the original surfaces. Hence, a great reduction in radiation heat loss is obtained by using these shields.

4. Derivation of general equation for view factor between black bodies. Suppose that we consider radiation between two parallel black planes of finite size as shown in Fig. 4.11-2a. Since the planes are not infinite in size, some of the radiation from surface 1 does not strike surface 2, and vice versa. Hence, the net radiation interchange is less, since some is lost to the surroundings. The fraction of radiation leaving surface 1 in all directions which is intercepted by surface 2 is called F_{12} and must be determined for each geometry by taking differential surface elements and integrating over the entire surface.

Before we can derive a general relationship for the view factor between two finite bodies, we must consider and discuss two quantities, a solid angle and the intensity of radiation. A solid angle ω is a dimensionless quantity which is a measure of an angle in solid geometry. In Fig. 4.11-3a the differential solid angle $d\omega_1$ is equal to the normal projection of dA_2 divided by the square of the distance between the point P and area dA_2:

$$d\omega_1 = \frac{dA_2 \cos \theta_2}{r^2}$$ (4.11-25)

The units of a solid angle are steradian or sr. For a hemisphere the number of sr subtended by this surface is 2π.

The intensity of radiation for a black body, I_B, is the rate of radiation emitted per unit area projected in a direction normal to the surface and per unit solid angle in a specified direction as shown in Fig. 4.11-3b. The projection of dA on the line between centers is $dA \cos \theta$.

$$I_B = \frac{dq}{dA \cos d\omega}$$ (4.11-26)

where q is in W and I_B is in W/m^2·sr. We assume that the black body is a diffuse surface which emits with equal intensity in all directions, that is, I = constant. The emissive power E_B which leaves a black-body plane surface is determined by integrating Eq. (4.11-26) over all

FIGURE 4.11-3. *Geometry for a solid angle and intensity of radiation: (a) solid-angle geometry, (b) intensity of radiation from emitting area dA.*

solid angles subtended by a hemisphere covering the surface. The final result is as follows [see references (C3, H1, K1) for details]:

$$E_B = \pi I_B \qquad (4.11\text{-}27)$$

where E_B is in W/m^2.

In order to determine the radiation heat-transfer rates between two black surfaces, we must determine the general case for the fraction of the total radiant heat that leaves a surface and arrives on a second surface. Using only black surfaces, we consider the case shown in Fig. 4.11-4, in which radiant energy is exchanged between area elements dA_1 and dA_2. The line r is the distance between the areas, and the angles between this line and the normals to the two surfaces are θ_1 and θ_2. The rate of radiant energy that leaves dA_1 in the direction given by the angle θ_1 is $I_{B1} \, dA \cos \theta_1$. The rate that leaves dA_1 and arrives on dA_2 is given by Eq. (4.11-28):

$$dq_{1 \to 2} = I_{B1} \, dA \cos \theta_1 \, d\omega_1 \qquad (4.11\text{-}28)$$

FIGURE 4.11-4. *Area elements for radiation shape factor.*

where $d\omega_1$ is the solid angle subtended by the area dA_2 as seen from dA_1. Combining Eqs. (4.11-25) and (4.11-28),

$$dq_{1\to2} = \frac{I_{B1}\,dA\cos\theta_1\cos\theta_2\,dA_2}{r^2} \tag{4.11-29}$$

From Eq. (4.11-27), $I_{B1} = E_{B1}/\pi$. Substituting E_{B1}/π for I_{B1} into Eq. (4.11-29),

$$dq_{1\to2} = \frac{E_{B1}\cos\theta_1\cos\theta_2\,dA_1\,dA_2}{\pi r^2} \tag{4.11-30}$$

The energy leaving dA_2 and arriving at dA_1 is

$$dq_{2\to1} = \frac{E_{B2}\cos\theta_2\cos\theta_1\,dA_2\,dA_1}{\pi r^2} \tag{4.11-31}$$

Substituting σT_1^4 for E_{B1} and σT_2^4 for E_{B2} from Eq. (4.11-4) and taking the difference of Eqs. (4.11-30) and (4.11-31) for the net heat flow,

$$dq_{12} = \sigma(T_1^4 - T_2^4)\frac{\cos\theta_1\cos\theta_2\,dA_1\,dA_2}{\pi r^2} \tag{4.11-32}$$

Performing the double integrations over surfaces A_1 and A_2 will yield the total net heat flow between the finite areas:

$$q_{12} = \sigma(T_1^4 - T_2^4)\int_{A_2}\int_{A_1}\frac{\cos\theta_1\cos\theta_2\,dA_1\,dA_2}{\pi r^2} \tag{4.11-33}$$

Equation (4.11-33) can also be written as

$$q_{12} = A_1 F_{12}\sigma(T_1^4 - T_2^4) = A_2 F_{21}\sigma(T_1^4 - T_2^4) \tag{4.11-34}$$

where F_{12} is a geometric shape factor or view factor and designates the fraction of the total radiation leaving A_1 which strikes A_2, and F_{21} represents the fraction leaving A_2 which strikes A_1. Also, the following relation exists:

$$A_1 F_{12} = A_2 F_{21} \tag{4.11-35}$$

which is valid for black surfaces and nonblack surfaces. The view factor F_{12} is then

$$F_{12} = \frac{1}{A_1}\int_{A_2}\int_{A_1}\frac{\cos\theta_1\cos\theta_2\,dA_1\,dA_2}{\pi r^2} \tag{4.11-36}$$

Values of the view factor can be calculated for a number of geometrical arrangements.

5. *View factors between black bodies for various geometries.* A number of basic relationships between view factors are given below.

The reciprocity relationship given by Eq. (4.11-35) is

$$A_1 F_{12} = A_2 F_{21} \tag{4.11-35}$$

This relationship can be applied to any two surfaces i and j:

$$A_i F_{ij} = A_j F_{ji} \tag{4.11-37}$$

FIGURE 4.11-5. *Radiant exchange between a flat surface and a hemisphere for Example 4.11-2.*

If surface A_1 can only see surface A_2, then $F_{12} = 1.0$.

If surface A_1 sees a number of surfaces $A_2, A_3, \ldots$, and all the surfaces form an enclosure, then the enclosure relationship is

$$F_{11} + F_{12} + F_{13} + \cdots = 1.0 \qquad \text{(4.11-38)}$$

If the surface A_1 cannot see itself (surface is flat or convex), $F_{11} = 0$.

EXAMPLE 4.11-2.   View Factor from a Plane to a Hemisphere

Determine the view factors between a plane A_1 covered by a hemisphere A_2 as shown in Fig. 4.11-5.

Solution: Since surface A_1 sees only A_2, the view factor $F_{12} = 1.0$. Using Eq. (4.11-35),

$$A_1 F_{12} = A_2 F_{21} \qquad \text{(4.11-35)}$$

The area $A_1 = \pi R^2$; $A_2 = 2\pi R^2$. Substituting into Eq. (4.11-35) and solving for F_{21},

$$F_{21} = F_{12} = \frac{A_1}{A_2} = (1.0)\frac{\pi R^2}{2\pi R^2} = \frac{1}{2}$$

Using Eq. (4.11-38) for surface A_1, $F_{11} = 1.0 - F_{12} = 1.0 - 1.0 = 0$. Also, writing Eq. (4.11-38) for surface A_2,

$$F_{22} + F_{21} = 1.0 \qquad \text{(4.11-39)}$$

Solving for F_{22}, $F_{22} = 1.0 - F_{21} = 1.0 - \frac{1}{2} = \frac{1}{2}$.

EXAMPLE 4.11-3.   Radiation Between Parallel Disks

In Fig. 4.11-6 a small disk of area A_1 is parallel to a large disk of area A_2, with A_1 centered directly below A_2. The distance between the centers of the disks is R and the radius of A_2 is a. Determine the view factor for radiant heat transfer from A_1 to A_2.

Solution: The differential area for A_2 is taken as the circular ring of radius x so that $dA_2 = 2\pi x\, dx$. The angle $\theta_1 = \theta_2$. Using Eq. (4.11-36),

$$F_{12} = \frac{1}{A_1} \int_{A_2} \int_{A_1} \frac{\cos\theta_1 \cos\theta_1\, dA_1 (2\pi x\, dx)}{\pi r^2}$$

In this case the area A_1 is very small compared to A_2, so dA_1 can be integrated to A_1 and the other terms inside the integral can be assumed constant. From the

FIGURE 4.11-6. *View factor for radiation from a small element to a parallel disk for Example 4.11-3.*

geometry shown, $r = (R^2 + x^2)^{1/2}$, $\cos \theta_1 = R/(R^2 + x^2)^{1/2}$. Making these substitutions into the equation for F_{12},

$$F_{12} = \int_0^a \frac{2R^2x\,dx}{(R^2 + x^2)^2}$$

Integrating,

$$F_{12} = \frac{a^2}{R^2 + a^2}$$

The integration of Eq. (4.11-36) has been performed for numerous geometrical configurations and values of F_{12} tabulated. Then,

$$q_{12} = F_{12}A_1\sigma(T_1^4 - T_2^4) = F_{21}A_2\sigma(T_1^4 - T_2^4) \qquad \textbf{(4.11-34)}$$

Radiation between parallel planes, directly opposed
1-2-3-4 Direct radiation between the planes, F_{12}
5-6-7-8 Planes connected by nonconducting but reradiating walls, $\overline{F}_{12}$
1-5 Disks   3-7 2:1 Rectangle
2-6 Squares 4-8 Long, narrow rectangles

Ratio of $\dfrac{\text{smaller side or diameter}}{\text{distance between planes}}$

FIGURE 4.11-7. *View factor between parallel planes directly opposed. (From W. H. McAdams, Heat Transmission, 3rd ed. New York: McGraw-Hill Book Company, 1954. With permission.)*

FIGURE 4.11-8. *View factor for adjacent perpendicular rectangles. [From H. C. Hottel, Mech. Eng., 52, 699 (1930). With permission.]*

where F_{12} is the fraction of the radiation leaving A_1 which is intercepted by A_2 and F_{21} the fraction reaching A_1 from A_2. Since the flux from 1 to 2 must equal that from 2 to 1, Eq. (4.11-34) becomes Eq. (4.11-35) as given previously:

$$A_1 F_{12} = A_2 F_{21} \qquad (4.11\text{-}35)$$

Hence, one selects the surface whose view factor can be determined most easily. For example, the view factor F_{12} for a small surface A_1 completely enclosed by a large surface A_2 is 1.0, since all the radiation leaving A_1 is intercepted by A_2. In Fig. 4.11-7 the view factors F_{12} between parallel planes are given, and in Fig. 4.11-8 the view factors for adjacent perpendicular rectangles. View factors for other geometries are given elsewhere (H1, K1, P3, W1).

4.11C View Factors When Surfaces Are Connected by Reradiating Walls

If the two black-body surfaces A_1 and A_2 are connected by nonconducting (refractory) but reradiating walls as in Fig. 4.11-2b, a larger fraction of the radiation from surface 1 is intercepted by 2. This view factor is called $\overline{F}_{12}$. The case of two surfaces connected by the walls of an enclosure such as a furnace is a common example of this. The general equation for this case assuming a uniform refractory temperature has been derived (M1, C3) for two radiant sources A_1 and A_2 which are not concave, so they do not see themselves:

$$\overline{F}_{12} = \frac{A_2 - A_1 F_{12}^2}{A_1 + A_2 - 2A_1 F_{12}} = \frac{1 - (A_1/A_2)F_{12}^2}{A_1/A_2 + 1 - 2(A_1/A_2)F_{12}} \qquad (4.11\text{-}40)$$

Also, as before,

$$A_1 \overline{F}_{12} = A_1 \overline{F}_{21} \qquad (4.11\text{-}41)$$

$$q_{12} = \overline{F}_{12} A_1 \sigma (T_1^4 - T_2^4) \tag{4.11-42}$$

The factor $\overline{F}_{12}$ for parallel planes is given in Fig. 4.11-7 and for other geometries can be calculated from Eq. (4.11-36). For view factors F_{12} and $\overline{F}_{12}$ for parallel tubes adjacent to a wall as in a furnace as well as for variation in refractory wall temperature, see elsewhere (M1, P3). If there are no reradiating walls,

$$F_{12} = \overline{F}_{12} \tag{4.11-43}$$

4.11D View Factors and Gray Bodies

A general and more practical case, which is the same as for Eq. (4.11-40) but with the surfaces A_1 and A_2 being gray with emissivities ε_1 and ε_2, will be considered. Nonconducting reradiating walls are present as before. Since the two surfaces are now gray, there will be some reflection of radiation, which will decrease the net radiant exchange between the surfaces below that for black surfaces. The final equations for this case are

$$q_{12} = \mathfrak{F}_{12} A_1 \sigma (T_1^4 - T_2^4) \tag{4.11-44}$$

$$\mathfrak{F}_{12} = \cfrac{1}{\cfrac{1}{\overline{F}_{12}} + \cfrac{A_1}{A_2}\left(\cfrac{1}{\varepsilon_2} - 1\right) + \left(\cfrac{1}{\varepsilon_1} - 1\right)} \tag{4.11-45}$$

where $\mathfrak{F}_{12}$ is the new view factor for two gray surfaces A_1 and A_2 which cannot see themselves and are connected by reradiating walls. If no refractory walls are present, F_{12} is used in place of $\overline{F}_{12}$ in Eq. (4.11-41). Again,

$$A_1 \mathfrak{F}_{12} = A_2 \mathfrak{F}_{21} \tag{4.11-46}$$

EXAMPLE 4.11-4. Radiation Between Infinite Parallel Gray Planes
Derive Eq. (4.11-22) by starting with the general equation for radiation between two gray bodies A_1 and A_2 which are infinite parallel planes having emissivities ε_1 and ε_2, respectively.

Solution: Since there are no reradiating walls, by Eq. (4.11-43) $\overline{F}_{12}$ becomes F_{12}. Also, since all the radiation from surface 1 is intercepted by surface 2, $F_{12} = 1.0$. Substituting into Eq. (4.11-45), noting that $A_1/A_2 = 1.0$,

$$\mathfrak{F}_{12} = \cfrac{1}{\cfrac{1}{\overline{F}_{12}} + \cfrac{A_1}{A_2}\left(\cfrac{1}{\varepsilon_2} - 1\right) + \left(\cfrac{1}{\varepsilon_1} - 1\right)} = \cfrac{1}{\cfrac{1}{1} + 1\left(\cfrac{1}{\varepsilon_2} - 1\right) + \left(\cfrac{1}{\varepsilon_1} - 1\right)}$$

$$= \cfrac{1}{\cfrac{1}{\varepsilon_1} + \cfrac{1}{\varepsilon_2} - 1}$$

Then using Eq. (4.11-44),

$$q_{12} = \mathfrak{F}_{12} A_1 \sigma (T_1^4 - T_2^4) = A_1 \sigma (T_1^4 - T_2^4) \cfrac{1}{\cfrac{1}{\varepsilon_1} + \cfrac{1}{\varepsilon_2} - 1}$$

This is identical to Eq. (4.11-22).

Chapter 4   Principles of Steady-State Heat Transfer

FIGURE 4.11-9. *Configuration for Example 4.11-5.*

EXAMPLE 4.11-5. *Complex View Factor for Perpendicular Rectangles*
Find the view factor F_{12} for the configuration shown in Fig. 4.11-9 of the rectangle with area A_2 displaced from the common edge of rectangle A_1 and perpendicular to A_1. The temperature of A_1 is T_1 and that of A_2 and A_3 is T_2.

Solution: The area A_3 is a fictitious area between areas A_2 and A_1. Designate the area A_2 plus A_3 as $A_{(23)}$. The view factor $F_{1(23)}$ for areas A_1 and $A_{(23)}$ can be obtained from Fig. 4.11-8 for adjacent perpendicular rectangles. Also, F_{13} can be obtained from Fig. 4.11-8. The radiation interchange between A_1 and $A_{(23)}$ is equal to that intercepted by A_2 and by A_3:

$$A_1 F_{1(23)} \sigma(T_1^4 - T_2^4) = A_1 F_{12} \sigma(T_1^4 - T_2^4) + A_1 F_{13}(T_1^4 - T_2^4) \quad \textbf{(4.11-47)}$$

Hence,

$$A_1 F_{1(23)} = A_1 F_{12} + A_1 F_{13} \quad \textbf{(4.11-48)}$$

Solving for F_{12},

$$F_{12} = F_{1(23)} - F_{13} \quad \textbf{(4.11-49)}$$

Methods similar to those used in this example can be employed to find the shape factors for a general orientation of two rectangles in perpendicular planes or parallel rectangles (C3, H1, K1).

EXAMPLE 4.11-6. *Radiation to a Small Package*
A small, cold package having an area A_1 and emissivity ε_1 is at temperature T_1. It is placed in a warm room with the walls at T_2 and an emissivity ε_2. Using Eq. (4.11-45), derive the view factor for this and the equation for the radiation heat transfer.

Solution: For the small surface A_1 completely enclosed by the enclosure A_2, $\bar{F}_{12} = F_{12}$ by Eq. (4.11-43), since there are no reradiating (refractory) walls. Also, $F_{12} = 1.0$, since all the radiation from A_1 is intercepted by the enclosure A_2 because A_1 does not have any concave surfaces and cannot "see" itself. Since A_2 is very large compared to A_1, $A_1/A_2 = 0$. Substituting into Eq. (4.11-45),

$$\mathscr{F}_{12} = \cfrac{1}{\cfrac{1}{\bar{F}_{12}} + \cfrac{A_1}{A_2}\left(\cfrac{1}{\varepsilon_2} - 1\right) + \left(\cfrac{1}{\varepsilon_1} - 1\right)} = \cfrac{1}{\cfrac{1}{1} + 0\left(\cfrac{1}{\varepsilon_2} - 1\right) + \cfrac{1}{\varepsilon_1} - 1} = \varepsilon_1$$

Substituting into Eq. (4.11-44),

$$q_{12} = \mathcal{F}_{12}A_1\sigma(T_1^4 - T_2^4) = \varepsilon_1 A_1\sigma(T_1^4 - T_2^4)$$

This is the same as Eq. (4.10-6) derived previously.

For solving complicated radiation problems involving more than four or five heat-transfer surfaces, matrix methods have been developed and are discussed in detail elsewhere (H1, K1).

4.11E Radiation in Absorbing Gases

1. Introduction to absorbing gases in radiation. As discussed in this section, solids and liquids emit radiation over a continuous spectrum. However, most gases that are monatomic or diatomic, such as He, Ar, H_2, O_2, and N_2, are virtually transparent to thermal radiation; that is, they emit practically no radiation and do not absorb radiation. Gases with a dipole moment and higher polyatomic gases emit significant amounts of radiation and also absorb radiant energy within the same bands in which they emit radiation. These gases include CO_2, H_2O, CO, SO_2, NH_3, and organic vapors.

For a particular gas, the width of the absorption or emission bands depends on the pressure and also the temperature. If an absorbing gas is heated, it radiates energy to the cooler surroundings. The net radiation heat-transfer rate between surfaces is decreased in these cases because the gas absorbs some of the radiant energy being transported between the surfaces.

2. Absorption of radiation by a gas. The absorption of radiation in a gas layer can be described analytically, since the absorption by a given gas depends on the number of molecules in the path of radiation. Increasing the partial pressure of the absorbing gas or the path length increases the amount of absorption. We define $I_{\lambda O}$ as the intensity of radiation at a particular wavelength before it enters the gas and $I_{\lambda L}$ as the intensity at the same wavelength after having traveled a distance of L in the gas. If the beam impinges on a gas layer of thickness dL, the decrease in intensity, dI_λ, is proportional to I_λ and dL:

$$dI_\lambda = -\alpha_\lambda I_\lambda \, dL \tag{4.11-50}$$

where I_λ is in W/m². Integrating,

$$I_{\lambda L} = I_{\lambda 0} e^{-\alpha_\lambda L} \tag{4.11-51}$$

The constant α_λ depends on the particular gas, its partial pressure, and the wavelength of radiation. This equation is called Beer's law. Gases frequently absorb only in narrow-wavelength bands.

3. Characteristic mean beam length of absorbing gas. The calculation methods for gas radiation are quite complicated. For the purpose of engineering calculations, Hottel (M1) has presented approximate methods for calculating radiation and absorption when gases such as CO_2 and water vapor are present. Thick layers of a gas absorb more energy than do thin layers. Hence, in addition to specifying the pressure and temperature of a gas, we must specify a characteristic length (mean beam length) of a gas mass to determine the emissivity and absorptivity of a gas. The mean beam length L depends on the specific geometry.

For a black differential receiving surface area dA located in the center of the base of a hemisphere of radius L containing a radiating gas, the mean beam length is L. The mean

TABLE 4.11-1. *Mean Beam Length for Gas Radiation to Entire Enclosure Surface (M1, R2, P3)*

Geometry of Enclosure	Mean Beam Length, L
Sphere, diameter D	$0.65D$
Infinite cylinder, diameter D	$0.95D$
Cylinder, length = diameter D	$0.60D$
Infinite parallel plates, separation distance D	$1.8D$
Hemisphere, radiation to element in base, radius R	R
Cube, radiation to any face, side D	$0.60D$
Volume surrounding bank of long tubes with centers on equilateral triangle, clearance = tube diameter D	$2.8D$

beam length has been evaluated for various geometries, as presented in Table 4.11-1. For other shapes, L can be approximated by

$$L = 3.6\frac{V}{A} \qquad (4.11\text{-}52)$$

where V is volume of the gas in m^3, A is surface area of the enclosure in m^2, and L is in m.

4. Emissivity, absorptivity, and radiation of a gas. Gas emissivities have been correlated and Fig. 4.11-10 gives the gas emissivity ε_G of CO_2 at a total pressure of the system of 1.0 atm abs. The p_G is the partial pressure of CO_2 in atm and L is the mean beam length in m. The emissivity ε_G is defined as the ratio of the rate of energy transfer from the hemispherical body of gas to a surface element at the midpoint divided by the rate of energy transfer from a black hemisphere surface of radius L and temperature T_G to the same element.

The rate of radiation emitted from the gas is $\sigma\varepsilon_G T_G^4$ in W/m^2 of receiving surface element, where ε_G is evaluated at T_G. If the surface element at the midpoint at T_1 is radiating heat back to the gas, the absorption rate of the gas will be $\sigma\alpha_G T_1^4$, where α_G is the absorptivity of the gas for black-body radiation from the surface at T_1. The α_G of CO_2 is determined from Fig. 4.11-10 at T_1, but instead of the parameter $p_G L$, the parameter $p_G L(T_1/T_G)$ is used. The resulting value from the chart is then multiplied by $(T_G/T_1)^{0.65}$ to give α_G. The net rate of radiant transfer between a gas at T_G and a black surface of finite area A_1 at T_1 is then

$$q = \sigma A(\varepsilon_G T_G^4 - \alpha_G T_1^4) \qquad (4.11\text{-}53)$$

When the total pressure is not 1.0 atm, a correction chart is available to correct the emissivity of CO_2. Charts are also available for water vapor (H1, K1, M1, P3). When both CO_2 and H_2O are present the total radiation is reduced somewhat, since each gas is somewhat opaque to radiation from the other gas. Charts for these interactions are also available (H1, K1, M1, P3).

EXAMPLE 4.11-7. Gas Radiation to a Furnace Enclosure

A furnace is in the form of a cube 0.3 m on a side inside, and these interior walls can be approximated as black surfaces. The gas inside at 1.0 atm total pressure and 1100 K contains 10 mol % CO_2 and the rest is O_2 and N_2. The small amount

FIGURE 4.11-10. *Total emissivity of the gas carbon dioxide at a total
pressure of 1.0 atm. (From W. H. McAdams, Heat
Transmission, 3rd ed. New York: McGraw-Hill Book
Company, 1954. With permission.)*

of water vapor present will be neglected. The walls of the furnace are maintained at 600 K by external cooling. Calculate the total heat transfer to the walls neglecting heat transfer by convection.

Solution: From Table 4.11-1, the mean beam length for radiation to a cube face is $L = 0.60D = 0.60(0.30) = 0.180$ m. The partial pressure of CO_2 is $p_G = 0.10(100) = 0.10$ atm. Then $p_G L = 0.10(0.180) = 0.0180$ atm·m. From Fig. 4.11-10, $\varepsilon_G = 0.064$ at $T_G = 1100$ K.

To obtain α_G, we evaluate α_G at $T_1 = 600$ K and $p_G L(T_1/T_G) = (0.0180)(600/1100) = 0.00982$ atm·m. From Fig. 4.11-10, the uncorrected value of $\alpha_G = 0.048$. Multiplying this by the correction factor $(T_G/T_1)^{0.65}$, the final correction value is

$$\alpha_G = 0.048(1100/600)^{0.65} = 0.0712$$

Substituting into Eq. (4.11-53),

$$\frac{q}{A} = \sigma(\varepsilon_G T_G^4 - \alpha_G T_1^4)$$

$$= (5.676 \times 10^{-8})[0.064(1100)^4 - 0.0712(600)^4]$$

$$= 4.795 \times 10^3 \text{ W/m}^2 = 4.795 \text{ kW/m}^2$$

For six sides, $A = 6(0.3 \times 0.3) = 0.540 \text{ m}^2$. Then,

$$q = 4.795(0.540) = 2.589 \text{ kW}$$

For the case where the walls of the enclosure are not black, some of the radiation striking the walls is reflected back to the other walls and into the gas. As an approximation when the emissivity of the walls is greater than 0.7, an effective emissivity ε' can be used:

$$\varepsilon' = \frac{\varepsilon + 1.0}{2} \qquad \textbf{(4.11-54)}$$

where ε is the actual emissivity of the enclosure walls. Then Eq. (4.11-53) is modified to give the following (M1):

$$q = \sigma A \varepsilon' (\varepsilon_G T_G^4 - \alpha_G T_1^4) \qquad \textbf{(4.11-55)}$$

Other approximate methods are available for gases containing suspended luminous flames, clouds of nonblack particles, refractory walls and absorbing gases present, and so on (M1, P3).

4.12 HEAT TRANSFER OF NON-NEWTONIAN FLUIDS

4.12A Introduction

Most of the studies on heat transfer with fluids have been done with Newtonian fluids. However, a wide variety of non-Newtonian fluids are encountered in the industrial chemical, biological, and food processing industries. To design equipment to handle these fluids, the flow-property constants (rheological constants) must be available or must be measured experimentally. Section 3.5 gave a detailed discussion of rheological constants for non-Newtonian fluids. Since many non-Newtonian fluids have high effective viscosities, they are often in laminar flow. Since the majority of non-Newtonian fluids are pseudoplastic fluids, which can usually be represented by the power law, Eq. (3.5-2), the discussion will be concerned with such fluids. For other fluids, the reader is referred to Skelland (S3).

4.12B Heat Transfer Inside Tubes

1. Laminar flow in tubes. A large portion of the experimental investigations have been concerned with heat transfer of non-Newtonian fluids in laminar flow through cylindrical tubes. The physical properties that are needed for heat-transfer coefficients are density, heat capacity, thermal conductivity, and the rheological constants K' and n' or K and n.

In heat transfer in a fluid in laminar flow, the mechanism is primarily one of conduction. However, for low flow rates and low viscosities, natural convection effects can be present. Since many non-Newtonian fluids are quite "viscous," natural convection effects are reduced substantially. For laminar flow inside circular tubes of power-law fluids, the equation of Metzner and Gluck (M2) can be used with highly "viscous" non-Newtonian fluids with negligible natural convection for horizontal or vertical tubes for the Graetz number $N_{Gz} > 20$ and $n' > 0.10$:

$$(N_{Nu})_a = \frac{h_a D}{k} = 1.75 \delta^{1/3} (N_{Gz})^{1/3} \left(\frac{\gamma_b}{\gamma_w} \right)^{0.14} \qquad \textbf{(4.12-1)}$$

where

$$\delta = \frac{3n' + 1}{4n'}$$ (4.12-2)

$$N_{Gz} = \frac{mc_p}{kL} = \frac{\pi}{4} \frac{Dv\rho}{\mu} \frac{c_p\mu}{k} \frac{D}{L} = \frac{\pi}{4} N_{Re} N_{Pr} \frac{D}{L}$$ (4.12-3)

The viscosity coefficients γ_b at temperature T_b and γ_w at T_w are defined as

$$\frac{\gamma_b}{\gamma_w} = \frac{K'_b 8^{n'-1}}{K'_w 8^{n'-1}} = \frac{K'_b}{K'_w} = \frac{K_b}{K_w}$$ (4.12-4)

The nomenclature is as follows: k in W/m·K, c_p in J/kg·K, ρ in kg/m³, flow rate m in kg/s, length of heated section of tube L in m, inside diameter D in m, the mean coefficient h_a in W/m²·K, and K and n' rheological constants (see Section 3.5). The physical properties and K_b are all evaluated at the mean bulk temperature T_b and K_w at the average wall temperature T_w.

The value of the rheological constant n' or n has been found not to vary appreciably over wide temperature ranges (S3). However, the rheological constant K' or K has been found to vary appreciably. A plot of log K' versus $1/T_{abs}$ (C1) or versus $T°C$ (S3) can often be approximated by a straight line. Often data for the temperature effect on K are not available. Since the ratio K_b/K_w is taken to the 0.14 power, this factor can sometimes be neglected without causing large errors. For a value of the ratio of 2:1, the error is only about 10%. A plot of log viscosity versus $1/T$ for Newtonian fluids is also often a straight line. The value of h_a obtained from Eq. (4.12-1) is the mean value to use over the tube length L with the arithmetic temperature difference ΔT_a:

$$\Delta T_a = \frac{(T_w - T_{bi}) + (T_w - T_{bo})}{2}$$ (4.12-5)

when T_w is the average wall temperature for the whole tube and T_{bi} is the inlet bulk temperature and T_{bo} the outlet bulk temperature. The heat flux q is

$$q = h_a A \, \Delta T_a = h_a(\pi DL) \, \Delta T_a$$ (4.12-6)

EXAMPLE 4.12-1. *Heating a Non-Newtonian Fluid in Laminar Flow*
A non-Newtonian fluid flowing at a rate of 7.56×10^{-2} kg/s inside a 25.4-mm-ID tube is being heated by steam condensing outside the tube. The fluid enters the heating section of the tube, which is 1.524 m long, at a temperature of 37.8°C. The inside wall temperature T_w is constant at 93.3°C. The mean physical properties of the fluid are $\rho = 1041$ kg/m³, $c_{pm} = 2.093$ kJ/kg·K, and $k = 1.212$ W/m·K. The fluid is a power-law fluid having the following flow-property (rheological) constants: $n = n' = 0.40$, which is approximately constant over the temperature range encountered, and $K = 139.9$ N·s^n/m² at 37.8°C and 62.5 at 93.3°C. For this fluid a plot of log K versus $T°C$ is approximately a straight line. Calculate the outlet bulk temperature of the fluid if it is in laminar flow.

Solution: The solution is trial and error, since the outlet bulk temperature T_{bo} of the fluid must be known in order to calculate h_a from Eq. (4.12-2). Assuming $T_{bo} = 54.4°C$ for the first trial, the mean bulk temperature T_b is $(54.4 + 37.8)/2$, or 46.1°C.

Plotting the two values of K given at 37.8 and 93.3°C as log K versus T°C and drawing a straight line through these two points, a value for K_b of 123.5 at $T_b = 46.1$°C is read from the plot. At $T_w = 93.3$°C, $K_w = 62.5$.

Next, δ is calculated using Eq. (4.12-2):

$$\delta = \frac{3n'+1}{4n'} = \frac{3(0.40)+1}{4(0.40)} = 1.375$$

Substituting into Eq. (4.12-3),

$$N_{Gz} = \frac{mc_p}{kL} = \frac{(7.56 \times 10^{-2})(2.093 \times 10^3)}{1.212(1.524)} = 85.7$$

From Eq. (4.12-4),

$$\frac{\gamma_b}{\gamma_w} = \frac{K_b}{K_w} = \frac{123.5}{62.5}$$

Then substituting into Eq. (4.12-1),

$$\frac{h_a D}{k} = \frac{h_a(0.0254)}{1.212} = 1.75 \, \delta^{1/3}(N_{Gz})^{1/3}\left(\frac{\gamma_b}{\gamma_w}\right)^{0.14}$$

$$= 1.75(1.375)^{1/3}(85.7)^{1/3}\left(\frac{123.5}{62.5}\right)^{0.14} \qquad \textbf{(4.12-1)}$$

Solving, $h_a = 448.3$ W/m$^2 \cdot$ K.

By a heat balance, the value of q in W is as follows:

$$q = mc_{pm}(T_{bo} - T_{bi}) \qquad \textbf{(4.12-7)}$$

This is equated to Eq. (4.12-6) to obtain

$$q = mc_{pm}(T_{bo} - T_{bi}) = h_a(\pi DL)\Delta T_a \qquad \textbf{(4.12-8)}$$

The arithmetic mean temperature difference ΔT_a by Eq. (4.12-5) is

$$\Delta T_a = \frac{(T_w - T_{bi}) + (T_w - T_{bo})}{2}$$

$$= \frac{(93.3 - 37.8) + (93.3 - T_{bo})}{2} = 74.4 - 0.5T_{bo}$$

Substituting the known values in Eq. (4.12-8) and solving for T_{bo},

$$(7.56 \times 10^{-2})(2.093 \times 10^3)(T_{bo} - 37.8)$$

$$= 448.3(\pi \times 0.0254 \times 1.524)(74.4 - 0.5T_{bo})$$

$$T_{bo} = 54.1°C$$

This value of 54.1°C is close enough to the assumed value of 54.5°C that a second trial is not needed. Only the value of K_b would be affected. Known values can be substituted into Eq. (3.5-11) for the Reynolds number to show that it is less than 2100 and that the flow is laminar.

For less "viscous" non-Newtonian power-law fluids in laminar flow, natural convection may affect the heat-transfer rates. Metzner and Gluck (M2) recommend use of an empirical correction to Eq. (4.12-1) for horizontal tubes.

2. Turbulent flow in tubes. For turbulent flow of power-law fluids through tubes. Clapp (C4) presents the following empirical equation for heat transfer:

$$N_{\text{Nu}} = \frac{h_L D}{k} = 0.0041(N_{\text{Re,gen}})^{0.99}\left[\frac{K' c_p}{k}\left(\frac{8V}{D}\right)^{n-1}\right]^{0.4} \tag{4.12-9}$$

where $N_{\text{Re,gen}}$ is defined by Eq. (3.5-11) and h_L is the heat-transfer coefficient based on the log mean temperature driving force. The fluid properties are evaluated at the bulk mean temperature. Metzner and Friend (M3) also give equations for turbulent heat transfer.

4.12C Natural Convection

Acrivos (A1, S3) gives relationships for natural convection heat transfer to power-law fluids from various geometries of surfaces such as spheres, cylinders, and plates.

4.13 SPECIAL HEAT-TRANSFER COEFFICIENTS

4.13A Heat Transfer in Agitated Vessels

1. Introduction. Many chemical and biological processes are often carried out in agitated vessels. As discussed in Section 3.4, the liquids are generally agitated in cylindrical vessels with an impeller mounted on a shaft and driven by an electric motor. Typical agitators and vessel assemblies have been shown in Figs. 3.4-1 and 3.4-3. Often it is necessary to cool or heat the contents of the vessel during agitation. This is usually done by heat-transfer surfaces, which may be in the form of cooling or heating jackets in the wall of the vessel or coils of pipe immersed in the liquid.

2. Vessel with heating jacket. In Fig. 4.13-1a, a vessel with a cooling or heating jacket is shown. When heating, the fluid entering is often steam, which condenses inside the jacket and leaves at the bottom. The vessel is equipped with an agitator and in most cases also with baffles (not shown).

Correlations for the heat-transfer coefficient from the agitated Newtonian liquid inside the vessel to the jacket walls of the vessel have the following form:

$$\frac{h D_t}{k} = a\left(\frac{D_a^2 N\rho}{\mu}\right)^b \left(\frac{c_p \mu}{k}\right)^{1/3}\left(\frac{\mu}{\mu_w}\right)^m \tag{4.13-1}$$

where h is the heat-transfer coefficient for the agitated liquid to the inner wall in $\text{W/m}^2 \cdot \text{K}$, D_t is the inside diameter of the tank in m, k is thermal conductivity in $\text{W/m} \cdot \text{K}$, D_a is diameter of agitator in m, N is rotational speed in revolutions per sec, ρ is fluid density in kg/m^3, and μ is liquid viscosity in $\text{Pa} \cdot \text{s}$. All the liquid physical properties are evaluated at the bulk liquid temperature except μ_w, which is evaluated at the wall temperature T_w. Below are listed some available correlations and the Reynolds-number range ($N'_{\text{Re}} = D_a^2 N\rho/\mu$).

FIGURE 4.13-1. *Heat transfer in agitated vessels: (a) vessel with heating jacket, (b) vessel with heating coils.*

1. Paddle agitator with no baffles (C5, U1)

$$a = 0.36, \quad b = \tfrac{2}{3}, \quad m = 0.21, \quad N'_{Re} = 300 \text{ to } 3 \times 10^5$$

2. Flat-blade turbine agitator with no baffles (B4)

$$a = 0.54, \quad b = \tfrac{2}{3}, \quad m = 0.14, \quad N'_{Re} = 30 \text{ to } 3 \times 10^5$$

3. Flat-blade turbine agitator with baffles (B4, B5)

$$a = 0.74, \quad b = \tfrac{2}{3}, \quad m = 0.14, \quad N'_{Re} = 500 \text{ to } 3 \times 10^5$$

4. Anchor agitator with no baffles (U1)

$$a = 1.0, \quad b = \tfrac{1}{2}, \quad m = 0.18, \quad N'_{Re} = 10 \text{ to } 300$$

$$a = 0.36, \quad b = \tfrac{2}{3}, \quad m = 0.18, \quad N'_{Re} = 300 \text{ to } 4 \times 10^4$$

5. Helical-ribbon agitator with no baffles (G4)

$$a = 0.633, \quad b = \tfrac{1}{2}, \quad m = 0.18, \quad N'_{Re} = 8 \text{ to } 10^5$$

Some typical overall U values for jacketed vessels for various process applications are tabulated in Table 4.13-1.

EXAMPLE 4.13-1. Heat-Transfer Coefficient in Agitated Vessel with Jacket

A jacketed 1.83-m-diameter agitated vessel with baffles is being used to heat a liquid which is at 300 K. The agitator is 0.61 m in diameter and is a flat-blade turbine rotating at 100 rpm. Hot water is in the heating jacket. The wall surface temperature is constant at 355.4 K. The liquid has the following bulk physical properties: $\rho = 961$ kg/m^3, $c_p = 2500$ J/kg·K, $k = 0.173$ W/m·K, and $\mu = 1.00$

TABLE 4.13-1. *Typical Overall Heat-Transfer Coefficients in Jacketed Vessels*

Fluid in Jacket	Fluid in Vessel	Wall Material	Agitation	U btu $h \cdot ft^2 \cdot °F$	U W $m^2 \cdot K$	Ref.
Steam	Water	Copper	None	150	852	(P1)
			Simple stirring	250	1420	
Steam	Paste	Cast iron	Double scrapers	125	710	(P1)
Steam	Boiling water	Copper	None	250	1420	(P1)
Steam	Milk	Enameled cast iron	None	200	1135	(P1)
			Stirring	300	1700	
Hot water	Cold water	Enameled cast iron	None	70	398	(P1)
Steam	Tomato purée	Metal	Agitation	30	170	(C1)

Pa · s at 300 K and 0.084 Pa · s at 355.4 K. Calculate the heat-transfer coefficient to the wall of the jacket.

Solution: The following are given:

$$D_t = 1.83 \text{ m} \qquad D_a = 0.61 \text{ m} \qquad N = 100/60 \text{ rev/s}$$

$$\mu(300 \text{ K}) = 1.00 \text{ Pa} \cdot \text{s} = 1.00 \text{ kg/m} \cdot \text{s}$$

$$\mu_w(355.4 \text{ K}) = 0.084 \text{ Pa} \cdot \text{s} = 0.084 \text{ kg/m} \cdot \text{s}$$

First, calculating the Reynolds number at 300 K,

$$N'_{Re} = \frac{D_a^2 N \rho}{\mu} = \frac{(0.61)^2(100/60)(961)}{1.00} = 596$$

The Prandtl number is

$$N_{Pr} = \frac{C_p \mu}{k} = \frac{2500(1.00)}{0.173} = 14\,450$$

Using Eq. (4.13-1) with $a = 0.74$, $b = \frac{2}{3}$, and $m = 0.14$,

$$\frac{hD_t}{k} = 0.74(N'_{Re})^{2/3}(N_{Pr})^{1/3}\left(\frac{\mu}{\mu_w}\right)^{0.14} \tag{4.13-1}$$

Substituting and solving for h,

$$\frac{h(1.83)}{0.173} = 0.74(596)^{2/3}(14\,450)^{1/3}\left(\frac{1000}{84}\right)^{0.14}$$

$$h = 170.6 \text{ W/m}^2 \cdot \text{K} \, (30.0 \text{ btu/h} \cdot \text{ft}^2 \cdot °F)$$

A correlation to predict the heat-transfer coefficient of a power-law non-Newtonian fluid in a jacketed vessel with a turbine agitator is also available elsewhere (C6).

3. *Vessel with heating coils.* In Fig. 4.13-1b, an agitated vessel with a helical heating or cooling coil is shown. Correlations for the heat-transfer coefficient to the outside surface of the coils in agitated vessels are listed below for various types of agitators.

For a paddle agitator with no baffles (C5),

$$\frac{hD_t}{k} = 0.87 \left(\frac{D_a^2 N \rho}{\mu} \right)^{0.62} \left(\frac{c_p \mu}{k} \right)^{1/3} \left(\frac{\mu}{\mu_w} \right)^{0.14} \tag{4.13-2}$$

This holds for a Reynolds-number range of 300 to 4×10^5.

For a flat-blade turbine agitator with baffles, see (O1).

When the heating or cooling coil is in the form of vertical tube baffles with a flat-blade turbine, the following correlation can be used (D1):

$$\frac{hD_o}{k} = 0.09 \left(\frac{D_a^2 N \rho}{\mu} \right)^{0.65} \left(\frac{c_p \mu}{k} \right)^{1/3} \left(\frac{D_a}{D_t} \right)^{1/3} \left(\frac{2}{n_b} \right)^{0.2} \left(\frac{\mu}{\mu_f} \right)^{0.4} \tag{4.13-3}$$

where D_o is the outside diameter of the coil tube in m, n_b is the number of vertical baffle tubes, and μ_f is the viscosity at the mean film temperature.

Perry and Green (P3) give typical values of overall heat-transfer coefficients U for coils immersed in various liquids in agitated and nonagitated vessels.

4.13B Scraped-Surface Heat Exchangers

Liquid–solid suspensions, viscous aqueous and organic solutions, and numerous food products, such as margarine and orange juice concentrate, are often cooled or heated in a scraped-surface exchanger. This consists of a double-pipe heat exchanger with a jacketed cylinder containing steam or cooling liquid and an internal shaft rotating and fitted with wiper blades, as shown in Fig. 4.13-2.

The viscous liquid product flows at low velocity through the central tube between the rotating shaft and the inner pipe. The rotating scrapers or wiper blades continually scrape the surface of liquid, preventing localized overheating and giving rapid heat transfer. In some cases this device is also called a *votator heat exchanger.*

FIGURE 4.13-2. *Scraped-surface heat exchanger.*

Skelland et al. (S4) give the following equation to predict the inside heat-transfer coefficient for the votator:

$$\frac{hD}{k} = \alpha \left(\frac{c_p \mu}{k}\right)^\beta \left(\frac{(D - D_S)v\rho}{\mu}\right)^{1.0} \left(\frac{DN}{v}\right)^{0.62} \left(\frac{D_S}{D}\right)^{0.55} (n_B)^{0.53} \qquad \textbf{(4.13-4)}$$

$$\alpha = 0.014 \quad \beta = 0.96 \qquad \text{for viscous liquids}$$

$$\alpha = 0.039 \quad \beta = 0.70 \qquad \text{for nonviscous liquids}$$

where D = diameter of vessel in m, D_S = diameter of rotating shaft in m, v = axial flow velocity of liquid in m/s, N = agitator speed in rev/s, and n_B = number of blades on agitator. Data cover a region of axial flow velocities of 0.076 to 0.38 m/min and rotational speeds of 100 to 750 rpm.

Typical overall heat-transfer coefficients in food applications are $U = 1700$ W/m^2·K (300 btu/h·ft^2·F) for cooling margarine with NH$_3$, 2270 (400) for heating applesauce with steam, 1420 (250) for chilling shortening with NH$_3$, and 2270 (400) for cooling cream with water (B6).

4.13C Extended Surface or Finned Exchangers

1. Introduction. The use of fins or extended surfaces on the outside of a heat-exchanger pipe wall to give relatively high heat-transfer coefficients in the exchanger is quite common. An automobile radiator is such a device, where hot water passes inside through a bank of tubes and loses heat to the air. On the outside of the tubes, extended surfaces receive heat from the tube walls and transmit it to the air by forced convection.

Two common types of fins attached to the outside of a tube wall are shown in Fig. 4.13-3. In Fig. 4.13-3a there are a number of longitudinal fins spaced around the tube wall and the direction of gas flow is parallel to the axis of the tube. In Fig. 4.13-3b the gas flows normal to the tubes containing many circular or transverse fins.

Figure 4.13-3. *Two common types of fins on a section of circular tube:*
(a) longitudinal fin, (b) circular or transverse fin.

The qualitative effect of using extended surfaces can be shown approximately in Eq. (4.13-5) for a fluid inside a tube having a heat-transfer coefficient of h_i and an outside coefficient of h_o:

$$\frac{1}{U_i A_i} = \sum R \simeq \frac{1}{h_i A_i} + R_{\text{metal}} + \frac{1}{h_o A_o} \tag{4.13-5}$$

The resistance R_{metal} of the wall can often be neglected. The presence of the fins on the outside increases A_o and hence reduces the resistance $1/h_o A_o$ of the fluid on the outside of the tube. For example, if we have h_i for condensing steam, which is very large, and h_o for air outside the tube, which is quite small, increasing A_o greatly reduces $1/h_o A_o$. This in turn greatly reduces the total resistance, which increases the heat-transfer rate. If the positions of the two fluids are reversed, with air inside and steam outside, little increase in heat transfer could be obtained by using fins.

Equation (4.13-5) is only an approximation, since the temperature on the outside surface of the bare tube is not the same as that at the end of the fin because of the added resistance to heat flow by conduction from the fin tip to the base of the fin. Hence, a unit area of fin surface is not as efficient as a unit area of bare tube surface at the base of the fin. A fin efficiency η_f has been mathematically derived for various geometries of fins.

2. Derivation of equation for fin efficiency. We will consider a one-dimensional fin exposed to a surrounding fluid at temperature T_∞ as shown in Fig. 4.13-4. At the base of the fin the temperature is T_0 and at point x it is T. At steady state, the rate of heat conducted into the element at x is $q_{x|x}$ and is equal to the rate of heat conducted out plus the rate of heat lost by convection:

$$q_{x|x} = q_{x|x+\Delta x} + q_c \tag{4.13-6}$$

Substituting Fourier's equation for conduction and the convection equation,

$$-kA \left.\frac{dT}{dx}\right|_x = -kA \left.\frac{dT}{dx}\right|_{x+\Delta x} + h(P\,\Delta x)(T - T_\infty) \tag{4.13-7}$$

FIGURE 4.13-4. *Heat balance for one-dimensional conduction and convection in a rectangular fin with constant cross-sectional area.*

where A is the cross-sectional area of the fin in m^2, P the perimeter of the fin in m, and $(P \Delta x)$ the area for convection. Rearranging Eq. (4.13-7), dividing by Δx, and letting Δx approach zero,

$$\frac{d^2T}{dx^2} - \frac{hP}{kA}(T - T_\infty) = 0 \tag{4.13-8}$$

Letting $\theta = T - T_\infty$, Eq. (4.13-8) becomes

$$\frac{d^2\theta}{dx^2} = \frac{hP}{kA}\theta = 0 \tag{4.13-9}$$

The first boundary condition is that $\theta = \theta_0 = T_0 - T_\infty$ at $x = 0$. For the second boundary condition needed to integrate Eq. (4.13-9), several cases can be considered, depending upon the physical conditions at $x = L$. In the first case, the end of the fin is insulated and $d\theta/dx = 0$ at $x = L$. In the second case, the fin loses heat by convection from the tip surface, so that $-k(dT/dx)_L = h(T_L - T_\infty)$. The solution using the second case is quite involved and will not be considered here. Using the first case, where the tip is insulated, integration of Eq. (4.13-9) gives

$$\frac{\theta}{\theta_0} = \frac{\cosh[m(L - x)]}{\cosh mL} \tag{4.13-10}$$

where $m = (hP/kA)^{1/2}$.

The heat lost by the fin is expressed as

$$q = -kA \left.\frac{dT}{dx}\right|_{x=0} \tag{4.13-11}$$

Differentiating Eq. (4.13-10) with respect to x and combining it with Eq. (4.13-11),

$$q = (hPkA)^{1/2}(T_0 - T_\infty)\tanh mL \tag{4.13-12}$$

In the actual fin the temperature T in the fin decreases as the tip of the fin is approached. Hence, the rate of heat transfer per unit area decreases as the distance from the tube base is increased. To indicate this effectiveness of the fin in transferring heat, the fin efficiency η_f is defined as the ratio of the actual heat transferred from the fin to the heat transferred if the entire fin were at the base temperature T_0:

$$\eta_f = \frac{(hPkA)^{1/2}(T_0 - T_\infty)\tanh mL}{h(PL)(T_0 - T_\infty)} = \frac{\tanh mL}{mL} \tag{4.13-13}$$

where PL is the entire surface area of fin.

The expression for mL is

$$mL = \left(\frac{hP}{kA}\right)^{1/2} L = \left[\frac{h(2w + 2t)}{k(wt)}\right]^{1/2} L \tag{4.13-14}$$

For fins which are thin, $2t$ is small compared to $2w$, and

$$mL = \left(\frac{2h}{kt}\right)^{1/2} L \tag{4.13-15}$$

FIGURE 4.13-5. *Fin efficiency η_f for various fins: (a) longitudinal or straight fins, (b) circular or transverse fins. (See Fig. 4.13-3 for the dimensions of the fins.)*

Equation (4.13-15) holds for a fin with an insulated tip. This equation can be modified to hold for the case where the fin loses heat from its tip. This can be done by extending the length of the fin by $t/2$, where the corrected length L_c to use in Eqs. (4.13-13)–(4.13-15) is

$$L_c = L + \frac{t}{2} \tag{4.13-16}$$

The fin efficiency calculated from Eq. (4.13-13) for a longitudinal fin is shown in Fig. 4.13-5a. In Fig. 4.13-5b, the fin efficiency for a circular fin is presented. Note that the abscissa on the curves is $L_c(h/kt)^{1/2}$ and not $L_c(2h/kt)^{1/2}$ as in Eq. (4.13-15).

EXAMPLE 4.13.-2. Fin Efficiency and Heat Loss from Fin

A circular aluminum fin as shown in Fig. 4.13-3b ($k = 222$ W/m · K) is attached to a copper tube having an outside radius of 0.04 m. The length of the fin is 0.04 m and the thickness is 2 mm. The outside wall or tube base is at 523.2 K and the external surrounding air at 343.2 K has a convective coefficient of 30 W/m² · K. Calculate the fin efficiency and rate of heat loss from the fin.

Solution: The given data are $T_0 = 523.2$ K, $T_\infty = 343.2$ K, $L = 0.04$ m, $r_1 = 0.04$ m, $t = 0.002$ m, $k = 222$ W/m · K, $h = 30$ W/m² · K. By Eq. (4.13-16), $L_c = L + t/2 = 0.040 + 0.002/2 = 0.041$ m. Then,

$$L_c\left(\frac{h}{kt}\right)^{1/2} = (0.041)\left[\frac{30}{222(0.002)}\right]^{1/2} = 0.337$$

Also, $(L_c + r_1)/r_1 = (0.041 + 0.040)/0.040 = 2.025$. Using Fig. 4.13-5b, $\eta_f = 0.89$. The heat transfer from the fin itself is

$$q_f = \eta_f h A_f (T_0 - T_\infty) \tag{4.13-17}$$

where A_f is the outside surface area (annulus) of the fin and is given by the following for both sides of the fin:

$$A_f = 2\pi[(L_c + r_1)^2 - (r_1)^2] \quad \text{(circular fin)}$$

$$A_f = 2\pi(L_c x w) \quad \text{(longitudinal fin)} \tag{4.13-18}$$

Hence,

$$A_f = 2\pi[(0.041 + 0.040)^2 - (0.040)^2] = 3.118 \times 10^{-2} \, \text{m}^2$$

Substituting into Eq. (4.13-17),

$$q_f = 0.89(30)(3.118 \times 10^{-2})(523.2 - 343.2) = 149.9 \, \text{W}$$

3. Overall heat-transfer coefficient for finned tubes. We consider here the general case similar to Fig. 4.3-3b, where heat transfer occurs from a fluid inside a cylinder or tube, through the cylinder metal wall A of thickness Δx_A, and then to the fluid outside the tube, where the tube has fins on the outside. The heat is transferred through a series of resistances. The total heat q leaving the outside of the tube is the sum of heat loss by convection from the base of the bare tube q_t and the loss by convection from the fins, q_f:

$$q = q_t + q_f = h_o A_t (T_0 - T_\infty) + h_o A_f \eta_f (T_0 - T_\infty) \tag{4.13-19}$$

This can be written as a resistance since the paths are in parallel:

$$q = (h_o A_t + h_o A_f \eta_f)(T_1 - T_\infty) = \frac{T_0 - T_\infty}{\dfrac{1}{h_o(A_t + A_f \eta_f)}} = \frac{T_0 - T_\infty}{R} \tag{4.13-20}$$

where A_t is the area of the bare tube between the fins, A_f the area of the fins, and h_o the outside convective coefficient. The resistance in Eq. (4.3-20) can be substituted for the resistance $(1/h_o A_o)$ in Eq. (4.3-15) for a bare tube to give the overall equation for a finned tube exchanger:

$$q = \frac{T_4 - T_1}{1/h_i A_i + \Delta x_A / k_A A_{A\,\text{lm}} + 1/h_o(A_t + A_f \eta_f)} = \frac{T_4 - T_1}{\Sigma R} \tag{4.13-21}$$

where T_4 is the temperature of the fluid inside the tube and T_1 the outside fluid temperature. Writing Eq. (4.13-21) in the form of an overall heat-transfer coefficient U_i based on the inside area A_i, $q = U_i A_i(T_4 - T_1)$ and

$$U_i = \frac{1}{1/h_i + \Delta x_A A_i / k_A A_{A\,\text{lm}} + A_i / h_o(A_t + A_f \eta_f)} \tag{4.13-22}$$

The presence of fins on the outside of the tube changes the characteristics of the fluid flowing past the tube (either flowing parallel to the longitudinal finned tube or transverse to the circular finned tube). Hence, the correlations for fluid flow parallel to or transverse to bare tubes cannot be used to predict the outside convective coefficient h_o. Correlations are available in the literature (K4, M1, P1, P3) for heat transfer to various types of fins.

4.14 DIMENSIONAL ANALYSIS IN HEAT TRANSFER

4.14A Introduction

As seen in many of the correlations for fluid flow and heat transfer, many dimensionless groups, such as the Reynolds number and Prandtl number, occur in these correlations. Dimensional analysis is often used to group the variables in a given physical situation into dimensionless parameters or numbers which can be useful in experimentation and correlating data.

An important way of obtaining these dimensionless groups is to use dimensional analysis of differential equations as described in Section 3.11. Another useful method is the Buckingham method, in which the listing of the significant variables in the particular physical problem is done first. Then we determine the number of dimensionless parameters into which the variables may be combined.

4.14B Buckingham Method

1. Heat transfer inside a pipe. The Buckingham theorem, given in Section 3.11, states that the function relationship among q quantities or variables whose units may be given in terms of u fundamental units or dimensions may be written as $(q - u)$ dimensionless groups.

As an additional example to illustrate the use of this method, let us consider a fluid flowing in turbulent flow at velocity v inside a pipe of diameter D and undergoing heat transfer to the wall. We wish to predict the dimensionless groups relating the heat-transfer coefficient h to the variables D, ρ, μ, c_p, k, and v. The total number of variables is $q = 7$.

The fundamental units or dimensions are $u = 4$ and are mass M, length L, time t, and temperature T. The units of the variables in terms of these fundamental units are as follows:

$$h = \frac{M}{t^3 T} \qquad D = L \qquad \rho = \frac{M}{L^3} \qquad \mu = \frac{M}{Lt} \qquad c_p = \frac{L^2}{t^2 T} \qquad k = \frac{ML}{t^3 T} \qquad v = \frac{T}{t}$$

Hence, the number of dimensionless groups or π's can be assumed to be $7 - 4$, or 3. Then

$$\pi_1 = f(\pi_2, \pi_3) \tag{4.14-1}$$

We will choose the four variables D, k, μ, and v to be common to all the dimensionless groups. Then the three dimensionless groups are

$$\pi_1 = D^a k^b \mu^c v^d \rho \tag{4.14-2}$$

$$\pi_2 = D^e k^f \mu^g v^h c_p \tag{4.14-3}$$

$$\pi_3 = D^i k^j \mu^k v^l h \tag{4.14-4}$$

For π_1, substituting the actual dimensions,

$$M^0 L^0 t^0 T^0 = 1 = L^a \left(\frac{ML}{t^3 T}\right)^b \left(\frac{M}{LT}\right)^c \left(\frac{L}{T}\right)^d \left(\frac{M}{L^3}\right) \tag{4.14-5}$$

Summing for each exponent,

$$(L) \quad 0 = a + b - c + d - 3$$
$$(M) \quad 0 = b + c + 1$$
$$(t) \quad 0 = -3b - c - d \tag{4.14-6}$$
$$(T) \quad 0 = -b$$

Solving these equations simultaneously, $a = 1$, $b = 0$, $c = -1$, and $d = 1$.

Substituting these values into Eq. (4.14-2),

$$\pi_1 = \frac{Dv\rho}{\mu} = N_{Re} \tag{4.14-7}$$

Repeating for π_2 and π_3 and substituting the actual dimensions,

$$\pi_2 = \frac{c_p\mu}{k} = N_{Pr} \tag{4.14-8}$$

$$\pi_3 = \frac{hD}{k} = N_{Nu} \tag{4.14-9}$$

Substituting π_1, π_2, and π_3 into Eq. (4.14-1) and rearranging,

$$\frac{hD}{k} = f\left(\frac{Dv\rho}{\mu}, \frac{c_p\mu}{k}\right) \tag{4.14-10}$$

This is in the form of the familiar equation for heat transfer inside pipes, Eq. (4.5-8).

This type of analysis is useful in empirical correlations of heat-transfer data. The importance of each dimensionless group, however, must be determined by experimentation (B1, M1).

2. *Natural convection heat transfer outside a vertical plane.* In the case of natural convection heat transfer from a vertical plane wall of length L to an adjacent fluid, different dimensionless groups should be expected as compared to forced convection inside a pipe, since velocity is not a variable. The buoyant force due to the difference in density between the cold and the heated fluid should be a factor. As seen in Eqs. (4.7-1) and (4.7-2), the buoyant force depends upon the variables β, g, ρ, and ΔT. Hence, the list of variables to be considered and their fundamental units are as follows:

$$L = L \qquad \rho = \frac{M}{L^3} \qquad \mu = \frac{M}{Lt} \qquad c_p = \frac{L^2}{t^2 T} \qquad \beta = \frac{1}{T}$$

$$g = \frac{L}{t^2} \qquad \Delta T = T \qquad h = \frac{M}{t^3 T} \qquad k = \frac{ML}{t^3 T}$$

The number of variables is $q = 9$. Since $u = 4$, the number of dimensionless groups or π's is $9 - 4$, or 5. Then $\pi_1 = f(\pi_2, \pi_3, \pi_4, \pi_5)$.

We will choose the four variables L, μ, k, and g to be common to all the dimensionless groups:

$$\pi_1 = L^a\mu^b k^c g^d \rho \qquad \pi_2 = L^e\mu^f k^g g^h c_p \qquad \pi_3 = L^i\mu^j k^k g^l \beta$$

$$\pi_4 = L^m\mu^n k^o g^p \Delta T \qquad \pi_5 = L^q\mu^r k^s g^t h$$

For π_1, substituting the dimensions,

$$1 = L^a\left(\frac{M}{Lt}\right)^b\left(\frac{ML}{t^3 T}\right)^c\left(\frac{L}{t^2}\right)^d\left(\frac{M}{L^3}\right) \tag{4.14-11}$$

Solving for the exponents as before, $a = \frac{3}{2}$, $b = -1$, $c = 0$, and $d = \frac{1}{2}$. Then π_1 becomes

$$\pi_1 = \frac{L^{3/2}\rho g^{1/2}}{\mu} \qquad \text{(4.14-12)}$$

Taking the square of both sides to eliminate fractional exponents,

$$\pi_1 = \frac{L^3\rho^2 g}{\mu^2} \qquad \text{(4.14-13)}$$

Repeating for the other π equations,

$$\pi_1 = \frac{L^3\rho^2 g}{\mu^2} \qquad \pi_2 = \frac{c_p\mu}{k} = N_{Pr} \qquad \pi_3 = \frac{L\mu g\beta}{k}$$

$$\pi_4 = \frac{k\,\Delta T}{L\mu g} \qquad \pi_5 = \frac{hL}{k} = N_{Nu}$$

Combining the dimensionless groups π_1, π_3, and π_4 as follows,

$$\pi_1\pi_3\pi_4 = \frac{L^3\rho^2 g}{\mu^2}\frac{L\mu g\beta}{k}\frac{k\,\Delta T}{L\mu g} = \frac{L^3\rho^2 g\beta\,\Delta T}{\mu^2} = N_{Gr} \qquad \text{(4.14-14)}$$

Equation (4.14-14) is the Grashof group given in Eq. (4.7-4). Hence,

$$N_{Nu} = f(N_{Gr}, N_{Pr}) \qquad \text{(4.14-15)}$$

4.15 NUMERICAL METHODS FOR STEADY-STATE CONDUCTION IN TWO DIMENSIONS

4.15A Analytical Equation for Conduction

In Section 4.4 we discussed methods for solving two-dimensional heat-conduction problems using graphical procedures and shape factors. In this section we consider analytical and numerical methods.

The equation for conduction in the x direction is as follows:

$$q_x = -kA\frac{\partial T}{\partial x} \qquad \text{(4.15-1)}$$

Now we shall derive an equation for steady-state conduction in two directions x and y. Referring to Fig. 4.15-1, a rectangular block Δx by Δy by L is shown. The total heat input to the block is equal to the output:

$$q_{x|x} + q_{y|y} = q_{x|x+\Delta x} + q_{y|y+\Delta y} \qquad \text{(4.15-2)}$$

Now, from Eq. (4.15-1),

$$q_{x|x} = -k(\Delta yL)\frac{\partial T}{\partial x}\bigg|_x \qquad \text{(4.15-3)}$$

Writing similar equations for the other three terms and substituting into Eq. (4.15-2),

$$-k(\Delta yL)\frac{\partial T}{\partial x}\bigg|_x - k(\Delta xL)\frac{\partial T}{\partial y}\bigg|_y = -k(\Delta yL)\frac{\partial T}{\partial x}\bigg|_{x+\Delta x} - k(\Delta xL)\frac{\partial T}{\partial y}\bigg|_{y+\Delta y} \qquad \text{(4.15-4)}$$

FIGURE 4.15-1. *Steady-state conduction in two directions.*

FIGURE 4.15-2. *Steady-state heat conduction in two directions in a semi-infinite plate.*

Dividing through by $\Delta x \, \Delta y L$ and letting Δx and Δy approach zero, we obtain the final equation for steady-state conduction in two directions:

$$\frac{\partial^2 T}{\partial x^2} + \frac{\partial^2 T}{\partial y^2} = 0 \qquad \textbf{(4.15-5)}$$

This is called the *Laplace equation.*. There are a number of analytical methods for solving this equation. In the method of separation of variables, the final solution is expressed as an infinite Fourier series (H1, G2, K1). We consider the case shown in Fig. 4.15-2. The solid is called a semi-infinite solid since one of its dimensions is ∞. The two edges or boundaries at $x = 0$ and $x = L$ are held constant at T_1 K. The edge at $y = 0$ is held at T_2. And at $y = \infty$, $T = T_1$. The solution relating T to position y and x is

$$\frac{T - T_1}{T_2 - T_1} = \frac{4}{\pi}\left[\frac{1}{1}e^{-(\pi/L)y} \sin \frac{1\pi x}{L} + \frac{1}{3}e^{-(3\pi/L)y} \sin \frac{3\pi x}{L} + \cdots \right] \qquad \textbf{(4.15-6)}$$

Other analytical methods are available and are discussed in many texts (C2, H1, G2, K1). A large number of such analytical solutions have been given in the literature. However, there are many practical situations where the geometry or boundary conditions are too complex for analytical solutions, so that finite-difference numerical methods are used. These are discussed in the next section.

4.15B Finite-Difference Numerical Methods

1. Derivation of the method. Since the advent of fast digital computers, solutions to many complex two-dimensional heat-conduction problems by numerical methods are readily possible. In deriving the equations we can start with the partial differential equation (4.15-5). Setting up the finite difference of $\partial^2 T/\partial x^2$,

$$\frac{\partial^2 T}{\partial x^2} = \frac{\partial(\partial T/\partial x)}{\partial x} = \frac{\dfrac{T_{n+1,m} - T_{n,m}}{\Delta x} - \dfrac{T_{n,m} - T_{n-1,m}}{\Delta x}}{\Delta x}$$

$$= \frac{T_{n+1,m} - 2T_{n,m} + T_{n-1,m}}{(\Delta x)^2} \tag{4.15-7}$$

where the index m stands for a given value of y, $m + 1$ stands for $y + 1\ \Delta y$, and n is the index indicating the position of T on the x scale. This is shown in Fig. 4.15-3. The two-dimensional solid is divided into squares. The solid inside a square is imagined to be concentrated at the center of the square, and this concentrated mass is a "node." Each node is imagined to be connected to the adjacent nodes by a small conducting rod as shown.

The finite difference of $\partial^2 T/\partial y^2$ is written in a similar manner:

$$\frac{\partial^2 T}{\partial y^2} = \frac{T_{n,m+1} - 2T_{n,m} + T_{n,m-1}}{(\Delta y^2)} \tag{4.15-8}$$

Substituting Eqs. (4.15-7) and (4.15-8) into Eq. (4.15-5) and setting $\Delta x = \Delta y$,

$$T_{n,m+1} + T_{n,m-1} + T_{n+1,m} + T_{n-1,m} - 4T_{n,m} = 0 \tag{4.15-9}$$

This equation states that the net heat flow into any point or node is zero at steady state. The shaded area in Fig. 4.15-3 represents the area on which the heat balance was made. Alternatively, Eq. (4.15-9) can be derived by making a heat balance on this shaded area. The total heat in for unit thickness is

$$\frac{k\ \Delta y}{\Delta x}(T_{n-1,m} - T_{n,m}) + \frac{k\ \Delta y}{\Delta x}(T_{n+1,m} - T_{n,m})$$

$$+ \frac{k\ \Delta x}{\Delta y}(T_{n,m+1} - T_{n,m}) + \frac{k\ \Delta x}{\Delta y}(T_{n,m-1} - T_{n,m}) = 0 \tag{4.15-10}$$

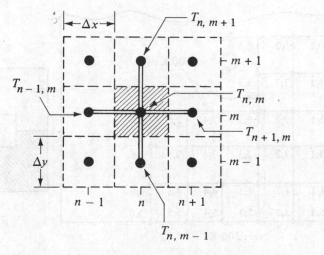

FIGURE 4.15-3. *Temperatures and arrangement of nodes for two-dimensional steady-state heat conduction.*

Rearranging, this becomes Eq. (4.15-9). In Fig. 4.15-3 the rods connecting the nodes act as fictitious heat-conducting rods.

To use the numerical method, Eq. (4.15-9) is written for each node or point. Hence, for N unknown nodes, N linear algebraic equations must be written and the system of equations solved for the various node temperatures. For a hand calculation using a modest number of nodes, the iteration method can be used to solve the system of equations.

2. Iteration method of solution. In using the iteration method, the right-hand side of Eq. (4.15-9) is set equal to a residual $\bar{q}_{n,m}$:

$$\bar{q}_{n,m} = T_{n-1,m} + T_{n+1,m} + T_{n,m+1} + T_{n,m-1} - 4T_{n,m} \tag{4.15-11}$$

Since $\bar{q}_{n,m} = 0$ at steady state, solving for $T_{n,m}$ in Eq. (4.15-11) or (4.15-9),

$$T_{n,m} = \frac{T_{n-1,m} + T_{n+1,m} + T_{n,m+1} + T_{n,m-1}}{4} \tag{4.15-12}$$

Equations (4.15-11) and (4.15-12) are the final equations to be used. Their use is illustrated in the following example.

EXAMPLE 4.15-1. Steady-State Heat Conduction in Two Directions
Figure 4.15-4 shows a cross section of a hollow rectangular chamber with inside dimensions 4×2 m and outside dimensions 8×8 m. The chamber is 20 m long. The inside walls are held at 600 K and the outside at 300 K. The k is 1.5 W/m·K. For steady-state conditions find the heat loss per unit chamber length. Use grids 1×1 m.

Solution: Since the chamber is symmetrical, one-fourth of the chamber (shaded part) will be used. Preliminary estimates will be made for the first approximation: $T_{1,2} = 450$ K, $T_{2,2} = 400$, $T_{3,2} = 400$, $T_{3,3} = 400$, $T_{3,4} = 450$,

FIGURE 4.15-4. *Square grid pattern for Example 4.15-1.*

$T_{3,5} = 500$, $T_{4,2} = 325$, $T_{4,3} = 350$, $T_{4,4} = 375$, and $T_{4,5} = 400$. Note that $T_{0,2} = T_{2,2}$, $T_{3,6} = T_{3,4}$, and $T_{4,6} = T_{4,4}$ by symmetry.

To start the calculation, one can select any interior point, but it is usually better to start near a boundary. Using $T_{1,2}$, we calculate the residual $\bar{q}_{1,2}$ by Eq. (4.15-11):

$$\bar{q}_{1,2} = T_{1,1} + T_{1,3} + T_{0,2} + T_{2,2} - 4T_{1,2}$$

$$= 300 + 600 + 400 + 400 - 4(450) = -100$$

Hence, $T_{1,2}$ is not at steady state. Next, we set $\bar{q}_{1,2}$ to 0 and calculate a new value of $T_{1,2}$ by Eq. (4.15-12):

$$T_{1,2} = \frac{T_{1,1} + T_{1,3} + T_{0,2} + T_{2,2}}{4} = \frac{300 + 600 + 400 + 400}{4} = 425$$

This new value of $T_{1,2}$ of 425 K will replace the old one of 450 and be used to calculate the other nodes. Next,

$$\bar{q}_{2,2} = T_{2,1} + T_{2,3} + T_{1,2} + T_{3,2} - 4T_{2,2}$$

$$= 300 + 600 + 425 + 400 - 4(400) = 125$$

Setting $\bar{q}_{2,2}$ to zero and using Eq. (4.15-12),

$$T_{2,2} = \frac{T_{2,1} + T_{2,3} + T_{1,2} + T_{3,2}}{4} = \frac{300 + 600 + 425 + 400}{4} = 431$$

Continuing for all the rest of the interior nodes,

$$\bar{q}_{3,2} = 300 + 400 + 431 + 325 - 4(400) = -144$$

Using Eq. (4.15-12), $T_{3,2} = 364$,

$$\bar{q}_{3,3} = 364 + 450 + 600 + 350 - 4(400) = 164$$

$$T_{3,3} = 441$$

$$\bar{q}_{3,4} = 441 + 500 + 600 + 375 - 4(450) = 116$$

$$T_{3,4} = 479$$

$$\bar{q}_{3,5} = 479 + 479 + 600 + 400 - 4(500) = -42$$

$$T_{3,5} = 489$$

$$\bar{q}_{4,2} = 300 + 350 + 364 + 300 - 4(325) = 14$$

$$T_{4,2} = 329$$

$$\bar{q}_{4,3} = 329 + 375 + 441 + 300 - 4(350) = 45$$

$$T_{4,3} = 361$$

$$\bar{q}_{4,4} = 361 + 400 + 479 + 300 - 4(375) = 40$$

$$T_{4,4} = 385$$

$$\bar{q}_{4,5} = 385 + 385 + 489 + 399 - 4(400) = -41$$

$$T_{4,5} = 390$$

Having completed one sweep across the grid map, we can start a second approximation, using, of course, the new values calculated. We can start again with $T_{1,2}$ or we can select the node with the largest residual. Starting with $T_{1,2}$ again,

$$\bar{q}_{1,2} = 300 + 600 + 431 + 431 - 4(425) = 62$$

$$T_{1,2} = 440$$

$$\bar{q}_{2,2} = 300 + 600 + 440 + 364 - 4(431) = -20$$

$$T_{2,2} = 426$$

This is continued until the residuals are as small as desired. The final values are as follows:

$$T_{1,2} = 441, \quad T_{2,2} = 432, \quad T_{3,2} = 384, \quad T_{3,3} = 461, \quad T_{3,4} = 485,$$

$$T_{3,5} = 490, \quad T_{4,2} = 340, \quad T_{4,3} = 372, \quad T_{4,4} = 387, \quad T_{4,5} = 391$$

To calculate the total heat loss from the chamber per unit chamber length, we use Fig. 4.15-5. For nodes $T_{2,4}$ to $T_{3,4}$ with $\Delta x = \Delta y$ and 1 m deep,

$$q = \frac{kA\,\Delta T}{\Delta x} = \frac{k[\Delta x(1)]}{\Delta x}(T_{2,4} - T_{3,4}) = k(T_{2,4} - T_{3,4}) \qquad \textbf{(4.15-13)}$$

The heat flux for nodes $T_{2,5}$ to $T_{3,5}$ and for $T_{1,3}$ to $T_{1,2}$ should be multiplied by $\frac{1}{2}$ because of symmetry. The total heat conducted is the sum of the five paths for one-fourth of the solid. For four duplicate parts,

$$q_{\mathrm{I}} = 4k\left[\tfrac{1}{2}(T_{1,3} - T_{1,2}) + (T_{2,3} - T_{2,2}) + (T_{2,3} - T_{3,3})\right.$$
$$\left. + (T_{2,4} - T_{3,4}) + \tfrac{1}{2}(T_{2,5} - T_{3,5})\right] \qquad \textbf{(4.15-14)}$$
$$= 4(1.5)\left[\tfrac{1}{2}(600 - 441) + (600 - 432) + (600 - 461)\right.$$
$$\left. + (600 - 485) + \tfrac{1}{2}(600 - 490)\right]$$
$$= 3340 \text{ W per } 1.0 \text{ m deep}$$

Also, the total heat conducted can be calculated using the nodes at the outside, as shown in Fig. 4.15-5. This gives $q_{\mathrm{II}} = 3430$ W. The average value is

$$q_{\mathrm{av}} = \frac{3340 + 3430}{2} = 3385 \text{ W per } 1.0 \text{ m deep}$$

If a larger number of nodes, that is, a smaller grid size, is used, a more accurate solution can be obtained. Using a grid size of 0.5 m instead of 1.0 m for Example 4.15-1, a q_{av} of 3250 W is obtained. If a very fine grid is used, more accuracy can be obtained, but a digital computer would be needed for the large number of calculations. Matrix methods are also available for solving a set of simultaneous equations on a computer. The iteration method used here is often called the Gauss–Seidel method. The simplest and most convenient method is to use a spreadsheet calculation with a computer. This avoids the complication of using complex matrix methods and so forth.

3. Equations for other boundary conditions. In Example 4.15-1 the conditions at the boundaries were such that the node points were known and constant. For the case where there is

     Chapter 4   Principles of Steady-State Heat Transfer

FIGURE 4.15-5. *Drawing for calculation of total heat conduction.*

convection at the boundary to a constant temperature T_∞, a heat balance on the node n, m in Fig. 4.15-6a is as follows, where heat in = heat out (K1):

$$\frac{k \, \Delta y}{\Delta x}(T_{n-1,m} - T_{n,m}) + \frac{k \, \Delta x}{2 \, \Delta y}(T_{n,m+1} - T_{n,m})$$

$$+ \frac{k \, \Delta x}{2 \, \Delta y}(T_{n,m-1} - T_{n,m}) = h \, \Delta y(T_{n,m} - T_\infty) \qquad \textbf{(4.15-15)}$$

FIGURE 4.15-6. *Other types of boundary conditions: (a) convection at a boundary, (b) insulated boundary, (c) exterior corner with convective boundary, (d) interior corner with convective boundary.*

Setting $\Delta x = \Delta y$, rearranging, and setting the resultant equation $= \bar{q}_{n,m}$ residual, the following results:

(a) For convection at a boundary,

$$\frac{h\,\Delta x}{k}T_\infty + \tfrac{1}{2}(2T_{n-1,m} + T_{n,m+1} + T_{n,m-1}) - T_{n,m}\left(\frac{h\,\Delta x}{k} + 2\right) = \bar{q}_{n,m} \quad \textbf{(4.15-16)}$$

In a similar manner, for the cases in Fig. 4.15-6:

(b) For an insulated boundary,

$$\tfrac{1}{2}(T_{n,m+1} + T_{n,m-1}) + T_{n-1,m} - 2T_{n,m} = \bar{q}_{n,m} \quad \textbf{(4.15-17)}$$

(c) For an exterior corner with convection at the boundary,

$$\frac{h\,\Delta x}{k}T_\infty + \tfrac{1}{2}(T_{n-1,m} + T_{n,m-1}) - \left(\frac{h\,\Delta x}{k} + 1\right)T_{n,m} = \bar{q}_{n,m} \quad \textbf{(4.15-18)}$$

(d) For an interior corner with convection at the boundary,

$$\frac{h\,\Delta x}{k}T_\infty + T_{n-1,m} + T_{n,m+1} + \tfrac{1}{2}(T_{n+1,m} + T_{n,m-1}) - \left(3 + \frac{h\,\Delta x}{k}\right)T_{n,m} = \bar{q}_{n,m}$$

$$\textbf{(4.15-19)}$$

For curved boundaries and other types of boundaries, see (C3, K1). To use Eqs. (4.15-16)–(4.15-19), the residual $\bar{q}_{n,m}$ is first obtained using the proper equation. Then $\bar{q}_{n,m}$ is set equal to zero and $T_{n,m}$ solved for in the resultant equation.

PROBLEMS

4.1-1. *Insulation in a Cold Room.* Calculate the heat loss per m² of surface area for a temporary insulating wall of a food cold storage room where the outside temperature is 299.9 K and the inside temperature 276.5 K. The wall is composed of 25.4 mm of corkboard having a k of 0.0433 W/m · K.

Ans. 39.9 W/m²

4.1-2. *Determination of Thermal Conductivity.* In determining the thermal conductivity of an insulating material, the temperatures were measured on both sides of a flat slab of 25 mm of the material and were 318.4 and 303.2 K. The heat flux was measured as 35.1 W/m². Calculate the thermal conductivity in btu/h · ft · °F and in W/m · K.

4.2-1. *Mean Thermal Conductivity in a Cylinder.* Prove that if the thermal conductivity varies linearly with temperature as in Eq. (4.1-11), the proper mean value k_m to use in the cylindrical equation is given by Eq. (4.2-3) as in a slab.

4.2-2. *Heat Removal of a Cooling Coil.* A cooling coil of 1.0 ft of 304 stainless-steel tubing having an inside diameter of 0.25 in. and an outside diameter of 0.40 in. is being used to remove heat from a bath. The temperature at the inside surface of the tube is 40°F and is 80°F on the outside. The thermal conductivity of 304 stainless steel is a function of temperature:

$$k = 7.75 + 7.78 \times 10^{-3}T$$

where k is in btu/h · ft · °F and T is in °F. Calculate the heat removal in btu/s and watts.

Ans. 1.225 btu/s, 1292 W

4.2-3. *Removal of Heat from a Bath.* Repeat Problem 4.2-2 but for a cooling coil made of 308 stainless steel having an average thermal conductivity of 15.23 W/m · K.

4.2-4. *Variation of Thermal Conductivity.* A flat plane of thickness Δx has one surface maintained at T_1 and the other at T_2. If the thermal conductivity varies according to temperature as

$$k = A + bT + cT^3$$

where a, b, and c are constants, derive an expression for the one-dimensional heat flux q/A.

4.2-5. *Temperature Distribution in a Hollow Sphere.* Derive Eq. (4.2-14) for the steady-state conduction of heat in a hollow sphere. Also, derive an equation which shows that the temperature varies hyperbolically with the radius r.

$$\textbf{Ans.} \quad \frac{T - T_1}{T_2 - T_1} = \frac{r_2}{r_2 - r_1}\left(1 - \frac{r_1}{r}\right)$$

4.3-1. *Insulation Needed for Food Cold Storage Room.* A food cold storage room is to be constructed of an inner layer of 19.1 mm of pine wood, a middle layer of cork board, and an outer layer of 50.8 mm of concrete. The inside wall surface temperature is $-17.8°C$ and the outside surface temperature is $29.4°C$ at the outer concrete surface. The mean conductivities are for pine, 0.151; cork, 0.0433; and concrete, 0.762 W/m · K. The total inside surface area of the room to use in the calculation is approximately 39 m^2 (neglecting corner and end effects). What thickness of cork board is needed to keep the heat loss to 586 W?

Ans. 0.128 m thickness

4.3-2. *Insulation of a Furnace.* A wall of a furnace 0.244 m thick is constructed of material having a thermal conductivity of 1.30 W/m · K. The wall will be insulated on the outside with material having an average k of 0.346 W/m · K, so the heat loss from the furnace will be equal to or less than 1830 W/m^2. The inner surface temperature is 1588 K and the outer 299 K. Calculate the thickness of insulation required.

Ans. 0.179 m

4.3-3. *Heat Loss Through Thermopane Double Window.* A double window called thermopane is one in which two layers of glass are separated by a layer of dry, stagnant air. In a given window, each of the glass layers is 6.35 mm thick separated by a 6.35-mm space of stagnant air. The thermal conductivity of the glass is 0.869 W/m · K and that of air is 0.026 over the temperature range used. For a temperature drop of 27.8 K over the system, calculate the heat loss for a window 0.914 m × 1.83 m. (*Note:* This calculation neglects the effect of the convective coefficient on one outside surface of one side of the window, the convective coefficient on the other outside surface, and convection inside the window.)

4.3-4. *Heat Loss from Steam Pipeline.* A steel pipeline, 2-in. schedule 40 pipe, contains saturated steam at 121.1°C. The line is covered with 25.4 mm of insulation. Assuming that the inside surface temperature of the metal wall is at 121.1°C and the outer surface of the insulation is at 26.7°C, calculate the heat loss for 30.5 m of pipe. Also, calculate the kg of steam condensed per hour in the pipe due to the heat loss. The average k for steel from Appendix A.3 is 45 W/m · K and the k for the insulation is 0.182.

Ans. 5384 W, 8.81 kg steam/h

4.3-5. *Heat Loss with Trial-and-Error Solution.* The exhaust duct from a heater has an inside diameter of 114.3 mm with ceramic walls 6.4 mm thick. The average $k = 1.52$ W/m · K. Outside this wall, an insulation of rock wool 102 mm thick is installed. The thermal conductivity of the rock wool is $k = 0.046 + 1.56 \times 10^{-4} \, T°C \, (W/m \cdot K)$. The inside surface temperature of the ceramic is $T_1 = 588.7$ K, and the outside surface temperature of the insulation is $T_3 = 311$ K. Calculate the heat loss for 1.5 m of duct and the interface temperature T_2 between the ceramic and the insulation. [Hint: The correct value of k_m for the insulation is that evaluated at the mean temperature of $(T_2 + T_3)/2$. Hence, for the first trial assume a mean temperature of, say, 448 K. Then calculate the heat loss and T_2. Using this new T_2, calculate a new mean temperature and proceed as before.]

4.3-6. Heat Loss by Convection and Conduction. A glass window with an area of 0.557 m^2 is installed in the wooden outside wall of a room. The wall dimensions are 2.44 × 3.05 m. The wood has a k of 0.1505 W/m · K and is 25.4 mm thick. The glass is 3.18 mm thick and has a k of 0.692. The inside room temperature is 299.9 K (26.7°C) and the outside air temperature is 266.5 K. The convection coefficient h_i on the inside wall of the glass and the wood is estimated as 8.5 W/m^2 · K; the outside h_o is also estimated as 8.5 for both surfaces. Calculate the heat loss through the wooden wall, through the glass, and the total.

Ans. 569.2 W (wood) (1942 btu/h), 77.6 W (glass) (265 btu/h),
646.8 W (total) (2207 btu/h)

4.3-7. Convection, Conduction, and Overall U. A gas at 450 K is flowing inside a 2-in. steel pipe, schedule 40. The pipe is insulated with 51 mm of lagging having a mean $k = 0.0623$ W/m · K. The convective heat-transfer coefficient of the gas inside the pipe is 30.7 W/m^2 · K and the convective coefficient on the outside of the lagging is 10.8. The air is at a temperature of 300 K.
(a) Calculate the heat loss per unit length of 1 m of pipe using resistances.
(b) Repeat, using the overall U_o based on the outside area A_o.

4.3-8. Heat Transfer in Steam Heater. Water at an average of 70°F is flowing in a 2-in. steel pipe, schedule 40. Steam at 220°F is condensing on the outside of the pipe. The convective coefficient for the water inside the pipe is $h = 500$ btu/h · ft^2 · °F and the condensing steam coefficient on the outside is $h = 1500$.
(a) Calculate the heat loss per unit length of 1 ft of pipe using resistances.
(b) Repeat, using the overall U_i based on the inside area A_i.
(c) Repeat, using U_o.

Ans. (a) $q = 26\,710$ btu/h (7.828 kW), (b) $U_i = 329.1$ btu/h · ft^2 · °F
(1869 W/m^2 · K), (c) $U_o = 286.4$ btu/h · ft^2 · °F (1626 W/m^2 · K)

4.3-9. Heat Loss from Temperature Measurements. A steel pipe carrying steam has an outside diameter of 89 mm. It is lagged with 76 mm of insulation having an average $k = 0.043$ W/m · K. Two thermocouples, one located at the interface between the pipe wall and the insulation and the other at the outer surface of the insulation, give temperatures of 115°C and 32°C, respectively. Calculate the heat loss in W per m of pipe.

4.3-10. Effect of Convective Coefficients on Heat Loss in Double Window. Repeat Problem 4.3-3 for heat loss in the double window. However, include a convective coefficient of $h = 11.35$ W/m^2 · K on one outside surface of one side of the window and an h of 11.35 on the other outside surface. Also calculate the overall U.

Ans. $q = 106.7$ W, $U = 2.29$ W/m^2 · K

4.3-11. Uniform Chemical Heat Generation. Heat is being generated uniformly by a chemical reaction in a long cylinder of radius 91.4 mm. The generation rate is constant at 46.6 W/m^3. The walls of the cylinder are cooled so that the wall temperature is held at

311.0 K. The thermal conductivity is 0.865 W/m · K. Calculate the center-line temperature at steady state.

Ans. $T_o = 311.112$ K

4.3-12. Heat of Respiration of a Food Product. A fresh food product is held in cold storage at 278.0 K. It is packed in a container in the shape of a flat slab with all faces insulated except for the top flat surface, which is exposed to the air at 278.0 K. For estimation purposes the surface temperature will be assumed to be 278 K. The slab is 152.4 mm thick and the exposed surface area is 0.186 m^2. The density of the foodstuff is 641 kg/m^3. The heat of respiration is 0.070 kJ/kg · h and the thermal conductivity is 0.346 W/m · K. Calculate the maximum temperature in the food product at steady state and the total heat given off in W. (*Note:* It is assumed in this problem that there is no air circulation inside the foodstuff. Hence, the results will be conservative, since circulation during respiration will reduce the temperature.)

Ans.   278.42 K, 0.353 W (1.22 btu/h)

4.3-13. Temperature Rise in Heating Wire. A current of 250 A is passing through a stainless-steel wire having a diameter of 5.08 mm. The wire is 2.44 m long and has a resistance of 0.0843 Ω. The outer surface is held constant at 427.6 K. The thermal conductivity is $k = 22.5$ W/m · K. Calculate the center-line temperature at steady state.

4.3-14. Critical Radius for Insulation. A metal steam pipe having an outside diameter of 30 mm has a surface temperature of 400 K and is to be insulated with an insulation having a thickness of 20 mm and a k of 0.08 W/m · K. The pipe is exposed to air at 300 K and a convection coefficient of 30 W/m^2 · K.
(a) Calculate the critical radius and the heat loss per m of length for the bare pipe.
(b) Calculate the heat loss for the insulated pipe assuming that the surface temperature of the pipe remains constant.

Ans.   (b) $q = 54.4$ W

4.4-1. Curvilinear-Squares Graphical Method. Repeat Example 4.4-1 but with the following changes:
(a) Select the number of equal temperature subdivisions between the isothermal boundaries to be five instead of four. Draw in the curvilinear squares and determine the total heat flux. Also calculate the shape factor S. Label each isotherm with the actual temperature.
(b) Repeat part (a), but in this case the thermal conductivity is not constant but $k = 0.85 (1 + 0.00040T)$, where T is temperature in K. [*Note:* To calculate the overall q, the mean value of k at the mean temperature is used. The spacing of the isotherms is independent of how k varies with T (M1). However, the temperatures corresponding to the individual isotherms are a function of how the value of k depends upon T. Write the equation for q' for a given curvilinear section using the mean value of k over the temperature interval. Equate this to the overall value of q divided by M or q/M. Then solve for the isotherm temperature.]

4.4-2. Heat Loss from a Furnace. A rectangular furnace with inside dimensions of $1.0 \times 1.0 \times 2.0$ m has a wall thickness of 0.20 m. The k of the walls is 0.95 W/m · K. The inside of the furnace is held at 800 K and the outside at 350 K. Calculate the total heat loss from the furnace.

Ans. $q = 25\ 171$ W

4.4-3. *Heat Loss from a Buried Pipe.* A water pipe whose wall temperature is 300 K has a diameter of 150 mm and a length of 10 m. It is buried horizontally in the ground at a depth of 0.40 m measured to the center line of the pipe. The ground surface temperature is 280 K and $k = 0.85$ W/m · K. Calculate the loss of heat from the pipe.

Ans. $q = 451.2$ W

4.5-1. *Heating Air by Condensing Steam.* Air is flowing through a tube having an inside diameter of 38.1 mm at a velocity of 6.71 m/s, average temperature of 449.9 K, and pressure of 138 kPa. The inside wall temperature is held constant at 204.4°C (477.6 K) by steam condensing outside the tube wall. Calculate the heat-transfer coefficient for a long tube and the heat-transfer flux.

Ans. $h = 39.38$ W/m^2 · K (6.94 btu/h · ft^2 · °F)

4.5-2. *Trial-and-Error Solution for Heating Water.* Water is flowing inside a horizontal $1\frac{1}{4}$-in. schedule 40 steel pipe at 37.8°C and a velocity of 1.52 m/s. Steam at 108.3°C is condensing on the outside of the pipe wall and the steam coefficient is assumed constant at 9100 W/m^2 · K.

(a) Calculate the convective coefficient h_i for the water. (Note that this is trial and error. A wall temperature on the inside must be assumed first.)
(b) Calculate the overall coefficient U_i based on the inside area and the heat-transfer flux q/A_i in W/m^2.

4.5-3. *Heat-Transfer Area and Use of Log Mean Temperature Difference.* A reaction mixture having a $c_{pm} = 2.85$ kJ/kg · K is flowing at a rate of 7260 kg/h and is to be cooled from 377.6 K to 344.3 K. Cooling water at 288.8 K is available and the flow rate is 4536 kg/h. The overall U_o is 653 W/m^2 · K.

(a) For counterflow, calculate the outlet water temperature and the area A_o of the exchanger.
(b) Repeat for cocurrent flow.

Ans. (a) $T_1 = 325.2$ K, $A_o = 5.43$ m^2; (b) $A_o = 6.46$ m^2

4.5-4. *Heating Water with Hot Gases and Heat-Transfer Area.* Water flowing at the rate of 13.85 kg/s is to be heated from 54.5 to 87.8°C in a heat exchanger by 54 430 kg/h of hot gas flowing counterflow and entering at 427°C ($c_{pm} = 1.005$ kJ/kg · K). The overall $U_o = 69.1$ W/m^2 · K. Calculate the exit-gas temperature and the heat-transfer area.

Ans. $T = 299.5$°C

4.5-5. *Cooling Oil and Overall U.* Oil flowing at the rate of 7258 kg/h with a $c_{pm} = 2.01$ kJ/kg · K is cooled from 394.3 K to 338.9 K in a counterflow heat exchanger by water entering at 294.3 K and leaving at 305.4 K. Calculate the flow rate of the water and the overall U_i if the A_i is 5.11 m^2.

Ans. 17 420 kg/h, $U_i = 686$ W/m^2 · K

4.5-6. *Laminar Flow and Heating of Oil.* A hydrocarbon oil having the same physical properties as the oil in Example 4.5-5 enters at 175°F inside a pipe having an inside diameter of 0.0303 ft and a length of 15 ft. The inside pipe surface temperature is constant at 325°F. The oil is to be heated to 250°F in the pipe. How many lb$_m$/h oil can be heated? (*Hint:* This solution is trial and error. One method is to assume a flow rate of, say, $m = 75$ lb mass/h. Calculate the N_{Re} and the value of h_a. Then make a heat balance to solve for q in terms of m. Equate this q to the q from the equation $q = h_a A \Delta T_a$. Solve for m. This is the new m to use for the second trial.)

Ans. $m = 84.2$ lb$_m$/h (38.2 kg/h)

4.5-7. *Heating Air by Condensing Steam.* Air at a pressure of 101.3 kPa and 288.8 K enters inside a tube having an inside diameter of 12.7 mm and a length of 1.52 m with a velocity of 24.4 m/s. Condensing steam on the outside of the tube maintains the inside wall temperature at 372.1 K. Calculate the convection coefficient of the air. (*Note:* This solution is trial and error. First assume an outlet temperature of the air.)

4.5-8. *Heat Transfer with a Liquid Metal.* The liquid metal bismuth at a flow rate of 2.00 kg/s enters a tube having an inside diameter of 35 mm at 425°C and is heated to 430°C in the tube. The tube wall is maintained at a temperature of 25°C above the liquid bulk temperature. Calculate the tube length required. The physical properties are as follows (H1): $k = 15.6$ W/m·K, $c_p = 149$ J/kg·K, $\mu = 1.34 \times 10^{-3}$ Pa·s.

4.6-1. *Heat Transfer from a Flat Plate.* Air at a pressure of 101.3 kPa and a temperature of 288.8 K is flowing over a thin, smooth, flat plate at 3.05 m/s. The plate length in the direction of flow is 0.305 m and its temperature is 333.2 K. Calculate the heat-transfer coefficient assuming laminar flow.

Ans. $h = 12.35$ W/m^2·K (2.18 btu/h·ft^2·°F)

4.6-2. *Chilling Frozen Meat.* Cold air at -28.9°C and 1 atm is recirculated at a velocity of 0.61 m/s over the exposed top flat surface of a piece of frozen meat. The sides and bottom of this rectangular slab of meat are insulated and the top surface is 254 mm by 254 mm square. If the surface of the meat is at -6.7°C, predict the average heat-transfer coefficient to the surface. As an approximation, assume that either Eq. (4.6-2) or (4.6-3) can be used, depending on the $N_{Re,L}$.

Ans. $h = 6.05$ W/m^2·K

4.6-3. *Heat Transfer to an Apple.* It is desired to predict the heat-transfer coefficient for air being blown past an apple lying on a screen with large openings. The air velocity is 0.61 m/s at 101.32 kPa pressure and 316.5 K. The surface of the apple is at 277.6 K and its average diameter is 114 mm. Assume that it is a sphere.

4.6-4. *Heating Air by a Steam Heater.* A total of 13 610 kg/h of air at 1 atm abs pressure and 15.6°C is to be heated by passing over a bank of tubes in which steam at 100°C is condensing. The tubes are 12.7 mm OD, 0.61 m long, and arranged in-line in a square pattern with $S_p = S_n = 19.05$ mm. The bank of tubes contains six transverse rows in the direction of flow and 19 rows normal to the flow. Assume that the tube surface temperature is constant at 93.33°C. Calculate the outlet air temperature.

4.7-1. *Natural Convection from an Oven Wall.* The oven wall in Example 4.7-1 is insulated so that the surface temperature is 366.5 K instead of 505.4 K. Calculate the natural convection heat-transfer coefficient and the heat-transfer rate per m of width. Use both Eq. (4.7-4) and the simplified equation. (*Note:* Radiation is being neglected in this calculation.) Use both SI and English units.

4.7-2. *Losses by Natural Convection from a Cylinder.* A vertical cylinder 76.2 mm in diameter and 121.9 mm high is maintained at 397.1 K at its surface. It loses heat by natural convection to air at 294.3 K. Heat is lost from the cylindrical side and the flat circular end at the top. Calculate the heat loss neglecting radiation losses. Use the simplified equations of Table 4.7-2 and those equations for the lowest range of N_{Gr} N_{Pr}. The equivalent L to use for the top flat surface is 0.9 times the diameter.

Ans. $q = 26.0$ W

4.7-3. *Heat Loss from a Horizontal Tube.* A horizontal tube carrying hot water has a surface temperature of 355.4 K and an outside diameter of 25.4 mm. The tube is exposed to room air at 294.3 K. What is the natural convection heat loss for a 1-m length of pipe?

4.7-4. *Natural Convection Cooling of an Orange.* An orange 102 mm in diameter having a surface temperature of 21.1°C is placed on an open shelf in a refrigerator held at

4.4°C. Calculate the heat loss by natural convection, neglecting radiation. As an approximation, the simplified equation for vertical planes can be used with L replaced by the radius of the sphere (M1). For a more accurate correlation, see (S2).

4.7-5. Natural Convection in Enclosed Horizontal Space. Repeat Example 4.7-3 but for the case where the two plates are horizontal and the bottom plate is hotter than the upper plate. Compare the results.

Ans. $q = 18.64$ W

4.7-6. Natural Convection Heat Loss in Double Window. A vertical double plate-glass window has an enclosed air-gap space of 10 mm. The window is 2.0 m high by 1.2 m wide. One window surface is at 25°C and the other at 10°C. Calculate the free convection heat-transfer rate through the air gap.

4.7-7. Natural Convection Heat Loss for Water in Vertical Plates. Two vertical square metal plates having dimensions of 0.40×0.40 m are separated by a gap of 12 mm and this enclosed space is filled with water. The average surface temperature of one plate is 65.6°C and the other plate is at 37.8°C. Calculate the heat-transfer rate through this gap.

4.7-8. Heat Loss from a Furnace. Two horizontal metal plates having dimensions of 0.8×1.0 m comprise the top of a furnace and are separated by a distance of 15 mm. The lower plate is at 400°C and the upper at 100°C, and air at 1 atm abs is enclosed in the gap. Calculate the heat-transfer rate between the plates.

4.8-1. Boiling Coefficient in a Jacketed Kettle. Predict the boiling heat-transfer coefficient for the vertical jacketed sides of the kettle given in Example 4.8-1. Then, using this coefficient for the sides and the coefficient from Example 4.8-1 for the bottom, predict the total heat transfer.

Ans. $T_w = 107.65$°C, $\Delta T = 7.65$ K, and h(vertical) $= 3560$ W/m$^2 \cdot$ K

4.8-2. Boiling Coefficient on a Horizontal Tube. Predict the boiling heat-transfer coefficient for water under pressure boiling at 250°F for a horizontal surface of $\frac{1}{16}$-in.-thick stainless steel having a k of 9.4 btu/h $\cdot$ ft $\cdot$ °F. The heating medium on the other side of this surface is a hot fluid at 290°F having an h of 275 btu/h $\cdot$ ft$^2 \cdot$ °F. Use the simplified equations. Be sure to correct this h value for the effect of pressure.

4.8-3. Condensation on a Vertical Tube. Repeat Example 4.8-2 but for a vertical tube 1.22 m (4.0 ft) high instead of 0.305 m (1.0 ft) high. Use SI and English units.

Ans. $h = 9438$ W/m$^2 \cdot$ K, 1663 btu/h $\cdot$ ft$^2 \cdot$ °F; $N_{Re} = 207.2$ (laminar flow)

4.8-4. Condensation of Steam on Vertical Tubes. Steam at 1 atm abs pressure and 100°C is condensing on a bank of five vertical tubes each 0.305 m high and having an OD of 25.4 mm. The tubes are arranged in a bundle spaced far enough apart that they do not interfere with each other. The surface temperature of the tubes is 97.78°C. Calculate the average heat-transfer coefficient and the total kg condensate per hour.

Ans. $h = 15\ 240$ W/m$^2 \cdot$ K

4.8-5. Condensation on a Bank of Horizontal Tubes. Steam at 1 atm abs pressure and 100°C is condensing on a horizontal tube bank with five layers of tubes ($N = 5$) placed one below the other. Each layer has four tubes (total tubes $= 4 \times 5 = 20$) and the OD of each tube is 19.1 mm. The tubes are each 0.61 m long and the tube surface temperature is 97.78°C. Calculate the average heat-transfer coefficient and the kg condensate per second for the whole condenser. Make a sketch of the tube bank.

4.9-1. Mean Temperature Difference in an Exchanger. A 1–2 exchanger with one shell pass and two tube passes is used to heat a cold fluid from 37.8°C to 121.1°C by using a hot fluid entering at 315.6°C and leaving at 148.9°C. Calculate the ΔT_{lm} and the mean temperature difference ΔT_m in K.

Ans. $\Delta T_{lm} = 148.9$ K, $\Delta T_m = 131.8$ K

4.9-2. *Cooling Oil by Water in an Exchanger.* Oil flowing at the rate of 5.04 kg/s ($c_{pm} = 2.09$ kJ/kg·K) is cooled in a 1–2 heat exchanger from 366.5 K to 344.3 K by 2.02 kg/s of water entering at 283.2 K. The overall heat-transfer coefficient U_o is 340 W/m²·K. Calculate the area required. (*Hint:* A heat balance must first be made to determine the outlet water temperature.)

4.9-3. *Heat Exchange Between Oil and Water.* Water is flowing at the rate of 1.13 kg/s in a 1–2 shell-and-tube heat exchanger and is heated from 45°C to 85°C by an oil having a heat capacity of 1.95 kJ/kg·K. The oil enters at 120°C and leaves at 85°C. Calculate the area of the exchanger if the overall heat-transfer coefficient is 300 W/m²·K.

4.9-4. *Outlet Temperature and Effectiveness of an Exchanger.* Hot oil at a flow rate of 3.00 kg/s ($c_p = 1.92$ kJ/kg·K) enters an existing counterflow exchanger at 400 K and is cooled by water entering at 325 K (under pressure) and flowing at a rate of 0.70 kg/s. The overall $U = 350$ W/m²·K and $A = 12.9$ m². Calculate the heat-transfer rate and the exit oil temperature.

4.10-1. *Radiation to a Tube from a Large Enclosure.* Repeat Example 4.10-1 but use the slightly more accurate Eq. (4.10-5) with two different emissivities.

Ans. $q = -2171$ W (-7410 btu/h)

4.10-2. *Baking a Loaf of Bread in an Oven.* A loaf of bread having a surface temperature of 373 K is being baked in an oven whose walls and the air are at 477.4 K. The bread moves continuously through the large oven on an open chain belt conveyor. The emissivity of the bread is estimated as 0.85, and the loaf can be assumed to be a rectangular solid 114.3 mm high × 114.3 mm wide × 330 mm long. Calculate the radiation heat-transfer rate to the bread, assuming that it is small compared to the oven and neglecting natural convection heat transfer.

Ans. $q = 278.4$ W (950 btu/h)

4.10-3. *Radiation and Convection from a Steam Pipe.* A horizontal oxidized steel pipe carrying steam and having an OD of 0.1683 m has a surface temperature of 374.9 K and is exposed to air at 297.1 K in a large enclosure. Calculate the heat loss for 0.305 m of pipe from natural convection plus radiation. For the steel pipe, use an ε of 0.79.

Ans. $q = 163.3$ W (557 btu/h)

4.10-4. *Radiation and Convection to a Loaf of Bread.* Calculate the total heat-transfer rate to the loaf of bread in Problem 4.10-2, including the radiation plus natural convection heat transfer. For radiation first calculate a value of h_r. For natural convection, use the simplified equations for the lower $N_{Gr}N_{Pr}$ range. For the four vertical sides, the equation for vertical planes can be used with an L of 114.3 mm. For the top surface, use the equation for a cooled plate facing upward, and for the bottom, a cooled plate facing downward. The characteristic L for a horizontal rectangular plate is the linear mean of the two dimensions.

4.10-5. *Heat Loss from a Pipe.* A bare stainless-steel tube having an outside diameter of 76.2 mm and an ε of 0.55 is placed horizontally in air at 294.2 K. The pipe surface temperature is 366.4 K. Calculate the value of $h_c + h_r$ for convection plus radiation and the heat loss for 3 m of pipe.

4.11-1. *Radiation Shielding.* Two very large and parallel planes each have an emissivity of 0.7. Surface 1 is at 866.5 K and surface 2 is at 588.8 K. Use SI and English units.
(a) What is the net radiation loss of surface 1?

(b) To reduce this loss, two additional radiation shields also having an emissivity of 0.7 are placed between the original surfaces. What is the new radiation loss?

Ans.   (a) 13 565 W/m², 4304 btu/h · ft²; (b) 4521 W/m², 1435 btu/h · ft²

4.11-2. Radiation from a Craft in Space. A space satellite in the shape of a sphere is traveling in outer space, where its surface temperature is held at 283.2 K. The sphere "sees" only outer space, which can be considered as a black body with a temperature of 0 K. The polished surface of the sphere has an emissivity of 0.1. Calculate the heat loss per m² by radiation.

Ans. $q_{12}/A_1 = 36.5$ W/m²

4.11-3. Radiation and Complex View Factor. Find the view factor F_{12} for the configuration shown in Fig. P4.11-3. The area A_4 and A_3 are fictitious areas (C3). The area $A_2 + A_4$ is called $A_{(24)}$ and $A_1 + A_3$ is called $A_{(13)}$. Areas $A_{(24)}$ and $A_{(13)}$ are perpendicular to each other. [*Hint:* Follow the methods in Example 4.11-5. First, write an equation similar to Eq. (4.11-48) which relates the interchange between A_3 and $A_{(24)}$. Then relate the interchange between $A_{(13)}$ and $A_{(24)}$. Finally, relate $A_{(13)}$ and A_4.]

Ans. $A_1 F_{12} = A_{(13)} F_{(13)(24)} + A_3 F_{34} - A_3 F_{3(24)} - A_{(13)} F_{(13)4}$

4.11-4. Radiation Between Parallel Surfaces. Two parallel surfaces each 1.83 × 1.83 m square are spaced 0.91 m apart. The surface temperature of A_1 is 811 K and that of A_2 is 533 K. Both are black surfaces.

(a) Calculate the radiant heat transfer between the two surfaces.

(b) Do the same as for part (a), but for the case where the two surfaces are connected by nonconducting reradiating walls.

(c) Repeat part (b), but A_1 has an emissivity of 0.8 and A_2 an emissivity of 0.7.

4.11-5. Radiation Between Adjacent Perpendicular Plates. Two adjacent rectangles are perpendicular to each other. The first rectangle is 1.52 × 2.44 m and the second 1.83 × 2.44 m, with the 2.44-m side common to both. The temperature of the first surface is 699 K and that of the second is 478 K. Both surfaces are black. Calculate the radiant heat transfer between the two surfaces.

4.11-6. View Factor for Complex Geometry. Using the dimensions given in Fig. P4.11-3, calculate the individual view factors and also F_{12}.

4.11-7. Radiation from a Surface to the Sky. A plane surface having an area of 1.0 m² is insulated on the bottom side and is placed on the ground exposed to the atmosphere at night. The upper surface is exposed to air at 290 K, and the convective heat-transfer coefficient from the air to the plane is 12 W/m² · K. The plane radiates to the clear

FIGURE P4.11-3.   *Geometric configuration for Problem 4.11-3.*

sky. The effective radiation temperature of the sky can be assumed as 80 K. If the plane is a black body, calculate the temperature of the plane at equilibrium.

Ans. $T = 266.5$ K $= -6.7°$C

4.11-8. *Radiation and Heating of Planes.* Two plane disks each 1.25 m in diameter are parallel and directly opposite each other. They are separated by a distance of 0.5 m. Disk 1 is heated by electrical resistance to 833.3 K. Both disks are insulated on all faces except the two faces directly opposite each other. Assume that the surroundings emit no radiation and that the disks are in space. Calculate the temperature of disk 2 at steady state and also the electrical energy input to disk 1. (*Hint:* The fraction of heat lost from area number 1 to space is $1 - F_{12}$.)

Ans. $F_{12} = 0.45$, $T_2 = 682.5$ K

4.11-9. *Radiation by Disks to Each Other and to Surroundings.* Two disks each 2.0 m in diameter are parallel and directly opposite each other and are separated by a distance of 2.0 m. Disk 1 is held at 1000 K by electric heating and disk 2 at 400 K by cooling water in a jacket at the rear of the disk. The disks radiate only to each other and to the surrounding space at 300 K. Calculate the electric heat input and also the heat removed by the cooling water.

4.11-10. *View Factor by Integration.* A small black disk is vertical, with an area of 0.002 m^2, and radiates to a vertical black plane surface that is 0.03 m wide and 2.0 m high and is opposite and parallel to the small disk. The disk source is 2.0 m away from the vertical plane and placed opposite the bottom of the plane. Determine F_{12} by integration of the view-factor equation.

Ans. $F_{12} = 0.00307$

4.11-11. *Gas Radiation to Gray Enclosure.* Repeat Example 4.11-7 but with the following changes:

(a) The interior walls are not black surfaces but gray surfaces with an emissivity of 0.75.

(b) The same conditions as part (a) with gray walls, but in addition heat is transferred by natural convection to the interior walls. Assume an average convective coefficient of 8.0 W/m$^2 \cdot$ K.

Ans. (b) q(convection + radiation) = 4.426 W

4.11-12. *Gas Radiation and Convection to a Stack.* A furnace discharges hot flue gas at 1000 K and 1 atm abs pressure containing 5% CO_2 into a stack having an inside diameter of 0.50 m. The inside walls of the refractory lining are at 900 K and the emissivity of the lining is 0.75. The convective heat-transfer coefficient of the gas has been estimated as 10 W/m$^2 \cdot$ K. Calculate the rate of heat transfer q/A from the gas by radiation plus convection.

4.12-1. *Laminar Heat Transfer of a Power-Law Fluid.* A non-Newtonian power-law fluid banana purée flowing at a rate of 300 lb$_m$/h inside a 1.0-in.-ID tube is being heated by a hot fluid flowing outside the tube. The banana purée enters the heating section of the tube, which is 5 ft long, at a temperature of 60°F. The inside wall temperature is constant at 180°F. The fluid properties as given by Charm (C1) are $\rho = 69.9$ lb$_m$/ft^3, $c_p = 0.875$ btu/lb$_m \cdot$ °F, and $k = 0.320$ btu/h $\cdot$ ft $\cdot$ °F. The fluid has the following rheological constants: $n = n' = 0.458$, which can be assumed constant, and $K = 0.146$ lb$_f \cdot$ s$^n \cdot$ ft^{-2} at 70°F and 0.0417 at 190°F. A plot of log K versus T°F can be assumed to be a straight line. Calculate the outlet bulk temperature of the fluid in laminar flow.

4.12-2. *Heating a Power-Law Fluid in Laminar Flow.* A non-Newtonian power-law fluid having the same physical properties and rheological constants as the fluid in Example

4.12-1 is flowing in laminar flow at a rate of 6.30×10^{-2} kg/s inside a 25.4-mm-ID tube. It is being heated by a hot fluid outside the tube. The fluid enters the heating section of the tube at 26.7°C and leaves the heating section at an outlet bulk temperature of 46.1°C. The inside wall temperature is constant at 82.2°C. Calculate the length of tube needed in m. (*Note:* In this case the unknown tube length L appears in the equation for h_a and in the heat-balance equation.)

Ans. $L = 1.722$ m

4.13-1. *Heat Transfer in a Jacketed Vessel with a Paddle Agitator.* A vessel with a paddle agitator and no baffles is used to heat a liquid at 37.8°C. A steam-heated jacket furnishes the heat. The vessel's inside diameter is 1.22 m; the agitator diameter is 0.406 m and it is rotating at 150 rpm. The wall surface temperature is 93.3°C. The physical properties of the liquid are $\rho = 977$ kg/m^3, $c_p = 2.72$ kJ/kg $\cdot$ K, $k = 0.346$ W/m $\cdot$ K, and $\mu = 0.100$ kg/m $\cdot$ s at 37.8°C and 7.5×10^{-3} at 93.3°C. Calculate the heat-transfer coefficient to the wall of the jacket.

4.13-2. *Heat Loss from Circular Fins.* Use the data and conditions from Example 4.13-2 and calculate the fin efficiency and rate of heat loss from the following different fin materials:
(a) Carbon steel ($k = 44$ W/m $\cdot$ K).
(b) Stainless steel ($k = 17.9$ W/m $\cdot$ K).

Ans. (a) $\eta_f = 0.66$, $q = 111.1$ W

4.13-3. *Heat Loss from Longitudinal Fin.* A longitudinal aluminum fin as shown in Fig. 4.13-3a ($k = 230$ W/m $\cdot$ K) is attached to a copper tube having an outside radius of 0.04 m. The length of the fin is 0.080 m and the thickness is 3 mm. The tube base is held at 450 K and the external surrounding air at 300 K has a convective coefficient of 25 W/m$^2 \cdot$ K. Calculate the fin efficiency and the heat loss from the fin per 1.0 m of length.

4.13-4. *Heat Transfer in Finned Tube Exchanger.* Air at an average temperature of 50°C is being heated by flowing outside a steel tube ($k = 45.1$ W/m $\cdot$ K) having an inside diameter of 35 mm and a wall thickness of 3 mm. The outside of the tube is covered with 16 longitudinal steel fins with a length $L = 13$ mm and a thickness of $t = 1.0$ mm. Condensing steam inside at 120°C has a coefficient of 7000 W/m$^2 \cdot$ K. The outside coefficient of the air has been estimated as 30 W/m$^2 \cdot$ K. Neglecting fouling factors and using a tube 1.0 m long, calculate the overall heat-transfer coefficient U_i based on the inside area A_i.

4.14-1. *Dimensional Analysis for Natural Convection.* Repeat the dimensional analysis for natural convection heat transfer to a vertical plate as given in Section 4.14. However, do as follows:
(a) Carry out all the detailed steps solving for all the exponents in the π's.
(b) Repeat, but in this case select the four variables L, μ, c_p, and g to be common to all the dimensionless groups.

4.14-2. *Dimensional Analysis for Unsteady-State Conduction.* For unsteady-state conduction in a solid, the following variables are involved: ρ, c_p, L (dimension of solid), t, k, and z (location in solid). Determine the dimensionless groups relating the variables.

Ans. $\pi_1 = \dfrac{kt}{\rho c_p L^2}$, $\pi_2 = \dfrac{z}{L}$

4.15-1. *Temperatures in a Semi-Infinite Plate.* A semi-infinite plate is similar to that in Fig. 4.15-2. At the surfaces $x = 0$ and $x = L$, the temperature is held constant at 200 K. At the surface $y = 0$, the temperature is held at 400 K. If $L = 1.0$ m, calculate the temperature at the point $y = 0.5$ m and $x = 0.5$ m at steady state.

4.15-2. Heat Conduction in a Two-Dimensional Solid. For two-dimensional heat conduction as given in Example 4.15-1, derive the equation to calculate the total heat loss from the chamber per unit length using the nodes at the outside. There should be eight paths for one-fourth of the chamber. Substitute the actual temperatures into the equation and obtain the heat loss.

Ans. $q = 3426$ W

4.15-3. Steady-State Heat Loss from a Rectangular Duct. A chamber that is in the shape of a long, hollow, rectangular duct has outside dimensions of 3×4 m and inside dimensions of 1×2 m. The walls are 1 m thick. The inside surface temperature is constant at 800 K and the outside constant at 200 K. The $k = 1.4$ W/m·K. Calculate the steady-state heat loss per unit m of length of duct. Use a grid size of $\Delta x = \Delta y = 0.5$ m. Also, use the outside nodes to calculate the total heat conduction. Use a spreadsheet for the calculation.

Ans. $q = 7428$ W

4.15-4. Two-Dimensional Heat Conduction and Different Boundary Conditions. A very long, solid piece of material 1 by 1 m square has its top face maintained at a constant temperature of 1000 K and its left face at 200 K. The bottom face and right face are exposed to an environment at 200 K and have a convection coefficient of $h = 10$ W/m²·K. The $k = 10$ W/m·K. Use a grid size of $\Delta x = \Delta y = \frac{1}{3}$ m and calculate the steady-state temperatures of the various nodes.

4.15-5. Nodal Point at Exterior Corner Between Insulated Surfaces. Derive the finite-difference equation for the case for the nodal point $T_{n,m}$ at an exterior corner between insulated surfaces. The diagram is similar to Fig. 4.15-6c except that the two boundaries are insulated.

Ans. $\bar{q}_{n,m} = \frac{1}{2}(T_{n-1,m} + T_{n,m-1}) - T_{n,m}$

REFERENCES

(A1) ACRIVOS, A. *A.I.Ch.E. J.,* **6,** 584 (1960).

(B1) BIRD, R. B., STEWART, W. E., and LIGHTFOOT, E. N. *Transport Phenomena.* New York: John Wiley & Sons, Inc., 1960.

(B2) BADGER, W. L., and BANCHERO, J. T. *Introduction to Chemical Engineering.* New York: McGraw-Hill Book Company, 1955.

(B3) BROMLEY, L. A. *Chem. Eng. Progr.,* **46,** 221 (1950).

(B4) BOWMAN, R. A., MUELLER, A. C., and NAGLE, W. M. *Trans. A.S.M.E.,* **62,** 283 (1940).

(B5) BROOKS, G., and SU, G. *Chem. Eng. Progr.,* **55,** 54 (1959).

(B6) BOLANOWSKI, J. P., and LINEBERRY, D. D. *Ind. Eng. Chem.,* **44,** 657 (1952).

(C1) CHARM, S. E. *The Fundamentals of Food Engineering,* 2nd ed. Westport, Conn.: Avi Publishing Co., Inc., 1971.

(C2) CARSLAW, H. S., and JAEGER, J. E. *Conduction of Heat in Solids,* 2nd ed. New York: Oxford University Press, Inc., 1959.

(C3) CHAPMAN, A. J. *Heat Transfer.* New York: Macmillan Publishing Co., Inc., 1960.

(C4) CLAPP, R. M. *International Developments in Heat Transfer,* Part III. New York: American Society of Mechanical Engineers, 1961.

(C5) CHILTON, T. H., DREW, T. B., and JEBENS, R. H. *Ind. Eng. Chem.,* **36,** 510 (1944).

(C6) CARREAU, P., CHAREST, G., and CORNEILLE, J. L. *Can. J. Chem. Eng.,* **44,** 3 (1966).

(C7)   CLAUSING, A. M. *Int. J. Heat Mass Transfer,* **9,** 791 (1966).

(D1)   DUNLAP, I. R., and RUSHTON, J. H. *Chem. Eng. Progr. Symp.,* **49**(5), 137 (1953).

(F1)   FUJII, T., and IMURA, H. *Int. J. Heat Mass Transfer,* **15,** 755 (1972).

(G1)   GRIMISON, E. D. *Trans. A.S.M.E.,* **59,** 583 (1937).

(G2)   GEANKOPLIS, C. J. *Mass Transport Phenomena.* Columbus, Ohio: Ohio State University Bookstores, 1972.

(G3)   GUPTA, A. S., CHAUBE, R. B., and UPADHYAY, S. N. *Chem. Eng. Sci.,* **29,** 839 (1974).

(G4)   GLUZ, M. D., and PAVLUSHENKO, L. S. *J. Appl. Chem., U.S.S.R.,* **39,** 2323 (1966).

(G5)   GLOBE, S., and DROPKIN, D. *J. Heat Transfer,* **81,** 24 (1959).

(H1)   HOLMAN, J. P. *Heat Transfer,* 4th ed. New York: McGraw-Hill Book Company, 1976.

(J1)   JACOB, M. *Heat Transfer,* Vol. 1. New York: John Wiley & Sons, Inc., 1949.

(J2)   JACOB, M., and HAWKINS, G. *Elements of Heat Transfer,* 3rd ed. New York: John Wiley & Sons, Inc., 1957.

(J3)   JACOB, M. *Heat Transfer,* Vol. 2. New York: John Wiley & Sons, Inc., 1957.

(K1)   KREITH, F., and BLACK, W. Z. *Basic Heat Transfer.* New York: Harper & Row, Publishers, 1980.

(K2)   KEYES, F. G. *Trans. A.S.M.E.,* **73,** 590 (1951); **74,** 1303 (1952).

(K3)   KNUDSEN, J. G., and KATZ, D. L. *Fluid Dynamics and Heat Transfer.* New York: McGraw-Hill Book Company, 1958.

(K4)   KERN, D. Q. *Process Heat Transfer.* New York: McGraw-Hill Book Company, 1950.

(L1)   LUBARSKY, B., and KAUFMAN, S. J. *NACA Tech. Note No. 3336* (1955).

(M1)   McADAMS, W. H. *Heat Transmission,* 3rd ed. New York: McGraw-Hill Book Company, 1954.

(M2)   METZNER, A. B., and GLUCK, D. F. *Chem. Eng. Sci.,* **12,** 185 (1960).

(M3)   METZNER, A. B., and FRIEND, P. S. *Ind. Eng. Chem.,* **51,** 879 (1959).

(N1)   NELSON, W. L. *Petroleum Refinery Engineering,* 4th ed. New York: McGraw-Hill Book Company, 1949.

(O1)   OLDSHUE, J. Y., and GRETTON, A. I. *Chem. Eng. Progr.,* **50,** 615 (1954).

(P1)   PERRY, R. H., and CHILTON, C. H. *Chemical Engineers' Handbook,* 5th ed. New York: McGraw-Hill Book Company, 1973.

(P2)   PERRY, J. H. *Chemical Engineers' Handbook,* 4th ed. New York: McGraw-Hill Book Company, 1963.

(P3)   PERRY, R. H., and GREEN, D. *Perry's Chemical Engineers' Handbook,* 6th ed. New York: McGraw-Hill Book Company, 1984.

(R1)   REID, R. C., PRAUSNITZ, J. M., and SHERWOOD, T. K. *The Properties of Gases and Liquids,* 3rd ed. New York: McGraw-Hill Book Company, 1977.

(R2)   ROHESENOW, W. M., and HARTNETT, J. P., eds. *Handbook of Heat Transfer.* New York: McGraw-Hill Book Company, 1973.

(S1)   SIEDER, E. N., and TATE, G. E. *Ind. Eng. Chem.,* **28,** 1429 (1936).

(S2)   STEINBERGER, R. L., and TREYBAL, R. E. *A.I.Ch.E. J.,* **6,** 227 (1960).

(S3)   SKELLAND, A. H. P. *Non-Newtonian Flow and Heat Transfer.* New York: John Wiley & Sons, Inc., 1967.

(S4)   SKELLAND, A. H. P., OLIVER, D. R., and TOOKE, S. *Brit. Chem. Eng.,* **7**(5), 346 (1962).

(U1)   UHL, V. W. *Chem. Eng. Progr. Symp.,* **51**(17), 93 (1955).

(W1)   WELTY, J. R., WICKS, C. E., and WILSON, R. E. *Fundamentals of Momentum, Heat and Mass Transfer,* 3rd ed. New York: John Wiley & Sons, Inc., 1984.

CHAPTER 5

Principles of
Unsteady-State
Heat Transfer

5.1 DERIVATION OF BASIC EQUATION

5.1A Introduction

In Chapter 4 we considered various heat-transfer systems in which the temperature at any given point and the heat flux were always constant over time, that is, in steady state. In the present chapter we will study processes in which the temperature at any given point in the system changes with time, that is, heat transfer is unsteady state or transient.

Before steady-state conditions can be reached in a process, some time must elapse after the heat-transfer process is initiated to allow the unsteady-state conditions to disappear. For example, in Section 4.2A we determined the heat flux through a wall at steady state. We did not consider the period during which one side of the wall was being heated up and the temperatures were increasing.

Unsteady-state heat transfer is important because of the large number of heating and cooling problems occurring industrially. In metallurgical processes it is necessary to predict cooling and heating rates for various geometries of metals in order to predict the time required to reach certain temperatures. In food processing, for example, the canning industry, perishable canned foods are heated by immersion in steam baths or chilled by immersion in cold water. In the paper industry wood logs are immersed in steam baths before processing. In most of these processes the material is suddenly immersed in a fluid of higher or lower temperature.

5.1B Derivation of Unsteady-State Conduction Equation

To derive the equation for unsteady-state conduction in one direction in a solid, we refer to Fig. 5.1-1. Heat is being conducted in the x direction in the cube Δx, Δy, Δz in size. For conduction in the x direction, we write

$$q_x = -kA \frac{\partial T}{\partial x} \qquad (5.1\text{-}1)$$

FIGURE 5.1-1. *Unsteady-state conduction in one direction.*

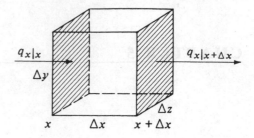

The term $\partial T/\partial x$ means the partial or derivative of T with respect to x, with the other variables, y, z, and time t, being held constant. Next, making a heat balance on the cube, we can write

rate of heat input + rate of generation

$$= \text{rate of heat output} + \text{rate of heat accumulation} \quad \textbf{(5.1-2)}$$

The rate of heat input to the cube is

$$\text{rate of heat input} = q_{x|x} = -k(\Delta y \, \Delta z) \left. \frac{\partial T}{\partial x} \right|_x \quad \textbf{(5.1-3)}$$

Also,

$$\text{rate of heat output} = q_{x|x+\Delta x} = -k(\Delta y \, \Delta z) \left. \frac{\partial T}{\partial x} \right|_{x+\Delta x} \quad \textbf{(5.1-4)}$$

The rate of accumulation of heat in the volume $\Delta x \, \Delta y \, \Delta z$ in time ∂t is

$$\text{rate of heat accumulation} = (\Delta x \, \Delta y \, \Delta z) \rho c_p \frac{\partial T}{\partial t} \quad \textbf{(5.1-5)}$$

The rate of heat generation in volume $\Delta x \, \Delta y \, \Delta z$ is

$$\text{rate of heat generation} = (\Delta x \, \Delta y \, \Delta z) \dot{q} \quad \textbf{(5.1-6)}$$

Substituting Eqs. (5.1-3)–(5.1-6) into (5.1-2) and dividing by $\Delta x \, \Delta y \, \Delta z$,

$$\dot{q} + \frac{-k\left(\left.\frac{\partial T}{\partial x}\right|_x - \left.\frac{\partial T}{\partial x}\right|_{x+\Delta x} \right)}{\Delta x} = \rho c_p \frac{\partial T}{\partial t} \quad \textbf{(5.1-7)}$$

Letting Δx approach zero, we have the second partial of T with respect to x or $\partial^2 T/\partial x^2$ on the left side. Then, rearranging,

$$\frac{\partial T}{\partial t} = \frac{k}{\rho c_p} \frac{\partial^2 T}{\partial x^2} + \frac{\dot{q}}{\rho c_p} = \alpha \frac{\partial^2 T}{\partial x^2} + \frac{\dot{q}}{\rho c_p} \quad \textbf{(5.1-8)}$$

where α is $k/\rho c_p$, thermal diffusivity. This derivation assumes constant k, ρ, and c_p. In SI units, $\alpha = \text{m}^2/\text{s}$, $T = \text{K}$, $t = \text{s}$, $k = \text{W/m} \cdot \text{K}$, $\rho = \text{kg/m}^3$, $\dot{q} = \text{W/m}^3$, and $c_p = \text{J/kg} \cdot \text{K}$. In English units, $\alpha = \text{ft}^2/\text{h}$, $T = {}^\circ\text{F}$, $t = \text{h}$, $k = \text{btu/h} \cdot \text{ft} \cdot {}^\circ\text{F}$, $\rho = \text{lb}_m/\text{ft}^3$, $\dot{q} = \text{btu/h} \cdot \text{ft}^3$, and $c_p = \text{btu/lb}_m \cdot {}^\circ\text{F}$.

For conduction in three dimensions, a similar derivation gives

$$\frac{\partial T}{\partial t} = \alpha \left(\frac{\partial^2 T}{\partial x^2} + \frac{\partial^2 T}{\partial y^2} + \frac{\partial^2 T}{\partial z^2} \right) + \frac{\dot{q}}{\rho c_p} \quad \textbf{(5.1-9)}$$

Chapter 5   Principles of Unsteady-State Heat Transfer

In many cases, unsteady-state heat conduction is occurring but the rate of heat generation is zero. Then Eqs. (5.1-8) and (5.1-9) become

$$\frac{\partial T}{\partial t} = \alpha \frac{\partial^2 T}{\partial x^2} \tag{5.1-10}$$

$$\frac{\partial T}{\partial t} = \alpha \left(\frac{\partial^2 T}{\partial x^2} + \frac{\partial^2 T}{\partial y^2} + \frac{\partial^2 T}{\partial z^2} \right) \tag{5.1-11}$$

Equations (5.1-10) and (5.1-11) relate the temperature T with position x, y, and z and time t. The solutions of Eqs. (5.1-10) and (5.1-11) for certain specific cases as well as for the more general cases are considered in much of the remainder of this chapter.

5.2 SIMPLIFIED CASE FOR SYSTEMS WITH NEGLIGIBLE INTERNAL RESISTANCE

5.2A Basic Equation

We begin our treatment of transient heat conduction by analyzing a simplified case. In this situation we consider a solid which has a very high thermal conductivity or very low internal conductive resistance compared to the external surface resistance, where convection occurs from the external fluid to the surface of the solid. Since the internal resistance is very small, the temperature within the solid is essentially uniform at any given time.

An example would be a small, hot cube of steel at T_0 K at time $t = 0$, suddenly immersed in a large bath of cold water at T_∞ which is held constant with time. Assume that the heat-transfer coefficient h in W/m² · K is constant with time. Making a heat balance on the solid object for a small time interval of time dt s, the heat transfer from the bath to the object must equal the change in internal energy of the object:

$$hA(T_\infty - T)dt = c_p \rho V \, dT \tag{5.2-1}$$

where A is the surface area of the object in m², T the average temperature of the object at time t in s, ρ the density of the object in kg/m³, and V the volume in m³. Rearranging the equation and integrating between the limits of $T = T_0$ when $t = 0$ and $T = T$ when $t = t$,

$$\int_{T=T_0}^{T=T} \frac{dT}{T_\infty - T} = \frac{hA}{c_p \rho V} \int_{t=0}^{t=t} dt \tag{5.2-2}$$

$$\frac{T - T_\infty}{T_0 - T_\infty} = e^{-(hA/c_p \rho V)t} \tag{5.2-3}$$

This equation describes the time–temperature history of the solid object. The term $c_p \rho V$ is often called the *lumped thermal capacitance* of the system. This type of analysis is often called the *lumped capacity method* or *Newtonian heating or cooling method*.

5.2B Equation for Different Geometries

In using Eq. (5.2-3) the surface/volume ratio of the object must be known. The basic assumption of negligible internal resistance was made in the derivation. This assumption is reasonably accurate when

$$N_{Bi} = \frac{hx_1}{k} < 0.1 \tag{5.2-4}$$

where hx_1/k is called the Biot number N_{Bi}, which is dimensionless, and x_1 is a characteristic dimension of the body obtained from $x_1 = V/A$. The Biot number compares the relative values of internal conduction resistance and surface convective resistance to heat transfer. For a sphere,

$$x_1 = \frac{V}{A} = \frac{4\pi r^3/3}{4\pi r^2} = \frac{r}{3} \qquad (5.2\text{-}5)$$

For a long cylinder,

$$x_1 = \frac{V}{A} = \frac{\pi D^2 L/4}{\pi DL} = \frac{D}{4} = \frac{r}{2} \qquad (5.2\text{-}6)$$

For a long square rod,

$$x_1 = \frac{V}{A} = \frac{(2x)^2 L}{4(2x)L} = \frac{x}{2} \qquad (x = \tfrac{1}{2}\ \text{thickness}) \qquad (5.2\text{-}7)$$

EXAMPLE 5.2-1. Cooling of a Steel Ball

A steel ball having a radius of 1.0 in. (25.4 mm) is at a uniform temperature of 800°F (699.9 K). It is suddenly plunged into a medium whose temperature is held constant at 250°F (394.3 K). Assuming a convective coefficient of $h = 2.0$ btu/h · ft^2 · °F (11.36 W/m^2 · K), calculate the temperature of the ball after 1 h (3600 s). The average physical properties are $k = 25$ btu/h · ft · °F (43.3 W/m · K), $\rho = 490$ lb$_m$/ft^3 (7849 kg/m^3), and $c_p = 0.11$ btu/lb$_m$ · °F (0.4606 kJ/kg · K). Use SI and English units.

Solution: For a sphere from Eq. (5.2-5),

$$x_1 = \frac{V}{A} = \frac{r}{3} = \frac{\frac{1}{12}}{3} = \tfrac{1}{36}\ \text{ft}$$

$$= \frac{25.4}{1000 \times 3} = 8.47 \times 10^{-3}\ \text{m}$$

From Eq. (5.2-4) for the Biot number,

$$N_{Bi} = \frac{hx_1}{k} = \frac{2(\frac{1}{36})}{25} = 0.00222$$

$$N_{Bi} = \frac{11.36(8.47 \times 10^{-3})}{43.3} = 0.00222$$

This value is <0.1; hence, the lumped capacity method can be used. Then,

$$\frac{hA}{c_p \rho V} = \frac{2}{0.11(490)(\frac{1}{36})} = 1.335\ \text{h}^{-1}$$

$$\frac{hA}{c_p \rho V} = \frac{11.36}{(0.4606 \times 1000)(7849)(8.47 \times 10^{-3})} = 3.71 \times 10^{-4}\ \text{s}^{-1}\,(1.335\ \text{h}^{-1})$$

Substituting into Eq. (5.2-3) for $t = 1.0$ h and solving for T,

$$\frac{T - T_\infty}{T_0 - T_\infty} = \frac{T - 250°F}{800 - 250} = e^{-(hA/c_p\rho V)t} = e^{-(1.335)(1.0)} \qquad T = 395°F$$

$$\frac{T - 394.3 \text{ K}}{699.9 - 394.3} = e^{-(3.71 \times 10^{-4})(3600)} \qquad T = 474.9 \text{ K}$$

5.2C Total Amount of Heat Transferred

The temperature of the solid at any time t can be calculated from Eq. (5.2-3). At any time t, the instantaneous rate of heat transfer $q(t)$ in W from the solid of negligible internal resistance can be calculated from

$$q(t) = hA(T - T_\infty) \tag{5.2-8}$$

Substituting the instantaneous temperature T from Eq. (5.2-3) into Eq. (5.2-8),

$$q(t) = hA(T_0 - T_\infty)e^{-(hA/c_p\rho V)t} \tag{5.2-9}$$

To determine the total amount of heat Q in W · s or J transferred from the solid from time $t = 0$ to $t = t$, we can integrate Eq. (5.2-9):

$$Q = \int_{t=0}^{t=t} q(t)\, d(t) = \int_{t=0}^{t=t} hA(t_0 - T_\infty)e^{-(hA/c_p\rho V)t}\, dt \tag{5.2-10}$$

$$Q = c_p\rho V(T_0 - T_\infty)[1 - e^{-(hA/c_p\rho V)t}] \tag{5.2-11}$$

EXAMPLE 5.2-2. Total Amount of Heat in Cooling
For the conditions in Example 5.2-1, calculate the total amount of heat removed up to time $t = 3600$ s.

Solution: From Example 5.2-1, $hA/c_p\rho V = 3.71 \times 10^{-4}$ s^{-1}. Also, $V = 4\pi r^3/3 = 4(\pi)(0.0254)^3/3 = 6.864 \times 10^{-5}$ m^3. Substituting into Eq. (5.2-11),

$$Q = (0.4606 \times 1000)(7849)(6.864 \times 10^{-5})(699.9 - 394.3)$$

$$\times [1 - e^{-(3.71 \times 10^{-4})(3600)}]$$

$$= 5.589 \times 10^4 \text{ J}$$

5.3 UNSTEADY-STATE HEAT CONDUCTION IN VARIOUS GEOMETRIES

5.3A Introduction and Analytical Methods

In Section 5.2 we considered a simplified case of negligible internal resistance where the object has a very high thermal conductivity. Now we will consider the more general situation where the internal resistance is not small, and hence the temperature is not constant in the solid. The first case that we shall consider is one where the surface convective resistance is negligible compared to the internal resistance. This could occur because of a very large heat-transfer coefficient at the surface or because of a relatively large conductive resistance in the object.

To illustrate an analytical method of solving this first case, we will derive the equation for unsteady-state conduction in the x direction only in a flat plate of thickness $2H$ as shown in

FIGURE 5.3-1. *Unsteady-state conduction in a flat plate with negligible surface resistance.*

Fig. 5.3-1. The initial profile of the temperature in the plate at $t = 0$ is uniform at $T = T_0$. At time $t = 0$, the ambient temperature is suddenly changed to T_1 and held there. Since there is no convection resistance, the temperature of the surface is also held constant at T_1. Since this is conduction in the x direction, Eq. (5.1-10) holds:

$$\frac{\partial T}{\partial t} = \alpha \frac{\partial^2 T}{\partial x^2} \qquad (5.1\text{-}10)$$

The initial and boundary conditions are

$$T = T_0, \qquad t = 0, \qquad x = x$$
$$T = T_1, \qquad t = t, \qquad x = 0 \qquad (5.3\text{-}1)$$
$$T = T_1, \qquad t = t, \qquad x = 2H$$

Generally, it is convenient to define a dimensionless temperature Y so that it varies between 0 and 1. Hence,

$$Y = \frac{T_1 - T}{T_1 - T_0} \qquad (5.3\text{-}2)$$

Substituting Eq. (5.3-2) into (5.1-10),

$$\frac{\partial Y}{\partial t} = \alpha \frac{\partial^2 Y}{\partial x^2} \qquad (5.3\text{-}3)$$

Redefining the boundary and initial conditions,

$$Y = \frac{T_1 - T_0}{T_1 - T_0} = 1, \qquad t = 0, \qquad x = x$$
$$Y = \frac{T_1 - T_1}{T_1 - T_0} = 0, \qquad t = t, \qquad x = 0 \qquad (5.3\text{-}4)$$
$$Y = \frac{T_1 - T_1}{T_1 - T_0} = 0, \qquad t = t, \qquad x = 2H$$

A convenient procedure to use to solve Eq. (5.3-3) is the method of separation of variables, which leads to a product solution

$$Y = e^{-a^2 \alpha t}(A \cos ax + B \sin ax)$$
(5.3-5)

where A and B are constants and a is a parameter. Applying the boundary and initial conditions of Eq. (5.3-4) to solve for these constants in Eq. (5.3-5), the final solution is an infinite Fourier series (G1):

$$\frac{T_1 - T_0}{T_1 - T_0} = \frac{4}{\pi}\left(\frac{1}{1}\exp\frac{-1^2\pi^2\alpha t}{4H^2}\sin\frac{1\pi x}{2H} + \frac{1}{3}\exp\frac{-3^2\pi^2\alpha t}{4H^2}\sin\frac{3\pi x}{2H}\right.$$

$$\left. + \frac{1}{5}\exp\frac{-5^2\pi^2\alpha t}{4H^2}\sin\frac{5\pi x}{2H} + \cdots\right)$$
(5.3-6)

Hence from Eq. (5.3-6), the temperature T at any position x and time t can be determined. However, these types of equations are very time-consuming to use, and convenient charts have been prepared, which are discussed in Sections 5.3B, 5.3C, 5.3D, and 5.3E, where a surface resistance is present.

5.3B Unsteady-State Conduction in a Semi-infinite Solid

In Fig. 5.3-2 a semi-infinite solid is shown that extends to ∞ in the $+x$ direction. Heat conduction occurs only in the x direction. Originally, the temperature in the solid is uniform at T_0. At time $t = 0$, the solid is suddenly exposed to or immersed in a large mass of ambient fluid at temperature T_1, which is constant. The convection coefficient h in W/m$^2 \cdot$ K or btu/h $\cdot$ ft$^2 \cdot$ °F is present and is constant; that is, a surface resistance is present. Hence, the temperature T_S at the surface is not the same as T_1.

The solution of Eq. (5.1-10) for these conditions has been obtained (S1) and is

$$\frac{T_1 - T_0}{T_1 - T_0} = 1 - Y$$

$$= \text{erfc}\frac{x}{2\sqrt{\alpha t}} - \exp\left[\frac{h\sqrt{\alpha t}}{k}\left(\frac{x}{\sqrt{\alpha t}} + \frac{h\sqrt{\alpha t}}{k}\right)\right]\text{erfc}\left(\frac{x}{2\sqrt{\alpha t}} + \frac{h}{k}\sqrt{\alpha t}\right)$$
(5.3-7)

where x is the distance into the solid from the surface in m (SI units), t = time in s, $\alpha = k/\rho c_p$ in m^2/s. In English units, x = ft, t = h, and α = ft^2/h. The function erfc is $(1 - \text{erf})$, where erf is the error function and numerical values are tabulated in standard tables and texts (G1, P1,

FIGURE 5.3-2.   *Unsteady-state conduction in a semi-infinite solid.*

FIGURE 5.3-3. *Unsteady-state heat conducted in a semi-infinite solid with surface convection. Calculated from Eq. (5.3-7)(S1).*

S1); Y is fraction of unaccomplished change $(T_1 - T)/(T_1 - T_0)$; and $1 - Y$ is fraction of change.

Figure 5.3-3, calculated using Eq. (5.3-7), is a convenient plot used for unsteady-state heat conduction into a semi-infinite solid with surface convection. If conduction into the solid is slow enough or h is very large, the top line with $h\sqrt{\alpha t}/k = \infty$ is used.

EXAMPLE 5.3-1. *Freezing Temperature in the Ground*

The depth in the soil of the earth at which freezing temperatures penetrate is often of importance in agriculture and construction. On a certain fall day, the temperature in the earth is constant at 15.6°C (60°F) to a depth of several meters. A cold wave suddenly reduces the air temperature from 15.6 to −17.8°C (0°F). The convective coefficient above the soil is 11.36 W/m² · K (2 btu/h · ft² · °F). The soil properties can be assumed as $\alpha = 4.65 \times 10^{-7}$ m²/s (0.018 ft²/h) and $k = 0.865$ W/m · K (0.5 btu/h · ft · °F). Neglect any latent heat effects. Use SI and English units.

(a) What is the surface temperature after 5 h?

(b) To what depth in the soil will the freezing temperature of 0°C (32°F) penetrate in 5 h?

Solution: This is a case of unsteady-state conduction in a semi-infinite solid. For part (a), the value of x which is the distance from the surface is $x = 0$ m.

Then the value of $x/2\sqrt{\alpha t}$ is calculated as follows for $t = 5$ h, $\alpha = 4.65 \times 10^{-7}$ m^2/s, $k = 0.865$ W/m·°C, and $h = 11.36$ W/m^2·°C. Using SI and English units,

$$\frac{x}{2\sqrt{\alpha t}} = \frac{0}{2\sqrt{(4.65 \times 10^{-7})(5 \times 3600)}} \qquad \frac{x}{2\sqrt{\alpha t}} = \frac{0}{2\sqrt{0.018(5)}}$$

Also,

$$\frac{h\sqrt{\alpha t}}{k} = \frac{11.36\sqrt{(4.65 \times 10^{-7})(5 \times 3600)}}{0.865} \qquad \frac{h\sqrt{\alpha t}}{k} = \frac{2\sqrt{0.018(5)}}{0.5}$$

$$= 1.2 \qquad\qquad\qquad\qquad = 1.2$$

Using Fig. 5.3-3, for $x/2\sqrt{\alpha t} = 0$ and $h\sqrt{\alpha t}/k = 1.2$, the value of $1 - Y = 0.63$ is read off the curve. Converting temperatures to K, $T_0 = 15.6°C + 273.2 = 288.8$ K (60°F) and $T_1 = -17.8°C + 273.2 = 255.4$ K (0°F). Then

$$1 - Y = \frac{T - T_0}{T_1 - T_0} = 0.63 = \frac{T - 288.8}{255.4 - 288.8}$$

Solving for T at the surface after 5 h,

$$T = 267.76 \text{ K} \quad \text{or} \quad -544°C\ (22.2°F)$$

For part (b), $T = 273.2$ K or 0°C, and the distance x is unknown. Substituting the known values,

$$\frac{T - T_0}{T_1 - T_0} = \frac{273.2 - 288.8}{255.4 - 288.8} = 0.467$$

From Fig. 5.3-3 for $(T - T_0)/(T_1 - T_0) = 0.467$ and $h\sqrt{\alpha t}/k = 1.2$, a value of 0.16 is read off the curve for $x/2\sqrt{\alpha t}$. Hence,

$$\frac{x}{2\sqrt{\alpha t}} = \frac{x}{2\sqrt{(4.65 \times 10^{-7})(5 \times 3600)}} = 0.16 \qquad \frac{x}{2\sqrt{\alpha t}} = \frac{x}{2\sqrt{0.018(5)}} = 0.16$$

Solving for x, the distance the freezing temperature penetrates in 5 h,

$$x = 0.0293 \text{ m} \ (0.096 \text{ ft})$$

5.3C Unsteady-State Conduction in a Large Flat Plate

A geometry that often occurs in heat-conduction problems is a flat plate of thickness $2x_1$ in the x direction and having large or infinite dimensions in the y and z directions, as shown in Fig. 5.3-4. Heat is being conducted only from the two flat and parallel surfaces in the x direction. The original uniform temperature of the plate is T_0; at time $t = 0$, the solid is exposed to an environment at temperature T_1 and unsteady-state conduction occurs. A surface resistance is present.

The numerical results of this case are presented graphically in Figs. 5.3-5 and 5.3-6. Figure 5.3-5, from Gurney and Lurie (G2), is a convenient chart for determining the temperatures at any position in the plate and at any time t. The dimensionless parameters used in this and subsequent unsteady-state charts in this section are given in Table 5.3-1 (x is the distance from the center of the flat plate, cylinder, or sphere; x_1 is one-half the thickness of the flat

FIGURE 5.3-4. *Unsteady-state conduction in a large flat plate.*

plate, radius of cylinder, or radius of sphere; x = distance from the surface for a semi-infinite solid.)

When $n = 0$, the position is at the center of the plate in Fig. 5.3-5. Often the temperature history at the center of the plate is quite important. A more accurate chart for determining only the center temperature is given in Fig. 5.3-6, the Heisler (H1) chart. Heisler (H1) has also prepared multiple charts for determining the temperatures at other positions.

EXAMPLE 5.3-2. Heat Conduction in a Slab of Butter

A rectangular slab of butter which is 46.2 mm thick at a temperature of 277.6 K (4.4°C) in a cooler is removed and placed in an environment at 297.1 K (23.9°C). The sides and bottom of the butter container can be considered to be insulated by the container side walls. The flat top surface of the butter is exposed to the environment. The convective coefficient is constant at 8.52 W/m$^2 \cdot$K. Calculate the temperature in the butter at the surface, at 25.4 mm below the surface, and at 46.2 mm below the surface at the insulated bottom after 5 h of exposure.

Solution: The butter can be considered as a large, flat plate with conduction vertically in the x direction. Since heat is entering only at the top face and the bottom face is insulated, the 46.2 mm of butter is equivalent to a half plate with

TABLE 5.3-1. *Dimensionless Parameters for Use in Unsteady-State Conduction Charts*

$$Y = \frac{T_1 - T}{T_1 - T_0} \qquad m = \frac{k}{hx_1}$$

$$1 - Y = \frac{T - T_0}{T_1 - T_0} \qquad n = \frac{x}{x_1}$$

$$X = \frac{\alpha t}{x_1^2}$$

SI units: α = m^2/s, T = K, t = s, x = m, x_1 = m, k = W/m$\cdot$K, h = W/m$^2 \cdot$K

English units: α = ft^2/h, T = °F, t = h, x = ft, x_1 = ft, k = btu/h$\cdot$ft$\cdot$°F, $\quad h$ = btu/h$\cdot$ft$^2 \cdot$°F

Cgs units: α = cm^2/s, T = °C, t = s, x = cm, x_1 = cm, k = cal/s$\cdot$cm$\cdot$°C, $\quad h$ = cal/s$\cdot$cm$^2 \cdot$°C

FIGURE 5.3-5. *Unsteady-state heat conduction in a large flat plate. [From H. P. Gurney and J. Lurie, Ind. Eng. Chem., 15, 1170 (1923).]*

FIGURE 5.3-6. Chart for determining temperature at the center of a large flat plate for unsteady-state heat conduction. [From H. P. Heisler, Trans. A.S.M.E., **69**, 227 (1947). With permission.]

thickness x_1 = 46.2 mm. In a plate with two exposed surfaces, as in Fig. 5.3-4, the center at $x = 0$ acts as an insulated surface, and both halves are mirror images of each other.

The physical properties of butter from Appendix A.4 are k = 0.197 W/m · K, c_p = 2.30 kJ/kg · K = 2300 J/kg · K, and ρ = 998 kg/m^3. The thermal diffusivity is

$$\alpha = \frac{k}{\rho c_p} = \frac{0.197}{998(2300)} = 8.58 \times 10^{-8}\ m^2/s$$

Also, x_1 = 46.2/1000 = 0.0462 m.

The parameters needed for use in Fig. 5.3-5 are

$$m = \frac{k}{hx_1} = \frac{0.197}{8.52(0.0462)} = 0.50$$

$$X = \frac{\alpha t}{x_1^2} = \frac{(8.58 \times 10^{-8})(5 \times 3600)}{(0.0462)^2} = 0.72$$

For the top surface, where $x = x_1 = 0.0462$ m,

$$n = \frac{x}{x_1} = \frac{0.0462}{0.0462} = 1.0$$

Then, using Fig. 5.3-5,

$$Y = 0.25 = \frac{T_1 - T}{T_1 - T_0} = \frac{297.1 - T}{297.1 - 277.6}$$

Solving, T = 292.2 K (19.0°C).

At the point 25.4 mm from the top surface, or 20.8 mm from the center, x = 0.0208 m, and

$$n = \frac{x}{x_1} = \frac{0.0208}{0.0462} = 0.45$$

From Fig. 5.3-5,

$$Y = 0.45 = \frac{T_1 - T}{T_1 - T_0} = \frac{297.1 - T}{297.1 - 277.6}$$

Solving, T = 288.3 K (15.1°C).

For the bottom point, or 0.0462 m from the top, $x = 0$ and

$$n = \frac{x}{x_1} = \frac{0}{x_1} = 0$$

Then, from Fig. 5.3-5,

$$Y = 0.50 = \frac{T_1 - T}{T_1 - T_0} = \frac{297.1 - T}{297.1 - 277.6}$$

Solving, T = 287.4 K (14.2°C). Alternatively, using Fig. 5.3-6, which is only for the center point, Y = 0.53 and T = 286.8 K (13.6°C).

5.3D Unsteady-State Conduction in a Long Cylinder

Here we consider unsteady-state conduction in a long cylinder where conduction occurs only in the radial direction. The cylinder is long so that either conduction at the ends can be neglected or the ends are insulated. Charts for this case are presented in Fig. 5.3-7 for determining the temperatures at any position and Fig. 5.3-8 for the center temperature only.

FIGURE 5.3-7. *Unsteady-state heat conduction in a long cylinder. [From H. P. Gurney and J. Lurie, Ind. Eng. Chem., **15**, 1170 (1923)]*

TABLE 10.6-1. *Packing Factors for Random and Structured Packing*

Type	Material	Nominal size, in.	Void fraction, ε	Surface area, a, ft^2/ft^3 (m^2/m^3)		Packing factor, F_p, ft^{-1} (m^{-1})		Relative mass-transfer coefficient, f_p
Random Packing								
Raschig Rings	Ceramic	1/2	0.64	111	(364)	580	(1900)	1.52
		1	0.74	58	(190)	179	(587)	1.20
		1 1/2	0.73	37	(121)	95	(312)	1.00
		2	0.74	28	(92)	65	(213)	0.85
Berl Saddles	Ceramic	1/2	0.62	142	(466)	240	(787)	1.58
		1	0.68	76	(249)	110	(361)	1.36
		2		32	(105)	45	(148)	
Pall Rings	Metal	1	0.94	63	(207)	56	(184)	1.61
		1 1/2	0.95	39	(128)	40	(131)	1.34
		2	0.96	31	(102)	27	(89)	1.14
Metal Intalox (IMTP)	Metal	1	0.97	70	(230)	41	(134)	1.78
		2	0.98	30	(98)	18	(59)	1.27
Nor-Pac	Plastic	1	0.92	55	(180)	25	(82)	
		2	0.94	31	(102)	12	(39)	
Hy-Pak	Metal	1	0.96	54	(177)	45	(148)	1.51
		2	0.97	29	(95)	26	(85)	1.07
	Plastic	1	0.92	55	(180)	25	(82)	
		2	0.94	31	(102)	12	(39)	
Structured Packing								
Mellapak	250Y	Metal	0.95	76	(249)	20	(66)	
	500Y			152	(499)	34	(112)	
Flexipac	2		0.93	68	(223)	22	(72)	
	4		0.98			6	(20)	
Gempak	2A		0.93	67	(220)	16	(52)	
	4A		0.91	138	(452)	32	(105)	
Norton Intalox	2T		0.97	65	(213)	17	(56)	1.98
	3T		0.97	54	(177)	13	(43)	1.94
Montz	B300			91	(299)	33	(108)	
Sulzer	CY	Wire Mesh	0.85	213	(700)	70	(230)	
	BX		0.90	150	(492)	21	(69)	

Data from Ref. (K1, L2, P2, S4). The relative mass-transfer coefficient, f_p, is discussed in Section 10.8B.

$v_G[\rho_G/(\rho_L - \rho_G)]^{0.5}F_p^{0.5}\nu^{0.05}$, capacity parameter

$(G_L/G_G)(\rho_G/\rho_L)^{0.5}$, flow parameter

FIGURE 10.6-6. *Pressure-drop correlation for structured packings by Kister and Gill (K2). (From H. Z. Kister,* Distillation Design, *New York: McGraw-Hill Book Company, 1992. With permission.)*

The following procedure can be used to determine the limiting flow rates and the tower diameter.

1. First, a suitable random packing or structured packing is selected, giving an F_p value.
2. A suitable liquid-to-gas ratio G_L/G_G is selected along with the total gas flow rate.
3. The pressure drop at flooding is calculated using Eq. (10.6-1), or if F_p is 60 or over, the $\Delta P_{flooding}$ is taken as 2.0 in./ft packing height.
4. Then the flow parameter is calculated, and using the pressure drop at flooding and either Fig. 10.6-5 or 10.6-6, the capacity parameter is read off the plot.
5. Using the capacity parameter, the value of G_G is obtained, which is the maximum value at flooding.
6. Using a suitable % of the flooding value of G_G for design, a new G_G and G_L are obtained. The pressure drop can also be obtained from Figure 10.6-5 or 10.6-6.
7. Knowing the total gas flow rate and G_G, the tower cross-sectional area and ID can be calculated.

4. Approximate design factors to use.   In using random packing, the radio of tower diameter to packing size should be 10/1 or greater. This is to ensure good liquid and gas distribution. For every 3 m (10 ft) height of packing, a liquid redistribution should be used to prevent channeling of liquid to the sides. Random-packed towers are generally used only for diameters of 1.0 m (3.3 ft) or less. Tray towers less than 0.6 m (2 ft) in diameter are usually not used because of cleaning and access problems.

The start of loading in packed towers is usually at about 65–70% of the flooding velocity (L2). For absorption, the tower should be designed using about 50–70% of the gas flooding velocity, with the high value used at high flow parameters. For atmospheric-pressure distillation, values of 70–80% can be used (S5). For distillation and structured packing, 80% of flooding is often used in design (L3). For tray towers, see Section 11.5.

EXAMPLE 10.6-1. *Pressure Drop and Tower Diameter for Ammonia Absorption*

Ammonia is being absorbed in a tower using pure water at 25°C and 1.0 atm abs pressure. The feed rate is 1440 lb_m/h (653.2 kg/h) and contains 3.0 mol % ammonia in air. The process design specifies a liquid-to-gas mass flow rate ratio G_L/G_G of 2/1 and the use of 1-in. metal Pall rings.

    (a) Calculate the pressure drop in the packing and gas mass velocity at flooding. Using 50% of the flooding velocity, calculate the pressure drop, gas and liquid flows, and tower diameter.

    (b) Repeat (a) above but use Mellapak 250Y structured packing.

Solution: The gas and liquid flows in the bottom of the tower are the largest, so the tower will be sized for these flows. Assume that approximately all of the ammonia is absorbed. The gas average mol wt is $28.97(0.97) + 17.0(0.03) = 28.61$. The weight fraction of ammonia is $0.03(17)/(28.61) = 0.01783$.

$$\rho_G = \left(\frac{492}{460 + 77}\right)\frac{(28.64)}{(359)} = 0.07309 \ lb_m/ft^3$$

Assuming the water is dilute, from Appendix A.2-4, the water viscosity $\mu = 0.8937$ cp. From A.2-3, the water density is $0.99708 \ gm/cm^3$. Then, $\rho_L = 0.99708(62.43) = 62.25 \ lb_m/ft^3$. Also, $\nu = \mu/\rho = 0.8937/0.99708 = 0.8963$ centistokes.

From Table 10.6-1, for 1-in. Pall rings, $F_p = 56 \ ft^{-1}$. Using Eq. 10.6-1, $\Delta P_{flood} = 0.115F_p^{0.7} = 0.115(56)^{0.7} = 1.925$ in. H_2O/ft packing height. The flow parameter for Fig. 10.6-5 is

$$(G_L/G_G)(\rho_G/\rho_L)^{0.5} = (2.0)(0.07309/62.25)^{0.5} = 0.06853$$

Using Fig. 10.6-5, for a flow parameter of 0.06853 (abscissa) and a pressure drop of 1.925 in./ft at flooding, a capacity parameter (ordinate) of 1.7 is read off the plot. Then, substituting into the capacity parameter equation and solving for ν_G,

$$1.7 = \nu_G[\rho_G/(\rho_L - \rho_G)]^{0.5} \ F_p^{0.5}\nu^{0.05}$$

$$= \nu_G\left[\frac{0.07309}{(62.25 - 0.07309)}\right]^{0.5}(56)^{0.5}(0.8963)^{0.05}$$

$\nu_G = 6.663 \ ft/s$. Then $G_G = \nu_G\rho_G = 6.663(0.07309) = 0.4870 \ lb_m/(s \cdot ft^2)$ at flooding. Using 50% of the flooding velocity for design, $G_G = 0.5(0.4870) = 0.2435 \ lb_m/(s \cdot ft^2)$ [$1.189 \ kg/(s \cdot m^2)$]. Also, the liquid flow rate $G_L = 2.0(0.2435) = 0.4870 \ lb_m/(s \cdot ft^2)$ [$2.378 \ kg/(s \cdot m^2)$].

To calculate the tower pressure drop at 50% of flooding, $G_G = 0.2435$ and $G_L = 0.4870$, the new capacity parameter is $0.5(1.7) = 0.85$. Using this value of 0.85 and the same flow parameter, 0.06853, a value of 0.18 in. water/ft is obtained from Fig. 10.6-5.

The tower cross-sectional area $= (1440/3600 \ lb_m/s)(1/0.2435 \ lb_m/(s \cdot ft^2)) = 1.6427 \ ft^2 = (\pi/4)D^2$. Solving, $D = 1.446$ ft (0.441 m). The amount of ammonia in the outlet water assuming all of the ammonia is absorbed is 0.01783(1440) = 25.68 lb. Since the liquid flow rate is 2 times the gas flow rate, the total liquid flow rate is 2.0(1440) = 2880 lb_m/hr. Hence, the flow rate of the pure inlet water is 2880 − 25.68 = 2858.3 lb_m/s.

For part (b), using Mellapak 250Y, F_p = 20 from Table 10.6-1. The Δp_{flood} = $0.115F_p^{0.7}$ = $0.115(20)^{0.7}$ = 0.936 in. water/ft. The flow parameter of 0.06853 is the same. Using Fig. 10.6-6, a capacity parameter = 1.38 at flooding is obtained. Then,

$$1.38 = \frac{G_G}{\rho_G}\left[\frac{\rho_G}{\rho_L - \rho_G}\right]^{0.5} F_p^{0.5} \nu^{0.05}$$

$$= \frac{(G_G)}{(0.07309)}\left[\frac{0.07309}{(62.25 - 0.07309)}\right]^{0.5}(20)^{0.5}(0.8963)^{0.05}$$

Solving, G_G = 0.6615 lb_m/(h · ft^2). For 50% flood, G_G = 0.5(0.6615) = 0.3308 lb_m/(s · ft^2) [1.615 kg/(s · m^2)]. Also, the liquid flow rate is G_L = 2(0.3308) = 0.6616 lb_m/(s · ft^2) [3.230 kg/(s · m^2)]. The new capacity parameter is 0.5(1.38) = 0.69. Using this and Fig. 10.6-6, a pressure drop of 0.11 in. water/ft is obtained.

The tower cross-sectional area = (1440/3600)(1/0.3308) = 1.209 ft^2 = $(\pi/4)D^2$. Solving, D = 1.241 ft (0.3784 m). Note that the tower with structured packing uses about 25% less cross-sectional area.

10.6D Design of Plate Absorption Towers

1. Operating-line derivation.   A plate (tray) absorption tower has the same process flow diagram as the countercurrent multiple-stage process in Fig. 10.3-2 and is shown as a vertical tray tower in Fig. 10.6-7. In the case of solute A diffusing through a stagnant gas (B) and then into a stagnant fluid, as in the absorption of acetone (A) from air (B) by water, the moles of inert or stagnant air and inert water remain constant throughout the entire tower. If the rates

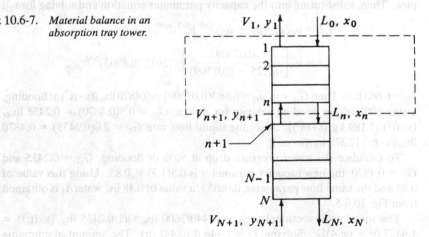

FIGURE 10.6-7.   *Material balance in an absorption tray tower.*

are V' kg mol inert air/s and L' kg mol inert solvent water/s or in kg mol inert/s $\cdot$ m^2 units (lb mol inert/h $\cdot$ ft^2), an overall material balance on component A in Fig. 10.6-7 is

$$L'\left(\frac{x_0}{1-x_0}\right) + V'\left(\frac{y_{N+1}}{1-y_{N+1}}\right) = L'\left(\frac{x_N}{1-x_N}\right) + V'\left(\frac{y_1}{1-y_1}\right) \qquad \textbf{(10.6-2)}$$

A balance around the dashed-line box gives

$$L'\left(\frac{x_0}{1-x_0}\right) + V'\left(\frac{y_{n+1}}{1-y_{n+1}}\right) = L'\left(\frac{x_n}{1-x_n}\right) + V'\left(\frac{y_1}{1-y_1}\right) \qquad \textbf{(10.6-3)}$$

where x is the mole fraction A in the liquid, y the mole fraction of A in the gas, L_n the total moles liquid/s, and V_{n+1} the total moles gas/s. The total flows/s of liquid and gas vary throughout the tower.

Equation (10.6-3) is the material balance or operating line for the absorption tower and is similar to Eq. (10.3-13) for a countercurrent-stage process, except that the inert streams L' and V' are used instead of the total flow rates L and V. Equation (10.6-3) relates the concentration y_{n+1} in the gas stream with x_n in the liquid stream passing it. The terms V', L', x_0, and y_1 are constant and are usually known or can be determined.

2. Graphical determination of the number of trays. A plot of the operating-line equation (10.6-3) as y versus x will give a curved line. If x and y are very dilute, the denominators $1 - x$ and $1 - y$ will be close to 1.0, and the line will be approximately straight, with a slope $\cong L'/V'$. The number of theoretical trays is determined by simply stepping off the number of trays, as done in Fig. 10.3-3 for a countercurrent multiple-stage process.

EXAMPLE 10.6-2. *Absorption of SO$_2$ in a Tray Tower*
A tray tower is to be designed to absorb SO$_2$ from an air stream by using pure water at 293 K (68°F). The entering gas contains 20 mol % SO$_2$ and that leaving 2 mol % at a total pressure of 101.3 kPa. The inert air flow rate is 150 kg air/h $\cdot$ m^2, and the entering water flow rate is 6000 kg water/h $\cdot$ m^2. Assuming an overall tray efficiency of 25%, how many theoretical trays and actual trays are needed? Assume that the tower operates at 293 K (20°C).

Solution: First calculating the molar flow rates,

$$V' = \frac{150}{29} = 5.18 \text{ kg mol inert air/h} \cdot \text{m}^2$$

$$L' = \frac{6000}{18.0} = 333 \text{ kg mol inert water/h} \cdot \text{m}^2$$

Referring to Fig. 10.6-7, $y_{N+1} = 0.20$, $y_1 = 0.02$, and $x_0 = 0$. Substituting into Eq. (10.6-2) and solving for x_N,

$$333\left(\frac{0}{1-0}\right) + 5.18\left(\frac{0.20}{1-0.20}\right) = 333\left(\frac{x_N}{1-x_N}\right) + 5.18\left(\frac{0.02}{1-0.02}\right)$$

$$x_N = 0.00355$$

FIGURE 10.6-8. *Theoretical number of trays for absorption of SO_2 in Example 10.6-2.*

Substituting into Eq. (10.6-3), using V' and L' as kg mol/h · m² instead of kg mol/s · m²,

$$333\left(\frac{0}{1-0}\right) + 5.18\left(\frac{y_{n+1}}{1-y_{n+1}}\right) = 333\left(\frac{x_n}{1-x_n}\right) + 5.18\left(\frac{0.02}{1-0.02}\right)$$

In order to plot the operating line, several intermediate points will be calculated. Setting $y_{n+1} = 0.07$ and substituting into the operating equation,

$$0 + 5.18\left(\frac{0.07}{1-0.07}\right) = 333\left(\frac{x_n}{1-x_n}\right) + 5.18\left(\frac{0.02}{1-0.02}\right)$$

Hence, $x_n = 0.000855$. To calculate another intermediate point, we set $y_{n+1} = 0.13$, and x_n is calculated as 0.00201. The two end points and the two intermediate points on the operating line are plotted in Fig. 10.6-8, as are the equilibrium data from Appendix A.3. The operating line is somewhat curved.

The number of theoretical trays is determined by stepping off the steps to give 2.4 theoretical trays. The actual number of trays is 2.4/0.25 = 9.6 trays.

10.6E   Design of Packed Towers for Absorption

1. Operating-line derivation. For the case of solute A diffusing through a stagnant gas and then into a stagnant fluid, an overall material balance on component A in Fig. 10.6-9 for a packed tower is (note the notation change in Fig. 10.6-9 with inlets y_1 and x_2)

$$L'\left(\frac{x_2}{1-x_2}\right) + V'\left(\frac{y_1}{1-y_1}\right) = L'\left(\frac{x_1}{1-x_1}\right) + V'\left(\frac{y_2}{1-y_2}\right) \tag{10.6-4}$$

where L' is kg mol inert liquid/s or kg mol inert liquid/s $\cdot$ m², V' is kg mol inert gas/s or kg mol inert gas/s $\cdot$ m², and y_1 and x_1 are mole fractions A in gas and liquid, respectively. The flows L' and V' are constant throughout the tower, but the total flows L and V are not constant.

A balance around the dashed-line box in Fig. 10.6-9 gives the operating-line equation:

$$L'\left(\frac{x}{1-x}\right) + V'\left(\frac{y_1}{1-y_1}\right) = L'\left(\frac{x_1}{1-x_1}\right) + V'\left(\frac{y}{1-y}\right) \qquad \textbf{(10.6-5)}$$

This equation, when plotted on yx coordinates, will give a curved line, as shown in Fig. 10.6-10a. Equation (10.6-5) can also be written in terms of partial pressure p_1 of A,

FIGURE 10.6-9. *Material balance for a countercurrent packed absorption tower.*

FIGURE 10.6-10. *Location of operating lines: (a) for absorption of A from V to L stream, (b) for stripping of A from L to V stream.*

where $y_1/(1 - y_1) = p_1/(P - p_1)$, and so on. If x and y are very dilute, $(1 - x)$ and $(1 - y)$ can be taken as 1.0 and Eq. (10.6-5) becomes

$$L'x + V'y_1 \cong L'x_1 + V'y \qquad (10.6-6)$$

This has a slope L'/V' and the operating line is essentially straight.

When the solute is being transferred from the L to the V stream, the process is called *stripping*. The operating line is below the equilibrium line, as shown in Fig. 10.6-10b.

2. Limiting and optimum L'/V' ratios. In the absorption process, the inlet gas flow V_1 (Fig. 10.6-9) and its composition y_1 are generally set. The exit concentration y_2 is also usually set by the designer, and the concentration x_2 of the entering liquid is often fixed by process requirements. Hence, the amount of the entering liquid flow L_2 or L' is open to choice.

In Fig. 10.6-11a the flow V_1 and the concentrations y_2, x_2, and y_1 are set. When the operating line has a minimum slope and touches the equilibrium line at point P, the liquid flow L' is a minimum at L'_{min}. The value of x_1 is a maximum at x_{1max} when L' is a minimum. At point P the driving forces $y - y^*$, $y - y_i$, $x^* - x$, and $x_i - x$ are all zero. To solve for L'_{min}, the values y_1 and x_{1max} are substituted into the operating-line equation. In some cases, if the equilibrium line is curved concavely downward, the minimum value of L is reached by the operating line becoming tangent to the equilibrium line instead of intersecting it.

The choice of the optimum L'/V' ratio to use in the design depends on an economic balance. In absorption, too high a value requires a large liquid flow and hence a large-diameter tower. The cost of recovering the solute from the liquid by distillation will be high. A small liquid flow results in a high tower, which is also costly. As an approximation, for absorption the optimum liquid flow rate can be taken as 1.2–1.5 times the limiting rate L'_{min}, with 1.5 usually used (S6).

For stripping or transfer of solute from L to V, where the operating line has a maximum slope and touches the equilibrium line at point P in Fig. 10.6-11b, then the gas flow is at the minimum V'_{min}. The value of y_2 is at a maximum at y_{2max}. As in absorption, the optimum gas flow rate is taken at about 1.5 times V'_{min}. In liquid extraction, covered later in Section 12.7, the same conditions for stripping hold for extracting solute from feed liquid L to solvent V.

3. Analytical equations for theoretical number of steps or trays. Analytical equations to calculate the number of theoretical trays N in an absorption tower are the same as Eqs. (10.3-22) and (10.3-25) for calculating the number of stages in countercurrent stage processes. These are as follows. (Note that the notation refers to Fig. 10.6-9 and not Fig. 10.3-3.)

For transfer of the solute from phase V to phase L (absorption),

$$N = \frac{\ln\left[\left(\dfrac{y_1 - mx_2}{y_2 - mx_2}\right)(1 - 1/A) + 1/A\right]}{\ln A} \qquad (10.6-7)$$

For transfer of the solute from phase L to phase V (stripping),

$$N = \frac{\ln\left[\left(\dfrac{x_2 - y_1/m}{x_1 - y_1/m}\right)(1 - A) + A\right]}{\ln(1/A)} \qquad (10.6-8)$$

where $A = L/mV$.

If the equilibrium line and/or operating line is slightly curved, m and $A = L/mV$ will vary. For absorption (referring to Fig. 10.6-9), at the bottom concentrated end tray, the slope m_1 or tangent at the point x_1 on the equilibrium line is used. At the dilute top tray, the slope m_2 of

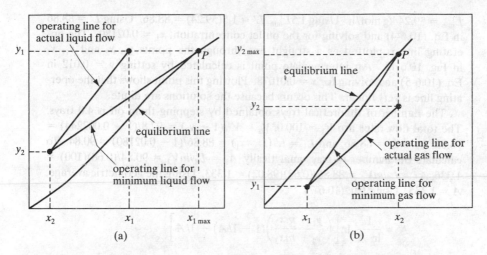

FIGURE 10.6-11. *Operating line for limiting conditions: (a) absorption, (b) stripping.*

the equilibrium line at point y_2 is used. Then $A_1 = L_1/m_1V_1$, $A_2 = L_2/m_2V_2$, and $A = \sqrt{A_1A_2}$. Also, the dilute m_2 is used in Eq. (10.6-7). For stripping, at the top or concentrated stage, the slope m_2 or tangent at point y_2 on the equilibrium line is used. At the bottom or dilute end, the slope m_1 at point x_1 on the equilibrium line is used. Then, $A_1 = L_1/m_1V_1$, $A_2 = L_2/m_2V_2$, and $A = \sqrt{A_1A_2}$. Again, the dilute m_1 is used in Eq. (10.6-8).

EXAMPLE 10.6-3. Minimum Liquid Flow Rate and Analytical Determination of Number of Trays

A tray tower is absorbing ethyl alcohol from an inert gas stream using pure water at 303 K and 101.3 kPa. The inlet gas stream flow rate is 100.0 kg mol/h and it contains 2.2 mol % alcohol. It is desired to recover 90% of the alcohol. The equilibrium relationship is $y = mx = 0.68x$ for this dilute stream. Using 1.5 times the minimum liquid flow rate, determine the number of trays needed. Do this graphically and also using the analytical equations.

Solution: The given data are $y_1 = 0.022$, $x_2 = 0$, $V_1 = 100.0$ kg mol/h, $m = 0.68$. Then $V' = V_1(1 - y_1) = 100.0(1 - 0.022) = 97.8$ kg mol inert/h. Moles alcohol/h in V_1 are $100 - 97.8 = 2.20$. Removing 90%, moles/h in outlet gas $V_2 = 0.10(2.20) = 0.220$. $V_2 = V' + 0.220 = 97.8 + 0.22 = 98.02$. $y_2 = 0.22/98.02 = 0.002244$. The equilibrium line is plotted in Fig. 10.6-12 along with y_2, x_2, and y_1. The operating line for minimum liquid flow L_{min} is drawn from y_2, x_2 to point P, touching the equilibrium line where $x_{1max} = y_1/m = 0.022/0.68 = 0.03235$. Substituting into the operating-line equation (10.6-4) and solving for L_{min},

$$L'\left(\frac{x_2}{1-x_2}\right) + V'\left(\frac{y_1}{1-y_1}\right) = L'\left(\frac{x_1}{1-x_1}\right) + V'\left(\frac{y_2}{1-y_2}\right)$$

$$L'_{min}\left(\frac{0}{1-0}\right) + 97.8\left(\frac{0.022}{1-0.022}\right)$$

$$= L'_{min}\left(\frac{0.03235}{1-0.03235}\right) + 97.8\left(\frac{0.002244}{1-0.002244}\right)$$

$L'_{min} = 59.24$ kg mol/h. Using $1.5L'_{min}$, $L' = 1.5(59.24) = 88.86$. Using $L' = 88.86$ in Eq. (10.6-4) and solving for the outlet concentration, $x_1 = 0.02180$. The operating line is plotted as a straight line through the points y_2, x_2 and y_1, x_1 in Fig. 10.6-12. An intermediate point is calculated by setting $y = 0.012$ in Eq. (10.6-5) and solving for $x = 0.01078$. Plotting this point shows that the operating line is very linear. This occurs because the solutions are dilute.

The number of theoretical trays obtained by stepping them off is 4.0 trays. The total flow rates are $V_1 = 100.0$, $V_2 = V'/(1 - y_2) = 97.8/(1 - 0.002244) = 98.02$, $L_2 = L' = 88.86$, and $L_1 = L'/(1 - x_1) = 88.86/(1 - 0.02180) = 90.84$. To calculate the number of trays analytically, $A_1 = L_1/mV_1 = 90.84/(0.68)(100) = 1.336$, $A_2 = L_2/mV_2 = 88.86/(0.68)(98.02) = 1.333$. Using the geometric average, $A = 1.335$. Using Eq. (10.6-7),

$$N = \frac{1}{\ln A} \, \ln\left[\left(\frac{y_1 - mx_2}{y_2 - mx_2} \right)(1 - 1/A) + 1/A \right]$$

$$= \frac{1}{\ln 1.335} \, \ln\left[\left(\frac{0.022 - 0}{0.002244 - 0} \right)(1 - 1/1.335) + 1/1.335 \right]$$

$N = 4.04$ theoretical steps, which agrees closely with the 4.0 steps obtained graphically.

4. Film and overall mass-transfer coefficients in packed towers. As discussed in Section 10.5, it is very difficult to measure experimentally the interfacial area A m^2 between phases L and V. Also, it is difficult to measure the film coefficients k'_x and k'_y and the overall coefficients K'_x

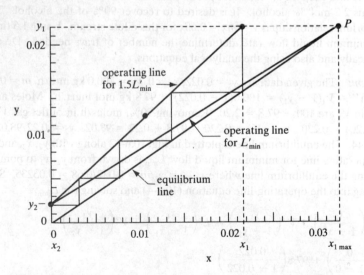

FIGURE 10.6-12. *Operating line for minimum and actual liquid flow in Example 10.6-3.*

and K'_y. Usually, experimental measurements in a packed tower yield a volumetric mass-transfer coefficient that combines the interfacial area and mass-transfer coefficient.

Defining a as interfacial area in m^2 per m^3 volume of packed section, the volume of packing in a height dz m (Fig. 10.6-9) is $S\,dz$, and

$$dA = aS\,dz \qquad (10.6-9)$$

where S is m^2 cross-sectional area of tower. The volumetric film and overall mass-transfer coefficients are then defined as

$$k'_y a = \frac{\text{kg mol}}{\text{s} \cdot m^3 \text{ packing} \cdot \text{mol frac}} \qquad k'_x a = \frac{\text{kg mol}}{\text{s} \cdot m^3 \text{ packing} \cdot \text{mol frac}} \qquad \text{(SI)}$$

$$K'_y a = \frac{\text{kg mol}}{\text{s} \cdot m^3 \text{ packing} \cdot \text{mol frac}} \qquad K'_x a = \frac{\text{kg mol}}{\text{s} \cdot m^3 \text{ packing} \cdot \text{mol frac}} \qquad \text{(SI)}$$

$$k'_y a = \frac{\text{lb mol}}{\text{h} \cdot ft^3 \text{ packing} \cdot \text{mol frac}} \qquad k'_x a = \frac{\text{lb mol}}{\text{h} \cdot ft^3 \text{ packing} \cdot \text{mol frac}} \qquad \text{(English)}$$

5. *Design method for packed towers using mass-transfer coefficients.* For absorption of A from stagnant B, the operating-line equation (10.6-5) holds. For the differential height of tower dz in Fig. 10.6-9, the moles of A leaving V equal the moles entering L:

$$d(Vy) = d(Lx) \qquad (10.6-10)$$

where V = kg mol total gas/s, L = kg mol total liquid/s, and $d(Vy) = d(Lx)$ = kg mol A transferred/s in height dz m. The kg mol A transferred/s from Eq. (10.6-10) must equal the kg mol A transferred/s from the mass-transfer equation for N_A. Equation (10.4-8) gives the flux N_A using the gas-film and liquid-film coefficients:

$$N_A = \frac{k'_y}{(1 - y_A)_{iM}}(y_{AG} - y_{Ai}) = \frac{k'_x}{(1 - x_A)_{iM}}(x_{Ai} - x_{AL}) \qquad (10.4-8)$$

where $(1 - y_A)_{iM}$ and $(1 - x_A)_{iM}$ are defined by Eqs. (10.4-6) and (10.4-7). Multiplying the left-hand side of Eq. (10.4-8) by dA and the two right-side terms by $aS\,dz$ from Eq. (10.6-9),

$$N_A\,dA = \frac{k'_y a}{(1 - y_A)_{iM}}(y_{AG} - y_{Ai})S\,dz = \frac{k'_x a}{(1 - x_A)_{iM}}(x_{Ai} - x_{AL})S\,dz \qquad (10.6-11)$$

where $N_A\,dA$ = kg mol A transferred/s in height dz m (lb mol/h).

Equating Eq. (10.6-10) to (10.6-11) and using y_{AG} for the bulk gas phase and x_{AL} for the bulk liquid phase,

$$d(Vy_{AG}) = \frac{k'_y a}{(1 - y_A)_{iM}}(y_{AG} - y_{Ai})S\,dz \qquad (10.6-12)$$

$$d(Lx_{AL}) = \frac{k'_x a}{(1 - x_A)_{iM}}(x_{Ai} - x_{AL})S\,dz \qquad (10.6-13)$$

Since $V' = V(1 - y_{AG})$ or $V = V'/(1 - y_{AG})$,

$$d(Vy_{AG}) = d\left(\frac{V'}{(1 - y_{AG})}y_{AG}\right) = V'\,d\left(\frac{y_{AG}}{1 - y_{AG}}\right) = \frac{V'\,dy_{AG}}{(1 - y_{AG})^2} \qquad (10.6-14)$$

Substituting V for $V'/(1 - y_{AG})$ in Eq. (10.6-14) and then equating Eq. (10.6-14) to (10.6-12),

$$\frac{V \, dy_{AG}}{1 - y_{AG}} = \frac{k_y' a}{(1 - y_A)_{iM}} (y_{AG} - y_{Ai}) S \, dz \qquad \textbf{(10.6-15)}$$

Repeating for Eq. (10.6-13), since $L = L'/(1 - x_{AL})$,

$$\frac{L \, dx_{AL}}{1 - x_{AL}} = \frac{k_x' a}{(1 - x_A)_{iM}} (x_{Ai} - x_{AL}) S \, dz \qquad \textbf{(10.6-16)}$$

Dropping the subscripts A, G, and L and integrating, the final equations are as follows using film coefficients:

$$\int_0^z dz = z = \int_{y_2}^{y_1} \frac{V \, dy}{\dfrac{k_y' a S}{(1 - y)_{iM}} (1 - y)(y - y_i)} \qquad \textbf{(10.6-17)}$$

$$\int_0^z dz = z = \int_{x_2}^{x_1} \frac{L \, dx}{\dfrac{k_x' a S}{(1 - x)_{iM}} (1 - x)(x_i - x)} \qquad \textbf{(10.6-18)}$$

In a similar manner, the final equations can be derived using overall coefficients:

$$z = \int_{y_2}^{y_1} \frac{V \, dy}{\dfrac{K_y' a S}{(1 - y)_{*M}} (1 - y)(y - y^*)} \qquad \textbf{(10.6-19)}$$

$$z = \int_{x_2}^{x_1} \frac{L \, dx}{\dfrac{K_x' a S}{(1 - x)_{*M}} (1 - x)(x^* - x)} \qquad \textbf{(10.6-20)}$$

In the general case, the equilibrium and the operating lines are usually curved, and $k_x' a$, $k_y' a$, $K_y' a$, and $K_x' a$ vary somewhat with total gas and liquid flows. Then Eqs. (10.6-17)–(10.6-20) must be integrated numerically or graphically. The methods for doing this for concentrated mixtures will be discussed in Section 10.7. Methods for dilute gases will be considered below.

10.6F Simplified Design Methods for Absorption of Dilute Gas Mixtures in Packed Towers

Since a considerable percentage of the absorption processes include absorption of a dilute gas A, these cases will be considered using a simplified design procedure.

The concentrations can be considered dilute for engineering design purposes when the mole fractions y and x in the gas and liquid streams are less than about 0.10, that is, 10%. The flows will vary by less than 10% and the mass-transfer coefficients by considerably less than this. As a result, the average values of the flows V and L and the mass-transfer coefficients at the top and bottom of the tower can be taken outside the integral. Likewise, the terms $(1 - y)_{iM}/(1 - y)$, $(1 - y)_{*M}/(1 - y)$, $(1 - x)_{iM}/(1 - x)$, and $(1 - x)_{*M}/(1 - x)$ can be taken outside and average values at the top and bottom of the tower used. (Often these terms are close to 1.0 and can be dropped out entirely.) Then Eqs. (10.6-17)–(10.6-20) become

$$z = \left[\frac{V}{k'_y aS}\frac{(1-y)_{iM}}{1-y}\right]_{av}\int_{y_2}^{y_1}\frac{dy}{y-y_i} \qquad (10.6\text{-}21)$$

$$z = \left[\frac{L}{k'_x aS}\frac{(1-x)_{iM}}{1-x}\right]_{av}\int_{x_2}^{x_1}\frac{dx}{x_i-x} \qquad (10.6\text{-}22)$$

$$z = \left[\frac{V}{K'_y aS}\frac{(1-y)_{*M}}{1-y}\right]_{av}\int_{y_2}^{y_1}\frac{dy}{y-y^*} \qquad (10.6\text{-}23)$$

$$z = \left[\frac{L}{K'_x aS}\frac{(1-x)_{*M}}{1-x}\right]_{av}\int_{x_2}^{x_1}\frac{dx}{x^*-x} \qquad (10.6\text{-}24)$$

Since the solutions are dilute, the operating line will be essentially straight. Assuming the equilibrium line is approximately straight over the range of concentrations used, $(y-y_i)$ varies linearly with y and also with x:

$$y - y_i = ky + b \qquad (10.6\text{-}25)$$

where k and b are constants. Therefore, the integral of Eq. (10.6-21) can be integrated to give the following:

$$\int_{y_2}^{y_1}\frac{dy}{y-y_i} = \frac{y_1-y_2}{(y-y_i)_M} \qquad (10.6\text{-}26)$$

where $(y-y_i)_M$ is the log mean driving force:

$$(y-y_i)_M = \frac{(y_1-y_{i1})-(y_2-y_{i2})}{\ln[(y_1-y_{i1})/(y_2-y_{i2})]} \qquad (10.6\text{-}27)$$

Similarly, Eq. (10.6-23) gives

$$(y-y^*)_M = \frac{(y_1-y_1^*)-(y_2-y_2^*)}{\ln[(y_1-y_1^*)/(y_2-y_2^*)]} \qquad (10.6\text{-}28)$$

If the term $(1-y)_{iM}/(1-y)$ is considered 1.0, then by substituting Eq. (10.6-26) into (10.6-21) and doing the same for Eqs. (10.6-22)–(10.6-24), the final results are as follows:

$$\frac{V}{S}(y_1-y_2) = k'_y az(y-y_i)_M \qquad (10.6\text{-}29)$$

$$\frac{L}{S}(x_1-x_2) = k'_x az(x_i-x)_M \qquad (10.6\text{-}30)$$

$$\frac{V}{S}(y_1-y_2) = K'_y az(y-y^*)_M \qquad (10.6\text{-}31)$$

$$\frac{L}{S}(x_1-x_2) = K'_x az(x^*-x)_M \qquad (10.6\text{-}32)$$

where the left side is the kg mol absorbed/s · m^2 (lb mol/h · ft^2) by material balance and the right-hand side is the rate equation for mass transfer. The value of V is the average $(V_1+V_2)/2$ and of L is $(L_1+L_2)/2$.

FIGURE 10.6-13. *Operating-line and interface compositions in a packed tower for absorption of dilute gases.*

Equations (10.6-29)–(10.6-32) can be used in slightly different ways. The general steps to follow are discussed below and shown in Fig. 10.6-13.

1. The operating-line equation (10.6-5) is plotted as in Fig. 10.6-13 as a straight line. Calculate V_1, V_2, and $V_{av} = (V_1 + V_2)/2$; also calculate L_1, L_2, and $L_{av} = (L_1 + L_2)/2$.

2. Average experimental values of the film coefficients $k'_y a$ and $k'_x a$ are available or may be obtained from empirical correlations. The interface compositions y_{i1} and x_{i1} at point y_1, x_1 in the tower are determined by plotting line P_1M_1, whose slope is calculated by Eq. (10.6-33):

$$\text{slope} = -\frac{k'_x a/(1-x)_{iM}}{k'_y a/(1-y)_{iM}} = -\frac{k_x a}{k_y a} \qquad (10.6\text{-}33)$$

$$\text{slope} \cong -\frac{k'_x a/(1-x_1)}{k'_y a/(1-y_1)} \qquad (10.6\text{-}34)$$

If terms $(1-x)_{iM}$ and $(1-y)_{iM}$ are used, the procedure is trial and error, as in Example 10.4-1. However, since the solutions are dilute, the terms $(1-x_1)$ and $(1-y_1)$ can be used in Eq. (10.6-34) without trial and error and with only a small error in slope. If the coefficients $k_y a$ and $k_x a$ are available for the approximate concentration range, they can be used, since they include the terms $(1-x)_{iM}$ and $(1-y)_{iM}$. For line P_2M_2 at the other end of the tower, values of y_{i2} and x_{i2} are determined using Eq. (10.6-33) or (10.6-34) and y_2 and x_2.

3. If the overall coefficient $K'_y a$ is being used, y_1^* and y_2^* are determined as shown in Fig. 10.6-13. If $K'_x a$ is used, x_1^* and x_2^* are obtained.

4. Calculate the log mean driving force $(y - y_i)_M$ by Eq. (10.6-27) if $k'_y a$ is used. For $K'_y a$, $(y - y^*)_M$ is calculated by Eq. (10.6-28). Using the liquid coefficients, the appropriate driving forces are calculated.

5. Calculate the column height z m by substituting into the appropriate form of Eqs. (10.6-29)–(10.6-32).

EXAMPLE 10.6-4. *Absorption of Acetone in a Packed Tower*
Acetone is being absorbed by water in a packed tower having a cross-sectional area of 0.186 m^2 at 293 K and 101.32 kPa (1 atm). The inlet air contains 2.6 mol %

acetone and outlet 0.5%. The gas flow is 13.65 kg mol inert air/h (30.1 lb mol/h). The pure water inlet flow is 45.36 kg mol water/h (100 lb mol/h). Film coefficients for the given flows in the tower are $k'_y a = 3.78 \times 10^{-2}$ kg mol/s · m³ · mol frac (8.50 lb mol/h · ft³ · mol frac) and $k'_x a = 6.16 \times 10^{-2}$ kg mol/s · m³ · mol frac (13.85 lb mol/h · ft³ · mol frac). Equilibrium data are given in Appendix A.3.

(a) Calculate the tower height using $k'_y a$.
(b) Repeat, using $k'_x a$.
(c) Calculate $K'_y a$ and the tower height.

Solution: From Appendix A.3 for acetone–water and $x_A = 0.0333$ mol frac, $p_A = 30/760 = 0.0395$ atm or $y_A = 0.0395$ mol frac. Hence, the equilibrium line is $y_A = m x_A$ or $0.0395 = m(0.0333)$. Then, $y = 1.186x$. This equilibrium line is plotted in Fig. 10.6-14. The given data are $L' = 45.36$ kg mol/h, $V' = 13.65$ kg mol/h, $y_1 = 0.026$, $y_2 = 0.005$, and $x_2 = 0$.

Substituting into Eq. (10.6-4) for an overall material balance using flow rates as kg mol/h instead of kg mol/s,

$$45.36\left(\frac{0}{1-0}\right) + 13.65\left(\frac{0.026}{1-0.026}\right) = 45.36\left(\frac{x_1}{1-x_1}\right) + 13.65\left(\frac{0.005}{1-0.005}\right)$$

$$x_1 = 0.00648$$

The points y_1, x_1 and y_2, x_2 are plotted in Fig. 10.6-14 and a straight line is drawn for the operating line.

Using Eq. (10.6-34) the approximate slope at y_1, x_1 is

$$\text{slope} \cong -\frac{k'_x a/(1-x_1)}{k'_y a/(1-y_1)} = -\frac{6.16 \times 10^{-2}/(1-0.00648)}{3.78 \times 10^{-2}/(1-0.026)} = -1.60$$

FIGURE 10.6-14. *Location of interface compositions for Example 10.6-4.*

Plotting this line through y_1, x_1, the line intersects the equilibrium line at $y_{i1} = 0.0154$ and $x_{i1} = 0.0130$. Also, $y_1^* = 0.0077$. Using Eq. (10.6-33) to calculate a more accurate slope, the preliminary values of y_{i1} and x_{i1} will be used in the trial-and-error solution. Substituting into Eq. (10.4-6),

$$(1 - y)_{iM} = \frac{(1 - y_{i1}) - (1 - y_1)}{\ln[(1 - y_{i1})/(1 - y_1)]}$$

$$= \frac{(1 - 0.0154) - (1 - 0.026)}{\ln[(1 - 0.0154)/(1 - 0.020)]} = 0.979$$

Using Eq. (10.4-7),

$$(1 - x)_{iM} = \frac{(1 - x_1) - (1 - x_{i1})}{\ln[(1 - x_1)/(1 - x_{i1})]}$$

$$= \frac{(1 - 0.00648) - (1 - 0.0130)}{\ln[(1 - 0.00648)/(1 - 0.0130)]} = 0.993$$

Substituting into Eq. (10.6-33),

$$\text{slope} = -\frac{k_x'a/(1 - x)_{iM}}{k_y'a/(1 - y)_{iM}} = -\frac{6.16 \times 10^{-2}/0.993}{3.78 \times 10^{-2}/0.929} = -1.61$$

Hence, the approximate slope and interface values are accurate enough.

For the slope at point y_2, x_2,

$$\text{slope} \cong -\frac{k_x'a/(1 - x_2)}{k_y'a/(1 - y_2)} = -\frac{6.16 \times 10^{-2}/(1 - 0)}{3.78 \times 10^{-2}/(1 - 0.005)} = -1.62$$

The slope changes little in the tower. Plotting this line, $y_{i2} = 0.0020$, $x_{i2} = 0.0018$, and $y_2^* = 0$.

Substituting into Eq. (10.6-27),

$$(y - y_i)_M = \frac{(y_1 - y_{i1}) - (y_2 - y_{i2})}{\ln[(y_1 - y_{i1})/(y_2 - y_{i2})]}$$

$$= \frac{(0.026 - 0.0154) - (0.005 - 0.0020)}{\ln[(0.026 - 0.0154)/(0.005 - 0.0020)]} = 0.00602$$

To calculate the total molar flow rates in kg mol/s,

$$V_1 = \frac{V'}{1 - y_1} = \frac{13.65/3600}{1 - 0.026} = 3.893 \times 10^{-3} \text{ kg mol/s}$$

$$V_2 = \frac{V'}{1 - y_2} = \frac{13.65/3600}{1 - 0.005} = 3.811 \times 10^{-3} \text{ kg mol/s}$$

$$V_{av} = \frac{V_1 + V_2}{2} = \frac{3.893 \times 10^{-3} + 3.811 \times 10^{-3}}{2} = 3.852 \times 10^{-3} \text{ kg mol/s}$$

$$L' \cong L_1 \cong L_2 \cong L_{av} = \frac{45.36}{3600} = 1.260 \times 10^{-2} \text{ kg mol/s}$$

For part (a), substituting into Eq. (10.6-29) and solving,

$$\frac{V_{av}}{S}(y_1 - y_2) = k_y' az(y - y_i)_M$$

$$\frac{3.852 \times 10^{-3}}{0.186}(0.0260 - 0.005) = (3.78 \times 10^{-2})z(0.00602)$$

$$z = 1.911 \text{ m } (6.27 \text{ ft})$$

For part (b), using an equation similar to Eq. (10.6-27),

$$(x_i - x)_M = \frac{(x_{i1} - x_1) - (x_{i2} - x_2)}{\ln[(x_{i1} - x_1)/(x_{i2} - x_2)]}$$

$$= \frac{(0.0130 - 0.00648) - (0.0018 - 0)}{\ln[(0.0130 - 0.00648)/(0.0018 - 0)]} = 0.00368$$

Substituting into Eq. (10.6-30) and solving,

$$\frac{1.260 \times 10^{-2}}{0.186}(0.00648 - 0) = (6.16 \times 10^{-2})z(0.00368)$$

$$z = 1.936 \text{ m}$$

This agrees with part (a) quite closely.

For part (c), substituting into Eq. (10.4-25) for point y_1, x_1,

$$(1 - y)_{*M} = \frac{(1 - y_1^*) - (1 - y_1)}{\ln[(1 - y_1^*)/(1 - y_1)]} = \frac{(1 - 0.0077) - (1 - 0.026)}{\ln[(1 - 0.0077)/(1 - 0.026)]} = 0.983$$

The overall mass-transfer coefficient $K_y'a$ at point y_1, x_1 is calculated by substituting into Eq. (10.4-24):

$$\frac{1}{K_y'a/(1 - y)_{*M}} = \frac{1}{k_y'a/(1 - y)_{iM}} + \frac{m'}{k_x'a/(1 - x)_{iM}}$$

$$\frac{1}{K_y'a/0.983} = \frac{1}{3.78 \times 10^{-2}/0.979} + \frac{1.186}{6.16 \times 10^{-2}/0.993}$$

$$K_y'a = 2.183 \times 10^{-2} \text{ kg mol/s} \cdot \text{m}^3 \cdot \text{mol frac}$$

Substituting into Eq. (10.6-28),

$$(y - y^*)_M = \frac{(y_1 - y_1^*) - (y_2 - y_2^*)}{\ln[(y_1 - y_1^*)/(y_2 - y_2^*)]}$$

$$= \frac{(0.0260 - 0.0077) - (0.0050 - 0)}{\ln[(0.0260 - 0.0077)/(0.0050 - 0)]} = 0.01025$$

Finally, substituting into Eq. (10.6-31),

$$\frac{3.852 \times 10^{-3}}{0.186}(0.0260 - 0.0050) = (2.183 \times 10^{-2})z(0.01025)$$

$$z = 1.944 \text{ m}$$

This is in agreement with parts (a) and (b).

10.6G Design of Packed Towers Using Transfer Units

1. Design for concentrated solutions. Another and in some ways more useful design method for packed towers is the use of the transfer-unit concept. For the most common case of A diffusing through stagnant and nondiffusing B, Eqs. (10.6-17)–(10.6-20) can be rewritten as

$$z = H_G \int_{y_2}^{y_1} \frac{(1 - y)_{iM} \, dy}{(1 - y)(y - y_i)} = H_G N_G \tag{10.6-35}$$

$$z = H_L \int_{x_2}^{x_1} \frac{(1 - x)_{iM} \, dx}{(1 - x)(x_i - x)} = H_L N_L \tag{10.6-36}$$

$$z = H_{OG} \int_{y_2}^{y_1} \frac{(1 - y)_{*M} \, dy}{(1 - y)(y - y^*)} = H_{OG} N_{OG} \tag{10.6-37}$$

$$z = H_{OL} \int_{x_2}^{x_1} \frac{(1 - x)_{*M} \, dx}{(1 - x)(x^* - x)} = H_{OL} N_{OL} \tag{10.6-38}$$

where

$$H_G = \frac{V}{k_y' aS} = \frac{V}{k_y a(1 - y)_{iM} S} \tag{10.6-39}$$

$$H_L = \frac{L}{k_x' aS} = \frac{L}{k_x a(1 - x)_{iM} S} \tag{10.6-40}$$

$$H_{OG} = \frac{V}{K_y' aS} = \frac{V}{K_y a(1 - y)_{*M} S} \tag{10.6-41}$$

$$H_{OL} = \frac{L}{K_x' aS} = \frac{L}{K_x a(1 - x)_{*M} S} \tag{10.6-42}$$

where $(1 - y)_{iM}$ is defined by Eq. (10.4-6), $(1 - x)_{iM}$ by Eq. (10.4-7), $(1 - y)_{*M}$ by Eq. (10.4-25), and $(1 - x)_{*M}$ by Eq. (10.4-27). The units of H are in m (ft). H_G is the height of a transfer unit based on the gas film. The values of the heights of transfer units are more constant than the mass-transfer coefficients. For example, $k_y' a$ is often proportional to $V^{0.7}$, so then $H_G \propto V^{1.0}/V^{0.7} \propto V^{0.3}$. The average values of the mass-transfer coefficients, $(1 - y)_{iM}$, $(1 - y)_{*M}$, $(1 - x)_{iM}$, and $(1 - x)_{*M}$, must be used in Eqs. (10.6-39)–(10.6-42).

The integrals on the right side of Eqs. (10.6-35)–(10.6-38) are the number of transfer units N_G, N_L, N_{OG}, and N_{OL}, respectively. The height of the packed tower is then

$$z = H_G N_G = H_L N_L = H_{OG} N_{OG} = H_{OL} N_{OL} \tag{10.6-43}$$

These equations are basically no different from those using mass-transfer coefficients. One still needs $k_y' a$ and $k_x' a$ to determine interface concentrations. Disregarding $(1 - y)_{iM}/(1 - y)$, which is near 1.0 in Eq. (10.6-35), the greater the amount of absorption $(y_1 - y_2)$ or the smaller the driving force $(y - y_i)$, the larger the number of transfer units N_G and the taller the tower.

2. Design for dilute solutions. When the solutions are dilute, with concentrations below 10%, the terms $(1 - y)_{iM}/(1 - y)$, $(1 - x)_{iM}/(1 - x)$, $(1 - y)_{*M}/(1 - y)$, and $(1 - x)_{*M}/(1 - x)$

in Eqs. (10.6-35)–(10.6-38) can be taken outside the integral and average values used. Since these are quite close to 1.0, they can be dropped out. The equations then become

$$z = H_G N_G = H_G \int_{y_2}^{y_1} \frac{dy}{y - y_i} \qquad (10.6\text{-}44)$$

$$z = H_L N_L = H_L \int_{x_2}^{x_1} \frac{dx}{x_i - x} \qquad (10.6\text{-}45)$$

$$z = H_{OG} N_{OG} = H_{OG} \int_{y_2}^{y_1} \frac{dy}{y - y^*} \qquad (10.6\text{-}46)$$

$$z = H_{OL} N_{OL} = H_{OL} \int_{x_2}^{x_1} \frac{dx}{x^* - x} \qquad (10.6\text{-}47)$$

If both the operating and equilibrium lines are straight and dilute, the integrals in Eqs. (10.6-44)–(10.6-47) can be integrated, giving the number of transfer units:

$$N_G = \frac{y_1 - y_2}{(y - y_i)_M} \qquad (10.6\text{-}48)$$

$$N_L = \frac{x_1 - x_2}{(x_i - x)_M} \qquad (10.6\text{-}49)$$

$$N_{OG} = \frac{(y_1 - y_2)}{(y - y^*)_M} \qquad (10.6\text{-}50)$$

$$N_{OL} = \frac{(x_1 - x_2)}{(x^* - x)_M} \qquad (10.6\text{-}51)$$

where $(y - y_i)_M$ is defined in Eq. (10.6-27) and $(y - y^*)_M$ in (10.6-28).

When the major resistance to mass transfer is in the gas phase, as in absorption of acetone from air by water, the overall number of transfer units based on the gas phase N_{OG} or the film N_G should be used. When the major resistance is in the liquid phase, as in absorption of O_2 by water or stripping of a slightly soluble solute from water, N_{OL} or N_L should be employed. This was also discussed in detail in Section 10.4D. Often the film coefficients are not available, and then it is more convenient to use N_{OG} or N_{OL}.

By combining the operating line with the integrals in Eqs. (10.6-46) and (10.6-47), using the equilibrium-line equation $y = mx$, and letting $A = L/mV$, different forms of the equations for absorption with N_{OG} and for stripping with N_{OL} are obtained:

$$N_{OG} = \frac{1}{(1 - 1/A)} \ln\left[(1 - 1/A)\left(\frac{y_1 - mx_2}{y_2 - mx_2} \right) + 1/A \right] \qquad (10.6\text{-}52)$$

$$N_{OL} = \frac{1}{(1 - A)} \ln\left[(1 - A)\left(\frac{x_2 - y_1/m}{x_1 - y_1/m} \right) + A \right] \qquad (10.6\text{-}53)$$

The values of m and A to use in the above equations when operating and/or equilibrium lines are slightly curved are discussed in detail in Section 10.6E for use with Eqs. (10.6-7) and (10.6-8).

When the operating and equilibrium lines are straight and not parallel, the number of overall gas-transfer units N_{OG} for absorption in Eq. (10.6-52) is related to the number of theoretical trays or stages N in Eq. (10.6-7) by

$$N_{OG} = \frac{N \ln A}{(1 - 1/A)} \qquad (10.6-54)$$

The height of a theoretical tray or stage, HETP, in m is related to H_{OG} by

$$\text{HETP} = H_{OG} \frac{\ln(1/A)}{(1 - A)/A} \qquad (10.6-55)$$

A detailed discussion of HETP is given in Section 11.5D. Note that if the operating and equilibrium lines are parallel ($A = 1.0$), then $H_{OG} = \text{HETP}$ and $N_{OG} = N$. Equations (10.6-7) and (10.6-8) can be used to analytically calculate N, the number of theoretical steps.

EXAMPLE 10.6-5. Use of Transfer Units and Analytical Equations for Packed Tower

Repeat Example 10.6-4 using transfer units and height of a transfer unit as follows:

   (a) Use H_G and N_G to calculate tower height.
   (b) Use H_{OG} and N_{OG} to calculate tower height.
   (c) Use Eq. (10.6-52) to calculate N_{OG} and tower height.
   (d) Using the analytical equations, calculate HETP from Eq. (10.6-55), number of theoretical steps N from Eq. (10.6-7), and tower height.

Solution: From Example 10.6-4, $k'_y a = 3.78 \times 10^{-2}$ kg mol/s $\cdot$ m$^2 \cdot$ mol frac, $K'_y a = 2.183 \times 10^{-2}$ kg mol/s $\cdot$ m$^2 \cdot$ mol frac, average $V = 3.852 \times 10^{-3}$ kg mol/s, and $S = 0.186$ m^2.

For part (a), from Eq. (10.6-39),

$$H_G = \frac{V}{k'_y aS} = \frac{3.852 \times 10^{-3}}{(3.78 \times 10^{-2})(0.186)} = 0.548 \text{ m}$$

From Eq. (10.6-27) in Example 10.6-4, $(y - y_i)_{iM} = 0.00602$. Also, $y_1 = 0.026$ and $y_2 = 0.005$. Then, using Eq. (10.6-48),

$$N_G = \frac{y_1 - y_2}{(y - y_i)_{iM}} = \frac{0.026 - 0.005}{0.00602} = 3.488 \text{ transfer units}$$

Substituting in Eq. (10.6-44),

$$z = H_G N_G = (0.548)(3.488) = 1.911 \text{ m } (6.27 \text{ ft})$$

For part (b), using Eq. (10.6-41),

$$H_{OG} = \frac{V}{K'_y aS} = \frac{3.852 \times 10^{-3}}{(2.183 \times 10^{-2})(0.186)} = 0.949 \text{ m}$$

From Eq. (10.6-28) in Example 10.6-4, $(y - y^*)_{*M} = 0.01025$. Then using Eq. (10.6-50),

$$N_{OG} = \frac{(y_1 - y_2)}{(y - y^*)_{*M}} = \frac{(0.026 - 0.005)}{0.01025} = 2.049 \text{ transfer units}$$

From Eq. (10.6-46),

$$z = H_{OG} N_{OG} = (0.949)(2.049) = 1.945 \text{ m (6.38 ft)}$$

Note that the number of transfer units $N_{OG} = 2.049$ is not the same as $N_G = 3.488$.

For part (c), from Example 10.6-4, $m = 1.186$, and the average $V = 3.852 \times 10^{-3}$, $L = 1.260 \times 10^{-2}$, $y_1 = 0.026$, $y_2 = 0.005$, and $x_2 = 0$.

Then $A = L/mV = 1.260 \times 10^{-2}/(1.186 \times 3.852 \times 10^{-3}) = 2.758$. Substituting into Eq. (10.6-52),

$$N_{OG} = \frac{1}{1 - 1/2.758} \ln\left[(1 - 1/2.758)\left(\frac{0.026 - 1.186 \times 0}{0.005 - 1.186 \times 0} \right) + \frac{1}{2.758} \right]$$

$$= 2.043 \text{ transfer units}$$

This compares closely with the value of 2.049 in part (b). Also, $z = H_{OG} N_{OG} = (0.949)(2.043) = 1.939$ m.

For part (d), to calculate HETP, Eq. (10.6-55) is used:

$$\text{HETP} = H_{OG} \frac{\ln(1/A)}{(1 - A)/A} = (0.949)\frac{\ln(1/2.758)}{(1 - 2.758)/2.758} = 1.510 \text{ m}$$

Using Eq. (10.6-7) to calculate N,

$$N = \frac{1}{\ln A} \ln\left[\left(\frac{y_1 - mx_2}{y_2 - mx_2} \right)(1 - 1/A) + 1/A \right]$$

$$= \frac{1}{\ln 2.758} \ln\left[\left(\frac{0.026 - 0}{0.005 - 0} \right)(1 - 1/2.758) + 1/2.758 \right]$$

$$N = 1.283 \text{ theoretical steps}$$

This compares with a value of 1.35 steps obtained graphically in Figure 10.6-14:

$$z = N(\text{HETP}) = 1.283(1.510 \text{ m}) = 1.938 \text{ m}$$

In order to relate H_{OG} to the film coefficients H_G and H_L, Eq. (10.4-24) is rewritten for dilute solutions:

$$\frac{1}{K_y'a} = \frac{1}{k_y'a} + \frac{m}{k_x'a} \tag{10.6-56}$$

Then, substituting $H_G = V/k_y'aS$, $H_L = L/k_x'aS$, and $H_{OG} = V/K_y'aS$ into Eq. (10.6-56) and canceling like terms,

$$H_{OG} = H_G + (mV/L)H_L \tag{10.6-57}$$

Similarly, using Eq. (10.4-26),

$$H_{OL} = H_L + (L/mV)H_G \tag{10.6-58}$$

Note that often in the literature, the terms H_y, H_x, H_{Oy}, and H_{Ox} are used instead of H_G, H_L, H_{OG}, and H_{OL}; they are identical to each other.

10.7 ABSORPTION OF CONCENTRATED MIXTURES IN PACKED TOWERS

In Section 10.6F simplified design methods were given for absorption of dilute gases in packed towers when the mole fractions in the gas and liquid streams were less than about 10%. Straight operating lines and approximately straight equilibrium lines are obtained. In concentrated gas mixtures the operating line and usually the equilibrium line will be substantially curved and $k'_x a$ and $k'_y a$ may vary with total flows. Then the design equations (10.6-17)–(10.6-20) must be integrated graphically or numerically:

$$\int_0^z dz = z = \int_{y_2}^{y_1} \frac{V\,dy}{\dfrac{k'_y aS}{(1-y)_{iM}}(1-y)(y-y_i)} \tag{10.6-17}$$

$$\int_0^z dz = z = \int_{x_2}^{x_1} \frac{L\,dx}{\dfrac{k'_x aS}{(1-x)_{iM}}(1-x)(x_i-x)} \tag{10.6-18}$$

$$\int_0^z dz = z = \int_{y_2}^{y_1} \frac{V\,dy}{\dfrac{K'_y aS}{(1-y)_{*M}}(1-y)(y-y^*)} \tag{10.6-19}$$

$$\int_0^z dz = z = \int_{x_2}^{x_1} \frac{L\,dx}{\dfrac{K'_x aS}{(1-x)_{*M}}(1-x)(x^*-x)} \tag{10.6-20}$$

The detailed general steps to follow are as follows:

1. The operating-line equation (10.6-5) and the equilibrium line are plotted.
2. The values of the film coefficients $k'_y a$ and $k'_x a$ are obtained from empirical equations. These two film coefficients are functions of G_y^n, kg total gas/s $\cdot$ m^2, and G_x^m, kg total liquid/s $\cdot$ m^2, where n and m are in the range 0.2–0.8. Using the operating-line-equation values, total V and L are calculated for different values of y and x in the tower and converted to G_y and G_x. Then values of $k'_y a$ and $k'_x a$ are calculated. If the variation between $k'_y a$ or $k'_x a$ at the top and bottom of the tower is small, an average value can be used.
3. Starting with the tower bottom at point $P_1(y_1, x_1)$, the interface compositions y_{i1}, x_{i1} are determined by plotting a line P_1M_1 with a slope calculated by Eq. (10.6-33). This line intersects the equilibrium line at the interface concentrations at point M_1:

$$\text{slope} = -\frac{k'_x a/(1-x)_{iM}}{k'_y a/(1-y)_{iM}} = -\frac{k_x a}{k_y a} \tag{10.6-33}$$

where $(1-y)_{iM}$ and $(1-x)_{iM}$ are determined from Eqs. (10.4-6) and (10.4-7), respectively. This is trial and error. As a first trial, $(1-x_1)$ can be used for $(1-x)_{iM}$ and $(1-y_1)$ for $(1-y)_{iM}$. The values of y_{i1} and x_{i1} determined in the first trial are used in Eq. (10.6-33) for the second trial.
4. At point $P_2(y_2, x_2)$ determine a new slope using Eq. (10.6-33) and repeating step 3. Do this for several intermediate points in the tower. This slope may vary throughout the tower.
5. Using the values of y_i and x_i, calculate the values of $f(y)$ as follows:

$$f(y) = \dfrac{V}{\dfrac{k_y'aS}{(1 - y)_{iM}}(1 - y)(y - y_i)} \qquad (10.7\text{-}1)$$

Then numerically or graphically integrate Eq. (10.6-17) between y_2 and y_1 to obtain the tower height. If $k_x'a$ or other coefficients are used, the appropriate functions indicated in Eqs. (10.6-18)–(10.6-20) are used. If the stream is quite dilute, $(1 - y)_{iM}$ or $(1 - x)_{iM}$ can be assumed to be 1.0.

EXAMPLE 10.7-1. Design of an Absorption Tower with a Concentrated Gas Mixture

A tower packed with 25.4-mm ceramic rings is to be designed to absorb SO_2 from air by using pure water at 293 K and 1.013×10^5 Pa abs pressure. The entering gas contains 20 mol % SO_2 and that leaving 2 mol %. The inert air flow is 6.53×10^{-4} kg mol air/s and the inert water flow is 4.20×10^{-2} kg mol water/s. The tower cross-sectional area is 0.0929 m^2. For dilute SO_2, the film mass-transfer coefficients at 293 K are, for 25.4-mm (1-in.) rings (W1),

$$k_y'a = 0.0594G_y^{0.7}G_x^{0.25} \qquad k_x'a = 0.152G_x^{0.82}$$

where $k_y'a$ is kg mol/s $\cdot$ m^3 $\cdot$ mol frac, $k_x'a$ is kg mol/s $\cdot$ m^3 $\cdot$ mol frac, and G_x and G_y are kg total liquid or gas, respectively, per sec per m^2 tower cross section. Calculate the tower height.

Solution: The given data are $V' = 6.53 \times 10^{-4}$ kg mol air/s (5.18 lb mol/h), $L' = 4.20 \times 10^{-2}$ kg mol/s (333 lb mol/h), $y_1 = 0.20$, $y_2 = 0.02$, and $x_2 = 0$.

Substituting into the overall material-balance equation (10.6-4),

$$L'\left(\frac{x_2}{1 - x_2}\right) + V'\left(\frac{y_1}{1 - y_1}\right) = L'\left(\frac{x_1}{1 - x_1}\right) + V'\left(\frac{y_2}{1 - y_2}\right)$$

$$4.20 \times 10^{-2}\left(\frac{0}{1 - 0}\right) + 6.53 \times 10^{-4}\left(\frac{0.2}{1 - 0.2}\right) = 4.20 \times 10^{-2}\left(\frac{x_1}{1 - x_1}\right)$$

$$+ 6.53 \times 10^{-4}\left(\frac{0.02}{1 - 0.02}\right)$$

Solving, $x_1 = 0.00355$. The operating line Eq. (10.6-5) is

$$4.20 \times 10^{-2}\left(\frac{x}{1 - x}\right) + 6.53 \times 10^{-4}\left(\frac{0.2}{1 - 0.2}\right) = 4.20 \times 10^{-2}\left(\frac{0.00355}{1 - 0.00355}\right)$$

$$+ 6.53 \times 10^{-4}\left(\frac{y}{1 - y}\right)$$

Setting $y = 0.04$ in the operating-line equation above and solving for x, $x = 0.000332$. Selecting other values of y and solving for x, points on the operating line were calculated as shown in Table 10.7-1 and plotted in Fig. 10.7-1 together with the equilibrium data from Appendix A.3.

The total molar flow V is calculated from $V = V'/(1 - y)$. At $y = 0.20$, $V = 6.53 \times 10^{-4}/(1 - 0.2) = 8.16 \times 10^{-4}$. Other values are calculated and tabu-

FIGURE 10.7-1. *Operating line and interface compositions for Example 10.7-1.*

lated in Table 10.7-1. The total mass flow G_y in $kg/s \cdot m^2$ is equal to the mass flow of air plus SO_2 divided by the cross-sectional area:

$$G_y = \frac{6.53 \times 10^{-4}(29) \text{ kg air/s} + 6.53 \times 10^{-4}\left(\dfrac{y}{1-y}\right)(64.1) \text{ kg } SO_2/s}{0.0929 \text{ m}^2}$$

Setting $y = 0.20$,

$$G_y = \frac{6.53 \times 10^{-4}(29) + 6.53 \times 10^{-4}\left(\dfrac{0.2}{1-0.2}\right)64.1}{0.0929} = 0.3164 \text{ kg/s} \cdot \text{m}^2$$

Similarly, G_y is calculated for all points and tabulated. For the liquid flow, $L = L'/(1-x)$. Also, for the total liquid mass flow rate,

$$G_x = \frac{4.20 \times 10^{-2}(18) + 4.20 \times 10^{-2}\left(\dfrac{x}{1-x}\right)64.1}{0.0929}$$

Calculated values of L and G_x for various values of x are tabulated in Table 10.7-1.
To calculate values of $k'_x a$, for $x = 0$, $G_x = 8.138$ and

$$k'_x a = 0.152 G_x^{0.82} = 0.152(8.138)^{0.82} = 0.848 \text{ kg mol/s} \cdot \text{m}^3 \cdot \text{mol frac}$$

TABLE 10.7-1. Calculated Data for Example 10.7-1

y	x	V	L	G_y	G_x	$k_y a$	$k_x a$	x_i	y_i	$1-y$	$(1-y)_{iM}$	$y-y_i$	$\dfrac{V}{k_y aS}\dfrac{(1-y)(y-y_i)}{(1-y)_{iM}}$ mol/m²·mol frac
0.02	0	6.66×10^{-4}	0.04200	0.2130	8.138	0.03398	0.848	0.00046	0.0090	0.980	0.985	0.0110	19.25
0.04	0.000332	6.80×10^{-4}	0.04201	0.2226	8.147	0.03504	0.849	0.00103	0.0235	0.960	0.968	0.0165	12.77
0.07	0.000855	7.02×10^{-4}	0.04203	0.2378	8.162	0.03673	0.850	0.00185	0.0476	0.930	0.941	0.0224	9.29
0.13	0.00201	7.51×10^{-4}	0.04208	0.2712	8.196	0.04032	0.853	0.00355	0.1015	0.870	0.885	0.0285	7.16
0.20	0.00355	8.16×10^{-4}	0.04215	0.3164	8.241	0.04496	0.857	0.00565	0.1685	0.800	0.816	0.0315	6.33

The rest of these values are calculated and given in Table 10.7-1. For the value of $k'_y a$, for $y = 0.02$, $G_y = 0.2130$, $G_x = 8.138$, and

$$k'_y a = 0.0594 G_y^{0.7} G_x^{0.25} = 0.0594(0.2130)^{0.7}(8.138)^{0.25}$$

$$= 0.03398 \text{ kg mol/s} \cdot \text{m}^3 \cdot \text{mol frac}$$

This and other calculated values of k'_y are tabulated. Note that these values vary considerably in the tower.

Next the interface compositions y_i and x_i must be determined for the given y and x values on the operating line. For the point $y_1 = 0.20$ and $x_1 = 0.00355$, we make a preliminary estimate of $(1 - y)_{iM} \cong 1 - y \cong 1 - 0.20 \cong 0.80$, together with the estimate of $(1 - x)_{iM} \cong 1 - x \cong 1 - 0.00355 \cong 0.996$. The slope of the line $P_1 M_1$ by Eq. (10.6-33) is approximately

$$\text{slope} = -\frac{k'_x a/(1 - x)_{iM}}{k'_y a/(1 - y)_{iM}} = -\frac{0.857/(0.996)}{0.04496/(0.80)} = -15.3$$

Plotting this on Fig. 10.7-1, $y_i = 0.1688$ and $x_i = 0.00566$. Using these values for the second trial in Eqs. (10.4-6) and (10.4-7),

$$(1 - y)_{iM} = \frac{(1 - 0.1688) - (1 - 0.20)}{\ln[(1 - 0.1688)/(1 - 0.20)]} = 0.816$$

$$(1 - x)_{iM} = \frac{(1 - 0.00355) - (1 - 0.00566)}{\ln[(1 - 0.00355)/(1 - 0.00566)]} = 0.995$$

The new slope by Eq. (10.6-33) is $(-0.857/0.995)/(0.04496/0.816) = -15.6$. Plotting, $y_i = 0.1685$ and $x_i = 0.00565$. This is shown as point M_1. This calculation is repeated until point y_2, x_2 is reached. The slope of Eq. (10.6-33) increases markedly in going up the tower, being -24.6 at the top of the tower. The values of y_i and x_i are given in Table 10.7-1.

In order to integrate Eq. (10.6-17), values of $(1 - y)$, $(1 - y)_{iM}$, and $(y - y_i)$ are needed and are tabulated in Table 10.7-1. Then for $y = 0.20$, $f(y)$ is calculated from Eq. (10.7-1):

$$f(y) = \frac{V}{\dfrac{k'_y a S}{(1 - y)_{iM}}(1 - y)(y - y_i)} = \frac{8.16 \times 10^{-4}}{\dfrac{0.04496(0.0929)}{0.816}(0.800)(0.0315)} = 6.33$$

This is repeated for other values of y from y_2 to y_1. Then the function $f(y)$ is used to numerically integrate Eq. (10.6-17), giving $z = 1.588$ m.

10.8 ESTIMATION OF MASS-TRANSFER COEFFICIENTS FOR PACKED TOWERS

10.8A Experimental Determination of Film Coefficients

The individual film mass-transfer coefficients $k'_y a$ and $k'_x a$ depend generally upon Schmidt number, gas and liquid mass velocities, and the size and shape of the packing. The interactions among these factors are quite complex. Hence, the correlations for mass-transfer coefficients are highly empirical. The reliability of these correlations is not too satisfactory.

Deviations of up to 25% are not uncommon. A major difficulty arises because it is an overall coefficient or resistance that is measured experimentally, which represents the two film resistances in series. To obtain the single-phase film coefficient, the experiment must be so arranged that the other film resistance is negligible or can be approximately calculated.

To measure the liquid film mass-transfer coefficient $k'_x a$, a system for absorption or desorption of very insoluble gases such as O_2 or CO_2 in water is used. The experiment gives $K'_x a$, which equals $k'_x a$ (which can give H_L), since the gas-phase resistance is negligible.

To measure the gas-phase film coefficient $k'_y a$, we desire to use a system such that the solute is very soluble in the liquid and the liquid-phase resistance is negligible. Most such systems, for example, NH_3–air–water, have a liquid-phase resistance of about 10%. By subtracting this known liquid-phase resistance (obtained by correcting $k'_x a$ data for absorption of CO_2 or O_2 to NH_3 data for $k'_x a$) from the overall resistance in Eq. (10.4-24), we obtain the coefficient $k'_y a$ or H_G. Details of these systems are discussed elsewhere (G1, S1, S2).

10.8B Correlations for Film Coefficients

Correlations for experimental coefficients can be expressed in terms of H_L and H_G or $k'_x a$ and $k'_y a$, which are related by Eqs. (10.6-39) and (10.6-40). For the first generation of packings, such as Raschig rings and Berl saddles, extensive correlations are available (T1). However, comprehensive data on the individual coefficients H_L and H_G for the newer packings, which have higher mass-transfer coefficients and capacity, are not generally available. These newer packings are more commonly used today.

However, as an alternative method for comparing the performance of different types and sizes of these newer random packings, the system CO_2–air–NaOH solution is often used (P2, S4). Air containing 1.0 mole CO_2 at 24°C (75°F) is absorbed in a packed tower using 1.0 N (4 wt %) NaOH solution (E2, E3, P2, S4). An overall coefficient $K_G a$ is measured.

In this system, the liquid film is controlling but the gas film resistance is not negligible. The fast chemical reaction between NaOH and CO_2 takes place close to the interface, which gives a steeper concentration gradient for CO_2 in the water film. Hence, the value of $K_G a$ is much larger than for absorption of CO_2 in water. Because of this, these experimental values are not used to predict the absorption for other systems in towers.

These experimental results, however, can be used to compare the performances of various packings. To do this, the ratio f_p of $K_G a$ for a given packing to that for $1\frac{1}{2}$-in. Raschig rings at a liquid velocity G_x of 5000 $lb_m/h \cdot ft^2$ (6.782 $kg/s \cdot m^2$) and G_y of 1000 $lb_m/h \cdot ft^2$ (1.356 $kg/s \cdot m^2$) is obtained; these are given in Table 10.6-1. The f_p value is a relative ratio of the total interfacial areas, since the reaction of CO_2 in NaOH solution takes place in the relatively static holdup pools and in the dynamic holdup. Some f_p data have been obtained at $G_y = 500\ lb_m/h \cdot ft^2$ instead of 1000 (E3). Eckert et al. (E2) showed that there is no effect of G_y in the range of 200–1000 $lb_m/h \cdot ft^2$ on the overall $K_G a$. This is expected where the liquid film resistance controls (S1). Values of f_p for various investigators agree within ±10% or less.

10.8C Predicting Mass-Transfer Film Coefficients

For estimating the performance $H_L(H_x)$ and $H_G(H_y)$ of a new packing, the values of f_p can be used to correct the experimental H_x values for oxygen absorption or desorption and the H_y value for NH_3 absorption with $1\frac{1}{2}$-in. Raschig rings. These values must also be corrected for Schmidt number, liquid viscosity, and flow rates.

1. *Gas film coefficient H_y.* Using the NH_3 absorption data corrected for the liquid film resistance of approximately 10%, H_G has been found to vary as G_y to an exponent between 0.3 and 0.4 (S1, T1) for values of G_y up to about 700 $lb_m/h \cdot ft^2$ (0.949 $kg/s \cdot m^2$). A value of 0.35 is used. For liquid flows of G_x from 500 to 5000 $lb_m/h \cdot ft^2$ (0.678–6.782 $kg/s \cdot m^2$), H_y varies as $G_x^{-0.4}$–$G_x^{-0.6}$, with the value of $G_x^{-0.5}$ used. Also, the value of H_y has been found to be proportional to $N_{Sc}^{0.5}$ of the gas phase. A value for H_y of 0.74 ft (0.226 m) is obtained from the correlation for $1\frac{1}{2}$-in. Raschig rings for the NH_3 system (S1) corrected for the small liquid film resistance of 10% at $G_x = 5000$ $lb_m/h \cdot ft^2$ (6.782 $kg/s \cdot m^2$) and $G_y = 500$ $lb_m/h \cdot ft^2$ (0.678 $kg/s \cdot m^2$). The value of $G_y = 500$ will be used instead of 1000, since there is no effect of G_y on f_p in this range. For the NH_3 system, $N_{Sc} = 0.66$ at 25°C. Then, for estimation of H_G for a new solute system and packing and flow rates of G_x and G_y using SI units,

$$H_G = H_y = \left(\frac{0.226}{f_p}\right)\left(\frac{N_{Sc}}{0.660}\right)^{0.5}\left(\frac{G_x}{6.782}\right)^{-0.5}\left(\frac{G_y}{0.678}\right)^{0.35} \tag{10.8-1}$$

where f_p for the new packing is given in Table 10.6-1 and H_G is in m.

2. *Liquid film coefficient H_x.* For gas flow rates up to loading or about 50% of the flooding velocity, the effect of G_y on H_x is small and can be neglected (S1). Using the oxygen desorption data, H_x is proportional to the liquid $N_{Sc}^{0.5}$. The $N_{Sc} = 372$ at 25°C for O_2 in water and the viscosity μ is 0.8937×10^{-3} $kg/m \cdot s$. Data for different packings show that H_x is proportional to (G_x/μ) to the 0.22–0.35 exponent, with an average of $(G_x/\mu)^{0.3}$. A value of $H_x = 1.17$ ft (0.357 m), where $G_x = 5000$ $lb_m/h \cdot ft^2$ is obtained from the correlation (S1) for the O_2 system and $1\frac{1}{2}$-in. Raschig rings. Then, to predict H_x for a new solute system and packing at velocities of G_x and G_y using SI units,

$$H_L = H_x = \left(\frac{0.357}{f_p}\right)\left(\frac{N_{Sc}}{372}\right)^{0.5}\left(\frac{G_x/\mu}{6.782/0.8937 \times 10^{-3}}\right)^{0.3} \tag{10.8-2}$$

These equations can be used for values of G_y up to almost 1000 $lb_m/h \cdot ft^2$ and G_x up to 5000 and remain below loading.

EXAMPLE 10.8-1. Prediction of Film Coefficients for CO_2 Absorption

Predict H_G, H_L, and H_{OL} for absorption of CO_2 from air by water in a dilute solution in a packed tower with $1\frac{1}{2}$-in. metal Pall rings at 303 K (30°C) and 101.32 kPa pressure. The flow rates are $G_x = 4.069$ $kg/s \cdot m^2$ (3000 $lb_m/h \cdot ft^2$) and $G_y = 0.5424$ $kg/s \cdot m^2$ (400 $lb_m/h \cdot ft^2$).

Solution: From Appendix A.3-18, for CO_2 at 1 atm, $p_A = 1.86 \times 10^3 x_A$. Hence, $y_A = p_A/1.0 = 1.86 \times 10^3 x_A$ (mole fraction units). Also, from Appendix A.3-3 for air at 303 K, $\mu = 1.866 \times 10^{-5}$ $kg/m \cdot s$ and the density $\rho = 1.166$ kg/m^3. The diffusivity for CO_2 at 276.2 K from Table 6.2-1 is 0.142×10^{-4} m^2/s. Correcting this to 303 K by Eq. (6.2-45), $D_{AB} = 0.142 \times 10^{-4} (303/276.2)^{1.75} = 0.1670 \times 10^{-4}$ m^2/s. Hence,

$$N_{Sc} = \frac{\mu}{\rho D} = \frac{1.866 \times 10^{-5}}{(1.166)(0.1670 \times 10^{-4})} = 0.958$$

From Table 10.6-1 the relative mass-transfer coefficient for $1\frac{1}{2}$-in. metal Pall rings compared to that for $1\frac{1}{2}$-in. Raschig rings is $f_p = 1.34$. Substituting into Eq. (10.8-1),

$$H_G = \frac{0.226}{1.34}\left(\frac{0.958}{0.660}\right)^{0.5}\left(\frac{4.069}{6.782}\right)^{-0.5}\left(\frac{0.5424}{0.678}\right)^{0.35} = 0.2426 \text{ m } (0.796 \text{ ft})$$

From Appendix A.2-4, the viscosity of water at 303 K is 0.8007×10^{-3} kg/m·s and the density $\rho = 995.68$ kg/m^3. At 298 K the viscosity of water is 0.8937×10^{-3} kg/s·m.

From Table 6.3-1, the D_{AB} of CO_2 in water is 2.00×10^{-9} m^2/s at 25°C. Using Eq. (6.3-9) to correct it to 303 K, $D_{AB} = (0.8937 \times 10^{-3}/0.8007 \times 10^{-3})(303/298)$ $(2.00 \times 10^{-9}) = 2.270 \times 10^{-9}$ m^2/s. Then,

$$N_{Sc} = \frac{\mu}{\rho D_{AB}} = \frac{0.8007 \times 10^{-3}}{995.68(2.270 \times 10^{-9})} = 354.3$$

Substituting into Eq. (10.8-2),

$$H_L = \left(\frac{0.357}{f_p}\right)\left(\frac{N_{Sc}}{372}\right)^{0.5}\left(\frac{G_x/\mu}{6.782/0.8937 \times 10^{-3}}\right)^{0.3}$$

$$H_L = \left(\frac{0.357}{1.34}\right)\left(\frac{354.3}{372}\right)^{0.5}\left(\frac{4.069/0.8007 \times 10^{-3}}{6.782/0.8937 \times 10^{-3}}\right)^{0.3} = 0.2306 \text{ m } (0.759 \text{ ft})$$

To calculate the value of H_{OL}, the molar flow rates are calculated, where for dilute air, $V = G_y/MW = 0.5424/28.97 = 0.01872$ kg mol/s·m^2, and for water, $L = G_x/MW = 4.069/18.0 = 0.2261$ kg mol/s·m^2. Substituting into Eq. (10.6-58),

$$H_{OL} = H_{Ox} = H_L + (L/mV)H_G$$

$$= 0.2306 + [(0.2261)/(1.86 \times 10^3 \times 0.01872)]0.2426$$

$$= 0.2306 + 0.001575 = 0.2322 \text{ m}$$

The percent resistance in the gas film is $0.001575(100)/0.2322 = 0.68\%$. This shows that for a very insoluble gas, even though H_G is similar in value to H_L, the large value of m causes the gas-phase resistance to be very small. Hence, $H_{OL} \cong H_L$. For a soluble gas like NH_3, where $m = 1.20$ at 303 K compared to 1.86×10^3 for CO_2, the percent resistance in the gas film would be about 90%. (See Problem 10.8-1.) The different gas and liquid Schmidt numbers for NH_3 would have only a small effect on the results.

10.9 HEAT EFFECTS AND TEMPERATURE VARIATIONS IN ABSORPTION

10.9A Heat Effects in Absorption

The temperature in an absorption tower can vary from the top to the bottom of the tower when the inlet gas contains a relatively high concentration of solute. Solute absorption by the liquid yields a heat of solution which raises the liquid temperature. Also, if evaporation of the solvent to the gas phase occurs, the liquid temperature is cooled. The curvature of the equilibrium line depends upon the absorption of the solute, the heat-transfer rate between phases, and the evaporation or condensation of the liquid solvent.

Calculated temperature profiles may also have a maximum in the tower. This can occur when the entering gas temperature is considerably below the exit solvent temperature and/or the volatile solvent evaporates. Solvent evaporation cools the liquid near the tower bottom and a temperature maximum occurs. Detailed rigorous heat and mass-balance equations are needed for mass transfer of the solute, mass transfer of the solvent, heat transfer between the gas and liquid, and enthalpy balances. Equations and examples are given by Sherwood et al. (S1), Stockar and Wilke (S7), and Treybal (T2). Note that in actual towers, intercoolers are often used to keep the towers isothermal.

10.9B Simplified Design Method

A simplified adiabatic design method is sometimes used when the entering gas contains solvent vapor and/or solvent evaporation occurs. Heat of solution of the solute is also included in the design. Then, using an overall enthalpy balance, the exit liquid temperature is calculated. This rise in liquid temperature can then be used to adjust the equilibrium-line curvature. First, an overall enthalpy balance is made which includes sensible heat for inlet and outlet gas temperatures, heat of solution of the solute, heat of vaporization of the solvent, and sensible heat for the inlet and the unknown outlet liquid temperature. This outlet temperature is then obtained.

The equilibrium line for the top entering liquid temperature is plotted, with the given slope at the dilute concentration. Next, an equilibrium line at this higher outlet liquid temperature is plotted. The outlet concentration x_1 is then located on this equilibrium line. Then, assuming a linear liquid temperature profile, the temperature of point x, which is halfway between the top and bottom concentrations, is obtained. This x value is then located on the equilibrium line for this new temperature. The final curved equilibrium line is plotted with the slope at the dilute end, through the x at the halfway point, and finally through the x_1 point. This method is illustrated in Example 10.9-1.

> ### EXAMPLE 10.9-1. Heat Balance for Nonisothermal Absorption Tower
> The gas feed at 20°C and 1 atm to a packed absorption tower contains 6.0 mol % of NH_3 (on a dry basis) in air. The inlet gas is saturated with water vapor. The absorbing pure liquid water enters at 25°C. The outlet gas contains 0.5% of NH_3 on a dry basis; it is assumed to be saturated with water vapor and leaves at 25°C. For a feed of 100 g mol dry gas, 190 g mol of pure water are to be used for absorption. The heat of solution for 1.0 g mol NH_3 gas absorbed in water is $\Delta H = -8310$ cal/g mol (S1). Equilibrium data (P1) are as follows for this system, where $y = mx$:
>
> | | 20°C | 25 | 30 | 35 | 40 | |
> |---|---|---|---|---|---|---|
> | x | | m | | | | *Interpolated |
> | 0.03077 | 0.778 | 1.005 | 1.266 | 1.578* | 1.924 | |

Solution: For the inlet gas, where $y_1 = 0.06$, the moles $NH_3 = 0.06(100) = 6.0$ and moles air $= 0.94(100) = 94.0$. For the outlet gas, where $y_2 = 0.005$, the moles air $= 94.0$ and moles $NH_3 = 94.0 [0.005/(1 - 0.005)] = 0.472$. The total is 94.472 moles. The moles NH_3 absorbed $= 6.0 - 0.472 = 5.528$. The outlet $x_1 = (5.528)/(190 + 5.528) = 0.0283$. From Appendix A.2-9, the latent heat of water at 25°C is (2442.3 J/g)(1/4.184 J/cal)(18.02 g/g mol) = 10 519 cal/g mol. The vapor pressure of water at 20°C = 2.346 kPa and at 25°C, 3.169 kPa.

The moles H_2O in the inlet gas at 20°C = (100.0)(2.346)/(101.325 − 2.346) = 2.370 moles vapor. In the outlet gas moles H_2O vapor = (94.472)(3.169)/

$(101.325 - 3.169) = 3.050$ moles vapor. The moles of H_2O vaporized $= 3.050 - 2.370 = 0.680$.

An enthalpy balance is made for ammonia gas and air in and liquid water at 25°C. For air, from Appendix A.3-3, $c_p = (1.0048 \text{ J/g}\cdot\text{K})(1/4.184 \text{ J/cal})$ $(28.972 \text{g/g mol}) = 6.957 \text{ cal/g mol}\cdot\text{K}$. For water vapor, from the Appendix, Fig. A.3-1, $c_p = 8.0 \text{ cal/g mol}\cdot\text{K}$, and for NH_3 gas, $c_p = 8.58 \text{ cal/g mol}\cdot\text{K}$. The sensible heat for the entering gas at 20°C is as follows. For air, the sensible heat $q = 94(6.957)(20 - 25) = -3270 \text{ cal}$. For water vapor, $q = (2.370)(8.0)(20 - 25) = -95 \text{ cal}$. For NH_3 gas, $q = (6.00)(8.58)(20 - 25) = -257 \text{ cal}$. The total sensible heat is $-3270 - 95 - 257 = -3622 \text{ cal}$. The latent heat of water vapor entering $q = 2.370(10\,519) = 24\,930 \text{ cal}$. The sensible heat of the entering liquid at 25°C is 0.

For the exit gas at 25°C, the sensible heat $= 0$. The latent heat of the water vapor $= 3.050(10\,519) = 32\,083 \text{ cal}$. The heat of solution of NH_3 absorption $= 5.528(-8310) = -45\,938 \text{ cal}$. From Appendix A.2-11, assuming dilute liquid water, $c_p = (1.000 \text{ cal/g}\cdot\text{K})(18.02 \text{ g/g mol}) = 18.02 \text{ cal/g mol}\cdot\text{K}$. The total g moles outlet liquid $= 190 + 5.528 - 0.68 = 194.85$. The sensible heat q of the outlet liquid $= (194.85)(18.02)(T_1 - 25) = 3511(T_1 - 25) \text{ cal}$, where T_1 is the unknown outlet temperature in °C. Equating the heat in to the heat out,

$$-3622 + 24\,930 = 0 + 32\,083 - 45\,938 + 3511(T_1 - 25)$$

Solving, $(T_1 - 25) = 10.02°C$, which is the temperature increase of the outlet liquid. The outlet $T_1 = 35.02°C$ or 35°C.

In Fig. 10.9-1, a straight operating line is plotted since the solution is dilute. The equilibrium line for 25°C is also shown with a slope $m = 1.005$ at the top of the tower. At the tower bottom, at 35°C, the exit $x_1 = 0.0283$. The equilibrium line at 35°C is shown. The point x_1 is located on this 35°C line and on the curved

FIGURE 10.9-1. *Operating line and curved equilibrium line for Example 10.9-1. The calculated linear temperature profile is also shown.*

equilibrium line for the tower. The assumed linear temperature profile is also shown. Selecting a value of $x = (0 + 0.0283)/2 = 0.0142$ with a temperature of $(35 + 25)/2$ or $30°C$, the point $x_1 = 0.0412$ is plotted on the $30°C$ equilibrium line. The final curved equilibrium line is plotted with a slope at the origin of 1.005 at $25°C$, through the point $x = 0.0142$ on the $30°C$ equilibrium line, and then through the point $x_1 = 0.0283$ on the $35°C$ equilibrium line. Since the equilibrium line is curved, the number of overall transfer units N_{Oy} can be obtained by numerical or graphical integration as before using Eq. (10.6-46).

PROBLEMS

10.2-1. *Equilibrium and Henry's Law Constant.* The partial pressure of CO_2 in air is 1.333×10^4 Pa and the total pressure is 1.133×10^5 Pa. The gas phase is in equilibrium with a water solution at 303 K. What is the value of x_A for CO_2 in equilibrium in the solution? See Appendix A.3 for the Henry's law constant.

Ans. $x_A = 7.07 \times 10^{-5}$ mol frac CO_2

10.2-2. *Gas Solubility in Aqueous Solution.* At 303 K the concentration of CO_2 in water is 0.90×10^{-4} kg CO_2/kg water. Using the Henry's law constant from Appendix A.3, what partial pressure of CO_2 must be kept in the gas to prevent the CO_2 from vaporizing from the aqueous solution?

Ans. $p_A = 6.93 \times 10^3$ Pa (0.0684 atm)

10.2-3. *Phase Rule for a Gas–Liquid System.* For the system SO_2–air–water, the total pressure is set at 1 atm abs and the partial pressure of SO_2 in the vapor is set at 0.20 atm. Calculate the number of degrees of freedom, F. What variables are unspecified and hence can be arbitrarily set?

10.3-1. *Equilibrium Stage Contact for Gas–Liquid System.* A gas mixture at 2.026×10^5 Pa total pressure containing air and SO_2 is brought into contact in a single-stage equilibrium mixer with pure water at 293 K. The partial pressure of SO_2 in the original gas is 1.52×10^4 Pa. The inlet gas contains 5.70 total kg mol and the inlet water 2.20 total kg mol. The exit gas and liquid leaving are in equilibrium. Calculate the amounts and compositions of the outlet phases. Use equilibrium data from Fig. 10.2-1.

Ans. $x_{A1} = 0.00495$, $y_{A1} = 0.0733$, $L_1 = 2.211$ kg mol, $V_1 = 5.69$ kg mol

10.3-2. *Absorption in a Countercurrent Stage Tower.* Repeat Example 10.3-2 using the same conditions but with the following change. Use a pure water flow to the tower of 108 kg mol H_2O/h, that is, 20% above the 90 used in Example 10.3-2. Determine the number of stages required graphically. Repeat, using the analytical Kremser equation.

10.3-3. *Stripping Taint from Cream by Steam.* Countercurrent stage stripping is to be used to remove a taint from cream. The taint is present in the original cream to the stripper at a concentration of 20 parts per million (ppm). For every 100 kg of cream entering per unit time, 50 kg of steam will be used for stripping. It is desired to reduce the concentration of the taint in the cream to 1 ppm. The equilibrium relation between the taint in the steam vapor and the liquid cream is $y_A = 10x_A$, where y_A is ppm of taint in the steam and x_A ppm in the cream (E1). Determine the number of theoretical stages needed. [*Hint:* In this case, for stripping from the liquid (L) stream to the vapor (V) stream, the operating line will be below the equilibrium line on the $y_A - x_A$ diagram. It is assumed that none of the steam condenses in the stripping. Use ppm in the material balances.]

Ans. Number stages = 1.85 (stepping down starting from the concentrated end)

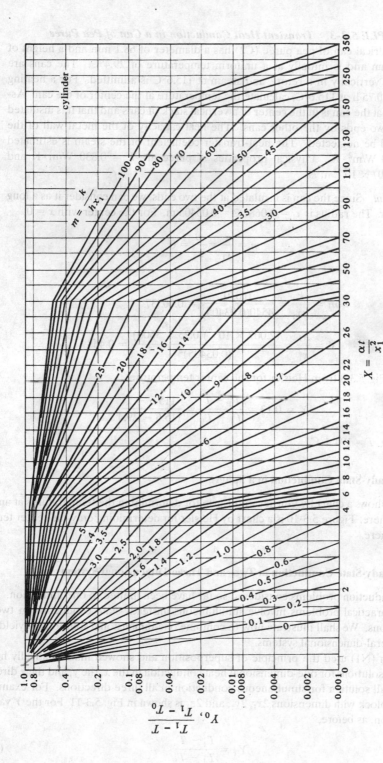

FIGURE 5.3-8. *Chart for determining temperature at the center of a long cylinder for unsteady-state heat conduction. [From H. P. Heisler, Trans. A.S.M.E., 69, 227 (1947). With permission.]*

The chart uses coordinates $X = \dfrac{\alpha t}{x_1^2}$ (horizontal axis) and $Y_0, \dfrac{T_1 - T_0}{T_1 - T}$ (vertical axis), with parameter $m = \dfrac{k}{h x_1}$.

EXAMPLE 5.3-3. *Transient Heat Conduction in a Can of Pea Purée*

A cylindrical can of pea purée (C2) has a diameter of 68.1 mm and a height of 101.6 mm and is initially at a uniform temperature of 29.4°C. The cans are stacked vertically in a retort, and steam at 115.6°C is admitted. For a heating time of 0.75 h at 115.6°C, calculate the temperature at the center of the can. Assume that the can is in the center of a vertical stack of cans and that it is insulated on its two ends by the other cans. The heat capacity of the metal wall of the can will be neglected. The heat-transfer coefficient of the steam is estimated as 4540 W/m²·K. Physical properties of purée are $k = 0.830$ W/m·K and $\alpha = 2.007 \times 10^{-7}$ m²/s.

Solution: Since the can is insulated at the two ends, we can consider it as a long cylinder. The radius is $x_1 = 0.0681/2 = 0.03405$ m. For the center with $x = 0$,

$$n = \frac{x}{x_1} = \frac{0}{x_1} = 0$$

Also,

$$m = \frac{k}{hx_1} = \frac{0.830}{4540(0.03405)} = 0.00537$$

$$X = \frac{\alpha t}{x_1^2} = \frac{(2.007 \times 10^{-7})(0.75 \times 3600)}{(0.03405)^2} = 0.468$$

Using Fig. 5.3-8 from Heisler for the center temperature,

$$Y = 0.13 = \frac{T_1 - T}{T_1 - T_0} = \frac{115.6 - T}{115.6 - 29.4}$$

Solving, $T = 104.4$°C.

5.3E Unsteady-State Conduction in a Sphere

Figure 5.3-9 shows a chart by Gurney and Lurie for determining the temperatures at any position in a sphere. Figure 5.3-10 is a chart by Heisler for determining only the center temperature in a sphere.

5.3F Unsteady-State Conduction in Two- and Three-Dimensional Systems

The heat-conduction problems considered so far have been limited to one dimension. However, many practical problems involve simultaneous unsteady-state conduction in two and three directions. We shall illustrate how to combine one-dimensional solutions to yield solutions for several-dimensional systems.

Newman (N1) used the principle of superposition and showed mathematically how to combine the solutions for one-dimensional heat conduction in the x, the y, and the z direction into an overall solution for simultaneous conduction in all three directions. For example, a rectangular block with dimensions $2x_1$, $2y_1$, and $2z_1$ is shown in Fig. 5.3-11. For the Y value in the x direction, as before,

$$Y_x = \frac{T_1 - T_x}{T_1 - T_0} \tag{5.3-8}$$

FIGURE 5.3-9. *Unsteady-state heat conduction in a sphere. [From H. P. Gurney and J. Lurie,
Ind. Eng. Chem., **15**, 1170 (1923).]*

where T_x is the temperature at time t and position x distance from the center line, as before.
Also, $n = x/x_1$, $m = k/hx_1$, and $X_x = \alpha t/x_1^2$, as before. Then for the y direction,

$$Y_y = \frac{T_1 - T_y}{T_1 - T_0} \qquad (5.3\text{-}9)$$

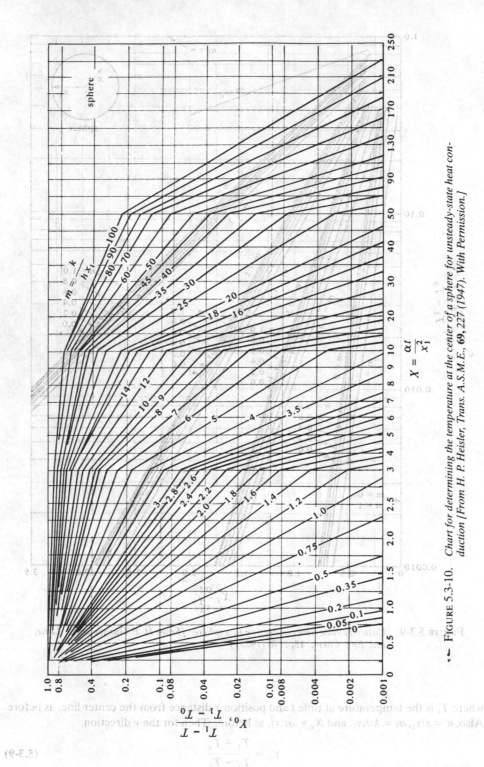

$$X = \frac{\alpha t}{x_1^2}$$

where T_1 is the temperature at time t and position x distance from the center line, as before.

Also $x = x_1/x_1 = k/hx_1$ and $X_v = \alpha t/x_1^2$ for the v direction

$$\frac{T_1 - T}{T_1 - T_0}$$

(5.3-9)

FIGURE 5.3-11. *Unsteady-state conduction in three directions in a rectangular block.*

and $n = y/y_1$, $m = k/hy_1$, and $X_y = \alpha t/y_1^2$. Similarly, for the z direction,

$$Y_z = \frac{T_1 - T_z}{T_1 - T_0} \tag{5.3-10}$$

Then, for simultaneous transfer in all three directions,

$$Y_{x,y,z} = (Y_x)(Y_y)(Y_z) = \frac{T_1 - T_{x,y,z}}{T_1 - T_0} \tag{5.3-11}$$

where $T_{x,y,z}$ is the temperature at the point x, y, z from the center of the rectangular block. The value of Y_x for the two parallel faces is obtained from Figs. 5.3-5 and 5.3-6 for conduction in a flat plate. The values of Y_y and Y_z are similarly obtained from the same charts.

For a short cylinder with radius x_1 and length $2y_1$, the following procedure is followed. First Y_x for the radical conduction is obtained from the figures for a long cylinder. Then Y_y for conduction between two parallel planes is obtained from Fig. 5.3-5 or 5.3-6 for conduction in a flat plate. Then,

$$Y_{x,y} = (Y_x)(Y_y) = \frac{T_1 - T_{x,y}}{T_1 - T_0} \tag{5.3-12}$$

EXAMPLE 5.3-4. Two-Dimensional Conduction in a Short Cylinder

Repeat Example 5.3-3 for transient conduction in a can of pea purée but assume that conduction also occurs from the two flat ends.

Solution: The can, which has a diameter of 68.1 mm and a height of 101.6 mm, is shown in Fig. 5.3-12. The given values from Example 5.3-3 are $x_1 = 0.03405$ m, $y_1 = 0.1016/2 = 0.0508$ m, $k = 0.830$ W/m·K, $\alpha = 2.007 \times 10^{-7}$ m^2/s, $h = 4540$ W/m^2·K, and $t = 0.75(3600) = 2700$ s.

For conduction in the x (radial) direction as calculated previously,

$$n = \frac{x}{x_1} = \frac{0}{x_1} = 0, \quad m = \frac{k}{hx_1} = \frac{0.830}{4540(0.03405)} = 0.00537$$

$$X = \frac{\alpha t}{x_1^2} = \frac{(2.007 \times 10^{-7})2700}{(0.03405)^2} = 0.468$$

FIGURE 5.3-12. *Two dimensional conduction in a short cylinder in Example 5.3-4.*

From Fig. 5.3-8 for the center temperature,

$$Y_x = 0.13$$

For conduction in the y (axial) direction for the center temperature,

$$n = \frac{y}{y_1} = \frac{0}{0.0508} = 0$$

$$m = \frac{k}{hy_1} = \frac{0.830}{4540(0.0508)} = 0.00360$$

$$X = \frac{\alpha t}{y_1^2} = \frac{(2.007 \times 10^{-7})2700}{(0.0508)^2} = 0.210$$

Using Fig. 5.3-6 for the center of a large plate (two parallel opposed planes),

$$Y_y = 0.80$$

Substituting into Eq. (5.3-12),

$$Y_{x,y} = (Y_x)(Y_y) = 0.13(0.80) = 0.104$$

Then,

$$\frac{T_1 - T_{x,y}}{T_1 - T_0} = \frac{115.6 - T_{x,y}}{115.6 - 29.4} = 0.104$$

$$T_{x,y} = 106.6°C$$

This compares with 104.4°C obtained in Example 5.3-3 for only radial conduction.

5.3G Charts for Average Temperature in a Plate, Cylinder, and Sphere with Negligible Surface Resistance

If the surface resistance is negligible, the curves given in Fig. 5.3-13 will give the total fraction of unaccomplished change, E, for slabs, cylinders, or spheres for unsteady-state conduction. The value of E is

$$E = \frac{T_1 - T_{av}}{T_1 - T_0} \tag{5.3-13}$$

FIGURE 5.3-13. *Unsteady-state conduction and average temperatures for negligible surface resistance. (From R. E. Treybal, Mass Transfer Operations, 2nd ed. New York: McGraw-Hill Book Company, 1968. With permission.)*

where T_0 is the original uniform temperature, T_1 is the temperature of the environment to which the solid is suddenly subjected, and T_{av} is the average temperature of the solid after t hours.

The values of E_a, E_b, and E_c are each used for conduction between a pair of parallel faces, as in a plate. For example, for conduction in the a and b directions in a rectangular bar,

$$E = E_a E_b \qquad \text{(5.3-14)}$$

For conduction from all three sets of faces,

$$E = E_a E_b E_c \qquad \text{(5.3-15)}$$

For conduction in a short cylinder $2c$ long and radius a,

$$E = E_c E_r \qquad \text{(5.3-16)}$$

5.4 NUMERICAL FINITE-DIFFERENCE METHODS FOR UNSTEADY-STATE CONDUCTION

5.4A Unsteady-State Conduction in a Slab

1. Introduction. As discussed in previous sections of this chapter, the partial differential equations for unsteady-state conduction in various simple geometries can be solved analytically if the boundary conditions are constant at $T = T_1$ with time. Also, in the solutions the initial profile of the temperature at $t = 0$ is uniform at $T = T_0$. The unsteady-state charts used also have these same boundary conditions and initial condition. However, when the boundary conditions are not constant with time and/or the initial conditions are not constant with position, numerical methods must be used.

Numerical calculation methods for unsteady-state heat conduction are similar to numerical methods for steady state discussed in Section 4.15. The solid is subdivided into sections or slabs of equal length and a fictitious node is placed at the center of each section. Then a heat balance is made for each node. This method differs from the steady-state method in that we have heat accumulation in a node for unsteady-state conduction. The methods are well suited for a spreadsheet calculation.

2. Equations for a slab. The unsteady-state equation for conduction in the x direction in a slab is

$$\frac{\partial T}{\partial t} = \alpha \frac{\partial^2 T}{\partial x^2} \tag{5.1-10}$$

This can be set up for a numerical solution by expressing each partial derivative as an actual finite difference in ΔT, Δt, and Δx. However, an alternative method will be used to derive the final result by making a heat balance. Figure 5.4-1 shows a slab centered at position n, represented by the shaded area. The slab has a width of Δx m and a cross-sectional area of A m^2. The node at position n having a temperature of T_n is placed at the center of the shaded sec-

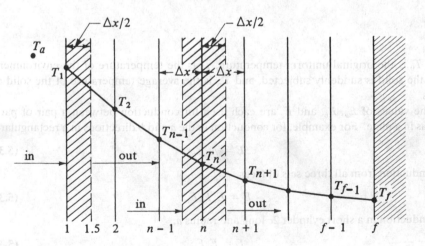

FIGURE 5.4-1. *Unsteady-state conduction in a slab.*

tion; this node represents the total mass and heat capacity of the section or slab. Each node is imagined to be connected to the adjacent node by a fictitious, small conducting rod. (See Fig. 4.15-3 for an example.)

The figure shows the temperature profile at a given instant of time t s. Making a heat balance on this node or slab, the rate of heat in – the rate of heat out = the rate of heat accumulation in Δt s:

$$\frac{kA}{\Delta x}({}_tT_{n-1} - {}_tT_n) - \frac{kA}{\Delta x}({}_tT_n - {}_tT_{n+1}) = \frac{(A\,\Delta x)\rho c_p}{\Delta t}({}_{t+\Delta t}T_n - {}_tT_n) \qquad (5.4\text{-}1)$$

where ${}_tT_n$ is the temperature at point n at time t and ${}_{t+\Delta t}T_n$ is the temperature at point n at time $t + 1\,\Delta t$ later. Rearranging and solving for ${}_{t+\Delta t}T_n$,

$$_{t+\Delta t}T_n = \frac{1}{M}\left[{}_tT_{n+1} + (M - 2){}_tT_n + {}_tT_{n-1}\right] \qquad (5.4\text{-}2)$$

where

$$M = \frac{(\Delta x)^2}{\alpha\,\Delta t} \qquad (5.4\text{-}3)$$

Note that in Eq. (5.4-2) the temperature ${}_{t+\Delta t}T_n$ at position or node n and at a new time $t + \Delta t$ is calculated from the three points which are known at time t, the starting time. This is called the *explicit method,* because the temperature at a new time can be calculated explicitly from the temperatures at the previous time. In this method the calculation proceeds directly from one time increment to the next until the final temperature distribution is calculated at the desired final time. Of course, the temperature distribution at the initial time and the boundary conditions must be known.

Once the value of Δx has been selected, then from Eq. (5.4-3) a value of M or the time increment Δt may be picked. For a given value of M, smaller values of Δx mean smaller values of Δt. The value of M must be as follows:

$$M \geq 2 \qquad (5.4\text{-}4)$$

If M is less than 2, the second law of thermodynamics is violated. It also can be shown that for stability and convergence of the finite-difference solution, M must be ≥ 2.

Stability means the errors in the solution do not grow exponentially as the solution proceeds but damp out. Convergence means that the solution of the difference equation approaches the exact solution of the partial differential equation as Δt and Δx go to zero with M fixed. Using smaller sizes of Δt and Δx increases the accuracy in general but greatly increases the number of calculations required. Hence, a digital computer is often ideally suited for this type of calculation using a spreadsheet.

3. Simplified Schmidt method for a slab. If the value of $M = 2$, then a great simplification of Eq. (5.4-2) occurs, giving the Schmidt method:

$$_{t+\Delta t}T_n = \frac{{}_tT_{n-1} + {}_tT_{n+1}}{2} \qquad (5.4\text{-}5)$$

This means that when a time $1\,\Delta t$ has elapsed, the new temperature at a given point n at $t + \Delta t$ is the arithmetic average of the temperatures at the two adjacent nodes $n + 1$ and $n - 1$ at the original time t.

5.4B Boundary Conditions for Numerical Method for a Slab

1. Convection at the boundary.   For the case where there is a finite convective resistance at the boundary and the temperature of the environment or fluid outside is suddenly changed to T_a, we can derive the following for a slab. Referring to Fig. 5.4-1, we make a heat balance on the outside half-element. The rate of heat in by convection − the rate of heat out by conduction = the rate of heat accumulations in Δt s:

$$hA(_tT_a - {}_tT_1) - \frac{kA}{\Delta x}(_tT_1 - {}_tT_2) = \frac{(A\,\Delta x/2)\rho c_p}{\Delta t}(_{t+\Delta t}T_{1.25} - {}_tT_{1.25}) \tag{5.4-6}$$

where $_tT_{1.25}$ is the temperature at the midpoint of the 0.5 Δx outside slab. As an approximation, the temperature T_1 at the surface can be used to replace that of $T_{1.25}$. Rearranging,

$$_{t+\Delta t}T_1 = \frac{1}{M}\left[2N_tT_a + [M - (2N + 2)]_tT_1 + 2_tT_2\right] \tag{5.4-7}$$

where

$$N = \frac{h\,\Delta x}{k} \tag{5.4-8}$$

Note that the value of M must be such that

$$M \geq 2N + 2 \tag{5.4-9}$$

2. Insulated boundary condition.   In the case for the boundary condition where the rear face is insulated, a heat balance is made on the rear $\frac{1}{2}\Delta x$ slab just as on the front $\frac{1}{2}\Delta x$ slab in Fig. 5.4-1. The resulting equation is the same as Eqs. (5.4-6) and (5.4-7), but $h = 0$ or $N = 0$ and $_tT_{f-1} = {}_tT_{f+1}$ because of symmetry.

$$_{t+\Delta t}T_f = \frac{1}{M}\left[(M - 2)_tT_f + 2_tT_{f-1}\right] \tag{5.4-10}$$

3. Alternative convective condition.   To use the equations above for a given problem, the same values of M, Δx, and Δt must be used. If N gets too large, so that M may be inconveniently too large, another form of Eq. (5.4-7) can be derived. By neglecting the heat accumulation in the front half-slab in Eq. (5.4-6),

$$_{t+\Delta t}T_1 = \frac{N}{N + 1}\,_{t+\Delta t}T_a + \frac{1}{N + 1}\,_{t+\Delta t}T_2 \tag{5.4-11}$$

Here the value of M is not restricted by the N value. This approximation works fairly well when a large number of increments in Δx are used so that the amount of heat neglected is small compared to the total.

4. Procedures for use of initial boundary temperature.   When the temperature of the environment outside is suddenly changed to T_a, the following procedures should be used.

1. When $M = 2$ and a hand calculation of a limited number of increments is used, a special procedure should be used in Eqs. (5.4-5) and (5.4-7) or (5.4-11). For the first time increment, one should use an average value for $_1T_a$ of $(T_a + {}_0T_1)/2$, where $_0T_1$ is the initial temperature at point 1. For all succeeding Δt values, the value of T_a should be used (D1, K1).

This special procedure for determining the value of T_a to use for the first time increment increases the accuracy of the numerical method, especially after a few time intervals. If T_a varies with time t, a new value can be used for each Δt interval.

2. When $M = 2$ and many time increments are used with a digital computer, this special procedure is not needed, and the same value of T_a is used for all time increments.

3. When $M = 3$ or more and a hand calculation of a limited number of increments or a digital-computer calculation of many increments is used, only one value of T_a is used for all time increments. Note that when $M = 3$ or more, many more calculations are needed compared to the case for $M = 2$. The most accurate results are obtained when $M = 4$, which is the preferred method, with slightly less accurate results for $M = 3$ (D1, K1, K2).

EXAMPLE 5.4-1. Unsteady-State Conduction and the Schmidt Numerical Method

A slab of material 1.00 m thick is at a uniform temperature of 100°C. The front surface is suddenly exposed to a constant environmental temperature of 0°C. The convective resistance is zero ($h = \infty$). The back surface of the slab is insulated. The thermal diffusivity $\alpha = 2.00 \times 10^{-5}$ m^2/s. Using five slices each 0.20 m thick and the Schmidt numerical method with $M = 2.0$, calculate the temperature profile at $t = 6000$ s. Use the special procedure for the first time increment.

Solution: Figure 5.4-2 shows the temperature profile at $t = 0$ and the environmental temperature of $T_a = 0$°C with five slices used. For the Schmidt method, $M = 2$. Substituting into Eq. (5.4-3) with $\alpha = 2.00 \times 10^{-5}$ and $\Delta x = 0.20$ and solving for Δt,

$$M = 2 = \frac{(\Delta x)^2}{\alpha \Delta t} = \frac{(0.20)^2}{(2.00 \times 10^{-5})\Delta t} \qquad \Delta t = 1000 \text{ s} \qquad \textbf{(5.4-3)}$$

FIGURE 5.4-2. *Temperature for numerical method, Example 5.4-1.*

This means that (6000 s)/(1000 s/increment), or six time increments, must be used to reach 6000 s.

For the front surface, where $n = 1$, the temperature $_1T_a$ to use for the first Δt time increment, as stated previously, is

$$_{-1}T_a = \frac{T_a + {_0}T_1}{2} = {_1}T_1 \qquad n = 1 \qquad \text{(5.4-12)}$$

where $_0T_1$ is the initial temperature at point 1. For the remaining time increments,

$$T_1 = T_a \qquad n = 1 \qquad \text{(5.4-13)}$$

To calculate the temperatures for all time increments for the slabs $n = 2$ to 5, using Eq. (5.4-5),

$$_{t+\Delta t}T_n = \frac{_tT_{n-1} + {_0}T_{n+1}}{2} \qquad n = 2, 3, 4, 5 \qquad \text{(5.4-14)}$$

For the insulated end for all time increments at $n = 6$, substituting $M = 2$ and $f = 6$ into Eq. (5.4-10),

$$_{t+\Delta t}T_6 = \frac{(2-2)_tT_6 + 2_tT_5}{2} = {_t}T_5 \qquad \text{(5.4-15)}$$

For the first time increment of $t + \Delta t$, and calculating the temperature at $n = 1$ by Eq. (5.4-12),

$$_{t+\Delta t}T_1 = \frac{T_a + {_0}T_1}{2} = \frac{0 + 100}{2} = 50°C = {_1}T_a$$

For $n = 2$, using Eq. (5.4-14),

$$_{t+\Delta t}T_2 = \frac{_tT_1 + {_t}T_3}{2} = \frac{50 + 100}{2} = 75$$

Continuing for $n = 3, 4, 5$, we have

$$_{t+\Delta t}T_3 = \frac{_tT_2 + {_t}T_4}{2} = \frac{100 + 100}{2} = 100$$

$$_{t+\Delta t}T_4 = \frac{_tT_3 + {_t}T_5}{2} = \frac{100 + 100}{2} = 100$$

$$_{t+\Delta t}T_5 = \frac{_tT_4 + {_t}T_6}{2} = \frac{100 + 100}{2} = 100$$

For $n = 6$, using Eq. (5.4-15),

$$_{t+\Delta t}T_6 = {_t}T_5 = 100$$

For 2 Δt, using Eq. (5.4-13) for $n = 1$, and continuing for $n = 2$ to 6, using Eqs. (5.4-14) and (5.4-15),

$$_{t+2\Delta t}T_1 = T_a = 0$$

$$_{t+2\Delta t}T_2 = \frac{_{t+\Delta t}T_1 + {_{t+\Delta t}}T_3}{2} = \frac{0 + 100}{2} = 50$$

$$_{t+2\Delta t}T_3 = \frac{_{t+\Delta t}T_2 + _{t+\Delta t}T_4}{2} = \frac{75 + 100}{2} = 87.5$$

$$_{t+2\Delta t}T_4 = \frac{_{t+\Delta t}T_3 + _{t+\Delta t}T_5}{2} = \frac{100 + 100}{2} = 100$$

$$_{t+2\Delta t}T_5 = \frac{_{t+\Delta t}T_4 + _{t+\Delta t}T_6}{2} = \frac{100 + 100}{2} = 100$$

$$_{t+2\Delta t}T_6 = _{t+\Delta t}T_5 = 100$$

For 3 Δt,

$$_{t+3\Delta t}T_1 = 0$$

$$_{t+3\Delta t}T_2 = \frac{0 + 87.5}{2} = 43.75$$

$$_{t+3\Delta t}T_3 = \frac{50 + 100}{2} = 75$$

$$_{t+3\Delta t}T_4 = \frac{87.5 + 100}{2} = 93.75$$

$$_{t+3\Delta t}T_5 = \frac{100 + 100}{2} = 100$$

$$_{t+3\Delta t}T_6 = 100$$

For 4 Δt,

$$_{t+4\Delta t}T_1 = 0$$

$$_{t+4\Delta t}T_2 = \frac{0 + 75}{2} = 37.5$$

$$_{t+4\Delta t}T_3 = \frac{43.75 + 93.75}{2} = 68.75$$

$$_{t+4\Delta t}T_4 = \frac{75 + 100}{2} = 87.5$$

$$_{t+4\Delta t}T_5 = \frac{93.75 + 100}{2} = 96.88$$

$$_{t+4\Delta t}T_6 = 100$$

For 5 Δt,

$$_{t+5\Delta t}T_1 = 0$$

$$_{t+5\Delta t}T_2 = \frac{0 + 68.75}{2} = 34.38$$

$$_{t+5\Delta t}T_3 = \frac{37.5 + 87.5}{2} = 62.50$$

$$_{t+5\Delta t}T_4 = \frac{68.75 + 96.88}{2} = 82.81$$

$$_{t+5\Delta t}T_5 = \frac{87.5 + 100}{2} = 93.75$$

$$_{t+5\Delta t}T_6 = 96.88$$

For 6 Δt (final time),

$$_{t+6\Delta t}T_1 = 0$$

$$_{t+6\Delta t}T_2 = \frac{0 + 62.5}{2} = 31.25$$

$$_{t+6\Delta t}T_3 = \frac{34.38 + 82.81}{2} = 58.59$$

$$_{t+6\Delta t}T_4 = \frac{62.50 + 93.75}{2} = 78.13$$

$$_{t+6\Delta t}T_5 = \frac{82.81 + 96.88}{2} = 89.84$$

$$_{t+6\Delta t}T_6 = 93.75$$

The temperature profiles for 3 Δt increments and the final time of 6 Δt increments are plotted in Fig. 5.4-2. This example shows how a hand calculation can be done. To increase the accuracy, more slab increments and more time increments are required. This, then, is ideally suited for computation using a spreadsheet with a computer.

EXAMPLE 5.4-2. Unsteady-State Conduction Using the Digital Computer
Repeat Example 5.4-1 using the digital computer. Use $\Delta x = 0.05$ m. Write the spreadsheet program and compare the final temperatures with Example 5.4-1. Use the explicit method of Schmidt for $M = 2$. Although not needed for many time increments using the digital computer, use the special procedure for the value of $_1T_a$ for the first time increment. Thus a direct comparison can be made with Example 5.4-1 of the effect of the number of increments on the results.

Solution: The number of slabs to use is 1.00 m/(0.05 m/slab) or 20 slabs. Substituting into Eq. (5.4-3) with $\alpha = 2.00 \times 10^{-5}$ m^2/s, $\Delta x = 0.05$ m, and $M = 2$, and solving for Δt,

$$M = 2 = \frac{(\Delta x)^2}{\alpha \, \Delta t} = \frac{(0.05)^2}{(2.00 \times 10^{-5})(\Delta t)}$$

$$\Delta t = 62.5 \text{ s}$$

Hence, $(6000/62.5) = 96$ time increments to be used. The value of n goes from $n = 1$ to 21.

The equations to use to calculate the temperatures are again Eqs. (5.4-12)–(5.4-15). However, the only differences are that in Eq. (5.4-14) n goes from 2 to 20, and in Eq. (5.4-15) $n = 21$, so that $_{t+\Delta t}T_{21} = {}_tT_{20}$.

The spreadsheet for these equations is easily written and is left up to the reader. The results are tabulated in Table 5.4-1 for comparison with Example 5.4-1, where only five slices were used. The table shows that the results for five

TABLE 5.4-1. *Comparison of Results for Examples 5.4-1 and 5.4-2*

Distance from Front Face	Results Using $\Delta x = 0.20$ m		Results Using $\Delta x = 0.05$ m	
		Temperature		Temperature
m	n	°C	n	°C
0	1	0.0	1	0.0
0.20	2	31.25	5	31.65
0.40	3	58.59	9	58.47
0.60	4	78.13	13	77.55
0.80	5	89.84	17	88.41
1.00	6	93.75	21	91.87

slices are reasonably close to those for 20 slices, with values in both cases deviating by 2% or less from each other.

As a rule-of-thumb guide for hand calculations, using a minimum of five slices and at least 8–10 time increments should give sufficient accuracy for most purposes. Only when very high accuracy is desired or several cases are to be solved is it desirable to solve the problem using a spreadsheet calculation with a computer.

EXAMPLE 5.4-3. Unsteady-State Conduction with Convective Boundary Condition

Use the same conditions as Example 5.4-1, but a convective coefficient of $h = 25.0$ W/m$^2 \cdot$ K is now present at the surface. The thermal conductivity $k = 10.0$ W/m $\cdot$ K.

Solution: Equations (5.4-7) and (5.4-8) can be used for convection at the surface. From Eq. (5.4-8), $N = h\Delta x/k = 25.0(0.20)/10.0 = 0.50$. Then $2N + 2 = 2(0.50) + 2 = 3.0$. However, by Eq. (5.4-9), the value of M must be equal to or greater than $2N + 2$. This means that a value of $M = 2$ cannot be used. We will select the preferred method where $M = 4.0$. [Another, less accurate alternative is to use Eq. (5.4-11) for convection, and then the value of M is not restricted by the N value.]

Substituting into Eq. (5.4-3) and solving for Δt,

$$M = 4 = \frac{(\Delta x)^2}{\alpha \Delta t} = \frac{(0.20)^2}{(2.00 \times 10^{-5})(\Delta t)} \qquad \Delta t = 500 \text{ s}$$

Hence, $6000/500 = 12$ time increments must be used.

For the first Δt time increment and for all time increments, the value of the environmental temperature T_a to use is $T_a = 0$°C since $M > 3$. For convection at the node or point $n = 1$ we use Eq. (5.4-7), where $M = 4$ and $N = 0.50$:

$$_{t+\Delta t}T_1 = \tfrac{1}{4}[2(0.5)T_a + [4 - (2 \times 0.5 + 2)]_t T_1 + 2_t T_2]$$

$$= 0.25T_a + 0.25_t T_1 + 0.50_t T_2 \qquad n = 1 \qquad \textbf{(5.4-16)}$$

For $n = 2, 3, 4, 5$, we use Eq. (5.4-2),

$$_{t+\Delta t}T_n = \tfrac{1}{4}[_tT_{n+1} + (4 - 2)_tT_n + _tT_{n-1}]$$

$$= 0.25_tT_{n+1} + 0.50_tT_n + 0.25_tT_{n-1} \quad n = 2, 3, 4, 5 \quad \textbf{(5.4-17)}$$

For $n = 6$ (insulated boundary), we use Eq. (5.4-10) and $f = 6$.

$$_{t+\Delta t}T_6 = \tfrac{1}{4}[(4 - 2)_tT_6 + 2_tT_5]$$

$$= 0.50_tT_6 + 0.50_tT_5 \quad n = 6 \quad \textbf{(5.4-18)}$$

For 1 Δt, for the first time increment of $t + \Delta t$, $T_a = 0$. Using Eq. (5.4-16) to calculate the temperature at node 1,

$$_{t+\Delta t}T_1 = 0.25(0) + 0.25(100) + 0.50(100) = 75.0$$

For $n = 2, 3, 4, 5$, using Eq. (5.4-17),

$$_{t+\Delta t}T_2 = 0.25_tT_3 + 0.50_tT_2 + 0.25_tT_1$$

$$= 0.25(100) + 0.50(100) + 0.25(100) = 100.0$$

Also, in a similar calculation, T_3, T_4, and $T_5 = 100.0$. For $n = 6$, using Eq. (5.4-18), $T_6 = 100.0$.

For 2 Δt, $T_a = 0$. Using Eq. (5.4-16),

$$_{t+2\Delta t}T_1 = 0.25(0) + 0.25(75.0) + 0.50(100) = 68.75$$

Using Eq. (5.4-17) for $n = 2, 3, 4, 5$,

$$_{t+2\Delta t}T_2 = 0.25(100) + 0.50(100) + 0.25(75.00) = 93.75$$

$$_{t+2\Delta t}T_3 = 0.25(100) + 0.50(100) + 0.25(100) = 100.0$$

Also, T_4 and $T_5 = 100.0$. For $n = 6$, using Eq. (5.4-18), $T_6 = 100.0$.

For 3 Δt, $T_a = 0$. Using Eq. (5.4-16),

$$_{t+3\Delta t}T_1 = 0.25(0) + 0.25(68.75) + 0.50(93.75) = 64.07$$

Using Eq. (5.4-17) for $n = 2, 3, 4, 5$,

$$_{t+3\Delta t}T_2 = 0.25(100) + 0.50(93.75) + 0.25(68.75) = 89.07$$

$$_{t+3\Delta t}T_3 = 0.25(100) + 0.50(100) + 0.25(93.75) = 98.44$$

$$_{t+3\Delta t}T_4 = 0.25(100) + 0.50(100) + 0.25(100) = 100.0$$

Also, $T_5 = 100.0$ and $T_6 = 100.0$.

In a similar manner the calculations can be continued for the remaining time until a total of 12 Δt increments have been used.

5.4C. Other Numerical Methods for Unsteady-State Conduction

1. Unsteady-state conduction in a cylinder. In deriving the numerical equations for unsteady-state conduction in a flat slab, the cross-sectional area was constant throughout. In a cylinder it changes radially. To derive the equation for a cylinder, Fig. 5.4-3 is used, where the cylinder is divided into concentric hollow cylinders whose walls are Δx m thick. Assuming a cylin-

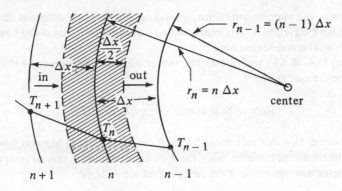

FIGURE 5.4-3. *Unsteady-state conduction in a cylinder.*

der 1 m long and making a heat balance on the slab at point n, the rate of heat in − rate of heat out = rate of heat accumulation:

$$\frac{k[2\pi(n + 1/2)\,\Delta x]}{\Delta x}({}_tT_{n+1} - {}_tT_n) - k\frac{[2\pi(n - 1/2)\,\Delta x]}{\Delta x}({}_tT_n - {}_tT_{n-1})$$

$$= \frac{2\pi n(\Delta x)^2\rho c_p}{\Delta t}({}_{t+\Delta t}T_n - {}_tT_n) \quad \textbf{(5.4-19)}$$

Rearranging, the final equation is

$$_{t+\Delta t}T_n = \frac{1}{M}\left[\frac{2n + 1}{2n}{}_tT_{n+1} + (M - 2){}_tT_n + \frac{2n - 1}{2n}{}_tT_{n-1}\right] \quad \textbf{(5.4-20)}$$

where $M = (\Delta x)^2/(\alpha\,\Delta t)$ as before. Also, at the center where $n = 0$,

$$_{t+\Delta t}T_0 = \frac{4}{M}{}_tT_1 + \frac{M - 4}{M}{}_tT_0 \quad \textbf{(5.4-21)}$$

To use Equations (5.4-20) and (5.4-21),

$$M \geq 4 \quad \textbf{(5.4-22)}$$

Equations for convection at the outer surface of the cylinder have been derived (D1). If the heat capacity of the outer half-slab is neglected,

$$_{t+\Delta t}T_n = \frac{nN}{\dfrac{2n - 1}{2} + nN}\,{}_{t+\Delta t}T_a + \frac{(2n - 1)/2}{\dfrac{2n - 1}{2} + nN}\,{}_{t+\Delta t}T_{n-1} \quad \textbf{(5.4-23)}$$

where T_n is the temperature at the surface and T_{n-1} the temperature at a position in the solid 1 Δx below the surface.

Equations for numerical methods for two-dimensional unsteady-state conduction have been derived and are available in a number of references (D1, K2).

2. Unsteady-state conduction and implicit numerical method.   In some practical problems the restrictions imposed on the value $M \geq 2$ by stability requirements may prove inconvenient.

Also, to minimize the stability problems, implicit methods using different finite-difference formulas have been developed. An important one of these formulas is the Crank–Nicolson method, which will be considered here.

In deriving Eqs. (5.4-1) and (5.4-2), the rate at which heat entered the slab in Fig. 5.4-1 was taken to be the rate at time t:

$$\text{Rate of heat in at } t = \frac{kA}{\Delta A}(_tT_{n-1} - {_tT_n}) \tag{5.4-24}$$

It was then assumed that this rate could be used during the whole interval from t to $t + \Delta t$. This is an approximation, however since the rate changes during this Δt interval. A better value would be the average value of the rate at t and at $t + \Delta t$, or

$$\text{average rate of heat in} = \frac{kA}{\Delta x}\left[\frac{(_tT_{n-1} - {_tT_n}) + (_{t+\Delta t}T_{n-1} - {_{t+\Delta t}T_n})}{2}\right] \tag{5.4-25}$$

For the heat leaving, a similar type of average is used. The final equation is

$$_{t+\Delta t}T_{n+1} - (2M + 2)_{t+\Delta t}T_n + {_{t+\Delta t}T_{n-1}} = -{_tT_{n+1}} + (2 - 2M)_tT_n - {_tT_{n-1}} \tag{5.4-26}$$

This means that now a new value of $_{t+\Delta t}T_n$ cannot be calculated only from values at time t, as in Eq. (5.4-2), but that all the new values of T at $t + \Delta t$ at all points must be calculated simultaneously. To do this, an equation similar to Eq. (5.4-26) is written for each of the internal points. Each of these equations and the boundary equations are linear algebraic equations. These then can be solved simultaneously by the standard methods, such as the Gauss–Seidel iteration technique, matrix inversion technique, and so on (G1, K1).

An important advantage of Eq. (5.4-26) is that the stability and convergence criteria are satisfied for all positive values of M. This means that M can have values less than 2.0. A disadvantage of the implicit method is the larger number of calculations needed for each time step. Explicit methods are simpler to use, but because of stability considerations, especially in complex situations, implicit methods are often preferred.

5.5 CHILLING AND FREEZING OF FOOD AND BIOLOGICAL MATERIALS

5.5A Introduction

Unlike many inorganic and organic materials which are relatively stable, food and other biological materials decay and deteriorate more or less rapidly with time at room temperature. This spoilage is due to a number of factors. Tissues of foods such as fruits and vegetables continue to undergo metabolic respiration after harvesting, and ripen and eventually spoil. Enzymes of the dead tissues of meats and fish remain active and induce oxidation and other deteriorating effects. Microorganisms attack all types of foods by decomposing the foods so that spoilage occurs; chemical reactions also occur, such as the oxidation of fats.

At low temperatures the growth rate of microorganisms will be slowed if the temperature is below that which is optimum for growth. Enzyme activity and chemical reaction rates are also reduced at low temperatures. The rates of most chemical and biological reactions in storage of chilled or frozen foods and biological materials are reduced by factors of $\frac{1}{2}$ to $\frac{1}{3}$ for each 10 K (10°C) drop in temperature.

Water plays an important part in these rates of deterioration, and it is present to a substantial percentage in most biological materials. To reach a temperature low enough for most of these rates to approximately cease, most of the water must be frozen. Materials such as food do not freeze at 0°C (32°F), as pure water does, but at a range of temperatures below 0°C. However, because of some of the physical effects of ice crystals and other effects, such as concentrating of solutions, chilling of biological materials is often used for preservation instead of freezing.

Chilling of materials involves removing the sensible heat and heat of metabolism and reducing the temperature, usually to a range of 4.4°C (40°F) to just above freezing. Essentially no latent heat of freezing is involved. The materials can be stored for a week or so up to a few months, depending on the product stored and the gaseous atmosphere. Each material has its optimum chill storage temperature.

In the freezing of food and biological materials, the temperature is reduced so that most of the water is frozen to ice. Depending on the final storage temperature, down to as low as −30°C, the materials can be stored for up to a year or so. Often in the production of frozen foods, they are first treated by blanching or scalding to destroy enzymes.

5.5B Chilling of Food and Biological Materials

In the chilling of food and biological materials, the temperature of the materials is reduced to the desired chill storage temperature, which can be about −1.1°C (30°F) to 4.4°C (40°F). For example, after slaughter, beef has a temperature of 37.8°C (100°F) to 40°C (104°F), and it is often cooled to about 4.4°C (40°F). Milk from cows must be chilled quickly to temperatures just above freezing. Some fish fillets at the time of packing are at a temperature of 7.2°C (45°F) to 10°C (50°F) and are chilled to close to 0°C.

These rates of chilling or cooling are governed by the laws of unsteady-state heat conduction discussed in Sections 5.1 to 5.4. The heat is removed by convection at the surface of the material and by unsteady-state conduction in the material. The fluid outside the foodstuff or biological materials is used to remove this heat; in many cases it is air. The air has previously been cooled by refrigeration to −1.1°C to +4.4°C, depending on the material and other conditions. The convective heat-transfer coefficients, which usually include radiation effects, can also be predicted by the methods in Chapter 4; for air the coefficient varies from about 8.5 to 40 W/m² · K (1.5 to 7 btu/h · ft² · °F), depending primarily on air velocity.

In some cases the fluid used for chilling is a liquid flowing over the surface, and the values of h can vary from about 280 to 1700 W/m² · K (50−300 btu/h · ft² · °F). In other cases, a contact or plate cooler is used, where chilled plates are in direct contact with the material. Then the temperature of the surface of the material is usually assumed to be equal or close to that of the contact plates. Contact freezers are used for freezing biological materials.

Where the food is packaged in boxes or the material is tightly covered by a film of plastic, this additional resistance must be considered. One method for doing this is to add the resistance of the package covering to that of the convective film:

$$R_T = R_P + R_C \tag{5.5-1}$$

where R_P is the resistance of covering, R_C the resistance of the outside convective film, and R_T the total resistance. Then, for each resistance,

$$R_C = \frac{1}{h_c A} \tag{5.5-2}$$

$$R_P = \frac{\Delta x}{k A} \tag{5.5-3}$$

$$R_T = \frac{1}{hA} \tag{5.5-4}$$

where h_c is the convective gas or liquid coefficient, A is the area, Δx is the thickness of the covering, k is the thermal conductivity of the covering, and h is the overall coefficient. The overall coefficient h is the one to use in the unsteady-state charts. This assumes a negligible heat capacity of the covering, which is usually the case. Also, it assumes that the covering closely touches the food material so there is no resistance between the covering and the food.

The major sources of error in using the unsteady-state charts are inadequate data on the density, heat capacity, and thermal conductivity of the foods and the prediction of the convective coefficient. Food materials are irregular anisotropic substances, whose physical properties are often difficult to evaluate. Also, if evaporation of water occurs on chilling, latent heat losses can affect the accuracy of the results.

EXAMPLE 5.5-1. Chilling Dressed Beef

Hodgson (H2) gives physical properties of beef carcasses during chilling of $\rho = 1073$ kg/m^3, $c_p = 3.48$ kJ/kg $\cdot$ K, and $k = 0.498$ W/m $\cdot$ K. A large slab of beef 0.203 m thick and initially at a uniform temperature of 37.8°C is to be cooled so that the center temperature is 10°C. Chilled air at 1.7°C (assumed constant) with an $h = 39.7$ W/m$^2 \cdot$ K is used. Calculate the time needed.

Solution: The thermal diffusivity α is

$$\alpha = \frac{k}{\rho c_p} = \frac{0.498}{(1073)(3.48 \times 1000)} = 1.334 \times 10^{-7} \text{ m}^2/\text{s}$$

Then, for the half-thickness x_1 of the slab,

$$x_1 = \frac{0.203}{2} = 0.1015 \text{ m}$$

For the center of the slab,

$$n = \frac{x}{x_1} = \frac{0}{x_1} = 0$$

Also,

$$m = \frac{k}{hx_1} = \frac{0.498}{(39.7)(0.1015)} = 0.123$$

$$T_1 = 1.7°C + 237.2 = 274.9 \text{ K} \qquad T_0 = 37.8 + 273.2 = 311.0 \text{ K}$$

$$T = 10 + 273.2 = 283.2 \text{ K}$$

$$Y = \frac{T_1 - T}{T_1 - T_0} = \frac{274.9 - 283.2}{274.9 - 311.0} = 0.230$$

Using Fig. 5.3-6 for the center of a large flat plate,

$$X = 0.90 = \frac{\alpha t}{x_1^2} = \frac{(1.334 \times 10^{-7})(t)}{(0.1015)^2}$$

Solving, $t = 6.95 \times 10^4$ s (19.3 h).

5.5C Freezing of Food and Biological Materials

1. Introduction.   In the freezing of food and other biological materials, the removal of sensible heat in chilling occurs first and then the removal of the latent heat of freezing. The latent heat of freezing water of 335 kJ/kg (144 btu/lb$_m$) is a substantial portion of the total heat removed on freezing. Other slight effects, such as the heats of solution of salts and so on, may be present but are quite small. Actually, when materials such as meats are frozen to $-29°C$, only about 90% of the water is frozen to ice, with the rest thought to be bound water (B1).

Riedel (R1) gives enthalpy–temperature–composition charts for the freezing of many different foods. These charts show that freezing does not occur at a given temperature but extends over a range of several degrees. As a consequence, there is no one freezing point with a single latent heat of freezing.

Since the latent heat of freezing is present in the unsteady-state process of freezing, the standard unsteady-state conduction equations and charts given in this chapter cannot be used for prediction of freezing times. A full analytical solution of the rate of freezing of food and biological materials is very difficult because of the variation of physical properties with temperature, the amount of freezing varying with temperature, and other factors. An approximate solution by Plank is often used.

2. Approximate solution of Plank for freezing.   Plank (P2) has derived an approximate solution for the time of freezing which is often sufficient for engineering purposes. The assumptions in the derivation are as follows. Initially, all the food is at the freezing temperature but is unfrozen. The thermal conductivity of the frozen part is constant. All the material freezes at the freezing point, with a constant latent heat. The heat transfer by conduction in the frozen layer occurs slowly enough that it is under pseudo-steady-state conditions.

In Fig. 5.5-1 a slab of thickness a m is cooled from both sides by convection. At a given time t s, a thickness of x m of frozen layer has formed on both sides. The temperature of the environment is constant at T_1 K and the freezing temperature is constant at T_f. An unfrozen layer in the center at T_f is present.

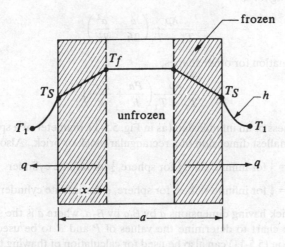

FIGURE 5.5-1.   *Temperature profile during freezing.*

The heat leaving at time t is q W. Since we are at pseudo-steady state, at time t, the heat leaving by convection on the outside is

$$q = hA(T_S - T_1) \qquad (5.5-5)$$

where A is the surface area. Also, the heat being conducted through the frozen layer of x thickness at steady state is

$$q = \frac{kA}{x}(T_f - T_S) \qquad (5.5-6)$$

where k is the thermal conductivity of the frozen material. In a given time dt s, a layer dx thick of material freezes. Then multiplying A times dx times ρ gives the kg mass frozen. Multiplying this by the latent heat λ in J/kg and dividing by dt,

$$q = \frac{A\,dx\,\rho\lambda}{dt} = A\rho\lambda\frac{dx}{dt} \qquad (5.5-7)$$

where ρ is the density of the unfrozen material.

Next, to eliminate T_S from Eqs. (5.5-5) and (5.5-6), Eq. (5.5-5) is solved for T_S and substituted into Eq. (5.5-6), giving

$$q = \frac{(T_f - T_1)A}{x/k + 1/h} \qquad (5.5-8)$$

Equating Eq. (5.5-8) to (5.5-7),

$$\frac{(T_f - T_1)A}{x/k + 1/h} = A\rho\lambda\frac{dx}{dt} \qquad (5.5-9)$$

Rearranging and integrating between $t = 0$ and $x = 0$, to $t = t$ and $x = a/2$,

$$(T_f - T_1)\int_0^t dt = \lambda\rho\int_0^{a/2}\left(\frac{x}{k} + \frac{1}{h}\right)dx \qquad (5.5-10)$$

Integrating and solving for t,

$$t = \frac{\lambda\rho}{T_f - T_1}\left(\frac{a}{2h} + \frac{a^2}{8k}\right) \qquad (5.5-11)$$

To generalize the equation for other shapes,

$$t = \frac{\lambda\rho}{T_f - T_1}\left(\frac{Pa}{h} + \frac{Ra^2}{k}\right) \qquad (5.5-12)$$

where a is the thickness of an infinite slab (as in Fig. 5.5-1), diameter of a sphere, diameter of a long cylinder, or smallest dimension of a rectangular block or brick. Also,

$P = \frac{1}{2}$ for infinite slab, $\frac{1}{6}$ for sphere, $\frac{1}{4}$ for infinite cylinder

$R = \frac{1}{8}$ for infinite slab, $\frac{1}{24}$ for sphere, $\frac{1}{16}$ for infinite cylinder

For a rectangular brick having dimensions a by $\beta_1 a$ by $\beta_2 a$, where a is the shortest side, Ede (B1) has prepared a chart to determine the values of P and R to be used to calculate t in Eq. (5.5-12). Equation (5.5-11) can also be used for calculation of thawing times by replacing the k of the frozen material by the k of the thawed material.

EXAMPLE 5.5-2.   Freezing of Meat

Slabs of meat 0.0635 m thick are to be frozen in an air-blast freezer at 244.3 K (−28.9°C). The meat is initially at the freezing temperature of 270.4 K (−2.8°C). The meat contains 75% moisture. The heat-transfer coefficient is $h = 17.0$ W/m^2·K. The physical properties are $\rho = 1057$ kg/m^3 for the unfrozen meat and $k = 1.038$ W/m·K for the frozen meat. Calculate the freezing time.

Solution: Since the latent heat of fusion of water to ice is 335 kJ/kg (144 btu/lb$_m$), for meat with 75% water,

$$\lambda = 0.75(335) = 251.2 \text{ kJ/kg}$$

The other given variables are $a = 0.0635$ m, $T_f = 270.4$ K, $T_1 = 244.3$ K, $\rho = 1057$ kg/m^3, $h = 17.0$ W/m^2·K, $k = 1.038$ W/m·K. Substituting into Eq. (5.5-11),

$$t = \frac{\lambda\rho}{T_f - T_1}\left(\frac{a}{2h} + \frac{a^2}{8k}\right) = \frac{(2.512 \times 10^5)1057}{270.4 - 244.3}\left[\frac{0.0635}{2(17.0)} + \frac{(0.0635)^2}{8(1.038)}\right]$$

$$= 2.395 \times 10^4 \text{ s (6.65 h)}$$

3. Other methods for calculating freezing times. Neumann (C1, C2) has derived a complicated equation for freezing in a slab. He assumes the following conditions. The surface temperature is the same as the environment, that is, no surface resistance. The temperature of freezing is constant. This method suffers from the limitation that a convection coefficient cannot be used at the surface, since it assumes no surface resistance. However, the method does include the effect of cooling from an original temperature, which may be above the freezing point.

Plank's equation does not make provision for an original temperature, which may be above the freezing point. An approximate method for calculating the additional time necessary to cool from temperature T_0 down to the freezing point T_f is as follows. Using the unsteady-state charts calculate the time for the average temperature in the material to reach T_f, assuming that no freezing occurs and using the physical properties of the unfrozen material. If there is no surface resistance, Fig. 5.3-13 can be used directly for this. If a resistance is present, the temperature at several points in the material will have to be obtained from the unsteady-state charts and the average temperature calculated from these point temperatures. This may be partially trial and error, since the time is unknown and must be assumed. If the average temperature calculated is not at the freezing point, a new time must be assumed. This is an approximate method since some material will actually freeze.

5.6 DIFFERENTIAL EQUATION OF ENERGY CHANGE

5.6A Introduction

In Sections 3.6 and 3.7 we derived a differential equation of continuity and a differential equation of momentum transfer for a pure fluid. These equations were derived because overall mass, energy, and momentum balances made on a finite volume in the earlier parts of Chapter 2 did not tell us what goes on inside a control volume. In the overall balances performed, a new balance was made for each new system studied. However, it is often easier to start with the differential equations of continuity and momentum transfer in general form and then simplify the equations by discarding unneeded terms for each specific problem.

In Chapter 4 on steady-state heat transfer and Chapter 5 on unsteady-state heat transfer, new overall energy balances were made on a finite control volume for each new situation. To progress further in our study of heat or energy transfer in flow and nonflow systems, we must use a differential volume to investigate in greater detail what goes on inside this volume. The balance will be made on a single phase and the boundary conditions at the phase boundary will be used for integration.

In the next section we derive a general differential equation of energy change: the conservation-of-energy equation. Then this equation is modified for certain special cases that occur frequently. Finally, applications of the uses of these equations are given. Cases for both steady-state and unsteady-state energy transfer are studied using this conservation-of-energy equation, which is perfectly general and holds for steady- or unsteady-state conditions.

5.6B Derivation of Differential Equation of Energy Change

As in the derivation of the differential equation of momentum transfer, we write a balance on an element of volume of size Δx, Δy, Δz which is stationary. We then write the law of conservation of energy, which is really the first law of thermodynamics for the fluid in this volume element at any time. The following is the same as Eq. (2.7-7) for a control volume given in Section 2.7.

$$\begin{pmatrix} \text{rate of} \\ \text{energy in} \end{pmatrix} - \begin{pmatrix} \text{rate of} \\ \text{energy out} \end{pmatrix} - \begin{pmatrix} \text{rate of external} \\ \text{work done by} \\ \text{system on surroundings} \end{pmatrix}$$

$$= \begin{pmatrix} \text{rate of} \\ \text{accumulation of} \\ \text{energy} \end{pmatrix} \quad \text{(5.6-1)}$$

As in momentum transfer, the transfer of energy into and out of the volume element is by convection and molecular transport or conduction. There are two kinds of energy being transferred. The first is internal energy U in J/kg (btu/lb$_m$) or any other set of units. This is the energy associated with random translational and internal motions of the molecules plus molecular interactions. The second is kinetic energy $\rho v^2/2$, which is the energy associated with the bulk fluid motion, where v is the local fluid velocity, m/s (ft/s). Hence, the total energy per unit volume is $(\rho U + \rho v^2/2)$. The rate of accumulation of energy in the volume element in m^3 (ft^3) is then

$$\Delta x \, \Delta y \, \Delta z \frac{\partial}{\partial t} \left(\rho U + \frac{\rho v^2}{2} \right) \quad \text{(5.6-2)}$$

The total energy entering by convection in the x direction at x minus that leaving at $x + \Delta x$ is

$$\Delta y \, \Delta z \left[v_x \left(\rho U + \frac{\rho v^2}{2} \right) \right]_x - \Delta y \, \Delta z \left[v_x \left(\rho U + \frac{\rho v^2}{2} \right) \right]_{x+\Delta x} \quad \text{(5.6-3)}$$

Similar equations can be written for the y and z directions using velocities v_y and v_z, respectively.

The net rate of energy entering the element by conduction in the x direction is

$$\Delta y \, \Delta z[(q_x)_x - (q_x)_{x+\Delta x}] \qquad (5.6\text{-}4)$$

Similar equations can be written for the y and z directions, where q_x, q_y, and q_z are the components of the heat flux vector q, which is in W/m^2 (btu/s $\cdot$ ft^2) or any other convenient set of units.

The net work done by the system on its surroundings is the sum of the following three parts for the x direction. For the net work done against the gravitational force,

$$-\rho \, \Delta x \, \Delta y \, \Delta z(v_x g_x) \qquad (5.6\text{-}5)$$

where g_x is gravitational force. The net work done against the static pressure p is

$$\Delta y \, \Delta z[(pv_x)_{x+\Delta x} - (pv_x)_x] \qquad (5.6\text{-}6)$$

where p is N/m^2 (lb$_f$/ft^2) or any other convenient set of units. For the net work against the viscous forces,

$$\Delta y \, \Delta z[(\tau_{xx}v_x + \tau_{xy}v_y + \tau_{xz}v_z)_{x+\Delta x} - (\tau_{xx}v_x + \tau_{xy}v_y + \tau_{xz}v_z)_x] \qquad (5.6\text{-}7)$$

In Section 3.7 these viscous forces are discussed in more detail.

Writing equations similar to (5.6-3)–(5.6-7) in all three directions; substituting these equations and Eq. (5.6-2) into (5.6-1); dividing by Δx, Δy, and Δz; and letting Δx, Δy, and Δz approach zero, we obtain

$$\frac{\partial}{\partial t}\left(\rho U + \frac{\rho v^2}{2}\right) = -\left[\frac{\partial}{\partial x} v_x\left(\rho U + \frac{\rho v^2}{2}\right) + \frac{\partial}{\partial y} v_y\left(\rho U + \frac{\rho v^2}{2}\right) + \frac{\partial}{\partial z} v_z\left(\rho U + \frac{\rho v^2}{2}\right)\right]$$

$$- \left(\frac{\partial q_x}{\partial x} + \frac{\partial q_y}{\partial y} + \frac{\partial q_z}{\partial z}\right) + \rho(v_x g_x + v_y g_y + v_z g_z)$$

$$- \left[\frac{\partial}{\partial x}(pv_x) + \frac{\partial}{\partial y}(pv_y) + \frac{\partial}{\partial z}(pv_z)\right]$$

$$- \left[\frac{\partial}{\partial x}(\tau_{xx}v_x + \tau_{xy}v_y + \tau_{xz}v_z) + \frac{\partial}{\partial z}(\tau_{yx}v_x + \tau_{yy}v_y + \tau_{yz}v_z)\right.$$

$$\left. + \frac{\partial}{\partial z}(\tau_{zx}v_x + \tau_{zy}v_y + \tau_{zz}v_z)\right] \qquad (5.6\text{-}8)$$

For further details of this derivation, see (B2).

Equation (5.6-8) is the final equation of energy change relative to a stationary point. However, it is not in a convenient form. We first combine Eq. (5.6-8) with the equation of continuity, Eq. (3.6-23), with the equation of motion, Eq. (3.7-13), and express the internal energy in terms of fluid temperature T and heat capacity. Then writing the resultant equation for a Newtonian fluid with constant thermal conductivity k, we obtain

$$\rho c_v \frac{DT}{Dt} = k\nabla^2 T - T\left(\frac{\partial p}{\partial T}\right)_\rho (\nabla \cdot v) + \mu\phi \qquad (5.6\text{-}9)$$

This equation utilizes Fourier's second law in three directions, where

$$k\nabla^2 T = k\left(\frac{\partial^2 T}{\partial x^2} + \frac{\partial^2 T}{\partial y^2} + \frac{\partial^2 T}{\partial z^2}\right) \qquad (5.6\text{-}10)$$

The viscous-dissipation term $\mu\phi$ is generally negligible except where extremely large velocity gradients exist. It will be omitted in the discussions to follow. Equation (5.6-9) is the equation of energy change for a Newtonian fluid with constant k in terms of the fluid temperature T.

5.6C   Special Cases of the Equation of Energy Change

The following special forms of Eq. (5.6-9) for a Newtonian fluid with constant thermal conductivity are commonly encountered. First, Eq. (5.6-9) will be written in rectangular coordinates without the $\mu\phi$ term:

$$\rho c_v \left(\frac{\partial T}{\partial t} + v_x \frac{\partial T}{\partial x} + v_y \frac{\partial T}{\partial y} + v_z \frac{\partial T}{\partial z} \right)$$

$$= k \left(\frac{\partial^2 T}{\partial x^2} + \frac{\partial^2 T}{\partial y^2} + \frac{\partial^2 T}{\partial z^2} \right) - T \left(\frac{\partial p}{\partial T} \right)_\rho \left(\frac{\partial v_x}{\partial x} + \frac{\partial v_y}{\partial y} + \frac{\partial v_z}{\partial z} \right) \quad (5.6\text{-}11)$$

1. Fluid at constant pressure.   The equations below can be used for constant-density fluids as well as for constant pressure.

$$\rho c_p \frac{DT}{Dt} = k \nabla^2 T \quad (5.6\text{-}12)$$

In rectangular coordinates,

$$\rho c_p \left(\frac{\partial T}{\partial t} + v_x \frac{\partial T}{\partial x} + v_y \frac{\partial T}{\partial y} + v_z \frac{\partial T}{\partial z} \right) = k \left(\frac{\partial^2 T}{\partial x^2} + \frac{\partial^2 T}{\partial y^2} + \frac{\partial^2 T}{\partial z^2} \right) \quad (5.6\text{-}13)$$

In cylindrical coordinates,

$$\rho c_p \left(\frac{\partial T}{\partial t} + v_r \frac{\partial T}{\partial r} + \frac{v_\theta}{r} \frac{\partial T}{\partial \theta} + v_z \frac{\partial T}{\partial z} \right) = k \left(\frac{\partial^2 T}{\partial r^2} + \frac{1}{r} \frac{\partial T}{\partial r} + \frac{1}{r^2} \frac{\partial^2 T}{\partial \theta^2} + \frac{\partial^2 T}{\partial z^2} \right) \quad (5.6\text{-}14)$$

In spherical coordinates,

$$\rho c_p \left(\frac{\partial T}{\partial t} + v_r \frac{\partial T}{\partial r} + \frac{v_\theta}{r} \frac{\partial T}{\partial \theta} + \frac{v_\phi}{r \sin\theta} \frac{\partial T}{\partial \phi} \right)$$

$$= k \left[\frac{1}{r^2} \frac{\partial}{\partial r} \left(r^2 \frac{\partial T}{\partial r} \right) + \frac{1}{r^2 \sin\theta} \frac{\partial}{\partial \theta} \left(\sin\theta \frac{\partial T}{\partial \theta} \right) + \frac{1}{r^2 \sin^2\theta} \frac{\partial^2 T}{\partial \phi^2} \right] \quad (5.6\text{-}15)$$

For definitions of cylindrical and spherical coordinates, see Section 3.6. If the velocity v is zero, DT/Dt becomes $\partial T/\partial t$.

2. Fluid at constant density

$$\rho c_p \frac{DT}{Dt} = k \nabla^2 T \quad (5.6\text{-}16)$$

Note that this is identical to Eq. (5.6-12) for constant pressure.

3. Solid.   Here we consider ρ is constant and $v = 0$.

$$\rho c_p \frac{\partial T}{\partial t} = k \nabla^2 T \quad (5.6\text{-}17)$$

This is often referred to as *Fourier's second law* of heat conduction. This also holds for a fluid with zero velocity at constant pressure.

4. Heat generation. If there is heat generation in the fluid by electrical or chemical means, then $\dot{q}$ can be added to the right side of Eq. (5.6-17).

$$\rho c_p \frac{\partial T}{\partial t} = k\nabla^2 T + \dot{q} \tag{5.6-18}$$

where $\dot{q}$ is the rate of heat generation in W/m^3 (btu/h·ft^3) or other suitable units. Viscous dissipation is also a heat source, but its inclusion greatly complicates problem solving because the equations for energy and motion are then coupled.

5. Other coordinate systems. Fourier's second law of unsteady-state heat conduction can be written as follows.

For rectangular coordinates,

$$\frac{\partial T}{\partial t} = \frac{k}{\rho c_p}\nabla^2 T = \alpha\left(\frac{\partial^2 T}{\partial x^2} + \frac{\partial^2 T}{\partial y^2} + \frac{\partial^2 T}{\partial z^2}\right) \tag{5.6-19}$$

where $\alpha = k/\rho c_p$, thermal diffusivity in m^2/s (ft^2/h).

For cylindrical coordinates,

$$\frac{\partial T}{\partial t} = \alpha\left(\frac{\partial^2 T}{\partial r^2} + \frac{1}{r}\frac{\partial T}{\partial r} + \frac{1}{r^2}\frac{\partial^2 T}{\partial \theta^2} + \frac{\partial^2 T}{\partial z^2}\right) \tag{5.6-20}$$

For spherical coordinates,

$$\frac{\partial T}{\partial t} = \alpha\left[\frac{1}{r^2}\frac{\partial}{\partial r}\left(r^2\frac{\partial T}{\partial r}\right) + \frac{1}{r^2\sin\theta}\frac{\partial}{\partial \theta}\left(\sin\theta\frac{\partial T}{\partial \theta}\right) + \frac{1}{r^2\sin^2\theta}\frac{\partial^2 T}{\partial \phi^2}\right] \tag{5.6-21}$$

5.6D Uses of Equation of Energy Change

In Section 3.8 we used the differential equations of continuity and motion to set up fluid-flow problems. We did this by discarding the terms that are zero or near zero and using the remaining equations to solve for the velocity and pressure distributions. This was done instead of making new mass and momentum balances for each new situation. In a similar manner, to solve problems of heat transfer, the differential equations of continuity, motion, and energy will be used, with the unneeded terms being discarded. Several examples will be given to illustrate the general methods used.

> *EXAMPLE 5.6-1. Temperature Profile with Heat Generation*
> A solid cylinder in which heat generation is occurring uniformly as $\dot{q}$ W/m^3 is insulated on the ends. The temperature of the surface of the cylinder is held constant at T_w K. The radius of the cylinder is $r = R$ m. Heat flows only in the radial direction. Derive the equation for the temperature profile at steady state if the solid has a constant thermal conductivity.

Solution: Equation (5.6-20) will be used for cylindrical coordinates. The term $\dot{q}/\rho c_p$ for generation will be added to the right side, giving

$$\frac{\partial T}{\partial t} = \frac{k}{\rho c_p}\left(\frac{\partial^2 T}{\partial r^2} + \frac{1}{r}\frac{\partial T}{\partial r} + \frac{1}{r^2}\frac{\partial^2 T}{\partial \theta^2} + \frac{\partial^2 T}{\partial z^2}\right) + \frac{\dot{q}}{\rho c_p} \qquad (5.6\text{-}22)$$

For steady state $\partial T/\partial t = 0$. Also, for conduction only in the radial direction, $\partial^2 T/\partial z^2 = 0$ and $\partial^2 T/\partial \theta^2 = 0$. This gives the following differential equation:

$$\frac{d^2 T}{dr^2} + \frac{1}{r}\frac{dT}{dr} = -\frac{\dot{q}}{k} \qquad (5.6\text{-}23)$$

This can be rewritten as

$$r\frac{d^2 T}{dr^2} + \frac{dT}{dr} = -\frac{\dot{q}r}{k} \qquad (5.6\text{-}24)$$

Note that Eq. (5.6-24) can be rewritten as follows:

$$\frac{d}{dr}\left(r\frac{dT}{dr}\right) = -\frac{\dot{q}r}{k} \qquad (5.6\text{-}25)$$

Integrating Eq. (5.6-25) once,

$$r\frac{dT}{dr} = -\frac{\dot{q}r^2}{2k} + K_1 \qquad (5.6\text{-}26)$$

where K_1 is a constant. Integrating again,

$$T = -\frac{\dot{q}r^2}{4k} + K_1 \ln r + K_2 \qquad (5.6\text{-}27)$$

where K_2 is a constant. The boundary conditions are when $r = 0$, $dT/dr = 0$ (by symmetry), and when $r = R$, $T = T_w$. The final equation is

$$T = \frac{\dot{q}\,(R^2 - r^2)}{4k} + T_w \qquad (5.6\text{-}28)$$

This is the same as Eq. (4.3-29), which was obtained by another method.

EXAMPLE 5.6-2.   Laminar Flow and Heat Transfer Using Equation of Energy Change

Using the differential equation of energy change, derive the partial differential equation and boundary conditions needed for the case of laminar flow of a constant-density fluid in a horizontal tube which is being heated. The fluid is flowing at a constant velocity v_z. At the wall of the pipe where the radius $r = r_0$, the heat flux is constant at q_0. The process is at steady state and it is assumed at $z = 0$ at the inlet that the velocity profile is established. Constant physical properties will be assumed.

Solution: From Example 3.8-3, the equation of continuity gives $\partial v_z/\partial z = 0$. Solution of the equation of motion for steady state using cylindrical coordinates gives the parabolic velocity profile:

$$v_z = v_{z\,\text{max}}\left[1 - \left(\frac{r}{r_0}\right)^2\right] \tag{5.6-29}$$

Since the fluid has a constant density, Eq. (5.6-14) in cylindrical coordinates will be used for the equation of energy change. For this case $v_r = 0$ and $v_\theta = 0$. Since this will be symmetrical, $\partial T/\partial\theta$ and $\partial^2 T/\partial\theta^2$ will be zero. For steady state, $\partial T/\partial t = 0$. Hence, Eq. (5.6-14) reduces to

$$v_z \frac{\partial T}{\partial z} = \frac{k}{\rho c_p}\left(\frac{\partial^2 T}{\partial r^2} + \frac{1}{r}\frac{\partial T}{\partial r} + \frac{\partial^2 T}{\partial z^2}\right) \tag{5.6-30}$$

Usually conduction in the z direction ($\partial^2 T/\partial z^2$ term) is small compared to the convective term $v_z\,\partial T/\partial z$ and can be dropped. Finally, substituting Eq. (5.6-29) into (5.6-30), we obtain

$$v_{z\,\text{max}}\left[1 - \left(\frac{r}{r_0}\right)^2\right]\frac{\partial T}{\partial z} = \frac{k}{\rho c_p}\left(\frac{\partial^2 T}{\partial r^2} + \frac{1}{r}\frac{\partial T}{\partial r}\right) \tag{5.6-31}$$

The boundary conditions are

At $z = 0$, $T = T_0$ (all r)

At $r = 0$, $T = $ finite

At $r = r_0$, $q_0 = -k\dfrac{\partial T}{\partial r}$ (constant)

For details on the actual solution of this equation, see Siegel et al. (S2).

5.7 BOUNDARY-LAYER FLOW AND TURBULENCE IN HEAT TRANSFER

5.7A Laminar Flow and Boundary-Layer Theory in Heat Transfer

In Section 3.10C an exact solution was obtained for the velocity profile for isothermal laminar flow past a flat plate. The solution of Blasius can be extended to include the convective heat-transfer problem for the same geometry and laminar flow. In Fig. 5.7-1 the thermal

FIGURE 5.7-1. *Laminar flow of fluid past a flat plate and thermal boundary layer.*

boundary layer is shown. The temperature of the fluid approaching the plate is T_∞ and that of the plate is T_S at the surface.

We start by writing the differential energy balance, Eq. (5.6-13):

$$\frac{\partial T}{\partial t} + v_x \frac{\partial T}{\partial x} + v_y \frac{\partial T}{\partial y} + v_z \frac{\partial T}{\partial z} = \frac{k}{\rho c_p} \left(\frac{\partial^2 T}{\partial x^2} + \frac{\partial^2 T}{\partial y^2} + \frac{\partial^2 T}{\partial z^2} \right) \tag{5.7-1}$$

If the flow is in the x and y directions, $v_z = 0$. At steady state, $\partial T/\partial t = 0$. Conduction is neglected in the x and z directions, so $\partial^2 T/\partial x^2 = \partial^2 T/\partial z^2 = 0$. Conduction occurs in the y direction. The result is

$$v_x \frac{\partial T}{\partial x} + v_y \frac{\partial T}{\partial y} = \frac{k}{\rho c_p} \frac{\partial^2 T}{\partial y^2} \tag{5.7-2}$$

The simplified momentum-balance equation used in the velocity boundary-layer derivation is very similar:

$$v_x \frac{\partial v_x}{\partial x} + v_y \frac{\partial v_x}{\partial y} = \frac{\mu}{\rho} \frac{\partial^2 v_x}{\partial y^2} \tag{3.10-5}$$

The continuity equation used previously is

$$\frac{\partial v_x}{\partial x} + \frac{\partial v_y}{\partial y} = 0 \tag{3.10-3}$$

Equations (3.10-5) and (3.10-3) were used by Blasius for solving the case for laminar boundary-layer flow. The boundary conditions used were

$$\frac{v_x}{v_\infty} = \frac{v_y}{v_\infty} = 0 \quad \text{at } y = 0$$

$$\frac{v_x}{v_\infty} = 1 \qquad \text{at } y = \infty \tag{5.7-3}$$

$$\frac{v_x}{v_\infty} = 1 \qquad \text{at } x = 0$$

The similarity between Eqs. (3.10-5) and (5.7-2) is obvious. Hence, the Blasius solution can be applied if $k/\rho c_p = \mu/\rho$. This means the Prandtl number $c_p \mu/k = 1$. Also, the boundary conditions must be the same. This is done by replacing the temperature T in Eq. (5.7-2) by the dimensionless variable $(T - T_S)/(T_\infty - T_S)$. The boundary conditions become

$$\frac{v_x}{v_\infty} = \frac{v_y}{v_\infty} = \frac{T - T_S}{T_\infty - T_S} = 0 \quad \text{at } y = 0$$

$$\frac{v_x}{v_\infty} = \frac{T - T_S}{T_\infty - T_S} = 1 \qquad \text{at } y = \infty \tag{5.7-4}$$

$$\frac{v_x}{v_\infty} = \frac{T - T_S}{T_\infty - T_S} = 1 \qquad \text{at } x = 0$$

We see that the equations and boundary conditions are identical for the temperature profile and the velocity profile. Hence, for any point x, y in the flow system, the dimensionless velocity variables v_x/v_∞ and $(T - T_S)/(T_\infty - T_S)$ are equal. The velocity-profile solution is the same as the temperature-profile solution.

This means that the transfer of momentum and heat are directly analogous, and the boundary-layer thickness δ for the velocity profile (hydrodynamic boundary layer) and the thermal boundary-layer thickness δ_T are equal. This is important for gases, where the Prandtl numbers are close to 1.

By combining Eqs. (3.10-7) and (3.10-8), the velocity gradient at the surface is

$$\left(\frac{\partial v_x}{\partial y}\right)_{y=0} = 0.332 \frac{v_\infty}{x} N_{Re,x}^{1/2} \tag{5.7-5}$$

where $N_{Re,x} = x v_\infty \rho / \mu$. Also,

$$\frac{v_x}{v_\infty} = \frac{T - T_S}{T_\infty - T_S} \tag{5.7-6}$$

Combining Eqs. (5.7-5) and (5.7-6),

$$\left(\frac{\partial T}{\partial y}\right)_{y=0} = (T_\infty - T_S)\left(\frac{0.332}{x} N_{Re,x}^{1/2}\right) \tag{5.7-7}$$

The convective equation can be related to the Fourier equation by the following, where q_y is in J/s or W (btu/h):

$$\frac{q_y}{A} = h_x(T_S - T_\infty) = -k\left(\frac{\partial T}{\partial y}\right)_{y=0} \tag{5.7-8}$$

Combining Eqs. (5.7-7) and (5.7-8),

$$\frac{h_x x}{k} = N_{Nu,x} - 0.332 N_{Re,x}^{1/2} \tag{5.7-9}$$

where $N_{Nu,x}$ is the dimensionless Nusselt number and h_x is the local heat-transfer coefficient at point x on the plate.

Pohlhausen (K1) was able to show that the relation between the hydrodynamic and thermal boundary layers for fluids with Prandtl number >0.6 gives approximately

$$\frac{\delta}{\delta_T} = N_{Pr}^{1/3} \tag{5.7-10}$$

As a result, the equation for the local heat-transfer coefficient is

$$h_x = 0.332 \frac{k}{x} N_{Re,x}^{1/2} N_{Pr}^{1/3} \tag{5.7-11}$$

Also,

$$\frac{h_x x}{k} = N_{Nu,x} = 0.332 N_{Re,x}^{1/2} N_{Pr}^{1/3} \tag{5.7-12}$$

The equation for the mean heat-transfer coefficient h from $x = 0$ to $x = L$ for a plate of width b and area bL is

$$h = \frac{b}{A} \int_0^L h_x \, dx$$

$$= \frac{1}{L} 0.332 k \left(\frac{\rho v_\infty}{\mu}\right)^{1/2} N_{Pr}^{1/3} \int_0^L \frac{dx}{x^{1/2}} \tag{5.7-13}$$

Integrating,

$$h = 0.644 \frac{k}{L} N_{Re,L}^{1/2} N_{Pr}^{1/3} \tag{5.7-14}$$

$$\frac{hL}{k} = N_{Nu} = 0.644 N_{Re,L}^{1/2} N_{Pr}^{1/3} \tag{5.7-15}$$

As pointed out previously, this laminar boundary layer on smooth plates holds up to a Reynolds number of about 5×10^5. In using the results above, the fluid properties are usually evaluated at the film temperature $T_f = (T_S + T_\infty)/2$.

5.7B Approximate Integral Analysis of the Thermal Boundary Layer

As discussed in the analysis of the hydrodynamic boundary layer, the Blasius solution is accurate but limited in its scope. Other, more complex systems cannot be solved by this method. The approximate integral analysis used by von Kármán to calculate the hydrodynamic boundary layer was covered in Section 3.10. This approach can be used to analyze the thermal boundary layer.

This method will be outlined briefly. First, a control volume, as previously given in Fig. 3.10-5, is used to derive the final energy integral expression:

$$\frac{k}{\rho c_p} \left(\frac{\partial T}{\partial y} \right)_{y=0} = \frac{d}{dx} \int_0^{\delta_T} v_x (T_\infty - T) \, dy \tag{5.7-16}$$

This equation is analogous to Eq. (3.10-48) combined with Eq. (3.10-51) for the momentum analysis, giving

$$\frac{\mu}{\rho} \left(\frac{\partial v_x}{\partial y} \right)_{y=0} = \frac{d}{dx} \int_0^{\delta} v_x (v_\infty - v_x) \, dy \tag{5.7-17}$$

Equation (5.7-16) can be solved if both a velocity profile and temperature profile are known. The assumed velocity profile used is Eq. (3.10-50):

$$\frac{v_x}{v_\infty} = \frac{3}{2} \frac{y}{\delta} - \frac{1}{2} \left(\frac{y}{\delta} \right)^3 \tag{3.10-50}$$

The same form of temperature profile is assumed:

$$\frac{T - T_S}{T_\infty - T_S} = \frac{3}{2} \frac{y}{\delta_T} - \frac{1}{2} \left(\frac{y}{\delta_T} \right)^3 \tag{5.7-18}$$

Substituting Eqs. (3.10-50) and (5.7-18) into the integral expression and solving,

$$N_{Nu,x} = 0.36 N_{Re,x}^{1/2} N_{Pr}^{1/3} \tag{5.7-19}$$

This is only about 8% greater than the exact result in Eq. (5.7-11), which indicates that this approximate integral method can be used with confidence in cases where exact solutions cannot be obtained.

In a similar fashion, the integral momentum analysis method used for the turbulent hydrodynamic boundary layer in Section 3.10 can be used for the thermal boundary layer in turbulent flow. Again, the Blasius $\frac{1}{7}$-power law is used for the temperature distribution. These give results that are quite similar to the experimental equations given in Section 4.6.

5.7C Prandtl Mixing Length and Eddy Thermal Diffusivity

1. Eddy momentum diffusivity in turbulent flow.   In Section 3.10F the total shear stress $\bar{\tau}_{yx}^{t}$ for turbulent flow was written as follows when the molecular and turbulent contributions are summed together:

$$\bar{\tau}_{yx}^{t} = -\rho\left(\frac{\mu}{\rho} + \varepsilon_t\right)\frac{d\bar{v}_x}{dy} \qquad (5.7\text{-}20)$$

The molecular momentum diffusivity μ/ρ in m²/s is a function only of the fluid molecular properties. However, the turbulent momentum eddy diffusivity ε_t depends on the fluid motion. In Eq. (3.10-29) we related ε_t to the Prandtl mixing length L as follows:

$$\varepsilon_t = L^2\left|\frac{d\bar{v}_x}{dy}\right| \qquad (3.10\text{-}29)$$

2. Prandtl mixing length and eddy thermal diffusivity.   We can derive the eddy thermal diffusivity α_t for turbulent heat transfer in a similar manner, as follows. Eddies or clumps of fluid are transported a distance L in the y direction. At this point L the clump of fluid differs in mean velocity from the adjacent fluid by the velocity v'_x, which is the fluctuating velocity component discussed in Section 3.10F. Energy is also transported the distance L with a velocity v'_y in the y direction together with the mass being transported. The instantaneous temperature of the fluid is $T = T' + \bar{T}$, where $\bar{T}$ is the mean value and T' the deviation from the mean value. This fluctuating T' is similar to the fluctuating velocity v'_x. The mixing length is small enough that the temperature difference can be written as

$$T' = L\frac{d\bar{T}}{dy} \qquad (5.7\text{-}21)$$

The rate of energy transported per unit area is q_y/A and is equal to the mass flux in the y direction times the heat capacity times the temperature difference:

$$\frac{q_y}{A} = \frac{-v'_y\rho c_p L}{dy}\frac{d\bar{T}}{dy} \qquad (5.7\text{-}22)$$

In Section 3.10F we assumed $v'_x \cong v'_y$ and that

$$v'_x = v'_y = L\left|\frac{d\bar{v}_x}{dy}\right| \qquad (5.7\text{-}23)$$

Substituting Eq. (5.7-23) into (5.7-22),

$$\frac{q_y}{A} = -\rho c_p L^2\left|\frac{d\bar{v}_x}{dy}\right|\frac{d\bar{T}}{dy} \qquad (5.7\text{-}24)$$

According to Eq. (3.10-29) the term $L^2|d\bar{v}_x/dy|$ is the momentum eddy diffusivity ε_t. When this term is in the turbulent heat-transfer equation (5.7-24), it is called α_t, eddy thermal diffusivity. Then Eq. (5.7-24) becomes

$$\frac{q_y}{A} = -\rho c_p \alpha_t \frac{d\bar{T}}{dy} \qquad (5.7\text{-}25)$$

Combining this with the Fourier equation written in terms of the molecular thermal diffusivity α,

$$\frac{q_y}{A} = -\rho c_p (\alpha + \alpha_t) \frac{d\overline{T}}{dy} \tag{5.7-26}$$

3. *Similarities among momentum, heat, and mass transport.* Equation (5.7-26) is similar to Eq. (5.7-20) for total momentum transport. The eddy thermal diffusivity α_t and the eddy momentum diffusivity ε_t have been assumed equal in the derivations. Experimental data show that this equality is only approximate. An eddy mass diffusivity for mass transfer has been defined in a similar manner using the Prandtl mixing length theory and is assumed equal to α_t and ε_t.

PROBLEMS

5.2-1. Temperature Response in Cooling a Wire. A small copper wire with a diameter of 0.792 mm and initially at 366.5 K is suddenly immersed in a liquid held constant at 311 K. The convection coefficient $h = 85.2$ W/m$^2 \cdot$ K. The physical properties can be assumed constant and are $k = 374$ W/m $\cdot$ K, $c_p = 0.389$ kJ/kg $\cdot$ K, and $\rho = 8890$ kg/m^3.
(a) Determine the time in seconds for the average temperature of the wire to drop to 338.8 K (one-half the initial temperature difference).
(b) Do the same but for $h = 11.36$ W/m$^2 \cdot$ K.
(c) For part (b), calculate the total amount of heat removed for a wire 1.0 m long.

Ans. (a) $t = 5.66$ s

5.2-2. Quenching Lead Shot in a Bath. Lead shot having an average diameter of 5.1 mm is at an initial temperature of 204.4°C. To quench the shot it is added to a quenching oil bath held at 32.2°C and falls to the bottom. The time of fall is 15 s. Assuming an average convection coefficient of $h = 199$ W/m$^2 \cdot$ K, what will be the temperature of the shot after the fall? For lead, $\rho = 11\,370$ kg/m^3 and $c_p = 0.138$ kJ/kg $\cdot$ K.

5.2-3. Unsteady-State Heating of a Stirred Tank. A vessel is filled with 0.0283 m^3 of water initially at 288.8 K. The vessel, which is well stirred, is suddenly immersed in a steam bath held at 377.6 K. The overall heat-transfer coefficient U between the steam and water is 1136 W/m$^2 \cdot$ K and the area is 0.372 m^2. Neglecting the heat capacity of the walls and agitator, calculate the time in hours to heat the water to 338.7 K. [*Hint:* Since the water is well stirred, its temperature is uniform. Show that Eq. (5.2-3) holds by starting with Eq. (5.2-1).]

5.3-1. Temperature in a Refractory Lining. A combustion chamber has a 2-in.-thick refractory lining to protect the outer shell. To predict the thermal stresses at start-up, the temperature 0.2 in. below the surface is needed 1 min after start-up. The following data are available. The initial temperature $T_0 = 100$°F, the hot gas temperature $T_1 = 3000$°F, $h = 40$ btu/h $\cdot$ ft$^2 \cdot$ °F, $k = 0.6$ btu/h $\cdot$ ft $\cdot$ °F, and $\alpha = 0.020$ ft^2/h. Calculate the temperature at a 0.2-in. depth and a 0.6-in. depth. Use Fig. 5.3-3 and justify its use by seeing if the lining acts as a semi-infinite solid during this 1-min period.

Ans. For $x = 0.2$ in., $(T - T_0)/(T_1 - T_0) = 0.28$ and $T = 912$°F (489°C); for $x = 0.6$ in., $(T - T_0)/(T_1 - T_0) = 0.02$ and $T = 158$°F (70°C)

5.3-2. Freezing Temperature in the Soil. The average temperature of the soil to a considerable depth is approximately 277.6 K (40°F) during a winter day. If the outside air temperature suddenly drops to 255.4 K (0°F) and stays there, how long will it take for a pipe 3.05 m (10 ft) below the surface to reach 273.2 K (32°F)? The convective coefficient is $h = 8.52$ W/m² · K (1.5 btu/h · ft² · °F). The soil physical properties can be taken as 5.16×10^{-7} m²/s (0.02 ft²/h) for the thermal diffusivity and 1.384 W/m · K (0.8 btu/h · ft · °F) for the thermal conductivity. (*Note:* The solution is trial and error, since the unknown time appears twice in the graph for a semi-infinite solid.)

5.3-3. Cooling a Slab of Aluminum. A large piece of aluminum that can be considered a semi-infinite solid initially has a uniform temperature of 505.4 K. The surface is suddenly exposed to an environment at 338.8 K with a surface convection coefficient of 455 W/m² · K. Calculate the time in hours for the temperature to reach 388.8 K at a depth of 25.4 mm. The average physical properties are $\alpha = 0.340$ m²/h and $k = 208$ W/m · K.

5.3-4. Transient Heating of a Concrete Wall. A wall made of concrete 0.305 m thick is insulated on the rear side. The wall at a uniform temperature of 10°C (283.2 K) is exposed on the front side to a gas at 843°C (1116.2 K). The convection coefficient is 28.4 W/m² · K, the thermal diffusivity is 1.74×10^{-3} m²/h, and the thermal conductivity is 0.935 W/m · K.

(a) Calculate the time for the temperature at the insulated face to reach 232°C (505.2 K).

(b) Calculate the temperature at a point 0.152 m below the surface at this same time.

Ans. (a) $\alpha t / x_1^2 = 0.25, t = 13.4$ h

5.3-5. Cooking a Slab of Meat. A slab of meat 25.4 mm thick originally at a uniform temperature of 10°C is to be cooked from both sides until the center reaches 121°C in an oven at 177°C. The convection coefficient can be assumed constant at 25.6 W/m² · K. Neglect any latent heat changes and calculate the time required. The thermal conductivity is 0.69 W/m · K and the thermal diffusivity 5.85×10^{-4} m²/h. Use the Heisler chart.

Ans. 0.80 h (2880 s)

5.3-6. Unsteady-State Conduction in a Brick Wall. A flat brick wall 1.0 ft thick is the lining on one side of a furnace. If the wall is at a uniform temperature of 100°F and one side is suddenly exposed to a gas at 1100°F, calculate the time for the furnace wall at a point 0.5 ft from the surface to reach 500°F. The rear side of the wall is insulated. The convection coefficient is 2.6 btu/h · ft² · °F and the physical properties of the brick are $k = 0.65$ btu/h · ft · °F and $\alpha = 0.02$ ft²/h.

5.3-7. Cooling a Steel Rod. A long steel rod 0.305 m in diameter is initially at a temperature of 588 K. It is immersed in an oil bath maintained at 311 K. The surface convective coefficient is 125 W/m² · K. Calculate the temperature at the center of the rod after 1 h. The average physical properties of the steel are $k = 38$ W/m · K and $\alpha = 0.0381$ m²/h.

Ans. $T = 391$ K

5.3-8. Effect of Size on Heat Processing Meat. An autoclave held at 121.1°C is being used to process sausage meat 101.6 mm in diameter and 0.61 m long which is originally at 21.1°C. After 2 h the temperature at the center is 98.9°C. If the diameter is increased to 139.7 mm, how long will it take for the center to reach 98.9°C? The heat-transfer coefficient to the surface is $h = 1100$ W/m² · K, which is very large, so the surface resistance can be considered negligible. (Show this.) Neglect the heat transfer from the ends of the cylinder. The thermal conductivity $k = 0.485$ W/m · K.

Ans. 3.78 h

5.3-9. *Temperature of Oranges on Trees During Freezing Weather.* In orange-growing areas, the freezing of the oranges on the trees during cold nights is of serious economic concern. If the oranges are initially at a temperature of 21.1°C, calculate the center temperature of the orange if exposed to air at −3.9°C for 6 h. The oranges are 102 mm in diameter and the convective coefficient is estimated as 11.4 W/m² · K. The thermal conductivity k is 0.431 W/m · K and α is 4.65×10^{-4} m²/h. Neglect any latent heat effects.

Ans. $(T_1 - T)/(T_1 - T_0) = 0.05$, $T = -2.65$°C

5.3-10. *Hardening a Steel Sphere.* To harden a steel sphere having a diameter of 50.8 mm, it is heated to 1033 K and then dunked into a large water bath at 300 K. Determine the time for the center of the sphere to reach 366.5 K. The surface coefficient can be assumed as 710 W/m² · K, k = 45 W/m · K, and α = 0.0325 m²/h.

5.3-11. *Unsteady-State Conduction in a Short Cylinder.* An aluminum cylinder is initially heated to a uniform temperature of 204.4°C. Then it is plunged into a large bath held at 93.3°C, where h = 568 W/m² · K. The cylinder has a diameter of 50.8 mm and is 101.6 mm long. Calculate the center temperature after 60 s. The physical properties are $\alpha = 9.44 \times 10^{-5}$ m²/s and k = 207.7 W/m · K.

5.3-12. *Conduction in Three Dimensions in a Rectangular Block.* A rectangular steel block 0.305 m by 0.457 m by 0.61 m is initially at 315.6°C. It is suddenly immersed in an environment at 93.3°C. Determine the temperature at the center of the block after 1 h. The surface convection coefficient is 34 W/m² · K. The physical properties are k = 38 W/m · K and α = 0.0379 m²/h.

5.4-1. *Schmidt Numerical Method for Unsteady-State Conduction.* A material in the form of an infinite plate 0.762 m thick is at an initial uniform temperature of 366.53 K. The rear face of the plate is insulated. The front face is suddenly exposed to a temperature of 533.2 K. The convective resistance at this face can be assumed as zero. Calculate the temperature profile after 0.875 h using the Schmidt numerical method with M = 2 and slabs 0.1524 m thick. The thermal diffusivity is 0.0929 m²/h.

Ans. Δt = 0.125 h, seven time increments needed

5.4-2. *Unsteady-State Conduction with Nonuniform Initial Temperature Profile.* Use the same conditions as in Problem 5.4-1 but with the following change. The initial temperature profile is not uniform but is 366.53 K at the front face and 422.1 K at the rear face with a linear variation between the two faces.

5.4-3. *Unsteady-State Conduction Using the Digital Computer.* Repeat Problem 5.4-2 but use the computer and a spreadsheet. Use slabs 0.03048 m thick and M = 2.0. Calculate the temperature profile after 0.875 h.

5.4-4. *Chilling Meat Using Numerical Methods.* A slab of beef 45.7 mm thick and initially at a uniform temperature of 283 K is being chilled by a surface contact cooler at 274.7 K on the front face. The rear face of the meat is insulated. Assume that the convection resistance at the front surface is zero. Using five slices and M = 2, calculate the temperature profile after 0.54 h. The thermal diffusivity is 4.64×10^{-4} m²/h.

Ans. Δt = 0.090 h, six time increments

5.4-5. *Cooling Beef with Convective Resistance.* A large slab of beef is 45.7 mm thick and is at an initial uniform temperature of 37.78°C. It is being chilled at the front surface in a chilled air blast at −1.11°C with a convective heat-transfer coefficient of h = 38.0 W/m² · K. The rear face of the meat is insulated. The thermal conductivity of the beef is k = 0.498 W/m · K and $\alpha = 4.64 \times 10^{-4}$ m²/h. Using a numerical method with five slices and M = 4.0, calculate the temperature profile after 0.27 h. [*Hint:*

Since there is a convective resistance, the value of N must be calculated. Also, Eq. (5.4-7) should be used.]

Ans. 17.16°C ($n = 1$), 28.22°C (2), 34.48°C (3), 37.00°C (4), 37.67°C (5), 37.77°C (6)

5.4-6. *Cooling Beef Using the Digital Computer.* Repeat Problem 5.4-5 using the digital computer. Use 20 slices and $M = 4.0$. Use a spreadsheet calculation.

5.4-7. *Convection and Unsteady-State Conduction.* For the conditions of Example 5.4-3, continue the calculations for a total of 12 time increments. Plot the temperature profile.

5.4-8. *Alternative Convective Boundary Condition for Numerical Method.* Repeat Example 5.4-3 but instead use the alternative boundary condition, Eq. (5.4-11). Also, use $M = 4$. Calculate the profile for the full 12 time increments.

5.4-9. *Numerical Method for Semi-infinite Solid and Convection.* A semi-infinite solid initially at a uniform temperature of 200°C is cooled at its surface by convection. The cooling fluid at a constant temperature of 100°C has a convective coefficient of $h = 250$ W/m$^2 \cdot$K. The physical properties of the solid are $k = 20$ W/m$\cdot$K and $\alpha = 4 \times 10^{-5}$ m^2/s. Using a numerical method with $\Delta x = 0.040$ m and $M = 4.0$, calculate the temperature profile after 50 s total time.

Ans. $T_1 = 157.72$, $T_2 = 181.84$, $T_3 = 194.44$, $T_4 = 198.93$, $T_5 = 199.90$°C

5.5-1. *Chilling Slab of Beef.* Repeat Example 5.5-1, where the slab of beef is cooled to 10°C at the center, but use air of 0°C at a lower value of $h = 22.7$ W/m$^2 \cdot$K.

Ans. $(T_1 - T)/(T_1 - T_0) = 0.265$, $X = 0.92$, $t = 19.74$ h

5.5-2. *Chilling Fish Fillets.* Codfish fillets originally at 10°C are packed to a thickness of 102 mm. Ice is packed on both sides of the fillets and wet-strength paper separates the ice and fillets. The surface temperature of the fish can be assumed as essentially 0°C. Calculate the time for the center of the fillets to reach 2.22°C and the temperature at this time at a distance of 25.4 mm from the surface. Also, plot temperature versus position for the slab. The physical properties are (B1) $k = 0.571$ W/m$\cdot$K, $\rho = 1052$ kg/m^3, and $c_p = 4.02$ kJ/kg$\cdot$K.

5.5-3. *Average Temperature in Chilling Fish.* Fish fillets having the same physical properties given in Problem 5.5-2 are originally at 10°C. They are packed to a thickness of 102 mm with ice on each side. Assuming that the surface temperature of the fillets is 0°C, calculate the time for the average temperature to reach 1.39°C. (*Note:* This is a case where the surface resistance is zero. Can Fig. 5.3-13 be used for this case?)

5.5-4. *Time to Freeze a Slab of Meat.* Repeat Example 5.5-2 using the same conditions except that a plate or contact freezer is used where the surface coefficient can be assumed as $h = 142$ W/m$^2 \cdot$K.

Ans. $t = 2.00$ h

5.5-5. *Freezing a Cylinder of Meat.* A package of meat containing 75% moisture and in the form of a long cylinder 5 in. in diameter is to be frozen in an air-blast freezer at -25°F. The meat is initially at the freezing temperature of 27°F. The heat-transfer coefficient is $h = 3.5$ btu/h$\cdot$ft$^2 \cdot$°F. The physical properties are $\rho = 64$ lb$_m$/ft^3 for the unfrozen meat and $k = 0.60$ btu/h$\cdot$ft$\cdot$°F for the frozen meat. Calculate the freezing time.

5.6-1. *Heat Generation Using Equation of Energy Change.* A plane wall with uniform internal heat generation of $\dot{q}$ W/m^3 is insulated at four surfaces, with heat conduction only in the x direction. The wall has a thickness of $2L$ m. The temperature at one wall at $x = +L$ and at the other wall at $x = -L$ is held constant at T_w K. Using the differential equation of energy change, Eq. (5.6-18), derive the equation for the final temperature profile.

$$\textbf{Ans.} \quad T = \frac{\dot{q}(L^2 - x^2)}{2k} + T_w$$

5.6-2. ***Heat Transfer in a Solid Using Equation of Energy Change.*** A solid of thickness L is at a uniform temperature of T_0 K. Suddenly the front surface temperature of the solid at $z = 0$ m is raised to T_1 at $t = 0$ and held there, and at $z = L$ at the rear to T_2 and held constant. Heat transfer occurs only in the z direction. For constant physical properties and using the differential equation of energy change, do as follows:
   (a) Derive the partial differential equation and the boundary conditions (B.C.) for unsteady-state energy transfer.
   (b) Do the same for steady state and integrate the final equation.

$$\textbf{Ans.} \quad \text{(a) } \partial T/\partial t = \alpha\, \partial^2 T/\partial z^2; \text{ B.C.(1): } t = 0, z = z, T = T_0; \text{ B.C.(2): } t = t, z = 0,$$
$$T = T_1; \text{ B.C.(3): } t = t, z = L, T = T_2; \text{ (b) } T = (T_2 - T_1)z/L + T_1$$

5.6-3. ***Radial Temperature Profile Using the Equation of Energy Change.*** Radial heat transfer is occurring by conduction through a long, hollow cylinder of length L with the ends insulated.
   (a) What is the final differential equation for steady-state conduction? Start with Fourier's second law in cylindrical coordinates, Eq. (5.6-20).
   (b) Solve the equation for the temperature profile from part (a) for the boundary conditions given as follows: $T = T_i$ for $r = r_i$, $T = T_o$ for $r = r_o$.
   (c) Using part (b), derive an expression for the heat flow q in W.

$$\textbf{Ans.} \quad T = T_i - \frac{T_i - T_o}{\ln(r_o/r_i)} \ln \frac{r}{r_i}$$

5.6-4. ***Heat Conduction in a Sphere.*** Radial energy flow is occurring in a hollow sphere with an inside radius of r_i and an outside radius of r_o. At steady state the inside surface temperature is constant at T_i and constant at T_o on the outside surface.
   (a) Using the differential equation of energy change, solve the equation for the temperature profile.
   (b) Using part (a), derive an expression for the heat flow in W.

5.6-5. ***Variable Heat Generation and Equation of Energy Change.*** A plane wall is insulated so that conduction occurs only in the x direction. The boundary conditions which apply at steady state are $T = T_0$ at $x = 0$ and $T = T_L$ at $x = L$. Internal heat generation per unit volume is occurring and varies as $\dot{q} = \dot{q}_0 e^{-\beta x/L}$, where $\dot{q}_0$ and β are constants. Solve the general differential equation of energy change for the temperature profile.

5.7-1. ***Thermal and Hydrodynamic Boundary Layer Thicknesses.*** Air at 294.3 K and 101.3 kPa with a free stream velocity of 12.2 m/s is flowing parallel to a smooth, flat plate held at a surface temperature of 383 K. Do the following:
   (a) At the critical $N_{Re,L} = 5 \times 10^5$, calculate the critical length $x = L$ of the plate, the thickness δ of the hydrodynamic boundary layer, and the thickness δ_T of the thermal boundary layer. Note that the Prandtl number is not 1.0.
   (b) Calculate the average heat-transfer coefficient over the plate covered by the laminar boundary layer.

5.7-2. ***Boundary-Layer Thicknesses and Heat Transfer.*** Air at 37.8°C and 1 atm abs flows at a velocity of 3.05 m/s parallel to a flat plate held at 93.3°C. The plate is 1 m wide. Calculate the following at a position 0.61 m from the leading edge:

(a) The thermal boundary-layer thickness δ_T and the hydrodynamic boundary-layer thickness δ.

(b) Total heat transfer from the plate.

REFERENCES

(B1) BLAKEBROUGH, N. *Biochemical and Biological Engineering Science,* Vol. 2. New York: Academic Press, Inc., 1968.

(B2) BIRD, R. B., STEWART, W. E., and LIGHTFOOT, E. N. *Transport Phenomena.* New York: John Wiley & Sons, Inc., 1960.

(C1) CARSLAW, H. S., and JAEGER, J. C. *Conduction of Heat in Solids.* Oxford: Clarendon Press, 1959.

(C2) CHARM, S. E. *The Fundamentals of Food Engineering,* 2nd ed. Westport, Conn.: Avi Publishing Co., Inc., 1971.

(D1) DUSINBERRE, G. M. *Heat Transfer Calculations by Finite Differences.* Scranton, Pa.: International Textbook Co., Inc., 1961.

(G1) GEANKOPLIS, C. J. *Mass Transport Phenomena.* Columbus, Ohio: Ohio State University Bookstores, 1972.

(G2) GURNEY, H. P., and LURIE, J. *Ind. Eng. Chem.,* **15,** 1170 (1923).

(H1) HEISLER, H. P. *Trans. A.S.M.E.,* **69,** 227 (1947).

(H2) HODGSON, T. *Fd. Inds. S. Afr.,* **16,** 41 (1964); *Int. Inst. Refrig. Annexe,* **1966,** 633 (1966).

(K1) KREITH, F. *Principles of Heat Transfer,* 2nd ed. Scranton, Pa.: International Textbook Company, 1965.

(K2) KREITH, F., and BLACK, W. Z. *Basic Heat Transfer.* New York: Harper & Row, Publishers, 1980.

(N1) NEWMAN, A. H. *Ind. Eng. Chem.,* **28,** 545 (1936).

(P1) PERRY, R. H., and CHILTON, C. H. *Chemical Engineers' Handbook,* 5th ed. New York: McGraw-Hill Book Company, 1973.

(P2) PLANK, R. Z. *Ges. Kalteind.,* **20,** 109 (1913); *Z. Ges. Kalteind. Bieh. Reih,* **10** (3), 1 (1941).

(R1) RIEDEL, L. *Kaltetchnik,* **8,** 374 (1956); **9,** 38 (1957); **11,** 41 (1959); **12,** 4 (1960).

(S1) SCHNEIDER, P. J. *Conduction Heat Transfer.* Reading, Mass.: Addison-Wesley Publishing Company, Inc., 1955.

(S2) SIEGEL, R., SPARROW, E. M., and HALLMAN, T. M. *Appl. Sci. Res.,* **A7,** 386 (1958).

CHAPTER 6

Principles of
Mass Transfer

6.1 INTRODUCTION TO MASS TRANSFER AND DIFFUSION

6.1A Similarity of Mass, Heat, and Momentum Transfer Processes

1. Introduction.   In Chapter 1 we noted that the various separation processes have certain basic principles which can be classified into three fundamental transfer (or "transport") processes: momentum transfer, heat transfer, and mass transfer. The fundamental process of *momentum transfer* occurs in such operations as fluid flow, mixing, sedimentation, and filtration. *Heat transfer* occurs in conductive and convective transfer of heat, evaporation, distillation, and drying.

The third fundamental transfer process, *mass transfer,* occurs in distillation, absorption, drying, liquid–liquid extraction, adsorption, ion exchange, crystallization, and membrane processes. When mass is being transferred from one distinct phase to another or through a single phase, the basic mechanisms are the same whether the phase is a gas, liquid, or solid. This was also shown for heat transfer, where the transfer of heat by conduction followed Fourier's law in a gas, solid, or liquid.

2. General molecular transport equation.   All three of the molecular transport processes— momentum, heat, and mass—are characterized by the same general type of equation, given in Section 2.3A:

$$\text{rate of a transfer process} = \frac{\text{driving force}}{\text{resistance}} \tag{2.3-1}$$

This can be written as follows for molecular diffusion of the property momentum, heat, or mass:

$$\psi_z = -\delta \frac{d\Gamma}{dz} \tag{2.3-2}$$

3. *Molecular diffusion equations for momentum, heat, and mass transfer.* Newton's equation for momentum transfer for constant density can be written as follows in a manner similar to Eq. (2.3-2):

$$\tau_{zx} = -\frac{\mu}{\rho}\frac{d(v_x\rho)}{dz} \tag{6.1-1}$$

where τ_{zx} is momentum transferred/$s \cdot m^2$, μ/ρ is kinematic viscosity in m^2/s, z is distance in m, and $v_x\rho$ is momentum/m^3, where the momentum has units of $kg \cdot m/s$.

Fourier's law for heat conduction can be written as follows for constant ρ and c_p:

$$\frac{q_z}{A} = -\alpha\frac{d(\rho c_p T)}{dz} \tag{6.1-2}$$

where q_z/A is heat flux in W/m^2, α is the thermal diffusivity in m^2/s, and $\rho c_p T$ is J/m^3.

The equation for molecular diffusion of mass is Fick's law and is also similar to Eq. (2.3-2). It is written as follows for constant total concentration in a fluid:

$$J_{Az}^* = -D_{AB}\frac{dc_A}{dz} \tag{6.1-3}$$

where J_{Az}^* is the molar flux of component A in the z direction due to molecular diffusion in kg mol A/$s \cdot m^2$, D_{AB} the molecular diffusivity of the molecule A in B in m^2/s, c_A the concentration of A in kg mol/m^3, and z the distance of diffusion in m. In cgs units J_{Az}^* is g mol A/$s \cdot cm^2$, D_{AB} is cm^2/s, and c_A is g mol A/cm^3. In English units, J_{Az}^* is lb mol/$h \cdot ft^2$, D_{AB} is ft^2/h, and c_A is lb mol/ft^3.

The similarity of Eqs. (6.1-1), (6.1-2), and (6.1-3) for momentum, heat, and mass transfer should be obvious. All the fluxes on the left-hand side of the three equations have as units transfer of a quantity of momentum, heat, or mass per unit time per unit area. The transport properties μ/ρ, α and D_{AB} all have units of m^2/s, and the concentrations are represented as momentum/m^3, J/m^3, or kg mol/m^3.

4. *Turbulent diffusion equations for momentum, heat, and mass transfer.* In Section 5.7C equations were given showing the similarities among momentum, heat, and mass transfer in turbulent transfer. For turbulent momentum transfer and constant density,

$$\tau_{zx} = -\left(\frac{\mu}{\rho} + \varepsilon_t\right)\frac{d(v_x\rho)}{dz} \tag{6.1-4}$$

For turbulent heat transfer for constant ρ and c_p,

$$\frac{q_z}{A} = -(\alpha + \alpha_t)\frac{d(\rho c_p T)}{dz} \tag{6.1-5}$$

For turbulent mass transfer for constant c,

$$J_{Az}^* = -(D_{AB} + \varepsilon_M)\frac{dc_A}{dz} \tag{6.1-6}$$

In these equations ε_t is the turbulent or eddy momentum diffusivity in m^2/s, α_t the turbulent or eddy thermal diffusivity in m^2/s, and ε_M the turbulent or eddy mass diffusivity in m^2/s. Again, these equations are quite similar to each other. Many of the theoretical equations and empirical correlations for turbulent transport to various geometries are also quite similar.

6.1B Examples of Mass-Transfer Processes

Mass transfer is important in many areas of science and engineering. Mass transfer occurs when a component in a mixture migrates in the same phase or from phase to phase because of a difference in concentration between two points. Many familiar phenomena involve mass transfer. Liquid in an open pail of water evaporates into still air because of the difference in concentration of water vapor at the water surface and the surrounding air. There is a "driving force" from the surface to the air. A piece of sugar added to a cup of coffee eventually dissolves by itself and diffuses to the surrounding solution. When newly cut and moist green timber is exposed to the atmosphere, the wood will dry partially when water in the timber diffuses through the wood to the surface and then to the atmosphere. In a fermentation process nutrients and oxygen dissolved in the solution diffuse to the microorganisms. In a catalytic reaction the reactants diffuse from the surrounding medium to the catalyst surface, where reaction occurs.

Many purification processes involve mass transfer. In uranium processing, a uranium salt in solution is extracted by an organic solvent. Distillation to separate alcohol from water involves mass transfer. Removal of SO_2 from flue gas is done by absorption in a basic liquid solution.

We can treat mass transfer in a manner somewhat similar to that used in heat transfer with Fourier's law of conduction. However, an important difference is that in molecular mass transfer, one or more of the components of the medium is moving. In heat transfer by conduction, the medium is usually stationary and only energy in the form of heat is being transported. This introduces some differences between heat and mass transfer that will be discussed in this chapter.

6.1C Fick's Law for Molecular Diffusion

Molecular diffusion or molecular transport can be defined as the transfer or movement of individual molecules through a fluid by means of the random, individual movements of the molecules. We can imagine the molecules traveling only in straight lines and changing direction by bouncing off other molecules after collision. Since the molecules travel in a random path, molecular diffusion is often called a *random-walk process*.

In Fig. 6.1-1 the *molecular diffusion process* is shown schematically. A random path that molecule *A* might take in diffusing through *B* molecules from point (1) to (2) is shown. If

FIGURE 6.1-1. *Schematic diagram of molecular diffusion process.*

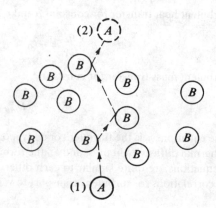

there are a greater number of A molecules near point (1) than at (2), then, since molecules diffuse randomly in both directions, more A molecules will diffuse from (1) to (2) than from (2) to (1). The net diffusion of A is from high- to low-concentration regions.

As another example, a drop of blue liquid dye is added to a cup of water. The dye molecules will diffuse slowly by molecular diffusion to all parts of the water. To increase this rate of mixing of the dye, the liquid can be mechanically agitated by a spoon and *convective mass transfer* will occur. The two modes of heat transfer, conduction and convective heat transfer, are analogous to molecular diffusion and convective mass transfer.

First, we will consider the diffusion of molecules when the whole bulk fluid is not moving but is stationary. Diffusion of the molecules is due to a concentration gradient. The general Fick's law equation can be written as follows for a binary mixture of A and B:

$$J^*_{Az} = -cD_{AB} \frac{dx_A}{dz} \qquad (6.1\text{-}7)$$

where c is total concentration of A and B in kg mol $A + B/m^3$, and x_A is the mole fraction of A in the mixture of A and B. If c is constant, then since $c_A = cx_A$,

$$c\, dx_A = d(cx_A) = dc_A \qquad (6.1\text{-}8)$$

Substituting into Eq. (6.1-7) we obtain Eq. (6.1-3) for constant total concentration:

$$J^*_{Az} = -D_{AB} \frac{dc_A}{dz} \qquad (6.1\text{-}3)$$

This equation is the one more commonly used in many molecular diffusion processes. If c varies some, an average value is often used with Eq. (6.1-3).

EXAMPLE 6.1-1. *Molecular Diffusion of Helium in Nitrogen*
A mixture of He and N_2 gas is contained in a pipe at 298 K and 1 atm total pressure which is constant throughout. At one end of the pipe at point 1 the partial pressure p_{A1} of He is 0.60 atm and at the other end 0.2 m (20 cm) $p_{A2} = 0.20$ atm. Calculate the flux of He at steady state if D_{AB} of the He–N_2 mixture is 0.687×10^{-4} m^2/s (0.687 cm^2/s). Use SI and cgs units.

Solution: Since total pressure P is constant, then c is constant, where c is as follows for a gas according to the perfect gas law:

$$PV = nRT \qquad (6.1\text{-}9)$$

$$\frac{n}{V} = \frac{P}{RT} = c \qquad (6.1\text{-}10)$$

where n is kg mol A plus B, V is volume in m^3, T is temperature in K, R is 8314.3 m$^3 \cdot$ Pa/kg mol $\cdot$ K or R is 82.057×10^{-3} m$^3 \cdot$ atm/kg mol $\cdot$ K, and c is kg mol A plus B/m^3. In cgs units, R is 82.057 cm$^3 \cdot$ atm/g mol $\cdot$ K.

For steady state the flux J^*_{Az} in Eq. (6.1-3) is constant. Also, D_{AB} for a gas is constant. Rearranging Eq. (6.1-3) and integrating,

$$J^*_{Az} \int_{z_1}^{z_2} dz = -D_{AB} \int_{c_{A1}}^{c_{A2}} dc_A$$

$$J^*_{AZ} = \frac{D_{AB}(c_{A1} - c_{A2})}{z_2 - z_1} \qquad (6.1\text{-}11)$$

Also, from the perfect gas law, $p_A V = n_A RT$, and

$$c_{A1} = \frac{p_{A1}}{RT} = \frac{n_A}{V} \tag{6.1-12}$$

Substituting Eq. (6.1-12) into (6.1-11),

$$J_{Az}^* = \frac{D_{AB}(p_{A1} - p_{A2})}{RT(z_2 - z_1)} \tag{6.1-13}$$

This is the final equation to use, which is in a form easily used for gases. Partial pressures are $p_{A1} = 0.6$ atm $= 0.6 \times 1.01325 \times 10^5 = 6.08 \times 10^4$ Pa and $p_{A2} = 0.2$ atm $= 0.2 \times 1.01325 \times 10^5 = 2.027 \times 10^4$ Pa. Then, using SI units,

$$J_{Az}^* = \frac{(0.687 \times 10^{-4})(6.08 \times 10^4 - 2.027 \times 10^4)}{8314(298)(0.20 - 0)}$$

$$= 5.63 \times 10^{-6} \text{ kg mol } A/\text{s} \cdot \text{m}^2$$

If pressures in atm are used with SI units,

$$J_{Az}^* = \frac{(0.687 \times 10^{-4})(0.60 - 0.20)}{(82.06 \times 10^{-3})(298)(0.20 - 0)} = 5.63 \times 10^{-6} \text{ kg mol } A/\text{s} \cdot \text{m}^2$$

For cgs units, substituting into Eq. (6.1-13),

$$J_{Az}^* = \frac{0.687(0.60 - 0.20)}{82.06(298)(20 - 0)} = 5.63 \times 10^{-7} \text{ g mol } A/\text{s} \cdot \text{cm}^2$$

Other driving forces (besides concentration differences) for diffusion also occur because of temperature, pressure, electrical potential, and other gradients. Details are given elsewhere (B3).

6.1D Convective Mass-Transfer Coefficient

When a fluid is flowing outside a solid surface in forced convection motion, we can express the rate of convective mass transfer from the surface to the fluid, or vice versa, by the following equation:

$$N_A = k_c(c_{L1} - c_{Li}) \tag{6.1-14}$$

where k_c is a mass-transfer coefficient in m/s, c_{L1} the bulk fluid concentration in kg mol A/m^3, and c_{Li} the concentration in the fluid next to the surface of the solid. This mass-transfer coefficient is very similar to the heat-transfer coefficient h and is a function of the system geometry, fluid properties, and flow velocity. In Chapter 7 we consider convective mass transfer in detail.

6.2 MOLECULAR DIFFUSION IN GASES

6.2A Equimolar Counterdiffusion in Gases

In Fig. 6.2-1 a diagram is given of two gases A and B at constant total pressure P in two large chambers connected by a tube where molecular diffusion at steady state is occurring. Stirring in each chamber keeps the concentrations in each chamber uniform. The partial pressure

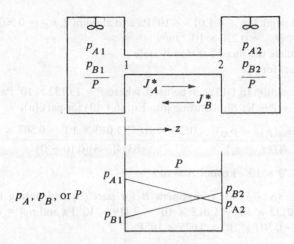

FIGURE 6.2-1. *Equimolar counterdiffusion of gases A and B.*

$p_{A1} > p_{A2}$ and $p_{B2} > p_{B1}$. Molecules of A diffuse to the right and B to the left. Since the total pressure P is constant throughout, the net moles of A diffusing to the right must equal the net moles of B to the left. If this is not so, the total pressure would not remain constant. This means that

$$J_{Az}^* = -J_{Bz}^* \tag{6.2-1}$$

The subscript z is often dropped when the direction is obvious. Writing Fick's law for B for constant c,

$$J_B^* = -D_{BA} \frac{dc_B}{dz} \tag{6.2-2}$$

Now since $P = p_A + p_B = $ constant, then

$$c = c_A + c_B \tag{6.2-3}$$

Differentiating both sides,

$$dc_A = -dc_B \tag{6.2-4}$$

Equating Eq. (6.1-3) to (6.2-2),

$$J_A^* = -D_{AB} \frac{dc_A}{dz} = -J_B^* = -(-)D_{BA} \frac{dc_B}{dz} \tag{6.2-5}$$

Substituting Eq. (6.2-4) into (6.2-5) and canceling like terms,

$$D_{AB} = D_{BA} \tag{6.2-6}$$

This shows that for a binary gas mixture of A and B, the diffusivity coefficient D_{AB} for A diffusing into B is the same as D_{BA} for B diffusing into A.

EXAMPLE 6.2-1. Equimolar Counterdiffusion

Ammonia gas (A) is diffusing through a uniform tube 0.10 m long containing N_2 gas (B) at 1.0132×10^5 Pa pressure and 298 K. The diagram is similar to

Fig. 6.2-1. At point 1, $p_{A1} = 1.013 \times 10^4$ Pa and at point 2, $p_{A2} = 0.507 \times 10^4$ Pa. The diffusivity $D_{AB} = 0.230 \times 10^{-4}$ m²/s.

  (a) Calculate the flux J_A^* at steady state.
  (b) Repeat for J_B^*.

Solution: Equation (6.1-13) can be used, where $P = 1.0132 \times 10^5$ Pa, $z_2 - z_1 = 0.10$ m, and $T = 298$ K. Substituting into Eq. (6.1-13) for part (a),

$$J_A^* = \frac{D_{AB}(p_{A1} - p_{A2})}{RT(z_2 - z_1)} = \frac{(0.23 \times 10^{-4})(1.013 \times 10^4 - 0.507 \times 10^4)}{8314(298)(0.10 - 0)}$$

$$= 4.70 \times 10^{-7} \text{ kg mol } A/\text{s} \cdot \text{m}^2$$

Rewriting Eq. (6.1-13) for component B for part (b) and noting that $p_{B1} = P - p_{A1} = 1.0132 \times 10^5 - 1.013 \times 10^4 = 9.119 \times 10^4$ Pa and $p_{B2} = P - p_{A2} = 1.0132 \times 10^5 - 0.507 \times 10^4 = 9.625 \times 10^4$ Pa,

$$J_B^* = \frac{D_{AB}(p_{B1} - p_{B2})}{RT(z_2 - z_1)} = \frac{(0.23 \times 10^{-4})(9.119 \times 10^4 - 9.625 \times 10^4)}{8314(298)(0.10 - 0)}$$

$$= -4.70 \times 10^{-7} \text{ kg mol } B/\text{s} \cdot \text{m}^2$$

The negative value for J_B^* means the flux goes from point 2 to point 1.

6.2B General Case for Diffusion of Gases A and B Plus Convection

Up to now we have considered Fick's law for diffusion in a stationary fluid; that is, there has been no net movement or convective flow of the entire phase of the binary mixture A and B. The diffusion flux J_A^* occurred because of the concentration gradient. The rate at which moles of A passed a fixed point to the right, which will be taken as a positive flux, is J_A^* kg mol $A/\text{s} \cdot \text{m}^2$. This flux can be converted to a velocity of diffusion of A to the right by

$$J_A^* \text{ (kg mol } A/\text{s} \cdot \text{m}^2) = v_{Ad}c_A\left(\frac{\text{m}}{\text{s}} \frac{\text{kg mol } A}{\text{m}^3}\right) \tag{6.2-7}$$

where v_{Ad} is the diffusion velocity of A in m/s.

Now let us consider what happens when the whole fluid is moving in bulk or convective flow to the right. The molar average velocity of the whole fluid relative to a stationary point is v_M m/s. Component A is still diffusing to the right, but now its diffusion velocity v_{Ad} is measured relative to the moving fluid. To a stationary observer A is moving faster than the bulk of the phase, since its diffusion velocity v_{Ad} is added to that of the bulk phase v_M. Expressed mathematically, the velocity of A relative to the stationary point is the sum of the diffusion velocity and the average or convective velocity:

$$v_A = v_{Ad} + v_M \tag{6.2-8}$$

where v_A is the velocity of A relative to a stationary point. Expressed pictorially,

$$\xrightarrow{\hspace{2cm}} v_A$$
$$\xrightarrow{\hspace{0.8cm}} \quad \xrightarrow{\hspace{0.8cm}}$$
$$v_{Ad} \qquad v_M$$

Multiplying Eq. (6.2-8) by c_A,

$$c_A v_A = c_A v_{Ad} + c_A v_M \tag{6.2-9}$$

Each of the three terms represents a flux. The first term, $c_A v_A$, can be represented by the flux N_A kg mol A/s $\cdot$ m^2. This is the total flux of A relative to the stationary point. The second term is J_A^*, the diffusion flux relative to the moving fluid. The third term is the convective flux of A relative to the stationary point. Hence, Eq. (6.2-9) becomes

$$N_A = J_A^* + c_A v_M \tag{6.2-10}$$

Let N be the total convective flux of the whole stream relative to the stationary point. Then,

$$N = c v_M = N_A + N_B \tag{6.2-11}$$

Or, solving for v_M,

$$v_M = \frac{N_A + N_B}{c} \tag{6.2-12}$$

Substituting Eq. (6.2-12) into (6.2-10),

$$N_A = J_A^* + \frac{c_A}{c}(N_A + N_B) \tag{6.2-13}$$

Since J_A^* is Fick's law, Eq. (6.1-7),

$$N_A = -c D_{AB} \frac{dx_A}{dz} + \frac{c_A}{c}(N_A + N_B) \tag{6.2-14}$$

Equation (6.2-14) is the final general equation for diffusion plus convection to use when the flux N_A is used, which is relative to a stationary point. A similar equation can be written for N_B.

$$N_B = -c D_{BA} \frac{dx_B}{dz} + \frac{c_B}{c}(N_A + N_B) \tag{6.2-15}$$

To solve Eq. (6.2-14) or (6.2-15), the relation between the flux N_A and N_B must be known. Equations (6.2-14) and (6.2-15) hold for diffusion in a gas, liquid, or solid.

For equimolar counterdiffusion, $N_A = -N_B$ and the convective term in Eq. (6.2-14) becomes zero. Then, $N_A = J_A^* = -N_B = -J_B^*$.

6.2C Special Case for A Diffusing Through Stagnant, Nondiffusing B

The case of diffusion of A through stagnant or nondiffusing B at steady state often occurs. In this case one boundary at the end of the diffusion path is impermeable to component B, so it cannot pass through. One example, shown in Fig. 6.2-2a, is in the evaporation of a pure liquid such as benzene (A) at the bottom of a narrow tube, where a large amount of inert or nondiffusing air (B) is passed over the top. The benzene vapor (A) diffuses through the air (B) in the tube. The boundary at the liquid surface at point 1 is impermeable to air, since air is insoluble in benzene liquid. Hence, air (B) cannot diffuse into or away from the surface. At point 2 the partial pressure $p_{A2} = 0$, since a large volume of air is passing by.

Another example, shown in Fig. 6.2-2b, occurs in the absorption of NH$_3$ (A) vapor which is in air (B) by water. The water surface is impermeable to the air, since air is only very slightly soluble in water. Thus, since B cannot diffuse, $N_B = 0$.

FIGURE 6.2-2. *Diffusion of A through stagnant, nondiffusing B: (a) benzene evaporating into air, (b) ammonia in air being absorbed into water.*

To derive the case for A diffusing in stagnant, nondiffusing B, $N_B = 0$ is substituted into the general Eq. (6.2-14):

$$N_A = -cD_{AB}\frac{dx_A}{dz} + \frac{c_A}{c}(N_A + 0)$$

(6.2-16)

The convective flux of A is $(c_A/c)(N_A + 0)$. Keeping the total pressure P constant, substituting $c = P/RT$, $p_A = x_A P$, and $c_A/c = p_A/P$ into Eq. (6.2-16),

$$N_A = -\frac{D_{AB}}{RT}\frac{dp_A}{dz} + \frac{p_A}{P}N_A$$

(6.2-17)

Rearranging and integrating,

$$N_A\left(1 - \frac{p_A}{P}\right) = -\frac{D_{AB}}{RT}\frac{dp_A}{dz}$$

(6.2-18)

$$N_A \int_{z_1}^{z_2} dz = -\frac{D_{AB}}{RT}\int_{p_{A1}}^{p_{A2}}\frac{dp_A}{1 - p_A/P}$$

(6.2-19)

$$N_A = \frac{D_{AB}P}{RT(z_2 - z_1)}\ln\frac{P - p_{A2}}{P - p_{A1}}$$

(6.2-20)

Equation (6.2-20) is the final equation to be used to calculate the flux of A. However, it is often written in another form. A log mean value of the inert B is defined as follows. Since $P = p_{A1} + p_{B1} = p_{A2} + p_{B2}$, $p_{B1} = P - p_{A1}$, and $p_{B2} = P - p_{A2}$,

$$p_{BM} = \frac{p_{B2} - p_{B1}}{\ln(p_{B2}/p_{B1})} = \frac{p_{A1} - p_{A2}}{\ln[(P - p_{A2})/(P - p_{A1})]}$$

(6.2-21)

Substituting Eq. (6.2-21) into (6.2-20),

$$N_A = \frac{D_{AB}P}{RT(z_2 - z_1)p_{BM}}(p_{A1} - p_{A2})$$

(6.2-22)

EXAMPLE 6.2-2. *Diffusion of Water Through Stagnant, Nondiffusing Air*

Water in the bottom of a narrow metal tube is held at a constant temperature of 293 K. The total pressure of air (assumed dry) is 1.01325×10^5 Pa (1.0 atm) and the temperature is 293 K (20°C). Water evaporates and diffuses through the air in the tube, and the diffusion path $z_2 - z_1$ is 0.1524 m (0.5 ft) long. The diagram is similar to Fig. 6.2-2a. Calculate the rate of evaporation at steady state in lb mol/h · ft^2 and kg mol/s · m^2. The diffusivity of water vapor at 293 K and 1 atm pressure is 0.250×10^{-4} m^2/s. Assume that the system is isothermal. Use SI and English units.

Solution: The diffusivity is converted to ft^2/h by using the conversion factor from Appendix A.1:

$$D_{AB} = 0.250 \times 10^{-4}(3.875 \times 10^4) = 0.969 \text{ ft}^2/\text{h}$$

From Appendix A.2 the vapor pressure of water at 20°C is 17.54 mm, or $p_{A1} = 17.54/760 = 0.0231$ atm $= 0.0231(1.01325 \times 10^5) = 2.341 \times 10^3$ Pa, $p_{A2} = 0$ (pure air). Since the temperature is 20°C (68°F), $T = 460 + 68 = 528°R = 293$ K. From Appendix A.1, $R = 0.730$ ft^3 · atm/lb mol · °R. To calculate the value of p_{BM} from Eq. (6.2-21),

$$p_{B1} = P - p_{A1} = 1.00 - 0.0231 = 0.9769 \text{ atm}$$

$$P_{B2} = P - p_{A2} = 1.00 - 0 = 1.00 \text{ atm}$$

$$p_{BM} = \frac{p_{B2} - p_{B1}}{\ln(p_{B2}/p_{B1})} = \frac{1.00 - 0.9769}{\ln(1.00/0.9769)} = 0.988 \text{ atm} = 1.001 \times 10^5 \text{ Pa}$$

Since p_{B1} is close to p_{B2}, the linear mean $(p_{B1} + p_{B2})/2$ could be used and would be very close to p_{BM}.

Substituting into Eq. (6.2-22) with $z_2 - z_1 = 0.5$ ft (0.1524 m),

$$N_A = \frac{D_{AB}P}{RT(z_2 - z_1)p_{BM}}(p_{A1} - p_{A2}) = \frac{0.969(1.0)(0.0231 - 0)}{0.730(528)(0.5)(0.988)}$$

$$= 1.175 \times 10^{-4} \text{ lb mol/h} \cdot \text{ft}^2$$

$$N_A = \frac{(0.250 \times 10^{-4})(1.01325 \times 10^5)(2.341 \times 10^3 - 0)}{8314(293)(0.1524)(1.001 \times 10^5)}$$

$$= 1.595 \times 10^{-7} \text{ kg mol/s} \cdot \text{m}^2$$

EXAMPLE 6.2-3. *Diffusion in a Tube with Change in Path Length*

Diffusion of water vapor in a narrow tube is occurring as in Example 6.2-2 under the same conditions. However, as shown in Fig. 6.2-2a, at a given time t, the level is z m from the top. As diffusion proceeds, the level drops slowly. Derive the equation for the time t_F for the level to drop from a starting point of z_0 m at $t = 0$ to z_F at $t = t_F$ s as shown.

Solution: We assume a pseudo-steady-state condition since the level drops very slowly. As time progresses, the path length z increases. At any time t, Eq. (6.2-22) holds; but the path length is z and Eq. (6.2-22) becomes as follows, where N_A and z are now variables:

$$N_A = \frac{D_{AB}P}{RTzp_{BM}}(p_{A1} - p_{A2}) \qquad \text{(6.2-23)}$$

Assuming a cross-sectional area of 1 m^2, the level drops dz m in dt s, and $\rho_A(dz \cdot 1)/M_A$ is the kg mol of A that have left and diffused. Then,

$$N_A \cdot 1 = \frac{\rho_A(dz \cdot 1)}{M_A \, dt} \qquad \text{(6.2-24)}$$

Equating Eq. (6.2-24) to (6.2-23), rearranging, and integrating between the limits of $z = z_0$ when $t = 0$ and $z = z_F$ when $t = t_F$,

$$\frac{\rho_A}{M_A}\int_{z_0}^{z_F} z \, dz = \frac{D_{AB}P(p_{A1} - p_{A2})}{RTp_{BM}}\int_0^{t_F} dt \qquad \text{(6.2-25)}$$

Solving for t_F,

$$t_F = \frac{\rho_A(z_F^2 - z_0^2)RTp_{BM}}{2M_AD_{AB}P(p_{A1} - p_{A2})} \qquad \text{(6.2-26)}$$

The method shown in Example 6.2-3 has been used to experimentally determine the diffusivity D_{AB}. In this experiment the starting path length z_0 is measured at $t = 0$ together with the final z_F at t_F. Then Eq. (6.2-26) is used to calculate D_{AB}.

6.2D Diffusion Through a Varying Cross-Sectional Area

So far, in the cases at steady state we have considered N_A and J_A^* as constants in the integrations. In these cases the cross-sectional area A m^2 through which the diffusion occurs has been constant with varying distance z. In some situations the area A may vary. Then it is convenient to define N_A as

$$N_A = \frac{\overline{N}_A}{A} \qquad \text{(6.2-27)}$$

where $\overline{N}_A$ is kg moles of A diffusing per second or kg mol/s. At steady state, $\overline{N}_A$ will be constant but not A for a varying area.

1. Diffusion from a sphere.   To illustrate the use of Eq. (6.2-27), the important case of diffusion to or from a sphere in a gas will be considered. This situation appears often, in such cases as the evaporation of a drop of liquid, the evaporation of a ball of naphthalene, and the diffusion of nutrients to a sphere-like microorganism in a liquid. In Fig. 6.2-3a is shown a sphere of fixed radius r_1 m in an infinite gas medium. Component (A) at partial pressure p_{A1} at the surface is diffusing into the surrounding stagnant medium (B), where $p_{A2} = 0$ at some large distance away. Steady-state diffusion will be assumed.

The flux N_A can be represented by Eq. (6.2-27), where A is the cross-sectional area $4\pi r^2$ at point r distance from the center of the sphere. Also, $\overline{N}_A$ is a constant at steady state:

$$N_A = \frac{\overline{N}_A}{4\pi r^2} \qquad \text{(6.2-28)}$$

(a)
(b)

FIGURE 6.2-3. *Diffusion through a varying cross-sectional area: (a) from a sphere to a surrounding medium, (b) through a circular conduit that is tapered uniformally.*

Since this is a case of A diffusing through stagnant, nondiffusing B, Eq. (6.2-18) will be used in its differential form and N_A will be equated to Eq. (6.2-28), giving

$$N_A = \frac{\overline{N}_A}{4\pi r^2} = -\frac{D_{AB}}{RT}\frac{dp_A}{(1 - p_A/P)dr} \tag{6.2-29}$$

Note that dr was substituted for dz. Rearranging and integrating between r_1 and some point r_2 a large distance away,

$$\frac{\overline{N}_A}{4\pi}\int_{r_1}^{r_2}\frac{dr}{r^2} = -\frac{D_{AB}}{RT}\int_{p_{A1}}^{p_{A2}}\frac{dp_A}{(1 - p_A/P)} \tag{6.2-30}$$

$$\frac{\overline{N}_A}{4\pi}\left(\frac{1}{r_1} - \frac{1}{r_2}\right) = \frac{D_{AB}P}{RT}\ln\frac{P - p_{A2}}{P - p_{A1}} \tag{6.2-31}$$

Since $r_2 \gg r_1$, $1/r_2 \cong 0$. Substituting p_{BM} from Eq. (6.2-21) into Eq. (6.2-31),

$$\frac{\overline{N}_A}{4\pi r_1^2} = N_{A1} = \frac{D_{AB}P}{RTr_1}\frac{p_{A1} - p_{A2}}{p_{BM}} \tag{6.2-32}$$

This equation can be simplified further. If p_{A1} is small compared to P (a dilute gas phase), $p_{BM} \cong P$. Also, setting $2r_1 = D_1$, diameter, and $c_{A1} = p_{A1}/RT$, we obtain

$$N_{A1} = \frac{2D_{AB}}{D_1}(c_{A1} - c_{A2}) \tag{6.2-33}$$

This equation can also be used for liquids, where D_{AB} is the diffusivity of A in the liquid.

EXAMPLE 6.2-4. *Evaporation of a Naphthalene Sphere*

A sphere of naphthalene having a radius of 2.0 mm is suspended in a large volume of still air at 318 K and 1.01325×10^5 Pa (1 atm). The surface temperature of the naphthalene can be assumed to be at 318 K and its vapor pressure at 318 K is 0.555 mm Hg. The D_{AB} of naphthalene in air at 318 K is 6.92×10^{-6} m²/s. Calculate the rate of evaporation of naphthalene from the surface.

Solution: The flow diagram is similar to Fig. 6.2-3a. $D_{AB} = 6.92 \times 10^{-6}$ m²/s, $p_{A1} = (0.555/760)(1.01325 \times 10^5) = 74.0$ Pa, $p_{A2} = 0$, $r_1 = 2/1000$ m, $R = 8314$ m³·Pa/kg mol·K, $p_{B1} = P - p_{A1} = 1.01325 \times 10^5 - 74.0 = 1.01251 \times$

10^5 Pa, $p_{B2} = P - p_{A2} = 1.01325 \times 10^5 - 0$. Since the values of p_{B1} and p_{B2} are close to each other,

$$p_{BM} = \frac{p_{B1} + p_{B2}}{2} = \frac{(1.0125 + 1.01325) \times 10^5}{2} = 1.0129 \times 10^5 \text{ Pa}$$

Substituting into Eq. (6.2-32),

$$N_{A1} = \frac{D_{AB}P(p_{A1} - p_{A2})}{RTr_1p_{BM}} = \frac{(6.92 \times 10^{-6})(1.01325 \times 10^5)(74.0 - 0)}{8314(318)(2/1000)(1.0129 \times 10^5)}$$

$$= 9.68 \times 10^{-8} \text{ kg mol } A/\text{s} \cdot \text{m}^2$$

If the sphere in Fig. 6.2-3a is evaporating, the radius r of the sphere decreases slowly with time. The equation for the time it takes for the sphere to evaporate completely can be derived by assuming pseudo-steady state and by equating the diffusion flux equation (6.2-32), where r is now a variable, to the moles of solid A evaporated per dt time and per unit area as calculated from a material balance. (See Problem 6.2-9 for this case.) The material-balance method is similar to Example 6.2-3. The final equation is

$$t_F = \frac{\rho_A r_1^2 RT p_{BM}}{2M_A D_{AB} P(p_{A1} - p_{A2})} \tag{6.2-34}$$

where r_1 is the original sphere radius, ρ_A the density of the sphere, and M_A the molecular weight.

2. *Diffusion through a conduit of nonuniform cross-sectional area.* In Fig. 6.2-3b component A is diffusion at steady state through a circular conduit which is tapered uniformally as shown. At point 1 the radius is r_1 and at point 2 it is r_2. At position z in the conduit, for A diffusing through stagnant, nondiffusing B,

$$N_A = \frac{\overline{N}_A}{\pi r^2} = -\frac{D_{AB}}{RT} \frac{dp_A}{(1 - p_A/P)dz} \tag{6.2-35}$$

Using the geometry shown, the variable radius r can be related to position z in the path as follows:

$$r = \left(\frac{r_2 - r_1}{z_2 - z_1}\right)z + r_1 \tag{6.2-36}$$

This value of r is then substituted into Eq. (6.2-35) to eliminate r and the equation integrated:

$$\frac{\overline{N}_A}{\pi} \int_{z_1}^{z_2} \frac{dz}{\left[\left(\dfrac{r_2 - r_1}{z_2 - z_1}\right)z + r_1\right]^2} = -\frac{D_{AB}}{RT} \int_{p_{A1}}^{p_{A2}} \frac{dp_A}{1 - p_A/P} \tag{6.2-37}$$

A case similar to this is given in Problem 6.2-10.

6.2E Diffusion Coefficients for Gases

1. *Experimental determination of diffusion coefficients.* A number of different experimental methods have been used to determine the molecular diffusivity for binary gas mixtures. Several of the important methods are as follows. One method is to evaporate a pure liquid in a narrow tube with a gas passed over the top, as shown in Fig. 6.2-2a. The fall in liquid level is measured with time and the diffusivity calculated from Eq. (6.2-26).

In another method, two pure gases having equal pressures are placed in separate sections of a long tube separated by a partition. The partition is slowly removed and diffusion proceeds. After a given time the partition is reinserted and the gas in each section analyzed. The diffusivities of the vapor of solids such as naphthalene, iodine, and benzoic acid in a gas have been obtained by measuring the rate of evaporation of a sphere. Equation (6.2-32) can be used. See Problem 6.2-9 for an example of this.

A method often used is the two-bulb method (N1). The apparatus consists of two glass bulbs with volumes V_1 and V_2 m^3 connected by a capillary of cross-sectional area A m^2 and length L whose volume is small compared to V_1 and V_2, as shown in Fig. 6.2-4. Pure gas A is added to V_1 and pure B to V_2 at the same pressures. The valve is opened, diffusion proceeds for a given time, and then the valve is closed and the mixed contents of each chamber are sampled separately.

The equations can be derived by neglecting the capillary volume and assuming each bulb is always of a uniform concentration. Assuming quasi-steady-state diffusion in the capillary,

$$J_A^* = -D_{AB}\frac{dc}{dz} = -\frac{D_{AB}(c_2 - c_1)}{L} \tag{6.2-38}$$

where c_2 is the concentration of A in V_2 at time t and c_1 in V_1. The rate of diffusion of A going to V_2 is equal to the rate of accumulation in V_2:

$$AJ_A^* = -\frac{D_{AB}(c_2 - c_1)A}{L} = V_2\frac{dc_2}{dt} \tag{6.2-39}$$

The average value c_{av} at equilibrium can be calculated by a material balance from the starting compositions c_1^0 and c_2^0 at $t = 0$:

$$(V_1 + V_2)c_{av} = V_1c_1^0 + V_2c_2^0 \tag{6.2-40}$$

A similar balance at time t gives

$$(V_1 + V_2)c_{av} = V_1c_1 + V_2c_2 \tag{6.2-41}$$

Substituting c_1 from Eq. (6.2-41) into (6.2-39), rearranging, and integrating between $t = 0$ and $t = t$, the final equation is

$$\frac{c_{av} - c_2}{c_{av} - c_2^0} = \exp\left[-\frac{D_{AB}(V_1 + V_2)}{(L/A)(V_2V_1)}t\right] \tag{6.2-42}$$

If c_2 is obtained by sampling at t, D_{AB} can be calculated.

2. Experimental diffusivity data. Some typical data are given in Table 6.2-1. Other data are tabulated in Perry and Green (P1) and Reid et al. (R1). The values range from about

FIGURE 6.2-4. *Diffusivity measurement of gases by the two-bulb method.*

TABLE 6.2-1. *Diffusion Coefficients of Gases at*
101.32 kPa Pressure

System	Temperature °C	K	Diffusivity [$(m^2/s)10^4$ or cm^2/s]	Ref.
$Air-NH_3$	0	273	0.198	(W1)
$Air-H_2O$	0	273	0.220	(N2)
	25	298	0.260	(L1)
	42	315	0.288	(M1)
$Air-CO_2$	3	276	0.142	(H1)
	44	317	0.177	
$Air-H_2$	0	273	0.611	(N2)
$Air-C_2H_5OH$	25	298	0.135	(M1)
	42	315	0.145	
$Air-CH_3COOH$	0	273	0.106	(N2)
$Air-n$-hexane	21	294	0.080	(C1)
$Air-$benzene	25	298	0.0962	(L1)
$Air-$toluene	25.9	298.9	0.086	(G1)
$Air-n$-butanol	0	273	0.0703	(N2)
	25.9	298.9	0.087	
H_2-CH_4	25	298	0.726	(C2)
H_2-N_2	25	298	0.784	(B1)
	85	358	1.052	
H_2-benzene	38.1	311.1	0.404	(H2)
H_2-Ar	22.4	295.4	0.83	(W2)
H_2-NH_3	25	298	0.783	(B1)
H_2-SO_2	50	323	0.61	(S1)
$H_2-C_2H_5OH$	67	340	0.586	(T1)
$He-Ar$	25	298	0.729	(S2)
$He-n$-butanol	150	423	0.587	(S2)
$He-$air	44	317	0.765	(H1)
$He-CH_4$	25	298	0.675	(C2)
$He-N_2$	25	298	0.687	(S2)
$He-O_2$	25	298	0.729	(S2)
$Ar-CH_4$	25	298	0.202	(C2)
CO_2-N_2	25	298	0.167	(W3)
CO_2-O_2	20	293	0.153	(W4)
N_2-n-butane	25	298	0.0960	(B2)
H_2O-CO_2	34.3	307.3	0.202	(S3)
$CO-N_2$	100	373	0.318	(A1)
CH_3Cl-SO_2	30	303	0.0693	(C3)
$(C_2H_5)_2O-NH_3$	26.5	299.5	0.1078	(S4)

0.05×10^{-4} m²/s, where a large molecule is present, to about 1.0×10^{-4} m²/s, where H_2 is present at room temperatures. The relation between diffusivity in m²/s and ft²/h is 1 m²/s $= 3.875 \times 10^4$ ft²/h.

3. Prediction of diffusivity for gases. The diffusivity of a binary gas mixture in the dilute gas region, that is, at low pressures near atmospheric, can be predicted using the kinetic theory of gases. The gas is assumed to consist of rigid spherical particles that are completely elastic on collision with another molecule, which implies that momentum is conserved.

In a simplified treatment it is assumed that there are no attractive or repulsive forces between the molecules. The derivation uses the mean free path λ, which is the average distance that a molecule has traveled between collisions. The final equation is

$$D_{AB} = \tfrac{1}{3}\bar{u}\lambda \tag{6.2-43}$$

where $\bar{u}$ is the average velocity of the molecules. The final equation obtained after substituting expressions for $\bar{u}$ and λ into Eq. (6.2-43) is approximately correct, since it correctly predicts D_{AB} proportional to 1/pressure and approximately predicts the temperature effect.

A more accurate and rigorous treatment must consider the intermolecular forces of attraction and repulsion between molecules as well as the different sizes of molecules A and B. Chapman and Enskog (H3) solved the Boltzmann equation, which uses a distribution function instead of the mean free path λ. To solve the equation, a relation between the attractive and repulsive forces between a given pair of molecules must be used. For a pair of nonpolar molecules, a reasonable approximation to the forces is the Lennard–Jones function.

The final relation for predicting the diffusivity of a binary gas pair of A and B molecules is

$$D_{AB} = \frac{1.8583 \times 10^{-7} T^{3/2}}{P\sigma_{AB}^2 \Omega_{D,AB}} \left(\frac{1}{M_A} + \frac{1}{M_B} \right)^{1/2} \tag{6.2-44}$$

where D_{AB} is the diffusivity in m²/s, T temperature in K, M_A molecular weight of A in kg mass/kg mol, M_B molecular weight of B, and P absolute pressure in atm. The term σ_{AB} is an "average collision diameter" and $\Omega_{D,AB}$ is a collision integral based on the Lennard–Jones potential. Values of σ_A and σ_B as well as $\Omega_{D,AB}$ can be obtained from a number of sources (B3, G2, H3, R1).

The collision integral $\Omega_{D,AB}$ is a ratio giving the deviation of a gas with interactions as compared to a gas of rigid, elastic spheres. This value would be 1.0 for a gas with no interactions. Equation (6.2-44) predicts diffusivities with an average deviation of about 8% up to about 1000 K (R1). For a polar–nonpolar gas mixture, Eq. (6.2-44) can be used if the correct force constant is used for the polar gas (M1, M2). For polar–polar gas pairs, the potential-energy function commonly used is the *Stockmayer potential* (M2).

The effect of concentration of A in B in Eq. (6.2-44) is not included. However, for real gases with interactions, the maximum effect of concentration on diffusivity is about 4% (G2). In most cases the effect is considerably less, and hence it is usually neglected.

Equation (6.2-44) is relatively complicated to use, and often some of the constants such as σ_{AB} are not available or are difficult to estimate. Hence, the semiempirical method of Fuller et al. (F1), which is much more convenient to use is often preferred. The equation was obtained by correlating many recent data and uses atomic volumes from Table 6.2-2, which are summed for each gas molecule. The equation is

$$D_{AB} = \frac{1.00 \times 10^{-7} T^{1.75} (1/M_A + 1/M_B)^{1/2}}{P[(\Sigma \, v_A)^{1/3} + (\Sigma \, v_B)^{1/3}]^2} \tag{6.2-45}$$

TABLE 6.2-2. *Atomic Diffusion Volumes for Use with the Fuller, Schettler, and Giddings Method* *

Atomic and structural diffusion volume increments, v

C	16.5	(Cl)	19.5
H	1.98	(S)	17.0
O	5.48	Aromatic ring	−20.2
(N)	5.69	Heterocyclic ring	−20.2

Diffusion volumes for simple molecules, $\sum v$

H_2	7.07	CO	18.9
D_2	6.70	CO_2	26.9
He	2.88	N_2O	35.9
N_2	17.9	NH_3	14.9
O_2	16.6	H_2O	12.7
Air	20.1	(CCl_2F_2)	114.8
Ar	16.1	(SF_6)	69.7
Kr	22.8	(Cl_2)	37.7
(Xe)	37.9	(Br_2)	67.2
Ne	5.59	(SO_2)	41.1

*Parentheses indicate that the value listed is based on only a few data points.

Source: Reprinted with permission from E. N. Fuller, P. D. Schettler, and J. C. Giddings, *Ind. Eng. Chem.,* **58,** 19(1966). Copyright by the American Chemical Society.

where $\sum v_A$ = sum of structural volume increments, Table 6.2-2, and D_{AB} = m²/s. This method can be used for mixtures of nonpolar gases or for a polar–nonpolar mixture. Its accuracy is not quite as good as that of Eq. (6.2-44).

The equation shows that D_{AB} is proportional to $1/P$ and to $T^{1.75}$. If an experimental value of D_{AB} is available at a given T and P and it is desired to have a value of D_{AB} at another T and P, one should correct the experimental value to the new T and P by means of the relationship $D_{AB} \propto T^{1.75}/P$.

4. Schmidt number of gases. The *Schmidt number* of a gas mixture of dilute A in B is dimensionless and is defined as

$$N_{Sc} = \frac{\mu}{\rho D_{AB}} \tag{6.2-46}$$

where μ is viscosity of the gas mixture, which is viscosity of B for a dilute mixture in Pa · s or kg/m · s, D_{AB} is diffusivity in m²/s, and ρ is the density of the mixture in kg/m³. For a gas the Schmidt number can be assumed independent of temperature over moderate ranges and independent of pressure up to about 10 atm or 10×10^5 Pa.

The Schmidt number is the dimensionless ratio of the molecular momentum diffusivity μ/ρ to the molecular mass diffusivity D_{AB}. Values of the Schmidt number for gases range from about 0.5 to 2. For liquids Schmidt numbers range from about 100 to over 10 000 for viscous liquids.

EXAMPLE 6.2-5. Estimation of Diffusivity of a Gas Mixture

Normal butanol (A) is diffusing through air (B) at 1 atm abs. Using the Fuller et al. method, estimate the diffusivity D_{AB} for the following temperatures and compare with the experimental data:

(a) For 0°C.
(b) For 25.9°C.
(c) For 0°C and 2.0 atm abs.

Solution: For part (a), $P = 1.00$ atm, $T = 273 + 0 = 273$ K, M_A (butanol) = 74.1, M_B (air) = 29. From Table 6.2-2,

$$\sum v_A = 4(16.5) + 10(1.98) + 1(5.48) = 91.28 \text{ (butanol)}$$

$$\sum v_B = 20.1 \text{ (air)}$$

Substituting into Eq. (6.2-45),

$$D_{AB} = \frac{1.0 \times 10^{-7}(273)^{1.75}(1/74.1 + 1/29)^{1/2}}{1.0[(91.28)^{1/3} + (20.1)^{1/3}]^2}$$

$$= 7.73 \times 10^{-6} \text{ m}^2/\text{s}$$

This value deviates by +10% from the experimental value of 7.03×10^{-6} m²/s from Table 6.2-1.

For part (b), $T = 273 + 25.9 = 298.9$. Substituting into Eq. (6.2-45), $D_{AB} = 9.05 \times 10^{-6}$ m²/s. This value deviates by +4% from the experimental value of 8.70×10^{-6} m²/s.

For part (c), the total pressure $P = 2.0$ atm. Using the value predicted in part (a) and correcting for pressure,

$$D_{AB} = 7.73 \times 10^{-6}(1.0/2.0) = 3.865 \times 10^{-6} \text{ m}^2/\text{s}$$

6.3 MOLECULAR DIFFUSION IN LIQUIDS

6.3A Introduction

Diffusion of solutes in liquids is very important in many industrial processes, especially in such separation operations as liquid–liquid extraction or solvent extraction, gas absorption, and distillation. Diffusion in liquids also occurs in many situations in nature, such as oxygenation of rivers and lakes by the air and diffusion of salts in blood.

It should be apparent that the rate of molecular diffusion in liquids is considerably slower than in gases. The molecules in a liquid are very close together compared to a gas. Hence, the molecules of the diffusing solute A will collide with molecules of liquid B more often and diffuse more slowly than in gases. In general, the diffusion coefficient in a gas will be on the order of magnitude of about 10^5 times greater than in a liquid. However, the flux in a gas is not that much greater, being only about 100 times faster, since the concentrations in liquids are considerably higher than in gases.

6.3B Equations for Diffusion in Liquids

Since the molecules in a liquid are packed together much more closely than in gases, the density and the resistance to diffusion in a liquid are much greater. Also, because of this closer spacing of the molecules, the attractive forces between molecules play an important role in diffusion. Since the kinetic theory of liquids is only partially developed, we write the equations for diffusion in liquids similar to those for gases.

In diffusion in liquids an important difference from diffusion in gases is that the diffusivities are often quite dependent on the concentration of the diffusing components.

1. Equimolar counterdiffusion. Starting with the general equation (6.2-14), we can obtain for equimolal counterdiffusion, where $N_A = -N_B$, an equation similar to Eq. (6.1-11) for gases at steady state:

$$N_A = \frac{D_{AB}(c_{A1} - c_{A2})}{z_2 - z_1} = \frac{D_{AB}c_{av}(x_{A1} - x_{A2})}{z_2 - z_1} \tag{6.3-1}$$

where N_A is the flux of A in kg mol A/s · m^2, D_{AB} the diffusivity of A in B in m^2/s, c_{A1} the concentration of A in kg mol A/m^3 at point 1, x_{A1} the mole fraction of A at point 1, and c_{av} defined by

$$c_{av} = \left(\frac{\rho}{M}\right)_{av} = \left(\frac{\rho_1}{M_1} + \frac{\rho_2}{M_2}\right)\bigg/ 2 \tag{6.3-2}$$

where c_{av} is the average total concentration of $A + B$ in kg mol/m^3, M_1 the average molecular weight of the solution at point 1 in kg mass/kg mol, and ρ_1 the average density of the solution in kg/m^3 at point 1.

Equation (6.3-1) uses the average value of D_{AB}, which may vary some with concentration, and the average value of c, which may also vary with concentration. Usually, the linear average of c is used, as in Eq. (6.3-2). The case of equimolar counterdiffusion in Eq. (6.3-1) only occurs very infrequently in liquids.

2. Diffusion of A through nondiffusing B. The most important case of diffusion in liquids is that where solute A is diffusing and solvent B is stagnant or nondiffusing. An example is a dilute solution of propionic acid (A) in a water (B) solution being contacted with toluene. Only the propionic acid (A) diffuses through the water phase, to the boundary, and then into the toluene phase. The toluene–water interface is a barrier to diffusion of B and $N_B = 0$. Such cases often occur in industry (T2). If Eq. (6.2-22) is rewritten in terms of concentrations by substituting $c_{av} = P/RT$, $c_{A1} = p_{A1}/RT$, and $x_{BM} = p_{BM}/P$, we obtain the equation for liquids at steady state:

$$N_A = \frac{D_{AB}c_{av}}{(z_2 - z_1)x_{BM}}(x_{A1} - x_{A2}) \tag{6.3-3}$$

where

$$x_{BM} = \frac{x_{B2} - x_{B1}}{\ln(x_{B2}/x_{B1})} \tag{6.3-4}$$

Note that $x_{A1} + x_{B1} = x_{A2} + x_{B2} = 1.0$. For dilute solutions x_{BM} is close to 1.0 and c is essentially constant. Then Eq. (6.3-3) simplifies to

$$N_A = \frac{D_{AB}(c_{A1} - c_{A2})}{z_2 - z_1} \qquad (6.3\text{-}5)$$

EXAMPLE 6.3-1. Diffusion of Ethanol (A) Through Water (B)

An ethanol (A)–water (B) solution in the form of a stagnant film 2.0 mm thick at 293 K is in contact at one surface with an organic solvent in which ethanol is soluble and water is insoluble. Hence, $N_B = 0$. At point 1 the concentration of ethanol is 16.8 wt % and the solution density is $\rho_1 = 972.8$ kg/m³. At point 2 the concentration of ethanol is 6.8 wt % and $\rho_2 = 988.1$ kg/m³ (P1). The diffusivity of ethanol is 0.740×10^{-9} m²/s (T2). Calculate the steady-state flux N_A.

Solution: The diffusivity is $D_{AB} = 0.740 \times 10^{-9}$ m²/s. The molecular weights of A and B are $M_A = 46.05$ and $M_B = 18.02$. For a wt % of 6.8, the mole fraction of ethanol (A) is as follows when using 100 kg of solution:

$$x_{A2} = \frac{6.8/46.05}{6.8/46.05 + 93.2/18.02} = \frac{0.1477}{0.1477 + 5.17} = 0.0277$$

Then $x_{B2} = 1 - 0.0277 = 0.9723$. Calculating x_{A1} in a similar manner, $x_{A1} = 0.0732$ and $x_{B1} = 1 - 0.0732 = 0.9268$. To calculate the molecular weight M_2 at point 2,

$$M_2 = \frac{100 \text{ kg}}{(0.1477 + 5.17)\text{kg mol}} = 18.75 \text{ kg/kg mol}$$

Similarly, $M_1 = 20.07$. From Eq. (6.3-2),

$$c_{av} = \frac{\rho_1/M_1 + \rho_2/M_2}{2} = \frac{972.8/20.07 + 988.1/18.75}{2} = 50.6 \text{ kg mol/m}^3$$

To calculate x_{BM} from Eq. (6.3-4), we can use the linear mean since x_{B1} and x_{B2} are close to each other:

$$x_{BM} = \frac{x_{B1} + x_{B2}}{2} = \frac{0.9268 + 0.9723}{2} = 0.949$$

Substituting into Eq. (6.3-3) and solving,

$$N_A = \frac{D_{AB}c_{av}}{(z_2 - z_1)x_{BM}}(x_{A1} - x_{A2}) = \frac{(0.740 \times 10^{-9})(50.6)(0.0732 - 0.0277)}{(2/1000)0.949}$$

$$= 8.99 \times 10^{-7} \text{ kg mol/s} \cdot \text{m}^2$$

6.3C Diffusion Coefficients for Liquids

1. Experimental determination of diffusivities. Several different methods are used to determine diffusion coefficients experimentally in liquids. In one method, unsteady-state diffusion in a long capillary tube is carried out and the diffusivity determined from the concentration profile. If the solute A is diffusing in B, the diffusion coefficient determined is D_{AB}. Also, the value of diffusivity is often very dependent upon the concentration of the diffusing solute A. For liquids, unlike gases, the diffusivity D_{AB} does not equal D_{BA}.

In a fairly common method a relatively dilute solution and a slightly more concentrated solution are placed in chambers on opposite sides of a porous membrane of sintered glass as shown in Fig. 6.3-1. Molecular diffusion takes place through the narrow passageways of the pores in the sintered glass while the two compartments are stirred. The effective diffusion length is $\tau\delta$, where the tortuosity $\tau > 1$ is a constant and corrects for the fact that the path is actually greater than δ cm. In this method, discussed by Bidstrup and Geankoplis (B4), the effective diffusion length is obtained by calibrating with a solute such as KCl having a known diffusivity.

To derive the equation, quasi-steady-state diffusion in the membrane is assumed:

$$N_A = \varepsilon D_{AB} = \frac{c - c'}{\tau\delta} \qquad (6.3\text{-}6)$$

where c is the concentration in the lower chamber at a time t, c' is the concentration in the upper chamber, and ε is the fraction of area of the glass open to diffusion. Making a balance on solute A in the upper chamber, where the rate in = rate out + rate of accumulation, making a similar balance on the lower chamber, using volume $V = V'$, and combining and integrating, the final equation is

$$\ln \frac{c_0 - c_0'}{c - c'} = \frac{2\varepsilon A}{\tau\delta V} D_{AB} t \qquad (6.3\text{-}7)$$

where $2\varepsilon A/\tau\delta V$ is a cell constant that can be determined using a solute of known diffusivity, such as KCl. The values c_0 and c_0' are initial concentrations and c and c' final concentrations.

2. Experimental liquid diffusivity data. Experimental diffusivity data for binary mixtures in the liquid phase are given in Table 6.3-1. All the data are for dilute solutions of the diffusing solute in the solvent. In liquids the diffusivities often vary quite markedly with concentration. Hence, the values in Table 6.3-1 should be used with some caution when outside the dilute range. Additional data are given in (P1). Values for biological solutes in solution are given in the next section. As noted in the table, the diffusivity values are quite small and in the range of about 0.5×10^{-9} to 5×10^{-9} m²/s for relatively nonviscous liquids. Diffusivities in gases are larger by a factor of 10^4–10^5.

FIGURE 6.3-1. *Diffusion cell for determination of diffusivity in a liquid.*

TABLE 6.3-1. *Diffusion Coefficients for Dilute Liquid Solutions*

Solute	Solvent	Temperature °C	K	Diffusivity $[(m^2/s)10^9$ or $(cm^2/s)10^5]$	Ref.
NH_3	Water	12	285	1.64	(N2)
		15	288	1.77	
O_2	Water	18	291	1.98	(N2)
		25	298	2.41	(V1)
CO_2	Water	25	298	2.00	(V1)
H_2	Water	25	298	4.8	(V1)
Methyl alcohol	Water	15	288	1.26	(J1)
Ethyl alcohol	Water	10	283	0.84	(J1)
		25	298	1.24	(J1)
n-Propyl alcohol	Water	15	288	0.87	(J1)
Formic acid	Water	25	298	1.52	(B4)
Acetic acid	Water	9.7	282.7	0.769	(B4)
		25	298	1.26	(B4)
Propionic acid	Water	25	298	1.01	(B4)
HCl (9 g mol/liter)	Water	10	283	3.3	(N2)
(2.5 g mol/liter)		10	283	2.5	(N2)
Benzoic acid	Water	25	298	1.21	(C4)
Acetone	Water	25	298	1.28	(A2)
Acetic acid	Benzene	25	298	2.09	(C5)
Urea	Ethanol	12	285	0.54	(N2)
Water	Ethanol	25	298	1.13	(H4)
KCl	Water	25	298	1.870	(P2)
KCl	Ethylene glycol	25	298	0.119	(P2)

6.3D Prediction of Diffusivities in Liquids

The equations for predicting diffusivities of dilute solutes in liquids are by necessity semi-empirical, since the theory for diffusion in liquids is not well established as yet. The Stokes–Einstein equation, one of the first theories, was derived for a very large spherical molecule (A) diffusing in a liquid solvent (B) of small molecules. Stokes' law was used to describe the drag on the moving solute molecule. Then the equation was modified by assuming that all molecules are alike and arranged in a cubic lattice, and by expressing the molecular radius in terms of the molar volume (W5),

$$D_{AB} = \frac{9.96 \times 10^{-16}T}{\mu V_A^{1/3}} \qquad (6.3\text{-}8)$$

where D_{AB} is diffusivity in m^2/s, T is temperature in K, μ is viscosity of solution in Pa·s or kg/m·s, and V_A is the solute molar volume at its normal boiling point in m^3/kg mol. This equation applies very well to very large unhydrated and sphere-like solute molecules of about 1000 molecular weight or greater (R1), or where the V_A is above about 0.500 m^3/kg mol (W5) in aqueous solution.

For smaller solute molar volumes, Eq. (6.3-8) does not hold. Several other theoretical derivations have been attempted, but the equations do not predict diffusivities very accurately. Hence, a number of semitheoretical expressions have been developed (R1). The Wilke–Chang (T3, W5) correlation can be used for most general purposes where the solute (A) is dilute in the solvent (B):

$$D_{AB} = 1.173 \times 10^{-16}(\phi M_B)^{1/2}\frac{T}{\mu_B V_A^{0.6}} \tag{6.3-9}$$

where M_B is the molecular weight of solvent B, μ_B is the viscosity of B in Pa·s or kg/m·s, V_A is the solute molar volume at the boiling point (L2), which can be obtained from Table 6.3-2, and ϕ is an "association parameter" of the solvent, where ϕ is 2.6 for water, 1.9 for methanol, 1.5 for ethanol, 1.0 for benzene, 1.0 for ether, 1.0 for heptane, and 1.0 for other unassociated solvents. When values of V_A are above 0.500 m^3/kg mol (500 cm^3/g mol), Eq. (6.3-8) should be used.

When water is the solute, values from Eq. (6.3-9) should be multiplied by a factor of 1/2.3 (R1). Equation (6.3-9) predicts diffusivities with a mean deviation of 10–15% for aqueous solutions and about 25% in nonaqueous solutions. Outside the range 278–313 K, the equation should be used with caution. For water as the diffusing solute, an equation by Reddy and Doraiswamy is preferred (R2). Skelland (S5) summarizes the correlations available for binary systems. Geankoplis (G2) discusses and gives an equation to predict diffusion in a ternary system, where a dilute solute A is diffusing in a mixture of B and C solvents. This case is often approximated in industrial processes.

EXAMPLE 6.3-2. Prediction of Liquid Diffusivity
Predict the diffusion coefficient of acetone (CH_3COCH_3) in water at 25° and 50°C using the Wilke–Chang equation. The experimental value is 1.28×10^{-9} m^2/s at 25°C (298 K).

Solution: From Appendix A.2 the viscosity of water at 25.0°C is $\mu_B = 0.8937 \times 10^{-3}$ Pa·s and at 50°C, 0.5494×10^{-3}. From Table 6.3-2 for CH_3COCH_3 with 3 carbons + 6 hydrogens + 1 oxygen,

$$V_A = 3(0.0148) + 6(0.0037) + 1(0.0074) = 0.0740 \text{ } m^3 kg \text{ mol}$$

For water the association parameter $\phi = 2.6$ and $M_B = 18.02$ kg mass/kg mol. For 25°C, $T = 298$ K. Substituting into Eq. (6.3-9),

$$D_{AB} = (1.173 \times 10^{-16})(\phi M_B)^{1/2}\frac{T}{\mu_B V_A^{0.6}}$$

$$= \frac{(1.173 \times 10^{-16})(2.6 \times 18.02)^{1/2}(298)}{(0.8937 \times 10^{-3})(0.0740)^{0.6}}$$

$$= 1.277 \times 10^{-9} \text{ } m^2/s$$

TABLE 6.3-2. *Atomic and Molar Volumes at the Normal Boiling Point*

Material	Atomic Volume $(m^3/kg\ mol)\ 10^3$	Material	Atomic Volume $(m^3/kg\ mol)\ 10^3$
C	14.8	Ring, 3-membered	-6
H	3.7	as in ethylene	
O (except as below)	7.4	oxide	
Doubly bound as	7.4	4-membered	-8.5
carbonyl		5-membered	-11.5
Coupled to two		6-membered	-15
other elements		Naphthalene ring	-30
In aldehydes, ketones	7.4	Anthracene ring	-47.5
In methyl esters	9.1		
In methyl ethers	9.9		
In ethyl esters	9.9		
In ethyl ethers	9.9		*Molecular Volume*
In higher esters	11.0		$(m^3/kg\ mol)\ 10^3$
In higher ethers	11.0	Air	29.9
In acids ($-OH$)	12.0	O_2	25.6
Joined to S, P, N	8.3	N_2	31.2
N		Br_2	53.2
Doubly bonded	15.6	Cl_2	48.4
In primary amines	10.5	CO	30.7
In secondary amines	12.0	CO_2	34.0
Br 27.0		H_2	14.3
Cl in RCHClR'	24.6	H_2O	18.8
Cl in RCl (terminal)	21.6	H_2S	32.9
F	8.7	NH_3	25.8
I	37.0	NO	23.6
S	25.6	N_2O	36.4
P	27.0	SO_2	44.8

Source: G. Le Bas, *The Molecular Volumes of Liquid Chemical Compounds.* New York: David McKay Co., Inc., 1915.

For 50°C or $T = 323$ K,

$$D_{AB} = \frac{(1.173 \times 10^{-16})(2.6 \times 18.02)^{1/2}(323)}{(0.5494 \times 10^{-3})(0.0740)^{0.6}}$$

$$= 2.251 \times 10^{-9}\ m^2/s$$

6.3E Prediction of Diffusivities of Electrolytes in Liquids

Electrolytes in aqueous solution such as KCl dissociate into cations and anions. Each ion diffuses at a different rate. If the solution is to remain electrically neutral at each point (assuming the absence of any applied electric-potential field), the cations and anions diffuse effectively as one component, and the ions have the same net motion or flux. Hence, the average diffusivity of the electrolyte KCl is a combination of the diffusion coefficients of the two ions. Its value is in between the diffusivity values for the two ions.

The well-known Nernst–Haskell equation for dilute, single-salt solutions can be used at 25°C to predict the overall diffusivity D_{AB} of the salt A in the solvent B (R1):

$$D_{AB}^o = 8.928 \times 10^{-10}T\frac{(1/n_+ + 1/n_-)}{(1/\lambda_+ + 1/\lambda_-)} \tag{6.3-10}$$

where D_{AB}^o is in cm^2/s, n_+ is the valence of the cation, n_- is the valence of the anion, and λ_+ and λ_- are the limiting ionic conductances in very dilute solutions in $(A/cm^2)(V/cm)$ (g equiv./cm^2). Values of the conductances are given in Table 6.3-3 at 25°C. The value of $T = 298.2$ in Eq. (6.3-10) when using values of λ_+ and λ_- at 25°C.

The diffusion coefficient of an individual ion i at 25°C can be calculated from

$$D_i = 2.662 \times 10^{-7}\frac{\lambda_i}{n_i} \tag{6.3-11}$$

Then Eq. (6.3-10) becomes as follows:

$$D_{AB}^o = \frac{n_+ + n_-}{n_-/D_+ + n_+/D_-} \tag{6.3-12}$$

To correct D_{AB}^o for temperature, first calculate D_{AB}^o at 25°C from Eq. (6.3-10) using the λ_+ and λ_- values given in Table 6.3-3 at 25°C. Then, multiply this D_{AB}^o at 25°C by $T/(334 \mu_w)$, where μ_w is the viscosity of water in cp at the new T (R1).

EXAMPLE 6.3-3. Diffusivities of Electrolytes

Predict the diffusion coefficients of dilute electrolytes for the following cases:
(a) For KCl at 25°C, predict D_{AB}^o and compare with the value in Table 6.3-1.
(b) Predict the value for KCl at 18.5°C. The experimental value is 1.7×10^{-5} cm^2/s (S9).
(c) For CaCl$_2$ predict D_{AB} at 25°C. Compare with the experimental value of 1.32×10^{-5} cm^2/s (C10). Also predict D_i of the ion Ca^{2+} and of Cl$^-$ and use Eq. (6.3-12).

Solution: For part (a) from Table 6.3-3, $\lambda_+(K^+) = 73.5$ and $\lambda_-(Cl^-) = 76.3$. Substituting into Eq. (6.3-10),

$$D_{AB}^o = 8.928 \times 10^{-10}(298.2)\frac{(1/1 + 1/1)}{(1/73.5 + 1/76.3)}$$

$$= 1.993 \times 10^{-5} \text{ cm}^2/s$$

The experimental value in Table 6.3-1 is 1.87×10^{-5} cm^2/s, which is reasonably close considering that this value is not at infinite dilution.

For part (b) the correction factor for temperature is $T/(334 \mu_w)$. For $T = 273.2 + 18.5 = 291.7$ K from Table A.2-4, $\mu_w = 1.042$ cp. Then $T/(334 \mu_w) = 291.7/(334 \times 1.042) = 0.8382$. Correcting the value of D_{AB}^o at 25°C to 18.5°C,

TABLE 6.3-3. *Limiting Ionic Conductances in Water at 25°C (R4)*

Anion	λ_-	Cation	λ_+
OH^-	197.6	H^+	349.8
Cl^-	76.3	Li^+	38.7
Br^-	78.3	Na^+	50.1
NO_3^-	71.4	K^+	73.5
$CH_3CO_2^-$	40.9	NH_4^+	73.4
$\frac{1}{2}SO_4^{2-}$	80	$\frac{1}{2}Ca^{2+}$	59.5
ClO_4^-	68.0	$\frac{1}{2}Zn^{2+}$	53
		$\frac{1}{2}La^{3+}$	69.5

Ionic conductances in $(A/cm^2)(V/cm)(g\ equiv./cm^2)$

$$D^o_{AB(185°C)} = 0.8382 D^o_{AB(25°C)} = 0.8382(1.993 \times 10^{-5})$$

$$= 1.671 \times 10^{-5}\ cm^2/s$$

This compares with the experimental value of $1.7 \times 10^{-5}\ cm^2/s$.

For part (c), for $CaCl_2$, from Table 6.3-3, $\lambda_+(Ca^{2+}/2) = 59.5$, $\lambda_-(Cl^-) = 76.3$, $n_+ = 2$, and $n_- = 1$. Again, using Eq. (6.3-10),

$$D^o_{AB} = 8.928 \times 10^{-10}(298.2)\frac{(1/2 + 1/1)}{(1/59.5 + 1/76.3)}$$

$$= 1.335 \times 10^{-5}\ cm^2/s$$

This compares well with the experimental value of 1.32×10^{-5} (C10).

To calculate the individual ion diffusivities at 25°C using Eq. (6.3-11),

$$D_{Ca^{2+}} = 2.662 \times 10^{-7}\frac{\lambda_+}{n_+} = 2.662 \times 10^{-7}\frac{(59.5)}{2} = 0.792 \times 10^{-5}\ cm^2/s$$

$$D_{Cl^-} = 2.662 \times 10^{-7}\frac{\lambda_-}{n_-} = 2.662 \times 10^{-7}\frac{(76.3)}{1} = 2.031 \times 10^{-5}\ cm^2/s$$

Substituting into Eq. (6.3-12) for 25°C,

$$D^o_{AB} = \frac{n_+ + n_-}{n_-/D_+ + n_+/D_-} = \frac{2 + 1}{1/(0.792 \times 10^{-5}) + 2/(2.031 \times 10^{-5})}$$

$$= 1.335 \times 10^{-5}\ cm^2/s$$

Hence, one can see that the diffusivity of the salt is in between that of the two ions.

6.4 MOLECULAR DIFFUSION IN BIOLOGICAL SOLUTIONS AND GELS

6.4A   Diffusion of Biological Solutes in Liquids

1. Introduction.   The diffusion of small solute molecules and especially macromolecules (*e.g.*, proteins) in aqueous solutions are important in the processing and storing of biological systems and in the life processes of microorganisms, animals, and plants. Food processing is an important area where diffusion plays an important role. In the drying of liquid solutions of fruit juice, coffee, and tea, water and frequently volatile flavor or aroma constituents are removed. These constituents diffuse through the liquid during evaporation.

In fermentation processes, nutrients, sugars, oxygen, and so on diffuse to the microorganisms, and waste products and at times enzymes diffuse away. In the artificial kidney machine various waste products diffuse through the blood solution to a membrane and then through the membrane to an aqueous solution.

Macromolecules in solution having molecular weights of tens of thousands or more were often called *colloids,* but now we know they generally form true solutions. The diffusion behavior of protein macromolecules in solution is affected by their large sizes and shapes, which can be random coils, rodlike, or globular (spheres or ellipsoids). Also, interactions of the large molecules with the small solvent and/or solute molecules affect the diffusion of the macromolecules as well as the small solute molecules.

Besides the Fickian diffusion to be discussed here, mediated transport often occurs in biological systems where chemical interactions occur. This latter type of transport will not be discussed here.

2. Interaction and "binding" in diffusion.   Protein macromolecules are very large compared to small solute molecules such as urea, KCl, and sodium caprylate, and often have a number of sites for interaction or "binding" of the solute or ligand molecules. An example is the binding of oxygen to hemoglobin in the blood. Human serum albumin protein binds most of the free fatty acids in the blood and increases their apparent solubility. Bovine serum albumin, which is in milk, binds 23 mol sodium caprylate/mol albumin when the albumin concentration is 30 kg/m^3 solution and the sodium caprylate is about 0.05 molar (G6). Hence, Fickian-type diffusion of macromolecules and small solute molecules can be greatly affected by the presence together of both types of molecules even in dilute solutions.

3. Experimental methods for determining diffusivity.   Methods for determining the diffusivity of biological solutes are similar to those discussed previously in Section 6.3 with some modifications. In the diaphragm diffusion cell shown in Fig. 6.3-1, the chamber is made of Lucite® or Teflon® instead of glass, since protein molecules bind to glass. Also, the porous membrane through which the molecular diffusion occurs is composed of cellulose acetate or other polymers (G5, G6, K1).

4. Experimental data for biological solutes.   Most of the experimental data in the literature on protein diffusivities have been extrapolated to zero concentration since the diffusivity is often a function of concentration. A tabulation of diffusivities of a few proteins and also of small solutes often present in biological systems is given in Table 6.4-1.

The diffusion coefficients for the large protein molecules are on the order of magnitude of 5×10^{-11} m^2/s compared to the values of about 1×10^{-9} m^2/s for the small solutes in Table 6.4-1. This means macromolecules diffuse at a rate about 20 times as slow as small solute molecules for the same concentration differences.

TABLE 6.4-1. *Diffusion Coefficients for Dilute Biological Solutes in Aqueous Solution*

Solute	Temperature		Diffusivity (m^2/s)	Molecular Weight	Ref.
	°C	K			
Urea	20	293	1.20×10^{-9}	60.1	(N2)
	25	298	1.378×10^{-9}		(G5)
Glycerol	20	293	0.825×10^{-9}	92.1	(G3)
Glycine	25	298	1.055×10^{-9}	75.1	(L3)
Sodium caprylate	25	298	8.78×10^{-10}	166.2	(G6)
Bovine serum albumin	25	298	6.81×10^{-11}	67 500	(C6)
Urease	25	298	4.01×10^{-11}	482 700	(C7)
	20	293	3.46×10^{-11}		(S6)
Soybean protein	20	293	2.91×10^{-11}	361 800	(S6)
Lipoxidase	20	293	5.59×10^{-11}	97 440	(S6)
Fibrinogen, human	20	293	1.98×10^{-11}	339 700	(S6)
Human serum albumin	20	293	5.93×10^{-11}	72 300	(S6)
γ-Globulin, human	20	293	4.00×10^{-11}	153 100	(S6)
Creatinine	37	310	1.08×10^{-9}	113.1	(C8)
Sucrose	37	310	0.697×10^{-9}	342.3	(C8)
	20	293	0.460×10^{-9}		(P3)

When the concentration of macromolecules such as proteins increases, the diffusion coefficient would be expected to decrease, since the diffusivity of small solute molecules decreases with increasing concentration. However, experimental data (G4, C7) show that the diffusivity of macromolecules such as proteins decreases in some cases and increases in others as protein concentration increases. Surface charges on the molecules appear to play a role in these phenomena.

When small solutes such as urea, KCl, and sodium caprylate, which are often present with protein macromolecules in solution, diffuse through these protein solutions, the diffusivity decreases with increasing polymer concentration (C7, G5, G6, N3). Experimental data for the diffusivity of the solute sodium caprylate (A) diffusing through bovine serum albumin (P) solution show that the diffusivity D_{AP} of A through P is markedly reduced as the protein (P) concentration is increased (G5, G6). A large part of the reduction is due to the binding of A to P so that there is less free A to diffuse. The rest is due to blockage by the large molecules.

5. Prediction of diffusivities for biological solutes. For predicting the diffusivity of small solutes alone in aqueous solution with molecular weights less than about 1000 or solute molar volumes less than about 0.500 m^3/kg mol, Eq. (6.3-9) should be used. For larger solutes the equations to be used are not as accurate. As an approximation the Stokes–Einstein equation (6.3-8) can be used:

$$D_{AB} = \frac{9.96 \times 10^{-16}T}{\mu V_A^{1/3}}$$

(6.3-8)

Probably a better approximate equation to use is the semiempirical equation of Polson (P3), which is recommended for a molecular weight above 1000. A modification of his equation to take into account different temperatures is as follows for dilute aqueous solutions:

$$D_{AB} = \frac{9.40 \times 10^{-15}T}{\mu(M_A)^{1/3}} \tag{6.4-1}$$

where M_A is the molecular weight of the large molecule A. When the shape of the molecule deviates greatly from a sphere, this equation should be used with caution.

EXAMPLE 6.4-1. Prediction of Diffusivity of Albumin

Predict the diffusivity of bovine serum albumin at 298 K in water as a dilute solution using the modified Polson equation (6.4-1) and compare with the experimental value in Table 6.4-1.

Solution: The molecular weight of bovine serum albumin (A) from Table 6.4-1 is $M_A = 67\,500$ kg/kg mol. The viscosity of water at 25°C is 0.8937×10^{-3} Pa·s and $T = 298$ K. Substituting into Eq. (6.4-1),

$$D_{AB} = \frac{9.40 \times 10^{-15}T}{\mu(M_A)^{1/3}} = \frac{(9.40 \times 10^{-15})298}{(0.8937 \times 10^{-3})(67\,500)^{1/3}}$$

$$= 7.70 \times 10^{-11} \text{ m}^2/\text{s}$$

This value is 11% higher than the experimental value of 6.81×10^{-11} m²/s.

6. Prediction of diffusivity of small solutes in protein solution. When a small solute (A) diffuses through a macromolecule (P) protein solution, Eq. (6.3-9) cannot be used for prediction for the small solute because of blockage to diffusion by the large molecules. The data needed to predict these effects are the diffusivity D_{AB} of solute A in water alone, the water of hydration on the protein, and an obstruction factor. A semitheoretical equation that can be used to approximate the diffusivity D_{AP} of A in globular-type protein P solutions is as follows, where only the blockage effect is considered (C8, G5, G6) and no binding is present:

$$D_{AP} = D_{AB}(1 - 1.81 \times 10^{-3}c_p) \tag{6.4-2}$$

where $c_p =$ kg P/m³. Then the diffusion equation is

$$N_A = \frac{D_{AP}(c_{A1} - c_{A2})}{z_2 - z_1} \tag{6.4-3}$$

where c_{A1} is concentration of A in kg mol A/m³.

7. Prediction of diffusivity with binding present. When A is in a protein solution P and binds to P, the diffusion flux of A is equal to the flux of unbound solute A in the solution plus the flux of the protein–solute complex. Methods for predicting this flux are available (G5, G6) when binding data have been experimentally obtained. The equation used is

$$D_{AP} = \left[D_{AB}(1 - 1.81 \times 10^{-3}c_p)\left(\frac{\% \text{ free } A}{100} \right) + D_P\left(\frac{\% \text{ bound } A}{100} \right) \right] \tag{6.4-4}$$

where D_P is the diffusivity of the protein alone in the solution, m²/s, and free A is that A not bound to the protein, which is determined from the experimental binding coefficient. Then

Eq. (6.4-3) is used to calculate the flux, where c_A is the total concentration of A in the solution.

6.4B Diffusion in Biological Gels

Gels can be looked upon as semisolid materials which are "porous." They are composed of macromolecules which are usually in dilute aqueous solution with the gel comprising a few wt % of the water solution. The "pores" or open spaces in the gel structure are filled with water. The rates of diffusion of small solutes in the gels are somewhat less than in aqueous solution. The main effect of the gel structure is to increase the path length for diffusion, assuming no electrical-type effects (S7).

Recent studies by electron microscopy (L4) have shown that the macromolecules of the gel agarose (a major constituent of agar) exist as long and relatively straight threads. This suggests a gel structure of loosely interwoven, extensively hydrogen-bonded polysaccharide macromolecules.

Some typical gels are agarose, agar, and gelatin. A number of organic polymers exist as gels in various types of solutions. To measure the diffusivity of solutes in gels, unsteady-state methods are used. In one method the gel is melted and poured into a narrow tube open at one end. After solidification, the tube is placed in an agitated bath containing the solute for diffusion. The solute leaves the solution at the gel boundary and diffuses through the gel itself. After a period of time the amount diffusing in the gel is determined to give the diffusion coefficient of the solute in the gel.

A few typical values of diffusivities of some solutes in various gels are given in Table 6.4-2. In some cases the diffusivity of the solute in pure water is given so that the decrease in diffusivity due to the gel can be seen. For example, from Table 6.4-2, at 278 K urea in water has a diffusivity of 0.880×10^{-9} m^2/s and in 2.9 wt % gelatin, has a value of 0.640×10^{-9} m^2/s, a decrease of 27%.

In both agar and gelatin the diffusivity of a given solute decreases more or less linearly with an increase in wt % gel. However, extrapolation to 0% gel gives a value smaller than that shown for pure water. It should be noted that in different preparations or batches of the same type of gel, the diffusivities can vary by as much as 10 to 20%.

EXAMPLE 6.4-2. Diffusion of Urea in Agar

A tube or bridge of a gel solution of 1.05 wt % agar in water at 278 K is 0.04 m long and connects two agitated solutions of urea in water. The urea concentration in the first solution is 0.2 g mol urea per liter solution and is 0 in the other. Calculate the flux of urea in kg mol/s · m^2 at steady state.

Solution: From Table 6.4-2 for the solute urea at 278 K, $D_{AB} = 0.727 \times 10^{-9}$ m^2/s. For urea diffusing through stagnant water in the gel, Eq. (6.3-3) can be used. However, since the value of x_{A1} is less than about 0.01, the solution is quite dilute and $x_{BM} \cong 1.00$. Hence, Eq. (6.3-5) can be used. The concentrations are $c_{A1} = 0.20/1000 = 0.0002$ g mol/cm^3 = 0.20 kg mol/m^3 and $c_{A2} = 0$. Substituting into Eq. (6.3-5),

$$N_A = \frac{D_{AB}(c_{A1} - c_{A2})}{z_2 - z_1} = \frac{0.727 \times 10^{-9}(0.20 - 0)}{0.04 - 0}$$

$$= 3.63 \times 10^{-9} \text{ kg mol/s} \cdot \text{m}^2$$

TABLE 6.4-2. *Typical Diffusivities of Solutes in Dilute Biological Gels in Aqueous Solution*

Solute	Gel	Wt % Gel in Solution	Temperature K	Temperature °C	Diffusivity (m^2/s)	Ref.
Sucrose	Gelatin	0	278	5	0.285×10^{-9}	(F2)
		3.8	278	5	0.209×10^{-9}	(F2)
		10.35	278	5	0.107×10^{-9}	(F2)
		5.1	293	20	0.252×10^{-9}	(F3)
Urea	Gelatin	0	278	5	0.880×10^{-9}	(F2)
		2.9	278	5	0.644×10^{-9}	(F2)
		5.1	278	5	0.609×10^{-9}	(F3)
		10.0	278	5	0.542×10^{-9}	(F2)
		5.1	293	20	0.859×10^{-9}	(F3)
Methanol	Gelatin	3.8	278	5	0.626×10^{-9}	(F3)
Urea	Agar	1.05	278	5	0.727×10^{-9}	(F3)
		3.16	278	5	0.591×10^{-9}	(F3)
		5.15	278	5	0.472×10^{-9}	(F3)
Glycerin	Agar	2.06	278	5	0.297×10^{-9}	(F3)
		6.02	278	5	0.199×10^{-9}	(F3)
Dextrose	Agar	0.79	278	5	0.327×10^{-9}	(F3)
Sucrose	Agar	0.79	278	5	0.247×10^{-9}	(F3)
Ethanol	Agar	5.15	278	5	0.393×10^{-9}	(F3)
NaCl (0.05 M)	Agarose	0	298	25	1.511×10^{-9}	(S7)
		2	298	25	1.398×10^{-9}	(S7)

6.5   MOLECULAR DIFFUSION IN SOLIDS

6.5A   Introduction and Types of Diffusion in Solids

Even though rates of diffusion of gases, liquids, and solids in solids are generally slower than rates in liquids and gases, mass transfer in solids is quite important in chemical and biological processing. Some examples are leaching of foods, such as soybeans, and of metal ores; drying of timber, salts, and foods; diffusion and catalytic reaction in solid catalysts; separation of fluids by membranes; diffusion of gases through polymer films used in packaging; and treating of metals at high temperatures by gases.

We can broadly classify transport in solids into two types of diffusion: diffusion that can be considered to follow Fick's law and does not depend primarily on the actual structure of the solid, and diffusion in porous solids where the actual structure and void channels are important. These two broad types of diffusion will be considered.

6.5B Diffusion in Solids Following Fick's Law

1. Derivation of equations. This type of diffusion in solids does not depend on the actual structure of the solid. The diffusion occurs when the fluid or solute diffusing is actually dissolved in the solid to form a more or less homogeneous solution—for example, in leaching, where the solid contains a large amount of water and a solute is diffusing through this solution, or in the diffusion of zinc through copper, where solid solutions are present. Also, the diffusion of nitrogen or hydrogen through rubber, or in some cases diffusion of water in foodstuffs, can be classified here, since equations of similar type can be used.

Generally, simplified equations are used. Using the general Eq. (6.2-14) for binary diffusion,

$$N_A = -cD_{AB}\frac{dx_A}{dz} + \frac{c_A}{c}(N_A + N_B) \tag{6.2-14}$$

the bulk-flow term, $(c_A/c)(N_A + N_B)$, even if present, is usually small, since c_A/c or x_A is quite small. Hence, it is neglected. Also, c is assumed constant, giving for diffusion in solids

$$N_A = -\frac{D_{AB}}{dz}\frac{dc_A}{dz} \tag{6.5-1}$$

where D_{AB} is diffusivity in m^2/s of A through B and is usually assumed constant, independent of pressure for solids. Note that $D_{AB} \neq D_{BA}$ in solids.

Integration of Eq. (6.5-1) for a solid slab at steady state gives

$$N_A = \frac{D_{AB}(c_{A1} - c_{A2})}{z_2 - z_1} \tag{6.5-2}$$

For the case of diffusion radially through a cylinder wall of inner radius r_1 and outer r_2 and length L,

$$\frac{N_A}{2\pi rL} = -D_{AB}\frac{dc_A}{dr} \tag{6.5-3}$$

$$N_A = D_{AB}(c_{A1} - c_{A2})\frac{2\pi L}{\ln(r_2/r_1)} \tag{6.5-4}$$

This case is similar to conduction heat transfer radially through a hollow cylinder, as shown in Fig. 4.3-2.

The diffusion coefficient D_{AB} in the solid as stated above is not dependent upon the pressure of the gas or liquid on the outside of the solid. For example, if CO_2 gas is outside a slab of rubber and is diffusing through the rubber, D_{AB} would be independent of p_A, the partial pressure of CO_2 at the surface. The solubility of CO_2 in the solid, however, is directly proportional to p_A. This is similar to the case of the solubility of O_2 in water being directly proportional to the partial pressure of O_2 in the air by Henry's law.

The solubility of a solute gas (A) in a solid is usually expressed as S in m^3 solute (at STP of 0°C and 1 atm) per m^3 solid per atm partial pressure of (A). Also, $S = cm^3(STP)/atm \cdot cm^3$ solid in the cgs system. To convert this to c_A concentration in the solid in kg mol A/m^3 using SI units,

$$c_A = \frac{S\,m^3(STP)/m^3\,solid \cdot atm}{22.414\ m^3(STP)/kg\ mol\ A}\,p_A\,atm = \frac{Sp_A}{22.414}\frac{kg\ mol\ A}{m^3\ solid} \tag{6.5-5}$$

Using cgs units,

$$c_A = \frac{Sp_A}{22\,414} \frac{\text{g mol } A}{\text{cm}^3 \text{ solid}}$$ (6.5-6)

EXAMPLE 6.5-1.   Diffusion of H_2 Through Neoprene Membrane

The gas hydrogen at 17°C and 0.010 atm partial pressure is diffusing through a membrane of vulcanized neoprene rubber 0.5 mm thick. The pressure of H_2 on the other side of the neoprene is zero. Calculate the steady-state flux, assuming that the only resistance to diffusion is in the membrane. The solubility S of H_2 gas in neoprene at 17°C is 0.051 m³ (at STP of 0°C and 1 atm)/m³ solid · atm and the diffusivity D_{AB} is 1.03×10^{-10} m²/s at 17°C.

Solution: A sketch showing the concentration is shown in Fig. 6.5-1. The equilibrium concentration c_{A1} at the inside surface of the rubber is, from Eq. (6.5-5),

$$c_{A1} = \frac{S}{22.414} p_{A1} = \frac{0.051(0.010)}{22.414} = 2.28 \times 10^{-5} \text{ kg mol } H_2/\text{m}^3 \text{ solid}$$

Since p_{A2} at the other side is 0, $c_{A2} = 0$. Substituting into Eq. (6.5-2) and solving,

$$N_A = \frac{D_{AB}(c_{A1} - c_{A2})}{z_2 - z_1} = \frac{(1.03 \times 10^{-10})(2.28 \times 10^{-5} - 0)}{(0.5 - 0)/1000}$$

$$= 4.69 \times 10^{-12} \text{ kg mol } H_2/\text{s} \cdot \text{m}^2$$

2. Permeability equations for diffusion in solids.   In many cases the experimental data for diffusion of gases in solids are not given as diffusivities and solubilities but as permeabilities, P_M, in m³ of solute gas A at STP (0°C and 1 atm press) diffusing per second per m² cross-sectional area through a solid 1 m thick under a pressure difference of 1 atm pressure. This can be related to Fick's equation (6.5-2) as follows:

$$N_A = \frac{D_{AB}(c_{A1} - c_{A2})}{z_2 - z_1}$$ (6.5-2)

From Eq. (6.5-5),

$$c_{A1} = \frac{Sp_{A1}}{22.414} \qquad c_{A2} = \frac{Sp_{A2}}{22.414}$$ (6.5-7)

FIGURE 6.5-1.   *Concentrations for Example 6.5-1.*

Substituting Eq. (6.5-7) into (6.5-2),

$$N_A = \frac{D_{AB}S(p_{A1} - p_{A2})}{22.414(z_2 - z_1)} = \frac{P_M(p_{A1} - p_{A2})}{22.414(z_2 - z_1)} \text{ kg mol/s} \cdot \text{m}^2 \qquad (6.5\text{-}8)$$

where the permeability P_M is

$$P_M = D_{AB}S \frac{\text{m}^3(\text{STP})}{\text{s} \cdot \text{m}^2 \text{C.S.} \cdot \text{atm/m}} \qquad (6.5\text{-}9)$$

Permeability (P_M) is also given in the literature in several other sets of units. For the cgs system, the permeability is given as $\text{cm}^3(\text{STP})/(\text{s} \cdot \text{cm}^2\text{C.S.} \cdot \text{atm/cm})$. In some cases in the literature the permeability is given as $\text{cm}^3(\text{STP})/(\text{s} \cdot \text{cm}^2\text{C.S.} \cdot \text{cm Hg/cm thickness})$. These are related as follows:

$$\frac{1.00 \text{ m}^3(\text{STP}) \cdot \text{m}}{\text{s} \cdot \text{m}^2\text{C.S.} \cdot \text{atm}} = \frac{10^4 \text{ cm}^3(\text{STP}) \cdot \text{cm}}{\text{s} \cdot \text{cm}^2 \cdot \text{atm}} \qquad (6.5\text{-}10)$$

$$\frac{1.0 \text{ m}^3(\text{STP}) \cdot \text{m}}{\text{s} \cdot \text{m}^2\text{C.S.} \cdot \text{atm}} = \frac{1.316 \times 10^2 \text{ cm}^3(\text{STP}) \cdot \text{cm}}{\text{s} \cdot \text{cm}^2\text{C.S.} \cdot \text{cmHg}} \qquad (6.5\text{-}11)$$

When there are several solids $1, 2, 3, \ldots$, in series and $L_1, L_2, \ldots$, represent the thickness of each, then Eq. (6.5-8) becomes

$$N_A = \frac{p_{A1} - p_{A2}}{22.414} \frac{1}{L_1/P_{M1} + L_2/P_{M2} + \cdots} \qquad (6.5\text{-}12)$$

where $p_{A1} - p_{A2}$ is the overall partial pressure difference.

3. Experimental diffusivities, solubilities, and permeabilities. Accurate prediction of diffusivities in solids is generally not possible because of the lack of knowledge of the theory of the solid state. Hence, experimental values are needed. Some experimental data for diffusivities, solubilities, and permeabilities are given in Table 6.5-1 for gases diffusing in solids and solids diffusing in solids.

For the simple gases such as He, H_2, O_2, N_2, and CO_2, with gas pressures up to 1 or 2 atm, the solubility in solids such as polymers and glasses generally follows Henry's law and Eq. (6.5-5) holds. Also, for these gases the diffusivity and permeability are independent of concentration, and hence pressure. For the effect of temperature T in K, the ln P_M is approximately a linear function of $1/T$. Also, the diffusion of one gas, say H_2, is approximately independent of the other gases present, such as O_2 and N_2.

For metals such as Ni, Cd, and Pt, where gases such as H_2 and O_2 are diffusing, it has been found experimentally that the flux is approximately proportional to $(\sqrt{p_{A1}} - \sqrt{p_{A2}})$, so Eq. (6.5-8) does not hold (B5). When water is diffusing through polymers, unlike the simple gases, P_M may depend somewhat on the relative pressure difference (C9, B5). Further data are available in monographs by Crank and Park (C9) and Barrer (B5).

EXAMPLE 6.5-2. Diffusion Through a Packaging Film Using Permeability
A polyethylene film 0.00015 m (0.15 mm) thick is being considered for use in packaging a pharmaceutical product at 30°C. If the partial pressure of O_2 outside the package is 0.21 atm and inside it is 0.01 atm, calculate the diffusion flux of O_2 at steady state. Use permeability data from Table 6.5-1. Assume that the

TABLE 6.5-1. *Diffusivities and Permeabilities in Solids*

Solute (A)	Solid (B)	T (K)	D_{AB}, Diffusion Coefficient $[m^2/s]$	Solubility, S $\left[\dfrac{m^3\ solute(STP)}{m^3\ solid \cdot atm}\right]$	Permeability, P_M $\left[\dfrac{m^3\ solute(STP)}{s \cdot m^2 \cdot atm/m}\right]$	Ref.
H_2	Vulcanized rubber	298	$0.85(10^{-9})$	0.040	$0.342(10^{-10})$	(B5)
O_2		298	$0.21(10^{-9})$	0.070	$0.152(10^{-10})$	(B5)
N_2		298	$0.15(10^{-9})$	0.035	$0.054(10^{-10})$	(B5)
CO_2		298	$0.11(10^{-9})$	0.90	$1.01(10^{-10})$	(B5)
H_2	Vulcanized neoprene	290	$0.103(10^{-9})$	0.051		(B5)
		300	$0.180(10^{-9})$	0.053		(B5)
H_2	Polyethylene	298			$6.53(10^{-12})$	(R3)
O_2		303			$4.17(10^{-12})$	(R3)
N_2		303			$1.52(10^{-12})$	(R3)
O_2	Nylon	303			$0.029(10^{-12})$	(R3)
N_2		303			$0.0152(10^{-12})$	(R3)
Air	English leather	298			$0.15{-}0.68 \times 10^{-4}$	(B5)
H_2O	Wax	306			$0.16(10^{-10})$	(B5)
H_2O	Cellophane	311			$0.91{-}1.82(10^{-10})$	(B5)
He	Pyrex glass	293			$4.86(10^{-15})$	(B5)
		373			$20.1(10^{-15})$	(B5)
He	SiO_2	293	$2.4{-}5.5(10^{-14})$	0.01		(B5)
H_2	Fe	293	$2.59(10^{-13})$			(B5)
Al	Cu	293	$1.3(10^{-34})$			(B5)

resistances to diffusion outside the film and inside are negligible compared to the resistance of the film.

Solution: From Table 6.5-1, $P_M = 4.17(10^{-12})$ m^3 solute(STP)/(s·m^2·atm/m). Substituting into Eq. (6.5-8),

$$N_A = \frac{P_M(p_{A1} - p_{A2})}{22.414(z_2 - z_1)} = \frac{4.17(10^{-12})(0.21 - 0.01)}{22.414(0.00015 - 0)}$$

$$= 2.480 \times 10^{-10}\ \text{kg mol/s} \cdot \text{m}^2$$

Note that a film made of nylon has a much smaller value of permeability P_M for O_2 and would make a more suitable barrier.

4. Membrane separation processes. In Chapter 13 a detailed discussion is given of the various membrane separation processes for gas separation by membranes, dialysis, reverse osmosis, ultrafiltration, and microfiltration.

6.5C Diffusion in Porous Solids That Depends on Structure

1. Diffusion of liquids in porous solids. In Section 6.5B we used Fick's law and treated the solid as a uniform homogeneous-like material with an experimental diffusivity D_{AB}. In this section we are concerned with porous solids that have pores or interconnected voids in the solid which affect the diffusion. A cross section of a typical porous solid is shown in Fig. 6.5-2.

For the situation where the voids are filled completely with liquid water, the concentration of salt in water at boundary 1 is c_{A1} and at point 2 is c_{A2}. The salt, in diffusing through the water in the void volume, takes a tortuous path which is unknown and greater than $(z_2 - z_1)$ by a factor τ, called *tortuosity*. Diffusion does not occur in the inert solid. For a dilute solution using Eq. (6.3-5) for diffusion of salt in water at steady state,

$$N_A = \frac{\varepsilon D_{AB}(c_{A1} - c_{A2})}{\tau(z_2 - z_1)} \tag{6.5-13}$$

where ε is the open void fraction, D_{AB} is the diffusivity of salt in water, and τ is a factor which corrects for the path longer than $(z_2 - z_1)$. For inert-type solids τ can vary from about 1.5 to 5. Often the terms are combined into an effective diffusivity:

$$D_{A\,\text{eff}} = \frac{\varepsilon}{\tau} D_{AB} \quad \text{m}^2/\text{s} \tag{6.5-14}$$

EXAMPLE 6.5-3. *Diffusion of KCl in Porous Silica*

A sintered solid of silica 2.0 mm thick is porous, with a void fraction ε of 0.30 and a tortuosity τ of 4.0. The pores are filled with water at 298 K. At one face the concentration of KCl is held at 0.10 g mol/liter, and fresh water flows rapidly past the other face. Neglecting any other resistance but that in the porous solid, calculate the diffusion of KCl at steady state.

Solution: The diffusivity of KCl in water from Table 6.3-1 is $D_{AB} = 1.87 \times 10^{-9}$ m²/s. Also, $c_{A1} = 0.10/1000 = 1.0 \times 10^{-4}$ g mol/cm³ = 0.10 kg mol/m³, and $c_{A2} = 0$. Substituting into Eq. (6.5-13),

$$N_A = \frac{\varepsilon D_{AB}(c_{A1} - c_{A2})}{\tau(z_2 - z_1)} = \frac{0.30(1.870 \times 10^{-9})(0.10 - 0)}{4.0(0.002 - 0)}$$

$$= 7.01 \times 10^{-9} \text{ kg mol KCl/s} \cdot \text{m}^2$$

FIGURE 6.5-2. *Sketch of a typical porous solid.*

2. *Diffusion of gases in porous solids.* If the voids shown in Fig. 6.5-2 are filled with gases, then a somewhat similar situation exists. If the pores are very large so that diffusion occurs only by Fickian-type diffusion, then Eq. (6.5-13) becomes, for gases,

$$N_A = \frac{\varepsilon D_{AB}(c_{A1} - c_{A2})}{\tau(z_2 - z_1)} = \frac{\varepsilon D_{AB}(p_{A1} - p_{A2})}{\tau RT(z_2 - z_1)} \qquad (6.5\text{-}15)$$

Again the value of the tortuosity must be determined experimentally. Diffusion is assumed to occur only through the voids or pores and not through the actual solid particles.

A correlation of tortuosity versus the void fraction of various unconsolidated porous media of beds of glass spheres, sand, salt, talc, and so on (S8) gives the following approximate values of τ for different values of ε: $\varepsilon = 0.2$, $\tau = 2.0$; $\varepsilon = 0.4$, $\tau = 1.75$; $\varepsilon = 0.6$, $\tau = 1.65$.

When the pores are quite small in size and on the order of magnitude of the mean free path of the gas, other types of diffusion occur, which are discussed in Section 7.6.

6.6 NUMERICAL METHODS FOR STEADY-STATE MOLECULAR DIFFUSION IN TWO DIMENSIONS

6.6A Derivation of Equations for Numerical Methods

1. Derivation of methods for steady state. In Fig. 6.6-1 a two-dimensional solid shown with unit thickness is divided into squares. The numerical methods for steady-state molecular diffusion are very similar to those for steady-state heat conduction discussed in Section 4.15. Hence, only a brief summary will be given here. The solid inside of a square is imagined to be concentrated at the center of the square at $c_{n,m}$ and is called a "node", which is connected to adjacent nodes by connecting rods through which the mass diffuses.

A total mass balance is made at steady state by stating that the sum of the molecular diffusion to the shaded area for unit thickness must equal zero:

$$\frac{D_{AB}\,\Delta y}{\Delta x}(c_{n-1,m} - c_{n,m}) + \frac{D_{AB}\,\Delta y}{\Delta x}(c_{n+1,m} - c_{n,m})$$

$$+ \frac{D_{AB}\,\Delta x}{\Delta y}(c_{n,m+1} - c_{n,m}) + \frac{D_{AB}\,\Delta x}{\Delta y}(c_{n,m-1} - c_{n,m}) = 0 \qquad (6.6\text{-}1)$$

where $c_{n,m}$ is concentration of A at node n,m in kg mol A/m^3. Setting $\Delta x = \Delta y$, and rearranging,

$$c_{n,m+1} + c_{n,m-1} + c_{n+1,m} + c_{n-1,m} - 4c_{n,m} = 0 \qquad (6.6\text{-}2)$$

FIGURE 6.6-1. *Concentrations and spacing of nodes for two-dimensional steady-state molecular diffusion.*

2. Iteration method of numerical solution. In order to solve Eq. (6.6-2), a separate equation is written for each unknown point giving N linear algebraic equations for N unknown points. For a hand calculation using a modest number of nodes, the iteration method can be used to solve the equations, where the right-hand side of Eq. (6.6-2) is set equal to a residual $\overline{N}_{n,m}$:

$$c_{n,m+1} + c_{n,m-1} + c_{n+1,m} + c_{n-1,m} - 4c_{n,m} = \overline{N}_{n,m} \tag{6.6-3}$$

Setting the equation equal to zero, $\overline{N}_{n,m} = 0$ for steady state and $c_{n,m}$ is calculated by

$$c_{n,m} = \frac{c_{n-1,m} + c_{n+1,m} + c_{n,m+1} + c_{n,m-1}}{4} \tag{6.6-4}$$

Equations (6.6-3) and (6.6-4) are the final equations to be used to calculate all the concentrations at steady state.

Example 4.15-1 for steady-state heat conduction illustrates the detailed steps for the iteration method, which are identical to those for steady-state diffusion.

Once the concentrations have been calculated, the flux can be calculated for each element as follows. Referring to Fig. 6.6-1, the flux for the node or element $c_{n,m}$ to $c_{n,m-1}$ is ($\Delta x = \Delta y$)

$$N = \frac{A D_{AB}}{\Delta y}(c_{n,m} - c_{n,m-1}) = \frac{[(\Delta x)(1)]D_{AB}}{\Delta y}(c_{n,m} - c_{n,m-1})$$

$$= D_{AB}(c_{n,m} - c_{n,m-1}) \tag{6.6-5}$$

where the area A is Δx times 1 m deep and N is kg mol A/s. Equations are written for the other appropriate elements and the sum of the fluxes calculated. This numerical method is well suited for use with a computer spreadsheet.

6.6B Equations for Special Boundary Conditions for Numerical Method

1. Equations for boundary conditions. When one of the nodal points $c_{n,m}$ is at a boundary where convective mass transfer is occurring to a constant concentration c_∞ in the bulk fluid shown in Fig. 6.6-2a, a different equation must be derived. Making a mass balance on the node n, m, where mass in = mass out at steady state,

$$\frac{D_{AB}\,\Delta y}{\Delta x}(c_{n-1,m} - c_{n,m}) + \frac{D_{AB}\,\Delta x}{2\,\Delta y}(c_{n,m+1} - c_{n,m})$$

$$+ \frac{D_{AB}\,\Delta x}{2\,\Delta y}(c_{n,m-1} - c_{n,m}) = k_c\,\Delta y(c_{n,m} - c_\infty) \tag{6.6-6}$$

where k_c is the convective mass-transfer coefficient in m/s defined by Eq. (6.1-14).

Setting $\Delta x = \Delta y$, rearranging, and setting the resultant equation equal to $\overline{N}_{n,m}$, the residual, the following results:

1. For convection at a boundary (Fig. 6.6-2a),

$$\frac{k_c\,\Delta x}{D_{AB}}c_\infty + \tfrac{1}{2}(2c_{n-1,m} + c_{n,m+1} + c_{n,m-1}) - c_{n,m}\left(\frac{k_c\,\Delta x}{D_{AB}} + 2\right) = \overline{N}_{n,m} \tag{6.6-7}$$

FIGURE 6.6-2. *Different boundary conditions for steady-state diffusion: (a) convection at a boundary, (b) insulated boundary, (c) exterior corner with convective boundary, (d) interior corner with convective boundary.*

This equation is similar to Eq. (4.15-16) for heat conduction and convection, with $k_c \, \Delta x / D_{AB}$ being used in place of $h \, \Delta x / k$. Similarly, Eqs. (6.6-8)–(6.6-10) have been derived for the other boundary conditions shown in Fig. 6.6-2.

2. For an insulated boundary (Fig. 6.6-2b),

$$\tfrac{1}{2}(c_{n,m+1} + c_{n,m-1}) + c_{n-1,m} - 2c_{n,m} = \overline{N}_{n,m} \qquad (6.6\text{-}8)$$

3. For an exterior corner with convection at the boundary (Fig. 6.6-2c),

$$\frac{k_c \, \Delta x}{D_{AB}} c_\infty + \tfrac{1}{2}(c_{n-1,m} + c_{n,m-1}) - \left(\frac{k_c \, \Delta x}{D_{AB}} + 1\right)c_{n,m} = \overline{N}_{n,m} \qquad (6.6\text{-}9)$$

4. For an interior corner with convection at the boundary (Fig. 6.6-2d),

$$\frac{k_c \, \Delta x}{D_{AB}} c_\infty + c_{n-1,m} + c_{n,m+1} + \tfrac{1}{2}(c_{n+1,m} + c_{n,m-1}) - \left(3 + \frac{k_c \, \Delta x}{D_{AB}}\right)c_{n,m} = \overline{N}_{n,m}$$

$$(6.6\text{-}10)$$

2. Boundary conditions with distribution coefficient. When Eq. (6.6-7) was derived, the distribution coefficient K between the liquid and the solid at the surface interface was 1.0. The distribution coefficient as shown in Fig. 6.6-3 is defined as

$$K = \frac{c_{n,mL}}{c_{n,m}} \qquad (6.6\text{-}11)$$

FIGURE 6.6-3. *Interface concentrations for convective mass transfer at a solid surface and an equilibrium distribution coefficient $K = c_{n,mL}/c_{n,m}$.*

where $c_{n,mL}$ is the concentration in the liquid adjacent to the surface and $c_{n,m}$ is the concentration in the solid adjacent to the surface. Then in deriving Eq. (6.6-6), the right-hand side $k_c \, \Delta y(c_{n,m} - c_\infty)$ becomes

$$k_c \, \Delta y(c_{n,mL} - c_\infty) \qquad (6.6\text{-}12)$$

where c_∞ is the concentration in the bulk fluid. Substituting $Kc_{n,m}$ for $c_{n,mL}$ from Eq. (6.6-11) into (6.6-12) and multiplying and dividing by K,

$$Kk_c \, \Delta y \left(\frac{Kc_{n,m}}{K} - \frac{c_\infty}{K} \right) = Kk_c \, \Delta y \left(c_{n,m} - \frac{c_\infty}{K} \right) \qquad (6.6\text{-}13)$$

Hence, whenever k_c appears as in Eq. (6.6-7), Kk_c should be substituted, and when c_∞ appears, c_∞/K should be used. Then Eq. (6.6-7) becomes as follows:

1. For convection at a boundary (Fig. 6.6-2a),

$$\left(\frac{Kk_c \, \Delta x}{D_{AB}} \right)\frac{c_\infty}{K} + \tfrac{1}{2}(2c_{n-1,m} + c_{n,m+1} + c_{n,m-1}) - c_{n,m}\left(\frac{Kk_c \, \Delta x}{D_{AB}} + 2 \right) = \overline{N}_{n,m}$$

$$(6.6\text{-}14)$$

Equations (6.6-9) and (6.6-10) can be rewritten in a similar manner as follows:

2. For an exterior corner with convection at the boundary (Fig. 6.6-2c),

$$\left(\frac{Kk_c \, \Delta x}{D_{AB}} \right)\frac{c_\infty}{K} + \tfrac{1}{2}(c_{n-1,m} + c_{n,m-1}) - \left(\frac{Kk_c \, \Delta x}{D_{AB}} + 1 \right)c_{n,m} = \overline{N}_{n,m} \qquad (6.6\text{-}15)$$

3. For an interior corner with convection at the boundary (Fig. 6.6-2d),

$$\left(\frac{Kk_c \, \Delta x}{D_{AB}} \right)\frac{c_\infty}{K} + c_{n-1,m} + c_{n,m+1} + \tfrac{1}{2}(c_{n+1,m} + c_{n,m-1}) - \left(3 + \frac{Kk_c \, \Delta x}{D_{AB}} \right)c_{n,m} = \overline{N}_{n,m}$$

$$(6.6\text{-}16)$$

EXAMPLE 6.6-1. Numerical Method for Convection and Steady-State Diffusion

For the two-dimensional hollow solid chamber shown in Fig. 6.6-4, determine the concentrations at the nodes as shown at steady state. At the inside surfaces the concentrations remain constant at 6.00×10^{-3} kg mol/m^3. At the outside surfaces the convection coefficient $k_c = 2 \times 10^{-7}$ m/s and $c_\infty = 2.00 \times 10^{-3}$ kg mol/m^3. The diffusivity in the solid is $D_{AB} = 1.0 \times 10^{-9}$ m^2/s. The grid size is $\Delta x = \Delta y = 0.005$ m. Also, determine the diffusion rates per 1.0 m depth. The distribution coefficient $K = 1.0$.

FIGURE 6.6-4. *Concentrations for hollow chamber for Example 6.6-1.*

Solution: To simplify the calculations, all the concentrations will be multiplied by 10^3. Since the chamber is symmetrical, we do the calculations on the $\frac{1}{8}$ shaded portion shown. The fixed known values are $c_{1,3} = 6.00$, $c_{1,4} = 6.00$, $c_\infty = 2.00$. Because of symmetry, $c_{1,2} = c_{2,3}$, $c_{2,5} = c_{2,3}$, $c_{2,1} = c_{3,2}$, $c_{3,3} = c_{3,5}$. To speed up the calculations, we will make estimates of the unknown concentrations as follows: $c_{2,2} = 3.80$, $c_{2,3} = 4.20$, $c_{2,4} = 4.40$, $c_{3,1} = 2.50$, $c_{3,2} = 2.70$, $c_{3,3} = 3.00$, $c_{3,4} = 3.20$.

For the interior points $c_{2,2}$, $c_{2,3}$, and $c_{2,4}$ we use Eqs. (6.6-3) and (6.6-4); for the corner convection point $c_{3,1}$, Eq. (6.6-9); for the other convection points $c_{3,2}$, $c_{3,3}$, $c_{3,4}$, Eq. (6.6-7). The term $k_c \, \Delta x/D_{AB} = (2 \times 10^{-7})(0.005)/(1.0 \times 10^{-9}) = 1.00$.

First approximation. Starting with $c_{2,2}$ we use Eq. (6.6-3) and calculate the residual $\overline{N}_{2,2}$:

$$c_{1,2} + c_{3,2} + c_{2,1} + c_{2,3} - 4c_{2,2} = \overline{N}_{2,2}$$

$$4.20 + 2.70 + 2.70 + 4.20 - 4(3.80) = -1.40$$

Hence, $c_{2,2}$ is not at steady state. Next we set $\overline{N}_{2,2}$ equal to zero and calculate a new value of $c_{2,2}$ from Eq. (6.6-4):

$$c_{2,2} = \frac{c_{1,2} + c_{3,2} + c_{2,1} + c_{2,3}}{4} = \frac{4.20 + 2.70 + 2.70 + 4.20}{4} = 3.45$$

This new value of $c_{2,2}$ replaces the old value.
For $c_{2,3}$,

$$c_{2,2} + c_{2,4} + c_{1,3} + c_{3,3} - 4c_{2,3} = \overline{N}_{2,3}$$

$$3.45 + 4.40 + 6.00 + 3.00 - 4(4.20) = 0.05$$

$$c_{2,3} = \frac{c_{2,2} + c_{2,4} + c_{1,3} + c_{3,3}}{4} = \frac{3.45 + 4.40 + 6.00 + 3.00}{4} = 4.21$$

For $c_{2,4}$,

$$c_{2,3} + c_{2,5} + c_{1,4} + C_{3,4} - 4c_{2,4} = \overline{N}_{2,4}$$

$$4.21 + 4.21 + 6.00 + 3.20 - 4(4.40) = 0.02$$

$$c_{2,4} = \frac{c_{2,3} + c_{2,5} + c_{1,4} + c_{3,4}}{4} = \frac{4.21 + 4.21 + 6.00 + 3.20}{4} = 4.41$$

For $c_{3,1}$, we use Eq. (6.6-9):

$$(1.0)c_\infty + \tfrac{1}{2}(c_{2,1} + c_{3,2}) - (1.0 + 1)c_{3,1} = \overline{N}_{3,1}$$

$$(1.0)2.00 + \tfrac{1}{2}(2.70 + 2.70) - 2.0(2.50) = -0.30$$

Setting Eq. (6.6-9) equal to zero and solving for $c_{3,1}$,

$$(1.0)2.00 + \tfrac{1}{2}(2.70 + 2.70) - (2.0)c_{3,1} = 0 \qquad c_{3,1} = 2.35$$

For $c_{3,2}$, we use Eq. (6.6-7):

$$(1.0)c_\infty + \tfrac{1}{2}(2 \times c_{2,2} + c_{3,1} + c_{3,3}) - (1.0 + 2)c_{3,2} = \overline{N}_{3,2}$$

$$(1.0)2.00 + \tfrac{1}{2}(2 \times 3.45 + 2.35 + 3.00) - (3.0)2.70 = 0.03$$

$$(1.0)2.00 + \tfrac{1}{2}(2 \times 3.45 + 2.35 + 3.00) - (3.0)c_{3,2} = 0 \qquad c_{3,2} = 2.71$$

For $c_{3,3}$,

$$(1.0)c_\infty + \tfrac{1}{2}(2 \times c_{2,3} + c_{3,2} + c_{3,4}) - (3.0)c_{3,3} = \overline{N}_{3,3}$$

$$(1.0)2.00 + \tfrac{1}{2}(2 \times 4.21 + 2.71 + 3.20) - (3.0)3.00 = 0.17$$

$$(1.0)2.00 + \tfrac{1}{2}(2 \times 4.21 + 2.71 + 3.20) - (3.0)c_{3,3} = 0 \qquad c_{3,3} = 3.06$$

For $c_{3,4}$,

$$(1.0)c_\infty + \tfrac{1}{2}(2 \times c_{2,4} + c_{3,3} + c_{3,5}) - (3.0)c_{3,4} = \overline{N}_{3,4}$$

$$(1.0)2.00 + \tfrac{1}{2}(2 \times 4.41 + 3.06 + 3.06) - (3.0)3.20 = -0.13$$

$$(1.0)2.00 + \tfrac{1}{2}(2 \times 4.41 + 3.06 + 3.06) - (3.0)c_{3,4} = 0 \qquad c_{3,4} = 3.16$$

Having completed one sweep across the grid map, we can perform a second approximation using the new values calculated, starting with $c_{2,2}$ or any other node. We continue until all the residuals are as small as desired. The final values after three approximations are $c_{2,2} = 3.47$, $c_{2,3} = 4.24$, $c_{2,4} = 4.41$, $c_{3,1} = 2.36$, $c_{3,2} = 2.72$, $c_{3,3} = 3.06$, $c_{3,4} = 3.16$.

To calculate the diffusion rates we first calculate the total convective diffusion rate, leaving the bottom surface at nodes $c_{3,1}$, $c_{3,2}$, $c_{3,3}$, and $c_{3,4}$ for 1.0 m depth:

$$N = k_c(\Delta x \cdot 1)\left[\frac{c_{3,1} - c_\infty}{2} + (c_{3,2} - c_\infty) + (c_{3,3} - c_\infty) + \frac{c_{3,4} - c_\infty}{2}\right]$$

$$= (2 \times 10^{-7})(0.005 \times 1)\left[\frac{2.36 - 2.00}{2} + (2.72 - 2.00)\right.$$

$$\left. +(3.06 - 2.00) + \frac{3.16 - 2.00}{2}\right] \times 10^{-3}$$

$$= 2.540 \times 10^{-12} \text{ kg mol/s}$$

Note that the first and fourth paths include only one-half of a surface. Next we calculate the total diffusion rate in the solid entering the top surface inside, using an equation similar to Eq. (6.6-5):

$$N = \frac{D_{AB}(\Delta x \cdot 1)}{\Delta y}\left[(c_{1,3} - c_{2,3}) + \frac{c_{1,4} - c_{2,4}}{2}\right]$$

$$= \frac{(1.0 \times 10^{-9})(0.005 \times 1)}{0.005}\left[(6.00 - 4.24) + \frac{6.00 - 4.41}{2}\right] \times 10^{-3}$$

$$= 2.555 \times 10^{-12} \text{ kg mol/s}$$

At steady state the diffusion rate leaving by convection should equal that entering by diffusion. These results indicate a reasonable check. Using smaller grids would give even more accuracy. Note that the results for the diffusion rate should be multiplied by 8.0 for the whole chamber.

PROBLEMS

6.1-1. *Diffusion of Methane Through Helium.* A gas of CH_4 and He is contained in a tube at 101.32 kPa pressure and 298 K. At one point the partial pressure of methane is $p_{A1} = 60.79$ kPa, and at a point 0.02 m distance away, $p_{A2} = 20.26$ kPa. If the total pressure is constant throughout the tube, calculate the flux of CH_4 (methane) at steady state for equimolar counterdiffusion.

Ans. $J_{Az}^* = 5.52 \times 10^{-5}$ kg mol A/s $\cdot$ m^2 $(5.52 \times 10^{-6}$ g mol A/s $\cdot$ cm$^2)$

6.1-2. *Diffusion of CO_2 in a Binary Gas Mixture.* The gas CO_2 is diffusing at steady state through a tube 0.20 m long having a diameter of 0.01 m and containing N_2 at 298 K. The total pressure is constant at 101.32 kPa. The partial pressure of CO_2 is 456 mm Hg at one end and 76 mm Hg at the other end. The diffusivity D_{AB} is 1.67×10^{-5} m^2/s at 298 K. Calculate the flux of CO_2 in cgs and SI units for equimolar counterdiffusion.

6.2-1. *Equimolar Counterdiffusion of a Binary Gas Mixture.* Helium and nitrogen gas are contained in a conduit 5 mm in diameter and 0.1 m long at 298 K and a uniform constant pressure of 1.0 atm abs. The partial pressure of He at one end of the tube is 0.060 atm and at the other end is 0.020 atm. The diffusivity can be obtained from Table 6.2-1. Calculate the following for steady-state equimolar counterdiffusion:
(a) Flux of He in kg mol/s $\cdot$ m^2 and g mol/s $\cdot$ cm^2.
(b) Flux of N_2.
(c) Partial pressure of He at a point 0.05 m from either end.

6.2-2. *Equimolar Counterdiffusion of NH_3 and N_2 at Steady State.* Ammonia gas (A) and nitrogen gas (B) are diffusing in counterdiffusion through a straight glass tube 2.0 ft (0.610 m) long with an inside diameter of 0.080 ft (24.4 mm) at 298 K and 101.32 kPa. Both ends of the tube are connected to large mixed chambers at 101.32 kPa. The partial pressure of NH_3 is constant at 20.0 kPa in one chamber and 6.666 kPa in the other. The diffusivity at 298 K and 101.32 kPa is 2.30×10^{-5} m^2/s.
(a) Calculate the diffusion of NH_3 in lb mol/h and kg mol/s.
(b) Calculate the diffusion of N_2.
(c) Calculate the partial pressures at a point 1.0 ft (0.305 m) in the tube and plot p_A, p_B, and P versus distance z.

Ans. (a) Diffusion of $NH_3 = 7.52 \times 10^{-7}$ lb mol A/h, 9.48×10^{-11} kg, mol A/s;
(c) $p_A = 1.333 \times 10^4$ Pa

6.2-3. *Diffusion of A Through Stagnant B and Effect of Type of Boundary on Flux.* Ammonia gas is diffusing through N_2 under steady-state conditions with N_2 nondiffusing since it is insoluble in one boundary. The total pressure is 1.013×10^5 Pa and the temperature is 298 K. The partial pressure of NH_3 at one point is 1.333×10^4 Pa, and at the other point 20 mm away it is 6.666×10^3 Pa. The D_{AB} for the mixture at 1.013×10^5 Pa and 298 K is 2.30×10^{-5} m^2/s.

(a) Calculate the flux of NH_3 in kg mol/s · m^2.

(b) Do the same as (a) but assume that N_2 also diffuses; that is, both boundaries are permeable to both gases and the flux is equimolar counterdiffusion. In which case is the flux greater?

Ans. (a) $N_A = 3.44 \times 10^{-6}$ kg mol/s · m^2

6.2-4. *Diffusion of Methane Through Nondiffusing Helium.* Methane gas is diffusing in a straight tube 0.1 m long containing helium at 298 K and a total pressure of 1.01325×10^5 Pa. The partial pressure of CH_4 is 1.400×10^4 Pa at one end and 1.333×10^3 Pa at the other end. Helium is insoluble in one boundary, and hence is nondiffusing or stagnant. The diffusivity is given in Table 6.2-1. Calculate the flux of methane in kg mol/s · m^2 at steady state.

6.2-5. *Mass Transfer from a Naphthalene Sphere to Air.* Mass transfer is occurring from a sphere of naphthalene having a radius of 10 mm. The sphere is in a large volume of still air at 52.6°C and 1 atm abs pressure. The vapor pressure of naphthalene at 52.6°C is 1.0 mm Hg. The diffusivity of naphthalene in air at 0°C is 5.16×10^{-6} m^2/s. Calculate the rate of evaporation of naphthalene from the surface in kg mol/s · m^2. [*Note:* The diffusivity can be corrected for temperature using the temperature-correction factor from the Fuller et al. equation (6.2-45).]

6.2-6. *Estimation of Diffusivity of a Binary Gas.* For a mixture of ethanol (CH_3CH_2OH) vapor and methane (CH_4), predict the diffusivity using the method of Fuller et al.

(a) At 1.0132×10^5 Pa and 298 and 373 K.

(b) At 2.0265×10^5 Pa and 298 K.

Ans. (a) $D_{AB} = 1.43 \times 10^{-5}$ m^2/s (298 K)

6.2-7. *Diffusion Flux and Effect of Temperature and Pressure.* Equimolar counterdiffusion is occurring at steady state in a tube 0.11 m long containing N_2 and CO gases at a total pressure of 1.0 atm abs. The partial pressure of N_2 is 80 mm Hg at one end and 10 mm at the other end. Predict the D_{AB} by the method of Fuller et al.

(a) Calculate the flux in kg mol/s · m^2 at 298 K for N_2.

(b) Repeat at 473 K. Does the flux increase?

(c) Repeat at 298 K but for a total pressure of 3.0 atm abs. The partial pressure of N_2 remains at 80 and 10 mm Hg, as in part (a). Does the flux change?

Ans. (a) $D_{AB} = 2.05 \times 10^{-5}$ m^2/s, $N_A = 7.02 \times 10^{-7}$ kg mol/s · m^2;
(b) $N_A = 9.92 \times 10^{-7}$ kg mol/s · m^2;
(c) $N_A = 2.34 \times 10^{-7}$ kg mol/s · m^2

6.2-8. *Evaporation Losses of Water in Irrigation Ditch.* Water at 25°C is flowing in a covered irrigation ditch below ground. Every 100 ft there is a vent line 1.0 in. inside diameter and 1.0 ft long to the outside atmosphere at 25°C. There are 10 vents in the 1000-ft ditch. The outside air can be assumed to be dry. Calculate the total evaporation loss of water in lb$_m$/d. Assume that the partial pressure of water vapor at the surface of the water is the vapor pressure, 23.76 mm Hg at 25°C. Use the diffusivity from Table 6.2-1.

6.2-9. Time to Completely Evaporate a Sphere. A drop of liquid toluene is kept at a uniform temperature of 25.9°C and is suspended in air by a fine wire. The initial radius $r_1 = 2.00$ mm. The vapor pressure of toluene at 25.9°C is $P_{A1} = 3.84$ kPa and the density of liquid toluene is 866 kg/m³.

(a) Derive Eq. (6.2-34) to predict the time t_F for the drop to evaporate completely in a large volume of still air. Show all steps.

(b) Calculate the time in seconds for complete evaporation.

Ans. (b) $t_F = 1388$ s

6.2-10. Diffusion in a Nonuniform Cross-Sectional Area. The gas ammonia (A) is diffusing at steady state through N_2 (B) by equimolar counterdiffusion in a conduit 1.22 m long at 25°C and a total pressure of 101.32 kPa abs. The partial pressure of ammonia at the left end is 25.33 kPa and at the other end 5.066 kPa. The cross section of the conduit is in the shape of an equilateral triangle, the length of each side of the triangle being 0.0610 m at the left end and tapering uniformly to 0.0305 m at the right end. Calculate the molar flux of ammonia. The diffusivity is $D_{AB} = 0.230 \times 10^{-4}$ m²/s.

6.3-1. Diffusion of A Through Stagnant B in a Liquid. The solute HCl (A) is diffusing through a thin film of water (B) 2.0 mm thick at 283 K. The concentration of HCl at point 1 at one boundary of the film is 12.0 wt % HCl (density $\rho_1 = 1060.7$ kg/m³), and at the other boundary at point 2 it is 6.0 wt % HCl ($\rho_2 = 1030.3$ kg/m³). The diffusion coefficient of HCl in water is 2.5×10^{-9} m²/s. Assuming steady state and one boundary impermeable to water, calculate the flux of HCl in kg mol/s · m².

Ans. $N_A = 2.372 \times 10^{-6}$ kg mol/s · m²

6.3-2. Diffusion of Ammonia in an Aqueous Solution. An ammonia (A)–water (B) solution at 278 K and 4.0 mm thick is in contact at one surface with an organic liquid at this interface. The concentration of ammonia in the organic phase is held constant and is such that the equilibrium concentration of ammonia in the water at this surface is 2.0 wt % ammonia (density of aqueous solution 991.7 kg/m³) and the concentration of ammonia in water at the other end of the film 4.0 mm away is 10 wt % (density 961.7 kg/m³). Water and the organic are insoluble in each other. The diffusion coefficient of NH_3 in water is 1.24×10^{-9} m²/s.

(a) At steady state, calculate the flux N_A in kg mol/s · m².

(b) Calculate the flux N_B. Explain.

6.3-3. Estimation of Liquid Diffusivity. It is desired to predict the diffusion coefficient of dilute acetic acid (CH_3COOH) in water at 282.9 K and at 298 K using the Wilke–Chang method. Compare the predicted values with the experimental values in Table 6.3-1.

Ans. $D_{AB} = 0.897 \times 10^{-9}$ m²/s (282.9 K), $D_{AB} = 1.396 \times 10^{-9}$ m²/s (288 K)

6.3-4. Estimation of Diffusivity of Methanol in H_2O. The diffusivity of dilute methanol in water has been determined experimentally to be 1.26×10^{-9} m²/s at 288 K.

(a) Estimate the diffusivity at 293 K using the Wilke–Chang equation.

(b) Estimate the diffusivity at 293 K by correcting the experimental value at 288 K to 293 K. (*Hint:* Do this by using the relationship $D_{AB} \propto T/\mu_B$.)

6.3-5. Estimation of Diffusivity of Electrolyte NaOH. Dilute NaOH is diffusing in an aqueous solution. Do as follows:

(a) Estimate the diffusivity of NaOH at 25°C. Also, calculate the diffusivity of the individual ions Na^+ and OH^-.

(b) Estimate the diffusivity of NaOH at 15°C.

Ans. (a) $D_{AB}^o = 2.128 \times 10^{-5}$ cm²/s; (b) $D_{AB}^o = 1.609 \times 10^{-5}$ cm²/s

6.3.6. *Estimation of Diffusivity of $LaCl_3$ and Temperature Effect.* Estimate the diffusion coefficient of the salt $LaCl_3$ in dilute aqueous solution at 25°C and at 35°C. Also, calculate the diffusion coefficient for the ions La^{3+} and Cl^- at 25°C. What percent increase in rate of diffusion will occur in going from 25 to 35°C if the same dilute concentration difference is present at both temperatures?

Ans. D^o_{AB} (35°C) = 1.649×10^{-5} cm²/s

6.4-1. *Prediction of Diffusivity of Enzyme Urease in Solution.* Predict the diffusivity of the enzyme urease in a dilute solution in water at 298 K using the modified Polson equation and compare the result with the experimental value in Table 6.4-1.

Ans. Predicted D_{AB} = 3.995×10^{-11} m²/s

6.4-2. *Diffusion of Sucrose in Gelatin.* A layer of gelatin in water 5 mm thick containing 5.1 wt % gelatin at 293 K separates two solutions of sucrose. The concentration of sucrose in the solution at one surface of the gelatin is constant at 2.0 g sucrose/100 mL solution, and 0.2 g/100 mL at the other surface. Calculate the flux of sucrose in kg sucrose/s · m² through the gel at steady state.

6.4-3. *Diffusivity of Oxygen in Protein Solution.* Oxygen is diffusing through a solution of bovine serum albumin (BSA) at 298 K. Oxygen has been shown not to bind to BSA. Predict the diffusivity D_{AP} of oxygen in a protein solution containing 11 g protein/100 mL solution. (*Note:* See Table 6.3-1 for the diffusivity of O_2 in water.)

Ans. D_{AP} = 1.930×10^{-9} m²/s

6.4-4. *Diffusion of Uric Acid in Protein Solution and Binding.* Uric acid (A) at 37°C is diffusing in an aqueous solution of proteins (P) containing 8.2 g protein/100 mL solution. Uric acid binds to the proteins, and over the range of concentrations present, 1.0 g mol of acid binds to the proteins for every 3.0 g mol of total acid present in the solution. The diffusivity D_{AB} of uric acid in water is 1.21×10^{-5} cm²/s and $D_P = 0.091 \times 10^{-5}$ cm²/s.

(a) Assuming no binding, predict the ratio D_{AP}/D_{AB} due only to blockage effects.

(b) Assuming blockage plus binding effects, predict the ratio D_{AP}/D_{AB}. Compare this with the experimental value for D_{AP}/D_{AB} of 0.616 (C8).

(c) Predict the flux in g uric acid/s · cm² for a concentration of acid of 0.05 g/L at point (1) and 0 g/L at point (2) a distance 1.5 μm away.

Ans. (c) N_A = 2.392×10^{-6} g/s · cm²

6.5-1. *Diffusion of CO_2 Through Rubber.* A flat plug 30 mm thick having an area of 4.0×10^{-4} m² and made of vulcanized rubber is used for closing an opening in a container. The gas CO_2 at 25°C and 2.0 atm pressure is inside the container. Calculate the total leakage or diffusion of CO_2 through the plug to the outside in kg mol CO_2/s at steady state. Assume that the partial pressure of CO_2 outside is zero. From Barrer (B5) the solubility of the CO_2 gas is 0.90 m³ gas (at STP of 0°C and 1 atm) per m³ rubber per atm pressure of CO_2. The diffusivity is 0.11×10^{-9} m²/s.

Ans. 1.178×10^{-13} kg mol CO_2/s

6.5-2. *Leakage of Hydrogen Through Neoprene Rubber.* Pure hydrogen gas at 2.0 atm abs pressure and 27°C is flowing past a vulcanized neoprene rubber slab 5 mm thick. Using the data from Table 6.5-1, calculate the diffusion flux in kg mol/s · m² at steady state. Assume no resistance to diffusion outside the slab and zero partial pressure of H_2 on the outside.

6.5-3. *Relation Between Diffusivity and Permeability.* The gas hydrogen is diffusing through a sheet of vulcanized rubber 20 mm thick at 25°C. The partial pressure of H_2

is 1.5 atm inside and 0 outside. Using the data from Table 6.5-1, calculate the following:
(a) The diffusivity D_{AB} from the permeability P_M and solubility S, and compare with the value in Table 6.5-1.
(b) The flux N_A of H_2 at steady state.

Ans. (b) $N_A = 1.144 \times 10^{-10}$ kg mol/s $\cdot$ m^2

6.5-4. *Loss from a Tube of Neoprene.* Hydrogen gas at 2.0 atm and 27°C is flowing in a neoprene tube 3.0 mm inside diameter and 11 mm outside diameter. Calculate the leakage of H_2 through a tube 1.0 m long in kg mol H_2/s at steady state.

6.5-5. *Diffusion Through Membranes in Series.* Nitrogen gas at 2.0 atm and 30°C is diffusing through a membrane of nylon 1.0 mm thick and polyethylene 8.0 mm thick in series. The partial pressure at the other side of the two films is 0 atm. Assuming no other resistances, calculate the flux N_A at steady state.

6.5-6. *Diffusion of CO$_2$ in a Packed Bed of Sand.* It is desired to calculate the rate of diffusion of CO_2 gas in air at steady state through a loosely packed bed of sand at 276 K and a total pressure of 1.013×10^5 Pa. The bed depth is 1.25 m and the void fraction ε is 0.30. The partial pressure of CO_2 is 2.026×10^3 Pa at the top of the bed and 0 Pa at the bottom. Use a τ of 1.87.

Ans. $N_A = 1.609 \times 10^{-9}$ kg mol CO_2/s $\cdot$ m^2

6.5-7. *Packaging to Keep Food Moist.* Cellophane is being used to keep food moist at 38°C. Calculate the loss of water vapor in g/d at steady state for a wrapping 0.10 mm thick and an area of 0.200 m^2 when the vapor pressure of water vapor inside is 10 mm Hg and the air outside contains water vapor at a pressure of 5 mm Hg. Use the larger permeability in Table 6.5-1.

Ans. 0.1663 g H$_2$O/day.

6.5-8. *Loss of Helium and Permeability.* A window of SiO$_2$ 2.0 mm thick and 1.0×10^{-4} m^2 in area is used to view the contents in a metal vessel at 20°C. Helium gas at 202.6 kPa is contained in the vessel. To be conservative use $D_{AB} = 5.5 \times 10^{-14}$ m^2/s from Table 6.5-1.
(a) Calculate the loss of He in kg mol/h at steady state.
(b) Calculate the permeability P_M.

Ans. (a) Loss = 8.833×10^{-15} kg mol He/h

6.6-1. *Numerical Method for Steady-State Diffusion.* Using the results from Example 6.6-1, calculate the total diffusion rate in the solid using the bottom nodes and paths of $c_{2,2}$ to $c_{3,2}$, $c_{2,3}$ to $c_{3,3}$, and so on. Compare with the other diffusion rates in Example 6.6-1.

Ans. $N = 2.555 \times 10^{-12}$ kg mol/s

6.6-2. *Numerical Method for Steady-State Diffusion with Distribution Coefficient.* Use the conditions given in Example 6.6-1 except that the distribution coefficient defined by Eq. (6.6-11) between the concentration in the liquid adjacent to the external surface and the concentration in the solid adjacent to the external surface is $K = 1.2$. Calculate the steady-state concentrations and the diffusion rates.

6.6-3. *Spreadsheet Solution for Steady-State Diffusion.* Use the conditions given in Example 6.6-1 but instead of using $\Delta x = 0.005$ m, use $\Delta x = \Delta y = 0.001$ m. The overall dimensions of the hollow chamber remain as in Example 6.6-1; the only difference is that more nodes will be used. Write the spreadsheet program and solve for the steady-state concentrations using the numerical method. Also, calculate the diffusion rates and compare with Example 6.6-1.

6.6-4. *Numerical Method with Fixed Surface Concentrations.* Steady-state diffusion is occurring in a two-dimensional solid as shown in Fig. 6.6-4. The grid $\Delta x = \Delta y = 0.010$ m. The diffusivity $D_{AB} = 2.00 \times 10^{-9}$ m^2/s. At the inside of the chamber the surface concentration is held constant at 2.00×10^{-3} kg mol/m^3. At the outside surfaces, the concentration is constant at 8.00×10^{-3}. Calculate the steady-state concentrations and the diffusion rates per m of depth.

REFERENCES

(A1) AMDUR, I., and SHULER, L. M. *J. Chem. Phys.,* **38,** 188 (1963).

(A2) ANDERSON, D. K., HALL. J. R., and BABB, A. L. *J. Phys. Chem.,* **62,** 404 (1958).

(B1) BUNDE, R. E. *Univ. Wisconsin Naval Res. Lab. Rept. No. CM-850,* August 1955.

(B2) BOYD, C. A., STEIN, N., STEINGRIMISSON, V., and RUMPEL, W. F. *J. Chem. Phys.,* **19,** 548 (1951).

(B3) BIRD, R. B., STEWART, W. E., and LIGHTFOOT, E. N. *Transport Phenomena.* New York: John Wiley & Sons, Inc., 1960.

(B4) BIDSTRUP, D. E., and GEANKOPLIS, C. J. *J. Chem. Eng. Data,* **8,** 170 (1963).

(B5) BARRER, R. M. *Diffusion in and Through Solids.* London: Cambridge University Press, 1941.

(C1) CARMICHAEL, L. T., SAGE, B. H., and LACEY, W. N. *A.I.Ch.E. J.,* **1,** 385 (1955).

(C2) CARSWELL, A. J., and STRYLAND, J. C. *Can. J. Phys.,* **41,** 708 (1963).

(C3) CHAKRABORTI, P. K., and GRAY, P. *Trans. Faraday Soc.,* **62,** 3331 (1961).

(C4) CHANG, S. Y. M.S. thesis, Massachusetts Institute of Technology, 1959.

(C5) CHANG, PIN, and WILKE, C. R. *J. Phys. Chem.,* **59,** 592 (1955).

(C6) CHARLWOOD, P. A. *J. Phys. Chem.,* **57,** 125 (1953).

(C7) CAMERON, J. R. M.S. thesis, Ohio State University, 1973.

(C8) COLTON, C. K., SMITH, K. A., MERRILL, E. W., and REECE, J. M. *Chem. Eng. Progr. Symp.,* **66**(99), 85 (1970).

(C9) CRANK, J., and PARK, G. S. *Diffusion in Polymers.* New York: Academic Press, Inc., 1968.

(C10) CUSSLER, E. L. *Diffusion Mass Transfer in Fluid Systems,* 2nd ed. New York: Cambridge University Press, 1997.

(F1) FULLER, E. N., SCHETTLER, P. D., and GIDDINGS, J. C. *Ind. Eng. Chem.,* **58,** 19 (1966).

(F2) FRIEDMAN, L., and KRAMER, E. O. *J. Am. Chem. Soc.,* **52,** 1298 (1930).

(F3) FRIEDMAN, L. *J. Am. Chem. Soc.,* **52,** 1305, 1311 (1930).

(G1) GILLILAND, E. R. *Ind. Eng. Chem.,* **26,** 681 (1934).

(G2) GEANKOPLIS, C. J. *Mass Transport Phenomena.* Columbus, Ohio: Ohio State University Bookstores, 1972.

(G3) GARNER, G. H., and MARCHANT, P. J. M. *Trans. Inst. Chem. Eng. (London),* **39,** 397 (1961).

(G4) GOSTING, L. S. *Advances in Protein Chemistry,* Vol. 1. New York: Academic Press, Inc., 1956.

(G5) GEANKOPLIS, C. J., OKOS, M. R., and GRULKE, E. A. *J. Chem. Eng. Data,* **23,** 40 (1978).

(G6) GEANKOPLIS, C. J., GRULKE, E. A., and OKOS, M. R. *Ind. Eng. Chem. Fund.,* **18,** 233 (1979).

(H1) HOLSEN, J. N., and STRUNK, M. R. *Ind. Eng. Chem. Fund.,* **3,** 143 (1964).

(H2) HUDSON, G. H., McCOUBREY, J. C., and UBBELOHDE, A. R. *Trans. Faraday Soc.,* **56,** 1144 (1960).

(H3) HIRSCHFELDER, J. O., CURTISS, C. F., and BIRD, R. B. *Molecular Theory of Gases and Liquids.* New York: John Wiley & Sons, Inc., 1954.

(H4) HAMMOND, B. R., and STOKES, R. H. *Trans. Faraday Soc.,* **49,** 890 (1953).

(J1)   JOHNSON, P. A., and BABB, A. L. *Chem. Revs.*, **56,** 387 (1956).

(K1)   KELLER, K. H., and FRIEDLANDER, S. K. *J. Gen. Physiol.*, **49,** 68 (1966).

(L1)   LEE, C. Y., and WILKE, C. R. *Ind. Eng. Chem.*, **46,** 2381 (1954).

(L2)   LE BAS, G. *The Molecular Volumes of Liquid Chemical Compounds.* New York: David McKay Co., Inc., 1915.

(L3)   LONGSWORTH, L. G. *J. Phys. Chem.*, **58,** 770 (1954).

(L4)   LANGDON, A. G., and THOMAS, H. C. *J. Phys. Chem.*, **75,** 1821 (1971).

(M1)   MASON, E. A., and MONCHICK, L. *J. Chem. Phys.*, **36,** 2746 (1962).

(M2)   MONCHICK, L., and MASON, E. A. *J. Chem. Phys.*, **35,** 1676 (1961).

(N1)   NEY, E. P., and ARMISTEAD, F. C. *Phys. Rev.*, **71,** 14 (1947).

(N2)   National Research Council, *International Critical Tables,* Vol. V. New York: McGraw-Hill Book Company, 1929.

(N3)   NARVARI, R. M., GAINER, J. L., and HALL, K. R. *A.I.Ch.E. J.*, **17,** 1028 (1971).

(P1)   PERRY, R. H., and GREEN, D. *Perry's Chemical Engineers' Handbook,* 6th ed. New York: McGraw-Hill Book Company, 1984.

(P2)   PERKINS, L. R., and GEANKOPLIS, C. J. *Chem. Eng. Sci.*, **24,** 1035 (1969).

(P3)   POLSON, A. *J. Phys. Colloid Chem.*, **54,** 649 (1950).

(R1)   REID, R. C., PRAUSNITZ, J. M., and SHERWOOD, T. K. *The Properties of Gases and Liquids,* 3rd ed. New York: McGraw-Hill Book Company, 1977.

(R2)   REDDY, K. A., and DORAISWAMY, L. K. *Ind. Eng. Chem. Fund.*, **6,** 77 (1967).

(R3)   ROGERS, C. E. *Engineering Design for Plastics.* New York: Reinhold Publishing Co., Inc., 1964.

(R4)   ROBINSON, R. A., and STOKES, R. H. *Electrolytic Solutions,* 2nd ed. New York: Academic Press, 1959.

(S1)   SCHAFER, K. L. *Z. Elecktrochem.*, **63,** 111 (1959).

(S2)   SEAGER, S. L., GEERTSON, L. R., and GIDDINGS, J. C. *J. Chem. Eng. Data*, **8,** 168 (1963).

(S3)   SCHWERTZ, F. A., and BROW, J. E. *J. Chem. Phys.*, **19,** 640 (1951).

(S4)   SRIVASTAVA, B. N., and SRIVASTAVA, I. B. *J. Chem. Phys.*, **38,** 1183 (1963).

(S5)   SKELLAND, A. H. P. *Diffusional Mass Transfer.* New York: McGraw-Hill Book Company, 1974.

(S6)   SORBER, H. A. *Handbook of Biochemistry, Selected Data for Molecular Biology.* Cleveland: Chemical Rubber Co., Inc., 1968.

(S7)   SPALDING, G. E. *J. Phys. Chem.*, **73,** 3380 (1969).

(S8)   SATTERFIELD, C. N. *Mass Transfer in Heterogeneous Catalysis.* Cambridge, Mass.: The MIT Press, 1978.

(S9)   SEADER, J. D., and HENLEY, E. J. *Separation Process Principles.* New York: John Wiley & Sons, 1998.

(T1)   TRAUTZ, M., and MULLER, W. *Ann. Physik*, **22,** 333 (1935).

(T2)   TREYBAL, R. E. *Liquid Extraction,* 2nd ed. New York: McGraw-Hill Book Company, 1963.

(T3)   TREYBAL, R. E. *Mass Transfer Operations,* 3rd ed. New York: McGraw-Hill Book Company, 1980.

(V1)   VIVIAN, J. E., and KING, C. J. *A.I.Ch.E. J.*, **10,** 220 (1964).

(W1)   WINTERGERST, V. E. *Ann. Physik*, **4,** 323 (1930).

(W2)   WESTENBERG, A. A., and FRAZIER, G. *J. Chem. Phys.*, **36,** 3499 (1962).

(W3)   WALKER, R. E., and WESTENBERG, A. A. *J. Chem. Phys.*, **29,** 1139 (1958).

(W4)   WALKER, R. E., and WESTENBERG, A. A. *J. Chem. Phys.*, **32,** 436 (1960).

(W5)   WILKE, C. R., and CHANG, PIN. *A.I.Ch.E. J.*, **1,** 264 (1955).

CHAPTER 7

Principles of Unsteady-State and Convective Mass Transfer

7.1 UNSTEADY-STATE DIFFUSION

7.1A Derivation of Basic Equation

In Chapter 6 we considered various mass-transfer systems where the concentration or partial pressure at any point and the diffusion flux were constant with time, hence at steady state. Before steady state can be reached, time must elapse after the mass-transfer process is initiated for the unsteady-state conditions to disappear.

In Section 2.3 a general property balance for unsteady-state molecular diffusion was made for the properties momentum, heat, and mass. For no generation present, this was

$$\frac{\partial \Gamma}{\partial t} = \delta \frac{\partial^2 \Gamma}{\partial z^2} \tag{2.13-12}$$

In Section 5.1 an unsteady-state equation for heat conduction was derived,

$$\frac{\partial T}{\partial t} = \alpha \frac{\partial^2 T}{\partial x^2} \tag{5.1-10}$$

The derivation of the unsteady-state diffusion equation in one direction for mass transfer is similar to that performed for heat transfer in obtaining Eq. (5.1-10). We refer to Fig. 7.1-1, where mass is diffusing in the x direction in a cube composed of a solid, stagnant gas, or stagnant liquid and having dimensions Δx, Δy, Δz. For diffusion in the x direction we write

$$N_{Ax} = -D_{AB} \frac{\partial c_A}{\partial x} \tag{7.1-1}$$

The term $\partial c_A / \partial x$ means the partial of c_A with respect to x or the rate of change of c_A with x when the other variable, time t, is kept constant.

Next we make a mass balance on component A in terms of moles for no generation:

$$\text{rate of input} = \text{rate of output} + \text{rate of accumulation} \tag{7.1-2}$$

FIGURE 7.1-1.   *Unsteady-state diffusion in one direction.*

The rate of input and rate of output in kg mol A/s are

$$\text{rate of input} = N_{Ax|x} = -D_{AB}\left.\frac{\partial c_A}{\partial x}\right|_x \tag{7.1-3}$$

$$\text{rate of output} = N_{Ax|x+\Delta x} = -D_{AB}\left.\frac{\partial c_A}{\partial x}\right|_{x+\Delta x} \tag{7.1-4}$$

The rate of accumulation is as follows for the volume $\Delta x\,\Delta y\,\Delta z$ m³:

$$\text{rate of accumulation} = (\Delta x\,\Delta y\,\Delta z)\frac{\partial c_A}{\partial t} \tag{7.1-5}$$

Substituting Eqs. (7.1-3), (7.1-4), and (7.1-5) into (7.1-2) and dividing by $\Delta x\,\Delta y\,\Delta z$,

$$-D_{AB}\frac{\left.\dfrac{\partial c_A}{\partial x}\right|_x - \left.\dfrac{\partial c_A}{\partial x}\right|_{x+\Delta x}}{\Delta x} = \frac{\partial c_A}{\partial t} \tag{7.1-6}$$

Letting Δx approach zero,

$$\frac{\partial c_A}{\partial t} = D_{AB}\frac{\partial^2 c_A}{\partial x^2} \tag{7.1-7}$$

The above holds for a constant diffusivity D_{AB}. If D_{AB} is a variable,

$$\frac{\partial c_A}{\partial t} = \frac{\partial(D_{AB}\,\partial c_A/\partial x)}{\partial x} \tag{7.1-8}$$

Equation (7.1-7) relates the concentration c_A with position x and time t. For diffusion in all three directions a similar derivation gives

$$\frac{\partial c_A}{\partial t} = D_{AB}\left(\frac{\partial^2 c_A}{\partial x^2} + \frac{\partial^2 c_A}{\partial y^2} + \frac{\partial^2 c_A}{\partial z^2}\right) \tag{7.1-9}$$

In the remainder of this section, the solutions of Eqs. (7.1-7) and (7.1-9) will be considered. Note the mathematical similarity between the equation for heat conduction,

$$\frac{\partial T}{\partial t} = \alpha\frac{\partial^2 T}{\partial x^2} \tag{5.1-6}$$

and Eq. (7.1-7) for diffusion. Because of this similarity, the mathematical methods used for solution of the unsteady-state heat-conduction equation can be used for unsteady-state mass transfer. This is discussed more fully in Sections 7.1B, 7.1C, and 7.7.

7.1B Diffusion in a Flat Plate with Negligible Surface Resistance

To illustrate an analytical method of solving Eq. (7.1-7), we will derive the solution for unsteady-state diffusion in the x direction for a plate of thickness $2x_1$, as shown in Fig. 7.1-2. For diffusion in one direction,

$$\frac{\partial c_A}{\partial t} = D_{AB} \frac{\partial^2 c_A}{\partial x^2} \tag{7.1-7}$$

Dropping the subscripts A and B for convenience,

$$\frac{\partial c}{\partial t} = D \frac{\partial^2 c}{\partial x^2} \tag{7.1-10}$$

The initial profile of the concentration in the plate at $t = 0$ is uniform at $c = c_0$ for all x values, as shown in Fig. 7.1-2. At time $t = 0$ the concentration of the fluid in the environment outside is suddenly changed to c_1. For a very high mass-transfer coefficient outside the surface resistance will be negligible and the concentration at the surface will be equal to that in the fluid, which is c_1.

The initial and boundary conditions are

$$c = c_0, \qquad t = 0, \qquad x = x, \qquad Y = \frac{c_1 - c_0}{c_1 - c_0} = 1$$

$$c = c_1, \qquad t = t, \qquad x = 0, \qquad Y = \frac{c_1 - c_1}{c_1 - c_0} = 0 \tag{7.1-11}$$

$$c = c_1, \qquad t = t, \qquad x = 2x_1, \qquad Y = \frac{c_1 - c_1}{c_1 - c_0} = 0$$

Redefining the concentration so it goes between 0 and 1,

$$Y = \frac{c_1 - c}{c_1 - c_0} \tag{7.1-12}$$

FIGURE 7.1-2. *Unsteady-state diffusion in a flat plate with negligible surface resistance.*

$$\frac{\partial Y}{\partial t} = D\frac{\partial^2 Y}{\partial x^2} \tag{7.1-13}$$

The solution of Eq. (7.1-13) is an infinite Fourier series and is identical to the solution of Eq. (5.1-6) for heat transfer:

$$Y = \frac{c_1 - c}{c_1 - c_0} = \frac{4}{\pi}\left[\frac{1}{1}\exp\left(-\frac{1^2\pi^2 X}{4}\right)\sin\frac{1\pi x}{2x_1} + \frac{1}{3}\exp\left(-\frac{3^2\pi^2 X}{4}\right)\sin\frac{3\pi x}{2x_1}\right.$$

$$\left. + \frac{1}{5}\exp\left(-\frac{5^2\pi^2 X}{4}\right)\sin\frac{5\pi x}{2x_1} + \cdots\right] \tag{7.1-14}$$

where

$X = Dt/x_1^2$, dimensionless

c = concentration at point x and time t in slab

$Y = (c_1 - c)/(c_1 - c_0)$ = fraction of unaccomplished change, dimensionless

$1 - Y = (c - c_0)/(c_1 - c_0)$ = fraction of change

Solution of equations similar to Eq. (7.1-14) are time-consuming; convenient charts for various geometries are available and will be discussed in the next section.

7.1C Unsteady-State Diffusion in Various Geometries

1. Convection and boundary conditions at the surface.   In Fig. 7.1-2 there was no convective resistance at the surface. However, in many cases when a fluid is outside the solid, convective mass transfer is occurring at the surface. A convective mass-transfer coefficient k_c, similar to a convective heat-transfer coefficient, is defined as follows:

$$N_A = k_c(c_{L1} - c_{Li}) \tag{7.1-15}$$

where k_c is a mass-transfer coefficient in m/s, c_{L1} is the bulk fluid concentration in kg mol A/m^3, and c_{Li} is the concentration in the fluid just adjacent to the surface of the solid. The coefficient k_c is an empirical coefficient and will be discussed more fully in Section 7.2.

In Fig. 7.1-3a the case where a mass-transfer coefficient is present at the boundary is shown. The concentration drop across the fluid is $c_{L1} - c_{Li}$. The concentration in the solid c_i at the surface is in equilibrium with c_{Li}.

In Fig. 7.1-3a the concentration c_{Li} in the liquid adjacent to the solid and c_i in the solid at the surface are in equilibrium and are equal. However, unlike heat transfer, where the temperatures are equal, the concentrations here are in equilibrium and are related by

$$K = \frac{c_{Li}}{c_i} \tag{7.1-16}$$

where K is the equilibrium distribution coefficient (similar to Henry's law coefficient for a gas and liquid). The value of K in Fig. 7.1-3a is 1.0.

In Fig. 7.1-3b the distribution coefficient $K > 1$ and $c_{Li} > c_i$, even though they are in equilibrium. Other cases are shown in Fig. 7.1-3c and d. This was also discussed in Section 6.6B.

FIGURE 7.1-3. *Interface conditions for convective mass transfer and an equilibrium distribution coefficient $K = c_{Li}/c_i$: (a) $K = 1$. (b) $K > 1$, (c) $K < 1$, (d) $K > 1$ and $k_c = \infty$.*

2. Relation between mass- and heat-transfer parameters. In order to use the unsteady-state heat-conduction charts in Chapter 5 for solving unsteady-state diffusion problems, the dimensionless variables or parameters for heat transfer must be related to those for mass transfer. In Table 7.1-1 the relations between these variables are tabulated. For $K \neq 1.0$, whenever k_c appears, it is given as Kk_c, and whenever c_1 appears, it is given as c_1/K.

3. Charts for diffusion in various geometries. The various heat-transfer charts for unsteady-state conduction can be used for unsteady-state diffusion and are as follows:

1. Semi-infinite solid, Fig. 5.3-3.
2. Flat plate, Figs. 5.3-5 and 5.3-6.
3. Long cylinder, Figs. 5.3-7 and 5.3-8.
4. Sphere, Figs. 5.3-9 and 5.3-10.
5. Average concentrations, zero convective resistance, Fig. 5.3-13.

EXAMPLE 7.1-1. Unsteady-State Diffusion in a Slab of Agar Gel

A solid slab of 5.15 wt % agar gel at 278 K is 10.16 mm thick and contains a uniform concentrations of urea of 0.1 kg mol/m^3. Diffusion is only in the x direction through two parallel flat surfaces 10.16 mm apart. The slab is suddenly immersed in pure turbulent water, so the surface resistance can be assumed to be negligible; that is, the convective coefficient k_c is very large. The diffusivity of urea in the agar from Table 6.4-2 is 4.72×10^{-10} m^2/s.

(a) Calculate the concentration at the midpoint of the slab (5.08 mm from the surface) and 2.54 mm from the surface after 10 h.

(b) If the thickness of the slab is halved, what would be the midpoint concentration in 10 h?

TABLE 7.1-1. *Relation Between Mass- and Heat-Transfer Parameters for Unsteady-State Diffusion**

Heat Transfer	Mass Transfer	
	$K = c_L/c = 1.0$	$K = c_L/c \neq 1.0$
$Y, \dfrac{T_1 - T}{T_1 - T_0}$	$\dfrac{c_1 - c}{c_1 - c_0}$	$\dfrac{c_1/K - c}{c_1/K - c_0}$
$1 - Y, \dfrac{T - T_0}{T_1 - T_0}$	$\dfrac{c - c_0}{c_1 - c_0}$	$\dfrac{c - c_0}{c_1/K - c_0}$
$X, \dfrac{\alpha t}{x_1^2}$	$\dfrac{D_{AB}t}{x_1^2}$	$\dfrac{D_{AB}t}{x_1^2}$
$\dfrac{x}{2\sqrt{\alpha t}}$	$\dfrac{x}{2\sqrt{D_{AB}t}}$	$\dfrac{x}{2\sqrt{D_{AB}t}}$
$m, \dfrac{k}{hx_1}$	$\dfrac{D_{AB}}{k_c x_1}$	$\dfrac{D_{AB}}{Kk_c x_1}$
$\dfrac{h}{k}\sqrt{\alpha t}$	$\dfrac{k_c}{D_{AB}}\sqrt{D_{AB}t}$	$\dfrac{Kk_c}{D_{AB}}\sqrt{D_{AB}t}$
$n, \dfrac{x}{x_1}$	$\dfrac{x}{x_1}$	$\dfrac{x}{x_1}$

*x is the distance from the center of the slab, cylinder, or sphere; for a semi-infinite slab, x is the distance from the surface, c_0 is the original uniform concentration in the solid, c_1 the concentration in the fluid outside the slab, and c the concentration in the solid at position x and time t.

Solution: For part (a), $c_0 = 0.10$ kg mol/m^3, $c_1 = 0$ for pure water, and c = concentration at distance x from center line and time t s. The equilibrium distribution coefficient K in Eq. (7.1-16) can be assumed to be 1.0, since the water in the aqueous solution in the gel and outside should be very similar in properties. From Table 7.1-1,

$$Y = \frac{c_1/K - c}{c_1/K - c_0} = \frac{0/1.0 - c}{0/1.0 - 0.10}$$

Also, $x_1 = 10.16/(1000 \times 2) = 5.08 \times 10^{-3}$ m (half-slab thickness), $x = 0$ (center), $X = D_{AB}t/x_1^2 = (4.72 \times 10^{-10})(10 \times 3600)/(5.08 \times 10^{-3})^2 = 0.658$. The relative position $n = x/x_1 = 0/5.08 \times 10^{-3} = 0$, and relative resistance $m = D_{AB}/Kk_c x_1 = 0$, since k_c is very large (zero resistance).

From Fig. 5.3-5 for $X = 0.658$, $m = 0$, and $n = 0$,

$$Y = 0.275 = \frac{0 - c}{0 - 0.10}$$

Solving, $c = 0.0275$ kg mol/m^3 for $x = 0$.

For the point 2.54 mm from the surface or 2.54 mm from center, $x = 2.54/1000 = 2.54 \times 10^{-3}$ m, $X = 0.658$, $m = 0$, $n = x/x_1 = 2.54 \times 10^{-3}/5.08 \times 10^{-3} = 0.5$. Then from Fig. 5.3-5, $Y = 0.172$. Solving, $c = 0.0172$ kg mol/m^3.

For part (b) and half the thickness, $X = 0.658/(0.5)^2 = 2.632$, $n = 0$, and $m = 0$. Hence, $Y = 0.0020$ and $c = 2.0 \times 10^{-4}$ kg mol/m^3.

EXAMPLE 7.1-2. Unsteady-State Diffusion in a Semi-infinite Slab

A very thick slab has a uniform concentration of solute A of $c_0 = 1.0 \times 10^{-2}$ kg mol A/m^3. Suddenly, the front face of the slab is exposed to a flowing fluid having a concentration $c_1 = 0.10$ kg mol A/m^3 and a convective coefficient $k_c = 2 \times 10^{-7}$ m/s. The equilibrium distribution coefficient $K = c_{Li}/c_i = 2.0$. Assuming that the slab is a semi-infinite solid, calculate the concentration in the solid at the surface ($x = 0$) and $x = 0.01$ m from the surface after $t = 3 \times 10^4$ s. The diffusivity in the solid is $D_{AB} = 4 \times 10^{-9}$ m^2/s.

Solution: To use Fig. 5.3-3, use Table 7.1-1.

$$\frac{Kk_c}{D_{AB}}\sqrt{D_{AB}t} = \frac{2.0(2 \times 10^{-7})}{4 \times 10^{-9}}\sqrt{(4 \times 10^{-9})(3 \times 10^4)} = 1.095$$

For $x = 0.01$ m from the surface in the solid,

$$\frac{x}{2\sqrt{D_{AB}t}} = \frac{0.01}{2\sqrt{(4 \times 10^{-9})(3 \times 10^4)}} = 0.457$$

From the chart, $1 - Y = 0.26$. Then, substituting into the equation for $(1 - Y)$ from Table 7.1-1 and solving,

$$1 - Y = \frac{c - c_0}{c_1/K - c_0} = \frac{c - 1 \times 10^{-2}}{(10 \times 10^{-2})/2 - (1 \times 10^{-2})} = 0.26$$

$$c = 2.04 \times 10^{-2} \text{ kg mol/m}^3 \qquad \text{(for } x = 0.01 \text{ m)}$$

For $x = 0$ m (i.e., at the surface of the solid),

$$\frac{x}{2\sqrt{D_{AB}t}} = 0$$

From the chart, $1 - Y = 0.62$. Solving, $c = 3.48 \times 10^{-2}$. This value is the same as c_i, as shown in Fig. 7.1-3b. To calculate the concentration c_{Li} in the liquid at the interface,

$$C_{Li} = Kc_i = 2.0(3.48 \times 10^{-2}) = 6.96 \times 10^{-2} \text{ kg mol/m}^3$$

A plot of these values will be similar to Fig. 7.1-3b.

4. Unsteady-state diffusion in more than one direction. In Section 5.3F a method was given for unsteady-state heat conduction, in which the one-dimensional solutions were combined to yield solutions for several-dimensional systems. The same method can be used for unsteady-state diffusion in more than one direction. Rewriting Eq. (5.3-11) for diffusion in a rectangular block in the x, y, and z directions,

$$Y_{x,y,z} = (Y_x)(Y_y)(Y_z) = \frac{c_1/K - c_{x,y,z}}{c_1/K - c_0} \qquad \textbf{(7.1-17)}$$

where $c_{x,y,z}$ is the concentration at the point x, y, z from the center of the block. The value of Y_x for the two parallel faces is obtained from Fig. 5.3-5 or 5.3-6 for a flat plate in the x direction. The values of Y_y and Y_z are similarly obtained from the same charts. For a short cylinder, an equation similar to Eq. (5.3-12) is used, and for average concentrations, ones similar to Eqs. (5.3-14), (5.3-15), and (5.3-16) are used.

7.2 CONVECTIVE MASS-TRANSFER COEFFICIENTS

7.2A Introduction to Convective Mass Transfer

In the previous sections of this chapter and in Chapter 6 we have emphasized molecular diffusion in stagnant fluids or fluids in laminar flow. In many cases the rate of diffusion is slow, and more rapid transfer is desired. To do this, the fluid velocity is increased until turbulent mass transfer occurs.

To have a fluid in convective flow usually requires the fluid to be flowing past another immiscible fluid or a solid surface. An example is a fluid flowing in a pipe, where part of the pipe wall is made by a slightly dissolving solid material such as benzoic acid. The benzoic acid dissolves and is transported perpendicular to the main stream from the wall. When a fluid is in turbulent flow and is flowing past a surface, the actual velocity of small particles of fluid cannot be described clearly as in laminar flow. In laminar flow the fluid flows in streamlines and its behavior can usually be described mathematically. However, in turbulent motion there are no streamlines; instead there are large eddies or "chunks" of fluid moving rapidly in seemingly random fashion.

When a solute A is dissolving from a solid surface, there is a high concentration of this solute in the fluid at the surface, and its concentration, in general, decreases as the distance from the wall increases. However, minute samples of fluid adjacent to each other do not always have concentrations close to each other. This occurs because eddies having solute in them move rapidly from one part of the fluid to another, transferring relatively large amounts of solute. This turbulent diffusion or eddy transfer is quite fast in comparison to molecular transfer.

Three regions of mass transfer can be visualized. In the first, which is adjacent to the surface, a thin, viscous sublayer film is present. Most of the mass transfer occurs by molecular diffusion, since few or no eddies are present. A large concentration drop occurs across this film as a result of the slow diffusion rate.

The transition or buffer region is adjacent to the first region. Some eddies are present, and the mass transfer is the sum of turbulent and molecular diffusion. There is a gradual transition in this region from the transfer by mainly molecular diffusion at one end to mainly turbulent at the other end.

In the *turbulent region* adjacent to the buffer region, most of the transfer is by turbulent diffusion, with a small amount by molecular diffusion. The concentration decrease is very small here since the eddies tend to keep the fluid concentration uniform. A more detailed discussion of these three regions is given in Section 3.10G.

A typical plot for the mass transfer of a dissolving solid from a surface to a turbulent fluid in a conduit is given in Fig. 7.2-1. The concentration drop from c_{A1} adjacent to the surface is very abrupt close to the surface and then levels off. This curve is very similar to the shapes found for heat and momentum transfer. The average or mixed concentration $\bar{c}_A$ is shown and is slightly greater than the minimum c_{A2}.

FIGURE 7.2-1. *Concentration profile in turbulent mass transfer from a surface to a fluid.*

7.2B Types of Mass-Transfer Coefficients

1. Definition of mass-transfer coefficient. Since our understanding of turbulent flow is incomplete, we attempt to write the equations for turbulent diffusion in a manner similar to that for molecular diffusion. For turbulent mass transfer for constant c, Eq. (6.1-6) is written as

$$J_A^* = -(D_{AB} + \varepsilon_M) \frac{dc_A}{dz} \tag{7.2-1}$$

where D_{AB} is the molecular diffusivity in m^2/s and ε_M the mass eddy diffusivity in m^2/s. The value of ε_M is variable and is near zero at the interface or surface and increases as the distance from the wall increases. We therefore use an average value $\bar{\varepsilon}_M$ since the variation of ε_M is not generally known. Integrating Eq. (7.2-1) between points 1 and 2,

$$J_{A1}^* = \frac{D_{AB} + \varepsilon_M}{z_2 - z_1} (c_{A1} - c_{A2}) \tag{7.2-2}$$

The flux J_{A1}^* is based on the surface area A_1 since the cross-sectional area may vary. The value of $z_2 - z_1$, the distance of the path, is often not known. Hence, Eq. (7.2-2) is simplified and is written using a convective mass-transfer coefficient k_c':

$$J_{A1}^* = k_c'(c_{A1} - c_{A2}) \tag{7.2-3}$$

where J_{A1}^* is the flux of A from the surface A_1 relative to the whole bulk phase, k_c' is $(D_{AB} + \bar{\varepsilon}_M)/(z_2 - z_1)$, an experimental mass-transfer coefficient in kg mol/s · m^2 · (kg mol/m^3) or simplified as m/s, and c_{A2} is the concentration at point 2 in kg mol A/m^3 or, more usually, the average bulk concentration $\bar{c}_{A2}$. This definition of a convective mass-transfer coefficient k_c' is quite similar to the convective heat-transfer coefficient h.

2. Mass-transfer coefficient for equimolar counterdiffusion. Generally, we are interested in N_A, the flux of A relative to stationary coordinates. We can start with the following equation, which is similar to that for molecular diffusion with the term ε_M added:

$$N_A = -c(D_{AB} + \varepsilon_M) \frac{dx_A}{dz} + x_A(N_A + N_B) \tag{7.2-4}$$

For the case of equimolar counterdiffusion, where $N_A = -N_B$, and integrating at steady state, calling $k_c' = (D_{AB} + \bar{\varepsilon}_M)/(z_2 - z_1)$,

$$N_A = k_c'(c_{A1} - c_{A2}) \tag{7.2-5}$$

Equation (7.2-5) is the defining equation for the mass-transfer coefficient. Often, however, we define the concentration in terms of mole fraction if a liquid or gas, or in terms of partial pressure if a gas. Hence, we can define the mass-transfer coefficient in several ways. If y_A is mole fraction in a gas phase and x_A in a liquid phase, then Eq. (7.2-5) can be written as follows for equimolar counterdiffusion:

$$\text{Gases:} \quad N_A = k_c'(c_{A1} - c_{A2}) = k_G'(p_{A1} - p_{A2}) = k_y'(y_{A1} - y_{A2}) \qquad \text{(7.2-6)}$$

$$\text{Liquids:} \quad N_A = k_c'(c_{A1} - c_{A2}) = k_L'(c_{A1} - c_{A2}) = k_x'(x_{A1} - x_{A2}) \qquad \text{(7.2-7)}$$

All of these mass-transfer coefficients can be related to each other. For example, using Eq. (7.2-6) and substituting $y_{A1} = c_{A1}/c$ and $y_{A2} = c_{A2}/c$ into the equation,

$$N_A = k_c'(c_{A1} - c_{A2}) = k_y'(y_{A1} - y_{A2}) = k_y'\left(\frac{c_{A1}}{c} - \frac{c_{A2}}{c}\right) = \frac{k_y'}{c}(c_{A1} - c_{A2}) \qquad \text{(7.2-8)}$$

Hence,

$$k_c' = \frac{k_y'}{c} \qquad \text{(7.2-9)}$$

These relations among mass-transfer coefficients, together with the various flux equations, are given in Table 7.2-1.

3. Mass-transfer coefficient for A diffusing through stagnant, nondiffusing B.   For A diffusing through stagnant, nondiffusing B, where $N_B = 0$, Eq. (7.2-4) gives for steady state

$$N_A = \frac{k_c'}{x_{BM}}(c_{A1} - c_{A2}) = k_c(c_{A1} - c_{A2})$$

$$= \frac{k_x'}{x_{BM}}(x_{A1} - x_{A2}) = k_x(x_{A1} - x_{A2}) \qquad \text{(7.2-10)}$$

where the x_{BM} and its counterpart y_{BM} are similar to Eq. (6.2-21) and k_c is the mass-transfer coefficient for A diffusing through stagnant B. Also,

$$x_{BM} = \frac{x_{B2} - x_{B1}}{\ln(x_{B2}/x_{B1})} \qquad y_{BM} = \frac{y_{B2} - y_{B1}}{\ln(y_{B2}/y_{B1})} \qquad \text{(7.2-11)}$$

Rewriting Eq. (7.2-10) using other units,

$$\text{(Gases):} \quad N_A = k_c(c_{A1} - c_{A2}) = k_G(p_{A1} - p_{A2}) = k_y(y_{A1} - y_{A2}) \qquad \text{(7.2-12)}$$

$$\text{(Liquids):} \quad N_A = k_c(c_{A1} - c_{A2}) = k_L(c_{A1} - c_{A2}) = k_x(x_{A1} - x_{A2}) \qquad \text{(7.2-13)}$$

Again all the mass-transfer coefficients can be related to each other and are given in Table 7.2-1. For example, setting Eq. (7.2-10) equal to (7.2-13),

$$N_A = \frac{k_c'}{x_{BM}}(c_{A1} - c_{A2}) = k_x(x_{A1} - x_{A2}) = k_x\left(\frac{c_{A1}}{c} - \frac{c_{A2}}{c}\right) \qquad \text{(7.2-14)}$$

Hence,

$$\frac{k_c'}{x_{BM}} = \frac{k_x}{c} \qquad \text{(7.2-15)}$$

TABLE 7.2-1. *Flux Equations and Mass-Transfer Coefficients*

Flux equations for equimolar counterdiffusion

Gases: $\quad N_A = k'_c(c_{A1} - c_{A2}) = k'_G(p_{A1} - p_{A2}) = k'_y(y_{A1} - y_{A2})$

Liquids: $\quad N_A = k'_c(c_{A1} - c_{A2}) = k'_L(c_{A1} - c_{A2}) = k'_x(x_{A1} - x_{A2})$

Flux equations for A diffusing through stagnant, nondiffusing B

Gases: $\quad N_A = k_c(c_{A1} - c_{A2}) = k_G(p_{A1} - p_{A2}) = k_y(y_{A1} - y_{A2})$

Liquids: $\quad N_A = k_c(c_{A1} - c_{A2}) = k_L(c_{A1} - c_{A2}) = k_x(x_{A1} - x_{A2})$

Conversions between mass-transfer coefficients

Gases:

$$k'_c c = k'_c \frac{P}{RT} = k_c \frac{p_{BM}}{RT} = k'_G P = k_G p_{BM} = k_y y_{BM} = k'_y = k_c y_{BM} c = k_G y_{BM} P$$

Liquids:

$$k'_c c = k'_L c = k_L x_{BM} c = k'_L \rho/M = k'_x = k_x x_{BM}$$

(where ρ is density of liquid and M is molecular weight)

Units of mass-transfer coefficients

	SI Units	Cgs Units	English Units
k_c, k_L, k'_c, k'_L	m/s	cm/s	ft/h
k_x, k_y, k'_x, k'_y	$\dfrac{\text{kg mol}}{\text{s} \cdot \text{m}^2 \cdot \text{mol frac}}$	$\dfrac{\text{g mol}}{\text{s} \cdot \text{cm}^2 \cdot \text{mol frac}}$	$\dfrac{\text{lb mol}}{\text{h} \cdot \text{ft}^2 \cdot \text{mol frac}}$
k_G, k'_G	$\dfrac{\text{kg mol}}{\text{s} \cdot \text{m}^2 \cdot \text{Pa}} \quad \dfrac{\text{kg mol}}{\text{s} \cdot \text{m}^2 \cdot \text{atm}}$ (preferred)	$\dfrac{\text{g mol}}{\text{s} \cdot \text{cm}^2 \cdot \text{atm}}$	$\dfrac{\text{lb mol}}{\text{h} \cdot \text{ft}^2 \cdot \text{atm}}$

EXAMPLE 7.2-1. *Vaporizing A and Convective Mass Transfer*

A large volume of pure gas B at 2 atm pressure is flowing over a surface from which pure A is vaporizing. The liquid A completely wets the surface, which is a blotting paper. Hence, the partial pressure of A at the surface is the vapor pressure of A at 298 K, which is 0.20 atm. The k'_y has been estimated to be 6.78×10^{-5} kg mol/s $\cdot$ m^2 $\cdot$ mol frac. Calculate N_A, the vaporization rate, and also the value of k_y and k_G.

Solution: This is the case of A diffusing through B, where the flux of B normal to the surface is zero, since B is not soluble in liquid A. $p_{A1} = 0.20$ atm and $p_{A2} = 0$ in the pure gas B. Also, $y_{A1} = p_{A1}/P = 0.20/2.0 = 0.10$ and $y_{A2} = 0$. We can use Eq. (7.2-12) with mole fractions:

$$N_A = k_y(y_{A1} - y_{A2}) \tag{7.2-12}$$

However, we have a value for k'_y which is related to k_y from Table 7.2-1 by

$$k_y y_{BM} = k'_y \tag{7.2-16}$$

The term y_{BM} is similar to x_{BM} and is, from Eq. (7.2-11),

$$y_{BM} = \frac{y_{B2} - y_{B1}}{\ln(y_{B2}/y_{B1})} \qquad\qquad \text{(7.2-11)}$$

$$y_{B1} = 1 - y_{A1} = 1 - 0.10 = 0.90 \qquad y_{B2} = 1 - y_{A2} = 1 - 0 = 1.0$$

Substituting into Eq. (7.2-11),

$$y_{BM} = \frac{1.0 - 0.90}{\ln(1.0/0.90)} = 0.95$$

Then, from Eq. (7.2-16),

$$k_y = \frac{k_y'}{y_{BM}} = \frac{6.78 \times 10^{-5}}{0.95} = 7.138 \times 10^{-5}\ \text{kg mol/s} \cdot \text{m}^2 \cdot \text{mol frac}$$

Also, from Table 7.2-1,

$$k_G y_{BM} P = k_y y_{BM} \qquad\qquad \text{(7.2-17)}$$

Hence, solving for k_G and substituting knowns,

$$k_G = \frac{k_y}{P} = \frac{7.138 \times 10^{-5}}{2 \times 1.01325 \times 10^5\ \text{Pa}} = 3.522 \times 10^{-10}\ \text{kg mol/s} \cdot \text{m}^2 \cdot \text{Pa}$$

$$k_G = \frac{k_y}{P} = \frac{7.138 \times 10^{-5}}{2.0\ \text{atm}} = 3.569 \times 10^{-5}\ \text{kg mol/s} \cdot \text{m}^2 \cdot \text{atm}$$

For the flux, using Eq. (7.2-12),

$$N_A = k_y(y_{A1} - y_{A2}) = 7.138 \times 10^{-5}(0.10 - 0) = 7.138 \times 10^{-6}\ \text{kg mol/s} \cdot \text{m}^2$$

Also,

$$p_{A1} = 0.20\ \text{atm} = 0.20(1.01325 \times 10^5) = 2.026 \times 10^4\ \text{Pa}$$

Using Eq. (7.2-12) again,

$$N_A = k_G(p_{A1} - p_{A2}) = 3.522 \times 10^{-10}(2.026 \times 10^4 - 0)$$
$$= 7.138 \times 10^{-6}\ \text{kg mol/s} \cdot \text{m}^2$$
$$N_A = k_G(p_{A1} - p_{A2}) = 3.569 \times 10^{-5}(0.20 - 0)$$
$$= 7.138 \times 10^{-6}\ \text{kg mol/s} \cdot \text{m}^2$$

Note that in this case, since the concentrations were dilute, y_{BM} is close to 1.0 and k_y and k_y' differ very little.

7.2C Mass Transfer Coefficients for General Case of A and B Diffusing and Convective Flow Using Film Theory

Equation (7.2-4) can be integrated assuming a simplified film theory where the mass transfer is assumed to occur through a thin film next to the wall of thickness δ_f and by molecular diffusion. Then the experimental value of k_c' for dilute solutions is used to determine the film thickness δ_f:

$$k_c' = \frac{D_{AB}}{\delta_f} \tag{7.2-18}$$

Rewriting Eq. (7.2-4),

$$N_A = -c \frac{D_{AB}}{dz} \frac{dx_A}{dz} + x_A(N_A + N_B) \tag{7.2-19}$$

The convective term is $x_A(N_A + N_B)$. Rearranging and integrating,

$$\frac{1}{cD_{AB}} \int_{z=0}^{z=\delta_f} dz = -\int_{x_{A1}}^{x_{A2}} \frac{dx_A}{N_A - x_A(N_A + N_B)} \tag{7.2-20}$$

$$N_A = \frac{N_A}{N_A + N_B} k_c'c \ln\left[\frac{N_A/(N_A + N_B) - x_{A2}}{N_A/(N_A + N_B) - x_{A1}}\right] \tag{7.2-21}$$

For $N_B = 0$, Eq. (7.2-21) reduces to Eq. (7.2-10).

7.2D Mass Transfer Coefficients under High Flux Conditions

The final Eq. (7.2-21) is a result of assuming the film theory where molecular diffusion occurs across the film δ_f. This assumes that this film thickness is unaffected by high fluxes and bulk or convective flow (diffusion-induced convection). As a result, other definitions of the mass-transfer coefficient that include this effect of diffusion-induced convection have been derived. One common method by Bird et al. (B1) and Skelland (S8) is given as follows for the case of A diffusing through stagnant, nondiffusing B where diffusion-induced convection is present.

Rewriting Eq. (7.2-19) for the flux N_A at the surface $z = 0$ where $x_A = x_{A1}$,

$$N_A = -cD_{AB}\left(\frac{dx_A}{dz}\right)_{z=0} + x_{A1}(N_A + 0) \tag{7.2-22}$$

Note that the convective term is defined in terms of x_{A1} and not the average value.

Defining a mass-transfer coefficient in terms of the diffusion flux,

$$-cD_{AB}\left(\frac{dx_A}{dz}\right)_{z=0} = k_c^0 c(x_{A1} - x_{A2}) \tag{7.2-23}$$

Substituting Eq. (7.2-23) into (7.2-22) and solving for N_A,

$$N_A = \frac{k_c^0 c(x_{A1} - x_{A2})}{1 - x_{A1}} \tag{7.2-24}$$

At low concentrations and fluxes, k_c^0 approaches k_c' for no bulk flow, or $N_A = k_c'c(x_{A1} - x_{A2})$.

In general, a coefficient k_c may be defined without regard to convective flow:

$$N_A = k_c c(x_{A1} - x_{A2}) \tag{7.2-25}$$

Combining (7.2-24) and (7.2-25),

$$k_c^0 = (1 - x_{A1})k_c \tag{7.2-26}$$

The relationship between k_c^0 or k_c for high flux and k_c' for low flux will be considered. These corrections or relationships will be derived using the film theory for the transfer of A by molecular diffusion and convective flow, with B being stagnant and nondiffusing. This has been done previously and is obtained by setting $N_B = 0$ in Eq. (7.2-21) to obtain the following, which is identical to Eq. (7.2-10):

$$N_A = \frac{k_c'}{x_{BM}}(c_{A1} - c_{A2}) = k_c (c_{A1} - c_{A2}) \qquad (7.2\text{-}27)$$

Hence, for the film theory,

$$\frac{k_c}{k_c'} = \frac{1}{x_{BM}} = \frac{k_x}{k_x'} \qquad (7.2\text{-}28)$$

Combining Eqs. (7.2-26) and (7.2-28),

$$\frac{k_c^0}{k_c'} = \frac{1 - x_{A1}}{x_{BM}} = \frac{k_x^0}{k_x'} \qquad (7.2\text{-}29)$$

For this film theory, Eqs. (7.2-28) and (7.2-29) are independent of the Schmidt number. These correction factors predicted by the film theory give results that are reasonably close to those using more complex theories—the penetration theory and boundary layer theory—which are discussed later in Section 7.9C. An advantage of this simple film theory is that it is quite useful in solving complex systems.

EXAMPLE 7.2-2. High Flux Correction Factors

Toluene A is evaporating from a wetted porous slab by having inert pure air at 1 atm flowing parallel to the flat surface. At a certain point the mass-transfer coefficient k_x' for very low fluxes has been estimated as 0.20 lb mol/hr·ft². The gas composition at the interface at this point is $x_{A1} = 0.65$. Calculate the flux N_A and the ratios k_c/k_c' or k_x/k_x' and k_c^0/k_c' or k_x^0/k_x' to correct for high flux.

Solution: For the flux N_A, using Eq. (7.2-11),

$$x_{BM} = \frac{x_{B2} - x_{B1}}{\ln(x_{B2}/x_{B1})} = \frac{1.00 - 0.35}{\ln(1.00/0.35)} = 0.619$$

Using Eq. (7.2-10) in terms of k_x', where $k_c'c = k_x'$,

$$N_A = \frac{k_x'}{x_{BM}}(x_{A1} - x_{A2}) = \frac{0.20}{0.619}(0.65 - 0) = 0.210 \text{ lb mol/hr·ft}^2$$

Using Eq. (7.2-28),

$$\frac{k_x}{k_x'} = \frac{k_c}{k_c'} = \frac{1}{x_{BM}} = \frac{1}{0.619} = 1.616$$

Then, $k_x = 1.616 k_x' = 1.616(0.20) = 0.323$ lb mol/hr·ft². Using Eq. (7.2-29),

$$\frac{k_x^0}{k_x'} = \frac{k_c^0}{k_c'} = \frac{1 - x_{A1}}{x_{BM}} = \frac{1 - 0.65}{0.619} = 0.565$$

and $k_x^0 = 0.565(0.200) = 0.113$ lb mol/hr·ft².

7.2E   Methods for Experimentally Determining Mass-Transfer Coefficients

Many different experimental methods have been employed to obtain mass-transfer coefficients. In determining the mass-transfer coefficient to a sphere, Steele and Geankoplis (S3) used a solid sphere of benzoic acid held rigidly by a rear support in a pipe. Before the run the sphere was weighed. After flow of the fluid for a timed interval, the sphere was removed, dried, and weighed again to give the amount of mass transferred, which was small compared to the weight of the sphere. From the mass transferred and the area of the sphere, the flux N_A was calculated. Then the driving force $(c_{AS} - 0)$ was used to calculate k_L, where c_{AS} is the solubility and the water contained no benzoic acid.

Another method used is to flow gases over various geometries wet with evaporating liquids. For mass transfer from a flat plate, a porous blotter wet with the liquid serves as the plate.

If the solution is quite dilute, then the mass-transfer coefficient measured is $k_c \cong k'_c$ and the dilute low flux coefficient k'_c or k'_x is experimentally obtained.

7.3   MASS-TRANSFER COEFFICIENTS FOR VARIOUS GEOMETRIES

7.3A   Dimensionless Numbers Used to Correlate Data

The experimental data for mass-transfer coefficients obtained using various kinds of fluids, different velocities, and different geometries are correlated using dimensionless numbers similar to those for heat and momentum transfer. Methods of dimensional analysis are discussed in Sections 3.11, 4.14, and 7.8.

The most important dimensionless number is the Reynolds number N_{Re}, which indicates degree of turbulence:

$$N_{Re} = \frac{Lv\rho}{\mu} \tag{7.3-1}$$

where L is diameter D_p for a sphere, diameter D for a pipe, or length L for a flat plate. The velocity v is the mass average velocity if in a pipe. In a packed bed the superficial velocity v' in the empty cross section is often used, or sometimes $v = v'/\varepsilon$ is used, where v is interstitial velocity and ε void fraction of bed.

The *Schmidt number* is

$$N_{Sc} = \frac{\mu}{\rho D_{AB}} \tag{7.3-2}$$

The viscosity μ and density ρ used are for the actual flowing mixture of solute A and fluid B. If the mixture is dilute, properties of the pure fluid B can be used. The Prandtl number $c_p\mu/k$ for heat transfer is analogous to the Schmidt number for mass transfer. The Schmidt number is the ratio of the shear component for diffusivity μ/ρ to the diffusivity for mass transfer D_{AB}; it physically relates the relative thickness of the hydrodynamic layer and mass-transfer boundary layer.

The *Sherwood number,* which is dimensionless, is

$$N_{Sh} = k'_c \frac{L}{D_{AB}} = k_c y_{BM} \frac{L}{D_{AB}} = \frac{k'_x}{c} \frac{L}{D_{AB}} = \cdots \tag{7.3-3}$$

Other substitutions from Table 7.2-1 can be made for k'_c in Eq. (7.3-3).

The *Stanton number* occurs often and is

$$N_{St} = \frac{k_c'}{v} = \frac{k_y'}{G_M} = \frac{k_G' P}{G_M} = \cdots \tag{7.3-4}$$

Again, substitution for k_c' can be made. $G_M = v\rho/M_{av} = vc$.

Often the mass-transfer coefficient is correlated as a dimensionless J_D factor, which is related to k_c' and N_{Sh} as follows:

$$J_D = \frac{k_c'}{v}(N_{Sc})^{2/3} = \frac{k_G' P}{G_M}(N_{Sc})^{2/3} = \cdots = N_{Sh}/(N_{Re}N_{Sc}^{1/3}) \tag{7.3-5}$$

For heat transfer a dimensionless J_H factor is as follows:

$$J_H = \frac{h}{c_p G}(N_{Pr})^{2/3} \tag{7.3-6}$$

7.3B Analogies Among Mass, Heat, and Momentum Transfer

1. Introduction.   In molecular transport of momentum, heat, or mass there are many similarities, which were pointed out in Chapters 2–6. The molecular diffusion equations of Newton for momentum, Fourier for heat, and Fick for mass are very similar, and we can say that we have analogies among these three molecular transport processes. There are also similarities in turbulent transport, as discussed in Sections 5.7C and 6.1A, where the flux equations were written using the turbulent eddy momentum diffusivity ε_t, the turbulent eddy thermal diffusivity α_t, and the turbulent eddy mass diffusivity ε_M. However, these similarities are not as well defined mathematically or physically and are more difficult to relate to each other.

A great deal of effort has been devoted in the literature to developing analogies among these three transport processes for turbulent transfer so as to allow prediction of one from any of the others. We discuss several next.

2. Reynolds analogy.   Reynolds was the first to note similarities in transport processes and relate turbulent momentum and heat transfer. Since then, mass transfer has also been related to momentum and heat transfer. We derive this analogy from Eqs. (6.1-4)–(6.1-6) for turbulent transport. For fluid flow in a pipe, for heat transfer from the fluid to the wall, Eq. (6.1-5) becomes as follows, where z is distance from the wall:

$$\frac{q}{A} = -\rho c_p(\alpha + \alpha_t)\frac{dT}{dz} \tag{7.3-7}$$

For momentum transfer, Eq. (6.1-4) becomes

$$\tau = -\rho\left(\frac{\mu}{\rho} + \varepsilon_t\right)\frac{dv}{dz} \tag{7.3-8}$$

Next we assume that α and μ/ρ are negligible and that $\alpha_t = \varepsilon_t$. Then dividing Eq. (7.3-7) by (7.3-8),

$$\left(\frac{\tau}{q/A}\right)c_p\, dT = dv \tag{7.3-9}$$

If we assume that heat flux q/A in a turbulent system is analogous to momentum flux τ, the ratio $\tau/(q/A)$ must be constant for all radial positions. We now integrate between conditions at the wall where $T = T_i$ and $v = 0$ to some point in the fluid where T is the same as the bulk T, and assume that the velocity at this point is the same as v_{av}, the bulk velocity. Also, q/A is understood to be the flux at the wall, as is the shear at the wall, written as τ_s. Hence,

$$\frac{\tau_s}{q/A} c_p (T - T_i) = v_{av} - 0 \tag{7.3-10}$$

Also, substituting $q/A = h(T - T_i)$ and $\tau_s = f v_{av}^2 \rho/2$ from Eq. (2.10-4) into Eq. (7.3-10),

$$\frac{f}{2} = \frac{h}{c_p v_{av} \rho} = \frac{h}{c_p G} \tag{7.3-11}$$

In a similar manner, using Eq. (6.1-6) for J_A^* and $J_A^* = k_c'(c_A - c_{Ai})$, we can relate this to Eq. (7.3-8) for momentum transfer. Then, the complete Reynolds analogy is

$$\frac{f}{2} = \frac{h}{c_p G} = \frac{k_c'}{v_{av}} \tag{7.3-12}$$

Experimental data for gas streams agree approximately with Eq. (7.3-12) if the Schmidt and Prandtl numbers arc near 1.0 and only skin friction is present in flow past a flat plate or inside a pipe. When liquids are present and/or form drag is present, the analogy is not valid.

3. *Other analogies.* The Reynolds analogy assumes that the turbulent diffusivities ε_t, α_t, and ε_M are all equal and that the molecular diffusivities μ/ρ, α, and D_{AB} are negligible compared to the turbulent diffusivities. When the Prandtl number $(\mu/\rho)/\alpha$ is 1.0, then $\mu/\rho = \alpha$; also, for $N_{Sc} = 1.0$, $\mu/\rho = D_{AB}$. Then, $(\mu/\rho + \varepsilon_t) = (\alpha + \alpha_t) = (D_{AB} + \varepsilon_M)$ and the Reynolds analogy can be obtained with the molecular terms present. However, the analogy breaks down when the viscous sublayer becomes important, since the eddy diffusivities diminish to zero and the molecular diffusivities become important.

Prandtl modified the Reynolds analogy by writing the regular molecular diffusion equation for the viscous sublayer and a Reynolds analogy equation for the turbulent core region. Then, since these processes are in series, these equations were combined to produce an overall equation (G1). The results again are poor for fluids where the Prandtl and Schmidt numbers differ from 1.0.

Von Kármán further modified the Prandtl analogy by considering the buffer region in addition to the viscous sublayer and the turbulent core. These three regions are shown in the universal velocity profile in Fig. 3.10-4. Again, an equation is written for molecular diffusion in the viscous sublayer using only the molecular diffusivity and a Reynolds analogy equation for the turbulent core. Both the molecular and eddy diffusivity are used in an equation for the buffer layer, where the velocity in this layer is used to obtain an equation for the eddy diffusivity. These three equations are then combined to give the von Kármán analogy. Since then, numerous other analogies have appeared (P1, S4).

4. *Chilton and Colburn J-factor analogy.* The most successful and most widely used analogy is the Chilton and Colburn J-factor analogy (C2). This analogy is based on experimental data for gases and liquids in both the laminar and turbulent flow regions and is written as follows:

$$\frac{f}{2} = J_H = \frac{h}{c_p G}(N_{Pr})^{2/3} = J_D = \frac{k_c'}{v_{av}}(N_{Sc})^{2/3} \tag{7.3-13}$$

Although this is an equation based on experimental data for both laminar and turbulent flow, it can be shown to satisfy the exact solution derived from laminar flow over a flat plate in Sections 3.10 and 5.7.

Equation (7.3-13) has been shown to be quite useful in correlating momentum, heat, and mass-transfer data. It permits the prediction of an unknown transfer coefficient when one of the other coefficients is known. In momentum transfer the friction factor is obtained for the total drag or friction loss, which includes form drag or momentum losses due to blunt objects as well as skin friction. For flow past a flat plate or in a pipe, where no form drag is present, $f/2 = J_H = J_D$. When form drag is present, as in flow in packed beds or past other blunt objects, $f/2$ is greater than J_H or J_D, and $J_H \cong J_D$.

7.3C Derivation of Mass-Transfer Coefficients in Laminar Flow

1. Introduction.   When a fluid is flowing in laminar flow and mass transfer by molecular diffusion is occurring, the equations are very similar to those for heat transfer by conduction in laminar flow. The phenomena of heat and mass transfer are not always completely analogous, since in mass transfer several components may be diffusing. Also, the flux of mass perpendicular to the direction of the flow must be small so as not to distort the laminar velocity profile.

In theory it is not necessary to have experimental mass-transfer coefficients for laminar flow, since the equations for momentum transfer and diffusion can be solved. However, in many actual cases it is difficult to describe mathematically the laminar flow for certain geometries, such as flow past a cylinder or in a packed bed. Hence, experimental mass-transfer coefficients are often obtained and correlated. A simplified theoretical derivation will be given for two cases of laminar flow.

2. Mass transfer in laminar flow in a tube.   We consider the case of mass transfer from a tube wall to a fluid inside in laminar flow, where, for example, the wall is made of solid benzoic acid which is dissolving in water. This is similar to heat transfer from a wall to the flowing fluid where natural convection is negligible. For fully developed flow, the parabolic velocity derived as Eqs. (2.6-18) and (2.6-20) is

$$v_x = v_{\max}\left[1 - \left(\frac{r}{R}\right)^2\right] = 2v_{\mathrm{av}}\left[1 - \left(\frac{r}{R}\right)^2\right] \tag{7.3-14}$$

where v_x is the velocity in the x direction at the distance r from the center. For steady-state diffusion in a cylinder, a mass balance can be made on a differential element where the rate in by convection plus diffusion equals the rate out radially by diffusion to give

$$v_x \frac{\partial c_A}{\partial x} = D_{AB}\left(\frac{1}{r}\frac{\partial c_A}{\partial r} + \frac{\partial^2 c_A}{\partial r^2} + \frac{\partial^2 c_A}{\partial x^2}\right) \tag{7.3-15}$$

Then, $\partial^2 c_A / \partial x^2 = 0$ if the diffusion in the x direction is negligible compared to that by convection. Combining Eqs. (7.3-14) and (7.3-15), the final solution (S1) is a complex series similar to the Graetz solution for heat transfer and a parabolic velocity profile.

If it is assumed that the velocity profile is flat, as in rodlike flow, the solution is more easily obtained (S1). A third solution, called the approximate *Leveque solution,* has been obtained, where there is a linear velocity profile near the wall and the solute diffuses only a short distance from the wall into the fluid. This is similar to the parabolic-velocity-profile solution at high flow rates. Experimental design equations are presented in Section 7.3D for this case.

3. Diffusion in a laminar falling film. In Section 2.9C we derived the equation for the velocity profile in a falling film shown in Fig. 7.3-1a. We will consider mass transfer of solute A into a laminar falling film, which is important in wetted-wall columns, in developing theories to explain mass transfer in stagnant pockets of fluids, and in turbulent mass transfer. The solute A in the gas is absorbed at the interface and then diffuses a distance into the liquid so that it has not penetrated the whole distance $x = \delta$ at the wall. At steady state the inlet concentration $c_A = 0$. The concentration profile of c_A at a point z distance from the inlet is shown in Fig. 7.3-1a.

A mass balance will be made on the element shown in Fig. 7.3-1b. For steady state, rate of input = rate of output:

$$N_{Ax|x}(1\ \Delta z) + N_{Az|z}(1\ \Delta x) = N_{Ax|x+\Delta x}(1\ \Delta z) + N_{Az|z+\Delta z}(1\ \Delta x) \qquad \textbf{(7.3-16)}$$

For a dilute solution the diffusion equation for A in the x direction is

$$N_{Ax} = -D_{AB}\frac{\partial c_A}{\partial x} + \text{zero convection} \qquad \textbf{(7.3-17)}$$

For the z direction the diffusion is negligible:

$$N_{Az} = 0 + c_A v_z \qquad \textbf{(7.3-18)}$$

Dividing Eq. (7.3-16) by $\Delta x\ \Delta z$, letting Δx and Δz approach zero, and substituting Eqs. (7.3-17) and (7.3-18) into the result, we obtain

$$v_z\frac{\partial c_A}{\partial z} - D_{AB}\frac{\partial^2 c_A}{\partial x^2} \qquad \textbf{(7.3-19)}$$

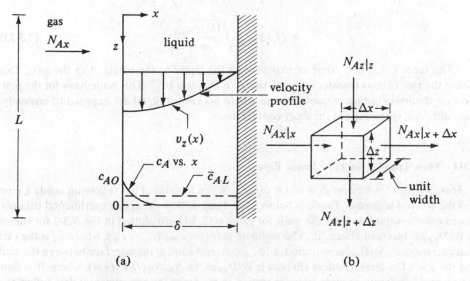

FIGURE 7.3-1. *Diffusion of solute A in a laminar falling film: (a) velocity profile and concentration profile, (b) small element for mass balance.*

From Eqs. (2.9-24) and (2.9-25), the velocity profile is parabolic and is $v_z = v_{z\,\text{max}}$ $[1 - (x/\delta^2)]$. Also, $v_{z\,\text{max}} = \frac{3}{2}v_{z\,\text{av}}$. If the solute has penetrated only a short distance into the fluid, that is, short contact times of $t = z/v_{\text{max}}$, then the A that has diffused has been carried along at the velocity $v_{z\,\text{max}}$, or v_{max} if the subscript z is dropped. Then Eq. (7.3-19) becomes

$$\frac{\partial c_A}{\partial (z/v_{\text{max}})} = D_{AB}\frac{\partial^2 c_A}{\partial x^2} \tag{7.3-20}$$

Using the boundary conditions of $c_A = 0$ at $z = 0$, $c_A = c_{A0}$ at $x = 0$, and $c_A = 0$ at $x = \infty$, we can integrate Eq. (7.3-20) to obtain

$$\frac{c_A}{c_{A0}} = \text{erfc}\left(\frac{x}{\sqrt{4D_{AB}z/v_{\text{max}}}}\right) \tag{7.3-21}$$

where erf y is the error function and erfc $y = 1 - \text{erf}\,y$. Values of erf y are standard tabulated functions.

To determine the local molar flux at the surface $x = 0$ at position z from the top entrance, we write (B1)

$$N_{Ax}(z)|_{x=0} = -D_{AB}\frac{\partial c_A}{\partial x}\bigg|_{x=0} = c_{A0}\sqrt{\frac{D_{AB}v_{\text{max}}}{\pi z}} \tag{7.3-22}$$

The total moles of A transferred per second to the liquid over the entire length $z = 0$ to $z = L$, where the vertical surface is unit width, is

$$N_A(L\cdot 1) = (1)\int_0^L (N_{Ax|x=0})\,dz$$

$$= (1)\int_0^L c_{A0}\left(\frac{D_{AB}v_{\text{max}}}{\pi}\right)^{1/2}\frac{1}{z^{1/2}}\,dz$$

$$= (L\cdot 1)c_{A0}\sqrt{\frac{4D_{AB}v_{\text{max}}}{\pi L}} \tag{7.3-23}$$

The term L/v_{max} is t_L, time of exposure of the liquid to the solute A in the gas. This means the rate of mass transfer is proportional to $D_{AB}^{0.5}$ and $1/t_L^{0.5}$. This is the basis for the penetration theory in turbulent mass transfer where pockets of liquid are exposed to unsteady-state diffusion (penetration) for short contact times.

7.3D Mass Transfer for Flow Inside Pipes

1. Mass transfer for laminar flow inside pipes. When a liquid or gas is flowing inside a pipe and the Reynolds number $Dv\rho/\mu$ is below 2100, laminar flow occurs. Experimental data obtained for mass transfer from the walls for gases (G2, L1) are plotted in Fig. 7.3-2 for values of $W/D_{AB}\rho L$ less than about 70. The ordinate is $(c_A - c_{A0})/(c_{Ai} - c_{A0})$, where c_A is the exit concentration, c_{A0} inlet concentration, and c_{Ai} concentration at the interface between the wall and the gas. The dimensionless abscissa is $W/D_{AB}\rho L$ or $N_{\text{Re}}N_{\text{Sc}}(D/L)(\pi/4)$, where W is flow in kg/s and L is length of mass-transfer section in m. Since the experimental data follow the rodlike plot, that line should be used. The velocity profile is assumed fully developed to parabolic form at the entrance.

FIGURE 7.3-2. *Data for diffusion in a fluid in streamline flow inside a pipe: filled circles, vaporization data of Gilliland and Sherwood; open circles, dissolving-solids data of Linton and Sherwood. [From W. H. Linton and T. K. Sherwood, Chem. Eng. Progr., 46, 258 (1950). With permission.]*

For liquids that have small values of D_{AB}, data follow the parabolic flow line, which is as follows for $W/D_{AB}\rho L$ over 400:

$$\frac{c_A - c_{A0}}{c_{Ai} - c_{A0}} = 5.5 \left(\frac{W}{D_{AB}\rho L} \right)^{-2/3} \tag{7.3-24}$$

2. Mass transfer for turbulent flow inside pipes. For turbulent flow when $Dv\rho/\mu > 2100$ for gases or liquids flowing inside a pipe,

$$N_{Sh} = k_c' \frac{D}{D_{AB}} = \frac{k_c p_{BM}}{P} \frac{D}{D_{AB}} = 0.023 \left(\frac{Dv\rho}{\mu} \right)^{0.83} \left(\frac{\mu}{\rho D_{AB}} \right)^{0.33} \tag{7.3-25}$$

The equation holds for N_{Sc} of 0.6 to 3000 (G2, L1). Note that the N_{Sc} for gases is in the range 0.5–3 and for liquids is above 100 in general. Equation (7.3-25) for mass transfer and Eq. (4.5-8) for heat transfer inside a pipe are similar to each other.

3. Mass transfer for flow inside wetted-wall towers. When a gas is flowing inside the core of a wetted-wall tower, the same correlations that are used for mass transfer of a gas in laminar or turbulent flow in a pipe are applicable. This means that Eqs. (7.3-24) and (7.3-25) can be used to predict mass transfer for the gas. For the mass transfer in the liquid film flowing down the wetted-wall tower, Eqs. (7.3-22) and (7.3-23) can be used for Reynolds numbers of $4\Gamma/\mu$ as defined by Eq. (2.9-29) up to about 1200, and the theoretically predicted values should be multiplied by about 1.5 because of ripples and other factors. These equations hold for short contact times or Reynolds numbers above about 100 (S1).

EXAMPLE 7.3-1. Mass Transfer Inside a Tube

A tube is coated on the inside with naphthalene and has an inside diameter of 20 mm and a length of 1.10 m. Air at 318 K and an average pressure of 101.3 kPa flows through this pipe at a velocity of 0.80 m/s. Assuming that the absolute pressure remains essentially constant, calculate the concentration of naphthalene in the exit air. Use the physical properties given in Example 6.2-4.

Solution: From Example 6.2-4, $D_{AB} = 6.92 \times 10^{-6}$ m^2/s and the vapor pressure $p_{Ai} = 74.0$ Pa or $c_{Ai} = p_{Ai}/RT = 74.0/(8314.3 \times 318) = 2.799 \times 10^{-5}$ kg mol/m^3. For air, from Appendix A.3, $\mu = 1.932 \times 10^{-5}$ Pa·s, $\rho = 1.114$ kg/m^3. The Schmidt number is

$$N_{Sc} = \frac{\mu}{\rho D_{AB}} = \frac{1.932 \times 10^{-5}}{1.114 \times 6.92 \times 10^{-6}} = 2.506$$

The Reynolds number is

$$N_{Re} = \frac{D v \rho}{\mu} = \frac{0.020(0.80)(1.114)}{1.932 \times 10^{-5}} = 922.6$$

Hence, the flow is laminar. Then,

$$N_{Re} N_{Sc} \frac{D}{L} \frac{\pi}{4} = 922.6(2.506) \frac{0.020}{1.10} \frac{\pi}{4} = 33.02$$

Using Fig. 7.3-2 and the rodlike flow line, $(c_A - c_{A0})/(c_{Ai} - c_{A0}) = 0.55$. Also, c_{A0}(inlet) = 0. Then, $(c_A - 0)/(2.799 \times 10^{-5} - 0) = 0.55$. Solving c_A (exit concentration) = 1.539×10^{-5} kg mol/m^3.

7.3E   Mass Transfer for Flow Outside Solid Surfaces

1. Mass transfer in flow parallel to flat plates. The mass transfer and vaporization of liquids from a plate or flat surface to a flowing stream is of interest in the drying of inorganic and biological materials, in the evaporation of solvents from paints, for plates in wind tunnels, and in flow channels in chemical process equipment.

When the fluid flows past a plate in a free stream in an open space the boundary layer is not fully developed. For gases or evaporation of liquids in the gas phase and for the laminar region of $N_{Re,L} = L v \rho/\mu$ less than 15 000, the data can be represented within ±25% by the equation (S4)

$$J_D = 0.664 N_{Re,L}^{-0.5} \tag{7.3-26}$$

Writing Eq. (7.3-26) in terms of the Sherwood number N_{Sh},

$$\frac{k_c' L}{D_{AB}} = N_{Sh} = 0.664 N_{Re,L}^{0.5} N_{Sc}^{1/3} \tag{7.3-27}$$

where L is the length of plate in the direction of flow. Also, $J_D = J_H = f/2$ for this geometry. For gases and $N_{Re,L}$ of 15 000–300 000, the data are represented within ±30% by $J_D = J_H = f/2$ as

$$J_D = 0.036 N_{Re,L}^{-0.2} \tag{7.3-28}$$

Experimental data for liquids are correlated within about ±40% by the following for a $N_{Re,L}$ of 600–50 000 (L2):

$$J_D = 0.99 N_{Re,L}^{-0.5} \tag{7.3-29}$$

EXAMPLE 7.3-2. Mass Transfer from a Flat Plate

A large volume of pure water at 26.1°C is flowing parallel to a flat plate of solid benzoic acid, where $L = 0.244$ m in the direction of flow. The water velocity is 0.061 m/s. The solubility of benzoic acid in water is 0.02948 kg mol/m^3. The diffusivity of benzoic acid is 1.245×10^{-9} m^2/s. Calculate the mass-transfer coefficient k_L and the flux N_A.

Solution: Since the solution is quite dilute, the physical properties of water at 26.1°C from Appendix A.2 can be used:

$$\mu = 8.71 \times 10^{-4} \, \text{Pa} \cdot \text{s}$$

$$\rho = 996 \, \text{kg/m}^3$$

$$D_{AB} = 1.245 \times 10^{-9} \, \text{m}^2/\text{s}$$

The Schmidt number is

$$N_{Sc} = \frac{8.71 \times 10^{-4}}{996(1.245 \times 10^{-9})} = 702$$

The Reynolds number is

$$N_{Re,L} = \frac{L v \rho}{\mu} = \frac{0.244(0.0610)(996)}{8.71 \times 10^{-4}} = 1.700 \times 10^4$$

Using Eq. (7.3-29),

$$J_D = 0.99 N_{Re,L}^{-0.5} = 0.99(1.700 \times 10^4)^{-0.5} = 0.00758$$

The definition of J_D from Eq. (7.3-5) is

$$J_D = \frac{k_c'}{v}(N_{Sc})^{2/3} \tag{7.3-5}$$

Solving for k_c', $k_c' = J_D v(N_{Sc})^{-2/3}$. Substituting known values and solving,

$$k_c' = 0.00758(0.0610)(702)^{-2/3} = 5.85 \times 10^{-6} \, \text{m/s}$$

In this case, diffusion is for A through nondiffusing B, so k_c in Eq. (7.2-10) should be used:

$$N_A = \frac{k_c'}{x_{BM}}(c_{A1} - c_{A2}) = k_c(c_{A1} - c_{A2}) \tag{7.2-10}$$

Since the solution is very dilute, $x_{BM} \cong 1.0$ and $k_c' \cong k_c$. Also, $c_{A1} = 2.948 \times 10^{-2}$ kg mol/m^3 (solubility) and $c_{A2} = 0$ (large volume of fresh water). Substituting into Eq. (7.2-10),

$$N_A = (5.85 \times 10^{-6})(0.02948 - 0) = 1.726 \times 10^{-7} \, \text{kg mol/s} \cdot \text{m}^2$$

2. Mass transfer for flow past single spheres. For flow past single spheres and for very low $N_{Re} = D_p v \rho / \mu$, where v is the average velocity in the empty test section before the sphere, the

Sherwood number, which is $k'_c D_p / D_{AB}$, should approach a value of 2.0. This can be shown from Eq. (6.2-33), which was derived for a stagnant medium. Rewriting Eq. (6.2-33) as follows, where D_p is the sphere diameter,

$$N_A = \frac{2D_{AB}}{D_p}(c_{A1} - c_{A2}) = k_c(c_{A1} - c_{A2}) \tag{7.3-30}$$

The mass-transfer coefficient k_c, which is k'_c for a dilute solution, is then

$$k'_c = \frac{2D_{AB}}{D_p} \tag{7.3-31}$$

Rearranging,

$$\frac{k'_c D_p}{D_{AB}} = N_{Sh} = 2.0 \tag{7.3-32}$$

Of course, natural convection effects could increase k'_c.

For gases, for a Schmidt number range of 0.6–2.7 and a Reynolds number range of 1–48 000, a modified equation (G1) can be used:

$$N_{Sh} = 2 + 0.552 N_{Re}^{0.53} N_{Sc}^{1/3} \tag{7.3-33}$$

This equation also holds for heat transfer, where the Prandtl number replaces the Schmidt number and the Nusselt number hD_p/k replaces the Sherwood number.

For liquids (G3) and a Reynolds number range of 2 to about 2000, the following can be used:

$$N_{Sh} = 2 + 0.95 N_{Re}^{0.50} N_{Sc}^{1/3} \tag{7.3-34}$$

For liquids and a Reynolds number of 2000–17 000, the following can be used (S5):

$$N_{Sh} = 0.347 N_{Re}^{0.62} N_{Sc}^{1/3} \tag{7.3-35}$$

EXAMPLE 7.3-3. Mass Transfer from a Sphere

Calculate the value of the mass-transfer coefficient and the flux for mass transfer from a sphere of naphthalene to air at 45°C and 1 atm abs flowing at a velocity of 0.305 m/s. The diameter of the sphere is 25.4 mm. The diffusivity of naphthalene in air at 45°C is 6.92×10^{-6} m²/s and the vapor pressure of solid naphthalene is 0.555 mm Hg. Use English and SI units.

Solution: In English units $D_{AB} = 6.92 \times 10^{-6}(3.875 \times 10^4) = 0.2682$ ft²/h. The diameter $D_p = 0.0254$ m $= 0.0254(3.2808) = 0.0833$ ft. From Appendix A.3 the physical properties of air will be used, since the concentration of naphthalene is low:

$$\mu = 1.93 \times 10^{-5} \, Pa \cdot s = 1.93 \times 10^{-5}(2.4191 \times 10^3) = 0.0467 \, lb_m/ft \cdot h$$

$$\rho = 1.113 \, kg/m^3 = \frac{1.113}{16.0185} = 0.0695 \, lb_m/ft^3$$

$$v = 0.305 \, m/s = 0.305(3600 \times 3.2808) = 3600 \, ft/h$$

Chapter 7   Principles of Unsteady-State and Convective Mass Transfer

The Schmidt number is

$$N_{Sc} = \frac{\mu}{\rho D_{AB}} = \frac{0.0467}{0.0695(0.2682)} = 2.505$$

$$N_{Sc} = \frac{1.93 \times 10^{-5}}{1.113(6.92 \times 10^{-6})} = 2.505$$

The Reynolds number is

$$N_{Re} = \frac{D_p v \rho}{\mu} = \frac{0.0833(3600)(0.0695)}{0.0467} = 446$$

$$N_{Re} = \frac{0.0254(0.3048)(1.113)}{1.93 \times 10^{-5}} = 446$$

Equation (7.3-33) for gases will be used:

$$N_{Sh} = 2 + 0.552(N_{Re})^{0.53}(N_{Sc})^{1/3} = 2 + 0.552(446)^{0.53}(2.505)^{1/3} = 21.0$$

From Eq. (7.3-3),

$$N_{Sh} = k_c' \frac{L}{D_{AB}} = k_c' \frac{D_p}{D_{AB}}$$

Substituting the knowns and solving,

$$21.0 = \frac{k_c'(0.0833)}{0.2682} \qquad k_c' = 67.6 \text{ ft/h}$$

$$21.0 = \frac{k_c'(0.0254)}{6.92 \times 10^{-6}} \qquad k_c' = 5.72 \times 10^{-3} \text{ m/s}$$

From Table 7.2-1,

$$k_c' c = k_c' \frac{P}{RT} = k_G' P$$

Hence, for $T = 45 + 273 = 318 \text{ K} = 318(1.8) = 574°R$,

$$k_G' = \frac{k_c'}{RT} = \frac{67.6}{(0.730)(573)} = 0.1616 \text{ lb mol/h} \cdot \text{ft}^2 \cdot \text{atm}$$

$$k_G' = \frac{5.72 \times 10^{-3}}{8314(318)} = 2.163 \times 10^{-9} \text{ kg mol/s} \cdot \text{m}^2 \cdot \text{Pa}$$

Since the gas is very dilute, $y_{BM} \cong 1.0$ and $k_G' \cong k_G$. Substituting into Eq. (7.2-12) for A diffusing through stagnant B and noting that $p_{A1} = 0.555/760 = 7.303 \times 10^{-4}$ atm $= 74.0$ Pa and $p_{A2} = 0$ (pure air),

$$N_A = k_G(p_{A1} - p_{A2}) = 0.1616(7.303 \times 10^{-4} - 0)$$

$$= 1.180 \times 10^{-4} \text{ lb mol/h} \cdot \text{ft}^2$$

$$= 2.163 \times 10^{-9}(74.0 - 0) = 1.599 \times 10^{-7} \text{ kg mol/s} \cdot \text{m}^2$$

The area of the sphere is

$$A = \pi D_p^2 = \pi (0.0833)^2 = 2.18 \times 10^{-2}\, \text{ft}^2$$

$$= (2.18 \times 10^{-2})\left(\frac{1}{3.2808}\right)^2 = 2.025 \times 10^{-3}\, \text{m}^2$$

Total amount evaporated $= N_A A = (1.18 \times 10^{-4})(2.18 \times 10^{-2}) = 2.572 \times 10^{-6}$ lb mol/h $= (1.599 \times 10^{-7})(2.025 \times 10^{-3}) = 3.238 \times 10^{-10}$ kg mol/s

3. Mass transfer to packed beds.   Mass transfer to and from packed beds occurs often in processing operations, including drying operations, adsorption or desorption of gases or liquids by solid particles such as charcoal, and mass transfer of gases and liquids to catalyst particles. By using a packed bed a large amount of mass-transfer area can be contained in a relatively small volume.

The void fraction in a bed is ε m^3 volume void space divided by the m^3 total volume of void space plus solid. The values range from 0.3 to 0.5 in general. Because of flow channeling, nonuniform packing, and so forth, accurate experimental data are difficult to obtain and data from different investigators can deviate considerably.

For a Reynolds number range of 10–10 000 for gases in a packed bed of spheres (D4), the recommended correlation with an average deviation of about ±20% and a maximum of about ±50% is

$$J_D = J_H = \frac{0.4548}{\varepsilon} N_{\text{Re}}^{-0.4069} \tag{7.3-36}$$

It has been shown (G4, G5) that J_D and J_H are approximately equal. The Reynolds number is defined as $N_{\text{Re}} = D_p v' \rho / \mu$, where D_p is diameter of the spheres and v' is the superficial mass average velocity in the empty tube without packing. For Eqs. (7.3-36)–(7.3-39) and Eqs. (7.3-5)–(7.3-6), v' is used.

For mass transfer of liquids in packed beds, the correlations of Wilson and Geankoplis (W1) should be used. For a Reynolds number $D_p v' \rho / \mu$ range of 0.0016–55 and a Schmidt number range of 165–70 000, the equation to use is

$$J_D = \frac{1.09}{\varepsilon} N_{\text{Re}}^{-2/3} \tag{7.3-37}$$

For liquids and a Reynolds number range of 55–1500 and a Schmidt number range of 165–10 690,

$$J_D = \frac{0.250}{\varepsilon} N_{\text{Re}}^{-0.31} \tag{7.3-38}$$

Or, as an alternate, Eq. (7.3-36) can be used for liquids for a Reynolds number range of 10–1500.

For fluidized beds of spheres, Eq. (7.3-36) can be used for gases and liquids and a Reynolds number range of 10–4000. For liquids in a fluidized bed and a Reynolds number range of 1–10 (D4),

$$\varepsilon J_D = 1.1068 N_{\text{Re}}^{-0.72} \tag{7.3-39}$$

If packed beds of solids other than spheres are used, approximate correction factors can be used with Eqs. (7.3-36)–(7.3-38) for spheres. This is done, for example, for a given non-spherical particle as follows. The particle diameter to use in the equations for predicting J_D is the diameter of a sphere with the same surface area as the given solid particle. The flux to these particles in the bed is then calculated using the area of the given particles. An alternative approximate procedure is given elsewhere (G6).

4. *Calculation method for packed beds.* To calculate the total flux in a packed bed, J_D is first obtained and then k_c in m/s from the J_D. Then, knowing the total volume V_b m^3 of the bed (void plus solids), the total external surface area A m^2 of the solids for mass transfer is calculated using Eqs. (7.3-40) and (7.3-41):

$$a = \frac{6(1 - \varepsilon)}{D_p} \tag{7.3-40}$$

where a is the m^2 surface area/m^3 total volume of bed when the solids are spheres, and

$$A = aV_b \tag{7.3-41}$$

To calculate the mass-transfer rate, the log mean driving force at the inlet and outlet of the bed should be used:

$$N_A A = A k_c \frac{(c_{Ai} - c_{A1}) - (c_{Ai} - c_{A2})}{\ln \dfrac{c_{Ai} - c_{A1}}{c_{Ai} - c_{A2}}} \tag{7.3-42}$$

where the final term is the log mean driving force: c_{Ai} is the concentration at the surface of the solid, in kg mol/m^3; c_{A1} is the inlet bulk fluid concentration; and c_{A2} is the outlet. The material-balance equation on the bulk stream is

$$N_A A = V(c_{A2} - c_{A1}) \tag{7.3-43}$$

where V is volumetric flow rate of fluid entering in m^3/s. Equations (7.3-42) and (7.3-43) must both be satisfied. The use of these two equations is similar to the use of the log mean temperature difference and heat balance in heat exchangers. These two equations can also be used for a fluid flowing in a pipe or past a flat plate, where A is the pipe wall area or plate area.

EXAMPLE 7.3-4. Mass Transfer of a Liquid in a Packed Bed

Pure water at 26.1°C flows at the rate of 5.514×10^{-7} m^3/s through a packed bed of benzoic-acid spheres having a diameter of 6.375 mm. The total surface area of the spheres in the bed is 0.01198 m^2 and the void fraction is 0.436. The tower diameter is 0.0667 m. The solubility of benzoic acid in water is 2.948×10^{-2} kg mol/m^3.
  (a) Predict the mass-transfer coefficient k_c. Compare with the experimental value of 4.665×10^{-6} m/s by Wilson and Geankoplis (W1).
  (b) Using the experimental value of k_c, predict the outlet concentration of benzoic acid in the water.

Solution: Since the solution is dilute, the physical properties of water will be used at 26.1°C from Appendix A.2. At 26.1°C, $\mu = 0.8718 \times 10^{-3}$ Pa · s, $\rho = 996.7$ kg/m^3. At 25.0°C, $\mu = 0.8940 \times 10^{-3}$ Pa · s, and from Table 6.3-1,

$D_{AB} = 1.21 \times 10^{-9}$ m²/s. To correct D_{AB} to 26.1°C using Eq. (6.3-9), $D_{AB} \propto T/\mu$. Hence,

$$D_{AB}(26.1°C) = (1.21 \times 10^{-9})\left(\frac{299.1}{298}\right)\left(\frac{0.8940 \times 10^{-3}}{0.8718 \times 10^{-3}}\right)$$

$$= 1.254 \times 10^{-9} \text{ m}^2/\text{s}$$

The tower cross-sectional area $= (\pi/4)(0.0667)^2 = 3.494 \times 10^{-3}$ m². Then $v' = (5.514 \times 10^{-7})/(3.494 \times 10^{-3}) = 1.578 \times 10^{-4}$ m/s. Then,

$$N_{Sc} = \frac{\mu}{\rho D_{AB}} = \frac{0.8718 \times 10^{-3}}{996.7(1.245 \times 10^{-9})} = 702.6$$

The Reynolds number is

$$N_{Re} = \frac{Dv'\rho}{\mu} = \frac{0.006375(1.578 \times 10^{-4})(996.7)}{0.8718 \times 10^{-3}} = 1.150$$

Using Eq. (7.3-37) and assuming $k_c = k_c'$ for dilute solutions,

$$J_D = \frac{1.09}{\varepsilon}(N_{Re})^{-2/3} = \frac{1.09}{0.436}(1.150)^{-2/3} = 2.277$$

Then, using Eq. (7.3-5) and solving,

$$J_D = \frac{k_c'}{v'}(N_{Sc})^{2/3} \qquad 2.277 = \frac{k_c'}{1.578 \times 10^{-4}}(702.6)^{2/3}$$

The predicted $k_c' = 4.447 \times 10^{-6}$ m/s. This compares with the experimental value of 4.665×10^{-6} m/s.

For part (b), using Eqs. (7.3-42) and (7.3-43),

$$Ak_c \frac{(c_{Ai} - c_{A1}) - (c_{Ai} - c_{A2})}{\ln \dfrac{c_{Ai} - c_{A1}}{c_{Ai} - c_{A2}}} = V(c_{A2} - c_{A1}) \qquad \textbf{(7.3-44)}$$

The values to substitute into Eq. (7.3-44) are $c_{Ai} = 2.948 \times 10^{-2}$, $c_{A1} = 0$, $A = 0.01198$, $V = 5.514 \times 10^{-7}$.

$$\frac{0.01198(4.665 \times 10^{-6})(c_{A2} - 0)}{\ln \dfrac{2.948 \times 10^{-2} - 0}{2.948 \times 10^{-2} - c_{A2}}} = (5.514 \times 10^{-7})(c_{A2} - 0)$$

Solving, $c_{A2} = 2.842 \times 10^{-3}$ kg mol/m³.

5. *Mass transfer for flow past single cylinders.* Experimental data have been obtained for mass transfer from single cylinders when the flow is perpendicular to the cylinder. The cylinders are long and mass transfer to the ends of the cylinder is not considered. For the Schmidt number range of 0.6 to 2.6 for gases and 1000 to 3000 for liquids and a Reynolds number range of 50 to 50 000, data from many references (B3, L1, M1, S4, V1) have been plotted, and the correlation to use is as follows:

$$J_D = 0.600(N_{Re})^{-0.487} \qquad \textbf{(7.3-45)}$$

The data scatter considerably by up to ±30%. This correlation can also be used for heat transfer, with $J_D = J_H$.

6. *Liquid metals mass transfer.* In recent years several correlations for mass-transfer coefficients of liquid metals have appeared in the literature. It has been found (G1) that with moderate safety factors, the correlations for nonliquid metals mass transfer may be used for liquid metals mass transfer. Care must be taken to ensure that the solid surface is wetted. Also, if the solid is an alloy, there may exist a resistance to diffusion in the solid phase.

7.4 MASS TRANSFER TO SUSPENSIONS OF SMALL PARTICLES

7.4A Introduction

Mass transfer from or to small suspended particles in an agitated solution occurs in a number of process applications. In liquid-phase hydrogenation, hydrogen diffuses from gas bubbles, through an organic liquid, and then to small suspended catalyst particles. In fermentation, oxygen diffuses from small gas bubbles, through the aqueous medium, and then to small suspended microorganisms.

For a liquid–solid dispersion, increased agitation over and above that necessary to freely suspend very small particles has very little effect on the mass-transfer coefficient k_L to the particle (B2). When the particles in a mixing vessel are just completely suspended, turbulence forces balance those due to gravity, and the mass-transfer rates are the same as for particles freely moving under gravity. With very small particles of, say, a few μm or so, which is the size of many microorganisms in fermentations and some catalyst particles, their size is smaller than eddies, which are about 100 μm or so in size. Hence, increased agitation will have little effect on mass transfer except at very high agitation.

For a gas–liquid–solid dispersion, such as in fermentation, the same principles hold. However, increased agitation increases the number of gas bubbles and hence the interfacial area. The mass-transfer coefficients from the gas bubble to the liquid and from the liquid to the solid are relatively unaffected.

7.4B Equations for Mass Transfer to Small Particles

1. *Mass transfer to small particles <0.6 mm.* Equations for predicting mass transfer to small particles in suspension have been developed which cover three size ranges of particles. The equation for particles <0.6 mm (600 μm) is discussed first.

The following equation has been shown to hold for predicting mass-transfer coefficients from small gas bubbles such as oxygen or air to the liquid phase or from the liquid phase to the surface of small catalyst particles, microorganisms, other solids, or liquid drops (B2, C3):

$$k'_L = \frac{2D_{AB}}{D_p} + 0.31 N_{Sc}^{-2/3} \left(\frac{\Delta \rho \, \mu_c g}{\rho_c^2} \right)^{1/3} \tag{7.4-1}$$

where D_{AB} is the diffusivity of the solute A in solution in m^2/s, D_p is the diameter of the gas bubble or the solid particle in m, μ_c is the viscosity of the solution in kg/m·s, $g = 9.80665$ m/s^2, $\Delta \rho = (\rho_c - \rho_p)$ or $(\rho_p - \rho_c)$, ρ_c is the density of the continuous phase in kg/m^3, and ρ_p is the density of the gas or solid particle. The value of $\Delta \rho$ is always positive.

The first term on the right in Eq. (7.4-1) is the molecular diffusion term, and the second term is that due to free fall or rise of the sphere due to gravitational forces. This equation has been experimentally checked for dispersions of low-density solids in agitated dispersions and for small gas bubbles in agitated systems.

EXAMPLE 7.4-1. Mass Transfer from Air Bubbles in Fermentation

Calculate the maximum rate of absorption of O_2 in a fermenter from air bubbles at 1 atm abs pressure having diameters of 100 μm at 37°C into water having a zero concentration of dissolved O_2. The solubility of O_2 from air in water at 37°C is 2.26×10^{-7} g mol O_2/cm^3 liquid or 2.26×10^{-4} kg mol O_2/m^3. The diffusivity of O_2 in water at 37°C is 3.25×10^{-9} m^2/s. Agitation is used to produce the air bubbles.

Solution: The mass-transfer resistance inside the gas bubble to the outside interface of the bubble can be neglected since it is negligible (B2). Hence, the mass-transfer coefficient k'_L outside the bubble is needed. The given data are

$$D_p = 100 \ \mu\text{m} = 1 \times 10^{-4} \text{ m} \qquad D_{AB} = 3.25 \times 10^{-9} \text{ m}^2/\text{s}$$

At 37°C,

$$\mu_c(\text{water}) = 6.947 \times 10^{-4} \text{ Pa} \cdot \text{s} = 6.947 \times 10^{-4} \text{ kg/m} \cdot \text{s}$$

$$\rho_c(\text{water}) = 994 \text{ kg/m}^3 \qquad \rho_p(\text{air}) = 1.13 \text{ kg/m}^3$$

$$N_{Sc} = \frac{\mu_c}{\rho_c D_{AB}} = \frac{6.947 \times 10^{-4}}{(994)(3.25 \times 10^{-9})} = 215$$

$$N_{Sc}^{2/3} = (215)^{2/3} = 35.9 \qquad \Delta\rho = \rho_c - \rho_p = 994 - 1.13 = 993 \text{ kg/m}^3$$

Substituting into Eq. (7.4-1),

$$k_L = \frac{2D_{AB}}{D_p} + 0.31 N_{Sc}^{-2/3} \left(\frac{\Delta\rho \, \mu_c g}{\rho_c^2} \right)^{1/3}$$

$$= \frac{2(3.25 \times 10^{-9})}{1 \times 10^{-4}} + \frac{0.31}{35.9} \left[\frac{993 \times 6.947 \times 10^{-4} \times 9.806}{(994)^2} \right]^{1/3}$$

$$= 6.50 \times 10^{-5} + 16.40 \times 10^{-5} = 2.290 \times 10^{-4} \text{ m/s}$$

The flux is as follows, assuming $k_L = k'_L$ for dilute solutions:

$$N_A = k_L(c_{A1} - c_{A2}) = 2.290 \times 10^{-4}(2.26 \times 10^{-4} - 0)$$

$$= 5.18 \times 10^{-8} \text{ kg mol } O_2/\text{s} \cdot \text{m}^2$$

Knowing the total number of bubbles and their area, the maximum possible rate of transfer of O_2 to the fermentation liquid can be calculated.

In Example 7.4-1, k_L was small. For mass transfer of O_2 in a solution to a microorganism with $D_p \cong 1 \ \mu$m, the term $2D_{AB}/D_p$ would be 100 times larger. Note that at large diameters the second term in Eq. (7.4-1) becomes small and the mass-transfer coefficient k_L becomes essentially independent of size D_p. In agitated vessels with gas introduced below the agitator in aqueous solutions, or when liquids are aerated with sintered plates, the gas bubbles are often in the size range covered by Eq. (7.4-1) (B2, C3, T1).

In aerated mixing vessels, the mass-transfer coefficients are essentially independent of the power input. However, as the power is increased, the bubble size decreases and the mass transfer coefficient continues to follow Eq. (7.4-1). The dispersions include those in which the solid particles are just completely suspended in mixing vessels. Increase in agitation intensity above the level needed for complete suspension of these small particles results in only a small increase in k_L (C3).

Equation (7.4-1) has also been shown to apply to heat transfer and can be written as follows (B2, C3):

$$N_{Nu} = \frac{hD_p}{k} = 2.0 + 0.31 N_{Pr}^{1/3}\left(\frac{D_p^3 \rho_c \, \Delta\rho g}{\mu_c^2}\right)^{1/3} \tag{7.4-2}$$

2. Mass transfer to large gas bubbles >2.5 mm. For large gas bubbles or liquid drops >2.5 mm, the mass-transfer coefficient can be predicted by

$$k_L' = 0.42 N_{Sc}^{-0.5}\left(\frac{\Delta\rho \, \mu_c g}{\rho_c^2}\right)^{1/3} \tag{7.4-3}$$

Large gas bubbles are produced when pure liquids are aerated in mixing vessels and sieve-plate columns (C1). In this case the mass-transfer coefficient k_L' or k_L is independent of the bubble size and is constant for a given set of physical properties. For the same physical properties the large-bubble Eq. (7.4-3) gives values of k_L about three to four times larger than Eq. (7.4-1) for small particles. Again, Eq. (7.4-3) shows that the k_L is essentially independent of agitation intensity in an agitated vessel and gas velocity in a sieve-tray tower.

3. Mass transfer to particles in transition region. In mass transfer in the transition region between small and large bubbles in the size range 0.6–2.5 mm, the mass-transfer coefficient can be approximated by assuming that it increases linearly with bubble diameter (B2, C3).

4. Mass transfer to particles in highly turbulent mixers. In the preceding three regions, the density difference between phases is sufficiently large to cause the force of gravity to primarily determine the mass-transfer coefficient. This also includes solids just completely suspended in mixing vessels. When agitation power is increased beyond that needed for suspension of solid or liquid particles and the turbulence forces become larger than the gravitational forces, Eq. (7.4-1) is not followed, and Eq. (7.4-4) should be used where small increases in k_L' are observed (B2, C3):

$$k_L' N_{Sc}^{2/3} = 0.13\left(\frac{(P/V)\mu_c}{\rho_c^2}\right)^{1/4} \tag{7.4-4}$$

where P/V is power input per unit volume as defined in Section 3.4. The data deviate substantially by up to 60% from this correlation. In the case of gas–liquid dispersions it is quite impractical for agitation systems to exceed gravitational forces.

The experimental data are complicated by the fact that very small particles are easily suspended, and if their size is on the order of the smallest eddies, the mass-transfer coefficient will remain constant until a large increase in power input is added above that required for suspension.

7.5 MOLECULAR DIFFUSION PLUS CONVECTION AND CHEMICAL REACTION

7.5A Different Types of Fluxes and Fick's Law

In Section 6.2B the flux J_A^* was defined as the molar flux of A in kg mol $A/s \cdot m^2$ relative to the molar average velocity v_M of the whole or bulk stream. Also, N_A was defined as the molar flux of A relative to stationary coordinates. Fluxes and velocities can also be defined in other ways. Table 7.5-1 lists the different types of fluxes and velocities often used in binary systems.

The velocity v is the mass average velocity of the stream relative to stationary coordinates and can be obtained by actually weighing the flow for a timed increment. It is related to the velocity v_A and v_B by

$$v = w_A v_A + w_B v_B = \frac{\rho_A}{\rho} v_A + \frac{\rho_B}{\rho} v_B \tag{7.5-1}$$

where w_A is ρ_A/ρ, the weight fraction of A; w_B is the weight fraction of B; and v_A is the velocity of A relative to stationary coordinates in m/s. The molar average velocity v_M in m/s is relative to stationary coordinates:

$$v_M = x_A v_A + x_B v_B = \frac{c_A}{c} v_A + \frac{c_B}{c} v_B \tag{7.5-2}$$

The molar diffusion flux relative to the molar average velocity v_M defined previously is

$$J_A^* = c_A(v_A - v_M) \tag{7.5-3}$$

The molar diffusion flux J_A relative to the mass average velocity v is

$$J_A = c_A(v_A - v) \tag{7.5-4}$$

Fick's law from Table 7.5-1 as given previously is relative to v_M:

$$J_A^* = -cD_{AB} \frac{dx_A}{dz} \tag{7.5-5}$$

TABLE 7.5-1. *Different Types of Fluxes and Velocities in Binary Systems*

	Mass Flux $(kg\ A/s \cdot m^2)$	Molar Flux $(kg\ mol\ A/s \cdot m^2)$
Relative to fixed coordinates	$n_A = \rho_A v_A$	$N_A = c_A v_A$
Relative to molar average velocity v_M	$j_A^* = \rho_A(v_A - v_M)$	$J_A^* = c_A(v_A - v_M)$
Relative to mass average velocity v	$j_A = \rho_A(v_A - v)$	$J_A = c_A(v_A - v)$

Relations Between Fluxes Above

$$N_A + N_B = c v_M \qquad N_A = n_A/M_A \qquad N_A = J_A + c_A v$$
$$J_A^* + J_B^* = 0 \qquad J_A = j_A/M_A \qquad n_A + n_B = \rho v$$
$$j_A + j_B = 0 \qquad N_A = J_A^* + c_A v_M \qquad n_A = j_A + \rho_A v$$

Different Forms of Fick's Law for Diffusion Flux
$$J_A^* = -cD_{AB}\ dx_A/dz \qquad j_A = -\rho D_{AB}\ dw_A/dz$$

Fick's law can also be defined in terms of a mass flux relative to v as given in Table 7.5-1:

$$j_A = -\rho D_{AB} \frac{dw_A}{dz} \tag{7.5-6}$$

EXAMPLE 7.5-1.   Proof of Mass Flux Equation
Table 7.5-1 gives the following relation:

$$j_A + j_B = 0 \tag{7.5-7}$$

Prove this relationship using the definitions of the fluxes in terms of velocities.

Solution: From Table 7.5-1, substituting $\rho_A(v_A - v)$ for j_A and $\rho_B(v_B - v)$ for j_B, and rearranging,

$$\rho_A v_A - \rho_A v + \rho_B v_B - \rho_B v = 0 \tag{7.5-8}$$

$$\rho_A v_A + \rho_B v_B - v(\rho_A + \rho_B) = 0 \tag{7.5-9}$$

Substituting Eq. (7.5-1) for v and ρ for $\rho_A + \rho_B$, the identity is proved.

7.5B   Equation of Continuity for a Binary Mixture

A general equation can be derived for a binary mixture of A and B for diffusion and convection that also includes the terms for unsteady-state diffusion and chemical reaction. We shall make a mass balance on component A on an element $\Delta x \, \Delta y \, \Delta z$ fixed in space as shown in Fig. 7.5-1. The general mass balance on A is

$$\begin{pmatrix} \text{rate of} \\ \text{mass } A \text{ in} \end{pmatrix} - \begin{pmatrix} \text{rate of} \\ \text{mass } A \text{ out} \end{pmatrix} + \begin{pmatrix} \text{rate of} \\ \text{generation of mass } A \end{pmatrix}$$

$$= \begin{pmatrix} \text{rate of} \\ \text{accumulation} \\ \text{of mass } A \end{pmatrix} \tag{7.5-10}$$

The rate of mass A entering in the direction relative to stationary coordinates is $(n_{Ax|x})\Delta y \, \Delta z$ kg A/s and leaving is $(n_{Ax|x+\Delta x})\Delta y \, \Delta z$. Similar terms can be written for the y and z direc-

FIGURE 7.5-1.   *Mass balance for A in a binary mixture.*

tions. The rate of chemical production of A is r_A kg A generated/s $\cdot$ m^3 volume and the total rate generated is $r_A(\Delta x \, \Delta y \, \Delta z)$ kg A/s. The rate of accumulation of A is $(\partial \rho_A/\partial t)\Delta x \, \Delta y \, \Delta z$. Substituting into Eq. (7.5-10) and letting Δx, Δy, and Δz approach zero,

$$\frac{\partial \rho_A}{\partial t} + \left(\frac{\partial n_{Ax}}{\partial x} + \frac{\partial n_{Ay}}{\partial y} + \frac{\partial n_{Az}}{\partial z}\right) = r_A \tag{7.5-11}$$

In vector notation,

$$\frac{\partial \rho_A}{\partial t} + (\nabla \cdot n_A) = r_A \tag{7.5-12}$$

Dividing both sides of Eq. (7.5-11) by M_A,

$$\frac{\partial c_A}{\partial t} + \left(\frac{\partial N_{Ax}}{\partial x} + \frac{\partial N_{Ay}}{\partial y} + \frac{\partial N_{Az}}{\partial z}\right) = R_A \tag{7.5-13}$$

where R_A is kg mol A generated/s $\cdot$ m^3. Substituting N_A and Fick's law from Table 7.5-1,

$$N_A = -cD_{AB}\frac{dx_A}{dz} + c_A v_M \tag{7.5-14}$$

and writing the equation for all three directions, Eq. (7.5-13) becomes

$$\frac{\partial c_A}{\partial t} + (\nabla \cdot c_A v_M) - (\nabla \cdot cD_{AB}\nabla x_A) = R_A \tag{7.5-15}$$

This is the final general equation.

7.5C Special Cases of the Equation of Continuity

1. Equation for constant c and D_{AB}. In diffusion with gases the total pressure P is often constant. Then, since $c = P/RT$, c is constant for constant temperature T. Starting with the general equation (7.5-15) and substituting $\nabla x_A = \nabla c_A/c$, we obtain

$$\frac{\partial c_A}{\partial t} + c_A(\nabla \cdot v_M) + (v_M \cdot \nabla c_A) - D_{AB}\nabla^2 c_A = R_A \tag{7.5-16}$$

2. Equimolar counterdiffusion for gases. For the special case of equimolar counterdiffusion of gases at constant pressure and no reaction, $c = $ constant, $v_M = 0$, $D_{AB} = $ constant, $R_A = 0$, and Eq. (7.5-15) becomes

$$\frac{\partial c_A}{\partial t} = D_{AB}\left(\frac{\partial^2 c_A}{\partial x^2} + \frac{\partial^2 c_A}{\partial y^2} + \frac{\partial^2 c_A}{\partial z^2}\right) \tag{7.1-9}$$

This equation is Eq. (7.1-9), derived previously, which is also used for unsteady-state diffusion of a dilute solute A in a solid or a liquid when D_{AB} is constant.

3. Equation for constant ρ and D_{AB} (liquids). In dilute liquid solutions, the mass density ρ and D_{AB} can often be considered constant. Starting with Eq. (7.5-12) we substitute $n_A = -\rho D_{AB}\nabla w_A + \rho_A v$ from Table 7.5-1 into this equation. Then using the fact that for constant ρ, $\nabla w_A = \nabla \rho_A / \rho$ and also that $(\nabla \cdot v) = 0$, substituting these into the resulting equation, and dividing both sides by M_A, we obtain

$$\frac{\partial c_A}{\partial t} + (v \cdot \nabla c_A) - D_{AB} \nabla^2 c_A = R_A \tag{7.5-17}$$

7.5D Special Cases of the General Diffusion Equation at Steady State

1. Introduction and physical conditions at the boundaries. The general equation for diffusion and convection of a binary mixture in one direction with no chemical reaction has been given previously:

$$N_A = -c D_{AB} \frac{dx_A}{dz} + \frac{c_A}{c}(N_A + N_B) \tag{6.2-14}$$

To integrate this equation at steady state, it is necessary to specify the boundary conditions at z_1 and z_2. In many mass-transfer problems the molar ratio N_A/N_B is determined by the physical conditions occurring at the two boundaries.

As an example, one boundary of the diffusion path may be impermeable to species B because B is insoluble in the phase at this boundary. Diffusion of ammonia (A) and nitrogen (B) through a gas phase to a water phase at the boundary is such a case, since nitrogen is essentially insoluble in water. Hence, $N_B = 0$, since at steady state N_B must have the same value at all points in the path of $z_2 - z_1$. In some cases, a heat balance in the adjacent phase at the boundary can determine the flux ratios. For example, if component A condenses at a boundary and releases its latent heat to component B, which vaporizes and diffuses back, the ratios of the latent heats determine the flux ratio.

In another example, the boundary concentration can be fixed by having a large volume of a phase flowing rapidly by with a given concentration x_{A1}. In some cases the concentration x_{A1} may be set by an equilibrium condition, whereby x_{A1} is in equilibrium with some fixed composition at the boundary. Chemical reactions can also influence the rates of diffusion and the boundary conditions.

2. Equimolar counterdiffusion. For the special case of equimolar counterdiffusion, where $N_A = -N_B$, Eq. (6.2-14) becomes, as shown previously, for steady state and constant c,

$$N_A = J_A^* = -c D_{AB} \frac{dx_A}{dz} = \frac{D_{AB}(c_{A1} - c_{A2})}{z_2 - z_1} \tag{7.5-18}$$

3. Diffusion of A through stagnant, nondiffusing B. For gas A diffusing through stagnant nondiffusing gas B, $N_B = 0$, and integration of Eq. (6.2-14) gives Eq. (6.2-22):

$$N_A = \frac{D_{AB} P}{RT(z_2 - z_1) p_{BM}}(p_{A1} - p_{A2}) \tag{6.2-22}$$

Several other more complicated cases of integration of Eq. (6.2-14) are considered next.

4. Diffusion and chemical reaction at a boundary. Often in catalytic reactions, where A and B are diffusing to and from a catalyst surface, the relation between the fluxes N_A and N_B at steady state is controlled by the stoichiometry of a reaction at a boundary. An example is gas A diffusing from the bulk gas phase to the catalyst surface, where it reacts instantaneously and irreversibly in a heterogeneous reaction as follows:

$$A \rightarrow 2B \tag{7.5-19}$$

Gas B then diffuses back, as shown in Fig. 7.5-2.

At steady state 1 mol of A diffuses to the catalyst for every 2 mol of B diffusing away, or $N_B = -2N_A$. The negative sign indicates that the fluxes are in opposite directions. Rewriting Eq. (6.2-14) in terms of mole fractions,

$$N_A = -cD_{AB} \frac{dx_A}{dz} + x_A(N_A + N_B) \tag{7.5-20}$$

Next, substituting $N_B = -2N_A$ into Eq. (7.5-20),

$$N_A = -cD_{AB} \frac{dx_A}{dz} + x_A(N_A - 2N_A) \tag{7.5-21}$$

Rearranging and integrating with constant c (P = constant), we obtain the following:

1. *Instantaneous surface reaction:*

$$N_A \int_{z_1=0}^{z_2=\delta} dz = -cD_{AB} \int_{x_{A1}}^{x_{A2}} \frac{dx_A}{1 + x_A} \tag{7.5-22}$$

$$N_A = \frac{cD_{AB}}{\delta} \ln \frac{1 + x_{A1}}{1 + x_{A2}} \tag{7.5-23}$$

Since the reaction is instantaneous, $x_{A2} = 0$, because no A can exist next to the catalyst surface. Equation (7.5-23) describes the overall rate of the process of diffusion plus instantaneous chemical reaction.

2. *Slow surface reaction.* If the heterogeneous reaction at the surface is not instantaneous but slow for the reaction $A \rightarrow 2B$, and the reaction is first order,

$$N_{Az=\delta} = k_1' c_A = k_1' c x_A \tag{7.5-24}$$

FIGURE 7.5-2. *Diffusion of A and heterogeneous reaction at a surface.*

where k_1' is the first-order heterogeneous reaction velocity constant in m/s. Equation (7.5-23) still holds for this case, but the boundary condition x_{A2} at $z = \delta$ is obtained by solving for x_A in Eq. (7.5-24),

$$x_A = x_{A2} = \frac{N_{Az=\delta}}{k_1'c} = \frac{N_A}{k_c'} \tag{7.5-25}$$

For steady state, $N_{Az=\delta} = N_A$. Substituting Eq. (7.5-25) into (7.5-23),

$$N_A = \frac{cD_{AB}}{\delta} \ln \frac{1 + x_{A1}}{1 + N_A/k_1'c} \tag{7.5-26}$$

The rate in Eq. (7.5-26) is less than in Eq. (7.5-23), since the denominator in the latter equation is $1 + x_{A2} = 1 + 0$ and in the former is $1 + N_A/k_1'c$.

EXAMPLE 7.5-2. Diffusion and Chemical Reaction at a Boundary

Pure gas A diffuses from point 1 at a partial pressure of 101.32 kPa to point 2 a distance 2.00 mm away. At point 2 it undergoes a chemical reaction at the catalyst surface and $A \rightarrow 2B$. Component B diffuses back at steady state. The total pressure is $P = 101.32$ kPa. The temperature is 300 K and $D_{AB} = 0.15 \times 10^{-4}$ m^2/s.

(a) For instantaneous rate of reaction, calculate x_{A2} and N_A.
(b) For a slow reaction where $k_1' = 5.63 \times 10^{-3}$ m/s, calculate x_{A2} and N_A.

Solution: For part (a), $p_{A2} = x_{A2} = 0$ since no A can exist next to the catalyst surface. Since $N_B = -2N_A$, Eq. (7.5-23) will be used as follows: $\delta = 2.00 \times 10^{-3}$ m, $T = 300$ K, $c = P/RT = 101.32 \times 10^3/(8314 \times 300) = 4.062 \times 10^{-2}$ kg mol/m^3, $x_{A1} = p_{A1}/P = 101.32 \times 10^3/101.32 \times 10^3 = 1.00$.

$$N_A = \frac{cD_{AB}}{\delta} \ln \frac{1 + x_{A1}}{1 + x_{A2}} = \frac{(4.062 \times 10^{-2})(0.15 \times 10^{-4})}{2.00 \times 10^{-3}} \ln \frac{1 + 1.00}{1 + 0}$$

$$= 2.112 \times 10^{-4} \text{ kg mol } A/\text{s} \cdot \text{m}^2$$

For part (b), from Eq. (7.5-25), $x_{A2} = N_A/k_1'c = N_A/(5.63 \times 10^{-3} \times 4.062 \times 10^{-2})$. Substituting into Eq. (7.5-26),

$$N_A = \frac{(4.062 \times 10^{-2})(0.15 \times 10^{-4})}{2.00 \times 10^{-3}} \ln \frac{1 + 1.00}{1 + N_A/(5.63 \times 10^{-3} \times 4.062 \times 10^{-2})}$$

Solving by trial and error, $N_A = 1.004 \times 10^{-4}$ kg mol $A/\text{s} \cdot \text{m}^2$. Then $x_{A2} = (1.004 \times 10^{-4})/(5.63 \times 10^{-3} \times 4.062 \times 10^{-2}) = 0.4390$.

Even though in part (a) of Example 7.5-2 the rate of reaction is instantaneous, the flux N_A is diffusion-controlled. As the reaction rate slows, the flux N_A is decreased also.

5. Diffusion and homogeneous reaction in a phase. Equation (7.5-23) was derived for the case of chemical reaction of A at the boundary on a catalyst surface. In some cases component A undergoes an irreversible chemical reaction in the homogeneous phase B while diffusing, as follows: $A \rightarrow C$. Assume that component A is very dilute in phase B, which can be a gas or a liquid. Then at steady state the equation for diffusion of A is as follows, where the bulk-flow term is dropped:

$$N_{Az} = -D_{AB}\frac{dc_A}{dz} + 0 \qquad (7.5\text{-}27)$$

Writing a material balance on A shown in Fig. 7.5-3 for the Δz element for steady state,

$$\begin{pmatrix}\text{rate of}\\ A \text{ in}\end{pmatrix} + \begin{pmatrix}\text{rate of}\\ \text{generation of } A\end{pmatrix} = \begin{pmatrix}\text{rate of}\\ A \text{ out}\end{pmatrix} + \begin{pmatrix}\text{rate of}\\ \text{accumulation of } A\end{pmatrix} \qquad (7.5\text{-}28)$$

The first-order reaction rate of A per m^3 volume is

$$\text{rate of generation} = -k'c_A \qquad (7.5\text{-}29)$$

where k' is the reaction velocity constant in s^{-1}. Substituting into Eq. (7.5-28) for a cross-sectional area of 1 m^2 with the rate of accumulation being 0 at steady state,

$$N_{Az|z}(1) - k'c_A(1)(\Delta z) = N_{Az|z+\Delta z}(1) + 0 \qquad (7.5\text{-}30)$$

Next we divide through by Δz and let Δz approach zero:

$$-\frac{dN_{Az}}{dz} = k'c_A \qquad (7.5\text{-}31)$$

Substituting Eq. (7.5-27) into (7.5-31),

$$\frac{d^2c_A}{dz^2} = \frac{k'}{D_{AB}}c_A \qquad (7.5\text{-}32)$$

The boundary conditions are $c_A = c_{A1}$ for $z = 0$ and $c_A = c_{A2}$ for $z = L$. Solving,

$$c_A = \frac{c_{A2}\sinh\left(\sqrt{\dfrac{k'}{D_{AB}}}\,z\right) + c_{A1}\sinh\left[\sqrt{\dfrac{k'}{D_{AB}}}(L-z)\right]}{\sinh\left(\sqrt{\dfrac{k'}{D_{AB}}}L\right)} \qquad (7.5\text{-}33)$$

This equation can be used at steady state to calculate c_A at any z and can be used for reactions in gases, liquids, or even solids, where the solute A is dilute.

FIGURE 7.5-3. *Homogeneous chemical reaction and diffusion in a fluid.*

As an alternative derivation of Eq. (7.5-32), we can use Eq. (7.5-17) for constant ρ and D_{AB}:

$$\frac{\partial c_A}{\partial t} + (v \cdot \nabla c_A) - D_{AB} \nabla^2 c_A = R_A \tag{7.5-17}$$

We set the first term $\partial c_A/\partial t = 0$ for steady state. Since we are assuming dilute solutions and neglecting the bulk flow term, $v = 0$, making the second term in Eq. (7.5-17) zero. For a first-order reaction of A where A disappears, $R_A = -k'c_A$ kg mol A generated/s $\cdot$ m³. Writing the diffusion term $-D_{AB} \nabla^2 c_A$ for the z direction only, we obtain

$$D_{AB} \frac{d^2 c_A}{dz^2} = k' c_A \tag{7.5-34}$$

which is, of course, identical to Eq. (7.5-32).

7.5E   Unsteady-State Diffusion and Reaction in a Semi-infinite Medium

Here we consider a case where dilute A is absorbed at the surface of a solid or stagnant fluid phase and then unsteady-state diffusion and reaction occur in the phase. The fluid or solid phase B is considered semi-infinite. At the surface, where $z = 0$, the concentration of c_A is kept constant at c_{A0}. The dilute solute A reacts by a first-order mechanism

$$A + B \rightarrow C \tag{7.5-35}$$

and the rate of generation is $-k'c_A$. The same diagram as in Fig. 7.5-3 holds. Using Eq. (7.5-30) but substituting $(\partial c_A/\partial t)(\Delta z)(1)$ for the rate of accumulation,

$$N_{Az|z}(1) - k'c_A(1)(\Delta z) = N_{Az|z+\Delta z}(1) + \left(\frac{\partial c_A}{\partial t}\right)(\Delta z)(1) \tag{7.5-36}$$

This becomes

$$\frac{\partial c_A}{\partial t} = D_{AB} \frac{\partial^2 c_A}{\partial z^2} - k'c_A \tag{7.5-37}$$

The initial and boundary conditions are

$$t = 0, \qquad c_A = 0 \quad \text{for } z > 0$$
$$z = 0, \qquad c_A = c_{A0} \quad \text{for } t > 0 \tag{7.5-38}$$
$$z = \infty, \qquad c_A = 0 \quad \text{for } t > 0$$

The solution by Danckwerts (D1) is

$$\frac{c_A}{c_{A0}} = \tfrac{1}{2} \exp(-z\sqrt{k'/D_{AB}}) \cdot \text{erfc}\left(\frac{z}{2\sqrt{t D_{AB}}} - \sqrt{k't}\right)$$
$$+ \tfrac{1}{2} \exp(z\sqrt{k'/D_{AB}}) \cdot \text{erfc}\left(\frac{z}{2\sqrt{t D_{AB}}} + \sqrt{k't}\right) \tag{7.5-39}$$

The total amount Q of A absorbed up to time t is

$$Q = c_{A0}\sqrt{D_{AB}/k'}[(k't + \tfrac{1}{2})\text{erf } \sqrt{k't} + \sqrt{k't/\pi}e^{-k't}] \tag{7.5-40}$$

where Q is kg mol A absorbed/m^2. Many actual cases are approximated by this case. The equation is useful where absorption occurs at the surface of a stagnant fluid or a solid and unsteady-state diffusion and reaction occur in the solid or fluid. The results can be used to measure the diffusivity of a gas in a solution, to determine reaction rate constants k' of dissolved gases, and to determine solubilities of gases in liquids with which they react. Details are given elsewhere (D3).

EXAMPLE 7.5-3. Reaction and Unsteady-State Diffusion

Pure CO_2 gas at 101.32 kPa pressure is absorbed into a dilute alkaline buffer solution containing a catalyst. The dilute, absorbed solute CO_2 undergoes a first-order reaction, with $k' = 35$ s^{-1} and $D_{AB} = 1.5 \times 10^{-9}$ m^2/s. The solubility of CO_2 is 2.961×10^{-7} kg mol/m$^3 \cdot$ Pa (D3). The surface is exposed to the gas for 0.010 s. Calculate the kg mol CO_2 absorbed/m^2 surface.

Solution: For use in Eq. (7.5-40), $k't = 35(0.01) = 0.350$. Also, $c_{A0} = 2.961 \times 10^{-7}$ (kg mol/m$^3 \cdot$ Pa)(101.32 $\times 10^3$ Pa) $= 3.00 \times 10^{-2}$ kg mol SO_2/m^3.

$$Q = (3.00 \times 10^{-2})\sqrt{1.5 \times 10^{-9}/35}[(0.35 + \tfrac{1}{2})\text{erf}\sqrt{0.35} + \sqrt{0.35/\pi}\,e^{-0.35}]$$
$$= 1.458 \times 10^{-7} \text{ kg mol } CO_2/\text{m}^2$$

7.5F Multicomponent Diffusion of Gases

The equations derived in this chapter have been for a binary system of A and B, which is probably the most important and most useful one. However, multicomponent diffusion sometimes occurs where three or more components $A, B, C, \ldots$ are present. The simplest case is for diffusion of A in a gas through a stagnant, nondiffusing mixture of $B, C, D, \ldots$ at constant total pressure. Hence, $N_B = 0, N_c = 0, \ldots$. The final equation derived using the Stefan–Maxwell method (G1) for steady-state diffusion is

$$N_A = \frac{D_{Am}P}{RT(z_2 - z_1)p_{iM}}(p_{A1} - p_{A2}) \tag{7.5-41}$$

where p_{iM} is the log mean of $p_{i1} = P - p_{A1}$ and $p_{i2} = P - p_{A2}$. Also,

$$D_{Am} = \frac{1}{x'_B/D_{AB} + x'_C/D_{AC} + \cdots} \tag{7.5-42}$$

where x'_B = mol B/mol inerts $= x_B/(1-x_A), x'_C = x_C/(1 - x_A), \ldots$.

EXAMPLE 7.5-4. Diffusion of A Through Nondiffusing B and C

At 298 K and 1 atm total pressure, methane (A) is diffusing at steady state through nondiffusing argon (B) and helium (C). At $z_1 = 0$, the partial pressures in atm are $p_{A1} = 0.4, p_{B1} = 0.4$, and $p_{C1} = 0.2$, and at $z_2 = 0.005$ m, $p_{A2} = 0.1, p_{B2} = 0.6$, and $p_{C2} = 0.3$. The binary diffusivities from Table 6.2-1 are $D_{AB} = 2.02 \times 10^{-5}$ m^2/s, $D_{AC} = 6.75 \times 10^{-5}$ m^2/s, and $D_{BC} = 7.29 \times 10^{-5}$ m^2/s. Calculate N_A.

Solution: At point 1, $x'_B = x_B/(1 - x_A) = 0.4/(1 - 0.4) = 0.667$. At point 2, $x'_B = 0.6/(1 - 0.1) = 0.667$. The value of x'_B is constant throughout the path. Also, $x'_C = x_C/(1 - x_A) = 0.2/(1 - 0.4) = 0.333$.

Substituting into Eq. (7.5-42),

$$D_{Am} = \frac{1}{x_B'/D_{AB} + x_C'/D_{AC}} = \frac{1}{0.667/2.02 \times 10^{-5} + 0.333/6.75 \times 10^{-5}}$$

$$= 2.635 \times 10^{-5} \, m^2/s$$

For calculating p_{iM}, $p_{i1} = P - p_{A1} = 1.0 - 0.4 = 0.6$ atm, $p_{i2} = P - p_{A2} = 1.0 - 0.1 = 0.90$. Then,

$$p_{iM} = \frac{p_{i2} - p_{i1}}{\ln(p_{i2}/p_{i1})} = \frac{0.90 - 0.60}{\ln(0.90/0.60)} = 0.740 \, atm = 7.496 \times 10^4 \, Pa$$

$$p_{A1} = 0.4(1.01325 \times 10^5) = 4.053 \times 10^4 \, Pa$$

$$p_{A2} = 0.1(1.01325 \times 10^5) = 1.013 \times 10^4 \, Pa$$

Substituting into Eq. (7.5-41),

$$N_A = \frac{D_{Am}P}{RT(z_2 - z_1)p_{iM}}(p_{A1} - p_{A2})$$

$$= \frac{(2.635 \times 10^{-5})(1.01325 \times 10^5)(4.053 - 1.013)(10^4)}{(8314)(298)(0.005 - 0)(7.496 \times 10^4)}$$

$$= 8.74 \times 10^{-5} \, kg \, mol \, A/s \cdot m^2$$

Using atm pressure units,

$$N_A = \frac{D_{Am}P}{RT(z_2 - z_1)p_{iM}}(p_{A1} - p_{A2}) = \frac{(2.635 \times 10^{-5})(1.0)(0.4 - 0.1)}{(82.06 \times 10^{-3})(298)(0.005 - 0)(0.740)}$$

$$= 8.74 \times 10^{-5} \, kg \, mol \, A/s \cdot m^2$$

A number of analytical solutions have been obtained for other cases, such as for equimolar diffusion of three components, diffusion of components A and B through stagnant C, and the general case of two or more components diffusing in a multicomponent mixture. These are discussed in detail with examples by Geankoplis (G1); the reader is referred there for further details.

7.6 DIFFUSION OF GASES IN POROUS SOLIDS AND CAPILLARIES

7.6A Introduction

In Section 6.5C diffusion in porous solids that depends on structure was discussed for liquids and gases. For gases it was assumed that the pores were very large and Fickian-type diffusion occurred. However, the pores are often small in diameter and the mechanism of diffusion is basically changed.

Diffusion of gases in small pores frequently occurs in heterogeneous catalysis where gases diffuse through very small pores to react on the surface of the catalyst. In freeze-drying of foods such as turkey meat, gaseous H_2O diffuses through very fine pores of the porous structure.

Since the pores or capillaries of porous solids are often small, the diffusion of gases may depend upon the diameter of the pores. We first define a mean free path λ, which is the average distance a gas molecule travels before it collides with another gas molecule:

$$\lambda = \frac{3.2\mu}{P} \sqrt{\frac{RT}{2\pi M}} \tag{7.6-1}$$

where λ is in m, μ is viscosity in Pa·s, P is pressure in N/m^2, T is temperature in K, M = molecular weight in kg/kg mol, and $R = 8.3143 \times 10^3$ N·m/kg mol·K. Note that low pressures give large values of λ. For liquids, since λ is so small, diffusion follows Fick's law.

In the next sections we shall consider what happens to the basic mechanisms of diffusion in gases as the relative value of the mean free path compared to the pore diameter varies. The total pressure P in the system will be constant, but partial pressures of A and B may be different.

7.6B Knudsen Diffusion of Gases

In Fig. 7.6-1a a gas molecule A at partial pressure p_{A1} at the entrance to a capillary is diffusing through the capillary having a diameter d m. The total pressure P is constant throughout. The mean free path λ is large compared to the diameter d. As a result, the molecule collides with the wall and molecule–wall collisions are important. This type of diffusion is called *Knudsen diffusion*.

The Knudsen diffusivity is independent of pressure P and is calculated from

$$D_{KA} = \frac{2}{3} \bar{r}\, \bar{v}_A \tag{7.6-2}$$

where D_{KA} is diffusivity in m^2/s, $\bar{r}$ is average pore radius in m, and $\bar{v}_A$ is the average molecular velocity for component A in m/s. Using the kinetic theory of gases to evaluate $\bar{v}_A$, the final equation for D_{KA} is

$$D_{KA} = 97.0\bar{r}\left(\frac{T}{M_A}\right)^{1/2} \tag{7.6-3}$$

where M_A is molecular weight of A in kg/kg mol and T is temperature in K.

EXAMPLE 7.6-1.   Knudsen Diffusivity of Hydrogen
A $H_2(A)-C_2H_6(B)$ gas mixture is diffusing in a pore of a nickel catalyst used for hydrogenation at 1.01325×10^5 Pa pressure and 373 K. The pore radius is 60 Å (angstrom). Calculate the Knudsen diffusivity D_{KA} of H_2.

FIGURE 7.6-1.   *Types of diffusion of gases in small capillary tubes: (a) Knudsen gas diffusion, (b) molecular or Fick's gas diffusion, (c) transition gas diffusion.*

Solution: Substituting into Eq. (7.6-3) for $\bar{r} = 6.0 \times 10^{-9}$ m, $M_A = 2.016$, and $T = 373$ K,

$$D_{KA} = 97.0\bar{r}\left(\frac{T}{M_A}\right)^{1/2} = 97.0(6.0 \times 10^{-9})\left(\frac{373}{2.016}\right)^{1/2}$$

$$= 7.92 \times 10^{-6} \text{ m}^2/\text{s}$$

The flux equation for Knudsen diffusion in a pore is

$$N_A = -D_{KA}\frac{dc_A}{dz} = -\frac{D_{KA}}{RT}\frac{dp_A}{dz} \tag{7.6-4}$$

Integrating between $z_1 = 0, p_A = p_{A1}$ and $z_2 = L, p_A = p_{A2}$,

$$N_A = \frac{D_{KA}P}{RTL}(x_{A1} - x_{A2}) = \frac{D_{KA}}{RTL}(p_{A1} - p_{A2}) \tag{7.6-5}$$

The diffusion of A for Knudsen diffusion is completely independent of B, since A collides with the walls of the pore and not with B. A similar equation can be written for component B.

When the Knudsen number N_{Kn} defined as

$$N_{Kn} = \frac{\lambda}{2\bar{r}} \tag{7.6-6}$$

is $\geq 10/1$, the diffusion is primarily Knudsen, and Eq. (7.6-5) predicts the flux to within about a 10% error. As N_{Kn} gets larger, this error decreases, since the diffusion approaches the Knudsen type.

7.6C Molecular Diffusion of Gases

As shown in Fig. 7.6-1b, when the mean free path λ is small compared to the pore diameter d or where $N_{Kn} \leq 1/100$, molecule–molecule collisions predominate and molecule–wall collisions are few. Ordinary molecular or Fickian diffusion holds and Fick's law predicts the diffusion to within about 10%. The error diminishes as N_{Kn} gets smaller since the diffusion approaches more closely the Fickian type.

The equation for molecular diffusion given in previous sections is

$$N_A = -\frac{D_{AB}P}{RT}\frac{dx_A}{dz} + x_A(N_A + N_B) \tag{7.6-7}$$

A flux ratio factor α can be defined as

$$\alpha = 1 + \frac{N_B}{N_A} \tag{7.6-8}$$

Combining Eqs. (7.6-7) and (7.6-8) and integrating for a path length of L cm,

$$N_A = \frac{D_{AB}P}{\alpha RTL}\ln\frac{1 - \alpha x_{A2}}{1 - \alpha x_{A1}} \tag{7.6-9}$$

If the diffusion is equimolar, $N_A = -N_B$ and Eq. (7.6-7) becomes Fick's law. The molecular diffusivity D_{AB} is inversely proportional to the total pressure P.

7.6D Transition-Region Diffusion of Gases

As shown in Fig. 7.6-1c, when the mean free path λ and pore diameter are intermediate in size between the two limits given for Knudsen and molecular diffusion, transition-type diffusion occurs, where molecule–molecule and molecule–wall collisions are important in diffusion.

The transition-region diffusion equation can be derived by adding the momentum loss due to molecule–wall collisions in Eq. (7.6-4) and that due to molecule–molecule collisions in Eq. (7.6-7) on a slice of capillary. No chemical reactions are occurring. The final differential equation is (G1)

$$N_A = -\frac{D_{NA}P}{RT}\frac{dx_A}{dz} \tag{7.6-10}$$

where

$$D_{NA} = \frac{1}{(1 - \alpha x_A)/D_{AB} + 1/D_{KA}} \tag{7.6-11}$$

This transition region diffusivity D_{NA} depends slightly on concentration x_A.

Integrating Eq. (7.6-10),

$$N_A = \frac{D_{AB}P}{\alpha RTL}\ln\frac{1 - \alpha x_{A2} + D_{AB}/D_{KA}}{1 - \alpha x_{A1} + D_{AB}/D_{KA}} \tag{7.6-12}$$

This equation has been shown experimentally to be valid over the entire transition region (R1). It reduces to the Knudsen equation at low pressures and to the molecular diffusion equation at high pressures. An equation similar to Eq. (7.6-12) can also be written for component B.

The term D_{AB}/D_{KA} is proportional to $1/P$. Hence, as the total pressure P increases, the term D_{AB}/D_{KA} becomes very small and N_A in Eq. (7.6-12) becomes independent of total pressure, since $D_{AB}P$ is independent of P. At low total pressures Eq. (7.6-12) becomes the Knudsen diffusion equation (7.6-5), and the flux N_A becomes directly proportional to P for constant x_{A1} and x_{A2}.

This is illustrated, in Fig. 7.6-2, for a fixed capillary diameter where the flux increases as total pressure increases and then levels off at high pressure. The relative position of the curve depends, of course, on the capillary diameter and the molecular and Knudsen diffusivities. Using only a smaller diameter, D_{KA} would be smaller, and the Knudsen flux line would be parallel to the existing line at low pressures. At high pressures the flux line would asymptotically approach the existing horizontal line, since molecular diffusion is independent of capillary diameter.

If A is diffusing in a catalytic pore and reacts at the surface at the end of the pore so that $A \to B$, then at steady state, equimolar counterdiffusion occurs, or $N_A = -N_B$. Then from Eq. (7.6-8), $\alpha = 1 - 1 = 0$. The effective diffusivity D_{NA} from Eq. (7.6-11) becomes

$$D'_{NA} = \frac{1}{1/D_{AB} + 1/D_{KA}} \tag{7.6-13}$$

The diffusivity is then independent of concentration and is constant. Integration of (7.6-10) then gives

$$N_A = \frac{D'_{NA}P}{RTL}(x_{A1} - x_{A2}) = \frac{D'_{NA}}{RTL}(p_{A1} - p_{A2}) \tag{7.6-14}$$

FIGURE 7.6-2. *Effect of total pressure P on the diffusion flux N_A in the transition region.*

This simplified diffusivity D'_{NA} is often used in diffusion in porous catalysts even when equimolar counterdiffusion is not occurring. It greatly simplifies the equations for diffusion and reaction to use this simplified diffusivity.

An alternative simplified diffusivity can be obtained by using an average value of x_A in Eq. (7.6-11), to give

$$D''_{NA} = \frac{1}{(1 - \alpha x_{A\,av})/D_{AB} + 1/D_{KA}} \tag{7.6-15}$$

where $x_{A\,av} = (x_{A1} + x_{A2})/2$. This diffusivity is more accurate than D'_{NA}. Integration of Eq. (7.6-10) gives

$$N_A = \frac{D''_{NA}P}{RTL}(x_{A1} - x_{A2}) = \frac{D''_{NA}}{RTL}(p_{A1} - p_{A2}) \tag{7.6-16}$$

7.6E   Flux Ratios for Diffusion of Gases in Capillaries

1. Diffusion in open system.   If diffusion in porous solids or channels with no chemical reaction is occurring where the total pressure P remains constant, then for an open binary counter-diffusing system, the ratio of N_A/N_B is constant in all of the three diffusion regimes and is (G1)

$$\frac{N_B}{N_A} = -\sqrt{\frac{M_A}{M_B}} \tag{7.6-17}$$

Hence,

$$\alpha = 1 - \sqrt{\frac{M_A}{M_B}} \tag{7.6-18}$$

In this case, gas flows past the two open ends of the system. However, when chemical reaction occurs, stoichiometry determines the ratio N_B/N_A, and not Eq. (7.6-17).

2. *Diffusion in closed system.* When molecular diffusion is occurring in a closed system, shown in Fig. 6.2-1, at constant total pressure P, equimolar counterdiffusion occurs.

EXAMPLE 7.6-2. *Transition-Region Diffusion of He and N_2*
A gas mixture at a total pressure of 0.10 atm abs and 298 K is composed of N_2 (A) and He (B). The mixture is diffusing through an open capillary 0.010 m long having a diameter of 5×10^{-6} m. The mole fraction of N_2 at one end is $x_{A1} = 0.8$ and at the other end is $x_{A2} = 0.2$. The molecular diffusivity D_{AB} is 6.98×10^{-5} m²/s at 1 atm, which is an average value determined by several investigators.
    (a) Calculate the flux N_A at steady state.
    (b) Use the approximate equations (7.6-14) and (7.6-16) for this case.

Solution: The given values are $T = 273 + 25 = 298$ K, $\bar{r} = 5 \times 10^{-6}/2 = 2.5 \times 10^{-6}$ m, $L = 0.01$ m, $P = 0.1(1.01325 \times 10^5) = 1.013 \times 10^4$ Pa, $x_{A1} = 0.8$, $x_{A2} = 0.2$, $D_{AB} = 6.98 \times 10^{-5}$ m²/s at 1 atm. Other values needed are $M_A = 28.02$ kg/kg mol, $M_B = 4.003$.
    The molecular diffusivity at 0.1 atm is $D_{AB} = 6.98 \times 10^{-5}/0.1 = 6.98 \times 10^{-4}$ m²/s. Substituting into Eq. (7.6-3) for the Knudsen diffusivity,

$$D_{KA} = 97.0(2.5 \times 10^{-6})\sqrt{298/28.02} = 7.91 \times 10^{-4}\ \text{m}^2/\text{s}$$

From Eq. (7.6-17),

$$\frac{N_B}{N_A} = -\sqrt{\frac{M_A}{M_B}} = -\sqrt{\frac{28.02}{4.003}} = -2.645$$

From Eq. (7.6-8),

$$\alpha = 1 + \frac{N_B}{N_A} = 1 - 2.645 = -1.645$$

Substituting into Eq. (7.6-12) for part (a),

$$N_A = \frac{(6.98 \times 10^{-4})(1.013 \times 10^4)}{(-1.645)(8314)(298)(0.01)} \ln \frac{1 + 1.645(0.2) + 6.98/7.91}{1 + 1.645(0.8) + 6.98/7.91}$$

$$= 6.40 \times 10^{-5}\ \text{kg mol/s} \cdot \text{m}^2$$

For part (b), the approximate equation (7.6-13) is used:

$$D'_{NA} = \frac{1}{1/D_{AB} + 1/D_{KA}} = \frac{1}{1/6.98 \times 10^{-4} + 1/7.91 \times 10^{-4}}$$

$$= 3.708 \times 10^{-4}\ \text{m}^2/\text{s}$$

Substituting into Eq. (7.6-14), the approximate flux is

$$N_A = \frac{D'_{NA}P}{RTL}(x_{A1} - x_{A2}) = \frac{(3.708 \times 10^{-4})(1.013 \times 10^4)}{8314(298)(0.01)}(0.8 - 0.2)$$

$$= 9.10 \times 10^{-5}\ \text{kg mol/s} \cdot \text{m}^2$$

Hence, the calculated flux is approximately 40% high when using the approximation of equimolar counterdiffusion ($\alpha = 0$).

The more accurate approximate equation (7.6-15) is used next. The average concentration is $x_{A\,av} = (x_{A1} + x_{A2})/2 = (0.8 + 0.2)/2 = 0.50$.

$$D''_{NA} = \frac{1}{(1 - \alpha x_{A\,av})/D_{AB} + 1/D_{KA}}$$

$$= \frac{1}{(1 + 1.645 \times 0.5)/(6.98 \times 10^{-4}) + 1/(7.91 \times 10^{-4})}$$

$$= 2.581 \times 10^{-4}\ \text{m}^2/\text{s}$$

Substituting into Eq. (7.6-16),

$$N_A = \frac{D''_{NA}}{RTL}(x_{A1} - x_{A2})$$

$$= \frac{(2.581 \times 10^{-4})(1.013 \times 10^4)}{8314(298)(0.01)}(0.8 - 0.2)$$

$$= 6.33 \times 10^{-5}\ \text{kg mol/s} \cdot \text{m}^2$$

In this case the flux is only -1.1% low.

7.6F Diffusion of Gases in Porous Solids

In actual diffusion in porous solids, the pores are not straight and cylindrical but irregular. Hence, the equations for diffusion in pores must be modified somewhat for actual porous solids. The problem is further complicated by the fact that the pore diameters vary and the Knudsen diffusivity is a function of pore diameter.

As a result of these complications, investigators often measure effective diffusivities $D_{A\,\text{eff}}$ in porous media, where

$$N_A = \frac{D_{A\,\text{eff}} P}{RTL}(x_{A1} - x_{A2}) \tag{7.6-19}$$

If a tortuosity factor τ is used to correct the length L in Eq. (7.6-16), and the right-hand side is multiplied by the void fraction ε, Eq. (7.6-16) becomes

$$N_A = \frac{\varepsilon D''_{NA}}{\tau}\frac{P}{RTL}(x_{A1} - x_{A2}) \tag{7.6-20}$$

Comparing Eqs. (7.6-19) and (7.6-20),

$$D_{A\,\text{eff}} = \frac{\varepsilon D''_{NA}}{\tau} \tag{7.6-21}$$

In some cases investigators measure $D_{A\,\text{eff}}$ but use D'_{NA} instead of the more accurate D''_{NA} in Eq. (7.6-21).

Experimental data (G4, S2, S6) show that τ varies from about 1.5 to over 10. A reasonable range for many commercial porous solids is about $2-6$ (S2). If the porous solid consists of a bidispersed system of micropores and macropores instead of a monodispersed pore system, the above approach should be modified (C4, S6).

Discussions and references for diffusion in porous inorganic-type solids, organic solids, and freeze-dried foods such as meat and fruit are given elsewhere (S2, S6).

Another type of diffusion that may occur is surface diffusion. When a molecular layer of adsorption occurs on the solid, the molecules can migrate on the surface. Details are given elsewhere (S2, S6).

7.7 NUMERICAL METHODS FOR UNSTEADY-STATE MOLECULAR DIFFUSION

7.7A Introduction

Unsteady-state diffusion often occurs in inorganic, organic, and biological solid materials. If the boundary conditions are constant with time, if they are the same on all sides or surfaces of the solid, and if the initial concentration profile is uniform throughout the solid, the methods described in Section 7.1 can be used. However, these conditions are not always fulfilled, in which case numerical methods must be used.

7.7B Unsteady-State Numerical Methods for Diffusion

1. Derivation for unsteady state for a slab. For unsteady-state diffusion in one direction, Eq. (7.1-9) becomes

$$\frac{\partial c_A}{\partial t} = D_{AB} \frac{\partial^2 c_A}{\partial x^2} \tag{7.7-1}$$

Since this equation is identical mathematically to the unsteady-state heat-conduction Eq. (5.10-10),

$$\frac{\partial T}{\partial t} = \alpha \frac{\partial^2 T}{\partial x^2} \tag{5.10-10}$$

identical mathematical methods can be used for solving both diffusion and conduction numerically.

Figure 7.7-1 shows a slab of width Δx centered at point n, represented by the shaded area. Making a mole balance of A on this slab at the time t when the rate in $-$ rate out = rate of accumulation in Δt s,

$$\frac{D_{AB} A}{\Delta x}(_t c_{n-1} - {}_t c_n) - \frac{D_{AB} A}{\Delta x}(_t c_n - {}_t c_{n+1}) = \frac{(A \, \Delta x)}{\Delta t}(_{t+\Delta t} c_n - {}_t c_n) \tag{7.7-2}$$

where A is cross-sectional area and $_{t+\Delta t} c_n$ is concentration at point n one Δt later. Rearranging,

$$_{t+\Delta t} c_n = \frac{1}{M}\left[_t c_{n+1} + (M - 2)_t c_n + {}_t c_{n-1}\right] \tag{7.7-3}$$

where M is a constant.

$$M = \frac{(\Delta x)^2}{D_{AB} \Delta t} \tag{7.7-4}$$

As in heat conduction, $M \geq 2$.

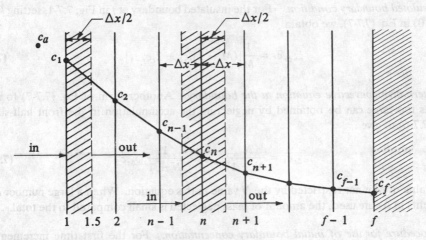

FIGURE 7.7-1. *Unsteady-state diffusion in a slab.*

In using Eq. (7.7-3), the concentration $_{t+\Delta t}C_n$ at position n and the new time $t + \Delta t$ is calculated explicitly from the known three points at t. In this calculation method, starting with the known concentrations at $t = 0$, the calculations proceed directly from one time increment to the next until the final time is reached.

2. Simplified Schmidt method for a slab. If the value of $M = 2$, a simplification of Eq. (7.7-3) occurs, giving the Schmidt method:

$$_{t+\Delta t}C_n = \frac{_tC_{n-1} + {}_tC_{n+1}}{2} \qquad (7.7\text{-}5)$$

7.7C Boundary Conditions for Numerical Methods for a Slab

1. Convection at a boundary. For the case where convection occurs outside in the fluid and the concentration of the fluid outside is suddenly changed to c_a, we can make a mass balance on the outside half-slab in Fig. 7.7-1. Following the methods used for heat transfer to derive Eq. (5.4-7), we write rate of mass entering by convection − rate of mass leaving by diffusion = rate of mass accumulation in Δt hours:

$$k_c A(_t c_a - {}_t c_1) - \frac{D_{AB} A}{\Delta x}(_t c_1 - {}_t c_2) = \frac{(A\,\Delta x/2)}{\Delta t}(_{t+\Delta t} c_{1.25} - {}_t c_{1.25}) \qquad (7.7\text{-}6)$$

where $_t c_{1.25}$ is the concentration at the midpoint of the 0.5 Δx outside slab. As an approximation, using $_t c_1$ for $_t c_{1.25}$ and rearranging Eq. (7.7-6),

$$_{t+\Delta t} c_1 = \frac{1}{M}[2N\,_t c_a + [M - (2N + 2)]_t c_1 + 2\,_t c_2] \qquad (7.7\text{-}7)$$

$$N = \frac{k_c \,\Delta x}{D_{AB}} \qquad (7.7\text{-}8)$$

where k_c is the convective mass-transfer coefficient in m/s. Again, note that $M \geq (2N + 2)$.

2. *Insulated boundary condition.*   For the insulated boundary at f in Fig. 7.7-1, setting $k_c = 0$ ($N = 0$) in Eq. (7.7-7), we obtain

$$_{t+\Delta t}c_f = \frac{1}{M}[(M - 2)_t c_f + 2_t c_{f-1}] \tag{7.7-9}$$

3. *Alternative convective equation at the boundary.*   Another form of Eq. (7.7-7) to use if N gets too large can be obtained by neglecting the accumulation in the front half-slab of Eq. (7.7-6) to give

$$_{t+\Delta t}c_1 = \frac{N}{N + 1}_{t+\Delta t}c_a + \frac{1}{N + 1}_{t+\Delta t}c_2 \tag{7.7-10}$$

The value of M is not restricted by the N value in this equation. When a large number of increments in Δx are used, the amount of mass neglected is small compared to the total.

4. *Procedure for use of initial boundary concentration.*   For the first time increment, we should use an average value for $_1 c_a$ of $(c_a + {}_0 c_1)/2$, where $_0 c_1$ is the initial concentration at point 1. For succeeding times, the full value of c_a should be used. This special procedure for the value of c_a increases the accuracy of the numerical method, especially after a few time intervals.

In Section 5.4B, concerning numerical methods for heat-transfer, a detailed discussion is given on the best value of M to use in Eq. (7.7-3). The most accurate results are obtained for $M = 4$.

5. *Boundary conditions with distribution coefficient.*   Equations for boundary conditions in Eqs. (7.7-7) and (7.7-10) were derived for the distribution coefficient K given in Eq. (7.7-7) being 1.0. When K is not 1.0, as in the boundary conditions for steady state, Kk_c should be substituted for k_c in Eq. (7.7-8) to become as follows (see also Sections 6.6B and 7.1C):

$$N = \frac{Kk_c \Delta x}{D_{AB}} \tag{7.7-11}$$

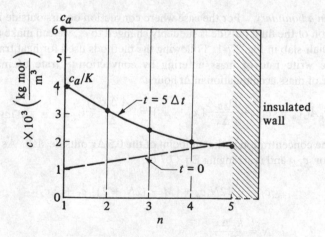

FIGURE 7.7-2.   *Concentrations for numerical method for unsteady-state diffusion, Example 7.7-1.*

Also, in Eqs. (7.7-7) and (7.7-10), the term c_a/K should be substituted for c_a.

Other cases, such as for diffusion between dissimilar slabs in series, resistance between slabs in series, and so on, are covered in detail elsewhere (G1), with actual numerical examples being given. In reference (G1) the implicit numerical method is discussed.

EXAMPLE 7.7-1. Numerical Solution for Unsteady-State Diffusion with a Distribution Coefficient

A slab of material 0.004 m thick has an initial concentration profile of solute A as follows, where x is distance in m from the exposed surface:

$x(m)$	Concentration $(kg\ mol\ A/m^3)$	Position, n
0	1.0×10^{-3}	1 (exposed)
0.001	1.25×10^{-3}	2
0.002	1.5×10^{-3}	3
0.003	1.75×10^{-3}	4
0.004	2.0×10^{-3}	5 (insulated)

The diffusivity $D_{AB} = 1.0 \times 10^{-9}$ m²/s. Suddenly, the top surface is exposed to a fluid having a constant concentration $c_a = 6 \times 10^{-3}$ kg mol A/m^3. The distribution coefficient $K = c_a/c_n = 1.50$. The rear surface is insulated, so that unsteady-state diffusion is occurring only in the x direction. Calculate the concentration profile after 2500 s. The convective mass-transfer coefficient k_c can be assumed as infinite. Use $\Delta x = 0.001$ m and $M = 2.0$.

Solution: Figure 7.7-2 shows the initial concentration profile for four slices and $c_a = 6 \times 10^{-3}$. Since $M = 2$, substituting into Eq. (7.7-4) with $\Delta x = 0.001$ m and solving for Δt,

$$M = 2 = \frac{(\Delta x)^2}{D_{AB}\ \Delta t} = \frac{(0.001)^2}{(1 \times 10^{-9})(\Delta t)}$$

$$\Delta t = 500\ s$$

Hence, 2500 s/(500 s/increment) or five time increments are needed.

For the front surface, where $n = 1$, the concentration to use for the first time increment, as stated previously, is

$$_1c_a = \frac{c_a/K + {}_0c_1}{2} = {}_1c_1 \quad (n = 1) \qquad \textbf{(7.7-12)}$$

where $_0c_1$ is the initial concentration at $n = 1$. For the remaining time increments,

$$c_1 = \frac{c_a}{K} \quad (n = 1) \qquad \textbf{(7.7-13)}$$

To calculate the concentrations for all time increments for slabs $n = 2, 3, 4$, using Eq. (7.7-5) for $M = 2$,

$$_{t+\Delta t}c_n = \frac{_tc_{n-1} + {}_tc_{n+1}}{2} \quad (n = 2, 3, 4) \qquad \textbf{(7.7-14)}$$

For the insulated end at $n = 5$, substituting $M = 2$ and $f = n = 5$ into Eq. (7.7-9),

$$_{t+\Delta t}c_5 = \frac{(2-2)_t c_5 + 2_t c_4}{2} = {}_t c_4 \quad (n = 5) \qquad \textbf{(7.7-15)}$$

For 1 Δt or $t + 1\ \Delta t$, the first time increment, calculating the concentration for $n = 1$ by Eq. (7.7-12),

$$_{t+\Delta t}c_1 = \frac{c_a/K + {}_0 c_1}{2} = \frac{6 \times 10^{-3}/1.5 + 1 \times 10^{-3}}{2} = 2.5 \times 10^{-3}$$

For $n = 2$, 3, and 4, using Eq. (7.7-14),

$$_{t+\Delta t}c_2 = \frac{_t c_{n-1} + {}_t c_{n+1}}{2} = \frac{_t c_1 + {}_t c_3}{2} = \frac{2.5 \times 10^{-3} + 1.5 \times 10^{-3}}{2} = 2 \times 10^{-3}$$

$$_{t+\Delta t}c_3 = \frac{_t c_2 + {}_t c_4}{2} = \frac{1.25 \times 10^{-3} + 1.75 \times 10^{-3}}{2} = 1.5 \times 10^{-3}$$

$$_{t+\Delta t}c_4 = \frac{_t c_3 + {}_t c_5}{2} = \frac{1.5 \times 10^{-3} + 2 \times 10^{-3}}{2} = 1.75 \times 10^{-3}$$

For $n = 5$, using Eq. (7.7-15),

$$_{t+\Delta t}c_5 = {}_t c_4 = 1.75 \times 10^{-3}$$

For 2 Δt, using Eq. (7.7-13) for $n = 1$, using Eq. (7.7-14) for $n = 2-4$, and using Eq. (7.7-15) for $n = 5$,

$$_{t+2\Delta t}c_1 = \frac{c_a}{K} = \frac{6 \times 10^{-3}}{1.5} = 4.0 \times 10^{-3} \qquad \text{(constant for rest of time)}$$

$$_{t+2\Delta t}c_2 = \frac{_{t+\Delta t}c_1 + {}_{t+\Delta t}c_3}{2} = \frac{4 \times 10^{-3} + 1.5 \times 10^{-3}}{2} = 2.75 \times 10^{-3}$$

$$_{t+2\Delta t}c_3 = \frac{_{t+\Delta t}c_2 + {}_{t+\Delta t}c_4}{2} = \frac{2 \times 10^{-3} + 1.75 \times 10^{-3}}{2} = 1.875 \times 10^{-3}$$

$$_{t+2\Delta t}c_4 = \frac{_{t+\Delta t}c_3 + {}_{t+\Delta t}c_5}{2} = \frac{1.5 \times 10^{-3} + 1.75 \times 10^{-3}}{2} = 1.625 \times 10^{-3}$$

$$_{t+2\Delta t}c_5 = {}_{t+\Delta t}c_4 = 1.75 \times 10^{-3}$$

For 3 Δt,

$$_{t+3\Delta t}c_1 = 4 \times 10^{-3}$$

$$_{t+3\Delta t}c_2 = \frac{4 \times 10^{-3} + 1.875 \times 10^{-3}}{2} = 2.938 \times 10^{-3}$$

$$_{t+3\Delta t}c_3 = \frac{2.75 \times 10^{-3} + 1.625 \times 10^{-3}}{2} = 2.188 \times 10^{-3}$$

$$_{t+3\Delta t}c_4 = \frac{1.875 \times 10^{-3} + 1.75 \times 10^{-3}}{2} = 1.813 \times 10^{-3}$$

$$_{t+3\Delta t}c_5 = 1.625 \times 10^{-3}$$

For 4 Δt,

$$_{t+4\Delta t}c_1 = 4 \times 10^{-3}$$

$$_{t+4\Delta t}c_2 = \frac{4 \times 10^{-3} + 2.188 \times 10^{-3}}{2} = 3.094 \times 10^{-3}$$

$$_{t+4\Delta t}c_3 = \frac{2.938 \times 10^{-3} + 1.813 \times 10^{-3}}{2} = 2.376 \times 10^{-3}$$

$$_{t+4\Delta t}c_4 = \frac{2.188 \times 10^{-3} + 1.625, \times 10^{-3}}{2} = 1.906 \times 10^{-3}$$

$$_{t+4\Delta t}c_5 = 1.813 \times 10^{-3}$$

For 5 Δt,

$$_{t+5\Delta t}c_1 = 4 \times 10^{-3}$$

$$_{t+5\Delta t}c_2 = \frac{4 \times 10^{-3} + 2.376 \times 10^{-3}}{2} = 3.188 \times 10^{-3}$$

$$_{t+5\Delta t}c_3 = \frac{3.094 \times 10^{-3} + 1.906 \times 10^{-3}}{2} = 2.500 \times 10^{-3}$$

$$_{t+5\Delta t}c_4 = \frac{2.376 \times 10^{-3} + 1.813 \times 10^{-3}}{2} = 2.095 \times 10^{-3}$$

$$_{t+5\Delta t}c_5 = 1.906 \times 10^{-3}$$

The final concentration profile is plotted in Fig. 7.7-2. To increase the accuracy, more slab increments and time increments are needed. This type of calculation is suitable for use with a computer spreadsheet.

7.8   DIMENSIONAL ANALYSIS IN MASS TRANSFER

7.8A   Introduction

The use of dimensional analysis enables us to predict the various dimensional groups which are very helpful in correlating experimental mass-transfer data. As we saw for fluid flow and heat transfer, the Reynolds number, Prandtl number, Grashof number, and Nusselt number are often used in correlating experimental data. The Buckingham theorem discussed in Sections 3.11 and 4.14 states that the functional relationship among q quantities or variables whose units may be given in terms of u fundamental units or dimensions may be written as $(q - u)$ dimensionless groups.

7.8B   Dimensional Analysis for Convective Mass Transfer

We consider a case of convective mass transfer where a fluid is flowing by forced convection in a pipe and mass transfer is occurring from the wall to the fluid. The fluid flows at a velocity v inside a pipe of diameter D, and we wish to relate the mass-transfer coefficient k_c' to the variables D, ρ, μ, v, and D_{AB}. The total number of variables is $q = 6$. The fundamental units or dimensions are $u = 3$ and are mass M, length L, and time t. The units of the variables are

$$k_c' = \frac{L}{t} \qquad \rho = \frac{M}{L^3} \qquad \mu = \frac{M}{Lt} \qquad v = \frac{L}{t} \qquad D_{AB} = \frac{L^2}{t} \qquad D = L$$

The number of dimensionless groups of π's are then $6 - 3$, or 3. Then,

$$\pi_1 = f(\pi_2, \pi_3) \tag{7.8-1}$$

We choose the variables D_{AB}, ρ, and D to be the variables common to all the dimensionless groups, which are

$$\pi_1 = D_{AB}^a \rho^b D^c k_c' \tag{7.8-2}$$

$$\pi_2 = D_{AB}^d \rho^e D^f v \tag{7.8-3}$$

$$\pi_3 = D_{AB}^g \rho^h D^i \mu \tag{7.8-4}$$

For π_1 we substitute the actual dimensions as follows:

$$1 = \left(\frac{L^2}{t}\right)^a \left(\frac{M}{L^3}\right)^b (L)^c \left(\frac{L}{t}\right) \tag{7.8-5}$$

Summing for each exponent,

$$(L) \quad 0 = 2a - 3b + c + 1$$

$$(M) \quad 0 = b \tag{7.8-6}$$

$$(t) \quad 0 = a - 1$$

Solving these equation simultaneously, $a = -1$, $b = 0$, $c = 1$. Substituting these values into Eq. (7.8-2),

$$\pi_1 = \frac{k_c' D}{D_{AB}} = N_{Sh} \tag{7.8-7}$$

Repeating for π_2 and π_3,

$$\pi_2 = \frac{v D}{D_{AB}} \tag{7.8-8}$$

$$\pi_3 = \frac{\mu}{\rho D_{AB}} = N_{Sc} \tag{7.8-9}$$

If we divide π_2 by π_3 we obtain the Reynolds number:

$$\frac{\pi_2}{\pi_3} = \frac{v D}{D_{AB}} \bigg/ \left(\frac{\mu}{\rho D_{AB}}\right) = \frac{D v \rho}{\mu} = N_{Re} \tag{7.8-10}$$

Hence, substituting into Eq. (7.8-1),

$$N_{Sh} = f(N_{Re}, N_{Sc}) \tag{7.8-11}$$

7.9 BOUNDARY-LAYER FLOW AND TURBULENCE IN MASS TRANSFER

7.9A Laminar Flow and Boundary-Layer Theory in Mass Transfer

In Section 3.10C an exact solution was obtained for the hydrodynamic boundary layer for isothermal laminar flow past a plate, and in Section 5.7A an extension of the Blasius solution was also used to derive an expression for convective heat transfer. In an analogous manner we use the Blasius solution for convective mass transfer for the same geometry and laminar

FIGURE 7.9-1. *Laminar flow of fluid past a flat plate and concentration boundary layer.*

flow. In Fig. 7.9-1 the concentration boundary layer is shown, where the concentration of the fluid approaching the plate is $c_{A\infty}$ and c_{AS} in the fluid adjacent to the surface.

We start by using the differential mass balance, Eq. (7.5-17), and simplifying it for steady state where $\partial c_A/\partial t = 0$; $R_A = 0$; flow only in the x and y directions, so $v_z = 0$; and neglecting diffusion in the x and z directions to give

$$v_x \frac{\partial c_A}{\partial x} + v_y \frac{\partial c_A}{\partial y} = D_{AB} \frac{\partial^2 c_A}{\partial y^2} \qquad (7.9\text{-}1)$$

The momentum boundary-layer equation is very similar:

$$v_x \frac{\partial v_x}{\partial x} + v_y \frac{\partial v_x}{\partial y} = \frac{\mu}{\rho} \frac{\partial^2 v_x}{\partial y^2} \qquad (3.10\text{-}5)$$

The thermal boundary-layer equation is also similar:

$$v_x \frac{\partial T}{\partial x} + v_y \frac{\partial T}{\partial y} = \frac{k}{\rho c_p} \frac{\partial^2 T}{\partial y^2} \qquad (5.7\text{-}2)$$

The continuity equation used previously is

$$\frac{\partial v_x}{\partial x} + \frac{\partial v_y}{\partial y} = 0 \qquad (3.10\text{-}3)$$

The dimensionless concentration boundary conditions are

$$\frac{v_x}{v_\infty} = \frac{T - T_S}{T_\infty - T_S} = \frac{c_A - c_{AS}}{c_{A\infty} - c_{AS}} = 0 \qquad \text{at } y = 0$$

$$\qquad\qquad (7.9\text{-}2)$$

$$\frac{v_x}{v_\infty} = \frac{T - T_S}{T_\infty - T_S} = \frac{c_A - c_{AS}}{c_{A\infty} - c_{AS}} = 1 \qquad \text{at } y = \infty$$

The similarity among the three differential equations (7.9-1), (3.10-5), and (5.7-2) is obvious, as is the similarity among the three sets of boundary conditions in Eq. (7.9-2). In Section 5.7A the Blasius solution was applied to convective heat transfer when $(\mu/\rho)/\alpha = N_{Pr} = 1.0$. We use the same type of solution for laminar convective mass transfer when $(\mu/\rho)/D_{AB} = N_{Sc} = 1.0$.

The velocity gradient at the surface was derived previously:

$$\left(\frac{\partial v_x}{\partial y}\right)_{y=0} = 0.332\frac{v_\infty}{x}N_{Re,x}^{1/2} \tag{5.7-5}$$

where $N_{Re,x} = xv_\infty\rho/\mu$. Also, from Eq. (7.9-2),

$$\frac{v_x}{v_\infty} = \frac{c_A - c_{AS}}{c_{A\infty} - c_{AS}} \tag{7.9-3}$$

Differentiating Eq. (7.9-3) and combining the result with Eq. (5.7-5),

$$\left(\frac{\partial c_A}{\partial y}\right)_{y=0} = (c_{A\infty} - c_{AS})\left(\frac{0.332}{x}N_{Re,x}^{1/2}\right) \tag{7.9-4}$$

The convective mass-transfer equation can be written as follows and related to Fick's equation for dilute solutions:

$$N_{Ay} = k'_c(c_{AS} - c_{A\infty}) = -D_{AB}\left(\frac{\partial c_A}{\partial y}\right)_{y=0} \tag{7.9-5}$$

Combining Eqs. (7.9-4) and (7.9-5),

$$\frac{k'_c x}{D_{AB}} = N_{Sh,x} = 0.332\,N_{Re,x}^{1/2} \tag{7.9-6}$$

This relationship is restricted to gases with a $N_{Sc} = 1.0$.

The relationship between the thickness δ of the hydrodynamic and δ_c of the concentration boundary layers where the Schmidt number is not 1.0 is

$$\frac{\delta}{\delta_c} = N_{Sc}^{1/3} \tag{7.9-7}$$

As a result, the equation for the local convective mass-transfer coefficient is

$$\frac{k'_c x}{D_{AB}} = N_{Sh,x} = 0.332\,N_{Re,x}^{1/2}N_{Sc}^{1/3} \tag{7.9-8}$$

We can obtain the equation for the mean mass-transfer coefficient k'_c from $x = 0$ to $x = L$ for a plate of width b by integrating as follows:

$$k'_c = \frac{b}{bL}\int_0^L k'_c\, dx \tag{7.9-9}$$

The result is

$$\frac{k'_c L}{D_{AB}} = N_{Sh} = 0.664\,N_{Re,L}^{1/2}N_{Sc}^{1/3} \tag{7.9-10}$$

This is similar to the heat-transfer equation for a flat plate, Eq. (5.7-15), and also agrees with the experimental mass-transfer equation (7.3-27) for a flat plate.

In Section 3.10 an approximate integral analysis was performed for the laminar hydrodynamic and the turbulent hydrodynamic boundary layers. This was also done in Section 5.7 for the thermal boundary layer. An approximate integral analysis can also be done in exactly the same manner for the laminar and turbulent concentration boundary layers.

7.9B Prandtl Mixing Length and Turbulent Eddy Mass Diffusivity

In many applications the flow in mass transfer is turbulent and not laminar. The turbulent flow of a fluid is quite complex as the fluid undergoes a series of random eddy movements throughout the turbulent core. When mass transfer is occurring, we refer to this as eddy mass diffusion. In Sections 3.10 and 5.7 we derived equations for turbulent eddy thermal diffusivity and momentum diffusivity using the Prandtl mixing length theory.

In a similar manner we can derive a relation for the turbulent eddy mass diffusivity, ε_M. Eddies are transported a distance L, called the Prandtl mixing length, in the y direction. At this point L the fluid eddy differs in velocity from the adjacent fluid by the velocity v'_x, which is the fluctuating velocity component given in Section 3.10F. The instantaneous rate of mass transfer of A at a velocity v'_y for a distance L in the y direction is

$$J^*_{Ay} = c'_A v'_y \tag{7.9-11}$$

where c'_A is the instantaneous fluctuating concentration. The instantaneous concentration of the fluid is $c_A = c'_A + \bar{c}_A$, where $\bar{c}_A$ is the mean value and c'_A the deviation from the mean value. The mixing length L is small enough that the concentration difference is

$$c'_A = L \frac{d\bar{c}_A}{dy} \tag{7.9-12}$$

The rate of mass transported per unit area is J^*_{Ay}. Combining Eqs. (7.9-11) and (7.9-12),

$$J^*_{Ay} = -v'_y L \frac{d\bar{c}_A}{dy} \tag{7.9-13}$$

From Eq. (5.7-23),

$$v'_y = v'_x = L \left| \frac{d\bar{v}_x}{dy} \right| \tag{7.9-14}$$

Substituting Eq. (7.9-14) into (7.9-13),

$$J^*_{Ay} = -L^2 \left| \frac{d\bar{v}_x}{dy} \right| \frac{d\bar{c}_A}{dy} \tag{7.9-15}$$

The term $L^2 |d\bar{v}_x/dy|$ is called the turbulent eddy mass diffusivity ε_M. Combining Eq. (7.9-15) with the diffusion equation in terms of D_{AB}, the total flux is

$$J^*_{Ay} = -(D_{AB} + \varepsilon_M) \frac{d\bar{c}_A}{dy} \tag{7.9-16}$$

The similarities between Eq. (7.9-16) for mass transfer and heat and momentum transfer have been pointed out in detail in Section 6.1A.

7.9C Models for Mass-Transfer Coefficients

1. Introduction. For many years mass-transfer coefficients, which were based primarily on empirical correlations, have been used in the design of process equipment. A better understanding of the mechanisms of turbulence is needed before we can give a theoretical explanation of convective mass-transfer coefficients. Several theories of convective mass transfer, such as the eddy diffusivity theory, have been presented in this chapter. In the following sections we present briefly some of these theories and discuss how they can be used to extend empirical correlations.

2. Film mass-transfer theory. The film theory, which is the simplest and most elementary theory, assumes the presence of a fictitious laminar film next to the boundary. This film, where only molecular diffusion is assumed to be occurring, has the same resistance to mass transfer as actually exists in the viscous, transition, and turbulent core regions. Then the actual mass-transfer coefficient k'_c is related to this film thickness δ_f by

$$J^*_A = k'_c(c_{A1} - c_{A2}) = \frac{D_{AB}}{\delta_f}(c_{A1} - c_{A2}) \tag{7.9-17}$$

$$k'_c = \frac{D_{AB}}{\delta_f} \tag{7.9-18}$$

The mass-transfer coefficient is proportional to $D_{AB}^{1.0}$. However, since we have shown that in Eq. (7.3-13) J_D is proportional to $(\mu/\rho D_{AB})^{2/3}$, then $k'_c \propto D_{AB}^{2/3}$. Hence, the film theory is not correct. The great advantage of the film theory is its simplicity where it can be used in complex situations such as simultaneous diffusion and chemical reaction.

3. Penetration theory. The penetration theory derived by Higbie and modified by Danckwerts (D3) was derived for diffusion or penetration into a laminar falling film for short contact times in Eq. (7.3-23) and is as follows:

$$k'_c = \sqrt{\frac{4D_{AB}}{\pi t_L}} \tag{7.9-19}$$

where t_L is the time of penetration of the solute in seconds. This was extended by Danckwerts. He modified this for turbulent mass transfer and postulated that a fluid eddy has a uniform concentration in the turbulent core and is swept to the surface and undergoes unsteady-state diffusion. Then the eddy is swept away to the eddy core and other eddies are swept to the surface and stay for a random amount of time. A mean surface renewal factor s in s^{-1} is defined as follows:

$$k'_c = \sqrt{D_{AB}s} \tag{7.9-20}$$

The mass-transfer coefficient k'_c is proportional to $D_{AB}^{0.5}$. In some systems, such as where liquid flows over packing and semistagnant pockets occur where the surface is being renewed, the results approximately follow Eq. (7.9-20). The value of s must be obtained experimentally. Others (D3, T2) have derived more complex combination film-surface renewal theories predicting a gradual change of the exponent on D_{AB} from 0.5 to 1.0 depending on turbulence and other factors. Penetration theories have been used in cases where diffusion and chemical reaction are occurring (D3).

4. Boundary-layer theory. The boundary-layer theory has been discussed in detail in Section 7.9 and is useful in predicting and correlating data for fluids flowing past solid surfaces. For laminar flow and turbulent flow the mass-transfer coefficient $k'_c \propto D_{AB}^{2/3}$. This has been experimentally verified for many cases.

PROBLEMS

7.1-1. *Unsteady-State Diffusion in a Thick Slab.* Repeat Example 7.1-2 but use a distribution coefficient $K = 0.50$ instead of 2.0. Plot the data.

$$\text{Ans.} \quad c = c_i = 5.75 \times 10^{-2} \cdot (x = 0),$$
$$c = 2.78 \times 10^{-2} \, (x = 0.01 \text{ m}), c_{Li} = 2.87 \times 10^{-2} \text{ kg mol/m}^3$$

7.1-2. *Plot of Concentration Profile in Unsteady-State Diffusion.* Using the same conditions as in Example 7.1-2, calculate the concentration at the points $x = 0, 0.005, 0.01,$ 0.015, and 0.02 m from the surface. Also calculate c_{Li} in the liquid at the interface. Plot the concentrations in a manner similar to Fig. 7.1-3b, showing interface concentrations.

7.1-3. *Unsteady-State Diffusion in Several Directions.* Use the same conditions as in Example 7.1-1 except that the solid is a rectangular block 10.16 mm thick in the x direction, 7.62 mm thick in the y direction, and 10.16 mm thick in the z direction, and diffusion occurs at all six faces. Calculate the concentration at the midpoint after 10 h.

$$\text{Ans.} \quad c = 6.20 \times 10^{-4} \text{ kg mol/m}^3$$

7.1-4. *Drying of Moist Clay.* A very thick slab of clay has an initial moisture content of $c_0 = 14$ wt %. Air is passed over the top surface to dry the clay. Assume a relative resistance of the gas at the surface of zero. The equilibrium moisture content at the surface is constant at $c_1 = 3.0$ wt %. The diffusion of the moisture in the clay can be approximated by a diffusivity of $D_{AB} = 1.29 \times 10^{-8}$ m^2/s. After 1.0 h of drying, calculate the concentration of water at points 0.005, 0.01, and 0.02 m below the surface. Assume that the clay is a semi-infinite solid and that the Y value can be represented using concentrations of wt % rather than kg mol/m^3. Plot the values versus x.

7.1-5. *Unsteady-State Diffusion in a Cylinder of Agar Gel.* A wet cylinder of agar gel at 278 K containing a uniform concentration of urea of 0.1 kg mol/m^3 has a diameter of 30.48 mm and is 38.1 mm long with flat, parallel ends. The diffusivity is 4.72×10^{-10} m^2/s. Calculate the concentration at the midpoint of the cylinder after 100 h for the following cases if the cylinder is suddenly immersed in turbulent pure water:
(a) For radial diffusion only.
(b) Diffusion occurs radially and axially.

7.1-6. *Drying of Wood.* A flat slab of Douglas fir wood 50.8 mm thick containing 30 wt % moisture is being dried from both sides (neglecting ends and edges). The equilibrium moisture content at the surface of the wood due to the drying air blown over it is held at 5 wt % moisture. The drying can be assumed to be represented by a diffusivity of 3.72×10^{-6} m^2/h. Calculate the time for the center to reach 10% moisture.

7.2-1. *Flux and Conversion of Mass-Transfer Coefficient.* A value of k_G was experimentally determined to be 1.08 lb mol/h $\cdot$ ft$^2 \cdot$ atm for A diffusing through stagnant B. For the same flow and concentrations it is desired to predict k'_G and the flux of A for equimolar counterdiffusion. The partial pressures are $p_{A1} = 0.20$ atm, $p_{A2} = 0.05$ atm, and $P = 1.0$ atm abs total. Use English and SI units.

$$\text{Ans.} \quad k'_G = 0.943 \text{ lb mol/h} \cdot \text{ft}^2 \cdot \text{atm}, 1.262 \times 10^{-8} \text{ kg mol/s} \cdot \text{m}^2 \cdot \text{Pa},$$
$$N_A = 0.1414 \text{ lb mol } A/\text{h} \cdot \text{ft}^2, 1.918 \times 10^{-4} \text{ kg mol/s} \cdot \text{m}^2$$

7.2-2. *Conversion of Mass-Transfer Coefficients.* Prove or show the following relationships, starting with the flux equations:
(a) Convert k'_c to k_y and k_G.
(b) Convert k_L to k_x and k'_x.
(c) Convert k_G to k_y and k_c.

7.2-3. Absorption of H_2S by Water. In a wetted-wall tower an air–H_2S mixture is flowing by a film of water that is flowing as a thin film down a vertical plate. The H_2S is being absorbed from the air to the water at a total pressure of 1.50 atm abs and 30°C. A value for k_c' of 9.567×10^{-4} m/s has been predicted for the gas-phase mass-transfer coefficient. At a given point the mole fraction of H_2S in the liquid at the liquid–gas interface is $2.0(10^{-5})$ and p_A of H_2S in the gas is 0.05 atm. The Henry's law equilibrium relation is p_A (atm) $= 609x_A$ (mole fraction in liquid). Calculate the rate of absorption of H_2S. (*Hint:* Call point 1 the interface and point 2 the gas phase. Then calculate p_{A1} from Henry's law and the given x_A. The value of p_{A2} is 0.05 atm.)

Ans. $N_A = -1.485 \times 10^{-6}$ kg mol/s $\cdot$ m^2

7.2-4. Effect of High Flux on Mass-Transfer Coefficients. Using the data from Example 7.2-2, also calculate the flux ratios k_x^0/k_x' for $x_{A1} = 0.20$ and $x_{A1} = 0.01$. Tabulate these ratios for the three values of x_{A1} and plot the ratio versus x_{A1}.

7.3-1. Mass Transfer from a Flat Plate to a Liquid. Using the data and physical properties of Example 7.3-2 calculate the flux for a water velocity of 0.152 m/s and a plate length of $L = 0.137$ m. Do not assume that $x_{BM} = 1.0$ but actually calculate its value.

7.3-2. Mass Transfer from a Pipe Wall. Pure water at 26.1°C is flowing at a velocity of 0.0305 m/s in a tube having an inside diameter of 6.35 mm. The tube is 1.829 m long, with the last 1.22 m having the walls coated with benzoic acid. Assuming that the velocity profile is fully developed, calculate the average concentration of benzoic acid at the outlet. Use the physical property data from Example 7.3-2. [*Hint:* First calculate the Reynolds number $Dv\rho/\mu$. Then calculate $N_{Re} N_{Sc}(D/L)(\pi/4)$, which is the same as $W/D_{AB}\rho L$.]

Ans. $(c_A - c_{A0})/(c_{Ai} - c_{A0}) = 0.0744$, $c_A = 2.193 \times 10^{-3}$ kg mol/m^3

7.3-3. Mass-Transfer Coefficient for Various Geometries. It is desired to estimate the mass-transfer coefficient k_G in kg mol/s $\cdot$ m$^2 \cdot$ Pa for water vapor in air at 338.6 K and 101.32 kPa flowing in a large duct past solids of different geometries. The velocity in the duct is 3.66 m/s. The water vapor concentration in the air is small, so the physical properties of air can be used. Water vapor is being transferred to the solids. Do this for the following geometries:
(a) A single 25.4-mm-diameter sphere.
(b) A packed bed of 25.4-mm spheres with $\varepsilon = 0.35$.

Ans. (a) $k_G = 1.984 \times 10^{-8}$ kg mol/s $\cdot$ m$^2 \cdot$ Pa (1.482 lb mol/h $\cdot$ ft$^2 \cdot$ atm)

7.3-4. Mass Transfer to Definite Shapes. Estimate the value of the mass-transfer coefficient in a stream of air at 325.6 K flowing in a duct past the following shapes made of solid naphthalene. The velocity of the air is 1.524 m/s at 325.6 K and 202.6 kPa. The D_{AB} of naphthalene in air is 5.16×10^{-6} m^2/s at 273 K and 101.3 kPa.
(a) For air flowing parallel to a flat plate 0.152 m in length.
(b) For air flowing past a single sphere 12.7 mm in diameter.

7.3-5. Mass Transfer to Packed Bed and Driving Force. Pure water at 26.1°C is flowing at a rate of 0.0701 ft^3/h through a packed bed of 0.251-in. benzoic-acid spheres having a total surface area of 0.129 ft^2. The solubility of benzoic acid in water is 0.00184 lb mol benzoic acid/ft^3 solution. The outlet concentration c_{A2} is 1.80×10^{-4} lb mol/ft^3. Calculate the mass-transfer coefficient k_c.

7.3-6. Mass Transfer in Liquid Metals. Mercury at 26.5°C is flowing through a packed bed of lead spheres having a diameter of 2.096 mm with a void fraction of 0.499. The superficial velocity is 0.02198 m/s. The solubility of lead in mercury is 1.721 wt %, the

Chapter 7   Principles of Unsteady-State and Convective Mass Transfer

Schmidt number is 124.1, the viscosity of the solution is 1.577×10^{-3} Pa·s, and the density is 13 530 kg/m³.

(a) Predict the value of J_D. Use Eq. (7.3-38) if applicable. Compare with the experimental value of $J_D = 0.076$ (D2).

(b) Predict the value of k_c for the case of A diffusing through nondiffusing B.

　　　　　　　　　　　　　　　　　　　　　Ans. (a) $J_D = 0.0784$; (b) $k_c = 6.986 \times 10^{-5}$ m/s

7.3-7. Mass Transfer from a Pipe and Log Mean Driving Force. Use the same physical conditions as in Problem 7.3-2, but the velocity in the pipe is now 3.05 m/s. Do as follows:

(a) Predict the mass-transfer coefficient k_c'. (Is this turbulent flow?)

(b) Calculate the average benzoic acid concentration at the outlet. [*Note:* In this case, Eqs. (7.3-42) and (7.3-43) must be used with the log mean driving force, where A is the surface area of the pipe.]

(c) Calculate the total kg mol of benzoic acid dissolved per second.

7.3-8. Derivation of Relation Between J_D and N_{Sh}. Equation (7.3-3) defines the Sherwood number and Eq. (7.3-5) defines the J_D factor. Derive the relation between N_{Sh} and J_D in terms of N_{Re} and N_{Sc}.

　　　　　　　　　　　　　　　　　　　　　Ans. $N_{Sh} = J_D N_{Re} N_{Sc}^{1/3}$

7.3-9. Driving Force to Use in Mass Transfer. Derive Eq. (7.3-42) for the log mean driving force to use for a fluid flowing in a packed bed or in a tube. (*Hint:* Start by making a mass balance and a diffusion rate balance over a differential area dA as follows:

$$N_A \, dA = k_c(c_{Ai} - c_A) dA = V \, dc_A$$

where V = m³/s flow rate. Assume dilute solutions.)

7.4-1. Maximum Oxygen Uptake of a Microorganism. Calculate the maximum possible rate of oxygen uptake at 37°C of microorganisms having a diameter of $\frac{2}{3}$ μm suspended in an agitated aqueous solution. It is assumed that the surrounding liquid is saturated with O_2 from air at 1 atm abs pressure. It will be assumed that the microorganism can utilize the oxygen much faster than it can diffuse to it. The microorganism has a density very close to that of water. Use physical-property data from Example 7.4-1. (*Hint:* Since the oxygen is consumed faster than it is supplied, the concentration c_{A2} at the surface is zero. The concentration c_{A1} in the solution is at saturation.)

　　　　　　　　　　　　Ans. $k_c = 9.75 \times 10^{-3}$ m/s, $N_A = 2.20 \times 10^{-6}$ kg mol O_2/s·m²

7.4-2. Mass Transfer of O_2 in Fermentation Process. A total of 5.0 g of wet microorganisms having a density of 1100 kg/m³ and a diameter of 0.667 μm are added to 0.100 L of aqueous solution at 37°C in a shaker flask for a fermentation. Air can enter through a porous stopper. Use physical property data from Example 7.4-1.

(a) Calculate the maximum rate possible for mass transfer of oxygen in kg mol O_2/s to the surface of the microorganisms, assuming that the solution is saturated with air at 101.32 kPa abs pressure.

(b) By material balances on other nutrients, the actual utilization of O_2 by the microorganisms is 6.30×10^{-6} kg mol O_2/s. What would be the actual concentration of O_2 in the solution as percent saturation during the fermentation?

　　　　　　　　　Ans. (a) $k_L' = 9.82 \times 10^{-3}$ m/s, $N_A A = 9.07 \times 10^{-5}$ kg mol O_2/s;
　　　　　　　　　(b) 6.95% saturation

7.5-1. Sum of Molar Fluxes. Prove the following equation using the definitions in Table 7.5-1:

$$N_A + N_B = c v_M$$

7.5-2. Proof of Derived Relation. Using the definitions from Table 7.5-1, prove the following:

$$j_A = n_A - w_A(n_A + n_B)$$

7.5-3. Different Forms of Fick's Law. Using Eq. (1), prove Eq. (2):

$$j_A = -\rho D_{AB} \frac{dw_A}{dz} \tag{1}$$

$$j_A = -\frac{c^2}{\rho} M_A M_B D_{AB} \frac{dx_A}{dz} \tag{2}$$

(*Hint:* First relate w_A to x_A. Then differentiate this equation to relate dw_A and dx_A. Finally, use $M = x_A M_A + x_B M_B$ to simplify.)

7.5-4. Other Form of Fick's Law. Show that the following form of Fick's law is valid:

$$c(v_A - v_B) = -\frac{cD_{AB}}{x_A x_B} \frac{dx_A}{dz}$$

(*Hint:* Start with $N_A = J_A^* + c_A v_M$. Substitute the expression for J_A^* from Table 7.5-1 and simplify.)

7.5-5. Different Form of Equation of Continuity. Starting with Eq. (7.5-12),

$$\frac{\partial \rho_A}{\partial t} + (\nabla \cdot n_A) = r_A \tag{7.5-12}$$

convert this to the following for constant ρ:

$$\frac{\partial \rho_A}{\partial t} + (v \cdot \nabla \rho_A) - (\nabla \cdot D_{AB} \nabla \rho_A) = r_A \tag{1}$$

[*Hint:* From Table 7.5-1, substitute $n_A = j_A + \rho_A v$ into Eq. (7.5-12). Note that $(\nabla \cdot v) = 0$ for constant ρ. Then substitute Fick's law in terms of j_A.]

7.5-6. Diffusion and Reaction at a Surface. Gas A is diffusing from a gas stream at point 1 to a catalyst surface at point 2 and reacts instantaneously and irreversibly as follows:

$$2A \rightarrow B$$

Gas B diffuses back to the gas stream. Derive the final equation for N_A at constant pressure P and steady state in terms of partial pressures.

$$\text{Ans.} \quad N_A = \frac{2D_{AB}P}{RT(z_2 - z_1)} \ln \frac{1 - p_{A2}/2P}{1 - p_{A1}/2P}$$

7.5-7. Unsteady-State Diffusion and Reaction. Solute A is diffusing at unsteady state into a semi-infinite medium of pure B and undergoes a first-order reaction with B. Solute A is dilute. Calculate the concentration c_A at points $z = 0, 4,$ and 10 mm from the surface for $t = 1 \times 10^5$ s. Physical property data are $D_{AB} = 1 \times 10^{-9}$ m²/s, $k' = 1 \times 10^{-4}$ s^{-1}, $c_{A0} = 1.0$ kg mol/m³. Also calculate the kg mol absorbed/m².

7.5-8. Multicomponent Diffusion. At a total pressure of 202.6 kPa and 358 K, ammonia gas (A) is diffusing at steady state through an inert, nondiffusing mixture of nitrogen (B) and hydrogen (C). The mole fractions at $z_1 = 0$ are $x_{A1} = 0.8$, $x_{B1} = 0.15$, and $x_{C1} = 0.05$; and at $z_2 = 4.0$ mm, $x_{A2} = 0.2$, $x_{B2} = 0.6$, and $x_{C2} = 0.2$. The diffusivities at 358 K and 101.3 kPa are $D_{AB} = 3.28 \times 10^{-5}$ m²/s and $D_{AC} = 1.093 \times 10^{-4}$ m²/s. Calculate the flux of ammonia.

Ans. $N_A = 4.69 \times 10^{-4}$ kg mol A/s·m²

7.5-9. Diffusion in Liquid Metals and Variable Diffusivity. The diffusion of tin (A) in liquid lead (B) at 510°C was carried out by using a 10.0-mm-long capillary tube and maintaining the mole fraction of tin at x_{A1} at the left end and x_{A2} at the right end of the tube. In the range of concentrations of $0.2 \leq x_A \leq 0.4$ the diffusivity of tin in lead has been found to be a linear function of x_A (S7):

$$D_{AB} = A + Bx_A$$

where A and B are constants and D_{AB} is in m²/s.
(a) Assuming the molar density to be constant at $c = c_A + c_B = c_{av}$, derive the final integrated equation for the flux N_A, assuming steady state and that A diffuses through stagnant B.
(b) For this experiment, $A = 4.8 \times 10^{-9}$, $B = -6.5 \times 10^{-9}$, $c_{av} = 50$ kg mol/m³, $x_{A1} = 0.4$, $x_{A2} = 0.2$. Calculate N_A.

Ans. (b) $N_A = 4.055 \times 10^{-6}$ kg mol A/s·m²

7.5-10. Diffusion and Chemical Reaction of Molten Iron in Process Metallurgy. In a steel-making process using molten pig iron containing carbon, a spray of molten iron particles containing 4.0 wt % carbon falls through a pure-oxygen atmosphere. The carbon diffuses through the molten iron to the surface of the drop, where it is assumed that it reacts instantly at the surface because of the high temperature, as follows, according to a first-order reaction:

$$C + \tfrac{1}{2}O_2(g) \rightarrow CO(g)$$

Calculate the maximum drop size allowable so that the final drop after a 2.0-s fall contains an average of 0.1 wt % carbon. Assume that the mass-transfer rate of gases at the surface is very great, so there is no outside resistance. Assume no internal circulation of the liquid. Hence, the decarburization rate is controlled by the rate of diffusion of carbon to the surface of the droplet. The diffusivity of carbon in iron is 7.5×10^{-9} m²/s (S7). (*Hint:* Can Fig. 5.3-13 be used for this case?)

Ans. radius = 0.217 mm

7.5-11. Effect of Slow Reaction Rate on Diffusion. Gas A diffuses from point 1 to a catalyst surface at point 2, where it reacts as follows: $2A \rightarrow B$. Gas B diffuses back a distance δ to point 1.
(a) Derive the equation for N_A for a very fast reaction using mole fraction units x_{A1}, and so on.
(b) For $D_{AB} = 0.2 \times 10^{-4}$ m²/s, $x_{A1} = 0.97$, $P = 101.32$ kPa, $\delta = 1.30$ mm, and $T = 298$ K, solve for N_A.
(c) Do the same as in part (a) but for a slow first-order reaction where k_1' is the reaction velocity constant.
(d) Calculate N_A and x_{A2} for part (c) where $k_1' = 0.53 \times 10^{-2}$ m/s.

Ans. (b) $N_A = 8.35 \times 10^{-4}$ kg mol/s·m²

7.5-12. Diffusion and Heterogeneous Reaction on Surface. In a tube of radius R m filled with a liquid, dilute component A is diffusing in the nonflowing liquid phase represented by

$$N_A = -D_{AB}\frac{dc_A}{dz}$$

where z is distance along the tube axis. The inside wall of the tube exerts a catalytic effect and decomposes A so that the heterogeneous rate of decomposition on the wall in kg mol A/s is equal to $kc_A A_w$, where k is a first-order constant and A_w is the wall area in m^2. Neglect any radial gradients (this means a uniform radial concentration).

Derive the differential equation for unsteady state for diffusion and reaction for this system. [*Hint:* First make a mass balance for A for a Δz length of tube as follows: rate of input (diffusion) + rate of generation (heterogeneous) = rate of output (diffusion) + rate of accumulation.]

Ans. $\dfrac{\partial c_A}{\partial t} = D_{AB}\dfrac{\partial^2 c_A}{\partial z^2} - \dfrac{2k}{R}c_A$

7.6-1. Knudsen Diffusivities. A mixture of He (A) and Ar (B) is diffusing at 1.013×10^5 Pa total pressure and 298 K through a capillary having a radius of 100 Å.
(a) Calculate the Knudsen diffusivity of He (A).
(b) Calculate the Knudsen diffusivity of Ar (B).
(c) Compare with the molecular diffusivity D_{AB}.

Ans. (a) $D_{KA} = 8.37 \times 10^{-6}$ m^2/s; (c) $D_{AB} = 7.29 \times 10^{-5}$ m^2/s

7.6-2. Transition-Region Diffusion. A mixture of He (A) and Ar (B) at 298 K is diffusing through an open capillary 15 mm long with a radius of 1000 Å. The total pressure is 1.013×10^5 Pa. The molecular diffusivity D_{AB} at 1.013×10^5 Pa is 7.29×10^{-5} m^2/s.
(a) Calculate the Knudsen diffusivity of He (A).
(b) Predict the flux N_A using Eq. (7.6-18) and Eq. (7.6-12) if $x_{A1} = 0.8$ and $x_{A2} = 0.2$. Assume steady state.
(c) Predict the flux N_A using the approximate Eqs. (7.6-14) and (7.6-16).

7.6-3. Diffusion in a Pore in the Transition Region. Pure H$_2$ gas (A) at one end of a noncatalytic pore of radius 50 Å and length 1.0 mm ($x_{A1} = 1.0$) is diffusing through this pore with pure C$_2$H$_6$ gas (B) at the other end at $x_{A2} = 0$. The total pressure is constant at 1013.2 kPa. The predicted molecular diffusivity of H$_2$–C$_2$H$_6$ is 8.60×10^{-5} m^2/s at 101.32 kPa and 373 K. Calculate the Knudsen diffusivity of H$_2$ and flux N_A of H$_2$ in the mixture at 373 K and steady state.

Ans. $D_{KA} = 6.60 \times 10^{-6}$ m^2/s, $N_A = 1.472 \times 10^{-3}$ kg mol A/s $\cdot$ m^2

7.6-4. Transition-Region Diffusion in Capillary. A mixture of nitrogen gas (A) and helium (B) at 298 K is diffusing through a capillary 0.10 m long in an open system with a diameter of 10 μm. The mole fractions are constant at $x_{A1} = 1.0$ and $x_{A2} = 0$. See Example 7.6-2 for physical properties.
(a) Calculate the Knudsen diffusivity D_{KA} and D_{KB} at the total pressures of 0.001, 0.1, and 10.0 atm.
(b) Calculate the flux N_A at steady state at these pressures.
(c) Plot N_A versus P on log–log paper. What are the limiting lines at lower pressures and very high pressures? Calculate and plot these lines.

7.7-1. Numerical Method for Unsteady-State Diffusion. A solid slab 0.01 m thick has an initial uniform concentration of solute A of 1.00 kg mol/m^3. The diffusivity of A in the solid is $D_{AB} = 1.0 \times 10^{-10}$ m^2/s. All surfaces of the slab are insulated except the top surface. The surface concentration is suddenly dropped to zero concentration and held there. Unsteady-state diffusion occurs in the one x direction with the rear surface insulated. Using a numerical method, determine the concentrations after 12×10^4 s. Use $\Delta x = 0.002$ m and $M = 2.0$. The value of K is 1.0.

Ans. $c_1 = 0$ (front surface, $x = 0$ m)
$c_2 = 0.3125$ kg mol/m^3 ($x = 0.002$ m)
$c_3 = 0.5859$ ($x = 0.004$ m)
$c_4 = 0.7813$ ($x = 0.006$ m)
$c_5 = 0.8984$ ($x = 0.008$ m)
$c_6 = 0.9375$ (insulated surface, $x = 0.01$ m)

7.7-2. Digital Computer and Unsteady-State Diffusion. Using the conditions of Problem 7.7-1, solve that problem by digital computer. Use $\Delta x = 0.0005$ m. Write the spreadsheet program and plot the final concentrations. Use the explicit method, $M = 2$.

7.7-3. Numerical Method and Different Boundary Condition. Use the same conditions as for Example 7.7-1, but in this case the rear surface is not insulated. At time $t = 0$ the concentration at the rear surface is also suddenly changed to $c_5 = 0$ and held there. Calculate the concentration profile after 2500 s. Plot the initial and final concentration profiles and compare with the final profile of Example 7.7-1.

7.8-1. Dimensional Analysis in Mass Transfer. A fluid is flowing in a vertical pipe and mass transfer is occurring from the pipe wall to the fluid. Relate the convective mass-transfer coefficient k_c' to the variables D, ρ, μ, v, D_{AB}, g, and $\Delta\rho$, where D is pipe diameter, L is pipe length, and $\Delta\rho$ is the density difference.

$$\textbf{Ans.} \quad \frac{k_c' D}{D_{AB}} = f\left(\frac{gL^3 \rho \, \Delta\rho}{\mu^2}, \frac{Dv\rho}{\mu}, \frac{\mu}{\rho D_{AB}} \right)$$

7.9-1. Mass Transfer and Turbulence Models. Pure water at a velocity of 0.11 m/s is flowing at 26.1°C past a flat plate of solid benzoic acid where $L = 0.40$ m. Do as follows:
(a) Assuming dilute solutions, calculate the mass-transfer coefficient k_c. Use physical-property data from Example 7.3-2.
(b) Using the film model, calculate the equivalent film thickness.
(c) Using the penetration model, calculate the time of penetration.
(d) Calculate the mean surface renewal factor using the modified penetration model.

Ans. (b) $\delta_f = 0.2031$ mm; (d) $s = 3.019 \times 10^{-2}$ s^{-1}

REFERENCES

(B1) BIRD, R. B., STEWART, W. E., and LIGHTFOOT, E. N. *Transport Phenomena.* New York: John Wiley & Sons, Inc., 1960.

(B2) BLAKEBROUGH, N. *Biochemical and Biological Engineering Science,* Vol. 1. New York: Academic Press, Inc., 1967.

(B3) BEDDINGTON, C. H., JR., and DREW, T. B. *Ind. Eng. Chem., 42,* 1164 (1950).

(C1) CARMICHAEL, L. T., SAGE, B. H., and LACEY, W. N. *A.I.Ch.E. J., 1,* 385 (1955).

(C2) CHILTON, T. H., and COLBURN, A. P. *Ind. Eng. Chem., 26,* 1183 (1934).

(C3) CALDERBANK, P. H., and MOO-YOUNG, M. B. *Chem. Eng. Sci., 16,* 39 (1961).

(C4) CUNNINGHAM, R. S., and GEANKOPLIS, C. J. *Ind. Eng. Chem. Fund., 7,* 535 (1968).

(D1) DANCKWERTS, P. V. *Trans. Faraday Soc., 46,* 300 (1950).

(D2) DUNN, W. E., BONILLA, C. F., FERSTENBERG, C., and GROSS, B. *A.I.Ch.E. J.,* **2,** 184 (1956).

(D3) DANCKWERTS, P. V. *Gas–Liquid Reactions.* New York: McGraw-Hill Book Company, 1970.

(D4) DWIVEDI, P. N., and UPADHYAY, S. N. *Ind. Eng. Chem., Proc. Des. Dev.,* **16,** 157 (1977).

(G1) GEANKOPLIS, C. J. *Mass Transport Phenomena.* Columbus, Ohio: Ohio State University Bookstores, 1972.

(G2) GILLILAND, E. R., and SHERWOOD, T. K. *Ind. Eng. Chem.,* **26,** 516 (1934).

(G3) GARNER, F. H., and SUCKLING, R. D. *A.I.Ch.E. J.,* **4,** 114 (1958).

(G4) GUPTA, A. S., and THODOS, G. *Ind. Chem. Eng. Fund.,* **3,** 218 (1964).

(G5) GUPTA, A. S., and THODOS, G. *A.I.Ch.E. J.,* **8,** 609 (1962).

(G6) GUPTA, A. S., and THODOS, G. *Chem. Eng. Progr.,* **58** (7), 58 (1962).

(L1) LINTON, W. H., JR., and SHERWOOD, T. K. *Chem. Eng. Progr.,* **46,** 258 (1950).

(L2) LITT, M., and FRIEDLANDER, S. K. *A.I.Ch.E. J.,* **5,** 483 (1959).

(M1) MCADAMS, W. H. *Heat Transmission,* 3rd ed. New York: McGraw-Hill Book Company, 1954.

(P1) PERRY, R. H., and GREEN, D. *Perry's Chemical Engineers' Handbook,* 6th ed. New York: McGraw-Hill Book Company, 1984.

(R1) REMICK, R. R., and GEANKOPLIS, C. J. *Ind. Eng. Chem. Fund.,* **12,** 214 (1973).

(S1) SEAGER, S. L., GEERTSON, L. R., and GIDDINGS, J. C. *J. Chem. Eng. Data,* **8,** 168 (1963).

(S2) SATTERFIELD, C. N. *Mass Transfer in Heterogeneous Catalysis.* Cambridge, Mass.: The MIT Press, 1970.

(S3) STEELE, L. R., and GEANKOPLIS, C. J. *A.I.Ch.E. J.,* **5,** 178 (1959).

(S4) SHERWOOD, T. K., PIGFORD, R. L., and WILKE, C. R. *Mass Transfer.* New York: McGraw-Hill Book Company, 1975.

(S5) STEINBERGER, W. L., and TREYBAL, R. E. *A.I.Ch.E. J.,* **6,** 227 (1960).

(S6) SMITH, J. M. *Chemical Engineering Kinetics,* 2nd ed. New York: McGraw-Hill Book Company, 1970.

(S7) SZEKELY, J., and THEMELIS, N. *Rate Phenomena in Process Metallurgy.* New York: Wiley-Interscience, 1971.

(S8) SKELLAND, A. H. P. *Diffusional Mass Transfer.* New York: Wiley-Interscience, 1974.

(T1) TREYBAL, R. E. *Mass Transfer Operations,* 3rd ed. New York: McGraw-Hill Book Company, 1980.

(T2) TOOR, H. L., and MARCHELLO, J. M. *A.I.Ch.E. J.,* **1,** 97 (1958).

(V1) VOGTLANDER, P. H., and BAKKER, C. A. P. *Chem. Eng. Sci.,* **18,** 583 (1963).

(W1) WILSON, E. J., and GEANKOPLIS, C. J. *Ind. Eng. Chem. Fund.,* **5,** 9 (1966).

PART 2

*Separation Process Principles
(Includes Unit Operations)*

CHAPTER 8

Evaporation

8.1 INTRODUCTION

8.1A Purpose

In Section 4.8 we discussed the case of heat transfer to a boiling liquid. An important instance of this type of heat transfer occurs quite often in the process industries and is given the general name *evaporation*. In evaporation the vapor from a boiling liquid solution is removed and a more concentrated solution remains. In the majority of cases the separation process called evaporation refers to the removal of water from an aqueous solution.

Typical examples of evaporation are concentration of aqueous solutions of sugar, sodium chloride, sodium hydroxide, glycerol, glue, milk, and orange juice. In these cases the concentrated solution is the desired product and the evaporated water is normally discarded. In a few cases, water, which contains a small amount of minerals, is evaporated to give a solids-free water to be used as boiler feed, for special chemical processes, or for other purposes. Evaporation processes to evaporate seawater to provide drinking water have been developed and used. In some cases, the primary purpose of evaporation is to concentrate a solution so that upon cooling, salt crystals will form and be separated. This special evaporation process, termed *crystallization,* is discussed in Chapter 12.

8.1B Processing Factors

The physical and chemical properties of the solution being concentrated and of the vapor being removed bear greatly on the type of evaporator used and the pressure and temperature of the process. Some of the properties which affect the processing methods are discussed next.

1. Concentration in the liquid. Usually, the liquid feed to an evaporator is relatively dilute, so its viscosity is low, similar to that of water, and relatively high heat-transfer coefficients are obtained. As evaporation proceeds, the solution may become very concentrated and quite viscous, causing the heat-transfer coefficient to drop markedly. Adequate circulation and/or turbulence must be present to keep the coefficient from becoming too low.

2. Solubility. As solutions are heated and the concentration of the solute or salt increases, the solubility limit of the material in solution may be exceeded and crystals may form. This may limit the maximum concentration in solution which can be obtained by evaporation. In Fig. 8.1-1 some solubilities of typical salts in water are shown as a function of temperature. In most cases the solubility of the salt increases with temperature. This means that when a hot, concentrated solution from an evaporator is cooled to room temperature, crystallization may occur.

3. Temperature sensitivity of materials. Many products, especially food and other biological materials, may be temperature-sensitive and degrade at higher temperatures or after pro- longed heating. Such products include pharmaceutical products; food products such as milk, orange juice, and vegetable extracts; and fine organic chemicals. The amount of degradation is a function of the temperature and the length of time.

4. Foaming or frothing. In some cases materials composed of caustic solutions, food solu- tions such as skim milk, and some fatty-acid solutions form a foam or froth during boiling. This foam accompanies the vapor coming out of the evaporator and entrainment losses occur.

5. Pressure and temperature. The boiling point of the solution is related to the pressure of the system. The higher the operating pressure of the evaporator, the higher the temperature at boiling. Also, as the concentration of the dissolved material in solution increases by evap- oration, the temperature of boiling may rise. This phenomenon is called *boiling-point rise* or *elevation* and is discussed in Section 8.4. To keep the temperatures low in heat-sensitive ma- terials, it is often necessary to operate under 1 atm pressure, that is, under vacuum.

6. Scale deposition and materials of construction. Some solutions deposit solid materials called *scale* on the heating surfaces. These could be formed by decomposition products or by decreases in solubility. The result is that the overall heat-transfer coefficient decreases, and

FIGURE 8.1-1. *Solubility curves for some typical salts in water.*

the evaporator must eventually be cleaned. The materials used in construction of the evaporator should be chosen to minimize corrosion.

8.2 TYPES OF EVAPORATION EQUIPMENT AND OPERATION METHODS

8.2A General Types of Evaporators

In evaporation, heat is added to a solution to vaporize the solvent, which is usually water. The heat is generally provided by the condensation of a vapor such as steam on one side of a metal surface, with the evaporating liquid on the other side. The type of equipment used depends primarily on the configuration of the heat-transfer surface and on the means employed to provide agitation or circulation of the liquid. The general types of equipment are discussed below.

1. Open kettle or pan. The simplest evaporator consists of an open pan or kettle in which the liquid is boiled. The heat is supplied by condensation of steam in a jacket or in coils immersed in the liquid. In some cases the kettle is direct-fired. These evaporators are inexpensive and simple to operate, but the heat economy is poor. In some cases, paddles or scrapers are used for agitation.

2. Horizontal-tube natural circulation evaporator. The horizontal-tube natural circulation evaporator is shown in Fig. 8.2-1a. The horizontal bundle of heating tubes is similar to the bundle of tubes in a heat exchanger. The steam enters the tubes, where it condenses. The steam condensate leaves at the other end of the tubes. The boiling liquid solution covers the tubes. The vapor leaves the liquid surface, often goes through some de-entraining device such as a baffle to prevent carryover of liquid droplets, and leaves out the top. This type of evaporator is relatively cheap and is used for nonviscous liquids with high heat-transfer coefficients and liquids that do not deposit scale. Since liquid circulation is poor, they are unsuitable for viscous liquids. In almost all cases, this evaporator and the types discussed below are operated continuously, that is, the feed enters at a constant rate and the concentrate leaves at a constant rate.

3. Vertical-type natural circulation evaporator. In this type of evaporator, vertical rather than horizontal tubes are used; the liquid is inside the tubes and the steam condenses outside the tubes. Because of boiling and decreases in density, the liquid rises in the tubes by natural circulation, as shown in Fig. 8.2-1b, and flows downward through a large, central open space or downcomer. This natural circulation increases the heat-transfer coefficient. This type of evaporator is not used with viscous liquids. It is often called the *short-tube evaporator*. A variation is the basket type, where vertical tubes are used but the heating element is held suspended in the body so there is an annular open space as the downcomer. In this way, it differs from the vertical natural circulation evaporator, which has a central instead of annular open space as the downcomer. The basket type is widely used in the sugar, salt, and caustic-soda industries.

4. Long-tube vertical-type evaporator. Since the heat-transfer coefficient on the steam side is very high compared to that on the evaporating-liquid side, high liquid velocities are desirable. In a long-tube vertical-type evaporator, shown in Fig. 8.2-1c, the liquid is inside the tubes. The tubes are 3 to 10 m long and the formation of vapor bubbles inside the tubes

FIGURE 8.2-1. *Different types of evaporators: (a) horizontal-tube type, (b) vertical-tube type, (c) long-tube vertical type, (d) forced-circulation type.*

causes a pumping action, which gives quite high liquid velocities. Generally, the liquid passes through the tubes only once and is not recirculated. Contact times can be quite low in this type. In some cases, as when the ratio of feed to evaporation rate is low, natural recirculation of the product through the evaporator is effected by adding a large pipe connection between the outlet concentrate line and the feed line. This is widely used for producing condensed milk.

5. *Falling-film-type evaporator.* A variation on the long-tube-type evaporator is the falling-film evaporator, wherein the liquid is fed to the top of the tubes and flows down the walls as a thin film. Vapor–liquid separation usually takes place at the bottom. This type is widely

used for concentrating heat-sensitive materials such as orange juice and other fruit juices, because the holdup time is very small (5 to 10 s or more) and the heat-transfer coefficients are high.

6. *Forced-circulation-type evaporator.* The liquid-film heat-transfer coefficient can be increased by pumping to cause forced circulation of the liquid inside the tubes. This could be done in the long-tube vertical type shown in Fig. 8.2-1c by adding a pipe connection shown with a pump between the outlet concentrate line and the feed line. In the forced-circulation type, however, the vertical tubes are usually shorter than in the long-tube type, as shown in Fig. 8.2-1d. Additionally, in some cases a separate and external horizontal heat exchanger is used. This type of evaporator is very useful for viscous liquids.

7. *Agitated-film evaporator.* The main resistance to heat transfer in an evaporator is on the liquid side. One way to increase turbulence in this film, and hence the heat-transfer coefficient, is by actual mechanical agitation of this liquid film. This is done in a modified falling-film evaporator with only a single, large, jacketed tube containing an internal agitator. Liquid enters at the top of the tube and as it flows downward, it is spread out into a turbulent film by the vertical agitator blades. The concentrated solution leaves at the bottom and vapor leaves through a separator and out the top. This type of evaporator is very useful with highly viscous materials, since the heat-transfer coefficient is greater than in forced-circulation evaporators. It is used with heat-sensitive viscous materials such as rubber latex, gelatin, antibiotics, and fruit juices. However, it has a high cost and small capacity. For interested readers, Perry and Green (P1) give more-detailed discussions and descriptions of evaporation equipment.

8. *Open-pan solar evaporator.* A very old yet still-used process is solar evaporation in open pans. Saltwater is put in shallow open pans or troughs and allowed to evaporate slowly in the sun to crystallize the salt.

8.2B Methods of Operation of Evaporators

1. *Single-effect evaporators.* A simplified diagram of a single-stage or single-effect evaporator is given in Fig. 8.2-2. The feed enters at T_F K and saturated steam at T_S enters the heat-exchange section. Condensed steam leaves as condensate or drips. Since the solution in the evaporator is assumed to be completely mixed, the concentrated product and the solution in the evaporator have the same composition and temperature T_1, which is the boiling point of

FIGURE 8.2-2. *Simplified diagram of single-effect evaporator.*

the solution. The temperature of the vapor is also T_1, since it is in equilibrium with the boiling solution. The pressure is P_1, which is the vapor pressure of the solution at T_1.

If the solution to be evaporated is assumed to be dilute and like water, then 1 kg of steam condensing will evaporate approximately 1 kg of vapor. This will hold if the feed entering has a temperature T_F near the boiling point.

The concept of an overall heat-transfer coefficient is used in the calculation of the rate of heat transfer in an evaporator. The general equation can be written

$$q = UA \; \Delta T = UA(T_S - T_1) \tag{8.2-1}$$

where q is the rate of heat transfer in W (btu/h), U is the overall heat-transfer coefficient in W/m$^2 \cdot$ K (btu/h $\cdot$ ft$^2 \cdot$ °F), A is the heat-transfer area in m^2 (ft^2), T_S is the temperature of the condensing steam in K (°F), and T_1 is the boiling point of the liquid in K (°F).

Single-effect evaporators are often used when the required capacity of operation is relatively small and/or the cost of steam is relatively cheap compared to the evaporator cost. However, for large-capacity operation, using more than one effect will markedly reduce steam costs.

2. Forward-feed multiple-effect evaporators. A single-effect evaporator as shown in Fig. 8.2-2 is wasteful of energy, since the latent heat of the vapor leaving is not used but is discarded. Much of this latent heat, however, can be recovered and reused by employing a multiple-effect evaporator. A simplified diagram of a forward-feed triple-effect evaporation system is shown in Fig. 8.2-3.

If the feed to the first effect is near the boiling point at the pressure in the first effect, 1 kg of steam will evaporate almost 1 kg of water. The first effect operates at a temperature that is high enough that the evaporated water serves as the heating medium to the second effect. Here, again, almost another kg of water is evaporated, which can then be used as the heating medium to the third effect. As a very rough approximation, almost 3 kg of water will be evaporated for 1 kg of steam in a three-effect evaporator. Hence, the *steam economy,* which is kg vapor evaporated/kg steam used, is increased. This also holds approximately for more than three effects. However, the increased steam economy of a multiple-effect evaporator is gained at the expense of the original first cost of these evaporators.

In forward-feed operation as shown in Fig. 8.2-3, the fresh feed is added to the first effect and flows to the next in the same direction as the vapor flow. This method of operation is

FIGURE 8.2-3. *Simplified diagram of forward-feed triple-effect evaporator.*

FIGURE 8.2-4. *Simplified diagram of backward-feed triple-effect evaporator.*

used when the feed is hot or when the final concentrated product might be damaged at high temperatures. The boiling temperatures decrease from effect to effect. This means that if the first effect is at $P_1 = 1$ atm abs pressure, the last effect will be under vacuum at a pressure P_3.

3. Backward-feed multiple-effect evaporators. In the backward-feed operation shown in Fig. 8.2-4 for a triple-effect evaporator, the fresh feed enters the last and coldest effect and continues on until the concentrated product leaves the first effect. This method of reverse feed is advantageous when the fresh feed is cold, since a smaller amount of liquid must be heated to the higher temperatures in the second and first effects. However, liquid pumps must be used in each effect, since the flow is from low to high pressure. This reverse-feed method is also used when the concentrated product is highly viscous. The high temperatures in the early effects reduce the viscosity and give reasonable heat-transfer coefficients.

4. Parallel-feed multiple-effect evaporators. Parallel feed in multiple-effect evaporators involves the adding of fresh feed and withdrawal of concentrated product from each effect. The vapor from each effect is still used to heat the next effect. This method of operation is mainly used when the feed is almost saturated and solid crystals are the product, as in the evaporation of brine to make salt.

8.3 OVERALL HEAT-TRANSFER COEFFICIENTS IN EVAPORATORS

The overall heat-transfer coefficient U in an evaporator is composed of the steam-side condensing coefficient, which has a value of about 5700 W/m$^2 \cdot$K (1000 btu/h$\cdot$ft$^2 \cdot$°F); the metal wall, which has a high thermal conductivity and usually a negligible resistance; the resistance of the scale on the liquid side; and the liquid film coefficient, which is usually inside the tubes.

The steam-side condensing coefficient outside the tubes can be estimated using Eqs. (4.8-20) through (4.8-26). The resistance due to scale formation usually cannot be predicted. Increasing the velocity of the liquid in the tubes greatly decreases the rate of scale formation, which is one important advantage of forced-circulation evaporators. The scale may be salts, such as calcium sulfate or sodium sulfate, which decrease in solubility with an increase in temperature and hence tend to deposit on the hot tubes.

For forced-circulation evaporators the coefficient h inside the tubes can be predicted if there is little or no vaporization inside the tube. The liquid hydrostatic head in the tubes prevents most boiling in the tubes. The standard equations for predicting the h value of liquids

TABLE 8.3-1. *Typical Heat-Transfer Coefficients for Various Evaporators* *
(B3, B4, L1, P1)

| | Overall U | |
Type of Evaporator	$W/m^2 \cdot K$	$btu/h \cdot ft^2 \cdot °F$
Short-tube vertical, natural circulation	1100–2800	200–500
Horizontal-tube, natural circulation	1100–2800	200–500
Long-tube vertical, natural circulation	1100–4000	200–700
Long-tube vertical, forced circulation	2300–11 000	400–2000
Agitated film	680–2300	120–400

*Generally, nonviscous liquids have the higher coefficients and viscous liquids the lower coefficients in the ranges given.

inside tubes can be used. Velocities used often range from 2 to 5 m/s (7 to 15 ft/s). The heat-transfer coefficient can be predicted from Eq. (4.5-8), using a constant of 0.028 instead of 0.027 (B1). If there is some or appreciable boiling in part or all of the tubes, use of the equation assuming no boiling will give conservative safe results (P1).

For long-tube vertical natural-circulation evaporators the heat-transfer coefficient is more difficult to predict, since there is a nonboiling zone in the bottom of the tubes and a boiling zone in the top. The length of the nonboiling zone depends on the heat transfer in the two zones and the pressure drop in the boiling two-phase zone. The film heat-transfer coefficient in the nonboiling zone can be estimated using Eq. (4.5-8) with a constant of 0.028. For the boiling two-phase zone, a number of equations are given by Perry and Green (P2).

For short-tube vertical evaporators the heat-transfer coefficients can be estimated by using the same methods as for long-tube vertical natural-circulation evaporators. Horizontal-tube evaporators have heat-transfer coefficients on the same order of magnitude as short-tube vertical evaporators.

For the agitated-film evaporator, the heat-transfer coefficient may be estimated using Eq. (4.13-4) for a scraped surface heat exchanger.

The methods given above are useful for actual evaporator design and/or for evaluating the effects of changes in operating conditions on the coefficients. In making preliminary designs or cost estimates, it is helpful to have available overall heat-transfer coefficients usually encountered in commercial practice. Some preliminary values and ranges of values for various types of evaporators are given in Table 8.3-1.

8.4 CALCULATION METHODS FOR SINGLE-EFFECT EVAPORATORS

8.4A Heat and Material Balances for Evaporators

The basic equation for solving for the capacity of a single-effect evaporator is Eq. (8.2-1), which can be written as

$$q = UA \, \Delta T \tag{8.4-1}$$

where ΔT K (°F) is the difference in temperature between the condensing steam and the boiling liquid in the evaporator. In order to solve Eq. (8.4-1) the value of q in W (btu/h) must be determined by making a heat and material balance on the evaporator shown in Fig. 8.4-1.

FIGURE 8.4-1. *Heat and mass balance for single-effect evaporator.*

The feed to the evaporator is F kg/h (lb$_m$/h) having a solids content of x_F mass fraction, temperature T_F, and enthalpy h_F J/kg (btu/lb$_m$). Coming out as a liquid is the concentrated liquid L kg/h (lb$_m$/h) having a solids content of x_L, temperature T_1, and enthalpy h_L. The vapor V kg/h (lb$_m$/h) is given off as pure solvent having a solids content of $y_V = 0$, temperature T_1, and enthalpy H_V. Saturated steam entering is S kg/h (lb$_m$/h) and has a temperature of T_S and enthalpy of H_S. The condensed steam leaving of S kg/h is assumed usually to be at T_S, the saturation temperature, with an enthalpy of h_S. This means that the steam gives off only its latent heat, λ, where

$$\lambda = H_S - h_S \tag{8.4-2}$$

Since the vapor V is in equilibrium with the liquid L, the temperatures of vapor and liquid are the same. Also, the pressure P_1 is the saturation vapor pressure of the liquid of composition x_L at its boiling point T_1. (This assumes no boiling-point rise.)

For the material balance, since we are at steady state, the rate of mass in = rate of mass out. Then, for a total balance,

$$F = L + V \tag{8.4-3}$$

For a balance on the solute (solids) alone,

$$Fx_F = Lx_L \tag{8.4-4}$$

For the heat balance, since the total heat entering = total heat leaving,

heat in feed + heat in steam
    = heat in concentrated liquid + heat in vapor + heat in condensed steam   (8.4-5)

This assumes no heat lost by radiation or convection. Substituting into Eq. (8.4-5),

$$Fh_F + SH_S = Lh_L + VH_V + Sh_S \tag{8.4-6}$$

Substituting Eq. (8.4-2) into (8.4-6),

$$Fh_F + S\lambda = Lh_L + VH_V \tag{8.4-7}$$

The heat q transferred in the evaporator is then

$$q = S(H_S - h_S) = S\lambda \tag{8.4-8}$$

In Eq. (8.4-7) the latent heat λ of steam at the saturation temperature T_S can be obtained from the steam tables in Appendix A.2. However, the enthalpies of the feed and products are often not available; these enthalpy–concentration data are available for only a few substances in solution. Hence, some approximations are made in order to make a heat balance. These are as follows:

1. It can be demonstrated as an approximation that the latent heat of evaporation of 1 kg mass of the water from an aqueous solution can be obtained from the steam tables using the temperature of the boiling solution T_1 (exposed surface temperature) rather than the equilibrium temperature for pure water at P_1.

2. If the heat capacities c_{pF} of the liquid feed and c_{pL} of the product are known, they can be used to calculate the enthalpies. (This neglects heats of dilution, which in most cases are not known.)

EXAMPLE 8.4-1.   Heat-Transfer Area in Single-Effect Evaporator

A continuous single-effect evaporator concentrates 9072 kg/h of a 1.0 wt % salt solution entering at 311.0 K (37.8°C) to a final concentration of 1.5 wt %. The vapor space of the evaporator is at 101.325 kPa (1.0 atm abs) and the steam supplied is saturated at 143.3 kPa. The overall coefficient $U = 1704$ W/m$^2 \cdot$K. Calculate the amounts of vapor and liquid product and the heat-transfer area required. Assume that, since it is dilute, the solution has the same boiling point as water.

Solution: The flow diagram is the same as in Fig. 8.4-1. For the material balance, substituting into Eq. (8.4-3),

$$F = L + V \tag{8.4-3}$$

$$9072 = L + V$$

Substituting into Eq. (8.4-4) and solving,

$$F x_F = L x_L \tag{8.4-4}$$

$$9072(0.01) = L(0.015)$$

$$L = 6048 \text{ kg/h of liquid}$$

Substituting into Eq. (8.4-3) and solving,

$$V = 3024 \text{ kg/h of vapor}$$

The heat capacity of the feed is assumed to be $c_{pF} = 4.14$ kJ/kg·K. (Often, for feeds of inorganic salts in water, the c_p can be assumed to be approximately that of water alone.) To make a heat balance using Eq. (8.4-7), it is convenient to select the boiling point of the dilute solution in the evaporator, which is assumed to be that of water at 101.32 kPa, $T_1 = 373.2$ K (100°C), as the datum temperature. Then H_V is simply the latent heat of water at 373.2 K, which from the steam tables in Appendix A.2 is 2257 kJ/kg (970.3 btu/lb$_m$). The latent heat λ of the steam at 143.3 kPa [saturation temperature $T_S = 383.2$ K (230°F)] is 2230 kJ/kg (958.8 btu/lb$_m$).

The enthalpy of the feed can be calculated from

$$h_F = c_{pF}(T_F - T_1) \tag{8.4-9}$$

Substituting into Eq. (8.4-7) with $h_L = 0$, since it is at the datum of 373.2 K,

$$9072(4.14)(311.0 - 373.2) + S(2230) = 6048(0) + 3024(2257)$$

$$S = 4108 \text{ kg steam/h}$$

The heat q transferred through the heating surface area A is, from Eq. (8.4-8),

$$q = S(\lambda) \qquad\qquad \textbf{(8.4-8)}$$

$$q = 4108(2230)(1000/3600) = 2\,544\,000 \text{ W}$$

Substituting into Eq. (8.4-1), where $\Delta T = T_S - T_1$,

$$q = 2\,544\,000 = UA\,\Delta T = 1704(A)(383.2 - 373.2)$$

Solving, $A = 149.3 \text{ m}^2$.

8.4B Effects of Processing Variables on Evaporator Operation

1. Effect of feed temperature. The inlet temperature of the feed has a large effect on the operation of the evaporator. In Example 8.4-1 the feed entering was at a temperature of 311.0 K, cold as compared to the boiling temperature of 373.2 K. About $\frac{1}{4}$ of the steam used for heating was used to heat the cold feed to the boiling point. Hence, only about $\frac{3}{4}$ of the steam was left for vaporization of the feed. If the feed is under pressure and enters the evaporator at a temperature above the boiling point in the evaporator, additional vaporization is obtained by flashing part of the entering hot feed. Preheating the feed can reduce the size of evaporator heat-transfer area needed.

2. Effect of pressure. In Example 8.4-1 a pressure of 101.32 kPa abs was used in the vapor space of the evaporator. This set the boiling point of the solution at 373.2 K and gave a ΔT for use in Eq. (8.4-1) of 383.2 − 373.2, or 10 K. In many cases a larger ΔT is desirable, since, as ΔT increases, the heating-surface area A and cost of the evaporator decrease. To reduce the pressure below 101.32 kPa, that is, to be under vacuum, a condenser and vacuum pump can be used. For example, if the pressure were reduced to 41.4 kPa, the boiling point of water would be 349.9 K and the new ΔT would be 383.2 − 349.9, or 33.3 K. A large decrease in heating-surface area would be obtained.

3. Effect of steam pressure. Using higher-pressure, saturated steam increases ΔT, which decreases the size and cost of the evaporator. However, high-pressure steam is more costly as well as often being more valuable as a source of power elsewhere. Hence, overall economic balances are really needed to determine the optimum steam pressures.

8.4C Boiling-Point Rise of Solutions

In the majority of cases in evaporation, the solutions are not dilute solutions such as those considered in Example 8.4-1. In most cases, the thermal properties of the solution being evaporated may differ considerably from those of water. The concentrations of the solutions are high enough that the heat capacity and boiling point are quite different from those for water.

For strong solutions of dissolved solutes the boiling-point rise due to the solutes in the solution usually cannot be predicted. However, a useful empirical law known as *Dühring's rule* can be applied. According to this rule, a straight line is obtained if the boiling point of a solution in °C or °F is plotted against the boiling point of pure water at the same pressure for

Boiling point of water (°C)

Boiling point of sodium hydroxide solution (°F)

Boiling point of sodium hydroxide solution (°C)

60 wt. % NaOH
50 wt. % NaOH
40 wt. % NaOH

30 wt. % NaOH
20 wt. % NaOH
10 wt. % NaOH
water

Boiling point of water (°F)

FIGURE 8.4-2. *Dühring lines for aqueous solutions of sodium hydroxide.*

a given concentration at different pressures. A different straight line is obtained for each given concentration. In Fig. 8.4-2 such a Dühring-line chart is given for solutions of sodium hydroxide in water. It is necessary to know the boiling point of a given solution at only two pressures to determine a line.

EXAMPLE 8.4-2.   Use of Dühring Chart for Boiling-Point Rise

As an example of use of the chart, the pressure in an evaporator is given as 25.6 kPa (3.72 psia) and a solution of 30% NaOH is being boiled. Determine the boiling temperature of the NaOH solution and the boiling-point rise BPR of the solution over that of water at the same pressure.

Solution: From the steam tables in Appendix A.2, the boiling point of water at 25.6 kPa is 65.6°C. From Fig. 8.4-2 for 65.6°C (150°F) and 30% NaOH, the boiling point of the NaOH solution is 79.5°C (175°F). The boiling-point rise is $79.5 - 65.6 = 13.9$°C (25°F).

In Perry and Green (P1) a chart is given for estimating the boiling-point rise of a large number of common aqueous solutions used in chemical and biological processes. In addition to the common salts and solutes, such as $NaNO_3$, NaOH, NaCl, and H_2SO_4, the biological solutes sucrose, citric acid, kraft solution, and glycerol are given. These biological solutes have quite small boiling-point-rise values compared to those of common salts.

8.4D Enthalpy–Concentration Charts of Solutions

If the heat of solution of the aqueous solution being concentrated in the evaporator is large, neglecting it could cause errors in the heat balances. This heat-of-solution phenomenon can be explained as follows. If pellets of NaOH are dissolved in a given amount of water, it is found that a considerable temperature rise occurs; that is, heat is evolved, called *heat of solution*. The amount of heat evolved depends on the type of substance and the amount of water used. Also, if a strong solution of NaOH is diluted to a lower concentration, heat is liberated. Conversely, if a solution is concentrated from a low to a high concentration, heat must be added.

In Fig. 8.4-3 an enthalpy–concentration chart for NaOH is given (M1), where the enthalpy is in kJ/kg (btu/lb_m) solution, temperature in °C (°F), and concentration in weight fraction NaOH in solution. Such enthalpy–concentration charts are usually not made for solutions having negligible heats of solution, since the heat capacities can be easily used to calculate enthalpies. Also, such charts are available for only a few solutions.

The enthalpy of the liquid water in Fig. 8.4-3 is referred to the same datum or reference state as in the steam tables, that is, liquid water at 0°C (273 K). This means that enthalpies from the figure can be used with those in the steam tables. In Eq. (8.4-7) values for h_F and h_L can be taken from Fig. 8.4-3 and values for λ and H_V from the steam tables. The uses of Fig. 8.4-3 will be better understood from the following example.

EXAMPLE 8.4-3. Evaporation of an NaOH Solution
An evaporator is used to concentrate 4536 kg/h (10 000 lb_m/h) of a 20% solution of NaOH in water entering at 60°C (140°F) to a product of 50% solids. The pressure of the saturated steam used is 172.4 kPa (25 psia) and the pressure in the vapor space of the evaporator is 11.7 kPa (1.7 psia). The overall heat-transfer coefficient is 1560 W/m$^2 \cdot$K (275 btu/h $\cdot$ ft$^2 \cdot$ °F). Calculate the steam used, the steam economy in kg vaporized/kg steam used, and the heating surface area in m^2.

Solution: The process flow diagram and nomenclature are the same as in Fig. 8.4-1. The given variables are $F = 4536$ kg/h, $x_F = 0.20$ wt fraction, $T_F = 60$°C, $P_1 = 11.7$ kPa, steam pressure $= 172.4$ kPa, and $x_L = 0.50$ wt fraction. For the overall material balance, substituting into Eq. (8.4-3),

$$F = 4536 = L + V \qquad \textbf{(8.4-3)}$$

Substituting into Eq. (8.4-4) and solving (8.4-3) and (8.4-4) simultaneously,

$$Fx_F = Lx_L$$

$$4536(0.20) = L(0.50)$$

$$L = 1814 \text{ kg/h} \qquad V = 2722 \text{ kg/h} \qquad \textbf{(8.4-4)}$$

FIGURE 8.4-3. *Enthalpy–concentration chart for the system NaOH–water.*
[Reference state liquid water at 0°C (273 K) or 32°F.] [From W. L.
McCabe, Trans. A.I.Ch.E., 31, 129 (1935). With permission.]

To determine the boiling point T_1 of the 50% concentrated solution, we first
obtain the boiling point of pure water at 11.7 kPa from the steam tables, Appendix A.2, as 48.9°C (120°F). From the Dühring chart, Fig. 8.4-2, for a boiling
point of water of 48.9°C and 50% NaOH, the boiling point of the solution is
$T_1 = 89.5°C$ (193°F). Hence,

$$\text{boiling-point rise} = T_1 - 48.9 = 89.5 - 48.9 = 40.6°C \ (73°F)$$

From the enthalpy–concentration chart (Fig. 8.4-3), for 20% NaOH at 60°C
(140°F), $h_f = 214$ kJ/kg (92 btu/lb$_m$). For 50% NaOH at 89.5°C (193°F), $h_L =$
505 kJ/kg (217 btu/lb$_m$).

For the superheated vapor V at 89.5°C (193°F) and 11.7 kPa [superheated
40.6°C (73°F) since the boiling point of water is 48.9°C (120°F) at 11.7 kPa], from
the steam tables, $H_V = 2667$ kJ/kg (1147 btu/lb$_m$). An alternative method for
calculating the H_V is first to obtain the enthalpy of saturated vapor at 48.9°C
(120°F) and 11.7 kPa of 2590 kJ/kg (1113.5 btu/lb$_m$). Then, using a heat capacity
of 1.884 kJ/kg · K for superheated steam with the superheat of (89.5 − 48.9)°C =
(89.5 − 48.9) K,

$$H_V = 2590 + 1.884(89.5 - 48.9) = 2667 \text{ kJ/kg}$$

For the saturated steam at 172.4 kPa, the saturation temperature from the steam tables is 115.6°C (240°F) and the latent heat is $\lambda = 2214$ kJ/kg (952 btu/lb$_m$).

Substituting into Eq. (8.4-7) and solving for S,

$$Fh_f + S\lambda = Lh_L + VH_V \qquad (8.4\text{-}7)$$

$$4535(214) + S(2214) = 1814(505) + 2722(2667)$$

$$S = 3255 \text{ kg steam/h}$$

Substituting into Eq. (8.4-8),

$$q = S\lambda = 3255(2214)\left(\frac{1}{3600}\right) = 2002 \text{ kW}$$

Substituting into Eq. (8.4-1) and solving,

$$2002(1000) = 1560(A)(115.6 - 89.5)$$

Hence, $A = 49.2$ m^2. Also, steam economy = 2722/3255 = 0.836.

8.5 CALCULATION METHODS FOR MULTIPLE-EFFECT EVAPORATORS

8.5A Introduction

In evaporation of solutions in a single-effect evaporator, a major cost is the cost of the steam used to evaporate the water. A single-effect evaporator is wasteful in terms of steam costs, since the latent heat of the vapor leaving the evaporator is usually not used. To reduce this cost, multiple-effect evaporators are used, which recover the latent heat of the vapor leaving and reuse it.

A three-effect evaporator, discussed briefly in Section 8.2B, is shown in Fig. 8.2-3. In this system each effect in itself acts as a single-effect evaporator. Raw steam is used as the heating medium to the first effect, which is boiling at temperature T_1 and pressure P_1. The vapor removed from the first effect is then used as the heating medium, condensing in the second effect and vaporizing water at temperature T_2 and pressure P_2 in this effect. To transfer heat from the condensing vapor to the boiling liquid in this second effect, the boiling temperature T_2 must be less than the condensing temperature. This means that the pressure P_2 in the second effect is lower than P_1 in the first effect. In a similar manner, vapor from the second effect is condensed in heating the third effect. Hence, pressure P_3 is less than P_2. If the first effect is operating at 1 atm abs pressure, the second and third effects will be under vacuum.

In the first effect, raw, dilute feed is added and is partly concentrated. Then this partly concentrated liquid (Fig. 8.2-3) flows to the second evaporator in series, where it is further concentrated. This liquid from the second effect flows to the third effect for final concentration.

When a multiple-effect evaporator is at steady-state operation, the flow rates and rate of evaporation in each effect are constant. The pressures, temperatures, and internal flow rates are automatically kept constant by the steady-state operation of the process itself. To change the concentration in the final effect, the feed rate to the first effect must be changed. The overall material balance made over the whole system and over each evaporator itself must be satisfied. If the final solution is too concentrated, the feed rate must be increased, and vice versa. Then the final solution will reach a new steady state at the desired concentration.

8.5B Temperature Drops and Capacity of Multiple-Effect Evaporators

1. Temperature drops in multiple-effect evaporators. The amount of heat transferred per hour in the first effect of a triple-effect evaporator with forward feed as in Fig. 8.2-3 will be

$$q_1 = U_1 A_1 \Delta T_1 \qquad (8.5\text{-}1)$$

where ΔT_1 is the difference between the condensing steam and the boiling point of the liquid, $T_S - T_1$. Assuming that the solutions have no boiling-point rise and no heat of solution and neglecting the sensible heat necessary to heat the feed to the boiling point, approximately all the latent heat of the condensing steam appears as latent heat in the vapor. This vapor then condenses in the second effect, giving up approximately the same amount of heat:

$$q_2 = U_2 A_2 \Delta T_2 \qquad (8.5\text{-}2)$$

This same reasoning holds for q_3. Since $q_1 = q_2 = q_3$, then, approximately,

$$U_1 A_1 \Delta T_1 = U_2 A_2 \Delta T_2 = U_3 A_3 \Delta T_3 \qquad (8.5\text{-}3)$$

In commercial practice the areas in all effects are usually equal and

$$\frac{q}{A} = U_1 \Delta T_1 = U_2 \Delta T_2 = U_3 \Delta T_3 \qquad (8.5\text{-}4)$$

Hence, the temperature drops ΔT in a multiple-effect evaporator are approximately inversely proportional to the values of U. Calling $\sum \Delta T$ as follows for no boiling-point rise,

$$\sum \Delta T = \Delta T_1 + \Delta T_2 + \Delta T_3 = T_S - T_3 \qquad (8.5\text{-}5)$$

Note that ΔT_1 °C = ΔT_1 K, ΔT_2 °C = ΔT_2 K, and so on. Since ΔT_1 is proportional to $1/U_1$, then

$$\Delta T_1 = \sum \Delta T \, \frac{1/U_1}{1/U_1 + 1/U_2 + 1/U_3} \qquad (8.5\text{-}6)$$

Similar equations can be written for ΔT_2 and ΔT_3.

2. Capacity of multiple-effect evaporators. A rough estimate of the capacity of a three-effect evaporator compared to a single-effect can be obtained by adding the value of q for each evaporator:

$$q = q_1 + q_2 + q_3 = U_1 A_1 \Delta T_1 + U_2 A_2 \Delta T_2 + U_3 A_3 \Delta T_3 \qquad (8.5\text{-}7)$$

If we make the assumptions that the value of U is the same in each effect and that the values of A are equal, Eq. (8.5-7) becomes

$$q = UA(\Delta T_1 + \Delta T_2 + \Delta T_3) = UA \, \Delta T \qquad (8.5\text{-}8)$$

where $\Delta T = \sum \Delta T = \Delta T_1 + \Delta T_2 + \Delta T_3 = T_S - T_3$.

If a single-effect evaporator is used with the same area A, the same value of U, and the same total temperature drop ΔT, then

$$q = UA \, \Delta T \qquad (8.5\text{-}9)$$

This, of course, gives the same capacity as for the multiple-effect evaporator. Hence, the increase in steam economy obtained by using multiple-effect evaporators is obtained at the expense of reduced capacity.

8.5C Calculations for Multiple-Effect Evaporators

In doing calculations for a multiple-effect evaporator system, the values to be obtained are usually the area of the heating surface in each effect, the kg of steam per hour to be supplied, and the amount of vapor leaving each effect, especially the last one. The given or known values are usually as follows: (1) steam pressure to the first effect, (2) final pressure in the vapor space of the last effect, (3) feed conditions and flow to the first effect, (4) the final concentration in the liquid leaving the last effect, (5) physical properties such as enthalpies and/or heat capacities of the liquid and vapors, and (6) overall heat-transfer coefficients in each effect. Usually, the areas of each effect are assumed equal.

The calculations are done using material balances, heat balances, and the capacity equations $q = UA \, \Delta T$ for each effect. A convenient way to solve these equations is by trial and error. The basic steps to follow are given as follows for a triple-effect evaporator.

8.5D Step-by-Step Calculation Methods for Triple-Effect Evaporators

1. From the known outlet concentration and pressure in the last effect, determine the boiling point in the last effect. (If a boiling-point rise is present, this can be determined from a Dühring-line plot.)
2. Determine the total amount of vapor evaporated by performing an overall material balance. For this first trial, apportion the total amount of vapor among the three effects. (Usually, equal amounts of vapor are produced in each effect, so that $V_1 = V_2 = V_3$ is assumed for the first trial.) Make a total material balance on effects 1, 2, and 3 to obtain L_1, L_2, and L_3. Then calculate the solids concentration in each effect by a solids balance on each effect.
3. Using Eq. (8.5-6), estimate the temperature drops ΔT_1, ΔT_2, and ΔT_3 in the three effects. Any effect that has an extra heating load, such as a cold feed, requires a proportionately larger ΔT. Then calculate the boiling point in each effect.

   [If a boiling-point rise (BPR) in °C is present, estimate the pressure in effects 1 and 2 and determine the BPR in each of the three effects. Only a crude pressure estimate is needed, since BPR is almost independent of pressure. Then the $\Sigma \, \Delta T$ available for heat transfer without the superheat is obtained by subtracting the sum of all three BPRs from the overall ΔT of $T_S - T_3$ (saturation). Using Eq. (8.5-6), estimate ΔT_1, ΔT_2, and ΔT_3. Then calculate the boiling point in each effect.]
4. Using heat and material balances in each effect, calculate the amount vaporized and the flows of liquid in each effect. If the amounts vaporized differ appreciably from those assumed in step 2, then steps 2, 3, and 4 can be repeated using the amounts of evaporation just calculated. (In step 2 only the solids balance is repeated.)
5. Calculate the value of q transferred in each effect. Using the rate equation $q = UA \, \Delta T$ for each effect, calculate the areas A_1, A_2, and A_3. Then calculate the average value A_m by

$$A_m = \frac{A_1 + A_2 + A_3}{3} \tag{8.5-10}$$

If these areas are reasonably close to each other, the calculations are complete and a second trial is not needed. If these areas are not almost equal, a second trial should be performed as follows.
6. To start trial 2, use the new values of L_1, L_2, L_3, V_1, V_2, and V_3 calculated by the heat balances in step 4 and calculate the new solids concentration in each effect by a solids balance on each effect.

7. Obtain new values $\Delta T'_1$, $\Delta T'_2$, and $\Delta T'_3$ from

$$\Delta T'_1 = \frac{\Delta T_1 A_1}{A_m} \qquad \Delta T'_2 = \frac{\Delta T_2 A_2}{A_m} \qquad \Delta T'_3 = \frac{\Delta T_3 A_3}{A_m} \qquad (8.5\text{-}11)$$

The sum $\Delta T'_1 + \Delta T'_2 + \Delta T'_3$ must equal the original $\sum \Delta T$. If not, proportionately readjust all $\Delta T'$ values so that this is so. Then calculate the boiling point in each effect.

[If a boiling-point rise is present, determine the new BPRs in the three effects using the new concentrations from step 6. To get a new value of $\sum \Delta T$ available for heat transfer, subtract the sum of all three BPRs from the overall ΔT. Calculate the new values of $\Delta T'$ by Eq. (8.5-11). The sum of the $\Delta T'$ values just calculated must be readjusted to the new $\sum \Delta T$ value. Then calculate the boiling point in each effect.] Step 7 is essentially a repeat of step 3 but using Eq. (8.5-11) to obtain a better estimate of the $\Delta T'$ values.

8. Using the new $\Delta T'$ values from step 7, repeat the calculations starting with step 4. Two trials are usually sufficient so that the areas are reasonably close to being equal.

EXAMPLE 8.5-1. *Evaporation of Sugar Solution in a Triple-Effect Evaporator*

A triple-effect forward-feed evaporator is being used to evaporate a sugar solution containing 10 wt % solids to a concentrated solution of 50%. The boiling-point rise of the solutions (independent of pressure) can be estimated from $BPR^\circ C = 1.78x + 6.22x^2$ ($BPR^\circ F = 3.2x + 11.2x^2$), where x is wt fraction of sugar in solution (K1). Saturated steam at 205.5 kPa (29.8 psia) [121.1°C (250°F) saturation temperature] is being used. The pressure in the vapor space of the third effect is 13.4 kPa (1.94 psia). The feed rate is 22 680 kg/h (50 000 lb$_m$/h) at 26.7°C (80°F). The heat capacity of the liquid solutions is (K1) $c_p = 4.19 - 2.35x$ kJ/kg · K (1.0 − 0.56x btu/lb$_m$ · °F). The heat of solution is considered to be negligible. The coefficients of heat transfer have been estimated as $U_1 = 3123$, $U_2 = 1987$, and $U_3 = 1136$ W/m^2 · K, or 550, 350, and 200 btu/h · ft^2 · °F. If each effect has the same surface area, calculate the area, the steam rate used, and the steam economy.

Solution: The process flow diagram is given in Fig. 8.5-1. Following the eight steps outlined, the calculations are as follows:

Step 1. For 13.4 kPa (1.94 psia), the saturation temperature is 51.67°C (125°F) from the steam tables. Using the equation for BPR for evaporator number 3 with $x = 0.5$,

$$BPR_3 = 1.78x + 6.22x^2 = 1.78(0.5) + 6.22(0.5)^2 = 2.45°C\ (4.4°F)$$

$$T_3 = 51.67 + 2.45 = 54.12°C\ (129.4°F)$$

Step 2. Making an overall and a solids balance to calculate the total amount vaporized $(V_1 + V_2 + V_3)$ and L_3,

$$F = 22\,680 = L_3 + (V_1 + V_2 + V_3)$$

$$Fx_F = 22\,680(0.1) = L_3(0.5) + (V_1 + V_2 + V_3)(0)$$

$$L_3 = 4536\ \text{kg/h}\ (10\,000\ \text{lb}_m/\text{h})$$

total vaporized $= (V_1 + V_2 + V_3) = 18\,144\ \text{kg/h}\ (40\,000\ \text{lb}_m/\text{h})$

$V_1 = 22{,}680 - L_1$ $V_2 = L_1 - L_2$ $V_3 = L_2 - 4536$

T_1 T_2 T_3

$F = 22\ 680$
$x_F = 0.1,\ T_F = 26.7^\circ C$
$S,\ 205.5\ kPa$
$T_{S1} = 121.1^\circ C$

(1)   (2)   (3)

13.7 kPa

T_{S1} T_{S2} T_{S3}

T_1 T_2 $L_3 = 4536$

L_1, x_1 L_2, x_2 $x_3 = 0.5,\ T_3$

FIGURE 8.5-1. *Flow diagram for triple-effect evaporation for Example 8.5-1.*

Assuming equal amount vaporized in each effect, $V_1 = V_2 = V_3 = 6048$ kg/h (13 333 lb$_m$/h). Making a total material balance on effects 1, 2, and 3 and solving,

(1) $F = 22\ 680 = V_1 + L_1 = 6048 + L_1,\quad L_1 = 16\ 632$ kg/h (33 667 lb$_m$/h)

(2) $L_1 = 16\ 632 = V_2 + L_2 = 6048 + L_2,\quad L_2 = 10\ 584$ (23 334)

(3) $L_2 = 10\ 584 = V_3 + L_3 = 6048 + L_3,\quad L_3 = 4536$ (10 000)

Making a solids balance on effects 1, 2, and 3 and solving for x,

(1) $22\ 680(0.1) = L_1 x_1 = 16\ 632(x_1),\quad x_1 = 0.136$

(2) $16\ 632(0.136) = L_2 x_2 = 10\ 584(x_2),\quad x_2 = 0.214$

(3) $10\ 584(0.214) = L_3 x_3 = 4536(x_3),\quad x_3 = 0.500$ (check balance)

Step 3. The BPR in each effect is calculated as follows:

(1) BPR$_1$ = $1.78x_1 + 6.22x_1^2 = 1.78(0.136) + 6.22(0.136)^2 = 0.36^\circ C\ (0.7^\circ F)$

(2) BPR$_2$ = $1.78(0.214) + 6.22(0.214)^2 = 0.65^\circ C\ (1.2^\circ F)$

(3) BPR$_3$ = $1.78(0.5) + 6.22(0.5)^2 = 2.45^\circ C\ (4.4^\circ F)$

$$\sum \Delta T \text{ available} = T_{S1} - T_3(\text{saturation}) - (\text{BPR}_1 + \text{BPR}_2 + \text{BPR}_3)$$

$$= 121.1 - 51.67 - (0.36 + 0.65 + 2.45) = 65.97^\circ C\ (118.7^\circ F)$$

Using Eq. (8.5-6) for ΔT_1 and similar equations for ΔT_2 and ΔT_3,

$$\Delta T_1 = \sum \Delta T \frac{1/U_1}{1/U_1 + 1/U_2 + 1/U_3} = \frac{(65.97)(1/3123)}{(1/3123) + (1/1987) + (1/1136)}$$

$$\Delta T_1 = 12.40^\circ C \qquad \Delta T_2 = 19.50^\circ C \qquad \Delta T_3 = 34.07^\circ C$$

However, since a cold feed enters effect number 1, this effect requires more heat. Increasing ΔT_1 and lowering ΔT_2 and ΔT_3 proportionately as a first estimate,

$$\Delta T_1 = 15.56^\circ C = 15.56\ K \qquad \Delta T_2 = 18.34^\circ C = 18.34\ K$$

$$\Delta T_3 = 32.07^\circ C = 32.07\ K$$

To calculate the actual boiling point of the solution in each effect,

(1) $T_1 = T_{S1} - \Delta T_1$

$= 121.1 - 15.56 = 105.54°C$

$T_{S1} = 121.1°C$ (condensing temperature of saturated steam to effect 1)

(2) $T_2 = T_1 - BPR_1 - \Delta T_2$

$= 105.54 - 0.36 - 18.34 = 86.84°C$

$T_{S2} = T_1 - BPR_1 = 105.54 - 0.36$

$= 105.18°C$ (condensing temperature of steam to effect 2)

(3) $T_3 = T_2 - BPR_2 - \Delta T_3$

$= 86.84 - 0.65 - 32.07 = 54.12°C$

$T_{S3} = T_2 - BPR_2$

$= 86.84 - 0.65 = 86.19°C$ (condensing temperature of steam to effect 3)

The temperatures in the three effects are as follows:

Effect 1	Effect 2	Effect 3	Condenser
$T_{S1} = 121.1°C$	$T_{S2} = 105.18$	$T_{S3} = 86.19$	$T_{S4} = 51.67$
$T_1 = 105.54$	$T_2 = 86.84$	$T_3 = 54.12$	

Step 4. The heat capacity of the liquid in each effect is calculated from the equation $c_p = 4.19 - 2.35x$:

$F: \quad c_p = 4.19 - 2.35(0.1) = 3.955$ kJ/kg·K

$L_1: \quad c_p = 4.19 - 2.35(0.136) = 3.869$

$L_2: \quad c_p = 4.19 - 2.35(0.214) = 3.684$

$L_3: \quad c_p = 4.19 - 2.35(0.5) = 3.015$

The values of the enthalpy H of the various vapor streams relative to water at 0°C as a datum are obtained from the steam table as follows:

Effect 1:

$T_1 = 105.54°C, \quad T_{S2} = 105.18\ (221.3°F), \quad BPR_1 = 0.36, \quad T_{S1} = 121.1\ (250°F)$

$H_1 = H_{S2}$(saturation enthalpy at T_{S2}) + 1.884(0.36°C superheat)

$= 2684 + 1.884(0.36) = 2685$ kJ/kg

$\lambda_{S1} = H_{S1}$(vapor saturation enthalpy) $- h_{S1}$(liquid enthalpy at T_{S1})

$= (2708 - 508) = 2200$ kJ/kg latent heat of condensation

Effect 2:

$T_2 = 86.84°C, \quad T_{S3} = 86.19, \quad BPR_2 = 0.65$

$H_2 = H_{S3} + 1.884(0.65) = 2654 + 1.884(0.65) = 2655$ kJ/kg

$\lambda_{S2} = H_1 - h_{S2} = 2685 - 441 = 2244$ kJ/kg

Effect 3:

$$T_3 = 54.12°C, \qquad T_{S4} = 51.67, \qquad BPR_3 = 2.45$$

$$H_3 = H_{S4} + 1.884(2.45) = 2595 + 1.884(2.45) = 2600 \text{ kJ/kg}$$

$$\lambda_{S3} = H_2 - h_{S3} = 2655 - 361 = 2294 \text{ kJ/kg}$$

(Note that the superheat corrections in this example are small and could possibly have been neglected. However, the corrections were used to demonstrate the method of calculation.) Flow relations to be used in heat balances are

$$V_1 = 22\,680 - L_1, \qquad V_2 = L_1 - L_2, \qquad V_3 = L_2 - 4536, \qquad L_3 = 4536$$

Write a heat balance on each effect. Using 0°C as a datum, since the values of H of the vapors are relative to 0°C (32°F), and noting that $(T_F - 0)°C = (T_F - 0)$ K and $(T_1 - 0)°C = (T_1 - 0)$ K,

(1) $$Fc_p(T_F - 0) + S\lambda_{S1} = L_1 c_p(T_1 - 0) + V_1 H_1$$

Substituting the known values,

$$22\,680(3.955)(26.7 - 0) + S(2200)$$
$$= L_1(3.869)(105.54 - 0) + (22\,680 - L_1)(2685)$$

(2) $$L_1 c_p(T_1 - 0) + V_1 \lambda_{S2} = L_2 c_p(T_2 - 0) + V_2 H_2$$

$$L_1(3.869)(105.54 - 0) + (22\,680 - L_1)(2244)$$
$$= L_2(3.684)(86.84 - 0) + (L_1 - L_2)(2655)$$

(3) $$L_2 c_p(T_2 - 0) + V_2 \lambda_{S3} = L_3 c_p(T_3 - 0) + V_3 H_3$$

$$L_2(3.684)(86.84 - 0) + (L_1 - L_2)(2294)$$
$$= 4536(3.015)(54.12 - 0) + (L_2 - 4536)(2600)$$

Solving the last two equations simultaneously for L_1 and L_2 and substituting into the first equation,

$$L_1 = 17\,078 \text{ kg/h} \qquad L_2 = 11\,068 \qquad L_3 = 4536$$

$$S = 8936 \qquad V_1 = 5602 \qquad V_2 = 6010 \qquad V_3 = 6532$$

The calculated values of V_1, V_2, and V_3 are close enough to the assumed values that steps 2, 3, and 4 do not need to be repeated. If the calculation were repeated, the calculated values of V_1, V_2, and V_3 would be used starting with step 2 and a solids balance in each effect would be made.

Step 5. Solving for the values of q in each effect and area,

$$q_1 = S\lambda_{S1} = \left(\frac{8936}{3600}\right)(2200 \times 1000) = 5.460 \times 10^6 \text{ W}$$

$$q_2 = V_1 \lambda_{S2} = \left(\frac{5602}{3600}\right)(2244 \times 1000) = 3.492 \times 10^6 \text{ W}$$

$$q_3 = V_2 \lambda_{S3} = \left(\frac{6010}{3600}\right)(2294 \times 1000) = 3.830 \times 10^6 \text{ W}$$

$$A_1 = \frac{q_1}{U_1\,\Delta T_1} = \frac{5.460 \times 10^6}{3123(15.56)} = 112.4 \text{ m}^2$$

$$A_2 = \frac{q_2}{U_2\,\Delta T_2} = \frac{3.492 \times 10^6}{1987(18.34)} = 95.8 \text{ m}^2$$

$$A_3 = \frac{q_3}{U_3\,\Delta T_3} = \frac{3.830 \times 10^6}{1136(32.07)} = 105.1 \text{ m}^2$$

The average area $A_m = 104.4 \text{ m}^2$. The areas differ from the average value by less than 10% and a second trial is not really necessary. However, a second trial will be made starting with step 6 to demonstrate the calculation methods used.

Step 6. Making a new solids balance on effects 1, 2, and 3, using the new $L_1 = 17\,078$, $L_2 = 11\,068$, and $L_3 = 4536$, and solving for x,

(1) $22\,680(0.1) = 17\,078(x_1)$, $x_1 = 0.133$

(2) $17\,078(0.133) = 11\,068(x_2)$, $x_2 = 0.205$

(3) $11\,068(0.205) = 4536(x_3)$, $x_3 = 0.500$ (check balance)

Step 7. The new BPR in each effect is then

(1) $\text{BPR}_1 = 1.78x_1 + 6.22x_1^2 = 1.78(0.133) + 6.22(0.133)^2 = 0.35°\text{C}$

(2) $\text{BPR}_2 = 1.78(0.205) + 6.22(0.205)^2 = 0.63°\text{C}$

(3) $\text{BPR}_3 = 1.78(0.5) + 6.22(0.5)^2 = 2.45°\text{C}$

$$\sum \Delta T \text{ available} = 121.1 - 51.67 - (0.35 + 0.63 + 2.45) = 66.00°\text{C}$$

The new values for ΔT are obtained using Eq. (8.5-11):

$$\Delta T_1' = \frac{\Delta T_1 A_1}{A_m} = \frac{15.56(112.4)}{104.4} = 16.77 \text{ K} = 16.77°\text{C}$$

$$\Delta T_2' = \frac{\Delta T_2 A_2}{A_m} = \frac{18.34(95.8)}{104.4} = 16.86°\text{C}$$

$$\Delta T_3' = \frac{\Delta T_3 A_3}{A_m} = \frac{32.07(105.1)}{104.4} = 32.34°\text{C}$$

$$\sum \Delta T = 16.77 + 16.86 + 32.34 = 65.97°\text{C}$$

These $\Delta T'$ values are readjusted so that $\Delta T_1' = 16.77$, $\Delta T_2' = 16.87$, $\Delta T_3' = 32.36$, and $\sum \Delta T = 16.77 + 16.87 + 32.36 = 66.00°\text{C}$. To calculate the actual boiling point of the solution in each effect,

(1) $T_1 = T_{S1} - \Delta T_1' = 121.1 - 16.77 = 104.33°\text{C}$, $T_{S1} = 121.1°\text{C}$

(2) $T_2 = T_1 - \text{BPR}_1 - \Delta T_2' = 104.33 - 0.35 - 16.87 = 87.11°\text{C}$

   $T_{S2} = T_1 - \text{BPR}_1 = 104.33 - 0.35 = 103.98°\text{C}$

(3) $T_3 = T_2 - \text{BPR}_2 - \Delta T_3' = 87.11 - 0.63 - 32.36 = 54.12°\text{C}$

   $T_{S3} = T_2 - \text{BPR}_2 = 87.11 - 0.63 = 86.48°\text{C}$

Step 8. Following step 4, the heat capacity of the liquid is $c_p = 4.19 - 2.35x$:

$$F: \quad c_p = 3.955 \text{ kJ/kg} \cdot \text{K}$$

$$L_1: \quad c_p = 4.19 - 2.35(0.133) = 3.877$$

$$L_2: \quad c_p = 4.19 - 2.35(0.205) = 3.708$$

$$L_3: \quad c_p = 3.015$$

The new values of the enthalpy H are as follows in each effect:

(1) $H_1 = H_{S2} + 1.884(°C \text{ superheat}) = 2682 + 1.884(0.35) = 2683 \text{ kJ/kg}$

$$\lambda_{S1} = H_{S1} - h_{S1} = 2708 - 508 = 2200 \text{ kJ/kg}$$

(2) $H_2 = H_{S3} + 1.884(0.63) = 2654 + 1.884(0.63) = 2655 \text{ kJ/kg}$

$$\lambda_{S2} = H_1 - h_{S2} = 2683 - 440 = 2243 \text{ kJ/kg}$$

(3) $H_3 = H_{S4} + 1.884(2.45) = 2595 + 1.884(2.45) = 2600 \text{ kJ/kg}$

$$\lambda_{S3} = H_2 - h_{S3} = 2655 - 362 = 2293 \text{ kJ/kg}$$

Writing a heat balance on each effect,

(1) $22\,680(3.955)(26.7 - 0) + S(2200)$
$$= L_1(3.877)(104.33 - 0) + (22\,680 - L_1)(2683)$$

(2) $L_1(3.877)(104.33 - 0) + (22\,680 - L_1)(2243)$
$$= L_2(3.708)(87.11 - 0) + (L_1 - L_2)(2655)$$

(3) $L_2(3.708)(87.11 - 0) + (L_1 - L_2)(2293)$
$$= 4536(3.015)(54.12 - 0) + (L_2 - 4536)(2600)$$

Solving,

$$L_1 = 17\,005 \text{ kg/h} \quad L_2 = 10\,952 \quad L_3 = 4536 \quad S = 8960 \text{ (steam used)}$$

$$V_1 = 5675 \quad V_2 = 6053 \quad V_3 = 6416$$

Note that these values from trial 2 differ very little from the trial 1 results. Following step 5, and solving for q in each effect and A,

$$q_1 = S\lambda_{S1} = \frac{8960}{3600}(2200 \times 1000) = 5.476 \times 10^6 \text{ W}$$

$$q_2 = V_1\lambda_{S2} = \frac{5675}{3600}(2243 \times 1000) = 3.539 \times 10^6 \text{ W}$$

$$q_3 = V_2\lambda_{S3} = \frac{6053}{3600}(2293 \times 1000) = 3.855 \times 10^6 \text{ W}$$

$$A_1 = \frac{q_1}{U_1 \, \Delta T_1'} = \frac{5.476 \times 10^6}{3123(16.77)} = 104.6 \text{ m}^2$$

$$A_2 = \frac{q_2}{U_2 \, \Delta T_2'} = \frac{3.539 \times 10^6}{1987(16.87)} = 105.6 \text{ m}^2$$

$$A_3 = \frac{q_3}{U_3 \, \Delta T_3'} = \frac{3.855 \times 10^6}{1136(32.36)} = 104.9 \text{ m}^2$$

The average area to use in each effect is $A_m = 105.0 \text{ m}^2$. Note that this value of 105.0 m^2 is quite close to the average value of 104.4 m^2 from the first trial.

$$\text{steam economy} = \frac{V_1 + V_2 + V_3}{S} = \frac{5675 + 6053 + 6416}{8960} = 2.025$$

8.6 CONDENSERS FOR EVAPORATORS

8.6A Introduction

In multiple-effect evaporators the vapors from the last effect are usually leaving under vacuum, that is, at less than atmospheric pressure. These vapors must be condensed and discharged as a liquid at atmospheric pressure. This is done by using cooling water to condense the vapors. The condenser can be a surface condenser, where the vapor to be condensed and the cooling liquid are separated by a metal wall, or a direct-contact condenser, where the vapor and cooling liquid are mixed directly.

8.6B Surface Condensers

Surface condensers are employed where actual mixing of the condensate with condenser cooling water is not desired. In general, they are shell-and-tube condensers, with the vapor on the shell side and cooling water in multipass flow on the tube side. Noncondensable gases such as air, CO_2, N_2, or another gas are usually present in the vapor stream. They may have entered as dissolved gases in the liquid feed or occur because of decomposition in the solutions. These noncondensable gases may be vented from any well-cooled point in the condenser. If the vapor being condensed is below atmospheric pressure, the condensed liquid leaving the surface condenser can be removed by pumping and the noncondensable gases by using a vacuum pump. Surface condensers are much more expensive and use more cooling water, so they are usually not used in cases where a direct-contact condenser is suitable.

8.6C Direct-Contact Condensers

In *direct-contact condensers* cooling water directly contacts and condenses the vapors. One of the most common types of direct-contact condenser is the countercurrent barometric condenser shown in Fig. 8.6-1. The vapor enters the condenser and is condensed by rising upward against a shower of cooling water droplets. The condenser is located on top of a long discharge tailpipe. The condenser is high enough above the discharge point in the tailpipe that the water column established in the pipe more than compensates for the difference in pressure between the low absolute pressure in the condenser and the atmosphere. The water can then discharge by gravity through a seal pot at the bottom. A height of about 10.4 m (34 ft) is used.

The barometric condenser is inexpensive and economical of water consumption. It can maintain a vacuum corresponding to a saturated vapor temperature within about 2.8 K (5°F) of the water temperature leaving the condenser. For example, if the discharge water is at 316.5 K (110°F), the pressure corresponding to 316.5 + 2.8 or 319.3 K is 10.1 kPa (1.47 psia).

The water consumption can be estimated by a simple heat balance for a barometric condenser. If the vapor flow to the condenser is V kg/h at temperature T_S and the water flow is

FIGURE 8.6-1. *Schematic of barometric condenser.*

W kg/h at an entering temperature of T_1 and a leaving temperature of T_2, the derivation is as follows:

$$VH_S + Wc_p(T_1 - 273.2) = (V + W)c_p(T_2 - 273.2) \qquad \text{(8.6-1)}$$

where H_S is the enthalpy from the steam tables of the vapor at T_S K and the pressure in the vapor stream. Solving,

$$\frac{W}{V} = \frac{\text{kg water}}{\text{kg vapor}} = \frac{H_S - c_p(T_2 - 273.2)}{c_p(T_2 - T_1)} \qquad \text{(8.6-2)}$$

The noncondensable gases can be removed from the condenser by a vacuum pump, either a mechanical pump or a steam-jet ejector. In the ejector high-pressure steam enters a nozzle at high speed and entrains the noncondensable gases from the space under vacuum.

Another type of direct-contact condenser is the jet barometric condenser. High-velocity jets of water act as both a vapor condenser and an entrainer of the noncondensables out of the tail pipe. Jet condensers usually require more water than the more-common barometric condensers and are more difficult to throttle at low vapor rates.

8.7 EVAPORATION OF BIOLOGICAL MATERIALS

8.7A Introduction and Properties of Biological Materials

The evaporation of many biological materials frequently differs from the evaporation of inorganic materials such as NaCl and NaOH and organic materials such as ethanol and acetic acid. Biological materials such as pharmaceuticals, milk, citrus juices, and vegetable extracts are usually quite heat-sensitive and often contain fine particles of suspended matter in solution. In addition, because of problems due to bacteria growth, the equipment must be designed for easy cleaning. Many biological materials in solution exhibit only a small boiling-point rise when concentrated. This is because suspended solids in a fine, dispersed form and dissolved solutes of large molecular weight contribute little to this rise.

The amount of degradation of biological materials on evaporation is a function of the temperature and length of time. To keep the temperature low, the evaporation must be done under vacuum, which reduces the boiling point of the solution. To keep the time of contact low, the equipment must provide for a low holdup time (contact time) for the material being evaporated. Typical types of equipment used and some biological materials processed are listed below. Detailed descriptions of the equipment are given in Section 8.2.

1. Long-tube vertical evaporator: condensed milk
2. Falling-film evaporator: fruit juices
3. Agitated-film (wiped-film) evaporator: rubber latex, gelatin, antibiotics, fruit juices
4. Heat-pump cycle evaporator: fruit juices, milk, pharmaceuticals

8.7B Fruit Juices

In the evaporation of fruit juices, such as orange juice, problems arise that are quite different from those associated with the evaporation of a typical salt such as NaCl. The fruit juices are heat-sensitive and the viscosity increases greatly as concentration increases. Also, solid suspended matter in fruit juices has a tendency to cling to the heating surface, thus causing overheating which leads to burning and spoilage of the matter (B2).

To reduce this tendency to stick and to reduce residence time, high rates of circulation over the heat-transfer surface are necessary. Since the material is heat-sensitive, low-temperature operation is also necessary. Hence, a fruit juice concentration plant usually employs a single and not a multiple evaporation unit. Vacuum is used to reduce the temperature of evaporation.

A typical fruit juice evaporation system using the heat-pump cycle is shown in the literature (P1, C1); it employs low-temperature ammonia as the heating fluid. A frozen concentrated citrus juice process is described by Charm (C1). The process uses a multistage falling-film evaporator. A major fault of concentrated orange juice is a flat flavor due to the loss of volatile constituents during evaporation. To overcome this, a portion of the fresh pulpy juice bypasses the evaporation cycle and is blended with the evaporated concentrate.

8.7C Sugar Solutions

Sugar (sucrose) is obtained primarily from sugarcane and sugar beets. Sugar tends to caramelize if kept at high temperatures for long periods (B2). The general tendency is to use short-tube evaporators of the natural circulation type. In the evaporation process for sugar solutions, a clear solution of sugar having a concentration of 10–13° Brix (10–13 wt %) is evaporated to 40–60° Brix (K1, S1).

The feed is first preheated by exhaust steam and then typically enters a six-effect forward-feed evaporator system. The first effect operates at a pressure in the vapor space of the evaporator of about 207 kPa (30 psia) [121.1°C (250°F) saturation temperature] and the last effect under vacuum at about 24 kPa (63.9°C saturation). Examples of the relatively small boiling-point rise of sugar solutions and the heat capacity are given in Example 8.5-1.

8.7D Paper-Pulp Waste Liquors

In the manufacture of paper pulp in the sulfate process, wood chips are digested or cooked and spent black liquor is obtained after washing the pulp. This solution contains primarily sodium carbonate and organic sulfide compounds. It is concentrated by evaporation in a six-effect system (K1, S1).

8.8. EVAPORATION USING VAPOR RECOMPRESSION

8.8A Introduction

In the single-effect evaporator, the vapor from the unit is generally condensed and discarded. In the multiple-effect evaporator, the pressure in each succeeding effect is lowered so that the boiling point of the liquid is also lowered in each effect. Hence, there is a temperature difference created for the vapor from one effect to condense in the next effect and boil the liquid to form vapor.

In a single-effect vapor-recompression (sometimes called vapor-compression) evaporator, the vapor is compressed so that its condensing or saturation temperature is increased. This compressed vapor is returned back to the heater of steam chest and condenses so that vapor is formed in the evaporator (B5, W1, Z1). In this manner the latent heat of the vapor is used and not discarded. The two types of vapor-recompression units are the mechanical and the thermal type.

8.8B Mechanical Vapor-Recompression Evaporator

In a mechanical vapor-recompression evaporator, a conventional single-effect evaporator similar to that in Fig. 8.2-2 is used, as shown in Fig. 8.8-1. The cold feed is preheated by exchange with the hot outlet liquid product and then flows to the unit. The vapor coming overhead does not go to a condenser but is sent to a centrifugal or positive-displacement compressor driven by an electric motor or steam. This compressed vapor or steam is sent back to the heat exchanger or steam chest. The compressed vapor condenses at a temperature higher than the boiling point of the hot liquid in the effect, and a temperature difference is set up. Vapor is again generated and the cycle repeated.

FIGURE 8.8-1. *Simplified process flow for mechanical vapor recompression evaporator.*

Sometimes it is necessary to add a small amount of makeup steam to the vapor line before the compressor (B5, K2). Also, a small amount of condensate may be added to the compressed vapor to remove any superheat, if present.

Vapor-recompression units generally operate at low optimum-temperature differences of 5–10°C. Hence, large heat-transfer areas are needed. These units usually have higher capital costs than multiple-effect units because of the larger area and the costs of the relatively expensive compressor and drive unit. The main advantage of vapor-recompression units is their lower energy costs. Using the steam equivalent of the power to drive the compressor, the steam economy is equivalent to a multiple-effect evaporator of up to 10 or more units (Z1).

Some typical applications of mechanical vapor-recompression units are evaporation of seawater to give distilled water, evaporation of kraft black liquor in the paper industry (L2), evaporation of heat-sensitive materials such as fruit juices, and crystallization of salts having inverse solubility curves, where the solubility decreases with increasing temperature (K2, M3).

Falling-film evaporators are well suited for vapor-recompression systems (W1) because they operate at low-temperature-difference values and have very little entrained liquid which can cause problems in the compressor. Vapor recompression has been used in distillation towers where the overhead vapor is recompressed and used in the reboiler as the heating medium (M2).

8.8C Thermal Vapor-Recompression Evaporator

A steam jet can also be used to compress the vapor, in what is called a thermal vapor-recompression evaporator. Its main disadvantages are the low efficiency of the steam jet, necessitating the removal of this excess heat, and the lack of flexibility to changes in process variables (M3). Steam jets are cheaper and more durable than mechanical compressors and can more easily handle large volumes of low-pressure vapors.

PROBLEMS

8.4-1. Heat-Transfer Coefficient in Single-Effect Evaporator. A feed of 4535 kg/h of a 2.0 wt % salt solution at 311 K enters continuously a single-effect evaporator and is being concentrated to 3.0%. The evaporation is at atmospheric pressure and the area of the evaporator is 69.7 m^2. Saturated steam at 383.2 K is supplied for heating. Since the solution is dilute, it can be assumed to have the same boiling point as water. The heat capacity of the feed can be taken as c_p = 4.10 kJ/kg · K. Calculate the amounts of vapor and liquid product and the overall heat-transfer coefficient U.

Ans. U = 1823 W/m^2 · K

8.4-2. Effects of Increased Feed Rate in Evaporator. Using the same area, value of U, steam pressure, evaporator pressure, and feed temperature as in Problem 8.4-1, calculate the amounts of liquid and vapor leaving and the liquid outlet concentration if the feed rate is increased to 6804 kg/h.

Ans. V = 1256 kg/h, L = 5548 kg/h, x_L = 2.45%

8.4-3. Effect of Evaporator Pressure on Capacity and Product Composition. Recalculate Example 8.4-1 but use an evaporator pressure of 41.4 kPa instead of 101.32 kPa abs. Use the same steam pressure, area A, and heat-transfer coefficient U in the calculations.

(a) Do this to obtain the new capacity or feed rate under these new conditions. The composition of the liquid product will be the same as before.

(b) Do this to obtain the new product composition if the feed rate is increased to 18 144 kg/h.

8.4-4. *Production of Distilled Water.* An evaporator having an area of 83.6 m^2 and $U = 2270$ W/m$^2 \cdot$ K is used to produce distilled water for a boiler feed. Tap water having 400 ppm dissolved solids at 15.6°C is fed to the evaporator operating at 1 atm pressure abs. Saturated steam at 115.6°C is available for use. Calculate the amount of distilled water produced per hour if the outlet liquid contains 800 ppm solids.

8.4-5. *Boiling-Point Rise of NaOH Solutions.* Determine the boiling temperature of the solution and the boiling-point rise for the following cases:

(a) A 30% NaOH solution boiling in an evaporator at a pressure of 172.4 kPa (25 psia).

(b) A 60% NaOH solution boiling in an evaporator at a pressure of 3.45 kPa (0.50 psia).

Ans. (a) Boiling point = 130.6°C, boiling-point rise = 15°C

8.4-6. *Boiling-Point Rise of Biological Solutes in Solution.* Determine the boiling-point rise for the following solutions of biological solutes in water. Use the figure in (P1), pp. 11–112.

(a) A 30 wt % solution of citric acid in water boiling at 220°F (104.4°C).

(b) A 40 wt % solution of sucrose in water boiling at 220°F (104.4°C).

Ans. (a) Boiling-point rise = 2.2°F (1.22°C)

8.4-7. *Effect of Feed Temperature on Evaporating an NaOH Solution.* A single-effect evaporator is concentrating a feed of 9072 kg/h of a 10 wt % solution of NaOH in water to a product of 50% solids. The pressure of the saturated steam used is 42 kPa (gage) and the pressure in the vapor space of the evaporator is 20 kPa (abs). The overall heat-transfer coefficient is 1988 W/m$^2 \cdot$ K. Calculate the steam used, the steam economy in kg vaporized/kg steam, and the area for the following feed conditions:

(a) Feed temperature of 288.8 K (15.6°C).

(b) Feed temperature of 322.1 K (48.9°C).

Ans. (a) $S = 8959$ kg/h of steam, $A = 296.9$ m^2

8.4-8. *Heat-Transfer Coefficient to Evaporate NaOH.* In order to concentrate 4536 kg/h of an NaOH solution containing 10 wt % NaOH to a 20 wt % solution, a single-effect evaporator is being used, with an area of 37.6 m^2. The feed enters at 21.1°C (294.3 K). Saturated steam at 110°C (383.2 K) is used for heating and the pressure in the vapor space of the evaporator is 51.7 kPa. Calculate the kg/h of steam used and the overall heat-transfer coefficient.

8.4-9. *Throughput of a Single-Effect Evaporator.* An evaporator is concentrating F kg/h at 311 K of a 20 wt % solution of NaOH to 50%. The saturated steam used for heating is at 399.3 K. The pressure in the vapor space of the evaporator is 13.3 kPa abs. The overall coefficient is 1420 W/m$^2 \cdot$ K and the area is 86.4 m^2. Calculate the feed rate F of the evaporator.

Ans. $F = 9072$ kg/h

8.4-10. *Surface Area and Steam Consumption of an Evaporator.* A single-effect evaporator is concentrating a feed solution of organic colloids from 5 to 50 wt %. The solution has a negligible boiling-point elevation. The heat capacity of the feed is $c_p = 4.06$ kJ/kg $\cdot$ K (0.97 btu/lb$_m \cdot$ °F) and the feed enters at 15.6°C (60°F). Saturated steam at 101.32 kPa is available for heating, and the pressure in the vapor space of the evaporator is 15.3 kPa. A total of 4536 kg/h (10 000 lb_m/h) of water is to be evaporated. The overall heat-transfer coefficient is 1988 W/m^2 · K (350 btu/h · °F). What is the required surface area in m^2 and the steam consumption?

8.4-11. *Evaporation of Tomato Juice Under Vacuum.* Tomato juice having a concentration of 12 wt % solids is being concentrated to 25% solids in a film-type evaporator. The maximum allowable temperature for the tomato juice is 135°F, which will be the temperature of the product. The feed enters at 100°F. Saturated steam at 25 psia is used for heating. The overall heat-transfer coefficient U is 600 btu/h · ft^2 · °F and the area A is 50 ft^2. The heat capacity of the feed c_p is estimated as 0.95 btu/lb_m · °F. Neglect any boiling-point rise if present. Calculate the feed rate of tomato juice to the evaporator.

8.4-12. *Concentration of Cane Sugar Solution.* A single-effect evaporator is being used to concentrate a feed of 10 000 lb_m/h of a cane sugar solution at 80°F and containing a sugar content of 15° Brix (degrees Brix is wt % sugar) to 30° Brix for use in a food process. Saturated steam at 240°F is available for heating. The vapor space in the evaporator will be at 1 atm abs pressure. The overall U = 350 btu/h · ft^2 · °F and the heat capacity of the feed is c_p = 0.91 btu/lb_m · °F. The boiling-point rise can be estimated from Example 8.5-1. The heat of solution can be considered negligible and neglected. Calculate the area required for the evaporator and the amount of steam used per hour.

Ans. Boiling-point rise = 2.0°F (1.1°C), A = 667 ft^2 (62.0 m^2)

8.5-1. *Boiling Points in a Triple-Effect Evaporator.* A solution with a negligible boiling-point rise is being evaporated in a triple-effect evaporator using saturated steam at 121.1°C (394.3 K). The pressure in the vapor of the last effect is 25.6 kPa abs. The heat-transfer coefficients are U_1 = 2840, U_2 = 1988, and U_3 = 1420 W/m^2 · K, and the areas are equal. Estimate the boiling point in each of the evaporators.

Ans. T_1 = 108.6°C (381.8 K)

8.5-2. *Evaporation of Sugar Solution in a Multiple-Effect Evaporator.* A triple-effect evaporator with forward feed is evaporating a sugar solution with negligible boiling-point rise (less than 1.0 K, which will be neglected) and containing 5 wt % solids to 25% solids. Saturated steam at 205 kPa abs is being used. The pressure in the vapor space of the third effect is 13.65 kPa. The feed rate is 22 680 kg/h and the temperature 299.9 K. The liquid heat capacity is c_p = 4.19 − 2.35 x, where c_p is in kJ/kg · K and x in wt fraction (K1). The heat-transfer coefficients are U_1 = 3123, U_2 = 1987, and U_3 = 1136 W/m^2 · K. Calculate the surface area of each effect if each effect has the same area, and the steam rate.

Ans. Area A = 99.1 m^2, steam rate S = 8972 kg/h

8.5-3. *Evaporation in Double-Effect Reverse-Feed Evaporators.* A feed containing 2 wt % dissolved organic solids in water is fed to a double-effect evaporator with reverse feed. The feed enters at 100°F and is concentrated to 25% solids. The boiling-point rise can be considered negligible, as can the heat of solution. Each evaporator has a 1000-ft^2 surface area, and the heat-transfer coefficients are U_1 = 500 and U_2 = 700 btu/h · ft^2 · °F. The feed enters evaporator number 2 and steam at 100 psia is fed to number 1. The pressure in the vapor space of evaporator number 2 is 0.98 psia. Assume that the heat capacity of all liquid solutions is that of liquid water. Calculate the feed rate F and the product rate L_1 of a solution containing 25% solids. (*Hint:* Assume a feed rate of, say, F = 1000 lb_m/h and a value of T_1. Calculate the area and T_1. Then calculate the actual feed rate by multiplying 1000 by 1000/calculated area.)

Ans. F = 133 800 lb_m/h (60 691 kg/h), L_1 = 10 700 lb_m/h (4853 kg/h)

8.5-4. *Concentration of NaOH Solution in Triple-Effect Evaporator.* A forced-circulation triple-effect evaporator using forward feed is to be used to concentrate a 10 wt % NaOH solution entering at 37.8°C to 50%. The steam used enters at 58.6 kPa gage. The absolute pressure in the vapor space of the third effect is 6.76 kPa. The feed rate is 13 608 kg/h. The heat-transfer coefficients are $U_1 = 6246$, $U_2 = 3407$, and $U_3 = 2271$ W/m$^2 \cdot$ K. All effects have the same area. Calculate the surface area and steam consumption.

Ans. $A = 97.3$ m^2, $S = 5284$ kg steam/h

8.5-5. *Triple-Effect Evaporator with Reverse Feed.* A feed rate of 20 410 kg/h of 10 wt % NaOH solution at 48.9°C is being concentrated in a triple-effect reverse-feed evaporator to produce a 50% solution. Saturated steam at 178.3°C is fed to the first evaporator and the pressure in the third effect is 10.34 kPa abs. The heat-transfer coefficient for each effect is assumed to be 2840 W/m$^2 \cdot$ K. Calculate the heat-transfer area and the steam consumption rate.

8.5-6. *Evaporation of Sugar Solution in Double-Effect Evaporator.* A double-effect evaporator with reverse feed is used to concentrate 4536 kg/h of a 10 wt % sugar solution to 50%. The feed enters the second effect at 37.8°C. Saturated steam at 115.6°C enters the first effect and the vapor from this effect is used to heat the second effect. The absolute pressure in the second effect is 13.65 kPa abs. The overall coefficients are $U_1 = 2270$ and $U_2 = 1705$ W/m$^2 \cdot$ K. The heating areas for both effects are equal. Use boiling-point-rise and heat-capacity data from Example 8.5-1. Calculate the area and steam consumption.

8.6-1. *Water Consumption and Pressure in Barometric Condenser.* The concentration of NaOH solution leaving the third effect of a triple-effect evaporator is 50 wt %. The vapor flow rate leaving is 5670 kg/h and this vapor goes to a barometric condenser. The discharge water from the condenser leaves at 40.5°C. Assuming that the condenser can maintain a vacuum in the third effect corresponding to a saturated vapor pressure of 2.78°C above 40.5°C, calculate the pressure in the third effect and the cooling-water flow to the condenser. The cooling water enters at 29.5°C. (*Note:* The vapor leaving the evaporator will be superheated because of the boiling-point rise.)

Ans. Pressure = 8.80 kPa abs, $W = 306\,200$ kg water/h

REFERENCES

(B1) BADGER, W. L., and BANCHERO, J. T. *Introduction to Chemical Engineering.* New York: McGraw-Hill Book Company, 1955.

(B2) BLAKEBROUGH, N. *Biochemical and Biological Engineering Science,* Vol. 2. New York: Academic Press, Inc., 1968.

(B3) BADGER, W. L., and MCCABE, W. L. *Elements of Chemical Engineering,* 2nd ed. New York: McGraw-Hill Book Company, 1936.

(B4) BROWN, G. G., et al. *Unit Operations.* New York: John Wiley & Sons, Inc., 1950.

(B5) BEESLEY, A. H., and RHINESMITH, R. D. *Chem. Eng. Progr.,* **76**(8), 37 (1980).

(C1) CHARM, S. E. *The Fundamentals of Food Engineering,* 2nd ed. Westport, Conn.: Avi Publishing Co., Inc., 1971.

(K1) KERN, D. Q. *Process Heat Transfer.* New York: McGraw-Hill Book Company, 1950.

(K2) KING, R. J. *Chem. Eng. Progr.,* **80**(7), 63 (1984).

(L1) LINDSEY, E. *Chem. Eng.,* **60**(4), 227 (1953).

(L2) LOGSDON, J. D. *Chem. Eng. Progr.,* **79**(9), 36 (1983).

(M1) MCCABE, W. L. *Trans. A.I.Ch.E.,* **31**, 129 (1935).

(M2) MEILI, A., and STUECHELI, A. *Chem. Eng.,* **94** (Feb. 16), 133 (1987).

(M3) MEHRA, D. K. *Chem. Eng.,* **93** (Feb. 3), 56 (1986).

(P1) PERRY, R. H., and GREEN, D. *Perry's Chemical Engineers' Handbook,* 7th ed. New York: McGraw-Hill Book Company, 1997.

(S1) SHREVE, R. N., and BRINK, J. A., JR. *Chemical Process Industries,* 4th ed. New York: McGraw-Hill Book Company, 1977.

(W1) WEIMER, L. D., DOLF, H. R., and AUSTIN, D. A. *Chem. Eng. Progr.,* **76**(11), 70 (1980).

(Z1) ZIMMER, A. *Chem. Eng. Progr.,* **76**(9), 37 (1980).

CHAPTER 9

*Drying of
Process Materials*

9.1 INTRODUCTION AND METHODS OF DRYING

9.1A Purposes of Drying

The discussions of drying in this chapter are concerned with the removal of water from process materials and other substances. The term "drying" is also used to refer to removal of other organic liquids, such as benzene or organic solvents, from solids. Many of the types of equipment and calculation methods discussed for removal of water can also be used for removal of organic liquids.

Drying generally means removal of relatively small amounts of water from material. Evaporation refers to removal of relatively large amounts of water from material. In evaporation the water is removed as vapor at its boiling point. In drying the water is usually removed as a vapor by air.

In some cases water may be removed mechanically from solid materials by means of presses, centrifuging, and other methods. This is cheaper than drying by thermal means for removal of water, which will be discussed here. The moisture content of the final dried product varies depending upon the type of product. Dried salt contains about 0.5% water, coal about 4%, and many food products about 5%. Drying is usually the final processing step before packaging and makes many materials, such as soap powders and dyestuffs, more suitable for handling.

Drying or dehydration of biological materials, especially foods, is used as a preservation technique. Microorganisms that cause food spoilage and decay cannot grow and multiply in the absence of water. Also, many enzymes that cause chemical changes in food and other biological materials cannot function without water. When the water content is reduced below about 10 wt %, the microorganisms are not active. However, it is usually necessary to lower the moisture content below 5 wt % in foods to preserve flavor and nutrition. Dried foods can be stored for extended periods of time.

Some biological materials and pharmaceuticals, which may not be heated for ordinary drying, may be freeze-dried, as discussed in Section 9.11. Also, in Section 9.12, sterilization of foods and other biological materials is discussed, which is another method often employed to preserve such materials.

9.1B General Methods of Drying

Drying methods and processes can be classified in several different ways. Drying processes can be classified as *batch,* where the material is inserted into the drying equipment and drying proceeds for a given period of time, or as *continuous,* where the material is continuously added to the dryer and dried material is continuously removed.

Drying processes can also be categorized according to the physical conditions used to add heat and remove water vapor: (1) in the first category, heat is added by direct contact with heated air at atmospheric pressure, and the water vapor formed is removed by the air; (2) in vacuum drying, the evaporation of water proceeds more rapidly at low pressures, and the heat is added indirectly by contact with a metal wall or by radiation (low temperatures can also be used under vacuum for certain materials that may discolor or decompose at higher temperatures); and (3) in freeze-drying, water is sublimed from the frozen material.

9.2 EQUIPMENT FOR DRYING

9.2A Tray Dryer

In *tray dryers,* which are also called shelf, cabinet, or compartment dryers, the material, which may be a lumpy solid or a pasty solid, is spread uniformly on a metal tray to a depth of 10 to 100 mm. Such a typical tray dryer, shown in Fig. 9.2-1, contains removable trays loaded in a cabinet.

Steam-heated air is recirculated by a fan over and parallel to the surface of the trays. Electrical heat is also used, especially for low heating loads. About 10 to 20% of the air passing over the trays is fresh air, the remainder being recirculated air.

After drying, the cabinet is opened and the trays are replaced with a new batch of trays. A modification of this type is the tray–truck type, where trays are loaded on trucks which are pushed into the dryer. This saves considerable time, since the trucks can be loaded and unloaded outside the dryer.

In the case of granular materials, the material can be loaded on screens which form the bottom of each tray. Then, in this through-circulation dryer, heated air passes through the permeable bed, yielding shorter drying times because of the greater surface area exposed to the air.

FIGURE 9.2-1. *Tray or shelf dryer.*

9.2B Vacuum-Shelf Indirect Dryers

Vacuum-shelf dryers are indirectly heated batch dryers similar to tray dryers. Such a dryer consists of a cabinet made of cast-iron or steel plates with tightly fitted doors so that it can be operated under vacuum. Hollow shelves of steel are fastened permanently inside the chamber and are connected in parallel to inlet and outlet steam headers. The trays containing the solids to be dried rest upon the hollow shelves. The heat is conducted through the metal walls and aided by radiation from the shelf above. For low-temperature operation, circulating warm water is used instead of steam for furnishing the heat to vaporize the moisture. The vapors usually pass to a condenser.

These dryers are used to dry expensive or temperature-sensitive or easily oxidizable materials. They are useful for handling materials with toxic or valuable solvents.

9.2C Continuous Tunnel Dryers

Continuous tunnel dryers are often batch truck or tray compartments operated in series, as shown in Fig. 9.2-2a. The solids are placed on trays or on trucks which move continuously through a tunnel with hot gases passing over the surface of each tray. The hot air flow can be countercurrent, cocurrent, or a combination. Many foods are dried in this way.

When granular particles of solids are to be dried, perforated or screen-belt continuous conveyors are often used, as in Fig. 9.2-2b. The wet granular solids are conveyed as a layer 25

FIGURE 9.2-2. *Continuous tunnel dryers: (a) tunnel dryer trucks with countercurrent air flow, (b) through-circulation screen conveyor dryer.*

FIGURE 9.2.3. *Schematic drawing of a direct-heat rotary dryer.*

to about 150 mm deep on a screen or perforated apron while heated air is blown upward through the bed or downward. The dryer consists of several sections in series, each with a fan and heating coils. A portion of the air is exhausted to the atmosphere by a fan. In some cases pasty materials can be preformed into cylinders and placed on the bed to be dried.

9.2D Rotary Dryers

A *rotary dryer* consists of a hollow cylinder which is rotated and usually slightly inclined toward the outlet. The wet granular solids are fed at the high end as shown in Fig. 9.2-3 and move through the shell as it rotates. The heating shown is by direct contact with hot gases in countercurrent flow. In some cases the heating is by indirect contact through the heated wall of the cylinder.

The granular particles move forward slowly a short distance before they are showered downward through the hot gases as shown. Many other variations of this rotary dryer are available; these are discussed elsewhere (P1).

9.2E Drum Dryers

A *drum dryer* consists of a heated metal roll, shown in Fig. 9.2-4, on the outside of which a thin layer of liquid or slurry is evaporated to dryness. The final dry solid is scraped off the roll, which is revolving slowly.

FIGURE 9.2.4. *Rotary-drum dryer.*

liquid feed

spray chamber

heated air →

exhaust gas

droplets

cyclone separator

solids

hopper

dry product

screw conveyor

FIGURE 9.2-5. *Process flow diagram of spray-drying apparatus.*

Drum dryers are suitable for handling slurries or pastes of solids in fine suspension and for solutions. The drum functions partly as an evaporator as well as a dryer. Other variations of the single-drum type are twin rotating drums with dip feeding or with top feeding to the two drums. Potato slurry is dried using drum dryers, to give potato flakes.

9.2F Spray Dryers

In a *spray dryer* a liquid or slurry solution is sprayed into a hot gas stream in the form of a mist of fine droplets. The water is rapidly vaporized from the droplets, leaving particles of dry solid which are separated from the gas stream. The flow of gas and liquid in the spray chamber may be countercurrent, cocurrent, or a combination.

The fine droplets are formed from the liquid feed by spray nozzles or high-speed rotating spray disks inside a cylindrical chamber, as shown in Fig. 9.2-5. It is necessary to ensure that the droplets or wet particles of solid do not strike and stick to solid surfaces before drying has taken place; hence, large chambers are used. The dried solids leave at the bottom of the chamber through a screw conveyor. The exhaust gases flow through a cyclone separator to remove any fines. The particles produced are usually light and quite porous. Dried milk powder is made from spray-drying milk.

9.2G Drying of Crops and Grains

In the drying of grain from a harvest, the grain contains about 30 to 35% moisture, and for safe storage for about 1 year should be dried to about 13 wt % moisture (H1). A typical continuous-flow dryer is shown in Fig. 9.2-6. In the drying bin the thickness of the layer of grain, through which the hot air passes, is 0.5 m or less. Unheated air in the bottom section cools the dry grain before it leaves. Other types of crop dryers and storage bins are described by Hall (H1).

FIGURE 9.2-6. *Vertical continuous-flow grain dryer.*

9.3 VAPOR PRESSURE OF WATER AND HUMIDITY

9.3A Vapor Pressure of Water

1. Introduction. In a number of the separation processes and transport processes, it is necessary to make calculations involving the properties of mixtures of water vapor and air. These calculations involve knowledge of the concentration of water vapor in air under various conditions of temperature and pressure, the thermal properties of these mixtures, and the changes occurring when these mixtures are brought into contact with water or with wet solids in drying.

Humidification involves the transfer of water from the liquid phase into a gaseous mixture of air and water vapor. Dehumidification involves the reverse transfer, whereby water vapor is transferred from the vapor state to the liquid state. Humidification and dehumidification can also refer to vapor mixtures of materials such as benzene, but most practical applications occur with water. To better understand humidity, it is first necessary to discuss the vapor pressure of water.

2. Vapor pressure of water and physical states. Pure water can exist in three different physical states: solid ice, liquid, and vapor. The physical state in which it exists depends on the pressure and temperature.

Figure 9.3-1 illustrates the various physical states of water and the pressure–temperature relationships at equilibrium. In Fig. 9.3-1 the regions of the solid, liquid, and vapor states are shown. Along the line AB, the phases liquid and vapor coexist. Along line AC, the phases ice and liquid coexist. Along line AD, ice and vapor coexist. If ice at point (1) is heated at constant pressure, the temperature rises and the physical condition is represented as moving horizontally. As the horizontal line crosses AC, the solid melts, and on crossing AB the liquid vaporizes. Moving from point (3) to (4), ice sublimes (vaporizes) to a vapor without becoming a liquid.

Liquid and vapor coexist in equilibrium along the line AB, which is the vapor-pressure line for water. Boiling occurs when the vapor pressure of the water is equal to the total pressure above the water surface. For example, at 100°C (212°F) the vapor pressure of water is 101.3 kPa (1.0 atm), and therefore it will boil at 1 atm pressure. At 65.6°C (150°F), from the steam tables in Appendix A.2, the vapor pressure of water is 25.7 kPa (3.72 psia). Hence, at 25.7 kPa and 65.6°C, water will boil.

solid region — liquid region

vapor region

Pressure

Temperature

FIGURE 9.3-1. *Phase diagram for water.*

If a pan of water is held at 65.6°C in a room at 101.3 kPa abs pressure, the vapor pressure of water will again be 25.7 kPa. This illustrates an important property of the vapor pressure of water, which is not influenced by the presence of an inert gas such as air; that is, the vapor pressure of water is essentially independent of the total pressure of the system.

9.3B Humidity and Humidity Chart

1. Definition of humidity. The humidity H of an air–water vapor mixture is defined as the **kg** of water vapor contained in 1 kg of dry air. The humidity so defined depends only on the partial pressure p_A of water vapor in the air and on the total pressure P (assumed throughout this chapter to be 101.325 kPa, 1.0 atm abs, or 760 mm Hg). Using the molecular weight of water (A) as 18.02 and of air as 28.97, the humidity H in kg H_2O/kg dry air, or in English units as lb H_2O/lb dry air, is as follows:

$$H \frac{\text{kg } H_2O}{\text{kg dry air}} = \frac{p_A}{P - p_A} \frac{\text{kg mol } H_2O}{\text{kg mol air}} \times \frac{18.02 \text{ kg } H_2O}{\text{kg mol } H_2O} \times \frac{1}{28.97 \text{ kg air/kg mol air}}$$

(9.3-1)

$$H = \frac{18.02}{28.97} \frac{p_A}{P - p_A}$$

Saturated air is air in which the water vapor is in equilibrium with liquid water at the given conditions of pressure and temperature. In this mixture the partial pressure of the water vapor in the air–water mixture is equal to the vapor pressure p_{AS} of pure water at the given temperature. Hence, the saturation humidity H_S is

$$H_S = \frac{18.02}{28.97} \frac{p_{AS}}{P - p_{AS}}$$

(9.3-2)

2. Percentage humidity. The percentage humidity H_P is defined as 100 times the actual humidity H of the air divided by the humidity H_S if the air were saturated at the same temperature and pressure:

$$H_P = 100 \frac{H}{H_S}$$

(9.3-3)

3. *Percentage relative humidity.* The amount of saturation of an air–water vapor mixture is also given as percentage relative humidity H_R using partial pressures:

$$H_R = 100 \frac{p_A}{p_{AS}} \tag{9.3-4}$$

Note that $H_R \neq H_P$, since H_P expressed in partial pressures by combining Eqs. (9.3-1), (9.3-2), and (9.3-3) is

$$H_P = 100 \frac{H}{H_S} = (100)\frac{18.02}{28.97}\frac{p_A}{P - p_A} \bigg/ \frac{18.02}{28.97}\frac{p_{AS}}{P - p_{AS}} = \frac{p_A}{p_{AS}}\frac{P - p_{AS}}{P - p_A}(100) \tag{9.3-5}$$

This, of course, is not the same as Eq. (9.3-4).

EXAMPLE 9.3-1. *Humidity from Vapor-Pressure Data*
The air in a room is at 26.7°C (80°F) and a pressure of 101.325 kPa and contains water vapor with a partial pressure $p_A = 2.76$ kPa. Calculate the following:
(a) Humidity, H.
(b) Saturation humidity, H_S, and percentage humidity, H_P.
(c) Percentage relative humidity, H_R.

Solution: From the steam tables at 26.7°C, the vapor pressure of water is $p_{AS} = 3.50$ kPa (0.507 psia). Also, $p_A = 2.76$ kPa and $P = 101.3$ kPa (14.7 psia). For part (a), using Eq. (9.3-1),

$$H = \frac{18.02}{28.97}\frac{p_A}{P - p_A} = \frac{18.02(2.76)}{28.97(101.3 - 2.76)} = 0.01742 \text{ kg H}_2\text{O/kg air}$$

For part (b), using Eq. (9.3-2), the saturation humidity is

$$H_S = \frac{18.02}{28.97}\frac{p_{AS}}{P - p_{AS}} = \frac{18.02(3.50)}{28.97(101.3 - 3.50)} = 0.02226 \text{ kg H}_2\text{O/kg air}$$

The percentage humidity, from Eq. (9.3-3), is

$$H_P = 100 \frac{H}{H_S} = \frac{100(0.01742)}{0.02226} = 78.3\%$$

For part (c), from Eq. (9.3-4), the percentage relative humidity is

$$H_R = 100 \frac{p_A}{p_{AS}} = \frac{100(2.76)}{3.50} = 78.9\%$$

4. *Dew point of an air–water vapor mixture.* The temperature at which a given mixture of air and water vapor would be saturated is called the *dew-point temperature* or simply the *dew point.* For example, at 26.7°C (80°F), the saturation vapor pressure of water is $p_{AS} = 3.50$ kPa (0.507 psia). Hence, the dew point of a mixture containing water vapor having a partial pressure of 3.50 kPa is 26.7°C. If an air–water vapor mixture is at 37.8°C (often called the dry bulb temperature, since this is the actual temperature a dry thermometer bulb would indicate in this mixture) and contains water vapor of $p_A = 3.50$ kPa, the mixture would not be saturated. On cooling to 26.7°C, the air would be saturated, that is, at the dew point. On further cooling, some water vapor would condense, since the partial pressure cannot be greater than the saturation vapor pressure.

5. *Humid heat of an air–water vapor mixture.* The humid heat c_s is the amount of heat in J (or kJ) required to raise the temperature of 1 kg of dry air plus the water vapor present by 1 K or 1°C. The heat capacity of air and water vapor can be assumed constant over the temperature ranges usually encountered at 1.005 kJ/kg dry air · K and 1.88 kJ/kg water vapor · K, respectively. Hence, for SI and English units,

$$c_S \text{ kJ/kg dry air} \cdot K = 1.005 + 1.88H \qquad \text{(SI)}$$

$$c_S \text{ btu/lb}_m \text{ dry air} \cdot °F = 0.24 + 0.45H \qquad \text{(English)}$$

(9.3-6)

[In some cases c_S will be given as $(1.005 + 1.88H)10^3 \text{ J/kg} \cdot K$.]

6. *Humid volume of an air–water vapor mixture.* The humid volume v_H is the total volume in m^3 of 1 kg of dry air plus the vapor it contains at 101.325 kPa (1.0 atm) abs pressure and the given gas temperature. Using the ideal gas law,

$$v_H \text{ m}^3\text{/kg dry air} = \frac{22.41}{273} T\,K \left(\frac{1}{28.97} + \frac{1}{18.02}H \right)$$

$$= (2.83 \times 10^{-3} + 4.56 \times 10^{-3}\,H)T\ K$$

$$v_H \text{ ft}^3\text{/lb}_m \text{ dry air} = \frac{359}{492} T°R \left(\frac{1}{28.97} + \frac{1}{18.02}H \right)$$

$$= (0.0252 + 0.0405H)T°R$$

(9.3-7)

For a saturated air–water vapor mixture, $H = H_S$, and v_H is the saturated volume.

7. *Total enthalpy of an air–water vapor mixture.* The total enthalpy of 1 kg of air plus its water vapor is H_y J/kg or kJ/kg dry air. If T_0 is the datum temperature chosen for both components, the total enthalpy is the sensible heat of the air–water vapor mixture plus the latent heat λ_0 in J/kg or kJ/kg water vapor of the water vapor at T_0. Note that $(T - T_0)°C = (T - T_0)$ K and that this enthalpy is referred to liquid water.

$$H_y \text{ kJ/kg dry air} = c_S(T - T_0) + H\lambda_0 = (1.005 + 1.88H)(T - T_0°C) + H\lambda_0$$

$$H_y \text{ btu/lb}_m \text{ dry air} = (0.24 + 0.45H)(T - T_0°F) + H\lambda_0$$

(9.3-8)

If the total enthalpy is referred to a base temperature T_0 of 0°C (32°F), the equation for H_y becomes

$$H_y \text{ kJ/kg dry air} = (1.005 + 1.88H)(T°C - 0) + 2501.4H \qquad \text{(SI)}$$

$$H_y \text{ btu/lb}_m \text{ dry air} = (0.24 + 0.45H)(T°F - 32) + 1075.4H \qquad \text{(English)}$$

(9.3-9)

8. *Humidity chart of air–water vapor mixtures.* A convenient chart of the properties of air–water vapor mixtures at 1.0 atm abs pressure is the humidity chart in Fig. 9.3-2. In this figure the humidity H is plotted versus the actual temperature of the air–water vapor mixture (dry bulb temperature).

The curve marked 100% running upward to the right gives the saturation humidity H_S as a function of temperature. In Example 9.3-1, for 26.7°C, H_S was calculated as 0.02226 kg H_2O/kg air. Plotting this point for 26.7°C (80°F) and $H_S = 0.02226$ on Fig. 9.3-2, it falls on the 100% saturated line.

FIGURE 9.3-2. *Humidity chart for mixtures of air and water vapor at a total pressure of 101.325 kPa (760 mm Hg). (From R. E. Treybal,* Mass-*Transfer Operations, 3rd ed. New York: McGraw-Hill Book Company, 1980. With permission.)*

Any point below the saturation line represents unsaturated air–water vapor mixtures. The curved lines below the 100% saturation line and running upward to the right represent unsaturated mixtures of definite percentage humidity H_P. Going downward vertically from the saturation line at a given temperature, the line between 100% saturation and zero humidity H (the bottom horizontal line) is divided evenly into 10 increments of 10% each.

All the percentage humidity lines H_P mentioned and the saturation humidity line H_S can be calculated from the data for vapor pressure of water.

EXAMPLE 9.3-2.   Use of Humidity Chart

Air entering a dryer has a temperature (dry bulb temperature) of 60°C (140°F) and a dew point of 26.7°C (80°F). Using the humidity chart, determine the actual humidity H, percentage humidity H_P, humid heat c_S, and humid volume v_H in SI and English units.

Solution: The dew point of 26.7°C is the temperature when the given mixture is at 100% saturation. Starting at 26.7°C (Fig. 9.3-2), and drawing a vertical line until it intersects the line for 100% humidity, a humidity of $H = 0.0225$ kg H_2O/kg dry air is read off the plot. This is the actual humidity of the air at 60°C. Stated in another way, if air at 60°C and having a humidity $H = 0.0225$ is cooled, its dew point will be 26.7°C. In English units, $H = 0.0225$ lb H_2O/lb dry air.

Locating this point where $H = 0.0225$ and $t = 60$°C on the chart, the percentage humidity H_P is found to be 14%, by linear interpolation vertically between the 10 and 20% lines. The humid heat for $H = 0.0225$ is, from Eq. (9.3-6),

$$c_S = 1.005 + 1.88(0.0225)$$

$$= 1.047 \text{ kJ/kg dry air} \cdot \text{K} \quad \text{or} \quad 1.047 \times 10^3 \text{ J/kg} \cdot \text{K}$$

$$c_S = 0.24 + 0.45(0.0225)$$

$$= 0.250 \text{ btu/lb}_m \text{ dry air} \cdot \text{°F} \quad \text{(English)}$$

The humid volume at 60°C (140°F), from Eq. (9.3-7), is

$$v_H = (2.83 \times 10^{-3} + 4.56 \times 10^{-3} \times 0.0225)(60 + 273)$$

$$= 0.977 \text{ m}^3\text{/kg dry air}$$

In English units,

$$v_H = (0.0252 + 0.0405 \times 0.0225)(460 + 140) = 15.67 \text{ ft}^3\text{/lb}_m \text{ dry air}$$

9.3C   Adiabatic Saturation Temperatures

Consider the process shown in Fig. 9.3-3, where the entering gas of air–water vapor mixture is contacted with a spray of liquid water. The gas leaves having a different humidity and temperature and the process is adiabatic. The water is recirculated, with some makeup water added.

The temperature of the water being recirculated reaches a steady-state temperature called the *adiabatic saturation temperature,* T_S. If the entering gas at temperature T having a humidity of H is not saturated, T_S will be lower than T. If the contact between the entering gas and the spray of droplets is enough to bring the gas and liquid to equilibrium, the leaving air is saturated at T_S, having a humidity H_S.

FIGURE 9.3-3. *Adiabatic air–water vapor saturator.*

Writing an enthalpy balance (heat balance) over the process, a datum of T_S is used. The enthalpy of the makeup H_2O is then zero. This means that the total enthalpy of the entering gas mixture = enthalpy of the leaving gas mixture, or, using Eq. (9.3-8),

$$c_S(T - T_S) + H\lambda_S = c_S(T_S - T_S) + H_S\lambda_S \qquad \textbf{(9.3-10)}$$

Or, rearranging, and using Eq. (9.3-6) for c_S,

$$\frac{H - H_S}{T - T_S} = -\frac{c_S}{\lambda_S} = \frac{1.005 + 1.88H}{\lambda_S} \qquad \text{(SI)}$$

$$\frac{H - H_S}{T - T_S} = \frac{0.24 + 0.45H}{\lambda_S} \qquad \text{(English)} \qquad \textbf{(9.3-11)}$$

Equation (9.3-11) is the equation of an adiabatic humidification curve when plotted on Fig. 9.3-2, which passes through the point H_S and T_S on the 100% saturation curve and other points of H and T. These series of lines, running upward to the left, are called *adiabatic humidification lines* or *adiabatic saturation lines*. Since c_S contains the term H, the adiabatic lines are not quite straight when plotted on the humidity chart.

If a given gas mixture at T_1 and H_1 is contacted for a sufficiently long time in an adiabatic saturator, it will leave saturated at H_{S1} and T_{S1}. The values of H_{S1} and T_{S1} are determined by following the adiabatic saturation line going through point T_1, H_1 until it intersects the 100% saturation line. If contact is not sufficient, the leaving mixture will be at a percentage saturation less than 100% but on the same line.

EXAMPLE 9.3-3. Adiabatic Saturation of Air

An air stream at 87.8°C having a humidity $H = 0.030$ kg H_2O/kg dry air is contacted in an adiabatic saturator with water. It is cooled and humidified to 90% saturation.

(a) What are the final values of H and T?
(b) For 100% saturation, what would be the values of H and T?

Solution: For part (a), the point $H = 0.030$ and $T = 87.8$°C is located on the humidity chart. The adiabatic saturation curve through this point is followed upward to the left until it intersects the 90% line at 42.5°C and $H = 0.0500$ kg H_2O/kg dry air.

For part (b), the same line is followed to 100% saturation, where $T = 40.5$°C and $H = 0.0505$ kg H_2O/kg dry air.

9.3D Wet Bulb Temperature

The adiabatic saturation temperature is the steady-state temperature attained when a large amount of water is contacted by the entering gas. The *wet bulb temperature* is the steady-state nonequilibrium temperature reached when a small amount of water is contacted under adiabatic conditions by a continuous stream of gas. Since the amount of liquid is small, the temperature and humidity of the gas are not changed, contrary to the case of adiabatic saturation, where the temperature and humidity of the gas are changed.

The method used to measure the wet bulb temperature is illustrated in Fig. 9.3-4, where a thermometer is covered by a wick or cloth. The wick is kept wet by water and is immersed in a flowing stream of air–water vapor having a temperature of T (dry bulb temperature) and humidity H. At steady state, water is evaporating to the gas stream. The wick and water are cooled to T_W and stay at this constant temperature. The latent heat of evaporation is exactly balanced by the convective heat flowing from the gas stream at T to the wick at a lower temperature T_W.

A heat balance on the wick can be made. The datum temperature is taken at T_W. The amount of heat lost by vaporization, neglecting the small sensible heat change of the vaporized liquid and radiation, is

$$q = M_A N_A \lambda_W A \tag{9.3-12}$$

where q is kW (kJ/s), M_A is the molecular weight of water, N_A is kg mol H_2O evaporating/ s · m², A is surface area m², and λ_W is the latent heat of vaporization at T_W in kJ/kg H_2O. In English units, q is btu/h, N_A is lb mol/h · ft², and λ_W is btu/lb$_m$ H_2O. The flux N_A is

$$N_A = \frac{k_y'}{x_{BM}}(y_W - y) = k_y(y_W - y) \tag{9.3-13}$$

where k_y' is the mass-transfer coefficient in kg mol/s · m² · mol frac, x_{BM} is the log mean inert mole fraction of the air, y_W is the mole fraction of water vapor in the gas at the surface, and y is the mole fraction in the gas. For a dilute mixture $x_{BM} \cong 1.0$ and $k_y' \cong k_y$. The relation between H and y is

$$y = \frac{H/M_A}{1/M_B + H/M_A} \tag{9.3-14}$$

where M_B is the molecular weight of air and M_A the molecular weight of H_2O. Since H is small, as an approximation,

$$y \cong \frac{H M_B}{M_A} \tag{9.3-15}$$

FIGURE 9.3-4. *Measurement of wet bulb temperature.*

Substituting Eq. (9.3-15) into (9.3-13) and then substituting the resultant into Eq. (9.3-12),

$$q = M_B k_y \lambda_W (H_W - H) A \qquad (9.3\text{-}16)$$

The rate of convective heat transfer from the gas stream at T to the wick at T_W is

$$q = h(T - T_W)A \qquad (9.3\text{-}17)$$

where h is the heat-transfer coefficient in $kW/m^2 \cdot K$ (btu/h $\cdot$ ft^2 $\cdot$ °F).

Equating Eq. (9.3-16) to (9.3-17) and rearranging,

$$\frac{H - H_W}{T - T_W} = -\frac{h/M_B k_y}{\lambda_W} \qquad (9.3\text{-}18)$$

Experimental data on the value of $h/M_B k_y$, called the *psychrometric ratio,* show that for water vapor–air mixtures, the value is approximately 0.96–1.005. Since this value is close to the value of c_S in Eq. (9.3-11), approximately 1.005, Eqs. (9.3-18) and (9.3-11) are almost the same. This means that the adiabatic saturation lines can also be used for wet bulb lines with reasonable accuracy. (Note that this is only true for water vapor and not for other vapors, such as benzene.) Hence, the wet bulb determination is often used to measure the humidity of an air–water vapor mixture.

EXAMPLE 9.3-4. *Wet Bulb Temperature and Humidity*

A water vapor–air mixture having a dry bulb temperature of $T = 60°C$ is passed over a wet bulb, as shown in Fig. 9.3-4, and the wet bulb temperature obtained is $T_W = 29.5°C$. What is the humidity of the mixture?

Solution: The wet bulb temperature of 29.5°C can be assumed to be the same as the adiabatic saturation temperature T_S, as discussed. Following the adiabatic saturation curve of 29.5°C until it reaches the dry bulb temperature of 60°C, the humidity is $H = 0.0135$ kg H$_2$O/kg dry air.

9.4 EQUILIBRIUM MOISTURE CONTENT OF MATERIALS

9.4A Introduction

As in other transfer processes, such as mass transfer, the process of drying of materials must be approached from the viewpoint of the equilibrium relationships together with the rate relationships. In most of the drying apparatus discussed in Section 9.2, material is dried in contact with an air–water vapor mixture. The equilibrium relationships between the air–water vapor and the solid material will be discussed in this section.

An important variable in the drying of materials is the humidity of the air in contact with a solid of given moisture content. Suppose that a wet solid containing moisture is brought into contact with a stream of air having a constant humidity H and temperature. A large excess of air is used, so its conditions remain constant. Eventually, after exposure of the solid sufficiently long for equilibrium to be reached, the solid will attain a definite moisture content. This is known as the *equilibrium moisture content* of the material under the specified humidity and temperature of the air. The moisture content is usually expressed on a dry basis as kg of water per kg of moisture-free (bone-dry) solid or kg H$_2$O/100 kg dry solid; in English units as lb H$_2$O/100 lb dry solid.

For some solids the value of the equilibrium moisture content depends on the direction from which equilibrium is approached. A different value for the equilibrium moisture content is obtained according to whether a wet sample is allowed to dry by desorption or a dry sample adsorbs moisture by adsorption. For drying calculations it is the desorption equilibrium that is the larger value and is of particular interest.

9.4B Experimental Data of Equilibrium Moisture Content for Inorganic and Biological Materials

1. Typical data for various materials. If the material contains more moisture than its equilibrium value in contact with a gas of a given humidity and temperature, it will dry until it reaches its equilibrium value. If the material contains less moisture than its equilibrium value, it will adsorb water until it reaches its equilibrium value. For air having 0% humidity, the equilibrium moisture value of all materials is zero.

The equilibrium moisture content varies greatly with the type of material for any given percent relative humidity, as shown in Fig. 9.4-1 for some typical materials at room tempera-

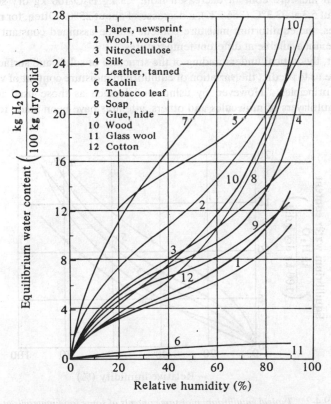

FIGURE 9.4-1. *Typical equilibrium moisture contents of some solids at approximately 298 K (25°C). [From National Research Council, International Critical Tables, Vol. II. New York: McGraw-Hill Book Company, 1929. Reproduced with permission of the National Academy of Sciences.]*

ture. Nonporous insoluble solids tend to have equilibrium moisture contents which are quite low, as shown for glass wool and kaolin. Certain spongy, cellular materials of organic and biological origin generally show large equilibrium moisture contents. Examples of these in Fig. 9.4-1 are wool, leather, and wood.

2. Typical food materials. In Fig. 9-4.2 the equilibrium moisture contents for some typical food materials are plotted versus percent relative humidity. These biological materials also show large values for equilibrium moisture content. Data in this figure and in Fig. 9.4-1 for biological materials show that at high percent relative humidities of about 60 to 80%, the equilibrium moisture content increases very rapidly with increases in relative humidity.

In general, at low relative humidities the equilibrium moisture content is greatest for food materials high in protein, starch, or other high-molecular-weight polymers and lower for food materials high in soluble solids. Crystalline salts and sugars as well as fats generally adsorb small amounts of water.

3. Effect of temperature. The equilibrium moisture content of a solid decreases somewhat with an increase in temperature. For example, for raw cotton at a relative humidity of 50%, the equilibrium moisture content decreased from 7.3 kg H_2O/100 kg dry solid at 37.8°C (311 K) to about 5.3 at 93.3°C (366.5 K), a decrease of about 25%. Often, for moderate temperature ranges, the equilibrium moisture content will be assumed constant when experimental data are not available at different temperatures.

At present, theoretical understanding of the structure of solids and surface phenomena does not enable us to predict the variation of equilibrium moisture content of various materials from first principles. However, by using models such as those used for adsorption isotherms of multilayers of molecules and others, attempts have been made to correlate ex-

FIGURE 9.4-2. *Typical equilibrium moisture contents of some food materials at approximately 298 K (25°C): (1) macaroni, (2) flour, (3) bread, (4) crackers, (5) egg albumin. [Curve (5) from ref. (E1). Curves (1) to (4) from National Research Council, International Critical Tables, Vol. II. New York: McGraw-Hill Book Company, 1929. Reproduced with permission of the National Academy of Sciences.]*

perimental data. Henderson (H2) gives an empirical relationship between equilibrium moisture content and percent relative humidity for some agricultural materials. In general, empirical relationships are not available for most materials, and equilibrium moisture contents must be determined experimentally. Also, equilibrium moisture relationships often vary from sample to sample of the same kind of material.

9.4C Bound and Unbound Water in Solids

In Fig. 9.4-1, if the equilibrium moisture content of a given material is continued to its intersection with the 100% humidity line, the moisture is called *bound water*. This water in the solid exerts a vapor pressure less than that of liquid water at the same temperature. If such a material contains more water than indicated by intersection with the 100% humidity line, it can still exert a vapor pressure only as high as that of ordinary water at the same temperature. This excess moisture content is called *unbound water*, and it is held primarily in the voids of the solid. Substances containing bound water are often called *hygroscopic materials*.

As an example, consider curve 10 for wood in Fig. 9.4-1. This intersects the curve for 100% humidity at about 30 kg H_2O/100 kg dry solid. Any sample of wood containing less than 30 kg H_2O/100 kg dry solid contains only bound water. If the wood sample contained 34 kg H_2O/100 kg dry solid, 4 kg H_2O would be unbound and 30 kg H_2O bound per 100 kg dry solid.

The bound water in a substance may exist under several different conditions. Moisture in cell or fiber walls may have solids dissolved in it and have a lower vapor pressure. Liquid water in capillaries of very small diameter will exert a lowered vapor pressure because of the concave curvature of the surface. Water in natural organic materials is in chemical and physical–chemical combination.

9.4D Free and Equilibrium Moisture of a Substance

Free moisture content in a sample is the moisture above the equilibrium moisture content. This free moisture is the moisture that can be removed by drying under the given percent relative humidity. For example, in Fig. 9.4-1 silk has an equilibrium moisture content of 8.5 kg H_2O/100 kg dry material in contact with air of 50% relative humidity and 25°C. If a sample contains 10 kg H_2O/100 kg dry material, only $10.0 - 8.5$, or 1.5, kg H_2O/100 kg dry material is removable by drying; this is the free moisture of the sample under these drying conditions.

In many texts and references, the moisture content is given as percent moisture on a dry basis. This is exactly the same as the kg H_2O/100 kg dry material multiplied by 100.

9.5 RATE-OF-DRYING CURVES

9.5A Introduction and Experimental Methods

1. Introduction. In the drying of various types of process materials from one moisture content to another, it is usually desired to estimate the size of dryer needed, the various operating conditions of humidity and temperature for the air used, and the time needed to perform the amount of drying required. As discussed in Section 9.4, equilibrium moisture contents of various materials cannot be predicted and must be determined experimentally. Similarly, since our knowledge of the basic mechanisms of rates of drying is quite incomplete, it is necessary in most cases to obtain some experimental measurements of drying rates.

2. *Experimental determination of rate of drying.* To experimentally determine the rate of drying for a given material, a sample is usually placed on a tray. If it is a solid material it should fill the tray so that only the top surface is exposed to the drying air stream. By suspending the tray from a balance in a cabinet or duct through which the air is flowing, the loss in weight of moisture during drying can be determined at different intervals without interrupting the operation.

In doing batch-drying experiments, certain precautions should be observed to obtain usable data under conditions that closely resemble those to be used in the large-scale operations. The sample should not be too small in weight and should be supported in a tray or frame similar to the large-scale one. The ratio of drying to nondrying surface (insulated surface) and the bed depth should be similar. The velocity, humidity, temperature, and direction of the air should be the same and constant to simulate drying under constant drying conditions.

9.5B Rate of Drying Curves for Constant-Drying Conditions

1. Conversion of data to rate-of-drying curve. Data obtained from a batch-drying experiment are usually obtained as W total weight of the wet solid (dry solid plus moisture) at different times t hours in the drying period. These data can be converted to rate-of-drying data in the following ways. First, the data are recalculated. If W is the weight of the wet solid in kg total water plus dry solid and W_S is the weight of the dry solid in kg,

$$X_t = \frac{W - W_S}{W_S} \frac{\text{kg total water}}{\text{kg dry solid}} \left(\frac{\text{lb total water}}{\text{lb dry solid}} \right) \tag{9.5-1}$$

For the given constant drying conditions, the equilibrium moisture content X^* kg equilibrium moisture/kg dry solid is determined. Then the free moisture content X in kg free water/kg dry solid is calculated for each value of X_t:

$$X = X_t - X^* \tag{9.5-2}$$

Using the data calculated from Eq. (9.5-2), a plot of free moisture content X versus time t in h is made, as in Fig. 9.5-1a. To obtain the rate-of-drying curve from this plot, the slopes of the tangents drawn to the curve in Fig. 9.5-1a can be measured, which give values of dX/dt at given values of t. The rate R is calculated for each point by

$$R = -\frac{L_S}{A} \frac{dX}{dt} \tag{9.5-3}$$

where R is drying rate in kg H_2O/h · m^2, L_S kg of dry solid used, and A exposed surface area for drying in m^2. In English units, R is lb$_m$ H_2O/h · ft^2, L_S is lb$_m$ dry solid, and A is ft^2. For obtaining R from Fig. 9.5-1a, a value of L_S/A of 21.5 kg/m^2 was used. The drying-rate curve is then obtained by plotting R versus the moisture content, as in Fig. 9.5-1b.

Another method for obtaining the rate-of-drying curve is to first calculate the weight loss ΔX for a Δt time. For example, if $X_1 = 0.350$ at a time $t_1 = 1.68$ h and $x_2 = 0.325$ at a time $t_2 = 2.04$ h, $\Delta X/\Delta t = (0.350 - 0.325)/(2.04 - 1.68)$. Then, using Eq. (9.5-4) and $L_S/A = 21.5$,

$$R = -\frac{L_S}{A} \frac{\Delta X}{\Delta t} = 21.5 \left(\frac{0.350 - 0.325}{2.04 - 1.68} \right) = 1.493$$

This rate R is the average over the period 1.68 to 2.04 h and should be plotted at the average concentration $X = (0.350 + 0.325)/2 = 0.338$.

2. *Plot of rate-of-drying curve.* In Fig. 9.5-1b the rate-of-drying curve for constant-drying conditions is shown. At zero time the initial free moisture content is shown at point A. In the beginning the solid is usually at a colder temperature than its ultimate temperature, and the evaporation rate will increase. Eventually, at point B, the surface temperature rises to its equilibrium value. Alternatively, if the solid is quite hot to start with, the rate may start at point A'. This initial unsteady-state adjustment period is usually quite short and it is often ignored in the analysis of times of drying.

(a)

(b)

FIGURE 9.5-1. *Typical drying-rate curve for constant drying conditions: (a) plot of data as free moisture versus time, (b) rate of drying curve as rate versus free moisture content.*

From point B to point C in Fig. 9.5-1a the line is straight, and hence the slope and rate are constant during this period. This *constant-rate-of-drying period* is shown as line BC in Fig. 9.5-1b.

At point C on both plots, the drying rate starts to decrease in the *falling-rate period* until it reaches point D. In this first falling-rate period, the rate shown as line CD in Fig. 9.5-1b is often linear.

At point D the rate of drying falls even more rapidly, until it reaches point E, where the equilibrium moisture content is X^* and $X = X^* - X^* = 0$. In some materials being dried, the region CD may be missing completely, or it may constitute all of the falling-rate period.

9.5C Drying in the Constant-Rate Period

Drying of different solids under different constant conditions of drying will often give curves of different shapes in the falling-rate period, but in general the two major portions of the drying-rate curve—constant-rate period and falling-rate period—are present.

In the constant-rate drying period, the surface of the solid is initially very wet and a continuous film of water exists on the drying surface. This water is entirely unbound water and it acts as if the solid were not present. The rate of evaporation under the given air conditions is independent of the solid and is essentially the same as the rate from a free liquid surface. Increased roughness of the solid surface, however, may lead to higher rates than from a flat surface.

If the solid is porous, most of the water evaporated in the constant-rate period is supplied from the interior of the solid. This period continues only as long as the water is supplied to the surface as fast as it is evaporated. Evaporation during this period is similar to that in determining the wet bulb temperature, and in the absence of heat transfer by radiation or conduction, the surface temperature is approximately the same as the wet bulb temperature.

9.5D Drying in the Falling-Rate Period

Point C in Fig. 9.5-1b is at the *critical free moisture content* X_C. At this point there is insufficient water on the surface to maintain a continuous film of water. The entire surface is no longer wetted, and the wetted area continually decreases in this first falling-rate period until the surface is completely dry, at point D in Fig. 9.5-1b.

The second falling-rate period begins at point D when the surface is completely dry. The plane of evaporation slowly recedes from the surface. Heat for the evaporation is transferred through the solid to the zone of vaporization. Vaporized water moves through the solid into the air stream.

In some cases no sharp discontinuity occurs at point D, and the change from partially wetted to completely dry conditions at the surface is so gradual that no distinct change is detectable.

The amount of moisture removed in the falling-rate period may be relatively small, but the time required may be long. This can be seen in Fig. 9.5-1. The period BC for constant-rate drying lasts for about 3.0 h and reduces X from 0.40 to about 0.19, a reduction of 0.21 kg H_2O/kg dry solid. The falling-rate period CE lasts about 9.0 h and reduces X only from 0.19 to 0.

9.5E Moisture Movements in Solids During Drying in the Falling-Rate Period

When drying occurs by evaporation of moisture from the exposed surface of a solid, moisture must move from the depths of the solid to the surface. The mechanisms of this movement affect the drying during the constant-rate and falling-rate periods. Some of the theories advanced to explain the various types of falling-rate curves will be briefly reviewed.

1. Liquid diffusion theory. According to this theory, diffusion of liquid moisture occurs when there is a concentration difference between the depths of the solid and the surface. This method of transport of moisture is usually found in nonporous solids where single-phase solutions are formed with the moisture, such as in paste, soap, gelatin, and glue. It is also found in drying the last portions of moisture from clay, flour, wood, leather, paper, starches, and textiles. In drying many food materials, the movement of water in the falling-rate period also occurs by diffusion.

The shapes of the moisture-distribution curves in the solid at given times are qualitatively consistent with the unsteady-state diffusion equations given in Chapter 7. The moisture diffusivity D_{AB} usually decreases with decreased moisture content, so that the diffusivities are usually average values over the range of concentrations used. Materials drying in this way are usually said to be drying by diffusion, although the actual mechanisms may be quite complicated. Since the rate of evaporation from the surface is quite fast, that is, the resistance is quite low, compared to the diffusion rate through the solid in the falling-rate period, the moisture content at the surface is at the equilibrium value.

The shape of a diffusion-controlled curve in the falling-rate period is similar to Fig. 9.5-2a. If the initial constant-rate drying is quite high, the first falling-rate period of unsaturated surface evaporation may not appear. If the constant-rate drying is quite low, the period of unsaturated surface evaporation is usually present in region CD in Fig. 9.5-1b and the diffusion-controlled curve is in region DE. Equations for calculating drying in this period where diffusion controls are given in Section 9.9. Also, Problem 7.1-4 for the drying of clay and Problem 7.1-6 for the drying of wood using diffusion theory are given in the Chapter 7 Problems.

2. Capillary movement in porous solids. When granular and porous solids such as clays, sand, soil, paint pigments, and minerals are being dried, unbound or free moisture moves

FIGURE 9.5-2. *Typical drying-rate curves: (a) diffusion-controlled falling-rate period, (b) capillary-controlled falling-rate period in a fine porous solid.*

through the capillaries and voids of the solids by *capillary action,* not by diffusion. This mechanism, involving surface tension, is similar to the movement of oil in a lamp wick.

A porous solid contains interconnecting pores and channels of varying pore sizes. As water is evaporated, a meniscus of liquid water is formed across each pore in the depths of the solid. This sets up capillary forces by the interfacial tension between the water and the solid. These capillary forces provide the driving force for moving water through the pores to the surface. Small pores develop greater forces than do large pores.

At the beginning of the falling-rate period at point C in Fig. 9.5-1b, the water is being brought to the surface by capillary action, but the surface layer of water starts to recede below the surface. Air rushes in to fill the voids. As the water is continuously removed, a point is reached where there is insufficient water left to maintain continuous films across the pores, and the rate of drying suddenly decreases at the start of the second falling-rate period at point D. Then the rate of diffusion of water vapor in the pores and rate of conduction of heat in the solid may become the main factors in drying.

In fine pores in solids, the rate-of-drying curve in the second falling-rate period may conform to the diffusion law; the curve is concave upward, as shown in Fig. 9.5-2b. For very porous solids, such as a bed of sand, where the pores are large, the rate-of-drying curve in the second falling-rate period is often straight, and hence the diffusion equations do not apply.

3. Effect of shrinkage. A factor often greatly affecting the drying rate is the shrinkage of the solid as moisture is removed. Rigid solids do not shrink appreciably, but colloidal and fibrous materials such as vegetables and other foodstuffs do undergo shrinkage. The most serious effect is that there may be developed a hard layer on the surface which is impervious to the flow of liquid or vapor moisture and slows the drying rate; examples are clay and soap. In many foodstuffs, if drying occurs at too high a temperature, a layer of closely packed, shrunken cells, which are sealed together, forms at the surface. This presents a barrier to moisture migration and is known as *case hardening.* Another effect of shrinkage is to cause the material to warp and change its structure. This can happen in drying wood.

Sometimes, to decrease these effects of shrinkage, it is desirable to dry with moist air. This decreases the rate of drying so that the effects of shrinkage on warping or hardening at the surface are greatly reduced.

9.6 CALCULATION METHODS FOR CONSTANT-RATE DRYING PERIOD

9.6A Method Using Experimental Drying Curve

1. Introduction. Probably the most important factor in drying calculations is the length of time required to dry a material from a given initial free moisture content X_1 to a final moisture content X_2. For drying in the constant-rate period, we can estimate the time needed by using experimental batch-drying curves or by using predicted mass- and heat-transfer coefficients.

2. Method using drying curve. To estimate the time of drying for a given batch of material, the best method is based on actual experimental data obtained under conditions where the feed material, relative exposed surface area, gas velocity, temperature, and humidity are essentially the same as in the final drier. Then the time required for the constant-rate period can be determined directly from the drying curve of free moisture content versus time.

EXAMPLE 9.6-1. Time of Drying from Drying Curve

A solid whose drying curve is represented by Fig. 9.5-1a is to be dried from a free moisture content $X_1 = 0.38$ kg H_2O/kg dry solid to $X_2 = 0.25$ kg H_2O/kg dry solid. Estimate the time required.

Solution: From Fig. 9.5-1a for $X_1 = 0.38$, t_1 is read off as 1.28 h. For $X_2 = 0.25$, $t_2 = 3.08$ h. Hence, the time required is

$$t = t_2 - t_1 = 3.08 - 1.28 = 1.80 \text{ h.}$$

3. Method using rate-of-drying curve for constant-rate period. Instead of using the drying curve, the rate-of-drying curve can be used. The drying rate R is defined by Eq. (9.5-3) as

$$R = -\frac{L_S}{A}\frac{dX}{dt} \qquad (9.5\text{-}3)$$

This can be rearranged and integrated over the time interval for drying from X_1 at $t_1 = 0$ to X_2 at $t_2 = t$:

$$t = \int_{t_1=0}^{t_2=t} dt = \frac{L_S}{A}\int_{X_2}^{X_1}\frac{dX}{R} \qquad (9.6\text{-}1)$$

If the drying takes place within the constant-rate period, so that both X_1 and X_2 are greater than the critical moisture content X_C, then $R = $ constant $= R_C$. Integrating Eq. (9.6-1) for the constant-rate period,

$$t = \frac{L_S}{AR_C}(X_1 - X_2) \qquad (9.6\text{-}2)$$

EXAMPLE 9.6-2. Drying Time from Rate-of-Drying Curve

Repeat Example 9.6-1 but use Eq. (9.6-2) and Fig. 9.5-1b.

Solution: As stated previously, a value of 21.5 for L_S/A was used to prepare Fig. 9.5-1b from 9.5-1a. From Fig. 9.5-1b, $R_C = 1.51$ kg H_2O/h·m^2. Substituting into Eq. (9.6-2),

$$t = \frac{L_S}{AR_C}(X_1 - X_2) = \frac{21.5}{1.51}(0.38 - 0.25) = 1.85 \text{ h}$$

This is close to the value of 1.80 h in Example 9.6-1.

9.6B Method Using Predicted Transfer Coefficients for Constant-Rate Period

1. Introduction. In the constant-rate period of drying, the surfaces of the grains of solid in contact with the drying air flow remain completely wetted. As stated previously, the rate of evaporation of moisture under a given set of air conditions is independent of the type of solid and is essentially the same as the rate of evaporation from a free liquid surface under the same conditions. However, surface roughness may increase the rate of evaporation.

During this constant-rate period, the solid is so wet that the water acts as if the solid were not there. The water evaporated from the surface is supplied from the interior of the solid.

The rate of evaporation from a porous material occurs by the same mechanism as that occurring at a wet bulb thermometer, which is essentially constant-rate drying.

2. Equations for predicting constant-rate drying. Drying of a material occurs by mass transfer of water vapor from the saturated surface of the material through an air film to the bulk gas phase or environment. The rate of moisture movement within the solid is sufficient to keep the surface saturated. The rate of removal of the water vapor (drying) is controlled by the rate of heat transfer to the evaporating surface, which furnishes the latent heat of evaporation for the liquid. At steady state, the rate of mass transfer balances the rate of heat transfer.

To derive the equation for drying, we neglect heat transfer by radiation to the solid surface and also assume no heat transfer by conduction from metal pans or surfaces. Conduction and radiation will be considered in Section 9.8. Assuming only heat transfer to the solid surface by convection from the hot gas to the surface of the solid and mass transfer from the surface to the hot gas (Fig. 9.6-1), we can write equations which are the same as those for deriving the wet bulb temperature T_W in Eq. (9.3-18).

The rate of convective heat transfer q in W (J/s, btu/h) from the gas at T°C (°F) to the surface of the solid at T_W°C, where $(T - T_W)$°C $= (T - T_W)$ K is

$$q = h(T - T_W)A \qquad (9.6\text{-}3)$$

where h is the heat-transfer coefficient in W/m² · K (btu/h · ft² · °F) and A is the exposed drying area in m² (ft²). The equation of the flux of water vapor from the surface is the same as Eq. (9.3-13) and is

$$N_A = k_y(y_W - y) \qquad (9.6\text{-}4)$$

Using the approximation from Eq. (9.3-15) and substituting into Eq. (9.6-4),

$$N_A = k_y \frac{M_B}{M_A}(H_W - H) \qquad (9.6\text{-}5)$$

The amount of heat needed to vaporize N_A kg mol/s · m² (lb mol/h · ft²) water, neglecting the small sensible heat changes, is the same as Eq. (9.3-12):

$$q = M_A N_A \lambda_W A \qquad (9.6\text{-}6)$$

where λ_W is the latent heat at T_W in J/kg (btu/lb$_m$).

Equating Eqs. (9.6-3) and (9.6-6) and substituting Eq. (9.6-5) for N_A,

$$R_C = \frac{q}{A\lambda_W} = \frac{h(T - T_W)}{\lambda_W} = k_y M_B(H_W - H) \qquad (9.6\text{-}7)$$

FIGURE 9.6-1. *Heat and mass transfer in constant-rate drying.*

Equation (9.6-7) is identical to Eq. (9.3-18) for the wet bulb temperature. Hence, in the absence of heat transfer by conduction and radiation, the temperature of the solid is at the wet bulb temperature of the air during the constant-rate drying period. Thus, the rate of drying R_C can be calculated using the heat-transfer equation $h(T - T_W)/\lambda_W$ or the mass-transfer equation $k_y M_B(H_W - H)$. However, it has been found more reliable to use the heat-transfer equation (9.6-8), since an error in determining the interface temperature T_W at the surface affects the driving force $(T - T_W)$ much less than it affects $(H_W - H)$.

$$R_C \text{ kg H}_2\text{O/h} \cdot \text{m}^2 = \frac{h}{\lambda_W}(T - T_W^\circ \text{ C})(3600) \quad \text{(SI)}$$

$$R_C \text{ lb}_m \text{ H}_2\text{O/h} \cdot \text{ft}^2 = \frac{h}{\lambda_W}(T - T_W \text{ °F}) \quad \text{(English)}$$

(9.6-8)

To predict R_C in Eq. (9.6-8), the heat-transfer coefficient must be known. For the case where the air is flowing parallel to the drying surface, Eq. (4.6-3) can be used for air. However, because the shape of the leading edge of the drying surface causes more turbulence, the following can be used for an air temperature of 45–150°C and a mass velocity G of 2450–29 300 kg/h · m^2 (500–6000 lb$_m$/h · ft^2) or a velocity of 0.61–7.6 m/s (2–25 ft/s):

$$h = 0.0204G^{0.8} \quad \text{(SI)}$$

$$h = 0.0128G^{0.8} \quad \text{(English)}$$

(9.6-9)

where in SI units G is $v\rho$ kg/h · m^2 and h is W/m^2 · K. In English units, G is in lb$_m$/h · ft^2 and h in btu/h · ft^2 · °F. When air flows perpendicular to the surface for a G of 3900–19 500 kg/h · m^2 or a velocity of 0.9–4.6 m/s (3–15 ft/s),

$$h = 1.17G^{0.37} \quad \text{(SI)}$$

$$h = 0.37G^{0.37} \quad \text{(English)}$$

(9.6-10)

Equations (9.6-8)–(9.6-10) can be used to estimate the rate of drying during the constant-rate period. However, when possible, experimental measurements of the drying rate are preferred.

To estimate the time of drying during the constant-rate period, substituting Eq. (9.6-7) into (9.6-2),

$$t = \frac{L_S \lambda_W(X_1 - X_2)}{Ah(T - T_W)} = \frac{L_S(X_1 - X_2)}{Ak_y M_B(H_W - H)}$$

(9.6-11)

EXAMPLE 9.6-3. Prediction of Constant-Rate Drying
An insoluble wet granular material is dried in a pan 0.457 × 0.457 m (1.5 × 1.5 ft) and 25.4 mm deep. The material is 25.4 mm deep in the pan, and the sides and bottom can be considered to be insulated. Heat transfer is by convection from an air stream flowing parallel to the surface at a velocity of 6.1 m/s (20 ft/s). The air is at 65.6°C (150°F) and has a humidity of 0.010 kg H$_2$O/kg dry air. Estimate the rate of drying for the constant-rate period using SI and English units.

Solution: For a humidity $H = 0.010$ and dry bulb temperature of 65.6°C, using the humidity chart, Fig. 9.3-2, the wet bulb temperature T_W is found to be 28.9°C (84°F) and $H_W = 0.026$ by following the adiabatic saturation line (the same as the wet bulb line) to the saturated humidity. Using Eq. (9.3-7) to calculate the humid volume,

$$v_H = (2.83 \times 10^{-3} + 4.56 \times 10^{-3}H)T$$
$$= (2.83 \times 10^{-3} + 4.56 \times 10^{-3} \times 0.01)(273 + 65.6)$$
$$= 0.974 \text{ m}^3/\text{kg dry air}$$

The density for 1.0 kg dry air + 0.010 kg H_2O is

$$\rho = \frac{1.0 + 0.010}{0.974} = 1.037 \text{ kg/m}^3 \ (0.0647 \text{ lb}_m/\text{ft}^3)$$

The mass velocity G is

$$G = v\rho = 6.1(3600)(1.037) = 22\,770 \text{ kg/h} \cdot \text{m}^2$$
$$G = v\rho = 20(3600)(0.0647) = 4660 \text{ lb}_m/\text{h} \cdot \text{ft}^2$$

Using Eq. (9.6-9),

$$h = 0.0204G^{0.8} = 0.0204(22\,770)^{0.8} = 62.45 \text{ W/m}^2 \cdot \text{K}$$

$$h = 0.0128G^{0.8} = 0.0128(4660)^{0.8} = 11.01 \text{ btu/h} \cdot \text{ft}^2 \cdot {}^\circ\text{F}$$

At $T_W = 28.9^\circ\text{C}$ (84°F), $\lambda_W = 2433$ kJ/kg (1046 btu/lb$_m$) from steam tables.
Substituting into Eq. (9.6-8) and noting that $(65.6 - 28.9)^\circ\text{C} = (65.6 - 28.9)$ K,

$$R_C = \frac{h}{\lambda_W}(T - T_W)(3600) = \frac{62.45}{2433 \times 1000}(65.6 - 28.9)(3600)$$
$$= 3.39 \text{ kg/h} \cdot \text{m}^2$$

$$R_C = \frac{11.01}{1046}(150 - 84) = 0.695 \text{ lb}_m/\text{h} \cdot \text{ft}^2$$

The total evaporation rate for a surface area of 0.457×0.457 m^2 is

$$\text{total rate} = R_C A = 3.39(0.457 \times 0.457) = 0.708 \text{ kg } H_2O/\text{h}$$
$$= 0.695(1.5 \times 1.5) = 1.564 \text{ lb}_m \, H_2O/\text{h}$$

9.6C Effect of Process Variables on Constant-Rate Period

As stated previously, experimental measurements of the drying rate are usually preferred over using the equations for prediction. However, these equations are quite helpful in predicting the effect of changing the drying-process variables when limited experimental data are available.

1. Effect of air velocity.   When conduction and radiation heat transfer are not present, the rate R_C of drying in the constant-rate region is proportional to h and hence to $G^{0.8}$ as given by Eq. (9.6-9) for air flow parallel to the surface. The effect of gas velocity is less important when radiation and conduction are present.

2. Effect of gas humidity.   If the gas humidity H is decreased for a given T of the gas, then from the humidity chart the wet bulb temperature T_W will decrease. Then, using Eq. (9.6-7),

R_C will increase. For example, if the original conditions are R_{C1}, T_1, T_{W1}, H_1, and H_{W1}, then if H_1 is changed to H_2 and H_{W1} is changed to H_{W2}, R_{C2} becomes

$$R_{C2} = R_{C1} \frac{T - T_{W2}}{T - T_{W1}} \frac{\lambda_{W1}}{\lambda_{W2}} = R_{C1} \frac{H_{W2} - H_2}{H_{W1} - H_1} \qquad \text{(9.6-12)}$$

However, since $\lambda_{W1} \cong \lambda_{W2}$,

$$R_{C2} = R_{C1} \frac{T - T_{W2}}{T - T_{W1}} = R_{C1} \frac{H_{W2} - H_2}{H_{W1} - H_1} \qquad \text{(9.6-13)}$$

3. Effect of gas temperature. If the gas temperature T is increased, T_W is also increased somewhat, but not as much as the increase in T. Hence, R_C increases as follows:

$$R_{C2} = R_{C1} \frac{T_2 - T_{W2}}{T_1 - T_{W1}} = R_{C1} \frac{H_{W2} - H_2}{H_{W1} - H_1} \qquad \text{(9.6-14)}$$

4. Effect of thickness of solid being dried. For heat transfer by convection only, the rate R_C is independent of the thickness x_1 of the solid. However, the time t for drying between fixed moisture contents X_1 and X_2 will be directly proportional to the thickness x_1. This is shown by Eq. (9.6-2), where increasing the thickness with a constant A will directly increase the amount of L_S kg dry solid.

5. Experimental effect of process variables. Experimental data tend to bear out the conclusions reached on the effects of material thickness, humidity, air velocity, and $T - T_W$.

9.7 CALCULATION METHODS FOR FALLING-RATE DRYING PERIOD

9.7A Method Using Numerical Integration

In the falling-rate drying period, as shown in Fig. 9.5-1b, the rate of drying R is not constant but decreases when drying proceeds past the critical free moisture content X_C. When the free moisture content X is zero, the rate drops to zero.

The time of drying for any region between X_1 and X_2 has been given by Eq. (9.6-1):

$$t = \frac{L_S}{A} \int_{X_2}^{X_1} \frac{dX}{R} \qquad \text{(9.6-1)}$$

If the rate is constant, Eq. (9.6-1) can be integrated to give Eq. (9.6-2). However, in the falling-rate period, R varies. For any shape of falling-rate drying curve, Eq. (9.6-1) can be integrated by plotting $1/R$ versus X and determining the area under the curve using graphical integration or numerical integration with a spreadsheet. (See Section 1.8 for methods of numerical integration.)

> ### EXAMPLE 9.7-1. *Numerical Integration in Falling-Rate Period*
> A batch of wet solid whose drying-rate curve is represented by Fig. 9.5-1b is to be dried from a free moisture content of $X_1 = 0.38$ kg H_2O/kg dry solid to $X_2 = 0.04$ kg H_2O/kg dry solid. The weight of the dry solid is $L_S = 399$ kg dry solid and

$A = 18.58 \text{ m}^2$ of top drying surface. Calculate the time for drying. Note that $L_S/A = 399/18.58 = 21.5 \text{ kg/m}^2$.

Solution: From Fig. 9.5-1b, the critical free moisture content is $X_C = 0.195 \text{ kg}$ $H_2O/\text{kg dry solid}$. Hence, the drying occurs in the constant-rate and falling-rate periods.

For the constant-rate period, $X_1 = 0.38$ and $X_2 = X_C = 0.195$. From Fig. 9.5-1b, $R_C = 1.51 \text{ kg } H_2O/\text{h} \cdot \text{m}^2$. Substituting into Eq. (9.6-2),

$$t = \frac{L_S}{AR_C}(X_1 - X_2) = \frac{399(0.38 - 0.195)}{(18.58)(1.51)} = 2.63 \text{ h}$$

For the falling-rate period, reading values of R for various values of X from Fig. 9.5-1b, the following table is prepared:

X	R	1/R	X	R	1/R
0.195	1.51	0.663	0.065	0.71	1.41
0.150	1.21	0.826	0.050	0.37	2.70
0.100	0.90	1.11	0.040	0.27	3.70

To determine this area by numerical integration using a spreadsheet, the calculations are given in the following table:

X	R	1/R	ΔX	(1/R)$_{av}$	(ΔX)(1/R)$_{av}$
0.195	0.51	0.663	0.045	0.745	0.0335
0.150	1.21	0.826	0.050	0.969	0.0485
0.100	0.90	1.111	0.035	1.260	0.0441
0.065	0.71	1.408	0.015	2.055	0.0308
0.050	0.37	2.702	0.010	3.203	0.0320
0.040	0.27	3.704		Total =	0.1889

The area of the first rectangle is the average height $(0.663 + 0.826)/2$, or 0.745, times the width ΔX $(0.195 - 0.150)$, or 0.045, giving 0.0335. Other values are similarly calculated, giving a total of 0.1889.

Substituting into Eq. (9.6-1),

$$t = \frac{L_S}{A} \int_{X_2}^{X_1} \frac{dX}{R} = \frac{399}{18.58}(0.1889) = 4.06 \text{ h}$$

The total time is $2.63 + 4.06 = 6.69 \text{ h}$.

9.7B Calculation Methods for Special Cases in Falling-Rate Region

In certain special cases in the falling-rate region, the equation for the time of drying, Eq. (9.6-1), can be integrated analytically.

1. Rate is a linear function of X. If both X_1 and X_2 are less than X_C and the rate R is linear in X over this region,

$$R = aX + b \qquad (9.7\text{-}1)$$

where a is the slope of the line and b is a constant. Differentiating Eq. (9.7-1) gives $dR = a\,dX$. Substituting this into Eq. (9.6-1),

$$t = \frac{L_S}{aA} \int_{R_2}^{R_1} \frac{dR}{R} = \frac{L_S}{aA} \ln \frac{R_1}{R_2} \qquad (9.7\text{-}2)$$

Since $R_1 = aX_1 + b$ and $R_2 = aX_2 + b$,

$$a = \frac{R_1 - R_2}{X_1 - X_2} \qquad (9.7\text{-}3)$$

Substituting Eq. (9.7-3) into (9.7-2),

$$t = \frac{L_S(X_1 - X_2)}{A(R_1 - R_2)} \ln \frac{R_1}{R_2} \qquad (9.7\text{-}4)$$

2. Rate is a linear function through origin. In some cases a straight line from the critical moisture content passing through the origin adequately represents the whole falling-rate period. In Fig. 9.5-1b this would be a straight line from C to E at the origin. Often, for lack of more detailed data, this assumption is made. Then, for a straight line through the origin, where the rate of drying is directly proportional to the free moisture content,

$$R = aX \qquad (9.7\text{-}5)$$

Differentiating, $dX = dR/a$. Substituting into Eq. (9.6-1),

$$t = \frac{L_S}{aA} \int_{R_2}^{R_1} \frac{dR}{R} = \frac{L_S}{aA} \ln \frac{R_1}{R_2} \qquad (9.7\text{-}6)$$

The slope a of the line is R_C/X_C, and for $X_1 = X_C$ at $R_1 = R_C$,

$$t = \frac{L_S X_C}{A R_C} \ln \frac{R_C}{R_2} \qquad (9.7\text{-}7)$$

Noting also that $R_C/R_2 = X_C/X_2$,

$$t = \frac{L_S X_C}{A R_C} \ln \frac{X_C}{X_2} \qquad (9.7\text{-}8)$$

or

$$R = R_C \frac{X}{X_C} \qquad (9.7\text{-}9)$$

EXAMPLE 9.7-2. Approximation of Straight Line for Falling-Rate Period
Repeat Example 9.7-1, but as an approximation assume a straight line for the rate R versus X through the origin from point X_C to $X = 0$ for the falling-rate period.

Solution: $R_C = 1.51$ kg $H_2O/h \cdot m^2$ and $X_C = 0.195$. Drying in the falling-rate region is from X_C to $X_2 = 0.040$. Substituting into Eq. (9.7-8),

$$t = \frac{L_S X_C}{A R_C} \ln \frac{X_C}{X_2} = \frac{399(0.195)}{18.58(1.51)} \ln \frac{0.195}{0.040}$$

$$= 4.39 \text{ h}$$

This value of 4.39 h compares favorably with the value of 4.06 h obtained in Example 9.7-1 by numerical integration.

9.8 COMBINED CONVECTION, RADIATION, AND CONDUCTION HEAT TRANSFER IN CONSTANT-RATE PERIOD

9.8A Introduction

In Section 9.6B an equation was derived for predicting the rate of drying in the constant-rate period. Equation (9.6-7) was derived assuming heat transfer to the solid by convection only from the surrounding air to the drying surface. Often the drying is done in an enclosure, where the enclosure surface radiates heat to the drying solid. Also, in some cases the solid may be resting on a metal tray, and heat transfer by conduction through the metal to the bottom of the solid may occur.

9.8B Derivation of Equation for Convection, Conduction, and Radiation

In Fig. 9.8-1 a solid material being dried by a stream of air is shown. The total rate of heat transfer to the drying surface is

$$q = q_C + q_R + q_K \qquad (9.8-1)$$

where q_C is the convective heat transfer from the gas at $T°C$ to the solid surface at $T_S°C$ in W (J/s), q_R is the radiant heat transfer from the surface at T_R to T_S in W (J/s), and q_K is the rate of heat transfer by conduction from the bottom in W. The rate of convective heat transfer is similar to Eq. (9.6-3) and is as follows, where $(T - T_S)°C = (T - T_S)$ K:

$$q_C = h_C(T - T_S)A \qquad (9.8-2)$$

FIGURE 9.8-1. *Heat and mass transfer in drying a solid from the top surface.*

where A is the exposed surface area in m^2. The radiant heat transfer is

$$q_R = h_R(T_R - T_S)A \tag{9.8-3}$$

where h_R is the radiant-heat-transfer coefficient defined by Eq. (4.10-10):

$$h_R = \varepsilon(5.676)\frac{\left(\dfrac{T_R}{100}\right)^4 - \left(\dfrac{T_S}{100}\right)^4}{T_R - T_S} \tag{4.10-10}$$

Note that in Eq. (4.10-10) T_R and T_S are in K. For the heat transfer by conduction from the bottom, the heat transfer is first by convection from the gas to the metal plate, then by conduction through the metal, and finally by conduction through the solid. Radiation to the bottom of the tray is often small if the tray is placed above another tray, and it will be neglected here. Also, if the gas temperatures are not too high, radiation from the top surface to the tray will be small. Hence, the heat by radiation should not be overemphasized. The heat by conduction is

$$q_K = U_K(T - T_S)A \tag{9.8-4}$$

$$U_K = \frac{1}{1/h_C + z_M/k_M + z_S/k_S} \tag{9.8-5}$$

where z_M is the metal thickness in m, k_M the metal thermal conductivity in W/m·K, z_S the solid thickness in m, and k_S the solid thermal conductivity. The value of h_C in Eq. (9.8-4) is assumed to be the same as in Eq. (9.8-2).

The equation for the rate of mass transfer is similar to Eq. (9.6-5) and is

$$N_A = k_y\frac{M_B}{M_A}(H_S - H) \tag{9.8-6}$$

Also, rewriting Eq. (9.6-6),

$$q = M_A N_A \lambda_S A \tag{9.8-7}$$

Combining Eqs. (9.8-1), (9.8-2), (9.8-3), (9.8-4), (9.8-6), and (9.8-7),

$$R_C = \frac{q}{A\lambda_S} = \frac{(h_C + U_K)(T - T_S) + h_R(T_R - T_S)}{\lambda_S} = k_y M_B(H_S - H) \tag{9.8-8}$$

This equation can be compared to Eq. (9.6-7), which gives the wet bulb temperature T_W when radiation and conduction are absent. Equation (9.8-8) gives surface temperature T_S greater than the wet bulb temperature T_W. Equation (9.8-8) must also intersect the saturated humidity line at T_S and H_S, and $T_S > T_W$ and $H_S > H_W$. The equation must be solved by trial and error.

To facilitate solution of Eq. (9.8-8), it can be rearranged (T1) in the following way:

$$\frac{(H_S - H)\lambda_S}{h_C/k_y M_B} = \left(1 + \frac{U_K}{h_C}\right)(T - T_S) + \frac{h_R}{h_C}(T_R - T_S) \tag{9.8-9}$$

The ratio $h_C/k_y M_B$ was shown in the wet bulb derivation of Eq. (9.3-18) to be approximately c_S in Eq. (9.3-6):

$$c_S = (1.005 + 1.88H)10^3 \; \text{J/kg·K} \tag{9.3-6}$$

EXAMPLE 9.8-1. Constant-Rate Drying When Radiation, Conduction, and Convection Are Present

An insoluble granular material wet with water is being dried in a pan 0.457×0.457 m and 25.4 mm deep. The material is 25.4 mm deep in the metal pan, which has a metal bottom of thickness $z_M = 0.610$ mm having a thermal conductivity $k_M = 43.3$ W/m·K. The thermal conductivity of the solid can be assumed as $k_S = 0.865$ W/m·K. Heat transfer is by convection from an air stream flowing parallel to the top drying surface and the bottom metal surface at a velocity of 6.1 m/s and having a temperature of 65.6°C and humidity $H = 0.010$ kg H_2O/kg dry air. The top surface also receives direct radiation from steam-heated pipes whose surface temperature $T_R = 93.3$°C. The emissivity of the solid is $\varepsilon = 0.92$. Estimate the rate of drying for the constant-rate period.

Solution: Some of the given values are as follows:

$$T = 65.6°C, \qquad z_S = 0.0254 \text{ m}, \qquad k_M = 43.3, \qquad k_S = 0.865$$

$$z_M = 0.00061 \text{ m} \qquad \varepsilon = 0.92, \qquad H = 0.010$$

The velocity, temperature, and humidity of the air are the same as in Example 9.6-3 and the convective coefficient was predicted as $h_C = 62.45$ W/m²·K.

The solution of Eq. (9.8-9) is by trial and error. The temperature T_S will be above the wet bulb temperature of $T_W = 28.9$°C and will be estimated as $T_S = 32.2$°C. Then $\lambda_S = 2424$ kJ/kg from the steam tables. To predict h_R from Eq. (4.10-10) for $\varepsilon = 0.92$, $T_1 = 93.3 + 273.2 = 366.5$ K, and $T_2 = 32.2 + 273.2 = 305.4$ K,

$$h_R = (0.92)(5.676)\frac{(366.5/100)^4 - (305.4/100)^4}{366.5 - 305.4} = 7.96 \text{ W/m}^2 \cdot \text{K}$$

Using Eq. (9.8-5),

$$U_K = \frac{1}{1/h_C + z_M/k_M + z_S/k_S} = \frac{1}{1/62.45 + 0.00061/43.3 + 0.0254/0.865}$$

$$= 22.04 \text{ W/m}^2 \cdot \text{K}$$

From Eq. (9.3-6),

$$c_S = (1.005 + 1.88H)10^3 = (1.005 + 1.88 \times 0.010)10^3$$

$$= 1.024 \times 10^3 \text{ J/kg} \cdot \text{K}$$

This can be substituted for $(h_C/k_y M_B)$ into Eq. (9.8-9). Also, substituting other knowns,

$$\frac{(H_S - 0.01)\lambda_S}{1.024 \times 10^3} = (1 + 22.04/62.45)(65.6 - T_S) + (7.96/62.45)(93.3 - T_S)$$

$$= 1.353(65.6 - T_S) + 0.1275(93.3 - T_S) \qquad \textbf{(9.8-10)}$$

For T_S assumed as 32.2°C, $\lambda_S = 2424 \times 10^3$ J/kg. From the humidity chart for $T_S = 32.2$°C, the saturation humidity $H_S = 0.031$. Substituting into Eq. (9.8-10) and solving for T_S,

$$\frac{(0.031 - 0.010)(2424 \times 10^3)}{1.024 \times 10^3} = 1.353(65.6 - T_S) + 0.1275(93.3 - T_S)$$

$$T_S = 34.4°C$$

For the second trial, assuming that $T_S = 32.5°C$, $\lambda_S = 2423 \times 10^3$, and H_S from the humidity chart at saturation is 0.032. Substituting into Eq. (9.8-10) while assuming that h_R does not change appreciably, a value of $T_S = 32.8°C$ is obtained. Hence, the final value is 32.8°C. This is 3.9°C greater than the wet bulb temperature of 28.9°C in Example 9.6-3, where radiation and conduction were absent.

Using Eq. (9.8-8),

$$R_C = \frac{(h_C + U_K)(T - T_S) + h_R(T_R - T_S)}{\lambda_S}(3600)$$

$$= \frac{(62.45 + 22.04)(65.6 - 32.8) + 7.96(93.3 - 32.8)}{2423 \times 10^3}(3600)$$

$$= 4.83 \text{ kg/h} \cdot \text{m}^2$$

This compares favorably with 3.39 kg/h · m² for Example 9.6-3 for no radiation or conduction.

9.9 DRYING IN FALLING-RATE PERIOD BY DIFFUSION AND CAPILLARY FLOW

9.9A Introduction

In the falling-rate period, the surface of the solid being dried is no longer completely wetted, and the rate of drying steadily falls with time. In Section 9.7 empirical methods were used to predict the time of drying. In one method the actual rate-of-drying curve was numerically or graphically integrated to determine the time of drying.

In another method an approximately straight line from the critical free moisture content to the origin at zero free moisture was assumed. Here the rate of drying was assumed to be a linear function of the free moisture content. The rate of drying R is defined by Eq. (9.5-3):

$$R = -\frac{L_S}{A}\frac{dX}{dt} \tag{9.5-3}$$

When R is a linear function of X in the falling-rate period,

$$R = aX \tag{9.7-5}$$

where a is a constant. Equating Eq. (9.7-5) to Eq. (9.5-3),

$$R = -\frac{L_S}{A}\frac{dX}{dt} = aX \tag{9.9-1}$$

Rearranging,

$$\frac{dX}{dt} = -\frac{aA}{L_S}X \tag{9.9-2}$$

In many instances, however, as mentioned briefly in Section 9.5E, the rate of moisture movement in the falling-rate period is governed by the rate of internal movement of the liquid by liquid diffusion or by capillary movement. These two mechanisms of moisture movement will be considered in more detail and the theories related to experimental data in the falling-rate region.

9.9B Liquid Diffusion of Moisture in Drying

When liquid diffusion of moisture controls the rate of drying in the falling-rate period, the equations for diffusion described in Chapter 7 can be used. Using the concentrations as X kg free moisture/kg dry solid instead of kg mol moisture/m^3, Fick's second law for unsteady-state diffusion, Eq. (7.10-10), can be written as

$$\frac{\partial X}{\partial t} = D_L \frac{\partial^2 X}{\partial x^2} \tag{9.9-3}$$

where D_L is the liquid diffusion coefficient in m^2/h and x is distance in the solid in m.

This type of diffusion is often characteristic of relatively slow drying in nongranular materials such as soap, gelatin, and glue, and in the later stages of drying of bound water in clay, wood, textiles, leather, paper, foods, starches, and other hydrophilic solids.

A major difficulty in analyzing diffusion drying data is that the initial moisture distribution is not uniform throughout the solid at the start if a drying period at constant rate precedes this falling-rate period. During diffusion-type drying, the resistance to mass transfer of water vapor from the surface is usually very small, and the diffusion in the solid controls the rate of drying. Then the moisture content at the surface is at the equilibrium value X^*. This means that the free moisture content X at the surface is essentially zero.

Assuming that the initial moisture distribution is uniform at $t = 0$, Eq. (9.9-3) may be integrated by the methods in Chapter 7 to give the following:

$$\frac{X_t - X^*}{X_{t1} - X^*} = \frac{X}{X_1} = \frac{8}{\pi^2} \left[e^{-D_L t(\pi/2x_1)^2} + \frac{1}{9} e^{-9D_L t(\pi/2x_1)^2} + \frac{1}{25} e^{-25D_L t(\pi/2x_1)^2} + \cdots \right] \tag{9.9-4}$$

where X = average free moisture content at time t h, X_1 = initial free moisture content at $t = 0$, X^* = equilibrium free moisture content, $x_1 = \frac{1}{2}$ the thickness of the slab when drying occurs from the top and bottom parallel faces, and x_1 = total thickness of slab if drying occurs only from the top face.

Equation (9.9-4) assumes that D_L is constant, but D_L is rarely constant; it varies with moisture content, temperature, and humidity. For long drying times, only the first term in Eq. (9.9-4) is significant, and the equation becomes

$$\frac{X}{X_1} = \frac{8}{\pi^2} e^{-D_L t(\pi/2x_1)^2} \tag{9.9-5}$$

Solving for the time of drying,

$$t = \frac{4x_1^2}{\pi^2 D_L} \ln \frac{8X_1}{\pi^2 X} \tag{9.9-6}$$

In this equation, if the diffusion mechanism starts at $X = X_C$, then $X_1 = X_C$. Differentiating Eq. (9.9-6) with respect to time and rearranging,

$$\frac{dX}{dt} = -\frac{\pi^2 D_L X}{4x_1^2} \tag{9.9-7}$$

Multiplying both sides by $-L_S/A$,

$$R = -\frac{L_S}{A}\frac{dX}{dt} = \frac{\pi^2 L_S D_L}{4x_1^2 A} X \tag{9.9-8}$$

Hence, Eqs. (9.9-7) and (9.9-8) state that when internal diffusion controls for long periods of time, the rate of drying is directly proportional to the free moisture X and the liquid diffusivity, and that the rate of drying is inversely proportional to the thickness squared. Or, stated as the time of drying between fixed moisture limits, the time varies directly as the square of the thickness. The drying rate should be independent of gas velocity and humidity.

EXAMPLE 9.9-1. Drying Slabs of Wood When Diffusion of Moisture Controls

The experimental average diffusion coefficient of moisture in a given wood is 2.97×10^{-6} m^2/h (3.20×10^{-5} ft^2/h). Large planks of wood 25.4 mm thick are dried from both sides by air having a humidity such that the equilibrium moisture content in the wood is $X^* = 0.04$ kg H$_2$O/kg dry wood. The wood is to be dried from a total average moisture content of $X_{t1} = 0.29$ to $X_t = 0.09$. Calculate the time needed.

Solution: The free moisture content $X_1 = X_{t1} - X^* = 0.29 - 0.04 = 0.25$, $X = X_t - X^* = 0.09 - 0.04 = 0.05$. The half-slab thickness $x_1 = 25.4/(2 \times 1000) = 0.0127$ m. Substituting into Eq. (9.9-6),

$$t = \frac{4x_1^2}{\pi^2 D_L}\ln\frac{8X_1}{\pi^2 X} = \frac{4(0.0127)^2}{\pi^2(2.97 \times 10^{-6})}\ln\frac{8 \times 0.25}{\pi^2 \times 0.05}$$

$$= 30.8 \text{ h}$$

Alternatively, Fig. 5.3-13 for the average concentration in a slab can be used. The ordinate $E_a = X/X_1 = 0.05/0.25 = 0.20$. Reading off the plot a value of $0.56 = D_L t/x_1^2$, substituting, and solving for t,

$$t = \frac{x_1^2(0.56)}{D_L} = \frac{(0.0127)^2(0.56)}{2.97 \times 10^{-6}} = 30.4 \text{ h}$$

9.9C Capillary Movement of Moisture in Drying

Water can flow from regions of high concentration to those of low concentration as a result of capillary action rather than by diffusion if the pore sizes of the granular materials are suitable.

The capillary theory (P1) assumes that a packed bed of nonporous spheres contains a void space between the spheres called *pores*. As water is evaporated, capillary forces are set up by the interfacial tension between the water and the solid. These forces provide the driving force for moving the water through the pores to the drying surface.

A modified form of Poiseuille's equation for laminar flow can be used in conjunction with the capillary-force equation to derive an equation for the rate of drying when flow is by capillary movement. If the moisture movement follows the capillary-flow equations, the rate of drying R will vary linearly with X. Since the mechanism of evaporation during this period is the same as during the constant-rate period, the effects of the variables gas velocity, temperature of the gas, humidity of the gas, and so on, will be the same as for the constant-rate drying period.

The defining equation for the rate of drying is

$$R = -\frac{L_S}{A}\frac{dX}{dt} \tag{9.5-3}$$

For the rate R varying linearly with X, given previously,

$$R = R_C \frac{X}{X_C} \tag{9.7-9}$$

$$t = \frac{L_S X_C}{A R_C}\ln\frac{X_C}{X_2} \tag{9.7-8}$$

We define t as the time when $X = X_2$ and

$$L_S = x_1 A \rho_S \tag{9.9-9}$$

where ρ_S = solid density kg dry solid/m^3. Substituting Eq. (9.9-9) and $X = X_2$ into Eq. (9.7-8),

$$t = \frac{x_1 \rho_S X_C}{R_C}\ln\frac{X_C}{X} \tag{9.9-10}$$

Substituting Eq. (9.6-7) for R_C,

$$t = \frac{x_1 \rho_S \lambda_W X_C}{h(T - T_W)}\ln\frac{X_C}{X} \tag{9.9-11}$$

Hence, Eqs. (9.9-10) and (9.9-11) state that when capillary flow controls in the falling-rate period, the rate of drying is inversely proportional to the thickness. The time of drying between fixed moisture limits varies directly as the thickness and depends upon the gas velocity, temperature, and humidity.

9.9D Comparison of Liquid Diffusion and Capillary Flow

To determine the mechanism of drying in the falling-rate period, the experimental data obtained for moisture content at various times using constant drying conditions are often analyzed as follows. The *unaccomplished moisture change,* defined as the ratio of free moisture present in the solid after drying for t hours to the total free moisture content present at the start of the falling-rate period, X/X_C, is plotted versus time on semilog paper. If a straight line is obtained, such as curve B in Fig. 9.9-1 using the upper scale for the abscissa, then either Eqs. (9.9-4)–(9.9-6) for diffusion or Eqs. (9.9-10) and (9.9-11) for capillary flow are applicable.

If the equations for capillary flow apply, the slope of the falling-rate drying line B in Fig. 9.9-1 is related to Eq. (9.9-10), which contains the constant drying rate R_C. The value of R_C is calculated from the measured slope of the line, which is $-R_C/x_1\rho_S X_C$, and if it agrees with the experimental value of R_C in the constant-drying period or the predicted value of R_C, the moisture movement is by capillary flow.

If the values of R_C do not agree, the moisture movement is by diffusion and the slope of line B in Fig. 9.9-1 from Eq. (9.9-6) should equal $-\pi^2 D_L/4x_1^2$. In actual practice, however, the diffusivity D_L is usually less at small moisture contents than at large moisture contents, and an average value of D_L is usually determined experimentally over the moisture range of interest.

FIGURE 9.9-1. *Plot of equations for falling-rate period: (A) Eq. (9.9-4) for moisture movement by diffusion, (B) Eq. (9.9-10) for moisture movement by capillary flow. (From R. H. Perry and C. H. Chilton, Chemical Engineers Handbook, 5th ed. New York: McGraw-Hill Book Company, 1973. With permission.)*

A plot of Eq. (9.9-4) is shown as line A, where $\ln(X/X_1)$ or $\ln(X/X_C)$ is plotted versus $D_L t/x_1^2$. This is the same plot as Fig. 5.3-13 for a slab and shows a curvature in the line for values of X/X_C between 1.0 and 0.6 and a straight line for $X/X_C < 0.6$.

When the experimental data show that the movement of moisture follows the diffusion law, the average experimental diffusivities can be calculated as follows for different concentration ranges. A value of X/X_C is chosen at 0.4, for example. From an experimental plot similar to curve B, Fig. 9.9-1, the experimental value of t is obtained. From curve A at $X/X_C = 0.4$, the theoretical value of $(D_L t/x_1^2)_{theor}$ is obtained. Then, by substituting the known values of t and x_1 into Eq. (9.9-12), the experimental average value of D_L over the range $X/X_C = 1.0-0.4$ is obtained:

$$D_L = \left(\frac{D_L t}{x_1^2}\right)_{theor} \frac{x_1^2}{t} \qquad (9.9\text{-}12)$$

This is repeated for various values of X/X_C. Values of D_L obtained for $X/X_C > 0.6$ are in error because of the curvature of line A.

FIGURE 9.9-2. *Plot of drying data for Example 9.9-2.*

EXAMPLE 9.9-2. *Diffusion Coefficient in the Tapioca Root*
Tapioca flour is obtained from drying and then milling the tapioca root. Experimental data on drying thin slices of the tapioca root 3 mm thick on both sides in the falling-rate period under constant-drying conditions are tabulated below. The time $t = 0$ is the start of the falling-rate period.

X/X_C	t (h)	X/X_C	t (h)	X/X_C	t (h)
1.0	0	0.55	0.40	0.23	0.94
0.80	0.15	0.40	0.60	0.18	1.07
0.63	0.27	0.30	0.80		

It has been determined that the data do not follow the capillary-flow equations but appear to follow the diffusion equations. Plot the data as X/X_C versus t on semilog coordinates and determine the average diffusivity of the moisture up to a value of $X/X_C = 0.20$.

Solution: In Fig. 9.9-2 the data are plotted as X/X_C on the log scale versus t on a linear scale and a smooth curve is drawn through the data. At $X/X_C = 0.20$, a value of $t = 1.02$ h is read off the plot. The value of $x_1 = 3$ mm/2 = 1.5 mm for drying from both sides. From Fig. 9.9-1, line A, for $X/X_C = 0.20$, $(D_L t/x_1^2)_{\text{theor}} = 0.56$. Then substituting into Eq. (9.9-12),

$$D_L = (D_L t/x_1^2)_{\text{theor}}\, \frac{x_1^2}{t} = \frac{0.56(1.5/1000)^2}{1.02 \times 3600} = 3.44 \times 10^{-10} \text{ m}^2/\text{s}$$

9.10   EQUATIONS FOR VARIOUS TYPES OF DRYERS

9.10A   Through-Circulation Drying in Packed Beds

For through-circulation drying, where the drying gas passes upward or downward through a bed of wet granular solids, both a constant-rate period and a falling-rate period of drying may result. Often the granular solids are arranged on a screen so that the gas passes through the screen and through the open spaces or voids between the solid particles.

1. Derivation of equations.   To derive the equations for this case, no heat losses will be assumed, so the system is adiabatic. The drying will be for unbound moisture in the wet granular solids. We shall consider a bed of uniform cross-sectional area A m^2, where a gas flow of G kg dry gas/h $\cdot$ m^2 cross section enters with a humidity of H_1. By a material balance on the gas at a given time, the gas leaves the bed with a humidity H_2. The amount of water removed from the bed by the gas is equal to the rate of drying at this time:

$$R = G(H_2 - H_1) \tag{9.10-1}$$

where R = kg H$_2$O/h $\cdot$ m^2 cross section and G = kg dry air/h $\cdot$ m^2 cross section.

In Fig. 9.10-1 the gas enters at T_1 and H_1 and leaves at T_2 and H_2. Hence, the temperature T and humidity H both vary through the bed. Making a heat balance over the short section dz m of the bed,

$$dq = -G c_S A \; dT \tag{9.10-2}$$

where A = m^2 cross-sectional area, q is the heat-transfer rate in W (J/s), and c_S is the humid heat of the air–water vapor mixture in Eq. (9.3-6). Note that G in this equation is in kg/s $\cdot$ m^2. The heat-transfer equation gives

$$dq = ha A \; dz(T - T_W) \tag{9.10-3}$$

where T_W = wet bulb temperature of solid, h is the heat-transfer coefficient in W/m$^2 \cdot$ K, and a is m^2 surface area of solids/m^3 bed volume. Equating Eq. (9.10-2) to (9.10-3), rearranging, and integrating,

$$\frac{ha}{G c_S} \int_0^z dz = -\int_{T_1}^{T_2} \frac{dT}{T - T_W} \tag{9.10-4}$$

FIGURE 9.10-1.   *Heat and material balances in a through-circulation dryer in a packed bed.*

$$\frac{haz}{Gc_S} = \ln\frac{T_1 - T_W}{T_2 - T_W} \tag{9.10-5}$$

where z = bed thickness = x_1 m.

For the constant-rate period of drying by air flowing parallel to a surface, Eq. (9.6-11) was derived:

$$t = \frac{L_S\lambda_W(X_1 - X_2)}{Ah(T - T_W)} = \frac{L_S(X_1 - X_2)}{Ak_yM_B(H_W - H)} \tag{9.6-11}$$

Using Eq. (9.9-9) and the definition of a, we obtain

$$\frac{L_S}{A} = \frac{\rho_S}{a} \tag{9.10-6}$$

Substituting Eq. (9.10-6) into (9.6-11) and setting $X_2 = X_C$ for drying to X_C, we obtain the equation for through-circulation drying in the constant-rate period:

$$t = \frac{\rho_S\lambda_W(X_1 - X_C)}{ah(T - T_W)} = \frac{\rho_S(X_1 - X_C)}{ak_yM_B(H_W - H)} \tag{9.10-7}$$

In a similar manner, Eq. (9.7-8) for the falling-rate period, which assumes that R is proportional to X, becomes, for through-circulation drying,

$$t = \frac{\rho_S\lambda_W X_C \ln(X_C/X)}{ah(T - T_W)} = \frac{\rho_S X_C \ln(X_C/X)}{ak_yM_B(H_W - H)} \tag{9.10-8}$$

Both Eqs. (9.10-7) and (9.10-8), however, hold for only one point in the bed in Fig. 9.10-1, since the temperature T of the gas varies throughout the bed. Hence, in a manner similar to the derivation in heat transfer, a log mean temperature difference can be used as an approximation for the whole bed in place of $T - T_W$ in Eqs. (9.10-7) and (9.10-8):

$$(T - T_W)_{LM} = \frac{(T_1 - T_W) - (T_2 - T_W)}{\ln[(T_1 - T_W)/(T_2 - T_W)]} = \frac{T_1 - T_2}{\ln[(T_1 - T_W)/(T_2 - T_W)]} \tag{9.10-9}$$

Substituting Eq. (9.10-5) for the denominator of Eq. (9.10-9) and substituting the value of T_2 from Eq. (9.10-5) into (9.10-9),

$$(T - T_W)_{LM} = \frac{(T_1 - T_W)(1 - e^{-haz/Gc_S})}{haz/Gc_S} \tag{9.10-10}$$

Substituting Eq. (9.10-10) into (9.10-7) for the constant-rate period and setting $x_1 = z$,

$$t = \frac{\rho_S\lambda_W x_1(X_1 - X_C)}{Gc_S(T_1 - T_W)(1 - e^{-hax_1/Gc_S})} \tag{9.10-11}$$

Similarly, for the falling-rate period an approximate equation is obtained:

$$t = \frac{\rho_S\lambda_W x_1 X_C \ln(X_C/X)}{Gc_S(T_1 - T_W)(1 - e^{-hax_1/Gc_S})} \tag{9.10-12}$$

A major difficulty with the use of Eq. (9.10-12) is that the critical moisture content is not easily estimated. Different forms of Eqs. (9.10-11) and (9.10-12) can also be derived, using humidity instead of temperature (T1).

2. Heat-transfer coefficients. For through-circulation drying, where the gases pass through a bed of wet granular solids, the following equations for estimating h for adiabatic evaporation of water can be used (G1, W1):

$$\left. \begin{array}{ll} h = 0.151 \dfrac{G_t^{0.59}}{D_p^{0.41}} & \text{(SI)} \\[3mm] h = 0.11 \dfrac{G_t^{0.59}}{D_p^{0.41}} & \text{(English)} \end{array} \right\} \quad \dfrac{D_p G_t}{\mu} > 350 \qquad \textbf{(9.10-13)}$$

$$\left. \begin{array}{ll} h = 0.214 \dfrac{G_t^{0.49}}{D_p^{0.51}} & \text{(SI)} \\[3mm] h = 0.15 \dfrac{G_t^{0.49}}{D_p^{0.51}} & \text{(English)} \end{array} \right\} \quad \dfrac{D_p G_t}{\mu} < 350 \qquad \textbf{(9.10-14)}$$

where h is in W/m$^2 \cdot$ K, D_p is diameter in m of a sphere having the same surface area as the particle in the bed, G_t is the total mass velocity entering the bed in kg/h $\cdot$ m^2, and μ is viscosity in kg/m $\cdot$ h. In English units, h is btu/h $\cdot$ ft$^2 \cdot$ °F, D_p is ft, G_t is lb$_m$/h $\cdot$ ft^2, and μ is lb$_m$/ft $\cdot$ h.

3. Geometry factors in a bed. To determine the value of a, m^2 surface area/m^3 of bed, in a packed bed for spherical particles having a diameter D_p m,

$$a = \frac{6(1 - \varepsilon)}{D_p} \qquad \textbf{(9.10-15)}$$

where ε is the void fraction in the bed. For cylindrical particles,

$$a = \frac{4(1 - \varepsilon)(h + 0.5D_c)}{D_c h} \qquad \textbf{(9.10-16)}$$

where D_c is diameter of cylinder in m and h is length of cylinder in m. The value of D_p to use in Eqs. (9.10-13) and (9.10-14) for a cylinder is the diameter of a sphere having the same surface area as the cylinder, as follows:

$$D_p = (D_c h + 0.5D_c^2)^{1/2} \qquad \textbf{(9.10-17)}$$

4. Equations for very fine particles. The equations derived for the constant- and falling-rate periods in packed beds hold for particles of about 3–19 mm in diameter in shallow beds about 10–65 mm thick (T1, M1). For very fine particles of 10–200 mesh (1.66–0.079 mm) and bed depth greater than 11 mm, the interfacial area a varies with the moisture content. Empirical expressions are available for estimating a and the mass-transfer coefficient (T1, A1).

EXAMPLE 9.10-1. Through-Circulation Drying in a Bed

A granular paste material is extruded into cylinders with a diameter of 6.35 mm and length of 25.4 mm. The initial total moisture content $X_{t1} = 1.0$ kg H$_2$O/kg dry solid and the equilibrium moisture is $X^* = 0.01$. The density of the dry solid is 1602 kg/m^3 (100 lb$_m$/ft^3). The cylinders are packed on a screen to a depth of $x_1 = 50.8$ mm. The bulk density of the dry solid in the bed is $\rho_S = 641$ kg/m^3. The inlet air has a humidity $H_1 = 0.04$ kg H$_2$O/kg dry air and a temperature $T_1 = 121.1$°C. The gas superficial velocity is 0.811 m/s and the gas passes through the bed. The total critical moisture content is $X_{tC} = 0.50$. Calculate the total time to dry the solids to $X_t = 0.10$ kg H_2O/kg dry solid.

Solution: For the solid,

$$X_1 = X_{t1} - X^* = 1.00 - 0.01 = 0.99 \text{ kg } H_2O/\text{kg dry solid}$$

$$X_C = X_{tC} - X^* = 0.50 - 0.01 = 0.49$$

$$X = X_t - X^* = 0.10 - 0.01 = 0.09$$

For the gas, $T_1 = 121.1°C$ and $H_1 = 0.04$ kg H_2O/kg dry air. The wet bulb temperature $T_W = 47.2°C$ and $H_W = 0.074$. The solid temperature is at T_W if radiation and conduction are neglected. The density of the entering air at $121.1°C$ and 1 atm is as follows:

$$v_H = (2.83 \times 10^{-3} + 4.56 \times 10^{-3} \times 0.04)(273 + 121.1) \quad \text{(9.3-7)}$$

$$= 1.187 \text{ m}^3/\text{kg dry air}$$

$$\rho = \frac{1.00 + 0.04}{1.187} = 0.876 \text{ kg dry air} + H_2O/\text{m}^3$$

The mass velocity of the dry air is

$$G = v\rho\left(\frac{1.0}{1.0 + 0.04}\right) = 0.811(3600)(0.876)\left(\frac{1}{1.04}\right) = 2459 \text{ kg dry air/h} \cdot \text{m}^2$$

Since the inlet $H_1 = 0.040$ and the outlet will be less than 0.074, an approximate average H of 0.05 will be used to calculate the total average mass velocity. The approximate average G_t is

$$G_t = 2459 + 2459(0.05) = 2582 \text{ kg air} + H_2O/\text{h} \cdot \text{m}^2$$

For the packed bed, the void fraction ε is calculated as follows for 1 m³ of bed containing solids plus voids. A total of 641 kg dry solid is present. The density of the dry solid is 1602 kg dry solid/m³ solid. The volume of the solids in 1 m³ of bed is then 641/1602, or 0.40 m³ solid. Hence, $\varepsilon = 1 - 0.40 = 0.60$. The solid cylinder length $h = 0.0254$ m. The diameter $D_c = 0.00635$ m. Substituting into Eq. (9.10-16),

$$a = \frac{4(1 - \varepsilon)(h + 0.5D_c)}{D_c h} = \frac{4(1 - 0.6)[0.0254 + 0.5(0.00635)]}{0.00635(0.0254)}$$

$$= 283.5 \text{ m}^2 \text{ surface area/m}^3 \text{ bed volume}$$

To calculate the diameter D_p of a sphere with the same area as the cylinder using Eq. (9.10-17),

$$D_p = (D_c h + 0.5D_c^2)^{1/2} = [0.00635 \times 0.0254 + 0.5(0.00635)^2]^{1/2}$$

$$= 0.0135 \text{ m}$$

The bed thickness $x_1 = 50.8$ mm $= 0.0508$ m.

To calculate the heat-transfer coefficient, the Reynolds number is first calculated. Assuming an approximate average air temperature of $93.3°C$, the viscosity of air is $\mu = 2.15 \times 10^{-5}$ kg/m$\cdot$s $= 2.15 \times 10^{-5}(3600) = 7.74 \times 10^{-2}$ kg/m$\cdot$h. The Reynolds number is

$$N_{Re} = \frac{D_p G_t}{\mu} = \frac{0.0135(2582)}{7.74 \times 10^{-2}} = 450$$

Using Eq. (9.10-13),

$$h = 0.151 \frac{G_t^{0.59}}{D_p^{0.41}} = \frac{0.151(2582)^{0.59}}{(0.0135)^{0.41}} = 90.9 \text{ W/m}^2 \cdot \text{K}$$

For $T_W = 47.2°$C, $\lambda_W = 2389$ kJ/kg, or 2.389×10^6 J/kg (1027 btu/lb$_m$), from steam tables. The average humid heat, from Eq. (9.3-6), is

$$c_S = 1.005 + 1.88H = 1.005 + 1.88(0.05) = 1.099 \text{ kJ/kg dry air} \cdot \text{K}$$

$$= 1.099 \times 10^3 \text{ J/kg} \cdot \text{K}$$

To calculate the time of drying for the constant-rate period using Eq. (9.10-11) and $G = 2459/3600 = 0.6831$ kg/s$\cdot$m^2,

$$t = \frac{\rho_S \lambda_W x_1 (X_1 - X_C)}{G c_S (T_1 - T_W)(1 - e^{-hax_1/Gc_S})}$$

$$= \frac{641(2.389 \times 10^6)(0.0508)(0.99 - 0.49)}{(0.683)(1.099 \times 10^3)(121.1 - 47.2)[1 - e^{-(90.9 \times 283.5 \times 0.0508)/(0.683 \times 1.099 \times 10^3)}]}$$

$$= 850 \text{ s} = 0.236 \text{ h}$$

For the time of drying for the falling-rate period, using Eq. (9.10-12),

$$t = \frac{\rho_S \lambda_W x_1 X_C \ln(X_C/X)}{G c_S (T_1 - T_W)(1 - e^{-hax_1/Gc_S})}$$

$$= \frac{641(2.389 \times 10^6)(0.0508)(0.49)\ln(0.49/0.09)}{(0.6831)(1.099 \times 10^3)(121.1 - 47.2)[1 - e^{-(90.9 \times 283.5 \times 0.0508)/(0.683 \times 1.099 \times 10^3)}]}$$

$$= 1412 \text{ s} = 0.392 \text{ h}$$

$$\text{total time } t = 0.236 + 0.392 = 0.628 \text{ h}$$

9.10B Tray Drying with Varying Air Conditions

For drying in a compartment or tray dryer where the air passes in parallel flow over the surface of the tray, the air conditions do not remain constant. Heat and material balances similar to those for through circulation must be made to determine the exit-gas temperature and humidity.

In Fig. 9.10-2 air is shown passing over a tray. It enters having a temperature of T_1 and humidity H_1 and leaves at T_2 and H_2. The spacing between the trays is b m and dry air flow is G kg dry air/s$\cdot$m^2 cross-sectional area. Writing a heat balance over a length dL_t of tray for a section 1 m wide,

$$dq = Gc_S(1 \times b) \, dT \tag{9.10-18}$$

FIGURE 9.10-2. *Heat and material balances in a tray dryer.*

The heat-transfer equation is

$$dq = h(1 \times dL_t)(T - T_W) \qquad \textbf{(9.10-19)}$$

Rearranging and integrating,

$$\frac{hL_t}{Gc_sb} = \ln \frac{T_1 - T_W}{T_2 - T_W} \qquad \textbf{(9.10-20)}$$

Defining a log mean temperature difference similar to Eq. (9.10-10) and substituting into Eqs. (9.6-11) and (9.7-8), we obtain the following. For the constant-rate period,

$$t = \frac{x_1 \rho_S L_t \lambda_W (X_1 - X_C)}{Gc_sb(T_1 - T_W)(1 - e^{-hL_t/Gc_sb})} \qquad \textbf{(9.10-21)}$$

For the falling-rate period, an approximate equation is obtained:

$$t = \frac{x_1 \rho_S L_t \lambda_W X_C \ln(X_C/X)}{Gc_sb(T_1 - T_W)(1 - e^{-hL_t/Gc_sb})} \qquad \textbf{(9.10-22)}$$

9.10C Material and Heat Balances for Continuous Dryers

1. Simple heat and material balances. In Fig. 9.10-3 a flow diagram is given for a continuous-type dryer where the drying gas flows countercurrently to the solids flow. The solid enters at a rate of L_S kg dry solid/h, having a free moisture content X_1 and a temperature T_{S1}. It leaves

FIGURE 9.10-3. *Process flow for a counter-current continuous dryer.*

at X_2 and T_{S2}. The gas enters at a rate G kg dry air/h, having a humidity H_2 kg H_2O/kg dry air and a temperature of T_{G2}. The gas leaves at T_{G1} and H_1.

For a material balance on the moisture,

$$GH_2 + L_S X_1 = GH_1 + L_S X_2 \qquad (9.10\text{-}23)$$

For a heat balance a datum of $T_0°C$ is selected. A convenient temperature is $0°C$ ($32°F$). The enthalpy of the wet solid is composed of the enthalpy of the dry solid plus that of the liquid as free moisture. The heat of wetting is usually neglected. The enthalpy of the gas H'_G in kJ/kg dry air is

$$H'_G = c_S(T_G - T_0) + H\lambda_0 \qquad (9.10\text{-}24)$$

where λ_0 is the latent heat of water at $T_0°C$, 2501 kJ/kg (1075.4 btu/lb$_m$) at $0°C$, and c_S is the humid heat, given as kJ/kg dry air $\cdot$ K:

$$c_S = 1.005 + 1.88H \qquad (9.3\text{-}6)$$

The enthalpy of the wet solid H'_S in kJ/kg dry solid, where $(T_S - T_0)°C = (T_S - T_0)$ K, is

$$H'_S = c_{pS}(T_S - T_0) + X c_{pA}(T_S - T_0) \qquad (9.10\text{-}25)$$

where c_{pS} is the heat capacity of the dry solid in kJ/kg dry solid $\cdot$ K and c_{pA} is the heat capacity of liquid moisture in kJ/kg $H_2O \cdot$ K. The heat of wetting or adsorption is neglected.

A heat balance on the dryer is

$$GH'_{G2} + L_S H'_{S1} = GH'_{G1} + L_S H'_{S2} + Q \qquad (9.10\text{-}26)$$

where Q is the heat loss in the dryer in kJ/h. For an adiabatic process $Q = 0$, and if heat is added, Q is negative.

EXAMPLE 9.10-2. Heat Balance on a Dryer

A continuous countercurrent dryer is being used to dry 453.6 kg dry solid/h containing 0.04 kg total moisture/kg dry solid to a value of 0.002 kg total moisture/kg dry solid. The granular solid enters at $26.7°C$ and is to be discharged at $62.8°C$. The dry solid has a heat capacity of 1.465 kJ/kg $\cdot$ K, which is assumed constant. Heating air enters at $93.3°C$, having a humidity of 0.010 kg H_2O/kg dry air, and is to leave at $37.8°C$. Calculate the air flow rate and the outlet humidity, assuming no heat losses in the dryer.

Solution: The flow diagram is given in Fig. 9.10-3. For the solid, $L_S = 453.6$ kg/h dry solid, $c_{pS} = 1.465$ kJ/kg dry solid $\cdot$ K, $X_1 = 0.040$ kg H_2O/kg dry solid, $c_{pA} = 4.187$ kJ/kg $H_2O \cdot$ K, $T_{S1} = 26.7°C$, $T_{S2} = 62.8°C$, $X_2 = 0.002$. (Note that X values used are X_t values.) For the gas, $T_{G2} = 93.3°C$, $H_2 = 0.010$ kg H_2O/kg dry air, and $T_{G1} = 37.8°C$.

Making a material balance on the moisture using Eq. (9.10-23),

$$GH_2 + L_S X_1 = GH_1 + L_S X_2$$

$$G(0.010) + 453.6(0.040) = GH_1 + 453.6(0.002) \qquad (9.10\text{-}27)$$

For the heat balance, the enthalpy of the entering gas at $93.3°C$, using $0°C$ as a datum, is, by Eq. (9.10-24), $\Delta T°C = \Delta T$ K and $\lambda_0 = 2501$ kJ/kg, from Table A.2-9,

$$H'_{G2} = c_S(T_{G2} - T_0) + H_2\lambda_0$$
$$= [1.005 + 1.88(0.010)](93.3 - 0) + 0.010(2501)$$
$$= 120.5 \text{ kJ/kg dry air}$$

For the exit gas,

$$H'_{G1} = c_S(T_{G1} - T_0) + H_1\lambda_0$$
$$= (1.005 + 1.88H_1)(37.8 - 0) + H_1(2501) = 37.99 + 2572H_1$$

For the entering solid, using Eq. (9.10-25),

$$H'_{S1} = c_{pS}(T_{S1} - T_0) + X_1 c_{pA}(T_{S1} - T_0)$$
$$= 1.465(26.7 - 0) + 0.040(4.187)(26.7 - 0) = 43.59 \text{ kJ/kg dry solid}$$
$$H'_{S2} = c_{pS}(T_{S2} - T_0) + X_2 c_{pA}(T_{S2} - T_0)$$
$$= 1.465(62.8 - 0) + 0.002(4.187)(62.8 - 0) = 92.53 \text{ kJ/kg}$$

Substituting into Eq. (9.10-26) for the heat balance with $Q = 0$ for no heat loss,

$$G(120.5) + 453.6(43.59) = G(37.99 + 2572H_1) + 453.6(92.53) + 0$$

$$(9.10\text{-}28)$$

Solving Eqs. (9.10-27) and (9.10-28) simultaneously,

$$G = 1166 \text{ kg dry air/h} \qquad H_1 = 0.0248 \text{ kg } H_2O/\text{kg dry air}$$

2. Air recirculation in dryers.   In many dryers it is desired to control the wet bulb temperature at which the drying of the solid occurs. Also, since steam costs are often important in heating the drying air, recirculation of the drying air is sometimes used to reduce costs and control humidity. Part of the moist, hot air leaving the dryer is recirculated (recycled) and combined with the fresh air. This is shown in Fig. 9.10-4. Fresh air having a temperature T_{G1} and humidity H_1 is mixed with recirculated air at T_{G2} and H_2 to give air at T_{G3} and H_3. This mixture is heated to T_{G4} with $H_4 = H_3$. After drying, the air leaves at a lower temperature T_{G2} and a higher humidity H_2.

The following material balances on the water can be made. For a water balance on the heater, noting that $H_6 = H_5 = H_2$,

$$G_1 H_1 + G_6 H_2 = (G_1 + G_6)H_4 \qquad (9.10\text{-}29)$$

FIGURE 9.10-4.   *Process flow for air recirculation in drying.*

Making a water balance on the dryer,

$$(G_1 + G_6)H_4 + L_S X_1 = (G_1 + G_6)H_2 + L_S C_2 \qquad \text{(9.10-30)}$$

In a similar manner heat balances can be made on the heater and dryer and on the overall system.

9.10D Continuous Countercurrent Drying

1. Introduction and temperature profiles. Drying continuously offers a number of advantages over batch-drying. Smaller sizes of equipment can often be used, and the product has a more uniform moisture content. In a continuous dryer the solid is moved through the dryer while in contact with a moving gas stream that may flow parallel or countercurrent to the solid. In countercurrent adiabatic operation, the entering hot gas contacts the leaving solid, which has been dried. In parallel adiabatic operation, the entering hot gas contacts the entering wet solid.

In Fig. 9.10-5 typical temperature profiles of the gas T_G and the solid T_S are shown for a continuous countercurrent dryer. In the preheat zone, the solid is heated up to the wet bulb or adiabatic saturation temperature. Little evaporation occurs here, and for low-temperature drying this zone is usually ignored. In the constant-rate zone, I, unbound and surface moisture are evaporated, and the temperature of the solid remains essentially constant at the adiabatic saturation temperature if heat is transferred by convection. The rate of drying would be constant here but the gas temperature is changing, as well as the humidity. The moisture content falls to the critical value X_C at the end of this period.

In zone II, unsaturated surface and bound moisture are evaporated and the solid is dried to its final value X_2. The humidity of the gas entering zone II is H_2 and it rises to H_C. The material-balance equation (9.10-23) may be used to calculate H_C as follows:

$$L_S(X_C - X_2) = G(H_C - H_2) \qquad \text{(9.10-31)}$$

where L_S is kg dry solid/h and G is kg dry gas/h.

FIGURE 9.10-5. *Temperature profiles for a continuous countercurrent dryer.*

2. *Equation for constant-rate period.* The rate of drying in the constant-rate region in zone I would be constant if it were not for the varying gas conditions. The rate of drying in this section is given by an equation similar to Eq. (9.6-7):

$$R = k_y M_B (H_W - H) = \frac{h}{\lambda W}(T_G - T_W) \qquad (9.10\text{-}32)$$

The time for drying is given by Eq. (9.6-1) using limits between X_1 and X_C:

$$t = \left(\frac{L_S}{A}\right) \int_{X_C}^{X_1} \frac{dX}{R} \qquad (9.10\text{-}33)$$

where A/L_S is the exposed drying surface m²/kg dry solid. Substituting Eq. (9.10-32) into (9.10-33) and $(G/L_S)\,dH$ for dX,

$$t = \frac{G}{L_S}\left(\frac{L_S}{A}\right) \frac{1}{k_y M_B} \int_{H_C}^{H_1} \frac{dH}{H_W - H} \qquad (9.10\text{-}34)$$

where G = kg dry air/h, L_S = kg dry solid/h, and A/L_S = m²/kg dry solid. This can be integrated graphically or numerically.

For the case where T_W or H_W is constant for adiabatic drying, Eq. (9.10-34) can be integrated:

$$t = \frac{G}{L_S}\left(\frac{L_S}{A}\right) \frac{1}{k_y M_B} \ln \frac{H_W - H_C}{H_W - H_1} \qquad (9.10\text{-}35)$$

The above can be modified by use of a log mean humidity difference:

$$\Delta H_{LM} = \frac{(H_W - H_C) - (H_W - H_1)}{\ln[(H_W - H_C)/(H_W - H_1)]} = \frac{H_1 - H_C}{\ln[(H_W - H_C)/(H_W - H_1)]} \qquad (9.10\text{-}36)$$

Substituting Eq. (9.10-36) into (9.10-35), an alternative equation is obtained:

$$t = \frac{G}{L_S}\left(\frac{L_S}{A}\right) \frac{1}{k_y M_B} \frac{H_1 - H_C}{\Delta H_{LM}} \qquad (9.10\text{-}37)$$

From Eq. (9.10-31), H_C can be calculated as follows:

$$H_C = H_2 + \frac{L_S}{G}(X_C - X_2) \qquad (9.10\text{-}38)$$

3. *Equation for falling-rate period.* For the situation where unsaturated surface drying occurs, H_W is constant for adiabatic drying, the rate of drying is directly dependent upon X as in Eq. (9.7-9), and Eq. (9.10-32) applies:

$$R = R_C \frac{X}{X_C} = k_y M_B (H_W - H)\frac{X}{X_C} \qquad (9.10\text{-}39)$$

Substituting Eq. (9.10-39) into (9.6-1),

$$t = \left(\frac{L_S}{A}\right) \frac{X_C}{k_y M_B} \int_{X_2}^{X_C} \frac{dX}{(H_W - H)X} \qquad (9.10\text{-}40)$$

Substituting $G\,dH/L_S$ for dX and $(H - H_2)G/L_S + X_2$ for X,

$$t = \frac{G}{L_S}\left(\frac{L_S}{A}\right)\frac{X_C}{k_y M_B} \int_{H_2}^{H_C} \frac{dH}{(H_W - H)[(H - H_2)G/L_S + X_2]} \qquad \text{(9.10-41)}$$

$$t = \frac{G}{L_S}\left(\frac{L_S}{A}\right)\frac{X_C}{k_y M_B} \frac{1}{(H_W - H_2)G/L_S + X_2} \ln \frac{X_C(H_W - H_2)}{X_2(H_W - H_C)} \qquad \text{(9.10-42)}$$

Again, to calculate H_C, Eq. (9.10-38) can be used.

These equations for the two periods can also be derived using the last part of Eq. (9.10-32) and temperatures instead of humidities.

9.11   FREEZE-DRYING OF BIOLOGICAL MATERIALS

9.11A   Introduction

Certain foodstuffs, pharmaceuticals, and biological materials, which may not be heated even to moderate temperatures in ordinary drying, may be freeze-dried. The substance to be dried is usually frozen by exposure to very cold air. In freeze-drying, the water is removed as a vapor by sublimation from the frozen material in a vacuum chamber. After the moisture sublimes to a vapor, it is removed by mechanical vacuum pumps or steam-jet ejectors.

As a rule, freeze-drying produces the highest-quality food product obtainable by any drying method. A prominent factor is the structural rigidity afforded by the frozen substance when sublimation occurs. This prevents collapse of the remaining porous structure after drying. When water is added later, the rehydrated product retains much of its original structural form. Freeze-drying of biological and food materials also has the advantage of little loss of flavor and aroma. The low temperatures involved minimize the degrading reactions which normally occur in ordinary drying processes. However, freeze-drying is an expensive form of dehydration for foods because of the slow drying rate and the use of vacuum.

Since the vapor pressure of ice is very small, freeze-drying requires very low pressures or high vacuum. If the water were in a pure state, freeze-drying at or near 0°C (273 K) at a pressure of 4580 μm (4.58 mm Hg abs) could be performed. (See Appendix A.2 for the properties of ice.) However, since the water usually exists in a solution or a combined state, the material must be cooled below 0°C to keep the water in the solid phase. Most freeze-drying is done at -10°C (263 K) or lower at pressures of about 2000 μm or less.

9.11B   Derivation of Equations for Freeze-Drying

In the freeze-drying process the original material is composed of a frozen core of material. As the ice sublimes, the plane of sublimation, which started at the outside surface, recedes, and a porous shell of material already dried remains. The heat for the latent heat of sublimation of 2838 kJ/kg (1220 btu/lb$_m$) ice is usually conducted inward through the layer of dried material. In some cases it is also conducted through the frozen layer from the rear. The vaporized water is transferred through the layer of dried material. Hence, heat and mass transfer are occurring simultaneously.

In Fig. 9.11-1 a material being freeze-dried is pictured. Heat by conduction, convection, and/or radiation from the gas phase reaches the dried surface and is then transferred by conduction to the ice layer. In some cases heat may also be conducted through the frozen mateconduction heat transfer

conduction heat transfer

dried material

frozen material

wall

water vapor

retreating ice front

FIGURE 9.11-1. *Heat and mass transfer in freeze drying.*

rial to reach the sublimation front or plane. The total drying time must be long enough that the final moisture content is below about 5 wt % to prevent degradation of the final material on storage. The maximum temperatures reached in the dried food and the frozen food must be low enough to keep degradation to a minimum.

The most widely used freeze-drying process is based upon the heat of sublimation being supplied from the surrounding gases to the sample surface. Then the heat is transferred by conduction through the dried material to the ice surface. A simplified model by Sandall et al. (S1) is shown in Fig. 9.11-2.

The heat flux to the surface of the material in Fig. 9.11-2 occurs by convection and in the dry solid by conduction to the sublimation surface. The heat flux to the surface is equal to that conducted through the dry solid, assuming pseudo-steady state:

$$q = h(T_e - T_s) = \frac{k}{\Delta L} \ (T_s - T_f) \qquad (9.11\text{-}1)$$

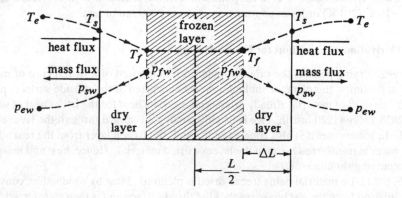

T_e T_s

frozen layer

T_s T_e

heat flux

T_f T_f

heat flux

mass flux

p_{fw} p_{fw}

mass flux

p_{sw}

p_{sw}

p_{ew}

p_{ew}

dry layer

dry layer

$\frac{L}{2}$

ΔL

FIGURE 9.11-2. *Model for uniformly retreating ice front in freeze drying.*

where q is heat flux in W (J/s), h is external heat-transfer coefficient in W/m² · K, T_e is external temperature of the gas in °C, T_s is surface temperature of the dry solid in °C, T_f is temperature of the sublimation front or ice layer in °C, k is thermal conductivity of the dry solid in W/m · K, and ΔL is the thickness of the dry layer in m. Note that $(T_s - T_f)$°C $= (T_s - T_f)$ K.

In a similar manner, the mass flux of the water vapor from the sublimation front is

$$N_A = \frac{D'}{RT\,\Delta L}(p_{fw} - p_{sw}) = k_g(p_{sw} - p_{ew}) \tag{9.11-2}$$

where N_A is flux of water vapor in kg mol/s · m², k_g is external mass-transfer coefficient in kg mol/s · m² · atm, p_{sw} is partial pressure of water vapor at the surface in atm, p_{ew} is partial pressure of water vapor in the external bulk gas phase in atm, T is the average temperature in the dry layer, D' is an average effective diffusivity in the dry layer in m²/s, and p_{fw} is the partial pressure of water vapor in equilibrium with the sublimation ice front in atm.

Equation (9.11-1) can be rearranged to give

$$q = \frac{1}{1/h + \Delta L/k}(T_e - T_f) \tag{9.11-3}$$

Also, Eq. (9.11-2) can be rearranged to give

$$N_A = \frac{1}{1/k_g + RT\,\Delta L/D'}(p_{fw} - p_{ew}) \tag{9.11-4}$$

The coefficients h and k_g are determined by the gas velocities and characteristics of the dryer and hence are constant. The values of T_e and p_{ew} are set by the external operating conditions. The values of k and D' are determined by the nature of the dried material.

The heat flux and mass flux at pseudo-steady state are related by

$$q = \Delta H_s\, N_A \tag{9.11-5}$$

where ΔH_s is the latent heat of sublimation of ice in J/kg mol. Also, p_{fw} is uniquely determined by T_f, since it is the equilibrium vapor pressure of ice at that temperature; or

$$p_{fw} = f(T_f) \tag{9.11-6}$$

Substituting Eqs. (9.11-3) and (9.11-4) into (9.11-5),

$$\frac{1}{1/h + \Delta L/k}(T_e - T_f) = \Delta H_s\, \frac{1}{1/k_g + RT\,\Delta L/D'}(p_{fw} - p_{ew}) \tag{9.11-7}$$

Also, substituting Eqs. (9.11-1) and (9.11-4) into (9.11-5),

$$\frac{1}{\Delta L/k}(T_s - T_f) = \Delta H_s\, \frac{1}{1/k_g + RT\,\Delta L/D'}(p_{fw} - p_{ew}) \tag{9.11-8}$$

As T_e and, hence, T_s are raised to increase the rate of drying, two limits may possibly be reached. First, the outer-surface temperature, T_s cannot be allowed to go too high because of thermal damage. Second, the temperature T_f must be kept well below the melting point. For the situation where $k/\Delta L$ is small compared to k_g and $D'/RT\,\Delta L$, the outer-surface temperature limit will be encountered first as T_s is raised. To further increase the drying rate, k must be raised. Hence, the process is considered to be heat-transfer-controlled. Most commercial freeze-drying processes are heat-transfer-controlled (K1).

In order to solve the given equations, ΔL is related to x, the fraction of the original free moisture remaining:

$$\Delta L = (1 - x)\frac{L}{2} \tag{9.11-9}$$

The rate of freeze-drying can be related to N_A by

$$N_A = \frac{L}{2}\frac{1}{M_A V_S}\left(-\frac{dx}{dt}\right) \tag{9.11-10}$$

where M_A is molecular weight of water, V_S is the volume of solid material occupied by a unit kg of water initially ($V_S = 1/X_0\rho_S$), X_0 is initial free moisture content in kg H_2O/kg dry solid, and ρ_S is bulk density of dry solid in kg/m^3.

Combining Eqs. (9.11-3), (9.11-5), (9.11-9), and (9.11-10), we obtain, for heat transfer,

$$\frac{L}{2}\frac{\Delta H_s}{M_A V_S}\left(-\frac{dx}{dt}\right) = \frac{1}{1/h + (1 - x)L/2k}(T_e - T_f) \tag{9.11-11}$$

Similarly, for mass transfer,

$$\frac{L}{2}\frac{1}{M_A V_S}\left(-\frac{dx}{dt}\right) = \frac{1}{1/k_g + RT(1 - x)L/2D'}(p_{fw} - p_{ew}) \tag{9.11-12}$$

Integrating Eq. (9.11-11) between the limits of $t = 0$ at $x_1 = 1.0$ and $t = t$ at $x_2 = x_2$, the equation for the time of drying to x_2 is as follows for h being very large (negligible external resistance):

$$t = \frac{L^2}{4kV_S}\frac{\Delta H_s}{M_A}\frac{1}{T_e - T_f}\left(x_1 - x_2 - \frac{x_1^2}{2} + \frac{x_2^2}{2}\right) \tag{9.11-13}$$

where $\Delta H_s/M_A$ is heat of sublimation in J/kg H_2O. For $x_2 = 0$, the slab is completely dry.

Assuming that the physical properties and mass- and heat-transfer coefficients are known, Eq. (9.11-8) can be used to calculate the ice-sublimation temperature T_f when the environment temperature T_e and the environment partial pressure p_{ew} are set. Since h is very large, $T_e \cong T_s$. Then Eq. (9.11-8) can be solved for T_f, since T_f and p_{fw} are related by the equilibrium-vapor-pressure relation, Eq. (9.11-6). In Eq. (9.11-8) the value to use for T can be approximated by $(T_f + T_s)/2$.

The uniformly retreating ice-front model was tested by Sandall et al. (S1) against actual freeze-drying data. The model satisfactorily predicted the drying times for removal of 65–90% of the total initial water (S1, K1). The temperature T_f of the sublimation interface did remain essentially constant as assumed in the derivation. However, during removal of the last 10–35% of the water, the drying rate slowed markedly and the actual time was considerably greater than the predicted time for this period.

The effective thermal conductivity k in the dried material has been found to vary significantly with the total pressure and with the type of gas present. Also, the type of material affects the value of k (S1, K1). The effective diffusivity D' of the dried material is a function of the structure of the material, Knudsen diffusivity, and molecular diffusivity (K1).

9.12 UNSTEADY-STATE THERMAL PROCESSING AND STERILIZATION OF BIOLOGICAL MATERIALS

9.12A Introduction

Materials of biological origin are usually not as stable as most inorganic and some organic materials. Hence, it is necessary to use certain processing methods to preserve biological materials, especially foods. Physical and chemical processing methods of preservation, such as drying, smoking, salting, chilling, freezing, and heating, are commonly used. Freezing and chilling of foods were discussed in Section 5.5 as methods of slowing the spoilage of biological materials. Also, in Section 9.11, freeze-drying of biological materials was discussed.

An important method is heat or thermal processing, whereby contaminating microorganisms that occur primarily on the outer surface of foods and cause spoilage and health problems are destroyed. This leads to longer storage times for food and other biological materials. A common method of preservation is to heat-seal cans of food. Likewise, thermal processing is used to sterilize aqueous fermentation media to be used in fermentation processes so that organisms that do not survive are unable to compete with the organism that is to be cultured.

The sterilization of food materials by heating destroys bacteria, yeast, molds, and so on, which cause spoilage, and also destroys pathogenic (disease-producing) organisms that may produce deadly toxins if not destroyed. The rate of destruction of microorganisms varies with the amount of heating and the type of organism. Some bacteria can exist in a vegetative growing form and in a dormant or spore form. The spore forms are much more resistant to heat. This mechanism of heat resistance is not clear.

For foods, it is necessary to kill essentially all the spores of *Clostridium botulinum,* which produces a toxin that is a deadly poison. Complete sterility with respect to this spore is the purpose of thermal processing. Since *Cl. botulinum* is so dangerous and often difficult to use, other spores, such as *Bacillus stearothermophilus,* which is a nonpathogenic organism of similar heat resistance, are often used for testing the heat-treating processes (A2, C1).

Temperature has a great effect on the growth rate of microorganisms, which have no temperature-regulating mechanism. Each organism has a certain optimal temperature range in which it grows best. If any microorganism is heated to a sufficiently high temperature for a sufficient time, it will be rendered sterile or killed.

The exact mechanism of thermal death of vegetative bacteria and spores is still somewhat uncertain. It is thought, however, to be due to the breakdown of enzymes, which are essential to the functioning of the living cell (B1).

9.12B Thermal Death-Rate Kinetics of Microorganisms

The destruction of microorganisms by heating means loss of viability and not destruction in the physical sense. If it is assumed that inactivation of a single enzyme in a cell will inactivate the cell, then in a suspension of organisms of a single species at a constant temperature, the death rate can be expressed as a first-order kinetic equation (A2). The rate of destruction (number dying per unit time) is proportional to the number of organisms:

$$\frac{dN}{dt} = -kN \qquad (9.12\text{-}1)$$

where N is the number of viable organisms at a given time, t is time in min, and k is a reaction velocity constant in min^{-1}. The reaction velocity constant is a function of temperature and the type of microorganism.

After rearranging, Eq. (9.12-1) can be integrated as follows:

$$\int_{N_0}^{N} \frac{dN}{N} = -\int_{t=0}^{t} k \, dt \tag{9.12-2}$$

$$\ln \frac{N_0}{N} = kt \tag{9.12-3}$$

where N_0 is the original number of organisms at $t = 0$ and N is the number at time t. Often N_0 is called the *contamination level* (original number of contaminating microbes before sterilization) and N the sterility level. Equation (9.12-3) can also be written as

$$N = N_0 \, e^{-kt} \tag{9.12-4}$$

Sometimes microbiologists use the term *decimal reduction time D*, which is the time in min during which the original number of viable microbes is reduced by $\frac{1}{10}$. Substituting into Eq. (9.12-4),

$$\frac{N}{N_0} = \frac{1}{10} = e^{-kD} \tag{9.12-5}$$

Taking the $\log_{10}$ of both sides and solving for D,

$$D = \frac{2.303}{k} \tag{9.12-6}$$

Combining Eqs. (9.12-3) and (9.12-6),

$$t = D \log_{10} \frac{N_0}{N} \tag{9.12-7}$$

If the $\log_{10}(N/N_0)$ is plotted versus t, a straight line should result from Eq. (9.12-3). Experimental data bear this out for vegetative cells and approximately for spores. Data for the vegetative cell *E. coli* (A1) at constant temperature follow this logarithmic death-rate curve. Bacterial-spore plots sometimes deviate somewhat from the logarithmic rate of death, particularly during a short period immediately following exposure to heat. However, for thermal-processing purposes for use with spores such as *Cl. botulinum,* a logarithmic-type curve is used.

To experimentally measure the microbial death rate, the spore or cell suspension in a solution is usually sealed in a capillary or test tube. A number of these tubes are then suddenly dipped into a hot bath for a given time. Then they are removed and immediately chilled. The number of viable organisms before and after exposure to the high temperature is then usually determined biologically by means of a plate count.

The effect of temperature on the reaction-rate constant k may be expressed by an Arrhenius-type equation:

$$k = ae^{-E/RT} \tag{9.12-8}$$

where a = an empirical constant, R is the gas constant in $kJ/g\ mol \cdot K$ ($cal/g \cdot mol \cdot K$), T is absolute temperature in K, and E is the activation energy in $kJ/g\ mol$ ($cal/g\ mol$). The value of

E is in the range 210 to about 418 kJ/g mol (50–100 kcal/g mol) for vegetative cells and spores (A2) and much lower for enzymes and vitamins.

Substituting Eq. (9.12-8) into (9.12-2) and integrating,

$$\ln \frac{N_0}{N} = a \int_{t=0}^{t} e^{-E/RT}\, dt \tag{9.12-9}$$

At constant temperature T, Eq. (9.12-9) becomes (9.12-3). Since k is a function of temperature, the decimal reduction time D, which is related to k by Eq. (9.12-6), is also a function of temperature. Hence, D is often written as D_T to show that it is temperature-dependent.

9.12C Determination of Thermal Process Time for Sterilization

For canned foods, *Cl. botulinum* is the primary organism to be reduced in number (S2). It has been established that the minimum adequate heating process should reduce the number of spores by a factor of 10^{-12}. This means that, since D is the time required to reduce the original number by 10^{-1}, substituting $N/N_0 = 10^{-12}$ into Eq. (9.12-4) and solving for t,

$$t = 12 \frac{2.303}{k} = 12D \tag{9.12-10}$$

Thus the time t is equal to $12D$ (often called the *12D concept*). This time in Eq. (9.12-10) to reduce the number by 10^{-12} is called the *thermal death time*. Usually, the sterility level N is a number much less than one organism. These times do not represent complete sterilization but a mathematical concept which has been found empirically to give effective sterilization.

Experimental data for thermal death rates of *Cl. botulinum*, when plotted as the decimal reduction time D_T at a given T versus the temperature T in °F on a semilog plot, give essentially straight lines over the range of temperatures used in food sterilization (S2). A typical thermal destruction curve is shown in Fig. 9.12-1. Actually, by combining Eqs. (9.12-6) and (9.12-8), it can be shown that the plot of $\log_{10} D_T$ versus $1/T$ (T in degrees absolute) is a straight line, but over small ranges of temperature a straight line is obtained when $\log_{10} D_T$ is plotted versus T°F or °C.

In Fig. 9.12-1 the term z represents the temperature range in °F for a 10:1 change in D_T. Since the plot is a straight line, the equation can be represented as

$$\log_{10} D_{T_2} - \log_{10} D_{T_1} = \frac{1}{z}(T_1 - T_2) \tag{9.12-11}$$

Letting $T_1 = 250°F$ (121.1°C), which is the standard temperature against which thermal processes are compared, and calling $T_2 = T$, Eq. (9.12-11) becomes

$$D_T = D_{250} \times 10^{(250-T)/z} \tag{9.12-12}$$

For the organism *Cl. botulinum* the experimental value of $z = 18°F$. This means that each increase in temperature of 18°F (10°C) will increase the death rate by a factor of 10. This compares with the factor of 2 for many chemical reactions for an 18°F increase in temperature.

Using Eq. (9.12-7),

$$t = D_T \log_{10} \frac{N_0}{N} \tag{9.12-7}$$

FIGURE 9.12-1. *Thermal destruction curve: plot of decimal reduction time versus temperature.*

Substituting $T = 250°F$ (121.1°C) as the standard temperature into this equation and substituting F_0 for t,

$$F_0 = D_{250} \log_{10} \frac{N_0}{N} \qquad (9.12\text{-}13)$$

where the F_0 value of a process is the time t in min at 250°F that will produce the same degree of sterilization as the given process at its temperature T. Combining Eqs. (9.12-7), (9.12-12), and (9.12-13), the F_0 of the given process at temperature T is

$$F_0 = t \cdot 10^{(T°C - 121.1)/(z°C)} \qquad \text{(SI)}$$

$$F_0 = t \cdot 10^{(T°F - 250)/(z°F)} \qquad \text{(English)} \qquad (9.12\text{-}14)$$

This is the F_0 value in min for the given thermal process at a given constant temperature $T°F$ and a given time t in min. Values for F_0 and z for adequate sterilization of *Cl. botulinum* vary somewhat with the type of food. Data are tabulated by Stumbo (S2) and Charm (C2) for various foods and microorganisms.

The effects of different but successive sterilization processes in a given material are additive. Hence, for several different temperature stages T_1, T_2, and so on, each having different times $t_1, t_2, \ldots$, the F_0 values for each stage are added to give the total F_0:

$$F_0 = t_1 \cdot 10^{(T_1 - 250)/z} + t_2 \cdot 10^{(T_2 - 250)/z} + \cdots \qquad \text{(English)} \qquad (9.12\text{-}15)$$

EXAMPLE 9.12-1. Sterilization of Cans of Food

Cans of a given food were heated in a retort for sterilization. The F_0 for *Cl. botulinum* in this type of food is 2.50 min and $z = 18°F$. The temperatures in the center of a can (the slowest-heating region) were measured and were approximately as follows, where the average temperature during each time period is listed: t_1 (0–20 min), $T_1 = 160°F$; t_2 (20–40 min), $T_2 = 210°F$; t_3 (40–73 min), $T_3 = 230°F$. Determine if this sterilization process is adequate. Use English and SI units.

Solution: For the three time periods, the data are as follows:

$$t_1 = 20 - 0 = 20 \text{ min}, \qquad T_1 = 160°F \ (71.1°C), \qquad z = 18°F \ (10°C)$$

$$t_2 = 40 - 20 = 20 \text{ min}, \qquad T_2 = 210°F \ (98.9°C)$$

$$t_3 = 73 - 40 = 33 \text{ min}, \qquad T_3 = 230°F \ (110°C)$$

Substituting into Eq. (9.12-15) and solving, using English and SI units,

$$F_0 = t_1 \cdot 10^{(T_1-250)/z} + t_2 \cdot 10^{(T_2-250)/z} + t_3 \cdot 10^{(T_3-250)/z} \qquad \textbf{(9.12-15)}$$

$$= (20)10^{(160-250)/18} + (20)10^{(210-250)/18} + (33)10^{(230-250)/18}$$

$$= 0.0020 + 0.1199 + 2.555 = 2.68 \text{ min} \qquad \text{(English)}$$

$$= (20)10^{(71.1-121.1)/10} + (20)10^{(98.9-121.1)/10} + (33)10^{(110-121.1)/10}$$

$$= 2.68 \text{ min} \qquad \text{(SI)}$$

Hence, this thermal processing is adequate, since only 2.50 min is needed for complete sterilization. Note that the time period at 160°F (71.1°C) contributes an insignificant amount to the final F_0. The major contribution is at 230°F (110°C), which is the highest temperature.

In the general case when cans of food are being sterilized in a retort, the temperature is not constant for a given time period but varies continuously with time. Hence, Eq. (9.12-15) can be modified and written for a continuously varying temperature T by taking small time increments of dt min for each value of T and summing. The final equation is

$$F_0 = \int_{t=0}^{t=t} 10^{(T°F-250)/(z°F)} \ dt \qquad \text{(English)}$$

$$\qquad\qquad\qquad\qquad\qquad\qquad\qquad\qquad\qquad\qquad \textbf{(9.12-16)}$$

$$F_0 = \int_{t=0}^{t=t} 10^{(T°C-121.1)/(z°C)} \ dt \qquad \text{(SI)}$$

This equation can be used as follows. Suppose that the temperature of a process is varying continuously and that a graph or table of values of T versus t is known or can be calculated by means of the unsteady-state methods given in Chapter 5. Equation (9.12-16) can be graphically integrated by plotting values of $10^{(T-250)/z}$ versus t and taking the area under the curve. In most cases a numerical integration is used to determine F_0. (See Section 1.8 for methods of numerical integration.)

In many cases the temperature of a process that is varying continuously with time is determined experimentally by measuring the temperature in the slowest-heating region. In cans this is the center of the can. Methods given in Chapter 5 for unsteady-state heating of short, fat cylinders by conduction can be used to predict the center temperature of the can as a function of time. However, these predictions can be somewhat in error, since physical and thermal properties of foods are difficult to measure accurately and often can vary. Also, trapped air in the container and unknown convection effects can affect the accuracy of predictions.

EXAMPLE 9.12-2. Thermal Process Evaluation by Numerical Integration

In the sterilization of a canned purée, the temperature in the slowest-heating region (center) of the can was measured, giving the following time–temperature data for the heating and holding time. The cooling-time data will be neglected as a safety factor.

t (min)	T (°F)		t (min)	T (°F)
0	80	(26.7°C)	40	225 (107.2°C)
15	165	(73.9)	50	230.5 (110.3)
25	201	(93.9)	64	235 (112.8)
30	212.5 (100.3)			

The F_0 value of *Cl. botulinum* is 2.45 min and z is 18°F. Calculate the F_0 value of the process above and determine if the sterilization is adequate.

Solution: In order to use Eq. (9.12-16), the values of $10^{(T-250)/z}$ must be calculated for each time. For $t = 0$ min, $T = 80°F$, and $z = 18°F$,

$$10^{(T-250)/z} = 10^{(80-250)/18} = 3.6 \times 10^{-10}$$

For $t = 15$ min, $T = 165°F$,

$$10^{(165-250)/18} = 0.0000189$$

For $t = 25$ min, $T = 201°F$,

$$10^{(201-250)/18} = 0.00189$$

For $t = 30$ min,

$$10^{(212.5-250)/18} = 0.00825$$

For $t = 40$ min,

$$10^{(225-250)/18} = 0.0408$$

For $t = 50$ min,

$$10^{(230.5-250)/18} = 0.0825$$

For $t = 64$ min,

$$10^{(235-250)/18} = 0.1465$$

These calculated values are then used in Eq. (9.12-16) to perform a numerical integration to give $F_0 = 2.50$ min. The process value of 2.50 min is greater than the required value of 2.45 min, and the sterilization is adequate.

9.12D Sterilization Methods Using Other Design Criteria

In types of thermal processing which are not necessarily involved with sterilization of foods, other types of design criteria are used. In foods the minimum adequate heat process should reduce the number of spores by a factor of 10^{-12}, that is, $N/N_0 = 10^{-12}$. However, in other batch-sterilization processes, such as in the sterilization of fermentation media, other criteria are often used. Often the equation for k, the reaction velocity constant for the specific organism to be used, is available:

$$k = ae^{-E/RT} \tag{9.12-8}$$

Then Eq. (9.12-9) is written as

$$\nabla = \ln \frac{N_0}{N} = a \int_{t=0}^{t} e^{-E/RT} \, dt = \int_{t=0}^{t} k \, dt \qquad (9.12\text{-}17)$$

where ∇ is the design criterion. Usually, the contamination level N_0 is available and either the sterility level N or the time of sterilization at a given temperature is the unknown. In either case a numerical or graphical integration is used to solve the problem.

In sterilization of food in a container, the time required to render the material safe is calculated at the slowest-heating region of the container (usually the center). Other regions of the container are usually heated to higher temperatures and are overtreated. Hence, another method used is based on the probability of survival in the whole container. These details are given by others (C2, S2). In still another processing method, a short-time, continuous-flow process is used instead of a batch process in a container (B2).

9.12E Pasteurization

The term *pasteurization* is used today to apply to a mild heat treatment of foods that is less drastic than sterilization. It is used to kill organisms that are relatively low in thermal resistance compared to those which the more drastic sterilization processes are designed to eliminate. Pasteurization usually involves killing vegetative microorganisms and not heat-resistant spores.

The most common process is the pasteurization of milk to kill *Mycobacterium tuberculosis*, which is a non-spore-forming bacterium. This pasteurization does not sterilize the milk but kills the *M. tuberculosis* and reduces the other bacterial count sufficiently so that the milk can be stored if refrigerated.

For the pasteurization of such foods as milk, fruit juices, and beer, the same mathematical and numerical procedures covered for sterilization processes in this section are used to accomplish the degree of sterilization desired in pasteurization (B1, S2). The times involved are much shorter and the temperatures used in pasteurization are much lower. Generally, the F_0 value is given as 150°F (65.6°C) or a similar temperature rather than 250°F as in sterilization. Also, the concept of the z value is employed, in which a rise in temperature of z°F will increase the death rate by a factor of 10. An F_0 value written as F_{150}^9 means the F value at 150°F with a z value of 9°F (S2).

In pasteurizing milk, batch and continuous processes are used. U.S. health regulations specify two equivalent sets of conditions; in one, the milk is held at 145°F (62.8°C) for 30 min, and in the other, at 161°F (71.7°C) for 15 s.

The general equations used for pasteurization are similar to sterilization and can be written as follows. Rewriting Eq. (9.12-13),

$$F_{T_1}^z = D_{T_1} \log_{10} \frac{N_0}{N} \qquad (9.12\text{-}18)$$

Rewriting Eq. (9.12-14),

$$F_{T_1}^z = t \cdot 10^{(T-T_1)/z} \qquad (9.12\text{-}19)$$

where T_1 is the standard temperature being used, such as 150°F, z is the value of z in °F for a tenfold increase in death rate, and T is the temperature of the actual process.

EXAMPLE 9.12-3. Pasteurization of Milk

A typical F value given for the thermal processing of milk in a tubular heat exchanger is $F_{150}^9 = 9.0$ min, and $D_{150} = 0.6$ min. Calculate the reduction in the number of viable cells under these conditions.

Solution: The z value is 9°F (5°C) and the temperature of the process is 150°F (65.6°C). Substituting into Eq. (9.12-18) and solving,

$$F_{150}^9 = 9.0 = 0.6 \log_{10} \frac{N_0}{N}$$

$$\frac{N_0}{N} = \frac{10^{15}}{1}$$

This gives a reduction in the number of viable cells of 10^{15}.

9.12F Effects of Thermal Processing on Food Constituents

Thermal processing is used to cause the death of various undesirable microorganisms, but it also causes undesirable effects, such as the reduction of certain nutritional values. Ascorbic acid (vitamin C) and thiamin and riboflavin (vitamins B_1 and B_2) are partially destroyed by thermal processing. The reduction of these desirable constituents can also be given kinetic parameters such as F_0 and z values in the same way as for sterilization and pasteurization. Examples and data are given by Charm (C2).

These same kinetic methods of thermal death rates can also be applied to predict the time for detecting a flavor change in a food product. Dietrich et al. (D1) determined a curve for the number of days to detect a flavor change in frozen spinach versus temperature of storage. The data followed Eq. (9.12-8) and a first-order kinetic relation.

PROBLEMS

9.3-1. Humidity from Vapor Pressure. The air in a room is at 37.8°C and a total pressure of 101.3 kPa abs containing water vapor with a partial pressure $p_A = 3.59$ kPa. Calculate:
(a) Humidity.
(b) Saturation humidity and percentage humidity.
(c) Percentage relative humidity.

9.3-2. Percentage and Relative Humidity. The air in a room has a humidity H of 0.021 kg H_2O/kg dry air at 32.2°C and 101.3 kPa abs pressure. Calculate:
(a) Percentage humidity H_P.
(b) Percentage relative humidity H_R.

Ans. (a) $H_P = 67.5\%$; (b) $H_R = 68.6\%$

9.3-3. Use of the Humidity Chart. The air entering a dryer has a temperature of 65.6°C (150°F) and dew point of 15.6°C (60°F). Using the humidity chart, determine the actual humidity and percentage humidity. Calculate the humid volume of this mixture and also calculate c_S using SI and English units.

Ans. $H = 0.0113$ kg H_2O/kg dry air, $H_P = 5.3\%$, $c_S = 1.026$ kJ/kg·K (0.245 btu/lb$_m$·°F), $v_H = 0.976$ m^3 air + water vapor/kg dry air

9.3-4. Properties of Air to a Dryer. An air–water vapor mixture going to a drying process has a dry bulb temperature of 57.2°C and a humidity of 0.030 kg H_2O/kg dry air. Using the humidity chart and appropriate equations, determine the percentage humidity, saturation humidity at 57.2°C, dew point, humid heat, and humid volume.

9.3-5. *Adiabatic Saturation Temperature.* Air at 82.2°C having a humidity $H = 0.0655$ kg H_2O/kg dry air is contacted in an adiabatic saturator with water. It leaves at 80% saturation.
(a) What are the final values of H and $T°C$?
(b) For 100% saturation, what would be the values of H and T?
            Ans.   (a) $H = 0.079$ kg H_2O/kg dry air, $T = 52.8°C$

9.3-6. *Adiabatic Saturation of Air.* Air enters an adiabatic saturator having a temperature of 76.7°C and a dew-point temperature of 40.6°C. It leaves the saturator 90% saturated. What are the final values of H and $T°C$?

9.3-7. *Humidity from Wet and Dry Bulb Temperatures.* An air–water vapor mixture has a dry bulb temperature of 65.6°C and a wet bulb temperature of 32.2°C. What is the humidity of the mixture?
            Ans. $H = 0.0175$ kg H_2O/kg dry air

9.3-8. *Humidity and Wet Bulb Temperature.* The humidity of an air–water vapor mixture is $H = 0.030$ kg H_2O/kg dry air. The dry bulb temperature of the mixture is 60°C. What is the wet bulb temperature?

9.3-9. *Dehumidification of Air.* Air having a dry bulb temperature of 37.8°C and a wet bulb temperature of 26.7°C is to be dried by first cooling to 15.6°C to condense water vapor and then heating to 23.9°C.
(a) Calculate the initial humidity and percentage humidity.
(b) Calculate the final humidity and percentage humidity. [*Hint*: Locate the initial point on the humidity chart. Then go horizontally (cooling) to the 100% saturation line. Follow this line to 15.6°C. Then go horizontally to the right to 23.9°C.]
            Ans.   (b) $H = 0.0115$ kg H_2O/kg dry air, $H_P = 60\%$

9.3-10. *Cooling and Dehumidifying Air.* Air entering an adiabatic cooling chamber has a temperature of 32.2°C and a percentage humidity of 65%. It is cooled by a cold water spray and saturated with water vapor in the chamber. After leaving, it is heated to 23.9°C. The final air has a percentage humidity of 40%.
(a) What is the initial humidity of the air?
(b) What is the final humidity after heating?

9.6-1. *Time for Drying in Constant-Rate Period.* A batch of wet solid was dried on a tray dryer using constant drying conditions and a thickness of material on the tray of 25.4 mm. Only the top surface was exposed. The drying rate during the constant-rate period was $R = 2.05$ kg H_2O/h · m² (0.42 lb$_m$ H_2O/h · ft²). The ratio L_S/A used was 24.4 kg dry solid/m² exposed surface (5.0 lb$_m$ dry solid/ft²). The initial free moisture was $X_1 = 0.55$ and the critical moisture content $X_C = 0.22$ kg free moisture/kg dry solid.
  Calculate the time to dry a batch of this material from $X_1 = 0.45$ to $X_2 = 0.30$ using the same drying conditions but a thickness of 50.8 mm, with drying from the top and bottom surfaces. (*Hint*: First calculate L_S/A for this new case.)
            Ans. $t = 1.785$ h

9.6-2. *Prediction of Effect of Process Variables on Drying Rate.* Using the conditions in Example 9.6-3 for the constant-rate drying period, do as follows:
(a) Predict the effect on R_C if the air velocity is only 3.05 m/s.
(b) Predict the effect if the gas temperature is raised to 76.7°C and H remains the same.

(c) Predict the effect on the time t for drying between moisture contents X_1 to X_2 if the thickness of material dried is 38.1 mm instead of 25.4 mm and the drying is still in the constant-rate period.

Ans. (a) $R_C = 1.947$ kg $H_2O/h \cdot m^2$ (0.399 lb_m $H_2O/h \cdot ft^2$);
(b) $R_C = 4.21$ kg $H_2O/h \cdot m^2$

9.6-3. *Prediction in Constant-Rate Drying Region.* A granular insoluble solid material wet with water is being dried in the constant-rate period in a pan 0.61 m $\times$ 0.61 m and the depth of material is 25.4 mm. The sides and bottom are insulated. Air flows parallel to the top drying surface at a velocity of 3.05 m/s and has a dry bulb temperature of $60°C$ and wet bulb temperature of $29.4°C$. The pan contains 11.34 kg of dry solid having a free moisture content of 0.35 kg H_2O/kg dry solid, and the material is to be dried in the constant-rate period to 0.22 kg H_2O/kg dry solid.
(a) Predict the drying rate and the time in hours needed.
(b) Predict the time needed if the depth of material is increased to 44.5 mm.

9.6-4. *Drying a Filter Cake in the Constant-Rate Region.* A wet filter cake in a pan 1 ft $\times$ 1 ft square and 1 in. thick is dried on the top surface with air at a wet bulb temperature of $80°F$ and a dry bulb temperature of $120°F$ flowing parallel to the surface at a velocity of 2.5 ft/s. The dry density of the cake is 120 lb_m/ft^3 and the critical free moisture content is 0.09 lb H_2O/lb dry solid. How long will it take to dry the material from a free moisture content of 0.20 lb H_2O/lb dry material to the critical moisture content?

Ans. $t = 13.3$ h

9.7-1. *Numerical Integration for Drying in Falling-Rate Region.* A wet solid is to be dried in a tray dryer under steady-state conditions from a free moisture content of $X_1 = 0.40$ kg H_2O/kg dry solid to $X_2 = 0.02$ kg H_2O/kg dry solid. The dry solid weight is 99.8 kg dry solid and the top surface area for drying is 4.645 m^2. The drying-rate curve can be represented by Fig. 9.5-1b.
(a) Calculate the time for drying using numerical integration in the falling-rate period.
(b) Repeat but use a straight line through the origin for the drying rate in the falling-rate period.

Ans. (a) t(constant rate) = 2.91 h, t(falling rate) = 6.65 h, t(total) = 9.56 h

9.7-2. *Drying Tests with a Foodstuff.* In order to test the feasibility of drying a certain foodstuff, drying data were obtained in a tray dryer with air flow over the top exposed surface having an area of 0.186 m^2. The bone-dry sample weight was 3.765 kg dry solid. At equilibrium after a long period, the wet sample weight was 3.955 kg H_2O + solid. Hence, $3.955 - 3.765$, or 0.190, kg of equilibrium moisture was present. The following sample weights versus time were obtained in the drying test:

Time (h)	Weight (kg)	Time (h)	Weight (kg)	Time (h)	Weight (kg)
0	4.944	2.2	4.554	7.0	4.019
0.4	4.885	3.0	4.404	9.0	3.978
0.8	4.808	4.2	4.241	12.0	3.955
1.4	4.699	5.0	4.150		

(a) Calculate the free moisture content X kg H_2O/kg dry solid for each data point and plot X versus time. (*Hint:* For 0 h, $4.944 - 0.190 - 3.765 = 0.989$ kg free moisture in 3.765 kg dry solid. Hence, $X = 0.989/3.765$.)

(b) Measure the slopes, calculate the drying rates R in kg $H_2O/h \cdot m^2$, and plot R versus X.

(c) Using this drying-rate curve, predict the total time to dry the sample from $X = 0.20$ to $X = 0.04$. Use numerical integration for the falling-rate period. What are the drying rate R_C in the constant-rate period and X_C?

Ans. (c) $R_C = 0.996$ kg $H_2O/h \cdot m^2$, $X_C = 0.12$, $t = 4.1$ h (total)

9.7-3. Prediction of Drying Time. A material was dried in a tray-type batch dryer using constant-drying conditions. When the initial free moisture content was 0.28 kg free moisture/kg dry solid, 6.0 h was required to dry the material to a free moisture content of 0.08 kg free moisture/kg dry solid. The critical free moisture content is 0.14. Assuming a drying rate in the falling-rate region, where the rate is a straight line from the critical point to the origin, predict the time to dry a sample from a free moisture content of 0.33 to 0.04 kg free moisture/kg dry solid. (*Hint:* First use the analytical equations for the constant-rate and the linear falling-rate periods with the known total time of 6.0 h. Then use the same equations for the new conditions.)

9.8-1. Drying of Biological Material in Tray Dryer. A granular biological material wet with water is being dried in a pan 0.305×0.305 m and 38.1 mm deep. The material is 38.1 mm deep in the pan, which is insulated on the sides and bottom. Heat transfer is by convection from an air stream flowing parallel to the top surface at a velocity of 3.05 m/s, having a temperature of 65.6°C and humidity $H = 0.010$ kg H_2O/kg dry air. The top surface receives radiation from steam-heated pipes whose surface temperature $T_R = 93.3$°C. The emissivity of the solid is $\varepsilon = 0.95$. It is desired to keep the surface temperature of the solid below 32.2°C so that decomposition will be kept low. Calculate the surface temperature and the rate of drying for the constant-rate period.

Ans. $T_S = 31.3$°C, $R_C = 2.583$ kg $H_2O/h \cdot m^2$

9.8-2. Drying When Radiation, Conduction, and Convection Are Present. A material is granular and wet with water and is being dried in a layer 25.4 mm deep in a batch-tray dryer pan. The pan has a metal bottom having a thermal conductivity of $k_M = 43.3$ W/m $\cdot$ K and a thickness of 1.59 mm. The thermal conductivity of the solid is $k_S = 1.125$ W/m $\cdot$ K. The air flows parallel to the top exposed surface and the bottom metal at a velocity of 3.05 m/s and a temperature of 60°C and humidity $H = 0.010$ kg H_2O/kg dry solid. Direct radiation heat from steam pipes having a surface temperature of 104.4°C falls on the exposed top surface, whose emissivity is 0.94. Estimate the surface temperature and the drying rate for the constant-rate period.

9.9-1. Diffusion Drying in Wood. Repeat Example 9.9-1 using the physical properties given but with the following changes:

(a) Calculate the time needed to dry the wood from a total moisture of 0.22 to 0.13. Use Fig. 5.3-13.

(b) Calculate the time needed to dry planks of wood 12.7 mm thick from $X_{t1} = 0.29$ to $X_t = 0.09$. Compare with the time needed for 25.4 mm thickness.

Ans. (b) $t = 7.60$ h (12.7 mm thick)

9.9-2. Diffusivity in Drying Tapioca Root. Using the data given in Example 9.9-2, determine the average diffusivity of the moisture up to a value of $X/X_C = 0.50$.

9.9-3. Diffusion Coefficient. Experimental drying data for a typical nonporous biological material obtained under constant drying conditions in the falling-rate region are tabulated below.

X/X_C	$t(h)$	X/X_C	$t(h)$
1.00	0	0.17	11.4
0.65	2.50	0.10	14.0
0.32	7.00	0.06	16.0

Drying from one side occurs, with the material having a thickness of 10.1 mm. The data appear to follow the diffusion equation. Determine the average diffusivity over the range $X/X_C = 1.0–0.10$.

9.10-1. Drying a Bed of Solids by Through Circulation. Repeat Example 9.10-1 for drying of a packed bed of wet cylinders by through circulation of the drying air. Use the same conditions except that the air velocity is 0.381 m/s.

9.10-2. Derivation of Equation for Through-Circulation Drying. Different forms of Eqs. (9.10-11) and (9.10-12) can be derived using humidity and mass-transfer equations rather than temperature and heat-transfer equations. This can be done by writing a mass-balance equation similar to Eq. (9.10-2) for a heat balance and a mass-transfer equation similar to Eq. (9.10-3).
(a) Derive the final equation for the time of drying in the constant-rate period using humidity and mass-transfer equations.
(b) Repeat for the falling-rate period.

$$\textbf{Ans.} \quad \text{(a)} \; t = \frac{\rho_S x_1 (X_1 - X_C)}{G(H_W - H_1)(1 - e^{-k_y M_B a x_1 / G})}$$

9.10-3. Through-Circulation Drying in the Constant-Rate Period. Spherical wet catalyst pellets having a diameter of 12.7 mm are being dried in a through-circulation dryer. The pellets are in a bed 63.5 mm thick on a screen. The solids are being dried by air entering with a superficial velocity of 0.914 m/s at 82.2°C and having a humidity $H = 0.01$ kg H_2O/kg dry air. The dry solid density is determined as 1522 kg/m^3, and the void fraction in the bed is 0.35. The initial free moisture content is 0.90 kg H_2O/kg solid and the solids are to be dried to a free moisture content of 0.45, which is above the critical free moisture content. Calculate the time for drying in this constant-rate period.

9.10-4. Material and Heat Balances on a Continuous Dryer. Repeat Example 9.10-2, making heat and material balances, but with the following changes. The solid enters at 15.6°C and leaves at 60°C. The gas enters at 87.8°C and leaves at 32.2°C. Heat losses from the dryer are estimated as 2931 W.

9.10-5. Drying in a Continuous Tunnel Dryer. A rate of feed of 700 lb$_m$ dry solid/h containing a free moisture content of $X_1 = 0.4133$ lb H_2O/lb dry solid is to be dried to $X_2 = 0.0374$ lb H_2O/lb dry solid in a continuous-counterflow tunnel dryer. A flow of 13 280 lb$_m$ dry air/h enters at 203°F with an $H_2 = 0.0562$ lb H_2O/lb dry air. The stock enters at the wet bulb temperature of 119°F and remains essentially constant in temperature in the dryer. The saturation humidity at 119°F from the humidity chart is $H_W = 0.0786$ lb H_2O/lb dry air. The surface area available for drying is $(A/L_S) = 0.30$ ft^2/lb$_m$ dry solid.

A small-batch experiment was performed using approximately the same constant-drying conditions, air velocity, and temperature of the solid as in the continuous dryer. The equilibrium critical moisture content was found to be $X_C = 0.0959$ lb H_2O/lb dry solid, and the experimental value of $k_y M_B$ was found as 30.15 lb$_m$ air/h·ft^2. In the falling-rate period, the drying rate was directly proportional to X.

For the continuous dryer, calculate the time in the dryer in the constant-rate zone and the falling-rate zone.

Ans. H_C = 0.0593 lb H_2O/lb dry air, H_1 = 0.0760 lb H_2O/lb dry air, t = 4.20 h in the constant-rate zone, t = 0.47 h in the falling-rate zone

9.10-6. *Air Recirculation in a Continuous Dryer.* The wet feed material to a continuous dryer contains 50 wt % water on a wet basis and is dried to 27 wt % by countercurrent air flow. The dried product leaves at the rate of 907.2 kg/h. Fresh air to the system is at 25.6°C and has a humidity of H = 0.007 kg H_2O/kg dry air. The moist air leaves the dryer at 37.8°C and H = 0.020 and part of it is recirculated and mixed with the fresh air before entering a heater. The heated mixed air enters the dryer at 65.6°C and H = 0.010. The solid enters at 26.7°C and leaves at 26.7°C. Calculate the fresh-air flow, the percent air leaving the dryer that is recycled, the heat added in the heater, and the heat loss from the dryer.

Ans. 32 094 kg fresh dry air/h, 23.08% recycled, 440.6 kW in heater

9.12-1. *Sterilizing Canned Foods.* In a sterilizing retort, cans of a given food were heated; the average temperature in the center of a can is approximately 98.9°C for the first 30 min. The average temperature for the next period is 110°C. If F_0 for the spore organism is 2.50 min and z = 10°C, calculate the time of heating at 110°C to make the process safe.

Ans. 29.9 min

9.12-2. *Temperature Effect on Decimal Reduction Time.* Prove by combining Eqs. (9.12-6) and (9.12-8) that a plot of $\log_{10} D_T$ versus $1/T$ (T in degrees absolute) is a straight line.

9.12-3. *Thermal Process Time for Pea Purée.* For cans of pea purée, F_0 = 2.45 min and z = 9.94°C (C2). Neglecting heatup time, determine the process time for adequate sterilization at 112.8°C at the center of the can.

Ans. t = 16.76 min

9.12-4. *Process Time for Adequate Sterilization.* The F_0 value for a given canned food is 2.80 min and z is 18°F (10°C). The center temperatures of a can of this food when heated in a retort were as follows for the time periods given: t_1 (0–10 min), T_1 = 140°F; t_2 (10–30 min), T_2 = 185°F; t_3 (30–50 min), T_3 = 220°F; t_4 (50–80 min), T_4 = 230°F; t_5 (80–100 min), T_5 = 190°F. Determine if adequate sterilization is obtained.

9.12-5. *Process Time and Numerical Integration.* The following time–temperature data were obtained for the heating, holding, and cooling of a canned food product in a retort, the temperature being measured in the center of the can:

t (min)	T (°F)	t (min)	T (°F)
0	110 (43.3°C)	80	232 (111.1)
20	165 (73.9)	90	225 (107.2)
40	205 (96.1)	100	160 (71.1)
60	228 (108.9)		

The F_0 value used is 2.60 min and z is 18°F (10°C). Calculate the F_0 value for this process and determine if the thermal processing is adequate. Use SI and English units.

9.12-6. *Sterility Level of Fermentation Medium.* The aqueous medium in a fermentor is being sterilized and the time–temperature data obtained are as follows:

Time (min)	0	10	20	25	30	35
Temperature (°C)	100	110	120	120	110	100

The reaction velocity constant k in min^{-1} for the contaminating bacterial spores can be represented as (A1)

$$k = 7.94 \times 10^{38} e^{-(68.7 \times 10^3)/1.987T}$$

where $T = K$. The contamination level $N_0 = 1 \times 10^{12}$ spores. Calculate the sterility level N at the end and ∇.

9.12-7. *Time for Pasteurization of Milk.* Calculate the time in min at 62.8°C for pasteurization of milk. The F_0 value to be used at 65.6°C is 9.0 min. The z value is 5°C.

Ans. $t = 32.7$ min

9.12-8. *Reduction in Number of Viable Cells in Pasteurization.* In a given pasteurization process the reduction in the number of viable cells used is 10^{15} and the F_0 value is 9.0 min. If the reduction is to be increased to 10^{16} because of increased contamination, what would be the new F_0 value?

REFERENCES

(A1)   ALLERTON, J., BROWNELL, L. E., and KATZ, D. L. *Chem. Eng. Progr.*, **45,** 619 (1949).

(A2)   AIBA, S., HUMPHREY, A. E., and MILLIS, N. F. *Biochemical Engineering,* 2nd ed. New York: Academic Press, Inc., 1973.

(B1)   BLAKEBROUGH, N. *Biochemical and Biological Engineering Science,* Vol. 2. New York: Academic Press, Inc., 1968.

(B2)   BATESON, R. N. *Chem. Eng. Progr. Symp. Ser.,* **67**(108), 44 (1971).

(C1)   CRUESS, W. V. *Commercial Fruit and Vegetable Products,* 4th ed. New York: McGraw-Hill Book Company, 1958.

(C2)   CHARM, S. E. *The Fundamentals of Food Engineering,* 2nd ed. Westport, Conn.: Avi Publishing Co., Inc., 1971.

(D1)   DIETRICH, W. C., BOGGS, M. M., NUTTING, M. D., and WEINSTEIN, N. E. *Food Technol.,* **14,** 522 (1960).

(E1)   EARLE, R. L. *Unit Operations in Food Processing.* Oxford: Pergamon Press, Inc., 1966.

(G1)   GAMSON, B. W., THODOS, G., and HOUGEN, O. A. *Trans. A.I.Ch.E.,* **39,** 1 (1943).

(H1)   HALL, C. W. *Processing Equipment for Agricultural Products.* Westport, Conn.: Avi Publishing Co., Inc., 1972.

(H2)   HENDERSON, S. M. *Agr. Eng.,* **33**(1), 29 (1952).

(K1)   KING, C. J. *Freeze Drying of Foods.* Boca Raton, Fla.: Chemical Rubber Co., Inc., 1971.

(M1)   MARSHALL, W. R., JR., and HOUGEN, O. A. *Trans. A.I.Ch.E.,* **38,** 91 (1942).

(P1)   PERRY, R. H., and GREEN, D. *Perry's Chemical Engineers' Handbook,* 6th ed. New York: McGraw-Hill Book Company, 1984.

(S1)   SANDALL, O. C., KING, C. J., and WILKE, C. R. *A.I.Ch.E. J.,* **13,** 428 (1967); *Chem. Eng. Progr.,* **64**(86), 43 (1968).

(S2)   STUMBO, C. R. *Thermobacteriology in Food Processing,* 2nd ed. New York: Academic Press, Inc., 1973.

(T1)   TREYBAL, R. E. *Mass Transfer Operations,* 3rd ed. New York: McGraw-Hill Book Company, 1980.

(W1)   WILKE, C. R., and HOUGEN, O. A. *Trans. A.I.Ch.E.,* **41,** 441 (1945).

CHAPTER 10

Stage and Continuous
Gas−Liquid Separation
Processes

10.1 TYPES OF SEPARATION PROCESSES AND METHODS

10.1A Introduction

Many chemical process materials and biological substances occur as mixtures of different components in the gas, liquid, or solid phase. In order to separate or remove one or more of the components from its original mixture, it must be contacted with another phase. The two phases are brought into more or less intimate contact with each other so that a solute or solutes can diffuse from one to the other. The two bulk phases are usually only somewhat miscible in each other. The two-phase pair can be gas−liquid, gas−solid, liquid−liquid, or liquid−solid. During the contact of the two phases the components of the original mixture redistribute themselves between the two phases. The phases are then separated by simple physical methods. By choosing the proper conditions and phases, one phase is enriched while the other is depleted in one or more components.

10.1B Types of Separation Processes

1. Absorption. When the two contacting phases are a gas and a liquid, this operation is called *absorption*. A solute A or several solutes are absorbed from the gas phase into the liquid phase in absorption. This process involves molecular and turbulent diffusion or mass transfer of solute A through a stagnant, nondiffusing gas B into a stagnant liquid C. An example is absorption of ammonia A from air B by the liquid water C. Usually, the exit ammonia−water solution is distilled to recover relatively pure ammonia.

Another example is absorbing SO_2 from the flue gases by absorption in alkaline solutions. In the hydrogenation of edible oils in the food industry, hydrogen gas is bubbled into oil and absorbed. The hydrogen in solution then reacts with the oil in the presence of a catalyst. The reverse of absorption is called *stripping* or *desorption*, and the same theories and basic principles hold. An example is the steam stripping of nonvolatile oils, in which the steam contacts the oil and small amounts of volatile components of the oil pass out with the steam.

When the gas is pure air and the liquid is pure water, the process is called *humidification.* *Dehumidification* involves removal of water vapor from air.

2. Distillation. In the *distillation* process, a volatile vapor phase and a liquid phase that vaporizes are involved. An example is distillation of an ethanol–water solution, where the vapor contains a concentration of ethanol greater than in the liquid. Another example is distillation of an ammonia–water solution to produce a vapor richer in ammonia. In the distillation of crude petroleum, various fractions, such as gasoline, kerosene, and heating oils, are distilled off.

3. Liquid–liquid extraction. When the two phases are liquids, where a solute or solutes are removed from one liquid phase to another liquid phase, the process is called *liquid–liquid extraction.* One example is extraction of acetic acid from a water solution by isopropyl ether. In the pharmaceutical industry, antibiotics in an aqueous fermentation solution are sometimes removed by extraction with an organic solvent.

4. Leaching. If a fluid is being used to extract a solute from a solid, the process is called *leaching.* Sometimes this process is also called *extraction.* Examples are leaching copper from solid ores by sulfuric acid and leaching vegetable oils from solid soybeans by organic solvents such as hexane. Vegetable oils are also leached from other biological products, such as peanuts, rape seeds, and sunflower seeds. Soluble sucrose is leached by water extraction from sugar cane and beets.

5. Membrane processing. Separation of molecules by the use of membranes is a relatively new separation process and is becoming more important. The relatively thin, solid membrane controls the rate of movement of molecules between two phases. It is used to remove salt from water, to purify gases, in food processing, and so on.

6. Crystallization. Solute components soluble in a solution can be removed from a solution by adjusting the conditions, such as temperature or concentration, so that the solubility of one or more of the components is exceeded and they *crystallize* out as a solid phase. Examples of this separation process are crystallization of sugar from solution and crystallization of metal salts in the processing of metal ore solutions.

7. Adsorption. In an *adsorption* process, one or more components of a liquid or gas stream are adsorbed on the surface or in the pores of a solid adsorbent and a separation is obtained. Examples include removal of organic compounds from polluted water, separation of paraffins from aromatics, and removal of solvents from air.

8. Ion exchange. In an *ion-exchange* process, certain ions are removed by an ion-exchange solid. This separation process closely resembles adsorption.

10.1C Processing Methods

Several methods of processing are used in the separations discussed above. The two phases, such as gas and liquid, or liquid and liquid, can be mixed together in a vessel and then separated. This is a *single-stage process.* Often the phases are mixed in one stage, separated, and then brought into contact again in a *multiple-stage process*. These two methods can be carried out batchwise or continuously. In still another general method, the two phases can be contacted continuously in a packed tower.

In this chapter, humidification and absorption will be considered; in Chapter 11, distillation; in Chapter 12, adsorption, ion exchange, liquid–liquid extraction, leaching, and crystallization; in Chapter 13, membrane processes; and in Chapter 14, mechanical–physical separations. In these processes the equilibrium relations between the two phases being considered must be known. This is discussed for gas–liquid systems in Section 10.2 and for the other systems in Chapters 11, 12, and 13.

10.2 EQUILIBRIUM RELATIONS BETWEEN PHASES

10.2A Phase Rule and Equilibrium

In order to predict the concentration of a solute in each of two phases in equilibrium, experimental equilibrium data must be available. If the two phases are not at equilibrium, the rate of mass transfer is proportional to the driving force, which is the departure from equilibrium. In all cases involving equilibria, two phases are involved, such as gas–liquid or liquid–liquid. The important variables affecting the equilibrium of a solute are temperature, pressure, and concentration.

The equilibrium between two phases in a given situation is restricted by the phase rule:

$$F = C - P + 2 \tag{10.2-1}$$

where P is the number of phases at equilibrium, C the number of total components in the two phases when no chemical reactions are occurring, and F the number of variants or degrees of freedom of the system. For example, for the gas–liquid system of CO_2–air–water, there are two phases and three components (considering air as one inert component). Then, by Eq. (10.2-1),

$$F = C - P + 2 = 3 - 2 + 2 = 3$$

This means that there are 3 degrees of freedom. If the total pressure and temperature are set, only one variable is left that can be set arbitrarily. If the mole fraction composition x_A of CO_2 (A) in the liquid phase is set, the mole fraction composition y_A or pressure p_A in the gas phase is automatically determined.

The phase rule does not tell us the partial pressure p_A in equilibrium with the selected x_A. The value of p_A must be determined experimentally. The two phases can, of course, be gas–liquid, liquid–solid, and so on. For example, the equilibrium distribution of acetic acid between a water phase and an isopropyl ether phase has been determined experimentally for various conditions.

10.2B Gas–Liquid Equilibrium

1. Gas–liquid equilibrium data. To illustrate the obtaining of experimental gas–liquid equilibrium data, the system SO_2–air–water will be considered. An amount of gaseous SO_2, air, and water are put in a closed container and shaken repeatedly at a given temperature until equilibrium is reached. Samples of the gas and liquid are analyzed to determine the partial pressure p_A in atm of SO_2 (A) in the gas and mole fraction x_A in the liquid. Figure 10.2-1

FIGURE 10.2-1. *Equilibrium plot for SO$_2$–water system at 293 K (20°C).*

shows a plot of data from Appendix A.3 of the partial pressure p_A of SO$_2$ in the vapor in equilibrium with the mole fraction x_A of SO$_2$ in the liquid at 293 K (20°C).

2. Henry's law. Often the equilibrium relation between p_A in the gas phase and x_A can be expressed by a straight-line Henry's law equation at low concentrations:

$$p_A = Hx_A \qquad\qquad (10.2\text{-}2)$$

where H is the Henry's law constant in atm/mole fraction for the given system. If both sides of Eq. (10.2-2) are divided by total pressure P in atm,

$$y_A = H'x_A \qquad\qquad (10.2\text{-}3)$$

where H' is the Henry's law constant in mole frac gas/mole frac liquid and is equal to H/P. Note that H' depends on total pressure, whereas H does not.

In Fig. 10.2-1 the data follow Henry's law up to a concentration x_A of about 0.005, where $H = 29.6$ atm/mol frac. In general, up to a total pressure of about 5×10^5 Pa (5 atm) the value of H is independent of P. Data for some common gases with water are given in Appendix A.3.

EXAMPLE 10.2-1. Dissolved Oxygen Concentration in Water
What will be the concentration of oxygen dissolved in water at 298 K when the solution is in equilibrium with air at 1 atm total pressure? The Henry's law constant is 4.38×10^4 atm/mol fraction.

Solution: The partial pressure p_A of oxygen (A) in air is 0.21 atm. Using Eq. (10.2-2),

$$0.21 = Hx_A = 4.38 \times 10^4 x_A$$

Solving, $x_A = 4.80 \times 10^{-6}$ mol fraction. This means that 4.80×10^{-6} mol O$_2$ is dissolved in 1.0 mol water plus oxygen, or 0.000853 part O$_2$/100 parts water.

10.3 SINGLE AND MULTIPLE EQUILIBRIUM CONTACT STAGES

10.3A Single-Stage Equilibrium Contact

In many operations of the chemical and other process industries, the transfer of mass from one phase to another occurs, usually accompanied by a separation of the components of the mixture, since one component will be transferred to a larger extent than will another component.

A single-stage process can be defined as one in which two different phases are brought into intimate contact with each other and then are separated. During the time of contact, intimate mixing occurs and the various components diffuse and redistribute themselves between the two phases. If mixing time is long enough, the components are essentially at equilibrium in the two phases after separation and the process is considered a single equilibrium stage.

A single equilibrium stage can be represented as in Fig. 10.3-1. The two entering phases, L_0 and V_2, of known amounts and compositions, enter the stage; mixing and equilibration occur; and the two exit streams, L_1 and V_1, leave in equilibrium with each other. Making a total mass balance,

$$L_0 + V_2 = L_1 + V_1 = M \tag{10.3-1}$$

where L is kg (lb_m), V is kg, and M is total kg.

Assuming that three components, A, B and C, are present in the streams and making a balance on A and C,

$$L_0 x_{A0} + V_2 y_{A2} = L_1 x_{A1} + V_1 y_{A1} = M x_{AM} \tag{10.3-2}$$

$$L_0 x_{C0} + V_2 y_{C2} = L_1 x_{C1} + V_1 y_{C1} = M x_{CM} \tag{10.3-3}$$

An equation for B is not needed since $x_A + x_B + x_C = 1.0$. The mass fraction of A in the L stream is x_A and is y_A in the V stream. The mass fraction of A in the M stream is x_{AM}.

To solve the three equations, the equilibrium relations between the components must be known. In Section 10.3B, this will be done for a gas–liquid system and in Chapter 11 for a vapor–liquid system. Note that Eqs. (10.3-1)–(10.3-3) can also be written using mole units, with L and V having units of moles and x_A and y_A units of mole fraction.

10.3B Single-Stage Equilibrium Contact for Gas–Liquid System

In the usual gas–liquid system the solute A is in the gas phase V, along with inert air B, and in the liquid phase L, along with inert water C. Assuming that air is essentially insoluble in the water phase and that water does not vaporize to the gas phase, the gas phase is a binary A–B and the liquid phase is a binary A–C. Using moles and mole fraction units, Eq. (10.3-1) holds for a single-stage process for the total material balance. Since component A is the only

FIGURE 10.3-1. *Single-stage equilibrium process.*

component that redistributes between the two phases, a balance on A can be written as follows:

$$L'\left(\frac{x_{A0}}{1 - x_{A0}}\right) + V'\left(\frac{y_{A2}}{1 - y_{A2}}\right) = L'\left(\frac{x_{A1}}{1 - x_{A1}}\right) + V'\left(\frac{y_{A1}}{1 - y_{A1}}\right) \qquad (10.3\text{-}4)$$

where L' is moles inert water C and V' is moles inert air B. Both L' and V' are constant and usually known.

To solve Eq. (10.3-4), the relation between y_{A1} and x_{A1} in equilibrium is given by Henry's law:

$$y_{A1} = H'x_{A1} \qquad (10.3\text{-}5)$$

If the solution is not dilute, equilibrium data in the form of a plot of p_A or y_A versus x_A must be available, as in Fig. 10.2-1.

EXAMPLE 10.3-1. Equilibrium Stage Contact for CO_2–Air–Water

A gas mixture at 1.0 atm pressure abs containing air and CO_2 is contacted in a single-stage mixer continuously with pure water at 293 K. The two exit gas and liquid streams reach equilibrium. The inlet gas flow rate is 100 kg mol/h, with a mole fraction of CO_2 of $y_{A2} = 0.20$. The liquid flow rate entering is 300 kg mol water/h. Calculate the amounts and compositions of the two outlet phases. Assume that water does not vaporize to the gas phase.

Solution: The flow diagram is the same as given in Fig. 10.3-1. The inert water flow is $L' = L_0 = 300$ kg mol/h. The inert air flow V' is obtained from Eq. (10.3-6):

$$V' = V(1 - y_A) \qquad (10.3\text{-}6)$$

Hence, the inert air flow is $V' = V_2(1 - y_{A2}) = 100(1 - 0.20) = 80$ kg mol/h. Substituting into Eq. (10.3-4) to make a balance on CO_2 (A),

$$300\left(\frac{0}{1 - 0}\right) + 80\left(\frac{0.20}{1 - 0.20}\right) = 300\left(\frac{x_{A1}}{1 - x_{A1}}\right) + 80\left(\frac{y_{A1}}{1 - y_{A1}}\right) \qquad (10.3\text{-}7)$$

At 293 K, the Henry's law constant from Appendix A.3 is $H = 0.142 \times 10^4$ atm/mol frac. Then $H' = H/P = 0.142 \times 10^4/1.0 = 0.142 \times 10^4$ mol frac gas/mol frac liquid. Substituting into Eq. (10.3-5),

$$y_{A1} = 0.142 \times 10^4 x_{A1} \qquad (10.3\text{-}8)$$

Substituting Eq. (10.3-8) into (10.3-7) and solving, $x_{A1} = 1.41 \times 10^{-4}$ and $y_{A1} = 0.20$. To calculate the total flow rates leaving,

$$L_1 = \frac{L'}{1 - x_{A1}} = \frac{300}{1 - 1.41 \times 10^{-4}} = 300 \text{ kg mol/h}$$

$$V_1 = \frac{V'}{1 - y_{A1}} = \frac{80}{1 - 0.20} = 100 \text{ kg mol/h}$$

In this case, since the liquid solution is so dilute, $L_0 \cong L_1$.

10.3C Countercurrent Multiple-Contact Stages

1. Derivation of general equation.   In Section 10.3A we used single-stage contact to transfer the solute A between the V and L phases. In order to transfer more solute from, say, the V_1 stream, the single-stage contact can be repeated by again contacting the V_1 stream leaving the first stage with fresh L_0. This can be repeated using multiple stages. However, this is wasteful of the L_0 stream and gives a dilute product in the outlet L_1 streams. To conserve use of the L_0 stream and to get a more concentrated product, countercurrent multiple-stage contacting is generally used. This is somewhat similar to countercurrent heat transfer in a heat exchanger, where the outlet heated stream approaches more closely the temperature of the inlet hot stream.

The process flow diagram for a countercurrent stage process is shown in Fig. 10.3-2. The inlet L stream is L_0 and the inlet V stream is V_{N+1} instead of V_2 as for a single-stage in Fig. 10.3-1. The outlet product streams are V_1 and L_N and the total number of stages is N. The component A is being exchanged between the V and L streams. The V stream is composed mainly of component B and the L stream of component C. Components B and C may or may not be somewhat miscible in each other. The two-phase system can be gas–liquid, vapor–liquid, liquid–liquid, or other.

Making a total overall balance on all stages,

$$L_0 + V_{N+1} = L_N + V_1 = M \tag{10.3-9}$$

where V_{N+1} is mol/h entering L_N is mol/h leaving the process, and M is the total flow. Note in Fig. 10.3-2 that any two streams leaving a stage are in equilibrium with each other. For example, in stage n, V_n and L_n are in equilibrium. For an overall component balance on $A, B,$ or C,

$$L_0 x_0 + V_{N+1} y_{N+1} = L_N x_N + V_1 y_1 = M x_M \tag{10.3-10}$$

where x and y are mole fractions. Flows in kg/h (lb_m/h) and mass fraction can also be used in these equations.

Making a total balance over the first n stages,

$$L_0 + V_{n+1} = L_n + V_1 \tag{10.3-11}$$

Making a component balance over the first n stages,

$$L_0 x_0 + V_{n+1} y_{n+1} = L_n x_n + V_1 y_1 \tag{10.3-12}$$

Solving for y_{n+1} in Eq. (10.3-12),

$$y_{n+1} = \frac{L_n x_n}{V_{n+1}} + \frac{V_1 y_1 - L_0 x_0}{V_{n+1}} \tag{10.3-13}$$

FIGURE 10.3-2.   *Countercurrent multiple-stage process.*

This is an important material-balance equation, often called an *operating line*. It relates the concentration y_{n+1} in the V stream with x_n in the L stream passing it. The terms V_1, y_1, L_0, and x_0 are constant and are usually known or can be determined from Eqs. (10.3-9)–(10.3-12).

2. Countercurrent contact with immiscible streams. An important case in which the solute A is being transferred occurs when the solvent stream V contains components A and B with no C and the solvent stream L contains A and C with no B. The two streams L and V are immiscible in each other, with only A being transferred. When Eq. (10.3-13) is plotted on an x-y plot (x_A and y_A of component A) such as Fig. 10.3-3, it is often curved, since the slope L_n/V_{n+1} of the operating line varies if the L and V streams vary from stage to stage.

In Fig. 10.3-3 the equilibrium line that relates the compositions of two streams leaving a stage in equilibrium with each other is plotted. To determine the number of ideal stages required to bring about a given separation or reduction of the concentration of A from y_{N+1} to y_1, the calculation is often done graphically. Starting at stage 1, y_1 and x_0 are on the operating line, Eq. (10.3-13), plotted in the figure. The vapor y_1 leaving is in equilibrium with the leaving x_1 and both compositions are on the equilibrium line. Then y_2 and x_1 are on the operating line and y_2 is in equilibrium with x_2, and so on. Each stage is represented by a step drawn on Fig. 10.3-3. The steps are continued on the graph until y_{N+1} is reached. Alternatively, we can start at y_{N+1} and draw the steps going to y_1.

If the streams L and V are dilute in component A, the streams are approximately constant and the slope L_n/V_{n+1} of Eq. (10.3-13) is nearly constant. Hence, the operating line is essentially a straight line on an x-y plot. In distillation, where only components A and B are present, Eq. (10.3-13) also holds for the operating line; this will be covered in Chapter 11. Cases where A, B, and C are appreciably soluble in each other often occur in liquid–liquid extraction and will be discussed in Chapter 12.

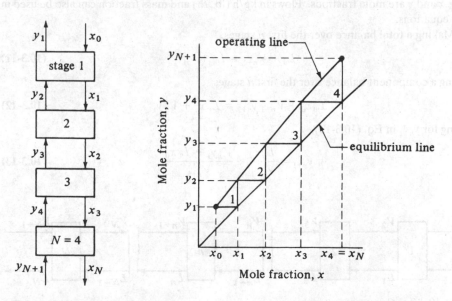

FIGURE 10.3-3. *Number of stages in a countercurrent multiple-stage contact process.*

Example 10.3-2. Absorption of Acetone in a Countercurrent Stage Tower
It is desired to absorb 90% of the acetone in a gas containing 1.0 mol % acetone in air in a countercurrent stage tower. The total inlet gas flow to the tower is 30.0 kg mol/h, and the total inlet pure water flow to be used to absorb the acetone is 90 kg mol H_2O/h. The process is to operate isothermally at 300 K and a total pressure of 101.3 kPa. The equilibrium relation for the acetone (A) in the gas–liquid is $y_A = 2.53x_A$. Determine the number of theoretical stages required for this separation.

Solution: The process flow diagram is similar to Fig. 10.3-3. Given values are $y_{AN+1} = 0.01$, $x_{A0} = 0$, $V_{N+1} = 30.0$ kg mol/h, and $L_0 = 90.0$ kg mol/h. Making an acetone material balance,

$$\text{amount of entering acetone} = y_{AN+1}V_{N+1} = 0.01(30.0) = 0.30 \text{ kg mol/h}$$

$$\text{entering air} = (1 - y_{AN+1})V_{N+1} = (1 - 0.01)(30.0)$$

$$= 29.7 \text{ kg mol air/h}$$

$$\text{acetone leaving in } V_1 = 0.10(0.30) = 0.030 \text{ kg mol/h}$$

$$\text{acetone leaving in } L_N = 0.90(0.30) = 0.27 \text{ kg mol/h}$$

$$V_1 = 29.7 + 0.03 = 29.73 \text{ kg mol air + acetone/h}$$

$$y_{A1} = \frac{0.030}{29.73} = 0.00101$$

$$L_N = 90.0 + 0.27 = 90.27 \text{ kg mol water + acetone/h}$$

$$x_{AN} = \frac{0.27}{90.27} = 0.00300$$

Since the flow of liquid varies only slightly from $L_0 = 90.0$ at the inlet to $L_N = 90.27$ at the outlet and V from 30.0 to 29.73, the slope L_n/V_{n+1} of the operating line in Eq. (10.3-13) is essentially constant. This line is plotted in Fig. 10.3-4

FIGURE 10.3-4. *Theoretical stages for countercurrent absorption in Example 10.3-2.*

together with the equilibrium relation $y_A = 2.53x_A$. Starting at point y_{A1}, x_{A0}, the stages are drawn as shown. About 5.2 theoretical stages are required.

10.3D Analytical Equations for Countercurrent Stage Contact

When the flow rates V and L in a countercurrent process are essentially constant, the operating-line equation (10.3-13) becomes straight. If the equilibrium line is also a straight line over the concentration range, simplified analytical expressions can be derived for the number of equilibrium stages in a countercurrent stage process.

Referring again to Fig. 10.3-2, Eq. (10.3-14) is an overall component balance on component A:

$$L_0x_0 + V_{N+1}y_{N+1} = L_Nx_N + V_1y_1 \tag{10.3-14}$$

Rearranging,

$$L_Nx_N - V_{N+1}y_{N+1} = L_0x_0 - V_1y_1 \tag{10.3-15}$$

Making a component balance for A on the first n stages,

$$L_0x_0 + V_{n+1}y_{n+1} = L_nx_n + V_1y_1 \tag{10.3-16}$$

Rearranging,

$$L_0x_0 - V_1y_1 = L_nx_n - V_{n+1}y_{n+1} \tag{10.3-17}$$

Equating Eq. (10.3-15) to (10.3-17),

$$L_nx_n - V_{n+1}y_{n+1} = L_Nx_N - V_{N+1}y_{N+1} \tag{10.3-18}$$

Since the molar flows are constant, $L_n = L_N = \text{constant} = L$ and $V_{n+1} = V_{N+1} = \text{constant} = V$. Then Eq. (10.3-18) becomes

$$L(x_n - x_N) = V(y_{n+1} - y_{N+1}) \tag{10.3-19}$$

Since y_{n+1} and x_{n+1} are in equilibrium and the equilibrium line is straight, $y_{n+1} = mx_{n+1}$. Also, $y_{N+1} = mx_{N+1}$. Substituting mx_{n+1} for y_{n+1} and calling $A = L/mV$, Eq. (10.3-19) becomes

$$x_{n+1} - Ax_n = \frac{y_{N+1}}{m} - Ax_N \tag{10.3-20}$$

where A is an absorption factor and is constant.

All factors on the right-hand side of Eq. (10.3-20) are constant. This equation is a linear first-order difference equation and can be solved by the calculus of finite-difference methods (G1, M1). The final derived equations are as follows.

For transfer of solute A from phase L to V (stripping),

$$\frac{x_0 - x_N}{x_0 - (y_{N+1}/m)} = \frac{(1/A)^{N+1} - (1/A)}{(1/A)^{N+1} - 1} \tag{10.3-21}$$

$$N = \frac{\ln\left[\dfrac{x_0 - (y_{N+1}/m)}{x_N - (y_{N+1}/m)}(1 - A) + A\right]}{\ln(1/A)} \tag{10.3-22}$$

When $A = 1$,

$$N = \frac{x_0 - x_N}{x_N - (y_{N+1}/m)} \qquad \text{(10.3-23)}$$

For transfer of solute A from phase V to L (absorption),

$$\frac{y_{N+1} - y_1}{y_{N+1} - mx_0} = \frac{A^{N+1} - A}{A^{N+1} - 1} \qquad \text{(10.3-24)}$$

$$N = \frac{\ln\left[\dfrac{y_{N+1} - mx_0}{y_1 - mx_0}\left(1 - \dfrac{1}{A}\right) + \dfrac{1}{A}\right]}{\ln A} \qquad \text{(10.3-25)}$$

When $A = 1$,

$$N = \frac{y_{N+1} - y_1}{y_1 - mx_0} \qquad \text{(10.3-26)}$$

The term A is often called the *absorption factor* and S the *stripping factor*, where $S = 1/A$. These equations can be used with any consistent set of units such as mass flow and mass fraction or molar flow and mole fraction. Such series of equations are often called *Kremser equations* and are convenient to use.

If the equilibrium line is not straight but curved somewhat, the slope will vary and, hence, m and $A = L/mV$ will vary. For absorption (referring to Fig. 10.3-3) at the concentrated end, the slope m_N or tangent of the equilibrium line at the concentrations y_N, x_N leaving this bottom stage N is used. This m_N is at point x_N on the equilibrium line. For the top or dilute end at stage 1 of the tower, the slope of the equilibrium line m_1 at the concentrations y_1, x_1 leaving this stage is employed. This m_1 is at point y_1 on the equilibrium line. Then $A_N = L_N/m_N V_{N+1}$ and $A_1 = L_0/m_1 V_1$. The geometric average is used, where $A = \sqrt{A_N A_1}$ (P1, T3). Also, the dilute m_1 is used in Eqs. (10.3-24)–(10.3-26).

For stripping at the top or concentrated stage, the slope m_1 or tangent to the equilibrium line at the concentrations y_1, x_1 leaving this stage is used. This m_1 is at point y_1 on the equilibrium line. At the bottom stage or dilute end of the tower, the slope m_N of the equilibrium line at the points y_N, x_N is used. This m_N is at x_N on the equilibrium line. Then, $A_N = L_N/m_N V_{N+1}$, $A_1 = L_0/m_1 V_1$, and $A = \sqrt{A_N A_1}$. Again the dilute m_N is used in Eqs. (10.3-21)–(10.3-23). Sometimes only the values of A and m at the dilute end are used since more of the stages are in this region.

Example 10.3-3. Number of Stages by Analytical Equation.
Repeat Example 10.3-2 but use the Kremser analytical equations for countercurrent stage processes.

Solution: At one end of the process at stage 1, $V_1 = 29.73$ kg mol/h, $y_{A1} = 0.00101$, $L_0 = 90.0$, and $x_{A0} = 0$. Also, the equilibrium relation is $y_A = 2.53x_A$ where $m = 2.53$. Then,

$$A_1 = \frac{L}{mV} = \frac{L_0}{mV_1} = \frac{90.0}{2.53 \times 29.73} = 1.20$$

At stage N, $V_{N+1} = 30.0$, $y_{AN+1} = 0.01$, $L_N = 90.27$, and $x_{AN} = 0.00300$.

$$A_N = \frac{L_N}{mV_{N+1}} = \frac{90.27}{2.53 \times 30.0} = 1.19$$

The geometric average $A = \sqrt{A_1 A_N} = \sqrt{1.20 \times 1.19} = 1.195$.

The acetone solute is transferred from the V to the L phase (absorption). Substituting into Eq. (10.3-25),

$$N = \frac{\ln\left[\frac{0.01 - 2.53(0)}{0.00101 - 2.53(0)}\left(1 - \frac{1}{1.195}\right) + \frac{1}{1.195}\right]}{\ln(1.195)} = 5.04 \text{ stages}$$

This compares closely with 5.2 stages obtained using the graphical method.

10.4 MASS TRANSFER BETWEEN PHASES

10.4A Introduction and Equilibrium Relations

1. Introduction to interphase mass transfer. In Chapter 7 we considered mass transfer from a fluid phase to another phase, which was most often a solid phase. The solute A was usually transferred from the fluid phase by convective mass transfer and through the solid by diffusion. In the present section we shall be concerned with the mass transfer of solute A from one fluid phase by convection and then through a second fluid phase by convection. For example, the solute may diffuse through a gas phase and then diffuse through and be absorbed in an adjacent and immiscible liquid phase. This occurs in the case of absorption of ammonia from air by water.

The two phases are in direct contact with each other, such as in a packed, tray, or spray-type tower, and the interfacial area between the phases is usually not well defined. In two-phase mass transfer, a concentration gradient will exist in each phase, causing mass transfer to occur. At the interface between the two fluid phases, equilibrium exists in most cases.

2. Equilibrium relations. Even when mass transfer is occurring, equilibrium relations are important to determine concentration profiles for predicting rates of mass transfer. In Section 10.2 the equilibrium relation in a gas–liquid system and Henry's law were discussed. In Section 7.1C a discussion covered equilibrium distribution coefficients between two phases. These equilibrium relations will be used in discussion of mass transfer between phases in this section.

10.4B Concentration Profiles in Interphase Mass Transfer

In the majority of mass-transfer systems, two phases, which are essentially immiscible in each other, are present together with an interface between these two phases. Assuming solute A is diffusing from the bulk gas phase G to the liquid phase L, it must pass through phase G, through the interface, and then into phase L in series. A concentration gradient must exist to cause this mass transfer through the resistances in each phase, as shown in Fig. 10.4-1. The average or bulk concentration of A in the gas phase in mole fraction units is y_{AG}, where $y_{AG} = p_A/P$, and in the bulk liquid phase in mole fraction units it is x_{AL}.

The concentration in the bulk gas phase y_{AG} decreases to y_{Ai} at the interface. The liquid concentration starts at x_{Ai} at the interface and falls to x_{AL}. At the interface, since there would

FIGURE 10.4-1. *Concentration profile of solute A diffusing through two phases.*

liquid-phase solution of A in liquid L | gas-phase mixture of A in gas G

y_{AG}

x_{Ai} y_{Ai}

x_{AL} N_A

interface

distance from interface

be no resistance to transfer across this interface, y_{Ai} and x_{Ai} are in equilibrium and are related by the equilibrium distribution relation

$$y_{Ai} = f(x_{Ai}) \qquad (10.4\text{-}1)$$

where y_{Ai} is a function of x_{Ai}. They are related by an equilibrium plot such as Fig. 10.1-1. If the system follows Henry's law, $y_A P$ or p_A and x_A are related by Eq. (10.2-2) at the interface.

Experimentally, the resistance at the interface has been shown to be negligible for most cases of mass transfer where chemical reactions do not occur, such as absorption of common gases from air to water and extraction of organic solutes from one phase to another. However, there are some exceptions. Certain surface-active compounds may concentrate at the interface and cause an "interfacial resistance" that slows down the diffusion of solute molecules. Theories for predicting when interfacial resistance may occur are often obscure and unreliable.

10.4C Mass Transfer Using Film Mass-Transfer Coefficients and Interface Concentrations

1. Equimolar counterdiffusion. For equimolar counterdiffusion the concentrations of Fig. 10.4-1 can be plotted on an x-y diagram as in Fig. 10.4-2. Point P represents the bulk phase compositions x_{AG} and x_{AL} of the two phases and point M the interface concentrations

FIGURE 10.4-2. *Concentration driving forces and interface concentrations in interphase mass transfer (equimolar counterdiffusion).*

y_{Ai} and x_{Ai}. For A diffusing from the gas to liquid and B in equimolar counterdiffusion from liquid to gas,

$$N_A = k'_y(y_{AG} - y_{Ai}) = k'_x(x_{Ai} - x_{AL}) \tag{10.4-2}$$

where k'_y is the gas-phase mass-transfer coefficient in kg mol/s · m^2 · mol frac (g mol/s · cm^2 · mol frac, lb mol/h · ft^2 · mol frac) and k'_x the liquid-phase mass-transfer coefficient in kg mol/s · m^2 · mol frac (g mol/s · cm^2 · mol frac, lb mol/h · ft^2 · mol frac). Rearranging Eq. (10.4-2),

$$-\frac{k'_x}{k'_y} = \frac{y_{AG} - y_{Ai}}{x_{AL} - x_{Ai}} \tag{10.4-3}$$

The driving force in the gas phase is $(y_{AG} - y_{Ai})$ and in the liquid phase it is $(x_{Ai} - x_{AL})$. The slope of the line PM is $-k'_x/k'_y$. This means that if the two film coefficients k'_x and k'_y are known, the interface compositions can be determined by drawing line PM with a slope $-k'_x/k'_y$ intersecting the equilibrium line.

The bulk-phase concentrations y_{AG} and x_{AL} can be determined by simply sampling the mixed bulk gas phase and sampling the mixed bulk liquid phase. The interface concentrations are determined by Eq. (10.4-3).

2. Diffusion of A through stagnant or nondiffusing B. For the common case of A diffusing through a stagnant gas phase and then through a stagnant liquid phase, the concentrations are shown in Fig. 10.4-3, where P again represents bulk-phase compositions and M interface compositions. The equations for A diffusing through a stagnant gas and then through a stagnant liquid are

$$N_A = k_y(y_{AG} - y_{Ai}) = k_x(x_{Ai} - x_{AL}) \tag{10.4-4}$$

Now,

$$k_y = \frac{k'_y}{(1 - y_A)_{iM}} \qquad k_x = \frac{k'_x}{(1 - x_A)_{iM}} \tag{10.4-5}$$

FIGURE 10.4-3. *Concentration driving forces and interface concentrations in interphase mass transfer (A diffusing through stagnant B).*

where

$$(1 - y_A)_{iM} = \frac{(1 - y_{Ai}) - (1 - y_{AG})}{\ln[(1 - y_{Ai})/(1 - y_{AG})]} \qquad \textbf{(10.4-6)}$$

$$(1 - x_A)_{iM} = \frac{(1 - x_{AL}) - (1 - x_{Ai})}{\ln[(1 - x_{AL})/(1 - x_{Ai})]} \qquad \textbf{(10.4-7)}$$

Then,

$$N_A = \frac{k'_y}{(1 - y_A)_{iM}}(y_{AG} - y_{Ai}) = \frac{k'_x}{(1 - x_A)_{iM}}(x_{Ai} - x_{AL}) \qquad \textbf{(10.4-8)}$$

Note that $(1 - y_A)_{iM}$ is the same as y_{BM} of Eq. (7.2-11) but is written for the interface, and $(1 - x_A)_{iM}$ is the same as x_{BM} of Eq. (7.2-11). Using Eq. (10.4-8) and rearranging,

$$\frac{-k'_x/(1 - x_A)_{iM}}{k'_y/(1 - y_A)_{iM}} = \frac{y_{AG} - y_{Ai}}{x_{AL} - x_{Ai}} \qquad \textbf{(10.4-9)}$$

The slope of the line PM in Fig. 10.4-3 to obtain the interface compositions is given by the left-hand side of Eq. (10.4-9). This differs from the slope of Eq. (10.4-3) for equimolar counterdiffusion by the terms $(1 - y_A)_{iM}$ and $(1 - x_A)_{iM}$. When A is diffusing through stagnant B and the solutions are dilute, $(1 - y_A)_{iM}$ and $(1 - x_A)_{iM}$ are close to 1.

A trial-and-error method is needed to use Eq. (10.4-9) to get the slope, since the left-hand side contains the terms y_{Ai} and x_{Ai} that are being sought. For the first trial $(1 - y_A)_{iM}$ and $(1 - x_A)_{iM}$ are assumed to be 1.0, and Eq. (10.4-9) is used to get the slope and y_{Ai} and x_{Ai} values. Then for the second trial, these values of y_{Ai} and x_{Ai} are used to calculate a new slope to get new values of y_{Ai} and x_{Ai}. This is repeated until the interface compositions do not change. Three trials are usually sufficient.

EXAMPLE 10.4-1. Interface Compositions in Interphase Mass Transfer

The solute A is being absorbed from a gas mixture of A and B in a wetted-wall tower with the liquid flowing as a film downward along the wall. At a certain point in the tower the bulk gas concentration $y_{AG} = 0.380$ mol fraction and the bulk liquid concentration is $x_{AL} = 0.100$. The tower is operating at 298 K and 1.013×10^5 Pa and the equilibrium data are as follows:

x_A	y_A	x_A	y_A
0	0	0.20	0.131
0.05	0.022	0.25	0.187
0.10	0.052	0.30	0.265
0.15	0.087	0.35	0.385

The solute A diffuses through stagnant B in the gas phase and then through a nondiffusing liquid.

Using correlations for dilute solutions in wetted-wall towers, the film mass-transfer coefficient for A in the gas phase is predicted as $k_y = 1.465 \times 10^{-3}$ kg mol $A/s \cdot m^2 \cdot$ mol frac (1.08 lb mol/h $\cdot$ ft$^2 \cdot$ mol frac) and for the liquid phase as

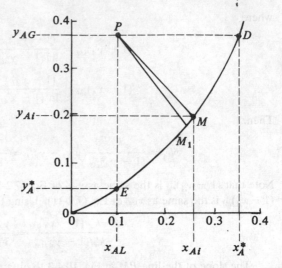

FIGURE 10.4-4. *Location of interface concentrations for Example 10.4-1.*

$k_x = 1.967 \times 10^{-3}$ kg mol A/s·m²·mol frac (1.45 lb mol/h·ft²·mol frac). Calculate the interface concentrations y_{Ai} and x_{Ai} and the flux N_A.

Solution: Since the correlations are for dilute solutions, $(1 - y_A)_{iM}$ and $(1 - x_A)_{iM}$ are approximately 1.0 and the coefficients are the same as k'_y and k'_x. The equilibrium data are plotted in Fig. 10.4-4. Point P is plotted at $y_{AG} = 0.380$ and $x_{AL} = 0.100$. For the first trial, $(1 - y_A)_{iM}$ and $(1 - x_A)_{iM}$ are assumed as 1.0 and the slope of line PM is, from Eq. (10.4-9),

$$-\frac{k'_x/(1 - x_A)_{iM}}{k'_y/(1 - y_A)_{iM}} = -\frac{1.967 \times 10^{-3}/1.0}{1.465 \times 10^{-3}/1.0} = -1.342$$

A line through point P with a slope of -1.342 is plotted in Fig. 10.4-4 intersecting the equilibrium line at M_1, where $y_{Ai} = 0.183$ and $x_{Ai} = 0.247$.

For the second trial we use y_{Ai} and x_{Ai} from the first trial to calculate the new slope. Substituting into Eqs. (10.4-6) and (10.4-7),

$$
\begin{aligned}
(1 - y_A)_{iM} &= \frac{(1 - y_{Ai}) - (1 - y_{AG})}{\ln[(1 - y_{Ai})/(1 - y_{AG})]} \\
&= \frac{(1 - 0.183) - (1 - 0.380)}{\ln[(1 - 0.183)/(1 - 0.380)]} = 0.715 \\
(1 - x_A)_{iM} &= \frac{(1 - x_{AL}) - (1 - x_{Ai})}{\ln[(1 - x_{AL})/(1 - x_{Ai})]} \\
&= \frac{(1 - 0.100) - (1 - 0.247)}{\ln[(1 - 0.100)/(1 - 0.247)]} = 0.825
\end{aligned}
$$

Substituting into Eq. (10.4-9) to obtain the new slope,

$$-\frac{k'_x/(1 - x_A)_{iM}}{k'_y/(1 - y_A)_{iM}} = -\frac{1.967 \times 10^{-3}/0.825}{1.465 \times 10^{-3}/0.715} = -1.163$$

A line through point P with a slope of -1.163 is plotted and intersects the equilibrium line at M, where $y_{Ai} = 0.197$ and $x_{Ai} = 0.257$.

Using these new values for the third trial, the following values are calculated:

$$(1 - y_A)_{iM} = \frac{(1 - 0.197) - (1 - 0.380)}{\ln[(1 - 0.197)/(1 - 0.380)]} = 0.709$$

$$(1 - x_A)_{iM} = \frac{(1 - 0.100) - (1 - 0.257)}{\ln[(1 - 0.100)/(1 - 0.257)]} = 0.820$$

$$-\frac{k'_x/(1 - x_A)_{iM}}{k'_y/(1 - y_A)_{iM}} = -\frac{1.967 \times 10^{-3}/0.820}{1.465 \times 10^{-3}/0.709} = -1.160$$

This slope of -1.160 is essentially the same as the slope of -1.163 for the second trial. Hence, the final values are $y_{Ai} = 0.197$ and $x_{Ai} = 0.257$ and are shown as point M.

To calculate the flux, Eq. (10.4-8) is used:

$$N_A = \frac{k'_y}{(1 - y_A)_{iM}}(y_{AG} - y_{Ai}) = \frac{1.465 \times 10^{-3}}{0.709}(0.380 - 0.197)$$

$$= 3.78 \times 10^{-4} \text{ kg mol/s} \cdot \text{m}^2$$

$$N_A = \frac{1.08}{0.709}(0.380 - 0.197) = 0.2785 \text{ lb mol/h} \cdot \text{ft}^2$$

$$N_A = \frac{k'_x}{(1 - x_A)_{iM}}(x_{Ai} - x_{AL}) = \frac{1.967 \times 10^{-3}}{0.820}(0.257 - 0.100)$$

$$= 3.78 \times 10^{-4} \text{ kg mol/s} \cdot \text{m}^2$$

Note that the flux N_A through each phase is the same as in the other phase, which should be the case at steady state.

10.4D Overall Mass-Transfer Coefficients and Driving Forces

1. *Introduction.* Film or single-phase mass-transfer coefficients k'_y and k'_x or k_y and k_x are often difficult to measure experimentally, except in certain experiments designed so that the concentration difference across one phase is small and can be neglected. As a result, overall mass-transfer coefficients K'_y and K'_x are measured based on the gas phase or liquid phase. This method is used in heat transfer, where overall heat-transfer coefficients are measured based on inside or outside areas instead of film coefficients.

The overall mass transfer K'_y is defined as

$$N_A = K'_y(y_{AG} - y_A^*) \tag{10.4-10}$$

where K'_y is based on the overall gas-phase driving force in kg mol/s $\cdot$ m^2 $\cdot$ mol frac, and y_A^* is the value that would be in equilibrium with x_{AL}, as shown in Fig. 10.4-2. Also, K'_x is defined as

$$N_A = K'_x(x_A^* - x_{AL}) \tag{10.4-11}$$

where K'_x is based on the overall liquid-phase driving force in kg mol/s $\cdot$ m^2 $\cdot$ mol frac and x_A^* is the value that would be in equilibrium with y_{AG}.

2. Equimolar counterdiffusion and/or diffusion in dilute solutions. Equation (10.4-2) holds for equimolar counterdiffusion, or, when the solutions are dilute, Eqs. (10.4-8) and (10.4-2) are identical:

$$N_A = k'_y(y_{AG} - y_{Ai}) = k'_x(x_{Ai} - x_{AL}) \tag{10.4-2}$$

From Fig. 10.4-2,

$$y_{AG} - y^*_A = (y_{AG} - y_{Ai}) + (y_{Ai} - y^*_A) \tag{10.4-12}$$

Between the points E and M the slope m' can be given as

$$m' = \frac{y_{Ai} - y^*_A}{x_{Ai} - x_{AL}} \tag{10.4-13}$$

Solving Eq. (10.4-13) for $(y_{Ai} - y^*_A)$ and substituting into Eq. (10.4-12),

$$y_{AG} - y^*_A = (y_{AG} - y_{Ai}) + m'(x_{Ai} - x_{AL}) \tag{10.4-14}$$

Then, on substituting Eqs. (10.4-10) and (10.4-2) into (10.4-14) and canceling out N_A,

$$\frac{1}{K'_y} = \frac{1}{k'_y} + \frac{m'}{k'_x} \tag{10.4-15}$$

The left-hand side of Eq. (10.4-15) is the total resistance based on the overall gas driving force and equals the gas film resistance $1/k'_y$ plus the liquid film resistance m'/k'_x.

In a similar manner, from Fig. 10.4-2,

$$x^*_A - x_{AL} = (x^*_A - x_{Ai}) + (x_{Ai} - x_{AL}) \tag{10.4-16}$$

$$m'' = \frac{y_{AG} - y_{Ai}}{x^*_A - x_{Ai}} \tag{10.4-17}$$

Proceeding as before,

$$\frac{1}{K'_x} = \frac{1}{m''k'_y} + \frac{1}{k'_x} \tag{10.4-18}$$

Several special cases of Eqs. (10.4-15) and (10.4-18) will now be discussed. The numerical values of k'_x and k'_y are very roughly similar. The values of the slopes m' and m'' are very important. If m' is quite small, so that the equilibrium curve in Fig. 10.4-2 is almost horizontal, a small value of y_A in the gas will give a large value of x_A in equilibrium in the liquid. The gas solute A is then very soluble in the liquid phase, and hence the term m'/k'_x in Eq. (10.4-15) is very small. Then,

$$\frac{1}{K'_y} \cong \frac{1}{k'_y} \tag{10.4-19}$$

and the major resistance is in the gas phase, or the "gas phase is controlling." The point M has moved down very close to E, so that

$$y_{AG} - y^*_A \cong y_{AG} - y_{Ai} \tag{10.4-20}$$

Similarly, when m'' is very large, the solute A is very insoluble in the liquid, $1/(m''k'_y)$ becomes small, and

$$\frac{1}{K'_x} \cong \frac{1}{k'_x} \tag{10.4-21}$$

The "liquid phase is controlling" and $x_{Ai} \cong x_A^*$. Systems for absorption of oxygen or CO_2 from air by water are similar to Eq. (10.4-21).

3. *Diffusion of A through stagnant or nondiffusing B.* For the case of A diffusing through nondiffusing B, Eqs. (10.4-8) and (10.4-14) hold and Fig. 10.4-3 is used:

$$N_A = \frac{k_y'}{(1 - y_A)_{iM}}(y_{AG} - y_{Ai}) = \frac{k_x'}{(1 - x_A)_{iM}}(x_{Ai} - x_{AL}) \qquad \textbf{(10.4-8)}$$

$$y_{AG} - y_A^* = (y_{AG} - y_{Ai}) + m'(x_{Ai} - x_{AL}) \qquad \textbf{(10.4-14)}$$

We must, however, define the equations for the flux using overall coefficients as follows:

$$N_A = \left[\frac{K_y'}{(1 - y_A)_{*M}}\right](y_{AG} - y_A^*) = \left[\frac{K_x'}{(1 - x_A)_{*M}}\right](x_A^* - x_{AL}) \qquad \textbf{(10.4-22)}$$

The bracketed terms are often written as follows:

$$K_y = \frac{K_y'}{(1 - y_A)_{*M}} \qquad K_x = \frac{K_x'}{(1 - x_A)_{*M}} \qquad \textbf{(10.4-23)}$$

where K_y is the overall gas mass-transfer coefficient for A diffusing through stagnant B and K_x the overall liquid mass-transfer coefficient. These two coefficients are concentration-dependent. Substituting Eqs. (10.4-8) and (10.4-22) into (10.4-14), we obtain

$$\frac{1}{K_y'/(1 - y_A)_{*M}} = \frac{1}{k_y'/(1 - y_A)_{iM}} + \frac{m'}{k_x'/(1 - x_A)_{iM}} \qquad \textbf{(10.4-24)}$$

where

$$(1 - y_A)_{*M} = \frac{(1 - y_A^*) - (1 - y_{AG})}{\ln[(1 - y_A^*)/(1 - y_{AG})]} \qquad \textbf{(10.4-25)}$$

Similarly, for K_x',

$$\frac{1}{K_x'/(1 - x_A)_{*M}} = \frac{1}{m''k_y'/(1 - y_A)_{iM}} + \frac{1}{k_x'/(1 - x_A)_{iM}} \qquad \textbf{(10.4-26)}$$

where

$$(1 - x_A)_{*M} = \frac{(1 - x_{AL}) - (1 - x_A^*)}{\ln[(1 - x_{AL})/(1 - x_A^*)]} \qquad \textbf{(10.4-27)}$$

It should be noted that the relations derived here also hold for any two-phase system, where y stands for one phase and x for the other phase. For example, for the extraction of the solute acetic acid (A) from water (y phase) by isopropyl ether (x phase), the same relations will hold.

EXAMPLE 10.4-2. *Overall Mass-Transfer Coefficients from Film Coefficients*

Using the same data as in Example 10.4-1, calculate the overall mass-transfer coefficient K_y', the flux, and the percent resistance in the gas and liquid films. Do this for the case of A diffusing through stagnant B.

Solution: From Fig. 10.4-4, $y_A^* = 0.052$, which is in equilibrium with the bulk liquid $x_{AL} = 0.10$. Also, $y_{AG} = 0.380$. The slope of chord m' between E and M from Eq. (10.4-13) is, for $y_{Ai} = 0.197$ and $x_{Ai} = 0.257$,

$$m' = \frac{y_{Ai} - y_A^*}{x_{Ai} - x_{AL}} = \frac{0.197 - 0.052}{0.257 - 0.100} = 0.923$$

From Example 10.4-1,

$$\frac{k_y'}{(1 - y_A)_{iM}} = \frac{1.465 \times 10^{-3}}{0.709} \qquad \frac{k_x'}{(1 - x_A)_{iM}} = \frac{1.967 \times 10^{-3}}{0.820}$$

Using Eq. (10.4-25),

$$(1 - y_A)_{*M} = \frac{(1 - y_A^*) - (1 - y_{AG})}{\ln[(1 - y_A^*)/(1 - y_{AG})]}$$

$$= \frac{(1 - 0.052) - (1 - 0.380)}{\ln[(1 - 0.052)/(1 - 0.380)]} = 0.733$$

Then, using Eq. (10.4-24),

$$\frac{1}{K_y'/0.773} = \frac{1}{1.465 \times 10^{-3}/0.709} + \frac{0.923}{1.967 \times 10^{-3}/0.820}$$

$$= 484.0 + 384.8 = 868.8$$

Solving, $K_y' = 8.90 \times 10^{-4}$. The percent resistance in the gas film is $(484.0/868.8)100 = 55.7\%$ and in the liquid film 44.3%. The flux is as follows, using Eq. (10.4-22):

$$N_A = \frac{K_y'}{(1 - y_A)_{*M}}(y_{AG} - y_A^*) = \frac{8.90 \times 10^{-4}}{0.773}(0.380 - 0.052)$$

$$= 3.78 \times 10^{-4} \text{ kg mol/s} \cdot \text{m}^2$$

This, of course, is the same flux value as was calculated in Example 10.4-1 using the film equations.

4. Discussion of overall coefficients. If the two-phase system is such that the major resistance is in the gas phase, as in Eq. (10.4-19), then to increase the overall rate of mass transfer, efforts should be centered on increasing the gas-phase turbulence, not the liquid-phase turbulence. For a two-phase system where the liquid film resistance is controlling, turbulence should be increased in this phase to increase rates of mass transfer.

To design mass-transfer equipment, the overall mass-transfer coefficient is synthesized from the individual film coefficients, as discussed in this section.

Generally, when the major resistance to mass transfer is in the gas phase, the overall mass transfer coefficient K_y' or the film coefficient k_y' is used. An example would be absorption of ammonia from air to water. When the major resistance is in the liquid phase, as in absorption of oxygen from air by water, K_x' or k_x' is used.

10.5 CONTINUOUS HUMIDIFICATION PROCESSES

10.5A Introduction and Types of Equipment for Humidification

1. Introduction to gas–liquid contactors. When a relatively warm liquid is brought into direct contact with gas that is unsaturated, some of the liquid is vaporized. The liquid temperature will drop mainly because of the latent heat of evaporation. This direct contact of a gas with a pure liquid occurs most often in contacting air with water. This is done for the following purposes: humidifying air for control of the moisture content of air in drying or air conditioning; dehumidifying air, where cold water condenses some water vapor from warm air; and water cooling, where evaporation of water to the air cools warm water.

In Chapter 9 the fundamentals of humidity and adiabatic humidification were discussed. In this section the performance and design of continuous air–water contactors is considered. The emphasis is on cooling of water, since this is the most important type of process in the process industries. There are many cases in industry in which warm water is discharged from heat exchangers and condensers when it would be more economical to cool and reuse it than to discard it.

2. Towers for water cooling. In a typical water-cooling tower, warm water flows countercurrent to an air stream. Typically, the warm water enters the top of a packed tower and cascades down through the packing, leaving at the bottom. Air enters at the bottom of the tower and flows upward through the descending water. The tower packing often consists of slats of plastic or of a packed bed. The water is distributed by troughs and overflows to cascade over slat gratings or packing that provides large interfacial areas of contact between the water and air in the form of droplets and films of water. The flow of air upward through the tower can be induced by the buoyancy of the warm air in the tower (natural draft) or by the action of a fan. Detailed descriptions of towers are given in other texts (B1, T1).

The water cannot be cooled below the wet bulb temperature. The driving force for the evaporation of the water is approximately the vapor pressure of the water less the vapor pressure it would have at the wet bulb temperature. The water can be cooled only to the wet bulb temperature, and in practice it is cooled to about 3 K or more above this. Only a small amount of water is lost by evaporation in cooling water. Since the latent heat of vaporization of water is about 2300 kJ/kg, a typical change of about 8 K in water temperature corresponds to an evaporation loss of about 1.5%. Hence, the total flow of water is usually assumed to be constant in calculations of tower size.

In humidification and dehumidification, intimate contact between the gas phase and liquid phase is needed for large rates of mass transfer and heat transfer. The gas-phase resistance controls the rate of transfer. Spray or packed towers are used to give large interfacial areas and to promote turbulence in the gas phase.

10.5B Theory and Calculations for Water-Cooling Towers

1. Temperature and concentration profiles at interface. In Fig. 10.5-1 the temperature profile and concentration profile in terms of humidity are shown at the water–gas interface. Water vapor diffuses from the interface to the bulk gas phase with a driving force in the gas phase of $(H_i - H_G)$ kg H_2O/kg dry air. There is no driving force for mass transfer in the liquid phase, since water is a pure liquid. The temperature driving force is $T_L - T_i$ in the liquid phase and $T_i - T_G$ K or °C in the gas phase. Sensible heat flows from the bulk liquid to the interface in

FIGURE 10.5-1. *Temperature and concentration profiles in upper part of cooling tower.*

the liquid. Sensible heat also flows from the interface to the gas phase. Latent heat also leaves the interface in the water vapor, diffusing to the gas phase. The sensible heat flow from the liquid to the interface equals the sensible heat flow in the gas plus the latent heat flow in the gas.

The conditions in Fig. 10.5-1 occur at the upper part of the cooling tower. In the lower part of the cooling tower, the temperature of the bulk water is higher than the wet bulb temperature of the air but may be below the dry bulb temperature. Then the direction of the sensible heat flow in Fig. 10.5-1 is reversed.

2. Rate equations for heat and mass transfer. We shall consider a packed water-cooling tower with air flowing upward and water countercurrently downward in the tower. The total interfacial area between the air and water phases is unknown, since the surface area of the packing is not equal to the interfacial area between the water droplets and the air. Hence, we define a quantity a, defined as m^2 of interfacial area per m^3 volume of packed section, or m^2/m^3. This is combined with the gas-phase mass-transfer coefficient k_G in kg mol/s · m^2 · Pa or kg mol/s · m^2 · atm to give a volumetric coefficient $k_G a$ in kg mol/s · m^3 volume · Pa or kg mol/s · m^3 · atm (lb mol/h · ft^3 · atm).

The process is carried out adiabatically; the various streams and conditions are shown in Fig. 10.5-2, where

L = water flow, kg water/s · m^2 (lb_m/h · ft^2)

T_L = temperature of water, °C or K (°F)

G = dry air flow, kg/s · m^2 (lb_m/h · ft^2)

T_G = temperature of air, °C or K (°F)

H = humidity of air, kg water/kg dry air (lb water/lb dry air)

H_y = enthalpy of air–water vapor mixture, J/kg dry air (btu/lb_m dry air)

FIGURE 10.5-2. *Continuous countercurrent adiabatic water cooling.*

The enthalpy H_y as given in Eq. (9.3-8) is

$$H_y = c_S(T - T_0) + H\lambda_0 = (1.005 + 1.88H)10^3(T - 0) + 2.501 \times 10^6 H \quad \text{(SI)}$$

$$H_y = c_S(T - T_0) + H\lambda_0 = (0.24 + 0.45H)(T - 32) + 1075.4H \quad \text{(English)}$$

$$\text{(9.3-8)}$$

The base temperature selected is 0°C or 273 K (32°F). Note that $(T - T_0)°C = (T - T_0)$ K.

Making a total heat balance for the dashed-line box shown in Fig. 10.5-2, an operating line is obtained:

$$G(H_y - H_{y1}) = Lc_L(T_L - T_{L1}) \tag{10.5-1}$$

This assumes that L is essentially constant, since only a small amount is evaporated. The heat capacity c_L of the liquid is assumed constant at 4.187×10^3 J/kg·K (1.00 btu/lb$_m$·°F). When plotted on a chart of H_y versus T_L, Eq. (10.5-1) is a straight line with a slope of Lc_L/G. Making an overall heat balance over both ends of the tower,

$$G(H_{y2} - H_{y1}) = Lc_L(T_{L2} - T_{L1}) \tag{10.5-2}$$

Again, making a heat balance for the dz column height and neglecting sensible-heat terms compared to the latent heat,

$$Lc_L\, dT_L = G\, dH_y \tag{10.5-3}$$

The total sensible heat transfer from the bulk liquid to the interface is (refer to Fig. 10.5-1)

$$Lc_L\, dT_L = G\, dH_y = h_L a\, dz(T_L - T_i) \qquad \text{(10.5-4)}$$

where $h_L a$ is the liquid-phase volumetric heat-transfer coefficient in $W/m^3 \cdot K$ (btu/h $\cdot$ ft^3 $\cdot$ °F) and T_i is the interface temperature.

For adiabatic mass transfer the rate of heat transfer due to the latent heat in the water vapor being transferred can be obtained from Eq. (9.3-16) by rearranging and using a volumetric basis:

$$\frac{q_\lambda}{A} = M_B k_G a P \lambda_0 (H_i - H_G)\, dz \qquad \text{(10.5-5)}$$

where q_λ/A is in W/m^2 (btu/h $\cdot$ ft^2), M_B = molecular weight of air, $k_G a$ is a volumetric mass-transfer coefficient in the gas in kg mol/s $\cdot$ m^3 $\cdot$ Pa, P = atm pressure in Pa, λ_0 is the latent heat of water in J/kg water, H_i is the humidity of the gas at the interface in kg water/kg dry air, and H_G is the humidity of the gas in the bulk gas phase in kg water/kg dry air. The rate of sensible heat transfer in the gas is

$$\frac{q_S}{A} = h_G a (T_i - T_G)\, dz \qquad \text{(10.5-6)}$$

where q_S/A is in W/m^2 and $h_G a$ is a volumetric heat-transfer coefficient in the gas in $W/m^3 \cdot K$.

Now from Fig. 10.5-1, Eq. (10.5-4) must equal the sum of Eqs. (10.5-5) and (10.5-6):

$$G\, dH_y = M_B k_G a P \lambda_0 (H_i - H_G) dz + h_G a (T_i - T_G)\, dz \qquad \text{(10.5-7)}$$

Equation (9.3-18) states that

$$\frac{h_G a}{M_B k_y a} \cong c_S \qquad \text{(10.5-8)}$$

Substituting $Pk_G a$ for $k_y a$,

$$\frac{h_G a}{M_B P k_G a} \cong c_S \qquad \text{(10.5-9)}$$

Substituting Eq. (10.5-9) into Eq. (10.5-7) and rearranging,

$$G d\, H_y = M_B k_G a P\, dz[(c_S T_i + \lambda_0 H_i) - (c_S T_G + \lambda_0 H_G)] \qquad \text{(10.5-10)}$$

Adding and subtracting $c_S T_0$ inside the brackets,

$$G\, dH_y = M_B k_G a P\, dz\{c_S(T_i - T_0) + H_i \lambda_0 - [c_S(T_G - T_0) + H_G \lambda_0]\} \qquad \text{(10.5-11)}$$

The terms inside the braces are $(H_{yi} - H_y)$, and Eq. (10.5-11) becomes

$$G\, dH_y = M_B k_G a P\, dz(H_{yi} - H_y) \qquad \text{(10.5-12)}$$

Integrating, the final equation to use for calculating the tower height is

$$\int_0^z dz = z = \frac{G}{M_B k_G a P} \int_{H_{y1}}^{H_{y2}} \frac{dH_y}{H_{yi} - H_y} \qquad \text{(10.5-13)}$$

If Eq. (10.5-4) is equated to Eq. (10.5-12) and the result rearranged,

$$-\frac{h_L a}{k_G a M_B P} = \frac{H_{yi} - H_y}{T_i - T_L}$$

(10.5-14)

10.5C Design of Water-Cooling Tower Using Film Mass-Transfer Coefficients

The tower design is done using the following steps:

1. The enthalpy of saturated air H_{yi} is plotted versus T_i on an H-versus-T plot as shown in Fig. 10.5-3. This enthalpy is calculated by means of Eq. (9.3-8) using the saturation humidity from the humidity chart for a given temperature, with 0°C (273 K) as a base temperature. Calculated values are tabulated in Table 10.5-1.

2. Knowing the entering air conditions T_{G1} and H_1, the enthalpy of this air H_{y1} is calculated from Eq. (9.3-8). The point H_{y1} and T_{L1} (desired leaving water temperature) is plotted in Fig. 10.5-3 as one point on the operating line. The operating line is plotted with a slope Lc_L/G and ends at point T_{L2}, which is the entering water temperature. This gives H_{y2}. Alternatively, H_{y2} can be calculated from Eq. (10.5-2).

3. Knowing $h_L a$ and $k_G a$, lines with a slope of $-h_L a/k_G a M_B P$ are plotted as shown in Fig. 10.5-3. From Eq. (10.5-14), point P represents H_y and T_L on the operating line, and point M represents H_{yi} and T_i, the interface conditions. Hence, line MS or $H_{yi} - H_y$ represents the driving force in Eq. (10.5-13).

4. The driving force $H_{yi} - H_y$ is computed for various values of T_L between T_{L1} and T_{L2}. Then the function $1/(H_{yi} - H_y)$ is integrated from H_{y1} to H_{y2} by numerical or graphical integration to obtain the value of the integral in Eq. (10.5-13). Finally, the height z is calculated from Eq. (10.5-13).

FIGURE 10.5-3. *Temperature enthalpy diagram and operating line for water-cooling tower.*

TABLE 10.5-1. *Enthalpies of Saturated Air–Water Vapor Mixtures (0°C Base Temperature)*

T_L		H_y		T_L		H_y	
		btu	J			btu	J
°F	°C	lb_m dry air	kg dry air	°F	°C	lb_m dry air	kg dry air
60	15.6	18.78	43.68×10^3	100	37.8	63.7	148.2×10^3
80	26.7	36.1	84.0×10^3	105	40.6	74.0	172.1×10^3
85	29.4	41.8	97.2×10^3	110	43.3	84.8	197.2×10^3
90	32.2	48.2	112.1×10^3	115	46.1	96.5	224.5×10^3
95	35.0	55.4	128.9×10^3	140	60.0	198.4	461.5×10^3

10.5D Design of Water-Cooling Tower Using Overall Mass-Transfer Coefficients

Often, only an overall mass-transfer coefficient $K_G a$ in kg mol/s · m³ · Pa or kg mol/s · m³ · atm is available, and Eq. (10.5-13) becomes

$$z = \frac{G}{M_B k_G a P} \int_{H_{y1}}^{H_{y2}} \frac{dH_y}{H_y^* - H_y} \tag{10.5-15}$$

The value of H_y^* is determined by going vertically from the value of H_y at point P up to the equilibrium line to give H_y^* at point R, as shown in Fig. 10.5-3. In many cases the experimental film coefficients $k_G a$ and $h_L a$ are not available. The few experimental data available indicate that $h_L a$ is quite large; the slope of the lines $-h_L a/(k_G a M_B P)$ in Eq. (10.5-14) would be very large and the value of H_{yi} would approach that of H_y^* in Fig. 10.5-3.

The tower design using the overall mass-transfer coefficient is done using the following steps:

1. The enthalpy–temperature data from Table 10.5-1 are plotted as shown in Fig. 10.5-3.
2. The operating line is calculated as in steps 1 and 2 for the film coefficients and plotted in Fig. 10.5-3.
3. In Fig. 10.5-3 point P represents H_y and T_L on the operating line and point R represents H_y^* on the equilibrium line. Hence, the vertical line RP or $H_y^* - H_y$ represents the driving force in Eq. (10.5-15).
4. The driving force $H_y^* - H_y$ is computed for various values of T_L between T_{L1} and T_{L2}. Then the function $1/(H_y^* - H_y)$ is integrated from H_{y1} to H_{y2} by numerical or graphical methods to obtain the value of the integral in Eq. (10.5-15). Finally, the height z is obtained from Eq. (10.5-15).

If experimental cooling data from an actual run in a cooling tower with known height z are available, then, using Eq. (10.5-15), the experimental value of $K_G a$ can be obtained.

EXAMPLE 10.5-1. *Design of Water-Cooling Tower Using Film Coefficients*
A packed countercurrent water-cooling tower using a gas flow rate of $G = 1.356$ kg dry air/s · m² and a water flow rate of $L = 1.356$ kg water/s · m² is to cool

FIGURE 10.5-4. *Graphical solution of Example 10.5-1.*

the water from $T_{L2} = 43.3°C$ (110°F) to $T_{L1} = 29.4°C$ (85°F). The entering air at 29.4°C has a wet bulb temperature of 23.9°C. The mass-transfer coefficient $k_G a$ is estimated as 1.207×10^{-7} kg mol/s·m³·Pa and $h_L a/k_G a M_B P$ as 4.187×10^4 J/kg·K (10.0 btu/lb$_m$·°F). Calculate the height of packed tower z. The tower operates at a pressure of 1.013×10^5 Pa.

Solution: Following the steps outlined, the enthalpies from the saturated air–water vapor mixtures from Table 10.5-1 are plotted in Fig. 10.5-4. The inlet air at $T_{G1} = 29.4°C$ has a wet bulb temperature of 23.9°C. The humidity from the humidity chart is $H_1 = 0.0165$ kg H$_2$O/kg dry air. Substituting into Eq. (9.3-8), noting that (29.4 − 0)°C = (29.4 − 0) K,

$$H_{y1} = (1.005 + 1.88 \times 0.0165)10^3(29.4 - 0) + 2.501 \times 10^6(0.0165)$$

$$= 7.17 \times 10^3 \text{ J/kg}$$

The point $H_{y1} = 71.7 \times 10^3$ and $T_{L1} = 29.4°C$ is plotted. Then substituting into Eq. (10.5-2) and solving,

$$1.356(H_{y2} - 71.7 \times 10^3) = 1.356(4.187 \times 10^3)(43.3 - 29.4)$$

$H_{y2} = 129.9 \times 10^3$ J/kg dry air (55.8 btu/lb$_m$). The point $H_{y2} = 129.9 \times 10^3$ and $T_{L2} = 43.3°C$ is also plotted, giving the operating line. Lines with slope $-h_L a/k_G a M_B P = -41.87 \times 10^3$ J/kg·K are plotted, giving H_{yi} and H_y values, which are tabulated in Table 10.5-2 along with derived values as shown. Values of the function $1/(H_{yi} - H_y)$ are used with numerical integration between the values $H_{y1} = 71.7 \times 10^3$ to $H_{y2} = 129.9 \times 10^3$ to obtain the integral

$$\int_{H_{y1}}^{H_{y2}} \frac{dH_y}{H_{yi} - H_y} = 1.82$$

H_{yi}	H_y	$H_{yi} - H_y$	$1/(H_{yi} - H_y)$
94.4×10^3	71.7×10^3	22.7×10^3	4.41×10^{-5}
108.4×10^3	83.5×10^3	24.9×10^3	4.02×10^{-5}
124.4×10^3	94.9×10^3	29.5×10^3	3.39×10^{-5}
141.8×10^3	106.5×10^3	35.3×10^3	2.83×10^{-5}
162.1×10^3	118.4×10^3	43.7×10^3	2.29×10^{-5}
184.7×10^3	129.9×10^3	54.8×10^3	1.82×10^{-5}

Substituting into Eq. (10.5-13),

$$z = \frac{G}{M_B k_G aP} \int \frac{dH_y}{H_{y_i} - H_y} = \frac{1.356}{29(1.207 \times 10^{-7})(1.013 \times 10^5)}(1.82)$$

$$= 6.98 \text{ m } (22.9 \text{ ft})$$

10.5E Minimum Value of Air Flow

Often the air flow G is not fixed but must be set for the design of the cooling tower. As shown in Fig. 10.5-5, for a minimum value of G, the operating line MN is drawn through the point H_{y1} and T_{L1} with a slope that touches the equilibrium line at T_{L2}, point N. If the equilibrium line is quite curved, line MN could become tangent to the equilibrium line at a point farther down the equilibrium line than point N. For the actual tower, a value of G greater than G_{min} must be used. Often, a value of G equal to 1.3 to 1.5 times G_{min} is used.

FIGURE 10.5-5. *Operating-line construction for minimum gas flow.*

10.5F Design of Water-Cooling Tower Using Height of a Transfer Unit

Often another form of the film mass-transfer coefficient is used in Eq. (10.5-13):

$$z = H_G \int_{H_{y1}}^{H_{y2}} \frac{dH_y}{H_{yi} - H_y} \tag{10.5-16}$$

$$H_G = \frac{G}{M_B k_G a P} \tag{10.5-17}$$

where H_G is the height of a gas enthalpy transfer unit in m, and the integral term is called the number of transfer units. The term H_G is often used since it is less dependent upon flow rates than $k_G a$.

In many cases another form of the overall mass-transfer coefficient $K_G a$ in kg mol/s $\cdot$ m^3 $\cdot$ Pa or kg mol/s $\cdot$ m^3 $\cdot$ atm is used, and Eq. (10.5-15) becomes

$$z = \frac{G}{M_B K_G a P} \int_{H_{y1}}^{H_{y2}} \frac{dH_y}{H_y^* - H_y} = H_{OG} \int_{H_{y1}}^{H_{y2}} \frac{dH_y}{H_y^* - H_y} \tag{10.5-18}$$

where H_{OG} is the height of an overall gas enthalpy transfer unit in m. The value of H_y^* is determined by going vertically from the value of H_y up to the equilibrium line, as shown in Fig. 10.5-3. This method should be used only when the equilibrium line is almost straight over the range used. However, the H_{OG} is often used even if the equilibrium line is somewhat curved because of the lack of film mass-transfer-coefficient data.

10.5G Temperature and Humidity of Air Stream in Tower

The procedures outlined above do not yield any information on the changes in temperature and humidity of the air–water vapor stream through the tower. If this information is of interest, a graphical method by Mickley (M2) is available. The equation used for the graphical method is derived by first setting Eq. (10.5-6) equal to $Gc_s dT_G$ and then combining it with Eqs. (10.5-12) and (10.5-9) to yield Eq. (10.5-19):

$$\frac{dH_y}{dT_G} = \frac{H_{yi} - H_y}{T_i - T_G} \tag{10.5-19}$$

10.5H Dehumidification Tower

For the cooling or humidification tower discussed above, the operating line lies below the equilibrium line, and water is cooled and air humidified. In a dehumidification tower, cool water is used to reduce the humidity and temperature of the air that enters. In this case the operating line is above the equilibrium line. Similar calculation methods are used (T1).

10.6 ABSORPTION IN PLATE AND PACKED TOWERS

10.6A Introduction to Absorption

As discussed briefly in Section 10.1B, absorption is a mass-transfer process in which a vapor solute A in a gas mixture is absorbed by means of a liquid in which the solute is more or less soluble. The gas mixture consists mainly of an inert gas and the solute. The liquid also is primarily immiscible in the gas phase; that is, its vaporization into the gas phase is relatively slight. A typical example is absorption of the solute ammonia from an air–ammonia mixture by water. Subsequently, the solute is recovered from the solution by distillation. In the reverse process of desorption or stripping, the same principles and equations hold.

Equilibrium relations for gas–liquid systems in absorption were discussed in Section 10.2, and such data are needed for design of absorption towers. Some data are tabulated in Appendix A.3. Other, more extensive data are available in Perry and Green (P1, P2).

10.6B   Equipment for Absorption and Distillation

1. Various types of tray (plate) towers for absorption and distillation.   In order to efficiently bring the vapor and liquid into contact in absorption and distillation, tray towers of the following types are often used.

1. *Sieve tray.*   The sieve tray shown in Fig. 10.6-1a is very common. Essentially the same tray is used in distillation and gas absorption. In the sieve tray, vapor bubbles up through simple holes in the tray through the flowing liquid. Hole sizes range from 3 to 12 mm in diameter, with 5 mm a common size. The vapor area of the holes varies between 5 to 15% of the tray area. The liquid is held on the tray surface and prevented from flowing down through the holes by the kinetic energy of the gas or vapor. The depth of liquid on the tray is maintained by an overflow, outlet weir. The overflow liquid flows into the downspout to the next tray below.
2. *Valve tray.*   A modification of the sieve tray is the valve tray shown in Fig. 10.6-1b. This consists of an opening in the tray and a lift-valve cover with guides to keep the cover properly positioned over the opening. This provides a variable open area which is varied by the vapor flow inhibiting leakage of liquid down the opening at low vapor rates. Hence, this type of tray can operate over a greater range of flow rates than the sieve tray, with a cost of only about 20% more than a sieve tray. The valve tray is being increasingly used today (S5).
3. *Bubble-cap tray.*   Bubble-cap trays have been used for over 100 years, but since 1950 they have been generally superseded by sieve-type or valve trays because of their cost, which is almost double that of sieve-type trays. In the bubble tray, the vapor or gas rises through

FIGURE 10.6-1.   *Tray contacting devices: (a) detail of sieve-tray tower, (b) detail of valve-tray tower.*

the opening in the tray into the bubble caps. Then the gas flows through slots in the periphery of each cap and bubbles upward through the flowing liquid. Details and design procedures for many of these and other types of trays are given elsewhere (B2, P2, T1). Efficiencies for the different types of trays are discussed in Section 11.5.

2. Structured packing for absorption and distillation. Structured packing has become competitive with conventional tray towers, especially in tower revamps where increased capacity and/or efficiency is desired (K1, L2). A typical corrugated-sheet packing is shown in Fig. 10.6-2 (F1). The thin corrugated-metal sheets are formed in a triangular cross-section, as shown in Fig. 10.6-2a. The vapor flow goes upward through the triangular channels, which are set at a 45° angle with the vertical. The sheets are arranged so the liquid flows downward in the opposite direction and spreads over the surfaces, as in a wetted-wall tower.

The corrugated sheets are assembled into an element whose height E, as shown in Fig. 10.6-2b, is about 20 to 30 cm tall (8–12 in.). A shorter height tends to increase the liquid and vapor spread in the horizontal plane. Each adjacent element is rotated 90° in the horizontal plane with respect to the layer below in order to spread the liquid and vapor uniformly in all radial planes. The ratios of B/h in Fig. 10.6-2a are in the range of 2/1 to 4/1. The size ranges of the triangle are typically: for B, 2.4–4.0 cm, for S, 1.7–2.6 cm, and for h, 1.2–1.8 cm (K1). Smaller sizes of the triangle mean that more sheets are present, giving a greater surface area. This results in a higher efficiency but smaller openings. However, the increased resistance to gas flow gives a lower capacity and a greater sensitivity to plugging (K1).

The open void fraction typically varies from 0.91 to 0.96 and the specific surface area from 165 to 330 m^2/m^3 volume (50 to 100 ft^2/ft^3). In many cases the packing sheet contains perforations or holes about 2–4 mm ID spaced 0.5–1.5 cm apart to help wet both the upper and lower sides of the sheet.

3. Packed towers for absorption and distillation. Packed towers are used for continuous countercurrent contacting of gas and liquid in absorption as well as for vapor–liquid contacting in distillation. The tower in Fig. 10.6-3 consists of a cylindrical column containing a gas inlet and distributing space at the bottom, a liquid inlet and distributing device at the top, a gas outlet at the top, a liquid outlet at the bottom, and a packing or filling in the tower. The gas

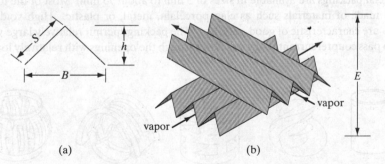

FIGURE 10.6-2. *Typical corrugated structured packing: (a) triangular cross section of flow channel; (b) flow-channel arrangement, with vapor flowing upward, indicated by arrows, and liquid downward. [From J. R. Fair and J. L. Bravo, Chem. Eng. Progr., 86, (Jan.), 19 (1990). With permission.]*

FIGURE 10.6-3. *Packed tower flows and characteristics for absorption.*

enters the distributing space below the packed section and rises upward through the openings or interstices in the packing and contacts the descending liquid flowing through the same openings. A large area of intimate contact between the liquid and gas is provided by the packing.

4. Types of random packing for absorption and distillation.   Many different types of tower packings have been developed and a number are used quite often. Common types of packing which are dumped at random in the tower are shown in Fig. 10.6-4. Such packings and other commercial packings are available in sizes of 3 mm to about 75 mm. Most of the tower packings are made of materials such as clay, porcelain, metal, or plastic. High void spaces of 65–95% are characteristic of good packings. The packings permit relatively large volumes of liquid to pass countercurrent to the gas flow through the openings with relatively low pressure

| (a) | (b) | (c) | (d) | (e) |

FIGURE 10.6-4.   *Typical random or dumped tower packings: (a) Raschig ring; (b) Berl saddle; (c) Pall ring; (d) Intalox metal, IMTP; (e) Jaeger Metal Tri-Pack.*

drops for the gas. These same types of packings are also used in vapor–liquid separation processes of distillation.

Ceramic Raschig rings and Berl saddles shown in Figs. 10.6-4a and b are older types of random packing and are seldom used now (K1). Pall rings (second-generation packing) shown in Fig. 10.6-4c, are made of plastic or metal; they are much more efficient and are still used now. They have porosities or void spaces of 0.90–0.96 and areas of 100–200 m^2/m^3 (30–60 ft^2/ft^3). The latest or third-generation packings are the Intalox metal type, shown in Fig. 10.6-4d, which is a combination of the Berl saddle and the Pall ring, and the Metal Tri-Pack, shown in Fig. 10.6-4e, which is a Pall ring in spherical shape. Porosities range from 0.95 to 0.98. Many other types of new packings are available. These third-generation packings are only slightly more efficient than the Pall rings.

Stacked packings having sizes of 75 mm or so and larger are also used. The packing is stacked vertically, with open channels running uninterruptedly through the bed. The advantage of the lower pressure drop of the gas is offset in part by the poorer gas–liquid contact in stacked packings. Typical stacked packings are wood grids, drip-point grids, spiral partition rings, and others.

10.6.C Pressure Drop and Flooding in Packed Towers

In a given packed tower with a given type and size of packing and with a definite flow of liquid, there is an upper limit to the rate of gas flow, called the *flooding velocity*. Above this gas velocity the tower cannot operate. At low gas velocities the liquid flows downward through the packing, essentially uninfluenced by the upward gas flow. As the gas flow rate is increased at low gas velocities, the pressure drop is proportional to the flow rate to the 1.8 power. At a gas flow rate called the *loading point*, the gas starts to hinder the liquid downflow, and local accumulations or pools of liquid start to appear in the packing. The pressure drop of the gas starts to rise at a faster rate. As the gas flow rate is increased, the liquid holdup or accumulation increases. At the flooding point, the liquid can no longer flow down through the packing and is blown out with the gas.

In an actual, operating tower, the gas velocity is well below flooding. The optimum economic gas velocity is about one-half or more of the flooding velocity. It depends upon a balance of economic factors including equipment cost, pressure drop, and processing variables. Pressure drop in the packing is an important consideration in design of a tower and is covered in detail below.

1. Pressure drop in random packings. Empirical correlations for various random packings based on experimental data are used to predict the pressure drop in the gas flow. The original correlation by Eckert (K1) correlated the gas and liquid flow rates and properties with pressure drop. The latest version has been replotted by Strigle (K1, S4) and is shown in Fig. 10.6-5. The line for $\Delta P = 2.0$ in. H_2O/ft has been extrapolated. The ordinate (capacity parameter) is $v_G[\rho_G/(\rho_L - \rho_G)]^{0.5} F_p^{0.5} \nu^{0.05}$ and the abscissa (flow parameter) is $(G_L/G_G)(\rho_G/\rho_L)^{0.5}$, where v_G is superficial gas velocity in ft/s, ρ_G is gas density in lb_m/ft^3, $v_G = G_G/\rho_G$, ρ_L is liquid density in lb_m/ft^3, F_p is a packing factor in ft^{-1}, ν is kinematic viscosity $\mu_L/(\rho_L/62.4)$ in centstokes, μ_L is liquid viscosity in cp, G_L is liquid mass velocity in $lb_m/(s \cdot ft^2)$, and G_G is gas mass velocity in $lb_m/(s \cdot ft^2)$. Note that this capacity parameter is not dimensionless and that only these units should be used. This correlation predicts pressure drops to an accuracy of ±11% (L2).

$v_G[\rho_G/(\rho_L - \rho_G)]^{0.5} F_p^{0.5} \nu^{0.05}$, capacity parameter

$(G_L/G_G)(\rho_G/\rho_L)^{0.5}$, flow parameter

FIGURE 10.6-5. *Pressure-drop correlation for random packings by Strigle. (From R. F. Strigle, Jr., Random Packings and Packed Towers, Houston: Gulf Publishing Company, 1987. With permission from Elsevier Science.)*

The packing factor F_p is almost inversely proportional to packing size. This packing factor F_p is determined empirically for each size and type of packing, and some data are given in Table 10.6-1. A very extensive list of values of F_p is given by Kister (K1).

2. Pressure drop in structured packings. An empirical correlation for structured packings is given in Fig. 10.6-6 by Kister and Gill (K1). They modified the Eckert correlation for random packings to better fit only the structured-packing data. An extrapolated line for $\Delta P = 0.05$ in. H_2O/ft and for $\Delta P = 2.0$ has been added. The packing factors F_p to be used for structured packing are those given in Table 10.6-1 and references (K1, L2, P2). The units on the ordinate and abscissa of Fig. 10.6-6 are the same as those for Fig. 10.6-5.

3. Flooding pressure drop in packed and structured packings. It is important for proper design to be able to predict the flooding pressure drop in towers and, hence, the limiting flow rates at flooding. Figures 10.6-5 and 10.6-6 do not predict flooding conditions. Kister and Gill (K2) have developed an empirical equation to predict the limiting pressure drop at flooding. This equation is

$$\Delta P_{flood} = 0.115 F_p^{0.7} \tag{10.6-1}$$

where ΔP_{flood} is in in. H_2O/ft height of packing and F_p is the packing factor in ft^{-1} given in Table 10.6-1 for random or structured packing. To convert from English to SI units, 1.00 in. H_2O/ft height = 83.33 mm H_2O/m height of packing. This can be used for packing factors from 9 up to 60. It predicts all of the data for flooding within ±15% and most for ±10%. At a packing factor of 60 or higher, Eq. (10.6-1) should not be used; instead, the pressure drop at flooding can be taken as 2.00 in. H_2O/ft (166.7 mm H_2O/m).

Chapter 10   Stage and Continuous Gas–Liquid Separation Processes

10.4-1. *Overall Mass-Transfer Coefficient from Film Coefficients.* Using the same data as in Example 10.4-1, calculate the overall mass-transfer coefficients K'_x and K_x, the flux, and the percent resistance in the gas film.

Ans. $K'_x = 1.173 \times 10^{-3}$ kg mol/s $\cdot$ m^2 $\cdot$ mol frac, $K_x = 1.519 \times 10^{-3}$, $N_A = 3.78 \times 10^{-4}$ kg mol/s $\cdot$ m^2, 36.7% resistance

10.4-2. *Interface Concentrations and Overall Mass-Transfer Coefficients.* Use the same equilibrium data and film coefficients k'_y and k'_x as in Example 10.4-1. However, use bulk concentrations of $y_{AG} = 0.25$ and $x_{AL} = 0.05$. Calculate the following:
(a) Interface concentrations y_{Ai} and x_{Ai} and flux N_A.
(b) Overall mass-transfer coefficients K'_y and K_y and flux N_A.
(c) Overall mass-transfer coefficient K'_x and flux N_A.

10.5-1. *Countercurrent Water-Cooling Tower.* A forced-draft countercurrent water-cooling tower is to cool water from 43.3 to 26.7°C. The air enters the bottom of the tower at 23.9°C with a wet bulb temperature of 21.1°C. The value of H_G for the flow conditions is $H_G = 0.533$ m. The heat-transfer resistance in the liquid phase will be neglected; that is, h_L is very large. Hence, values of H^*_y should be used. Calculate the tower height needed if 1.5 times the minimum air rate is used.

10.5-2. *Minimum Gas Rate and Height of Water-Cooling Tower.* It is planned to cool water from 110°F to 85°F in a packed countercurrent water-cooling tower using entering air at 85°F with a wet bulb temperature of 75°F. The water flow is 2000 lb$_m$/h $\cdot$ ft^2 and the air flow is 1400 lb$_m$ air/h $\cdot$ ft^2. The overall mass-transfer coefficient is $K_G a = 6.90$ lb mol/h $\cdot$ ft^3 $\cdot$ atm.
(a) Calculate the minimum air rate that can be used.
(b) Calculate the tower height needed if the air flow of 1400 lb$_m$ air/h $\cdot$ ft^2 is used.

Ans. (a) $G_{min} = 935$ lb$_m$ air/h $\cdot$ ft^2 (4241 kg air/h $\cdot$ m^2); (b) $z = 21.8$ ft (6.64 m)

10.5-3. *Design of Water-Cooling Tower.* Recalculate Example 10.5-1, but calculate the minimum air rate and use 1.75 times the minimum air rate.

10.5-4. *Effect of Changing Air Conditions on Cooling Tower.* For the cooling tower in Example 10.5-1, to what temperature will the water be cooled if the entering air enters at 29.4°C but the wet bulb temperature is 26.7°C? The same gas and liquid flow rates are used. The water enters at 43.3°C, as before. (*Hint:* In this case T_{L1} is the unknown. The tower height is the same as in Example 10.5-1. The slope of the operating line is as before. The solution is trial and error. Assume a value of T_{L1} that is greater than 29.4°C. Do numerical or graphical integration to see if the same height is obtained.)

10.6-1. *Amount of Absorption in a Tray Tower.* An existing tower contains the equivalent of 3.0 theoretical trays and is being used to absorb SO_2 from air by pure water at 293 K and 1.013×10^5 Pa. The entering gas contains 20 mol % SO_2 and the inlet air flow rate is 150 kg inert air/h $\cdot$ m^2. The entering water rate is 6000 kg/h $\cdot$ m^2. Calculate the outlet composition of the gas. (*Hint:* This is a trial-and-error solution. Assume an outlet gas composition of, say, $y_1 = 0.01$. Plot the operating line and determine the number of theoretical trays needed. If this number is not 3.0 trays, assume another value of y_1, and so on.)

Ans. $y_1 = 0.009$

10.6-2. *Analytical Method for Number of Trays in Absorption.* Use the analytical equations in Section 10.6 for countercurrent tray contact to calculate the number of theoretical trays needed for Example 10.6-3 using $1.3L'_{min}$.

10.6-3. *Absorption of Ammonia in a Tray Tower.* A tray tower is to be used to remove 99% of the ammonia from an entering air stream containing 6 mol % ammonia at 293 K and 1.013×10^5 Pa. The entering pure water flow rate is 188 kg H_2O/h $\cdot$ m^2 and the inert air flow is 128 kg air/h $\cdot$ m^2. Calculate the number of theoretical trays needed. Use equilibrium data from Appendix A.3. For the dilute end of the tower, plot an expanded diagram to step off the number of trays more accurately.

$\qquad$ **Ans.** $y_1 = 0.000639$ (exit), $x_N = 0.0260$ (exit), 3.8 theoretical trays

10.6-4. *Minimum Liquid Flow in a Packed Tower.* The gas stream from a chemical reactor contains 25 mol % ammonia and the rest inert gases. The total flow is 181.4 kg mol/h to an absorption tower at 303 K and 1.013×10^5 Pa pressure, where water containing 0.005 mol frac ammonia is the scrubbing liquid. The outlet gas concentration is to be 2.0 mol % ammonia. What is the minimum flow L'_{min}? Using 1.5 times the minimum, plot the equilibrium and operating lines.

$\qquad$ **Ans.** $L'_{min} = 262.6$ kg mol/h

10.6-5. *Steam Stripping and Number of Trays.* A relatively nonvolatile hydrocarbon oil contains 4.0 mol % propane and is being stripped by direct superheated steam in a stripping tray tower to reduce the propane content to 0.2%. The temperature is held constant at 422 K by internal heating in the tower at 2.026×10^5 Pa pressure. A total of 11.42 kg mol of direct steam is used for 300 kg mol of total entering liquid. The vapor–liquid equilibria can be represented by $y = 25x$, where y is mole fraction propane in the steam and x is mole fraction propane in the oil. Steam can be considered as an inert gas and will not condense. Plot the operating and equilibrium lines and determine the number of theoretical trays needed.

$\qquad$ **Ans.** 5.6 theoretical trays (stepping down from the tower top)

10.6-6. *Absorption of Ammonia in Packed Tower.* A gas stream contains 4.0 mol % NH_3 and its ammonia content is reduced to 0.5 mol % in a packed absorption tower at 293 K and 1.013×10^5 Pa. The inlet pure water flow is 68.0 kg mol/h and the total inlet gas flow is 57.8 kg mol/h. The tower diameter is 0.747 m. The film mass-transfer coefficients are $k'_y a = 0.0739$ kg mol/s $\cdot$ m^3 $\cdot$ mol frac and $k'_x a = 0.169$ kg mol/s $\cdot$ m^3 $\cdot$ mol frac. Using the design methods for dilute gas mixtures, do as follows:

(a) Calculate the tower height using $k'_y a$.

(b) Calculate the tower height using $K'_y a$.

$\qquad$ **Ans.** (a) $z = 2.362$ m (7.75 ft)

10.6-7. *Tower Height Using Overall Mass-Transfer Coefficient.* Repeat Example 10.6-4, using the overall liquid mass-transfer coefficient $K'_x a$ to calculate the tower height.

10.6-8. *Experimental Overall Mass-Transfer Coefficient.* In a tower 0.254 m in diameter absorbing acetone from air at 293 K and 101.32 kPa using pure water, the following experimental data were obtained. Height of 25.4-mm Raschig rings = 4.88 m, $V' = 3.30$ kg mol air/h, $y_1 = 0.01053$ mol frac acetone, $y_2 = 0.00072$, $L' = 9.03$ kg mol water/h, $x_1 = 0.00363$ mol frac acetone. Calculate the experimental value of $K_y a$.

10.6-9. *Conversion to Transfer-Unit Coefficients from Mass-Transfer Coefficients.* Experimental data on absorption of dilute acetone in air by water at 80°F and 1 atm abs pressure in a packed tower with 25.4-mm Raschig rings were obtained. The inert gas flow was 95 lb$_m$ air/h $\cdot$ ft^2 and the pure water flow was 987 lb$_m$/h $\cdot$ ft^2. The experimental coefficients are $k_G a = 4.03$ lb mol/h $\cdot$ ft^3 $\cdot$ atm and $k_L a = 16.6$ lb mol/h $\cdot$ ft^3 $\cdot$ lb mol/ h $\cdot$ ft^3. The equilibrium data can be expressed by $c_A = 1.37 p_A$, where c_A = lb mol/ft^3 and p_A = atm partial pressure of acetone.

(a) Calculate the film height of transfer units H_G and H_L.

(b) Calculate H_{OG}.

Ans. $H_{OG} = 0.957$ ft (0.292 m)

10.6-10. *Height of Tower Using Transfer Units.* Repeat Example 10.6-4 but use transfer units and calculate H_L, N_L, and tower height.

10.6-11. *Experimental Value of H_{OG}.* Using the experimental data given in Problem 10.6-8, calculate the number of transfer units N_{OG} and the experimental value of H_{OG}.

Ans. $H_{OG} = 1.265$ m

10.6-12. *Pressure Drop and Tower Diameter.* Use the same conditions as in Example 10.6-1 but with the following changes. The gas feed rate is 2000 lb_m/h and the design ratio of G_L/G_G is 2.2/1. Using 60% of flooding and 1 in Intalox packing, calculate the pressure drop, gas and liquid flows, and tower diameter.

Ans. $\Delta p = 0.250$ in. water/ft packing, $D = 1.452$ ft (0.4425 m)

10.6-13. *Minimum Liquid Flow Rate in Absorption.* Using the data from Example 10.6-3, calculate the number of trays graphically and analytically for an operating flow rate of 1.3 times the minimum liquid flow rate.

Ans. $N = 5.34$ steps (analytical)

10.6-14. *Experimental Height of Transfer Unit and Analytical Equations.* A packed tower 4.0 m tall is used to absorb ethyl alcohol from an inert gas by 90 kg mol/h of pure water at 303 K and 101.3 kPa. The total gas stream flow rate of 100 kg mol/h contains 2.0 mol % alcohol and the exit concentration is 0.20 mol %. The equilibrium relation is $y = mx = 0.68x$ for this dilute stream. Using the analytical equations, calculate the number of theoretical trays N, the number of transfer units N_{OG}, H_{OG}, and HETP.

Ans. $H_{OG} = 0.860$ m (2.823 ft), $N = 4.016$ trays

10.7-1. *Liquid Film Coefficients and Design of SO_2 Tower.* Using the data for Example 10.7-1, calculate the height of the tower using Eq. (10.6-18), which is based on the liquid film mass-transfer coefficient $k'_x a$. [*Note:* The interface values x_i have already been obtained.]

Ans. $z = 1.586$ m

10.7-2. *Design of SO_2 Tower Using Overall Coefficients.* Using the data for Example 10.7-1, calculate the tower height using the overall mass-transfer coefficient $K'_y a$. [*Hint:* Calculate $K'_y a$ at the top of the tower and at the bottom of the tower from the film coefficients. Then use a linear average of the two values for the design. Obtain the values of y^* from the operating- and equilibrium-line plot. Numerically or graphically integrate Eq. (10.6-19), keeping $K'_y a$ outside the integral.]

10.7-3. *Height of Packed Tower Using Transfer Units.* For Example 10.7-1, calculate the tower height using the H_G and the number of transfer units N_G. [*Hint:* Calculate H_G at the tower top using Eq. (10.6-39) and at the tower bottom. Use the linear average value for H_G. Calculate the number of transfer units N_G by numerical or graphical integration of the integral of Eq. (10.6-35). Then calculate the tower height.]

Ans. $H_G = 0.2036$ m (average value)

10.7-4 *Design of Absorption Tower Using Transfer Units.* The gas SO_2 is being scrubbed from a gas mixture by pure water at 303 K and 1.013×10^5 Pa. The inlet gas contains 6.00 mol % SO_2 and the outlet 0.3 mol % SO_2. The tower cross-sectional area of packing is 0.426 m^2. The inlet gas flow is 13.65 kg mol inert air/h and the inlet water flow is 984 kg mol inert water/h. The mass-transfer coefficients are $H_L = 0.436$ m and

$k_G a = 6.06 \times 10^{-7}$ kg mol/s·m³·Pa and are to be assumed constant in the tower for the given concentration range. Use equilibrium data from Appendix A.3. By numerical or graphical integration, determine N_G. Calculate the tower height. (*Note:* The equilibrium line is markedly curved, so numerical or graphical integration is necessary even for this dilute mixture.)

Ans. $N_G = 8.47$ transfer units, $z = 1.311$ m

10.8-1. *Correction of Film Coefficients for NH₃ Absorption.* Use the same system and conditions given in Example 10.8-1, except that NH_3 is being absorbed instead of CO_2. The flow rates are the same. Predict H_G, H_L, H_{OG}, and percent resistance in the liquid phase.

Ans. $H_{OG} = 0.2244$ m, % resistance = 9.4%

10.8-2. *Prediction of Film Coefficients for Acetone Absorption.* Predict H_G, H_L, and H_{OG} for absorption of acetone from air by water in a dilute aqueous solution using 2-in. Intalox metal IMTP packing at 20°C and 1 atm abs pressure. The flow rates are $G_x = 3.391$ kg/s·m² (2500 lb$_m$/h·ft²) and $G_y = 0.678$ kg/s·m² (500 lb$_m$/h·ft²). Use equilibrium data from Appendix A.3-21 and the diffusivity for acetone in water from Table 6.3-1. The diffusivity of acetone in air at 1 atm abs is 0.109×10^{-4} m²/s at 0°C (P1).

Ans. $H_G = 0.3416$ m, $H_{OG} = 0.3921$ m

10.9-1. *Nonisothermal Absorption Tower.* Use the same operating conditions as in Example 10.9-1 for absorption of NH₃ except for the following change. The inlet gas temperature is 15°C and it is saturated with water vapor. Calculate the outlet water temperature T_1 and the overall number of transfer units N_{Oy} by numerical or graphical integration.

Ans. $T_1 = 32.05°C$

REFERENCES

(B1) BADGER, W. L., and BANCHERO, J. T. *Introduction to Chemical Engineering.* New York: McGraw-Hill Book Company, 1955.

(B2) *Bubble Tray Design Manual.* American Institute of Chemical Engineers, New York, 1958.

(E1) EARLE, R. L. *Unit Operations in Food Processing.* Oxford: Pergamon Press, Inc., 1966.

(E2) ECKERT, J. S., FOOTE, E. H., and HUNTINGTON, R. L. *Chem. Eng. Progr.,* **54**(1), 70 (1958).

(E3) ECKERT J. S., FOOTE, E. H., ROLLISON, L. R., and WALTER, L. F. *Ind. Eng. Chem.,* **59**(2), 41 (1967).

(F1) FAIR, J. R., and BRAVO, J. L. *Chem. Eng. Progr.,* **86** (Jan.), 19 (1990).

(G1) GEANKOPLIS, C. J. *Mass Transport Phenomena.* Columbus, Ohio: Ohio State University Bookstores, 1972.

(K1) KISTER, H. Z. *Distillation Design.* New York: McGraw-Hill Book Company, 1992.

(K2) KISTER, H. Z., and GILL, D. R. *Chem. Eng. Progr.,* **87** (Feb.), 32 (1991).

(L1) LEVA, M. *Tower Packings and Packed Tower Design,* 2nd ed. Akron, Ohio: U.S. Stoneware, Inc., 1953.

(L2) LUDWIG, E. E. *Applied Process Design for Chemical and Petroleum Plants,* Vol. 2, 3rd ed. Houston: Gulf Publishing Company, 1997.

(M1) MICKLEY, H. S., SHERWOOD, T K., and REED, C. E. *Applied Mathematics in Chemical Engineering,* 2nd ed. New York: McGraw-Hill Book Company, 1957.

(M2) MICKLEY, H. S. *Chem. Eng. Progr.,* **45,** 739 (1949).

(P1)   PERRY, R. H., and GREEN, D. *Perry's Chemical Engineers' Handbook,* 6th ed. New York: McGraw-Hill Book Company, 1984.

(P2)   PERRY, R. H., and GREEN, D. *Perry's Chemical Engineers' Handbook,* 7th ed. New York: McGraw-Hill Book Company, 1997.

(S1)   SHERWOOD, T. K., PIGFORD, R. L., and WILKIE, C. R. *Mass Transfer.* New York: McGraw-Hill Book Company, 1975.

(S2)   SHULMAN, H. L., and coworkers. *A.I.Ch.E. J.,* **1,** 274 (1955); **9,** 479(1963).

(S3)   SHERWOOD, T. K., and HOLLOWAY, F. A. L. *Trans. A.I.Ch.E.,* **30,** 39 (1940).

(S4)   STRIGLE, R. F., JR. *Packed Tower Design and Applications: Random and Structured Packings,* 2nd ed. Houston: Gulf Publishing Company, 1994.

(S5)   SCHWEITZER, P. A. *Handbook of Separation Techniques for Chemical Engineers.* New York: McGraw-Hill Book Company, 1997.

(S6)   SEADER, J. D., and HENLEY, E. J. *Separation Process Principles.* New York: John Wiley & Sons, Inc., 1998.

(S7)   STOCKAR, U., and WILKE, C. R. *Ind. Eng. Chem. Fund.,* **16**(1), 88, 94 (1977).

(T1)   TREYBAL, R. E. *Mass Transfer Operations,* 3rd ed. New York: McGraw-Hill Book Company, 1980.

(T2)   TREYBAL, R. E. *Mass Transfer Operations.* New York: McGraw-Hill Book Company, 1955.

(T3)   TREYBAL, R. E. *Liquid Extraction,* 2nd ed. New York: McGraw-Hill Book Company, 1963.

(W1)   WHITNEY, R. P., and VIVIAN, J. E. *Chem. Eng. Progr.,* **45,** 323 (1949).

CHAPTER 11

Vapor–Liquid
Separation Processes

11.1 VAPOR–LIQUID EQUILIBRIUM RELATIONS

11.1A Phase Rule and Raoult's Law

As in the gas–liquid systems, the equilibrium in vapor–liquid systems is restricted by the phase rule, Eq. (10.2-1). As an example we shall use the ammonia–water, vapor–liquid system. For two components and two phases, F from Eq. (10.2-1) is 2 degrees of freedom. The four variables are temperature, pressure, and the composition y_A of NH_3 in the vapor phase and x_A in the liquid phase. The composition of water (B) is fixed if y_A or x_A is specified, since $y_A + y_B = 1.0$ and $x_A + x_B = 1.0$. If the pressure is fixed, only one more variable can be set. If we set the liquid composition, the temperature and vapor composition are automatically set.

An ideal law, *Raoult's law,* can be defined for vapor–liquid phases in equilibrium:

$$p_A = P_A x_A \tag{11.1-1}$$

where p_A is the partial pressure of component A in the vapor in Pa (atm), P_A is the vapor pressure of pure A in Pa (atm), and x_A is the mole fraction of A in the liquid. This law holds only for ideal solutions, such as benzene–toluene, hexane–heptane, and methyl alcohol–ethyl alcohol, which are usually substances very similar to each other. Many systems that are ideal or nonideal solutions follow Henry's law in dilute solutions.

11.1B Boiling-Point Diagrams and *x-y* Plots

Often the vapor–liquid equilibrium relations for a binary mixture of A and B are given as a boiling-point diagram, shown in Fig. 11.1-1 for the system benzene (A)–toluene (B) at a total pressure of 101.32 kPa. The upper line is the saturated vapor line (the *dew-point line*) and the lower line is the saturated liquid line (the *bubble-point line*). The two-phase region is in the region between these two lines.

In Fig. 11.1-1, if we start with a cold liquid mixture of $x_{A1} = 0.318$ and heat the mixture, it will start to boil at 98°C (371.2 K), and the composition of the first vapor in equilib-

Mole fraction benzene in liquid,
x_A, or vapor, y_A

FIGURE 11.1-1. *Boiling point diagram for benzene (A)–toluene*
(B) at 101.325 kPa (1 atm) total pressure.

rium is $y_{A1} = 0.532$. As we continue boiling, the composition x_A will move to the left since y_A is richer in A.

The system benzene–toluene follows Raoult's law, so the boiling-point diagram can be calculated from the pure vapor-pressure data in Table 11.1-1 and the following equations:

$$p_A + p_B = P \tag{11.1-2}$$

$$P_A x_A + P_B(1 - x_A) = P \tag{11.1-3}$$

$$y_A = \frac{p_A}{P} = \frac{P_A x_A}{P} \tag{11.1-4}$$

EXAMPLE 11.1-1. Use of Raoult's Law for Boiling-Point Diagram
Calculate the vapor and liquid compositions in equilibrium at 95°C (368.2 K) for benzene–toluene using the vapor pressure from Table 11.1-1 at 101.32 kPa.

Solution: At 95°C from Table 11.1-1 for benzene, $P_A = 155.7$ kPa and $P_B = 63.3$ kPa. Substituting into Eq. (11.1-3) and solving,

$$155.7(x_A) + 63.3(1 - x_A) = 101.32 \text{ kPa (760 mm Hg)}$$

Hence, $x_A = 0.411$ and $x_B = 1 - x_A = 1 - 0.411 = 0.589$. Substituting into Eq. (11.1-4),

$$y_A = \frac{P_A x_A}{P} = \frac{155.7(0.411)}{101.32} = 0.632$$

TABLE 11.1-1. *Vapor-Pressure and Equilibrium-Mole-Fraction Data*
for Benzene–Toluene System

| Temperature | | Vapor Pressure | | | | Mole Fraction Benzene at 101.325 kPa | |
| | | Benzene | | Toluene | | | |
K	°C	kPa	mm Hg	kPa	mm Hg	x_A	y_A
353.3	80.1	101.32	760			1.000	1.000
358.2	85	116.9	877	46.0	345	0.780	0.900
363.2	90	135.5	1016	54.0	405	0.581	0.777
368.2	95	155.7	1168	63.3	475	0.411	0.632
373.2	100	179.2	1344	74.3	557	0.258	0.456
378.2	105	204.2	1532	86.0	645	0.130	0.261
383.8	110.6	240.0	1800	101.32	760	0	0

A common method of plotting the equilibrium data is shown in Fig. 11.1-2, where y_A is plotted versus x_A for the benzene–toluene system. The 45° line is given to show that y_A is richer in component A than is x_A.

The boiling-point diagram in Fig. 11.1-1 is typical of an ideal system following Raoult's law. Nonideal systems differ considerably. In Fig. 11.1-3a the boiling-point diagram is shown for a maximum-boiling azeotrope. The maximum temperature T_{max} corresponds to a concentration x_{Az} and $x_{Az} = y_{Az}$ at this point. The plot of y_A versus x_A would show the curve crossing the 45° line at this point. Acetone–chloroform is an example of such a system. In Fig. 11.1-3b a minimum-boiling azeotrope is shown with $y_{Az} = x_{Az}$ at T_{min}. Ethanol–water is such a system.

FIGURE 11.1-2. *Equilibrium diagram for system benzene (A)–toluene (B) at 101.32 kPa (1 atm).*

FIGURE 11.1-3. *Equilibrium boiling-point diagrams: (a) maximum-boiling azeotrope,*
(b) minimum-boiling azeotrope.

11.2 SINGLE-STAGE EQUILIBRIUM CONTACT FOR VAPOR–LIQUID SYSTEM

If a vapor–liquid system is being considered, where the stream V_2 is a vapor and L_0 is a liquid, and the two streams are brought into contact in a single equilibrium stage which is quite similar to Fig. 10.3-1, the boiling point or the x-y equilibrium diagram must be used, because an equilibrium relation similar to Henry's law is not available. Since we are considering only two components, A and B, only Eqs. (10.3-1) and (10.3-2) are used for the material balances. If sensible heat effects are small and the latent heats of both compounds are the same, then when 1 mol of A condenses, 1 mol of B must vaporize. Hence, the total moles of vapor V_2 entering will equal V_1 leaving. Also, moles $L_0 = L_1$. This case is called one of *constant molal overflow*. An example is the benzene–toluene system.

EXAMPLE 11.2-1. Equilibrium Contact of Vapor–Liquid Mixture
A vapor at the dew point and 101.32 kPa containing a mole fraction of 0.40 benzene (A) and 0.60 toluene (B) and 100 kg mol total is brought into contact with 110 kg mol of a liquid at the boiling point containing a mole fraction of 0.30 benzene and 0.70 toluene. The two streams are contacted in a single stage, and the outlet streams leave in equilibrium with each other. Assume constant molal overflow. Calculate the amounts and compositions of the exit streams.

Solution: The process flow diagram is the same as in Fig. 10.3-1. The given values are $V_2 = 100$ kg mol, $y_{A2} = 0.40$, $L_0 = 110$ kg mol, and $x_{A0} = 0.30$. For constant molal overflow, $V_2 = V_1$ and $L_0 = L_1$. Substituting into Eq. (10.3-2) to make a material balance on component A,

$$L_0 x_{A0} + V_2 y_{A2} = L_1 x_{A1} + V_1 y_{A1} \qquad \textbf{(10.3-2)}$$

$$110(0.30) + 100(0.40) = 110 x_{A1} + 100 y_{A1} \qquad \textbf{(11.2-1)}$$

To solve Eq. (11.2-1), the equilibrium relation between y_{A1} and x_{A1} in Fig. 11.1-1 must be used. This is by trial and error, since an analytical expression is not available that relates y_A and x_A.

FIGURE 11.2-1. *Solution to Example 11.2-1.*

First, we assume that $x_{A1} = 0.20$ and substitute into Eq. (11.2-1) to solve for y_{A1}:

$$110(0.30) + 100(0.40) = 110(0.20) + 100y_{A1}$$

Solving, $y_{A1} = 0.51$. The equilibrium relations for benzene–toluene are plotted in Fig. 11.2-1. It is evident that $y_{A1} = 0.51$ and $x_{A1} = 0.20$ do not fall on the curve. This point is plotted on the graph. Next, assuming that $x_{A1} = 0.40$ and solving, $y_{A1} = 0.29$. This point is also plotted in Fig. 11.2-1. Assuming that $x_{A1} = 0.30$, $y_{A1} = 0.40$. A straight line is drawn between these three points which represents Eq. (11.2-1). At the intersection of this line with the equilibrium curve, $y_{A1} = 0.455$ and $x_{A1} = 0.25$, which agree with Eq. (11.2-1).

11.3 SIMPLE DISTILLATION METHODS

11.3A Introduction

The separation process known as distillation is a method for separating the various components of a liquid solution which depends upon the distribution of these components between a vapor phase and a liquid phase. All components are present in both phases. The vapor phase is created from the liquid phase by vaporization at the boiling point.

The basic requirement for the separation of components by distillation is that the composition of the vapor be different from the composition of the liquid with which it is in equilibrium at the boiling point of the liquid. Distillation is concerned with solutions where all components are appreciably volatile, such as ammonia–water or ethanol–water solutions, where both components will be in the vapor phase. In evaporation, by contrast, of a solution of salt and water, for example the water is vaporized but the salt is not. The process of absorption differs from distillation in that one of the components in absorption is essentially insoluble in the liquid phase. An example is absorption of ammonia from air by water, where air is insoluble in the water–ammonia solution.

11.3B Relative Volatility of Vapor–Liquid Systems

In Fig. 11.1-2, the equilibrium diagram for a binary mixture of A and B, the greater the distance between the equilibrium line and the 45° line, the greater the difference between the vapor composition y_A and liquid composition x_A. Hence, the separation is more easily made. A numerical measure of this separation is the relative volatility α_{AB}. This is defined as the ratio of the concentration of A in the vapor to the concentration of A in the liquid divided by the ratio of the concentration of B in the vapor to the concentration of B in the liquid:

$$\alpha_{AB} = \frac{y_A/x_A}{y_B/x_B} = \frac{y_A/x_A}{(1 - y_A)/(1 - x_A)} \tag{11.3-1}$$

where α_{AB} is the relative volatility of A with respect to B in the binary system.

If the system obeys Raoult's law, as does the benzene–toluene system,

$$y_A = \frac{P_A x_A}{P} \qquad y_B = \frac{P_B x_B}{P} \tag{11.3-2}$$

Substituting Eq. (11.3-2) into (11.3-1) for an ideal system,

$$\alpha_{AB} = \frac{P_A}{P_B} \tag{11.3-3}$$

Equation (11.3-1) can be rearranged to give

$$y_A = \frac{\alpha x_A}{1 + (\alpha - 1)x_A} \tag{11.3-4}$$

where $\alpha = \alpha_{AB}$. When the value of α is above 1.0, a separation is possible. The value of α may change as concentration changes. When binary systems follow Raoult's law, the relative volatility often varies only slightly over a large concentration range at constant total pressure.

EXAMPLE 11.3-1. Relative Volatility for Benzene–Toluene System
Using the data from Table 11.1-1, calculate the relative volatility for the benzene–toluene system at 85°C (358.2 K) and 105°C (378.2 K).

Solution: At 85°C, substituting into Eq. (11.3-3) for a system following Raoult's law,

$$\alpha = \frac{P_A}{P_B} = \frac{116.9}{46.0} = 2.54$$

Similarly at 105°C,

$$\alpha = \frac{204.2}{86.0} = 2.38$$

The variation in α is about 7%.

11.3C Equilibrium or Flash Distillation

1. Introduction to distillation methods. Distillation can be carried out by either of two main methods in practice. The first method of distillation involves the production of a vapor by boiling the liquid mixture to be separated in a single stage and recovering and condensing the

FIGURE 11.3-1. *Equilibrium or flash distillation.*

vapors. No liquid is allowed to return to the single-stage still to contact the rising vapors. The second method of distillation involves the returning of a portion of the condensate to the still. The vapors rise through a series of stages or trays, and part of the condensate flows downward through the series of stages or trays countercurrent to the vapors. This second method is called *fractional distillation, distillation with reflux,* or *rectification.*

There are three important types of distillation that occur in a single stage or still and that do not involve rectification. The first of these is equilibrium or flash distillation, the second is simple batch or differential distillation, and the third is simple steam distillation.

2. Equilibrium or flash distillation. In *equilibrium* or *flash distillation,* which occurs in a single stage, a liquid mixture is partially vaporized. The vapor is allowed to come to equilibrium with the liquid, and the vapor and liquid phases are then separated. This can be done batchwise or continuously.

In Fig. 11.3-1 a binary mixture of components A and B flowing at the rate of F mol/h into a heater is partially vaporized. Then the mixture reaches equilibrium and is separated. The composition of F is x_F mole fraction of A. A total material balance on component A is as follows:

$$Fx_F = Vy + Lx \tag{11.3-5}$$

Since $L = F - V$, Eq. (11.3-5) becomes

$$Fx_F = Vy + (F - V)x \tag{11.3-6}$$

Usually, the moles per hour of feed F, moles per hour of vapor V, and moles per hour of L are known or set. Hence, there are two unknowns x and y in Eq. (11.3-6). The other relationship needed in order to solve Eq. (11.3-6) is the equilibrium line. A convenient method to use is to plot Eq. (11.3-6) on the x-y equilibrium diagram. The intersection of the equation and the equilibrium line is the desired solution. This is similar to Example 11.2-1 and shown in Fig. 11.2-1.

11.3D Simple Batch or Differential Distillation

In *simple batch* or *differential distillation,* liquid is first charged to a heated kettle. The liquid charge is boiled slowly and the vapors are withdrawn as rapidly as they form to a condenser, where the condensed vapor (distillate) is collected. The first portion of vapor condensed will be richest in the more volatile component A. As vaporization proceeds, the vaporized product becomes leaner in A.

FIGURE 11.3-2. *Simple batch or differential distillation.*

V moles vapor to condenser
y

L moles liquid
x

In Fig. 11.3-2 a simple still is shown. Originally, a charge of L_1 moles of components A and B with a composition of x_1 mole fraction of A is placed in the still. At any given time, there are L moles of liquid left in the still with composition x, and the composition of the vapor leaving in equilibrium is y. A differential amount dL is vaporized.

The composition in the still pot changes with time. In deriving the equation for this process, we assume that a small amount of dL is vaporized. The composition of the liquid changes from x to $x - dx$ and the amount of liquid from L to $L - dL$. A material balance on A can be made, where the original amount = the amount left in the liquid + the amount of vapor:

$$xL = (x - dx)(L - dL) + y\, dL \qquad (11.3\text{-}7)$$

Multiplying out the right side,

$$xL = xL - x\, dL - L\, dx + dx\, dL + y\, dL \qquad (11.3\text{-}8)$$

Neglecting the term $dx\, dL$ and rearranging,

$$\frac{dL}{L} = \frac{dx}{y - x} \qquad (11.3\text{-}9)$$

Integrating,

$$\int_{L_2}^{L_1} \frac{dL}{L} = \ln \frac{L_1}{L_2} = \int_{x_2}^{x_1} \frac{dx}{y - x} \qquad (11.3\text{-}10)$$

where L_1 is the original moles charged, L_2 the moles left in the still, x_1 the original composition, and x_2 the final composition of liquid.

The equilibrium curve gives the relationship between y and x. The integration of Eq. (11.3-10) can be done by calculating values of $f(x) = 1/(y - x)$ and numerically or graphically integrating Eq. (11.3-10) between x_1 and x_2. Equation (11.3-10) is known as the *Rayleigh equation.* The average composition of total material distilled, y_{av}, can be obtained by material balance:

$$L_1 x_1 = L_2 x_2 + (L_1 - L_2) y_{av} \qquad (11.3\text{-}11)$$

EXAMPLE 11.3-2. Simple Differential Distillation

A mixture of 100 mol containing 50 mol % *n*-pentane and 50 mol % *n*-heptane is distilled under differential conditions at 101.3 kPa until 40 mol is distilled. What is the average composition of the total vapor distilled and the composition of the liquid left? The equilibrium data are as follows, where x and y are mole fractions of n-pentane:

x	y	x	y	x	y
1.000	1.000	0.398	0.836	0.059	0.271
0.867	0.984	0.254	0.701	0	0
0.594	0.925	0.145	0.521		

Solution: The given values to be used in Eq. (11.3-10) are $L_1 = 100$ mol, $x_1 = 0.50$, $L_2 = 60$ mol, and V (moles distilled) $= 40$ mol. Substituting into Eq. (11.3-10),

$$\ln \frac{100}{60} = 0.510 = \int_{x_2}^{x_1=0.5} \frac{dx}{y-x} \qquad \textbf{(11.3-12)}$$

The unknown is x_2, the composition of the liquid L_2 at the end of the differential distillation. To solve this by numerical integration, equilibrium values of y versus x are plotted so values of y can be obtained from this curve at small intervals of x. Alternatively, instead of plotting, the equilibrium data can be fitted to a polynomial function. For $x = 0.594$, the equilibrium value of $y = 0.925$. Then $f(x) = 1/(y - x) = 1/(0.925 - 0.594) = 3.02$. Other values of $f(y)$ are similarly calculated.

The numerical integration of Eq. (11.3-10) is performed from $x_1 = 0.5$ to x_2 such that the integral $= 0.510$ by Eq. (11.3-12) in Fig. 11.3-3. Hence, $x_2 = 0.277$. Substituting into Eq. (11.3-11) and solving for the average composition of the 40 mol distilled,

$$100(0.50) = 60(0.277) + 40(y_{av})$$

$$y_{av} = 0.835$$

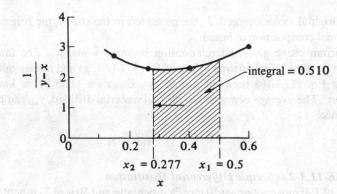

FIGURE 11.3-3. *Numerical integration for Example 11.3-2.*

11.3E Simple Steam Distillation

At atmospheric pressure high-boiling liquids cannot be purified by distillation, since the components of the liquid may decompose at the high temperatures required. Often the high-boiling substances are essentially insoluble in water, so a separation at lower temperatures can be obtained by *simple steam distillation*. This method is often used to separate a high-boiling component from small amounts of nonvolatile impurities.

If a layer of liquid water (A) and an immiscible high-boiling component (B) such as a hydrocarbon are boiled at 101.3 kPa abs pressure, then, by the phase rule, Eq. (10.2-1), for three phases and two components,

$$F = 2 - 3 + 2 = 1 \text{ degree of freedom}$$

Hence, if the total pressure is fixed, the system is fixed. Since there are two liquid phases, each will exert its own vapor pressure at the prevailing temperature and cannot be influenced by the presence of the other. When the sum of the separate vapor pressures equals the total pressure, the mixture boils and

$$P_A + P_B = P \tag{11.3-13}$$

where P_A is vapor pressure of pure water A and P_B is vapor pressure of pure B. Then the vapor composition is

$$y_A = \frac{P_A}{P} \qquad y_B = \frac{P_B}{P} \tag{11.3-14}$$

As long as the two liquid phases are present, the mixture will boil at the same temperature, giving a vapor of constant composition y_A. The temperature is found by using the vapor-pressure curves for pure A and pure B.

Note that by steam distillation, as long as liquid water is present, the high-boiling component B vaporizes at a temperature well below its normal boiling point without using a vacuum. The vapors of water (A) and high-boiling component (B) are usually condensed in a condenser and the resulting two immiscible liquid phases separated. This method has the disadvantage that large amounts of heat must be used to evaporate the water simultaneously with the high-boiling compound.

The ratio moles of B distilled to moles of A distilled is

$$\frac{n_B}{n_A} = \frac{P_B}{P_A} \tag{11.3-15}$$

Steam distillation is sometimes used in the food industry for the removal of volatile taints and flavors from edible fats and oils. In many cases vacuum distillation is used instead of steam distillation to purify high-boiling materials. The total pressure is quite low so that the vapor pressure of the system reaches the total pressure at relatively low temperatures.

Van Winkle (V1) derives equations for steam distillation where an appreciable amount of a nonvolatile component is present with the high-boiling component. This involves a three-component system. He also considers other cases for binary batch, continuous, and multicomponent batch steam distillation.

11.4 DISTILLATION WITH REFLUX AND McCABE–THIELE METHOD

11.4A Introduction to Distillation with Reflux

Rectification (fractionation) or stage distillation with reflux, from a simplified point of view, can be considered to be a process in which a series of flash-vaporization stages are arranged in a series in such a manner that the vapor and liquid products from each stage flow counter-current to each other. The liquid in a stage is conducted or flows to the stage below and the vapor from a stage flows upward to the stage above. Hence, in each stage a vapor stream V and a liquid stream L enter, are mixed and equilibrated, and a vapor and a liquid stream leave in equilibrium. This process flow diagram was shown in Fig. 10.3-1 for a single stage and an example given in Example 11.2-1 for a benzene–toluene mixture.

For the countercurrent contact with multiple stages in Fig. 10.3-2, the material-balance or operating-line equation (10.3-13) was derived, which relates the concentrations of the vapor and liquid streams passing each other in each stage. In a distillation column the stages (referred to as *sieve plates* or *trays*) in a distillation tower are arranged vertically, as shown schematically in Fig. 11.4-1.

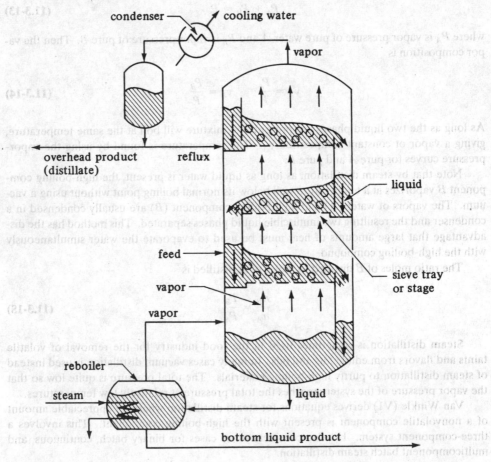

FIGURE 11.4-1. *Process flow of a fractionating tower containing sieve trays.*

The feed enters the column in Fig. 11.4-1 somewhere in the middle of the column. If the feed is liquid, it flows down to a sieve tray or stage. Vapor enters the tray and bubbles through the liquid on this tray as the entering liquid flows across. The vapor and liquid leaving the tray are essentially in equilibrium. The vapor continues up to the next tray or stage, where it is again contacted with a downflowing liquid. In this case the concentration of the more volatile component (the lower-boiling component A) is being increased in the vapor from each stage going upward and decreased in the liquid from each stage going downward. The final vapor product coming overhead is condensed in a condenser and a portion of the liquid product (distillate) is removed, which contains a high concentration of A. The remaining liquid from the condenser is returned (refluxed) as a liquid to the top tray.

The liquid leaving the bottom tray enters a reboiler, where it is partially vaporized, and the remaining liquid, which is lean in A or rich in B, is withdrawn as liquid product. The vapor from the reboiler is sent back to the bottom stage or tray. Only three trays are shown in the tower of Fig. 11.4-1. In most cases the number of trays is much greater. In the sieve tray the vapor enters through an opening and bubbles up through the liquid to provide intimate contact between the liquid and vapor on the tray. In a theoretical tray the vapor and liquid leaving are in equilibrium. The reboiler can be considered as a theoretical stage or tray.

11.4B McCabe–Thiele Method of Calculation for Number of Theoretical Stages

1. Introduction and assumptions. A mathematical–graphical method for determining the number of theoretical trays or stages needed for a given separation of a binary mixture of A and B has been developed by McCabe and Thiele. The method uses material balances around certain parts of the tower, which give operating lines somewhat similar to Eq. (10.3-13), and the x-y equilibrium curve for the system.

The main assumption made in the McCabe–Thiele method is that there must be equimolar overflow through the tower between the feed inlet and the top tray and the feed inlet and bottom tray. This is shown in Fig. 11.4-2, where liquid and vapor streams enter a tray, are equilibrated, and leave. A total material balance gives

$$V_{n+1} + L_{n-1} = V_n + L_n \tag{11.4-1}$$

A component balance on A gives

$$V_{n+1} y_{n+1} + L_{n-1} x_{n-1} = V_n y_n + L_n x_n \tag{11.4-2}$$

where V_{n+1} is mol/h of vapor from tray $n + 1$, L_n is mol/h liquid from tray n, y_{n+1} is mole fraction of A in V_{n+1}, and so on. The compositions y_n and x_n are in equilibrium and the temperature of the tray n is T_n. If T_n is taken as a datum, it can be shown by a heat balance that the sensible heat differences in the four streams are quite small if heats of solution are negligible.

FIGURE 11.4-2. *Vapor and liquid flows entering and leaving a tray.*

V_n, y_n

V_{n+1}, y_{n+1}

$n-1$

L_{n-1}, x_{n-1}

n

L_n, x_n

$n+1$

FIGURE 11.4-3. *Distillation column showing material-balance sections for McCabe–Thiele method.*

Hence, only the latent heats in streams V_{n+1} and V_n are important. Since molar latent heats for chemically similar compounds are almost the same, $V_{n+1} = V_n$ and $L_n = L_{n-1}$. Therefore, we have constant molal overflow in the tower.

2. Equations for enriching section. In Fig. 11.4-3 a continuous-distillation column is shown, with feed being introduced to the column at an intermediate point and an overhead distillate product and a bottoms product being withdrawn. The upper part of the tower above the feed entrance is called the *enriching section,* since the entering feed of binary components A and B is enriched in this section, so that the distillate is richer in A than the feed. The tower is at steady state.

An overall material balance around the entire column in Fig. 11.4-3 states that the entering feed of F mol/h must equal the distillate D in mol/h plus the bottoms W in mol/h:

$$F = D + W \qquad\qquad (11.4\text{-}3)$$

A total material balance on component A gives

$$Fx_F = Dx_D + Wx_W \qquad\qquad (11.4\text{-}4)$$

In Fig. 11.4-4a the distillation-tower section above the feed, the enriching section, is shown schematically. The vapor from the top tray having a composition y_1 passes to the condenser, where it is condensed so that the resulting liquid is at the boiling point. The reflux stream L mol/h and distillate D mol/h have the same composition, so $y_1 = x_D$. Since equimolal overflow is assumed, $L_1 = L_2 = L_n$ and $V_1 = V_2 = V_n = V_{n+1}$.

Making a total material balance over the dashed-line section in Fig. 11.4-4a,

$$V_{n+1} = L_n + D \qquad\qquad (11.4\text{-}5)$$

FIGURE 11.4-4. *Material balance and operating line for enriching section: (a) schematic of tower, (b) operating and equilibrium lines.*

Making a balance on component A,

$$V_{n+1}y_{n+1} = L_n x_n + Dx_D \qquad (11.4-6)$$

Solving for y_{n+1}, the enriching-section operating line is

$$y_{n+1} = \frac{L_n}{V_{n+1}}x_n + \frac{Dx_D}{V_{n+1}} \qquad (11.4-7)$$

Since $V_{n+1} = L_n + D$, $L_n/V_{n+1} = R/(R + 1)$ and Eq. (11.4-7) becomes

$$y_{n+1} = \frac{R}{R + 1}x_n + \frac{x_D}{R + 1} \qquad (11.4-8)$$

where $R = L_n/D$ = reflux ratio = constant. Equation (11.4-7) is a straight line on a plot of vapor composition versus liquid composition. It relates the compositions of two streams passing each other and is plotted in Fig. 11.4-4b. The slope is L_n/V_{n+1} or $R/(R + 1)$, as given in Eq. (11.4-8). It intersects the $y = x$ line (45° diagonal line) at $x = x_D$. The intercept of the operating line at $x = 0$ is $y = x_D/(R + 1)$.

The theoretical stages are determined by starting at x_D and stepping off the first plate to x_1. Then y_2 is the composition of the vapor passing the liquid x_1. In a similar manner, the other theoretical trays are stepped off down the tower in the enriching section to the feed tray.

3. Equations for stripping section. Making a total material balance over the dashed-line section in Fig. 11.4-5a for the stripping section of the tower below the feed entrance,

$$V_{m+1} = L_m - W \qquad (11.4-9)$$

Making a balance on component A,

$$V_{m+1}y_{m+1} = L_m x_m - Wx_W \qquad (11.4-10)$$

FIGURE 11.4-5. *Material balance and operating line for stripping section: (a) schematic of tower,
(b) operating and equilibrium lines.*

Solving for y_{m+1}, the stripping-section operating line is

$$y_{m+1} = \frac{L_m}{V_{m+1}} x_m - \frac{W x_W}{V_{m+1}} \tag{11.4-11}$$

Again, since equimolal flow is assumed, $L_m = L_N = $ constant and $V_{m+1} = V_N = $ constant.
Equation (11.4-11) is a straight line when plotted as y versus x in Fig. 11.4-5b, with a slope of
L_m/V_{m+1}. It intersects the $y = x$ line at $x = x_W$. The intercept at $x = 0$ is $y = -W x_W/V_{m+1}$.

Again the theoretical stages for the stripping section are determined by starting at x_W,
going up to y_W, and then across to the operating line, and so on.

4. Effect of feed conditions. The condition of the feed stream F entering the tower determines the relation between the vapor V_m in the stripping section and V_n in the enriching section as well as between L_m and L_n. If the feed is part liquid and part vapor, the vapor will add
to V_m to give V_n.

For convenience, we represent the condition of the feed by the quantity q, which is
defined as

$$q = \frac{\text{heat needed to vaporize 1 mol of feed at entering conditions}}{\text{molar latent heat of vaporization of feed}} \tag{11.4-12}$$

If the feed enters at its boiling point, the numerator of Eq. (11.4-12) is the same as the denominator, and $q = 1.0$. Equation (11.4-12) can also be written in terms of enthalpies:

$$q = \frac{H_V - H_F}{H_V - H_L} \tag{11.4-13}$$

FIGURE 11.4-6. *Relationship between flows above and below the feed entrance.*

where H_V is the enthalpy of the feed at the dew point, H_L the enthalpy of the feed at the boiling point (bubble point), and H_F the enthalpy of the feed at its entrance conditions. If the feed enters as vapor at the dew point, $q = 0$. For cold liquid feed $q > 1.0$, for superheated vapor $q < 0$, and for the feed being part liquid and part vapor, q is the fraction of feed that is liquid.

We can also look at q as the number of moles of saturated liquid produced on the feed plate by each mole of feed added to the tower. In Fig. 11.4-6 a diagram shows the relationship between flows above and below the feed extrance. From the definition of q, the following equations hold:

$$L_m = L_n + qF \qquad (11.4\text{-}14)$$

$$V_n = V_m + (1 - q)F \qquad (11.4\text{-}15)$$

The point of intersection of the enriching and the stripping operating-line equations on an x-y plot can be derived as follows. Rewriting Eqs. (11.4-6) and (11.4-10) as follows without the tray subscripts:

$$V_n y = L_n x + D x_D \qquad (11.4\text{-}16)$$

$$V_m y = L_m x - W x_W \qquad (11.4\text{-}17)$$

where the y and x values are the point of intersection of the two operating lines. Subtracting Eq. (11.4-16) from (11.4-17),

$$(V_m - V_n)y = (L_m - L_n)x - (D x_D + W x_W) \qquad (11.4\text{-}18)$$

Substituting Eqs. (11.4-4), (11.4-14), and (11.4-15) into Eq. (11.4-18) and rearranging,

$$y = \frac{q}{q - 1}x - \frac{x_F}{q - 1} \qquad (11.4\text{-}19)$$

This equation is the q-line equation and is the locus of the intersection of the two operating lines. Setting $y = x$ in Eq. (11.4-19), the intersection of the q-line equation with the 45° line is $y = x = x_F$, where x_F is the overall composition of the feed.

In Fig. 11.4-7 the q line is plotted for various feed conditions given below the figure. The slope of the q line is $q/(q - 1)$. For example, for the liquid below the boiling point, $q > 1$, and the slope is >1.0, as shown. The enriching and operating lines are plotted for the case of a feed of part liquid and part vapor, and the two lines intersect on the q line. A convenient way

FIGURE 11.4-7. Location of the q line for various feed conditions: liquid below boiling point (q > 1), liquid at boiling point (q = 1), liquid + vapor (0 < q < 1), saturated vapor (q = 0).

to locate the stripping operating line is to first plot the enriching operating line and the q line. Then draw the stripping line between the intersection of the q line and enriching operating line and the point $y = x = x_W$.

5. *Location of the feed tray in a tower and number of trays.* To determine the number of theoretical trays needed in a tower, the stripping and operating lines are drawn to intersect on the q line, as shown in Fig. 11.4-8. Starting at the top at x_D, the trays are stepped off. For trays 2 and 3, the steps can go to the enriching operating line, as shown in Fig. 11.4-8a. At step 4 the step goes to the stripping line. A total of about 4.6 theoretical steps are needed. The feed enters on tray 4.

For the correct method, the shift is made on step 2 to the stripping line, as shown in Fig. 11.4-8b. A total of only about 3.7 steps are needed, with the feed on tray 2. To keep the number of trays to a minimum, the shift from the enriching to the stripping operating line should be made at the first opportunity after passing the operating-line intersection.

In Fig. 11.4-8b the feed is part liquid and part vapor, since $0 < q < 1$. Hence, in adding the feed to tray 2, the vapor portion of the feed is separated and added beneath plate 2 and the liquid added to the liquid from above entering tray 2. If the feed is all liquid, it should be added to the liquid flowing to tray 2 from the tray above. If the feed is all vapor, it should be added below tray 2 and join the vapor rising from the plate below.

Since a reboiler is considered a theoretical step, when the vapor y_W is in equilibrium with x_W, as in Fig. 11.4-5b, the number of theoretical trays in a tower is equal to the number of theoretical steps minus one.

EXAMPLE 11.4-1. Rectification of a Benzene–Toluene Mixture

A liquid mixture of benzene–toluene is to be distilled in a fractionating tower at 101.3 kPa pressure. The feed of 100 kg mol/h is liquid, containing 45 mol % ben-

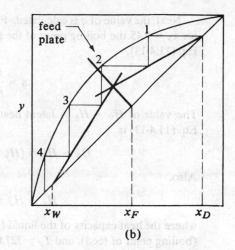

FIGURE 11.4-8. *Method of stepping off number of theoretical trays and location of feed plate: (a) improper location of feed on tray 4, (b) proper location of feed on tray 2 to give minimum number of steps.*

zene and 55 mol % toluene, and enters at 327.6 K (130°F). A distillate containing 95 mol % benzene and 5 mol % toluene and a bottoms containing 10 mol % benzene and 90 mol % toluene are to be obtained. The reflux ratio is 4:1. The average heat capacity of the feed is 159 kJ/kg mol · K (38 btu/lb mol · °F) and the average latent heat 32 099 kJ/kg mol (13 800 btu/lb mol). Equilibrium data for this system are given in Table 11.1-1 and Fig. 11.1-1. Calculate the kg moles per hour distillate, kg moles per hour bottoms, and the number of theoretical trays needed.

Solution: The given data are $F = 100$ kg mol/h, $x_F = 0.45$, $x_D = 0.95$, $x_W = 0.10$, and $R = L_n/D = 4$. For the overall material balance substituting into Eq. (11.4-3),

$$F = D + W \tag{11.4-3}$$

$$100 = D + W$$

Substituting into Eq. (11.4-4) and solving for D and W,

$$Fx_F = Dx_D + Wx_W \tag{11.4-4}$$

$$100(0.45) = D(0.95) + (100 - D)(0.10)$$

$$D = 41.2 \text{ kg mol/h} \qquad W = 58.8 \text{ kg mol/h}$$

For the enriching operating line, using Eq. (11.4-8),

$$y_{n+1} = \frac{R}{R+1}x_n + \frac{x_D}{R+1} = \frac{4}{4+1}x_n + \frac{0.95}{4+1} = 0.800x_n + 0.190$$

The equilibrium data from Table 11.1-1 and the enriching operating line above are plotted in Fig. 11.4-9.

Next, the value of q is calculated. From the boiling-point diagram, Fig. 11.1-1, for $x_F = 0.45$ the boiling point of the feed is 93.5°C or 366.7 K (200.3°F). From Eq. (11.4-13),

$$q = \frac{H_V - H_F}{H_V - H_L} \qquad \text{(11.4-13)}$$

The value of $H_V - H_L$ = latent heat = 32 099 kJ/kg mol. The numerator of Eq. (11.4-13) is

$$H_V - H_F = (H_V - H_L) + (H_L - H_F) \qquad \text{(11.4-20)}$$

Also,

$$H_L - H_F = c_{pL}(T_B - T_F) \qquad \text{(11.4-21)}$$

where the heat capacity of the liquid feed c_{pL} = 159 kJ/kg mol·K, T_B = 366.7 K (boiling point of feed), and T_F = 327.6 K (inlet feed temperature). Substituting Eqs. (11.4-20) and (11.4-21) into (11.4-13),

$$q = \frac{(H_V - H_L) + c_{pL}(T_B - T_F)}{H_V - H_L} \qquad \text{(11.4-22)}$$

Substituting the known values into Eq. (11.4-22),

$$q = \frac{32\,099 + 159(366.7 - 327.6)}{32\,099} = 1.195 \qquad \text{(SI)}$$

$$q = \frac{13\,800 + 38(200.3 - 130)}{13\,800} = 1.195 \qquad \text{(English)}$$

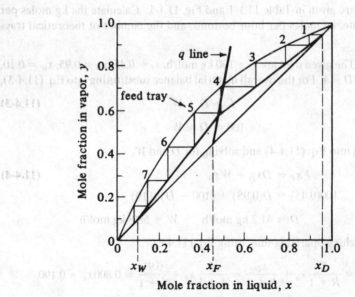

FIGURE 11.4-9. *McCabe–Thiele diagram for distillation of benzene–toluene for Example 11.4-1.*

From Eq. (11.4-19), the slope of the q line is

$$\frac{q}{q - 1} = \frac{1.195}{1.195 - 1} = 6.12$$

The q line is plotted in Fig. 11.4-9 starting at the point $y = x_F = 0.45$ with a slope of 6.12.

The stripping operating line is drawn connecting the point $y = x = x_W = 0.10$ with the intersection of the q line and the enriching operating line. Starting at the point $y = x = x_D$, the theoretical steps are drawn in, as shown in Fig. 11.4-9. The number of theoretical steps is 7.6, or 7.6 steps minus a reboiler, which gives 6.6 theoretical trays. The feed is introduced on tray 5 from the top.

11.4C Total and Minimum Reflux Ratio for McCabe–Thiele Method

1. Total reflux. In distillation of a binary mixture A and B, the feed conditions, distillate composition, and bottoms composition are usually specified and the number of theoretical trays are to be calculated. However, the number of theoretical trays needed depends upon the operating lines. To fix the operating lines, the reflux ratio $R = L_n/D$ at the top of the column must be set.

One of the limiting values of reflux ratio is that of total reflux, or $R = \infty$. Since $R = L_n/D$ and, by Eq. (11.4-5),

$$V_{n+1} = L_n + D \tag{11.4-5}$$

then L_n is very large, as is the vapor flow V_n. This means that the slope $R/(R + 1)$ of the enriching operating line becomes 1.0 and the operating lines of both sections of the column coincide with the 45° diagonal line, as shown in Fig. 11.4-10.

The number of theoretical trays required is obtained as before by stepping off the trays from the distillate to the bottoms. This gives the minimum number of trays that can possibly

FIGURE 11.4-10. *Total reflux and minimum number of trays by McCabe–Thiele method.*

be used to obtain the given separation. In actual practice, this condition can be realized by returning all the overhead condensed vapor V_1 from the top of the tower back to the tower as reflux, that is, total reflux. Also, all the liquid in the bottoms is reboiled. Hence, all the products distillate and bottoms are reduced to zero flow, as is the fresh feed to the tower.

This condition of total reflux can also be interpreted as requiring infinite sizes of condenser, reboiler, and tower diameter for a given feed rate.

If the relative volatility α of the binary mixture is approximately constant, the following analytical expression by Fenske can be used to calculate the minimum number of theoretical steps N_m when a total condenser is used:

$$N_m = \frac{\log\left(\dfrac{x_D}{1 - x_D}\dfrac{1 - x_W}{x_W}\right)}{\log \alpha_{av}} \qquad \text{(11.4-23)}$$

For small variations in α, $\alpha_{av} = (\alpha_1 \alpha_W)^{1/2}$, where α_1 is the relative volatility of the overhead vapor and α_W is the relative volatility of the bottoms liquid.

2. Minimum reflux ratio. The minimum reflux ratio can be defined as the reflux ratio R_m that will require an infinite number of trays for the given desired separation of x_D and x_W. This corresponds to the minimum vapor flow in the tower, and hence the minimum reboiler and condenser sizes. This case is shown in Fig. 11.4-11. If R is decreased, the slope of the enriching operating line $R/(R + 1)$ is decreased, and the intersection of this line and the stripping line with the q line moves farther from the 45° line and closer to the equilibrium line. As a result, the number of steps required to give a fixed x_D and x_W increases. When the two operating lines touch the equilibrium line, a "pinch point" at y' and x' occurs, where the number

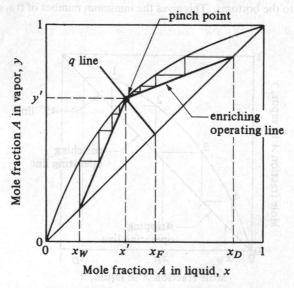

FIGURE 11.4-11. *Minimum reflux ratio and infinite num-*
ber of trays by McCabe–Thiele method.

FIGURE 11.4-12. *Minimum reflux ratio and infinite number of trays when operating line is tangent to equilibrium line.*

of steps required becomes infinite. The slope of the enriching operating line is as follows from Fig. 11.4-11, since the line passes through the points x', y', and x_D ($y = x_D$):

$$\frac{R_m}{R_m + 1} = \frac{x_D - y'}{x_D - x'} \qquad (11.4\text{-}24)$$

In some cases, where the equilibrium line has an inflection in it as shown in Fig. 11.4-12, the operating line at minimum reflux will be tangent to the equilibrium line.

3. Operating and optimum reflux ratio. For the case of total reflux, the number of plates is a minimum, but the tower diameter is infinite. This corresponds to an infinite cost of tower as well as steam and cooling water. This is one limit in the tower operation. Also, for minimum reflux, the number of trays is infinite, which again gives an infinite cost. These are the two limits in operation of the tower.

The actual operating reflux ratio to use lies between these two limits. To select the proper value of R requires a complete economic balance on the fixed costs of the tower and operating costs. The optimum reflux ratio to use for lowest total cost per year is between the minimum R_m and total reflux. This has been shown for many cases to be at an operating reflux ratio between $1.2R_m$ and $1.5R_m$.

EXAMPLE 11.4-2. Minimum Reflux Ratio and Total Reflux in Rectification

For the rectification in Example 11.4-1, where a benzene–toluene feed is being distilled to give a distillate composition of $x_D = 0.95$ and a bottoms composition of $x_W = 0.10$, calculate the following:

(a) Minimum reflux ratio R_m.
(b) Minimum number of theoretical plates at total reflux.

Solution: For part (a), the equilibrium line is plotted in Fig. 11.4-13 and the q-line equation is also shown for $x_F = 0.45$. Using the same x_D and x_W as in Example 11.4-1, the enriching operating line for minimum reflux is plotted as a

FIGURE 11.4-13. *Graphical solution for minimum reflux ratio R_m and total reflux for Example 11.4-2.*

dashed line and intersects the equilibrium line at the same point at which the q line intersects. Reading off the values of $x' = 0.49$ and $y' = 0.702$, substituting into Eq. (11.4-24), and solving for R_m,

$$\frac{R_m}{R_m + 1} = \frac{x_D - y'}{x_D - x'} = \frac{0.95 - 0.702}{0.95 - 0.49}$$

Hence, the minimum reflux ratio $R_m = 1.17$.

For the case of total reflux in part (b), the theoretical steps are drawn as shown in Fig. 11.4-13. The minimum number of theoretical steps is 5.8, which gives 4.8 theoretical trays plus a reboiler.

11.4D Special Cases for Rectification Using McCabe–Thiele Method

1. Stripping-column distillation. In some cases the feed to be distilled is not supplied to an intermediate point in a column but is added to the top of the stripping column, as shown in Fig. 11.4-14a. The feed is usually a saturated liquid at the boiling point, and the overhead product V_D is the vapor rising from the top plate, which goes to a condenser with no reflux or liquid returned to the tower.

The bottoms product W usually has a high concentration of the less volatile component B. Hence, the column operates as a stripping tower, with the vapor removing the more volatile A from the liquid as it flows downward. Assuming constant molar flow rates, a material balance of the more volatile component A around the dashed line in Fig. 11.4-14a gives, on rearrangement,

$$y_{m+1} = \frac{L_m}{V_{m+1}} x_m - \frac{W x_W}{V_{m+1}} \tag{11.4-25}$$

FIGURE 11.4-14. *Material balance and operating line for stripping tower: (a) flows in tower, (b) operating and equilibrium line.*

This stripping-line equation is the same as the stripping-line equation for a complete tower given as Eq. (11.4-11). It intersects the $y = x$ line at $x = x_W$, and the slope is constant at L_m/V_{m+1}.

If the feed is saturated liquid, then $L_m = F$. If the feed is cold liquid below the boiling point, the q line should be used and $q > 1$:

$$L_m = qF \qquad (11.4\text{-}26)$$

In Fig. 11.4-14 the stripping operating-line equation (11.4-25) is plotted and the q line, Eq. (11.4-19), is also shown for $q = 1.0$. Starting at x_F, the steps are drawn down the tower.

EXAMPLE 11.4-3. Number of Trays in Stripping Tower

A liquid feed at the boiling point of 400 kg mol/h containing 70 mol % benzene (A) and 30 mol % toluene (B) is fed to a stripping tower at 101.3 kPa pressure. The bottoms product flow is to be 60 kg mol/h containing only 10 mol % A and the rest B. Calculate the kg mol/h overhead vapor, its composition, and the number of theoretical steps required.

Solution: Referring to Fig. 11.4-14a, the known values are $F = 400$ kg mol/h, $x_F = 0.70$, $W = 60$ kg mol/h, and $x_W = 0.10$. The equilibrium data from Table 11.1-1 are plotted in Fig. 11.4-15. Making an overall material balance,

$$F = W + V_D$$

$$400 = 60 + V_D$$

FIGURE 11.4-15. *Stripping tower for Example 11.4-3.*

Solving, $V_D = 340$ kg mol/h. Making a component A balance and solving,

$$Fx_F = Wx_W + V_D y_D$$

$$400(0.70) = 60(0.10) + 340(y_D)$$

$$y_D = 0.806$$

For a saturated liquid, the q line is vertical and is plotted in Fig. 11.4-15. The operating line is plotted through the point $y = x_W = 0.10$ and the intersection of $y_D = 0.806$ with the q line. Alternatively, Eq. (11.4-25) can be used, with a slope of $L_m/V_{m+1} = 400/340$. Stepping off the trays from the top, 5.3 theoretical steps or 4.3 theoretical trays plus a reboiler are needed.

2. Enriching-column distillation. Enriching towers are also used at times, where the feed enters the bottom of the tower as a vapor. The overhead distillate is produced in the same manner as in a complete fractionating tower and is usually quite rich in the more volatile component A. The liquid bottoms is usually comparable to the feed in composition, being slightly leaner in component A. If the feed is saturated vapor, the vapor in the tower $V_n = F$. Enriching-line equation (11.4-7) holds, as does the q-line equation (11.4-19).

3. Rectification with direct steam injection. Generally, the heat to a distillation tower is applied to one side of a heat exchanger (reboiler) and the steam does not come into direct contact with the boiling solution, as shown in Fig. 11.4-5. However, when an aqueous solution of more volatile A and water B is being distilled, the heat required may be provided by the use of open steam injected directly at the bottom of the tower. The reboiler exchanger is then not needed.

FIGURE 11.4-16. *Use of direct steam injection: (a) schematic of tower, (b) operating and equilibrium lines.*

The steam is injected as small bubbles into the liquid in the tower bottom, as shown in Fig. 11.4-16a. The vapor leaving the liquid is then in equilibrium with the liquid if sufficient contact is obtained. Making an overall balance on the tower and a balance on A,

$$F + S = D + W \tag{11.4-27}$$

$$Fx_F + Sy_S = Dx_D + Wx_W \tag{11.4-28}$$

where S = mol/h of steam and $y_S = 0$ = mole fraction of A in steam. The enriching operating-line equation is the same as for indirect steam.

For the stripping-line equation, an overall balance and a balance on component A are as follows:

$$L_m + S = V_{m+1} + W \tag{11.4-29}$$

$$L_m x_m + S(0) = V_{m+1} y_{m+1} + Wx_W \tag{11.4-30}$$

Solving for y_{m+1} in Eq. (11.4-30),

$$y_{m+1} = \frac{L_m}{V_{m+1}} x_m - \frac{Wx_W}{V_{m+1}} \tag{11.4-31}$$

For saturated steam entering, $S = V_{m+1}$ and hence, by Eq. (11.4-29), $L_m = W$. Substituting into Eq. (11.4-31), the stripping operating line is

$$y_{m+1} = \frac{W}{S}x_m - \frac{W}{S}x_W \qquad\qquad \textbf{(11.4-32)}$$

When $y = 0$, $x = x_W$. Hence, the stripping line passes through the point $y = 0$, $x = x_W$, as shown in Fig. 11.4-16b, and is continued to the x axis. Also, for the intersection of the stripping line with the 45° line, when $y = x$ in Eq. (11.4-32), $x = Wx_W/(W - S)$.

For a given reflux ratio and overhead distillate composition, the use of open steam rather than closed requires an extra fraction of a stage, since the bottom step starts below the $y = x$ line (Fig. 11.4-16b). The advantage of open steam lies in simpler construction of the heater, which is a sparger.

4. Rectification tower with side stream. In certain situations, intermediate product or side streams are removed from sections of the tower between the distillate and the bottoms. The side stream may be vapor or liquid and may be removed at a point above the feed entrance or below, depending on the composition desired.

The flows for a column with a liquid side stream removed above the feed inlet are shown in Fig. 11.4-17. The top enriching operating line above the liquid side stream and the stripping operating line below the feed are found in the usual way. The equation for the q line is also unaffected by the side stream and is found as before. The liquid side stream alters the

FIGURE 11.4-17. *Process flow for a rectification tower with a liquid side stream.*

Chapter 11 Vapor–Liquid Separation Processes

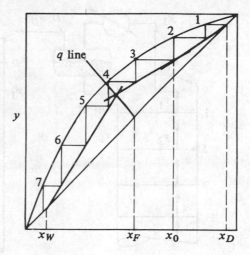

FIGURE 11.4-18. *McCabe–Thiele plot for a tower with a liquid side stream above the feed.*

liquid rate below it, and hence the material balance or operating line in the middle portion between the feed and liquid side stream plates as well.

Making a total material balance on the top portion of the tower, as shown in the dashed-line box in Fig. 11.4-17,

$$V_{S+1} = L_S + O + D \qquad \text{(11.4-33)}$$

where O is mol/h saturated liquid removed as a side stream. Since the liquid side stream is saturated,

$$L_n = L_S + O \qquad \text{(11.4-34)}$$

$$V_{S+1} = V_{n+1} \qquad \text{(11.4-35)}$$

Making a balance on the most volatile component,

$$V_{S+1}y_{S+1} = L_S x_S + O x_O + D x_D \qquad \text{(11.4-36)}$$

Solving for y_{S+1}, the operating line for the region between the side stream and the feed is

$$y_{S+1} = \frac{L_S}{V_{S+1}} x_S + \frac{O x_O + D x_D}{V_{S+1}} \qquad \text{(11.4-37)}$$

The slope of this line is L_S/V_{S+1}. The line can be located as shown in Fig. 11.4-18 by the q line, which determines the intersection of the stripping line and Eq. (11.4-37), or it may be fixed by the specification of x_O, the side-stream composition. The step on the McCabe–Thiele diagram must be at the intersection of the two operating lines at x_O in an actual tower. If this does not occur, the reflux ratio can be altered slightly to change the steps.

5. Partial condensers. In a few cases it may be desired to remove the overhead distillate product as a vapor instead of a liquid. This can also occur when the low boiling point of the distillate makes complete condensation difficult. The liquid condensate in a partial condenser is returned to the tower as reflux and the vapor removed as product, as shown in Fig. 11.4-19.

FIGURE 11.4-19. *Partial condenser where the vapor and liquid leave in equilibrium: (a) process flow diagram, (b) McCabe-Thiele plot.*

If the time of contact between the vapor product and the liquid is sufficient, the partial condenser is a theoretical stage. Then the composition x_R of the liquid reflux is in equilibrium with the vapor composition y_D, where $y_D = x_D$. If the cooling in the condenser is rapid and the vapor and liquid do not reach equilibrium, only a partial stage separation is obtained.

11.5   DISTILLATION AND ABSORPTION EFFICIENCIES FOR TRAY AND PACKED TOWERS

11.5A   Tray Efficiencies

In all the previous discussions of theoretical trays or stages in distillation, we assumed that the vapor leaving a tray was in equilibrium with the liquid leaving. However, if the time of contact and the degree of mixing on the tray are insufficient, the streams will not be in equilibrium. As a result the efficiency of the stage or tray will not be 100%. This means that we must use more actual trays for a given separation than the theoretical number of trays determined by calculation. The discussions in this section apply to both absorption and distillation tray towers.

Three types of tray or plate efficiency are used: *overall tray efficiency* E_O, *Murphree tray efficiency* E_M, and *point or local tray efficiency* E_{MP} (sometimes called *Murphree point efficiency*). These will be considered individually.

11.5B   Types of Tray Efficiencies

1. Overall tray efficiency. The *overall tray* or *plate efficiency* E_O concerns the entire tower and is simple to use, but it is the least fundamental. It is defined as the ratio of the number of theoretical or ideal trays needed in an entire tower to the number of actual trays used:

$$E_O = \frac{\text{number of ideal trays}}{\text{number of actual trays}} \qquad \textbf{(11.5-1)}$$

For example, if eight theoretical steps are needed and the overall efficiency is 60%, the number of theoretical trays is eight minus a reboiler, or seven trays. The actual number of trays is 7/0.60, or 11.7 trays.

2. Murphree tray efficiency. The *Murphree tray efficiency* E_M is defined as follows:

$$E_M = \frac{y_n - y_{n+1}}{y_n^* - y_{n+1}} \qquad \textbf{(11.5-2)}$$

where y_n is the average actual concentration of the mixed vapor leaving the tray n as shown in Fig. 11.5-1, y_{n+1} the average actual concentration of the mixed vapor entering tray n, and y_n^* the concentration of the vapor that would be in equilibrium with the liquid of concentration x_n leaving the tray to the downcomer.

The liquid entering the tray has a concentration of x_{n-1}; as it travels across the tray, its concentration drops to x_n at the outlet. Hence, there is a concentration gradient in the liquid as it flows across the tray. The vapor entering the tray comes in contact with liquid of different concentrations, and the outlet vapor will not be uniform in concentration.

3. Point efficiency. The *point* or *local efficiency* E_{MP} on a tray is defined as

$$E_{MP} = \frac{y_n' - y_{n+1}'}{y_n'^* - y_{n+1}'} \qquad \textbf{(11.5-3)}$$

where y_n' is the concentration of the vapor at a specific point in plate n as shown in Fig. 11.5-1, y_{n+1}' the concentration of the vapor entering the plate n at the same point, and $y_n'^*$ the concentration of the vapor that would be in equilibrium with x_n' at the same point. Since y_n' cannot be greater than $y_n'^*$, the local efficiency cannot be greater than 1.00 or 100%.

In small-diameter towers, the vapor flow sufficiently agitates the liquid so that it is uniform on the tray. Then the concentration of the liquid leaving is the same as that on the tray.

FIGURE 11.5-1. *Vapor and liquid compositions on a sieve tray and tray efficiency.*

Then $y'_n = y_n$, $y'_{n+1} = y_{n+1}$, and $y'^*_n = y^*_n$. The point efficiency then equals the Murphree tray efficiency, or $E_M = E_{MP}$.

In large-diameter columns, incomplete mixing of the liquid occurs on the trays. Some vapor will contact the entering liquid x_{n-1}, which is richer in component A than x_n. This will give a richer vapor at this point than at the exit point, where x_n leaves. Hence, the tray efficiency E_M will be greater than the point efficiency E_{MP}. The value of E_M can be related to E_{MP} by integration of E_{MP} over the entire tray.

11.5C Relationship Between Tray Efficiencies

The relationship between E_{MP} and E_M can be derived mathematically if the amount of liquid mixing is specified together with the amount of vapor mixing. Derivations for three different sets of assumptions are given by Robinson and Gilliland (R1). However, experimental data are usually needed to obtain amounts of mixing. Semitheoretical methods for predicting E_{MP} and E_M are summarized in detail by Van Winkle (V1).

When the Murphree tray efficiency E_M is known or can be predicted, the overall tray efficiency E_O can be related to E_M by several methods. In the first method, an analytical expression is as follows when the slope m of the equilibrium line is constant as well as the slope L/V of the operating line:

$$E_O = \frac{\log[1 + E_M(mV/L - 1)]}{\log(mV/L)} \tag{11.5-4}$$

If the equilibrium and operating lines of the tower are not straight, a graphical method employing the McCabe–Thiele diagram can be used to determine the actual number of trays when the Murphree tray efficiency is known. In Fig. 11.5-2 a diagram is given for an actual plate as compared with an ideal plate. The triangle acd represents an ideal plate and the smaller triangle abe the actual plate. For the case shown, the Murphree efficiency $E_M =$

FIGURE 11.5-2. *Use of Murphree plate efficiency to determine actual number of trays.*

0.60 = ba/ca. The dashed line going through point b is drawn so that ba/ca for each tray is 0.60. The trays are stepped off using this efficiency, and the total number of steps gives the actual number of trays needed. The reboiler is considered to be one theoretical tray, so the true equilibrium curve is used for this tray, as shown. In Fig. 11.5-2, 6.0 actual trays plus a reboiler are obtained.

11.5D Efficiency of Random-Packed and Structured Packed Towers

In tray towers, a theoretical tray is defined as a tray in which equilibrium is attained between the gas or vapor leaving and the liquid leaving the tray. In random-packed or structured packed towers, the same approach is used, where the HETP in m (ft) is defined as the height of the packed column necessary to give a separation equal to one theoretical plate. The design of mass-transfer towers requires evaluation of the number of theoretical stages or transfer units. Hence, the height of packing H in m (ft) required to perform a given separation is

$$H = n(\text{HETP}) \tag{11.5-5}$$

where n is the number of theoretical stages needed. Using the number-of-transfer-units method, the height H is

$$H = H_{OG} N_{OG} \tag{11.5-6}$$

where H_{OG} is the overall height of a transfer unit in m (ft) and N_{OG} is the number of transfer units.

The HETP and overall height of a transfer unit H_{OG} can be related by the following equation, which is the same as Eq. (10.6-55):

$$\text{HETP} = H_{OG} \frac{\ln[m/(L/V)]}{m/(L/V) - 1} \tag{11.5-7}$$

where m is the slope of the equilibrium line in mole fraction units and L and V are molar flow rates. If the operating line and equilibrium line are parallel, then HETP = H_{OG}. In distillation, the operating and equilibrium lines diverge below the feed point and converge above, so that the average mV/L is about 1.0 and HETP $\cong$ HTU for distillation. This is usually not true for absorption or stripping towers. Although the HETP concept lacks a sound theoretical basis, unlike the mass-transfer and H_{OG} concepts, it is simple and easy to use in computer equilibrium stage-to-stage calculations in distillation and is widely used to estimate packing height (S3). It is especially useful in multicomponent systems.

For a tray tower, the HETP can be defined as

$$\text{HETP} = \frac{T}{E_0} \tag{11.5-8}$$

where E_0 is the overall tray efficiency and T is the tray spacing, which varies from about 0.3 m for a 0.5-m-diameter tower, 0.6 m for a 1.0-m-diameter tower, to about 0.8 m (2.6 ft) for much larger towers over 4 m in diameter.

11.5E Estimation of Efficiencies of Tray and Packed Towers

In order to design the number of trays or packing heights needed, efficiencies must be obtained.

1. Efficiency of tray towers. For estimating the overall tray efficiency of bubble-tray towers for distillation, the O'Connell (O1) correlation can be used (K2) with about a ±10% error. The following equation for these data from Lockett (L1) can be used for sieve and valve trays as well, but predictions will be slightly conservative:

$$E_0 = 0.492(\mu_L\alpha)^{-0.245} \tag{11.5-9}$$

where E_0 is fraction efficiency, α is relative volatility of the two key components at the average tower temperature, and μ_L is the molar average viscosity in cp of the liquid feed at the average tower temperature of the top and the bottom. Most typical efficiencies are between 40 and 80%.

To estimate the overall tray efficiency for absorption towers, the O'Connell correlation (O1) can be used. This correlation is represented by the equation (S3)

$$\log E_0 = 1.597 - 0.199 \log(mM_L\mu_L/\rho_L) - 0.0896[\log(mM_L\mu_L/\rho_L)]^2 \tag{11.5-10}$$

where E_0 is overall average % tray efficiency, M_L is the average molecular weight of the liquid, m is the slope of the equilibrium line in mole fraction units, ρ_L is the liquid density in lb_m/ft^3, and μ_L is molar average liquid viscosity in cp at the average tower temperature. The average deviation of the data is ±16.3% and the maximum is 157%. This can be used for bubble-cap, sieve, and valve-type trays. Note that these tray efficiencies are quite low and in the range of 1% to 50%, with typical values of 10 to 30%.

2. Efficiency of random-packed towers. For estimates for random packing, Eq. (11.5-11) can be used to determine the HETP for second- and third-generation packings only (S2):

$$HETP = 0.0180d_p \quad \text{(SI)}$$
$$HETP = 1.5d_p \quad \text{(English)} \tag{11.5-11}$$

where HETP is in m and d_p is packing diameter in mm. In English units, HETP is in ft and d_p is in in. Also, for small-diameter towers, where the tower diameter D is less than 0.60 m (2 ft), HETP = D, but not less than 0.3 m (1 ft).

For vacuum service (S3),

$$HETP = 0.0180d_p + 0.15 \quad \text{(SI)}$$
$$HETP = 1.5d_p + 0.50 \quad \text{(English)} \tag{11.5-12}$$

The above equations are useful for low-viscosity liquids. For absorption with high-viscosity liquids, the values of HETP are much greater, with values of 1.5 to 1.8 m (5 to 6 ft).

3. Efficiency of structured packing in towers. For approximate estimates of the efficiency of structured packings at low to moderate pressure with low viscosity liquids (K4),

$$HETP = 100/a + 0.10 \quad \text{(SI)}$$
$$HETP = 100/a + 0.33 \quad \text{(English)} \tag{11.5-13}$$

where HETP is in m and a is surface area in m^2/m^3. In English units, HETP is in ft and a in ft^2/ft^3. The value added of 0.10 m gives the estimate a conservative bias (K4). Values of HETP range from about 0.3 to 0.6 m (1.0 to 2.0 ft). For wire mesh (gauze), structured-packing values range from 0.1 to 0.3 m (0.3 to 1.0 ft).

EXAMPLE 11.5-1. Estimation of Tray and Packing Efficiencies and Tower Height

A liquid feed of benzene–toluene is being distilled under the same conditions as in Ex. 11.4-1. The number of theoretical steps needed is calculated as 7.6. The feed composition $x_F = 0.45$, $x_D = 0.95$, and $x_W = 0.10$. Do as follows:

(a) Using valve trays, calculate the overall efficiency E_0 and the tower height. Assume a tray spacing T of 0.6 m.

(b) Using 2-in. metal Pall rings, calculate the HETP and the tower height.

(c) Using Flexipac No. 2 structured packing, calculate the tower height.

Solution: For part (a), from Fig. 11.1-1 at 1 atm abs and $x_W = 0.10$, the boiling temperature is 106.5°C. At the top, for $x_D = 0.95$, the dew point is 82.3°C. The average is $(106.5 + 82.3)/2$ or 94.4°C.

Using Table A.3-12 and Fig. A.3-4 at 94.4°C, the viscosity of benzene is 0.26 cp, and of toluene, 0.295 cp. The molar average viscosity is $\mu_L = 0.45(0.26) + 0.55(0.295) = 0.279$ cp.

From Table 11.1-1, the vapor pressure of benzene P_A at 94.4°C is 153.3 kPa, and for toluene, $P_B = 62.2$ kPa. Hence, the average relative volatility $\alpha = 153.3/62.2 = 2.465$.

Using Eq. (11.5-9), $E_0 = 0.492(\mu_L \alpha)^{-0.245} = 0.492 \, (0.279 \times 2.465)^{-0.245} = 0.539$. Using Eq. (11.5-8), HETP $= T/E_0 = 0.6/0.539 = 1.113$ m/theoretical steps. The number of tray theoretical steps $= 7.6 - 1$ step for the reboiler, or 6.6 steps. Hence, tower tray height $H = 1.113(6.6) = 7.35$ m.

For part (b), for 2-in. (25.4×2 mm) Pall rings, Eq. (11.5-11) gives

$$\text{HETP} = 0.0180 d_p = 0.0180(25.4 \times 2) = 0.914 \text{ m}$$

For 6.6 theoretical steps, tower height $H = 0.914(6.6) = 6.03$ m.

For part (c), for Flexipac No. 2 structured packing and using Table 10.6-1, $a = 223$ m/m^2. From Eq. (11.5-13),

$$\text{HETP} = 100/a + 0.10 = 100/223 + 0.10 = 0.548 \text{ m}$$

$$\text{Tower height } H = 0.548(6.6) = 3.617 \text{ m}$$

11.5F Flooding Velocity and Diameter of Tray Towers

In tray towers the maximum vapor velocity can be limited either by entrainment of small liquid droplets or by the liquid handling capacity of the tray downcomer whereby the liquid in the downcomer backs up to the next tray. The general basis for design uses the allowable-vapor-velocity concept. The equation by Fair (F1) for estimating the maximum allowable vapor velocity for sieve, bubble-cap, or valve trays is

$$v_{max} = K_v \left(\frac{\sigma}{20} \right)^{0.2} \sqrt{\frac{\rho_L - \rho_V}{\rho_V}} \tag{11.5-14}$$

where v_{max} is the allowable vapor velocity in ft/s based on the total cross-sectional area minus the area of one downcomer, σ is the surface tension of the liquid in dyn/cm (mN/m), and ρ_L and ρ_V are liquid and gas densities, kg/m^3 or lb$_m$/ft^3. The value of K_v in ft/s is obtained from Fig. 11.5-3, where L and V are total flow rates in kg/h or lb$_m$/h. As a rule-of-thumb, the value

FIGURE 11.5-3. *Estimation of K_v value for allowable vapor velocity. (From Fair, J. R., Petro/Chem. Eng., 33(10), 45 (1961). With permission.)*

of K_v should be multiplied by a factor of 0.91 to account for the downspout area of 9% of the tray (T2).

The Eq. (11.5-14) holds for nonfoaming systems. For many absorbers the K_v should be multiplied by 0.90 or so to account for foaming (S3). For the final design the above v_{max} should be multiplied by 0.80 to be 20% below flooding. For organic liquids a typical value of σ is about 20–25 dyn/cm. For water with a surface tension of about 72 dyn/cm, the flooding velocity is larger by a factor of about $(72/22.5)^{0.20}$, or 1.26/1.

EXAMPLE 11.5-2. *Tray Diameter of a Valve-Tray Absorption Tower*

A valve-tray absorption tower is being used to absorb and recover ethyl alcohol vapor in air by pure water. The tower operates at 30°C and a pressure of 110 kPa abs. The entering gas contains 2.0 mol % ethyl alcohol in water, and 95% of the alcohol is recovered in the outlet water. The inlet pure aqueous flow is 186 kg mol/h and the inlet gas flow is 211.7 kg mol/h. Calculate the required tower diameter. A tray spacing of 0.610 m (2.0 ft) will be assumed. Use a factor of 0.95 for possible foaming.

Solution: The molecular weight of the entering air at the tower bottom where the flow rates are the greatest is

$$M = 0.98(29.0) + 0.02(46.1) = 29.34 \text{ kg/kg mol}$$

The density of the vapor is

$$\rho_V = \frac{29.34 \text{ kg/kg mol}}{(22.414 \text{ m}^3/\text{kg mol})} \frac{(273.2)(110)}{(273.2 + 30)(101.325)}$$

$$= 1.280 \text{ kg/m}^3$$

The mass flow rate of the gas is $V = 211.7(29.34) = 6211$ kg/h. Moles ethyl alcohol absorbed = $0.95(0.02)(211.7) = 4.02$. The outlet aqueous flow rate $L = 186.0 + 4.02 = 190.02$ kg mol/h. The liquid mass flow rate is

$$L = 186.0(18) + 4.02(46.1) = 3533 \text{ kg/h}$$

The outlet water density, assuming a dilute solution at 30°C, from Appendix A.2-3 is $\rho_L = 0.995(1000) = 995$ kg/m³. Then,

$$\frac{L}{V}\left(\frac{\rho_V}{\rho_L}\right)^{0.5} = \frac{(3533)}{(6211)}\left(\frac{1.280}{995}\right)^{0.5} = 0.02040$$

Using Fig. 11.5-3 for a 24-in. tray spacing, $K_v = 0.385$ ft/s. Substituting into Eq. (11.5-14) and using a surface tension of 70 (slightly less than water),

$$v_{max} = 0.385\left(\frac{70}{20}\right)^{0.2}\sqrt{\frac{995 - 1.280}{1.280}} = 13.78 \text{ ft/s}$$

Multiplying the above by 0.91 to account for downspout area, by 0.95 for foaming, and by 0.80 for 80% of flooding,

$$v_{design} = 13.78(0.91)(0.95)(0.80)$$

$$= 9.531 \text{ ft/s} \quad \text{or} \quad 2.905 \text{ m/s}$$

The tower cross-section equals

$$\frac{(6211 \text{ kg/h})}{(3600 \text{ s/h})} \frac{1}{(1.28 \text{ kg/m}^3)} \frac{1}{(2.905 \text{ m/s})} = 0.464 \text{ m}^2$$

Solving for the diameter, $\pi D^2/4 = 0.464$. Then, $D = 0.7686$ m (2.522 ft).

11.6 FRACTIONAL DISTILLATION USING ENTHALPY–CONCENTRATION METHOD

11.6A Enthalpy–Concentration Data

1. Introduction. In Section 11.4B the McCabe–Thiele method was used to calculate the number of theoretical steps or trays needed for a given separation of a binary mixture of *A* and *B* by rectification or fractional distillation. The main assumptions in the method are that the latent heats are equal, sensible heat differences are negligible, and constant molal overflow occurs in each section of the distillation tower. In this section we shall consider fractional distillation using enthalpy–concentration data where the molal overflow rates are not necessarily constant. The analysis will be made using enthalpy as well as material balances.

2. Enthalpy–concentration data.

An enthalpy–concentration diagram for a binary vapor–liquid mixture of A and B takes into account latent heats, heats of solution or mixing, and sensible heats of the components of the mixture. The following data are needed to construct such a diagram at a constant pressure: (1) heat capacity of the liquid as a function of temperature, composition, and pressure; (2) heat of solution as a function of temperature and composition; (3) latent heats of vaporization as a function of composition and pressure or temperature; and (4) boiling point as a function of pressure, composition, and temperature.

The diagram at a given constant pressure is based on arbitrary reference states of liquid and temperature, such as 273 K (32°F). The saturated liquid line in enthalpy h kJ/kg (btu/lb$_m$) or kJ/kg mol is calculated by

$$h = x_A c_{pA}(T - T_0) + (1 - x_A)c_{pB}(T - T_0) + \Delta H_{sol} \tag{11.6-1}$$

where x_A is wt or mole fraction A, T is boiling point of the mixture in K (°F) or °C, T_0 is reference temperature, K, c_{pA} is the liquid heat capacity of the component A in kJ/kg·K (btu/lb$_m$·°F) or kJ/kg mol·K, c_{pB} is heat capacity of B, and ΔH_{sol} is heat of solution at T_0 in kJ/kg (btu/lb$_m$) or kJ/kg mol. If heat is evolved on mixing, the ΔH_{sol} will be a negative value in Eq. (11.6-1). Often, the heats of solution are small, as in hydrocarbon mixtures, and are neglected.

The saturated vapor enthalpy line of H kJ/kg (btu/lb$_m$) or kJ/kg mol of a vapor composition y_A is calculated by

$$H = y_A[\lambda_A + c_{py_A}(T - T_0)] + (1 - y_A)[\lambda_B + c_{py_B}(T - T_0)] \tag{11.6-2}$$

where c_{py_A} is the vapor heat capacity for A and c_{py_B} for B. The latent heats λ_A and λ_B are the values at the reference temperature T_0. Generally, the latent heat is given as λ_{Ab} at the normal boiling point T_{bA} of the pure component A and λ_{Bb} for B. Then to correct this to the reference temperature T_0 for use in Eq. (11.6-2),

$$\lambda_A = c_{pA}(T_{bA} - T_0) + \lambda_{Ab} - c_{py_A}(T_{bA} - T_0) \tag{11.6-3}$$

$$\lambda_B = c_{pB}(T_{bB} - T_0) + \lambda_{Bb} - c_{py_B}(T_{bB} - T_0) \tag{11.6-4}$$

In Eq. (11.6-3) the pure liquid is heated from T_0 to T_{bA}, vaporized at T_{bA}, and then cooled as a vapor to T_0. Similarly, Eq. (11.6-4) also holds for λ_B. For convenience, the reference temperature T_0 is often taken as equal to the boiling point of the lower-boiling component A. This means $\lambda_A = \lambda_{Ab}$. Hence, only λ_{Bb} must be corrected to λ_B.

EXAMPLE 11.6-1. Enthalpy–Concentration Plot for Benzene–Toluene

Prepare an enthalpy–concentration plot for benzene–toluene at 1 atm pressure. Equilibrium data are given in Table 11.1-1 and Figs. 11.1-1 and 11.1-2. Physical property data are given in Table 11.6-1.

Solution: A reference temperature of $T_0 = 80.1$°C will be used for convenience so that the liquid enthalpy of pure benzene ($x_A = 1.0$) at the boiling point will be zero. For the first point, we will select pure toluene ($x_A = 0$). For liquid toluene at the boiling point of 110.6°C, using Eq. (11.6-1) with zero heat of solution and data from Table 11.6-1,

$$h = x_A c_{pA}(T - 80.1) + (1 - x_A)c_{pB}(T - 80.1) + 0 \tag{11.6-5}$$

$$h = 0 + (1 - 0)(167.5)(110.6 - 80.1) = 5109 \text{ kJ/kg mol}$$

TABLE 11.6-1. *Physical Property Data for Benzene and Toluene*

Component	Boiling Point, (°C)	Heat Capacity, (kJ/kg mol · K)		Latent Heat of Vaporization (kJ/kg mol)
		Liquid	Vapor	
Benzene (A)	80.1	138.2	96.3	30 820
Toluene (B)	110.6	167.5	138.2	33 330

For the saturated vapor enthalpy line, Eq. (11.6-2) is used. However, we must first calculate λ_B at the reference temperature $T_0 = 80.1°C$, using Eq. (11.6-4):

$$\lambda_B = c_{pB}(T_{bB} - T_0) + \lambda_{Bb} - c_{pyB}(T_{bB} - T_0) \qquad \textbf{(11.6-4)}$$

$$= 167.5(110.6 - 80.1) + 33\,330 - 138.2(110.6 - 80.1)$$

$$= 34\,224 \text{ kJ/kg mol}$$

To calculate H, Eq. (11.6-2) is used, and $y_A = 0$:

$$H = y_A[\lambda_A + c_{pyA}(T - T_0)] + (1 - y_A)[\lambda_B + c_{pyB}(T - T_0)] \qquad \textbf{(11.6-2)}$$

$$= 0 + (1.0 - 0)[34\,224 + 138.2(110.6 - 80.1)]$$

$$= 38\,439 \text{ kJ/kg mol}$$

For pure benzene, $x_A = 1.0$ and $y_A = 1.0$. Using Eq. (11.6-5), since $T = T_0 = 80.1$, $h = 0$. For the saturated vapor enthalpy, using Eq. (11.6-2) and $T = 80.1$,

$$H = 1.0[30\,820 + 96.3(80.1 - 80.1)] + 0 = 30\,820$$

Selecting $x_A = 0.50$, the boiling point $T_b = 92°C$ and the temperature of saturated vapor for $y_A = 0.50$ is 98.8°C from Fig. 11.1-1. Using Eq. (11.6-5) for the saturated liquid enthalpy at the boiling point,

$$h = 0.5(138.2)(92 - 80.1) + (1 - 0.5)(167.5)(92 - 80.1) = 1820$$

Using Eq. (11.6-2) for $y_A = 0.5$, the saturated vapor enthalpy at 98.8°C is

$$H = 0.5[30\,820 + 96.3(98.8 - 80.1)]$$

$$+ (1 - 0.5)[34\,224 + 138.2(98.8 - 80.1)] = 34\,716$$

Selecting $x_A = 0.30$ and $y_A = 0.30$, $h = 2920$ and $H = 36\,268$. Also, for $x_A = 0.80$ and $y_A = 0.80$, $h = 562$ and $H = 32\,380$. These values are tabulated in Table 11.6-2 and plotted in Fig. 11.6-1.

Some properties of the enthalpy–concentration plot are as follows. The region in between the saturated vapor line and the saturated liquid line is the two-phase liquid–vapor region. From Table 11.1-1, for $x_A = 0.411$, the vapor in equilibrium is $y_A = 0.632$. These two points are plotted in Fig. 11.6-1; this tie line represents the enthalpies and compositions of the

Saturated Liquid		Saturated Vapor	
Mole fraction, x_A	Enthalpy, h, (kJ/kg mol)	Mole fraction, y_A	enthalpy, H, (kJ/kg mol)
0	5109	0	38 439
0.30	2920	0.30	36 268
0.50	1820	0.50	34 716
0.80	562	0.80	32 380
1.00	0	1.00	30 820

FIGURE 11.6-1. *Enthalpy-concentration plot for benzene-toluene mixture at 1.0 atm abs.*

liquid and vapor phases in equilibrium. Other tie lines can be drawn in a similar manner. The region below the *h*-versus-x_A line represents liquid below the boiling point.

11.6B Distillation in Enriching Section of Tower

To analyze the enriching section of a fractionating tower using enthalpy–concentration data, we make an overall and a component balance in Fig. 11.6-2:

$$V_{n+1} = L_n + D \qquad \textbf{(11.6-6)}$$

$$V_{n+1} y_{n+1} = L_n x_n + D x_D \qquad \textbf{(11.6-7)}$$

FIGURE 11.6-2. *Enriching section of distillation tower.*

Equation (11.6-7) can be rearranged to give the enriching-section operating line:

$$y_{n+1} = \frac{L_n}{V_{n+1}} x_n + \frac{Dx_D}{V_{n+1}} \qquad \textbf{(11.6-8)}$$

This is the same as Eq. (11.4-7) for the McCabe–Thiele method, but now the liquid and vapor flow rates V_{n+1} and L_n may vary throughout the tower, and Eq. (11.6-8) will not be a straight line on an x-y plot.

Making an enthalpy balance,

$$V_{n+1} H_{n+1} = L_n h_n + D h_D + q_c \qquad \textbf{(11.6-9)}$$

where q_c is the condenser duty, kJ/h or kW (btu/h). An enthalpy balance can be made just around the condenser:

$$q_c = V_1 H_1 - L h_D - D h_D \qquad \textbf{(11.6-10)}$$

By combining Eqs. (11.6-9) and (11.6-10) to eliminate q_c, an alternative form is obtained:

$$V_{n+1} H_{n+1} = L_n h_n + V_1 H_1 - L h_D \qquad \textbf{(11.6-11)}$$

Substituting the value of L_n from Eq. (11.6-6) into (11.6-11),

$$V_{n+1} H_{n+1} = (V_{n+1} - D) h_n + V_1 H_1 - L h_D \qquad \textbf{(11.6-12)}$$

Equations (11.6-8) and (11.6-12) are the final working equations for the enriching section.

In order to plot the operating line Eq. (11.6-8), the terms V_{n+1} and L_n must be determined from Eq. (11.6-12). If the reflux ratio is set, V_1 and L are known. The values H_1 and h_D can be determined by means of Eqs. (11.6-1) and (11.6-2) or from an enthalpy–concentration plot. If a value of x_n is selected, it is a trial-and-error solution to obtain H_{n+1}, since y_{n+1} is not known. The steps to follow are given below:

1. Select a value of x_n. Assume $V_{n+1} = V_1 = L + D$ and $L_n = L$. Then using these values in Eq. (11.6-8), calculate an approximate value for y_{n+1}. This assumes a straight operating line.

2. Using this y_{n+1}, obtain H_{n+1}, and obtain h_n using x_n. Substitute these values into Eq. (11.6-12) and solve for V_{n+1}. Obtain L_n from Eq. (11.6-6).
3. Substitute into Eq. (11.6-8) and solve for y_{n+1}.
4. If the calculated value of y_{n+1} does not equal the assumed value of y_{n+1}, repeat steps 2–3. Generally, a second trial is not needed. Assume another value of x_n and repeat steps 1–4.
5. Plot the curved operating line for the enriching section. Generally, only a few values for the flows L_n and V_{n+1} are needed to determine the operating line, which is slightly curved.

11.6C Distillation in Stripping Section of Tower

To analyze the stripping section of a distillation tower, an overall and a component material balance are made on Fig. 11.4-5a:

$$L_m = W + V_{m+1} \tag{11.6-13}$$

$$L_m x_m = W x_W + V_{m+1} y_{m+1} \tag{11.6-14}$$

$$y_{m+1} = \frac{L_m}{V_{m+1}} x_m - \frac{W x_W}{V_{m+1}} \tag{11.6-15}$$

Making an enthalpy balance with q_R kJ/h or kW(btu/h) entering the reboiler in Fig. 11.4-5a, and substituting $(V_{m+1} + W)$ for L_m from Eq. (11.6-13),

$$V_{m+1} H_{m+1} = (V_{m+1} + W) h_m + q_R - W h_W \tag{11.6-16}$$

Making an overall enthalpy balance in Fig. 11.4-3,

$$q_R = D h_D + W h_W + q_c - F h_F \tag{11.6-17}$$

The final working equations to use are Eqs. (11.6-15)–(11.6-17).

Using a method similar to that for the enriching section to solve the equations, select a value of y_{m+1} and calculate an approximate value for x_m from Eq. (11.6-15), assuming constant molal overflow. Then calculate V_{m+1} and L_m from Eqs. (11.6-16) and (11.6-13). Then use Eq. (11.6-15) to determine x_m. Compare this calculated value of x_m with the assumed value.

EXAMPLE 11.6-2. Distillation Using Enthalpy–Concentration Method
A liquid mixture of benzene–toluene is being distilled under the same conditions as in Example 11.4-1, except that a reflux ratio of 1.5 times the minimum reflux ratio is to be used. The value $R_m = 1.17$ from Example 11.4-2 will be used. Use enthalpy balances to calculate the flow rates of the liquid and vapor at various points in the tower and plot the curved operating lines. Determine the number of theoretical stages needed.

Solution: The given data are as follows: $F = 100$ kg mol/h, $x_F = 0.45$, $x_D = 0.95$, $x_W = 0.10$, $R = 1.5 R_m = 1.5(1.17) = 1.755$, $D = 41.2$ kg mol/h, $W = 58.8$ kg mol/h. The feed enters at 54.4°C and $q = 1.195$. The flows at the top of the tower are calculated as follows:

$$\frac{L}{D} = 1.755; \qquad L = 1.755(41.2) = 72.3;$$

$$V_1 = L + D = 72.3 + 41.2 = 113.5$$

From Fig. 11.1-1, the saturation temperature at the top of the tower for $y_1 = x_D = 0.95$ is 82.3°C. Using Eq. (11.6-2),

$$H_1 = 0.95[30\,820 + 96.3(82.3 - 80.1)]$$

$$+ (1 - 0.95)[34\,224 + 138.2(82.3 - 80.1)] = 31\,206$$

This value of 31 206 could also have been obtained from the enthalpy–concentration plot, Fig. 11.6-1. The boiling point of the distillate D is obtained from Fig. 11.1-1 and is 81.1°C. Using Eq. (11.6-5),

$$h_D = 0.95(138.2)(81.1 - 80.1) + (1 - 0.95)(167.5)(81.1 - 80.1) = 139$$

Again, this value could have been obtained from Fig. 11.6-1.

Following the procedure outlined for the enriching section for step 1, a value of $x_n = 0.55$ is selected. Assuming a straight operating line for Eq. (11.6-8), an approximate value of y_{n+1} is obtained:

$$y_{n+1} = \frac{72.3}{113.5}x_n + \frac{41.2}{113.5}(0.95) = 0.637(x_n) + 0.345$$

$$= 0.637(0.55) + 0.345 = 0.695$$

Starting with step 2 and using Fig. 11.6-1, for $x_n = 0.55$, $h_n = 1590$, and for $y_{n+1} = 0.695$, $H_{n+1} = 33\,240$. Substituting into Eq. (11.6-12) and solving,

$$V_{n+1}(33\,240) = (V_{n+1} - 41.2)1590 + 113.5(31\,206) - 72.3(139)$$

$$V_{n+1} = 109.5$$

Using Eq. (11.6-6),

$$109.5 = L_n + 41.2 \quad \text{or} \quad L_n = 68.3$$

For step 3, substituting into Eq. (11.6-8),

$$y_{n+1} = \frac{68.3}{109.5}(0.55) + \frac{41.2}{109.5}(0.95) = 0.700$$

This calculated value of $y_{n+1} = 0.700$ is sufficiently close to the approximate value of 0.695 that no further trials are needed.

Selecting another value for $x_n = 0.70$ and using Eq. (11.6-8), an approximate value of y_{n+1} is calculated:

$$y_{n+1} = \frac{72.3}{113.5}(0.70) + \frac{41.2}{113.5}(0.95) = 0.791$$

Using Fig. 11.6-1 for $x_n = 0.70$, $h_n = 1000$, and for $y_{n+1} = 0.791$, $H_{n+1} = 32\,500$. Substituting into Eq. (11.6-12) and solving,

$$V_{n+1}(32\,500) = (V_{n+1} - 41.2)1000 + 113.5(31\,206) - 72.3(139)$$

$$V_{n+1} = 110.8$$

Using Eq. (11.6-6),

$$L_n = 110.8 - 41.2 = 69.6$$

Substituting into Eq. (11.6-8),

$$y_{n+1} = \frac{69.6}{110.8}(0.70) + \frac{41.2}{110.8}(0.95) = 0.793$$

In Fig. 11.6-3, the points for the curved operating line in the enriching section are plotted. This line is approximately straight and is very slightly above that for constant molal overflow.

Using Eq. (11.6-10), the condenser duty is calculated:

$$q_c = 113.5(31\,206) - 72.3(139) - 41.2(139)$$

$$= 3\,526\,100 \text{ kJ/h}$$

To obtain the reboiler duty q_R, values for h_W and h_F are needed. Using Fig. 11.6-1 for $x_W = 0.10$, $h_W = 4350$. The feed is at 54.5°C. Using Eq. (11.6-5),

$$h_F = 0.45(138.2)(54.5 - 80.1) + (1 - 0.45)(167.5)(54.5 - 80.1)$$

$$= -3929$$

FIGURE 11.6-3. *Plot of curved operating lines using enthalpy–concentration method for Example 11.6-2. Solid lines are for enthalpy–concentration method and dashed lines for constant molal overflow.*

Chapter 11   Vapor–Liquid Separation Processes

Using Eq. (11.6-17),

$$q_R = 41.2(139) + 58.8(4350) + 3\ 526\ 100 - 100(-3929)$$

$$= 4\ 180\ 500\ \text{kJ/h}$$

Using Fig. 11.4-5 and making a material balance below the bottom tray and around the reboiler,

$$L_N = W + V_W \qquad\qquad \textbf{(11.6-18)}$$

Rewriting Eq. (11.6-16) for this bottom section,

$$V_W H_W = (V_W + W)h_N + q_R - W h_W \qquad\qquad \textbf{(11.6-19)}$$

From the equilibrium diagram, Fig. 11.1-2, for $x_W = 0.10$, $y_W = 0.207$, which is the vapor composition leaving the reboiler.

For equimolal overflow in the stripping section, using Eqs. (11.4-14) and (11.4-15),

$$L_m = L_n + qF = 72.3 + 1.195(100) = 191.8 \qquad\qquad \textbf{(11.4-14)}$$

$$V_{m+1} = V_{n+1} - (1 - q)F$$

$$= 113.5 - (1 - 1.195)100 = 133.0 \qquad\qquad \textbf{(11.4-15)}$$

Selecting $y_{m+1} = y_W = 0.207$, and using Eq. (11.6-15), an approximate value of $x_m = x_N$ is obtained:

$$y_{m+1} = \frac{L_m}{V_{m+1}} x_m - \frac{W x_w}{V_{m+1}} \qquad\qquad \textbf{(11.6-15)}$$

$$0.207 = \frac{191.8}{133.0}(x_N) - \frac{58.8}{133.0}(0.10)$$

Solving, $x_N = 0.174$. From Fig. (11.6-1), for $x_N = 0.174$, $h_N = 3800$, and for $y_W = 0.207$, $H_W = 37\ 000$. Substituting into Eq. (11.6-19),

$$V_W(37\ 000) = (V_W + 58.8)(3800) + 4\ 180\ 500 - 58.8(4350)$$

Solving, $V_W = 125.0$. Using Eq. (11.6-18), $L_N = 183.8$. Substituting into Eq. (11.6-15) and solving for x_N,

$$0.207 = \frac{183.8}{125.0}(x_N) - \frac{58.8}{125.0}(0.10)$$

$$x_N = 0.173$$

This value of 0.173 is quite close to the approximate value of 0.174.

Assuming a value of $y_{m+1} = 0.55$ and using Eq. (11.6-15), an approximate value of x_m is obtained:

$$y_{m+1} = 0.55 = \frac{191.8}{133.0}(x_m) - \frac{58.8}{133.0}(0.10)$$

$$x_m = 0.412$$

From Fig. (11.6-1), for $x_m = 0.412$, $h_m = 2300$, and for $y_{m+1} = 0.55$, $H_m = 34\,400$. Substituting into Eq. (11.6-16),

$$V_{m+1}(34\,400) = (V_{m+1} + 58.8)(2300) + 4\,180\,500 - 58.8(4350)$$

Solving, $V_{m+1} = 126.5$. Using Eq. (11.6-13),

$$L_m = W + V_{m+1} = 58.8 + 126.5 = 185.3$$

Substituting into Eq. (11.6-15) and solving for x_m,

$$y_{m+1} = 0.55 = \frac{185.3}{126.5}x_m - \frac{58.8}{126.5}(0.1)$$

$$x_m = 0.407$$

This value of 0.407 is sufficiently close to the approximate value of 0.412 that no further trials are needed. The two points calculated for the stripping section are plotted in Fig. 11.6-3. This stripping line is also approximately straight and is very slightly above the operating line for constant molal overflow.

Using the operating line for the enthalpy balance method, the number of theoretical steps is 10.4. Using the equimolal method, 9.9 steps are obtained. This difference would be larger if the reflux ratio of 1.5 times R_m were decreased to, say, 1.2 or 1.3. At larger reflux ratios, this difference in number of steps would be less.

Note that in Example 11.6-2, in the stripping section the vapor flow increases slightly from 125.0 to 126.5 in going from the reboiler to near the feed tray. These values are lower than the value of 133.0 obtained assuming equimolal overflow. Similar conclusions hold for the enriching section. The enthalpy–concentration method is useful in calculating the internal vapor and liquid flows at any point in the column. These data are then used in sizing the trays. Also, calculations of q_c and q_R are used in designing the condenser and reboiler. This method is very applicable to design using a computer solution for binary and multicomponent mixtures to make tray-to-tray mass and enthalpy balances for the whole tower. The more restrictive Ponchon–Savarit graphical method for only binary mixtures is available (K3, T2).

11.7   DISTILLATION OF MULTICOMPONENT MIXTURES

11.7A   Introduction to Multicomponent Distillation

In industry many of the distillation processes involve the separation of more than two components. The general principles of design for multicomponent distillation towers are the same in many respects as those described for binary systems. There is one mass balance for each component in the multicomponent mixture. Enthalpy or heat balances are made which are similar to those for the binary case. Equilibrium data are used to calculate boiling points and dew points. The concepts of minimum reflux and total reflux as limiting cases are also used.

1. Number of distillation towers needed.   In binary distillation, one tower was used to separate the two components A and B into relatively pure components, with A in the overhead and B in the bottoms. However, in a multicomponent mixture of n components, $n - 1$ frac-

FIGURE 11.7-1. *Separation of a ternary system of A, B, and C.*

tionators will be required for separation. For example, for a three-component system of components A, B, and C, where A is the most volatile and C the least volatile, two columns will be needed, as shown in Fig. 11.7-1. The feed of A, B, and C is distilled in column 1, and A and B are removed in the overhead and C in the bottoms. Since the separation in this column is between B and C, the bottoms containing C will contain a small amount of B and often a negligible amount of A (often called trace component). The amount of the trace component A in the bottoms can usually be neglected if the relative volatilities are reasonably large. In column 2 the feed of A and B is distilled, with A in the distillate containing a small amount of component B and a much smaller amount of C. The bottoms containing B will also be contaminated with a small amount of C and A. Alternately, column 1 could be used to remove A overhead, with B plus C being fed to column 2 for separation of B and C.

2. Design calculation methods. In multicomponent distillation, as in binary, ideal stages or trays are assumed in the stage-to-stage calculations. Using equilibrium data, equilibrium calculations are used to obtain the boiling point and equilibrium vapor composition from a given liquid composition or the dew point and liquid composition from a given vapor composition. Material balances and heat balances similar to those described in Section 11.6 are then used to calculate the flows to and from the adjacent stages. These stage-to-stage design calculations involve trial-and-error calculations, and high-speed digital computers are generally used to provide rigorous solutions.

In a design the conditions of the feed are generally known or specified (temperature, pressure, composition, flow rate). Then, in most cases, the calculation procedure follows either of two general methods. In the first method, the desired separation or split between two of the components is specified and the number of theoretical trays is calculated for a selected reflux ratio. It is clear that with more than two components in the feed, the complete compositions of the distillate and bottoms are not then known, and trial-and-error procedures must be used. In the second method, the number of stages in the enriching section and stripping section and the reflux ratio are specified or assumed and the separation of the components is calculated using assumed liquid and vapor flows and temperatures for the first trial. This approach is often preferred for computer calculations (H2, P1). In the trial-and-error procedures, the design method of Thiele and Geddes (P1, S1, T1), which is reliable, is often used to calculate resulting distillate and bottoms compositions together with tray temperatures and compositions. Various combinations and variations of the above rigorous calculation methods are available in the literature (H2, P1, S1) and will not be considered further.

The variables in the design of a distillation column are all interrelated, and there are only a certain number of these which may be fixed in the design. For a more detailed discussion of the specification of these variables, see Kwauk (K2).

3. *Shortcut calculation methods.* In the remainder of this chapter, shortcut calculation methods for the approximate solution of multicomponent distillation are considered. These methods are quite useful for studying a large number of cases rapidly to help orient the designer, determine approximate optimum conditions, or provide information for a cost estimate. Before discussing these methods, equilibrium relationships and calculation methods of bubble point, dew point, and flash vaporization for multicomponent systems will be covered.

11.7B Equilibrium Data in Multicomponent Distillation

For multicomponent systems which can be considered ideal, Raoult's law can be used to determine the composition of the vapor in equilibrium with the liquid. For example, for a system composed of four components, A, B, C, and D,

$$p_A = P_A x_A, \qquad p_B = P_B x_B, \qquad p_C = P_C x_C, \qquad p_D = P_D x_D \qquad (11.7\text{-}1)$$

$$y_A = \frac{p_A}{P} = \frac{P_A}{P} x_A, \qquad y_B = \frac{P_B}{P} x_B, \qquad y_C = \frac{P_C}{P} x_C, \qquad y_D = \frac{P_D}{P} x_D \qquad (11.7\text{-}2)$$

In hydrocarbon systems, because of nonidealities, the equilibrium data are often represented by

$$y_A = K_A x_A, \qquad y_B = K_B x_B, \qquad y_C = K_C x_C, \qquad y_D = K_D x_D \qquad (11.7\text{-}3)$$

where K_A is the vapor–liquid equilibrium constant or distribution coefficient for component A. These K values for light hydrocarbon systems (methane to decane) have been determined semiempirically and each K is a function of temperature and pressure. Convenient K factor charts are available from Depriester (D1) and Hadden and Grayson (H1). For light hydrocarbon systems, K is generally assumed not to be a function of composition, which is sufficiently accurate for most engineering calculations. Note that for an ideal system, $K_A = P_A/P$, and so on. As an example, data for the hydrocarbons n-butane, n-pentane, n-hexane, and n-heptane are plotted in Fig. 11.7-2 at 405.3 kPa (4.0 atm) absolute (D1, H1).

The relative volatility α_i for each individual component in a multicomponent mixture can be defined in a manner similar to that for a binary mixture. If component C in a mixture, of A, B, C, and D is selected as the base component,

$$\alpha_i = \frac{K_i}{K_C}, \qquad \alpha_A = \frac{K_A}{K_C}, \qquad \alpha_B = \frac{K_B}{K_C}, \qquad \alpha_C = \frac{K_C}{K_C} = 1.0, \qquad \alpha_D = \frac{K_D}{K_C} \qquad (11.7\text{-}4)$$

The values of K_i will be a stronger function of temperature than the α_i values, since the K_i lines in Fig. 11.7-2 all increase with temperature in a similar manner.

11.7C Boiling Point, Dew Point, and Flash Distillation

1. Boiling point. At a specified pressure, the boiling point or bubble point of a given multicomponent mixture must satisfy the relation $\sum y_i = 1.0$. For a mixture of A, B, C, and D, with C as the base component,

$$\sum y_i = \sum K_i x_i = K_C \sum \alpha_i x_i = 1.0 \qquad (11.7\text{-}5)$$

The calculation is a trial-and-error process, as follows. First a temperature is assumed and the values of α_i are calculated from the values of K_i at this temperature. Then the value of K_C is

FIGURE 11.7-2. *Equilibrium K values for light hydrocarbon systems at 405.3 kPa (4.0 atm) absolute.*

calculated from $K_C = 1.0/\sum \alpha_i x_i$. The temperature corresponding to the calculated value of $K_C = 1.0/\sum \alpha_i x_i$. The temperature corresponding to the calculated value of K_C is compared to the assumed temperature. If the values differ, the calculated temperature is used for the next iteration. After the final temperature is known, the vapor composition is calculated from

$$y_i = \frac{\alpha_i x_i}{\sum (\alpha_i x_i)} \qquad (11.7\text{-}6)$$

2. *Dew point.* For the dew-point calculation, which is also trial and error,

$$\sum x_i = \sum \left(\frac{y_i}{K_i}\right) = \left(\frac{1}{K_C}\right) \sum \left(\frac{y_i}{\alpha_i}\right) = 1.0 \qquad (11.7\text{-}7)$$

The value of K_C is calculated from $K_C = 1.0/\sum \alpha_i x_i$. After the final temperature is known, the liquid composition is calculated from

$$x_i = \frac{y_i/\alpha_i}{\sum (y_i/\alpha_i)} \tag{11.7-8}$$

EXAMPLE 11.7-1. Boiling Point of a Multicomponent Liquid

A liquid feed to a distillation tower at 405.3 kPa abs is fed to a distillation tower. The composition in mole fractions is as follows: n-butane ($x_A = 0.40$), n-pentane ($x_B = 0.25$), n-hexane ($x_C = 0.20$), n-heptane ($x_D = 0.15$). Calculate the boiling point and the vapor in equilibrium with the liquid.

Solution: First a temperature of 65°C is assumed and the values of K obtained from Fig. 11.7-2. Using component C (n-hexane) as the base component, the following values are calculated using Eq. (11.7-5) for the first trial:

		Trial 1 (65°C)			Trial 3 (70°C) Final			
Comp.	x_i	K_i	$\dfrac{K_i}{K_C} = \alpha_i$	$\alpha_i x_i$	K_i	α_i	$\alpha_i x_i$	y_i
A	0.40	1.68	6.857	2.743	1.86	6.607	2.643	0.748
B	0.25	0.63	2.571	0.643	0.710	2.522	0.631	0.178
C	0.20	0.245	1.000	0.200	0.2815	1.000	0.200	0.057
D	0.15	0.093	0.380	0.057	0.110	0.391	0.059	0.017
	1.00		$\sum \alpha_i x_i$ =	3.643		$\sum \alpha_i x_i$ =	3.533	1.000

$K_C = 1/\sum \alpha_i x_i = 1/3.643 = 0.2745$ (69°C) $K_C = 1/3.533 = 0.2830$ (70°C)

The calculated value of K_C is 0.2745, which corresponds to 69°C, Fig. 11.7-2. Using 69°C for trial 2, a temperature of 70°C is obtained. Using 70°C for trial 3, the calculations shown give a final calculated value of 70°C, which is the bubble point. Values of y_i are calculated from Eq. (11.7-6).

3. Flash distillation of multicomponent mixture. For flash distillation, the process flow diagram is shown in Fig. 11.3-1. Defining $f = V/F$ as the fraction of the feed vaporized and $(1 - f) = L/F$ as the fraction of the feed remaining as liquid, and making a component i balance as in Eq. (11.3-6), the following is obtained:

$$y_i = \frac{f - 1}{f} x_i + \frac{x_{iF}}{f} \tag{11.7-9}$$

where y_i is the composition of i in the vapor, in equilibrium with x_i in the liquid after vaporization. For equilibrium, $y_i = K_i x_i = K_C \alpha_i x_i$, where $\alpha_i = K_i/K_C$. Then Eq. (11.7-9) becomes

$$y_i = K_C \alpha_i x_i = \frac{f - 1}{f} x_i + \frac{x_{iF}}{f} \tag{11.7-10}$$

Solving for x_i and summing for all components,

$$\sum x_i = \sum \frac{x_{iF}}{f(K_C \alpha_i - 1) + 1} = 1.0 \tag{11.7-11}$$

This is solved by trial and error by first assuming a temperature if the fraction f vaporized has been set. When the $\sum x_i$ values add up to 1.0, the proper temperature has been chosen. The composition of the vapor y_i can be obtained from $y_i = K_C \alpha_i x_i$ or by a material balance.

11.7D Key Components in Multicomponent Distillation

Fractionation of a multicomponent mixture in a distillation tower will allow separation only between two components. For a mixture of A, B, C, D, and so on, a separation in one tower can only be made between A and B, or B and C, and so on. The components separated are called the *light key*, which is the more volatile (identified by the subscript L), and the *heavy key* (H). The components more volatile than the light key are called *light components* and will be present in the bottoms in small amounts. The components less volatile than the heavy key are called *heavy components* and will be present in the distillate in small amounts. The two key components are present in significant amounts in both the distillate and bottoms.

11.7E Total Reflux for Multicomponent Distillation

1. Minimum stages for total reflux. Just as in binary distillation, the minimum number of theoretical stages or steps, N_m, can be determined for multicomponent distillation for total reflux. The Fenske equation (11.4-23) also applies to any two components in a multicomponent system. When applied to the heavy key H and the light key L, it becomes

$$N_m = \frac{\log[(x_{LD}D/x_{HD}D)(x_{HW}W/x_{LW}W)]}{\log(\alpha_{L,av})} \tag{11.7-12}$$

where x_{LD} is mole fraction of light key in distillate, x_{LW} is mole fraction in bottoms, x_{HD} is mole fraction of heavy key in distillate, and x_{HW} is mole fraction in bottoms. The average value of α_L of the light key is calculated from α_{LD} at the top temperature (dew point) of the tower and α_{LW} at the bottoms temperature:

$$\alpha_{L,av} = \sqrt{\alpha_{LD}\alpha_{LW}} \tag{11.7-13}$$

Note that the distillate dew-point and bottoms boiling-point estimation is partially trial and error, since the distribution of the other components in the distillate and bottoms is not known and can affect these values.

2. Distribution of other components. To determine the distribution or concentration of other components in the distillate and bottoms at total reflux, Eq. (11.7-12) can be rearranged and written for any other component i as follows:

$$\frac{x_{iD}D}{x_{iW}W} = (\alpha_{i,av})^{N_m}\frac{x_{HD}D}{x_{HW}W} \tag{11.7-14}$$

These concentrations of the other components determined at total reflux can be used as approximations with finite and minimum reflux ratios. More accurate methods for finite and minimum reflux are available elsewhere (H2, S1, V1).

EXAMPLE 11.7-2. Calculation of Top and Bottom Temperatures and Total Reflux

The liquid feed of 100 mol/h at the boiling point given in Example 11.7-1 is fed to a distillation tower at 405.3 kPa and is to be fractionated so that 90% of the

n-pentane (B) is recovered in the distillate and 90% of the n-hexane (C) in the bottoms. Calculate the following:

(a) Moles per hour and composition of distillate and bottoms.
(b) Top temperature (dew point) of distillate and boiling point of bottoms.
(c) Minimum stages for total reflux and distribution of other components in the distillate and bottoms.

Solution: For part (a), material balances are made for each component, with component n-pentane (B) being the light key (L) and n-hexane (C) the heavy key (H). For the overall balance,

$$F = D + W \qquad (11.7\text{-}15)$$

For component B, the light key,

$$x_{BF}F = 0.25(100) = 25.0 = y_{BD}D + x_{BW}W \qquad (11.7\text{-}16)$$

Since 90% of B is in the distillate, $y_{BD}D = (0.90)(25) = 22.5$. Hence, $x_{BW}W = 2.5$. For component C, the heavy key,

$$x_{CF}F = 0.20(100) = 20.0 = y_{CD}D + x_{CW}W \qquad (11.7\text{-}17)$$

Also, 90% of C is in the bottoms, and $x_{CW}W = 0.90(20) = 18.0$. Then, $y_{CD}D = 2.0$. For the first trial, it is assumed that no component D (heavier than the heavy key C) is in the distillate and no light A in the bottoms. Hence, moles A in distillate $= y_{AD}D = 0.40(100) = 40.0$. Also, moles D in bottoms $= x_{DW}W = 0.15(100) = 15.0$. These values are tabulated below.

Comp.	Feed. F x_F	x_FF	Distillate, D $y_D = x_D$	y_DD	Bottoms, W x_W	x_WW
A	0.40	40.0	0.620	40.0	0	0
B (lt key L)	0.25	25.0	0.349	22.5	0.070	2.5
C (hy key H)	0.20	20.0	0.031	2.0	0.507	18.0
D	0.15	15.0	0	0	0.423	15.0
	1.00	$F = 100.0$	1.000	$D = 64.5$	1.000	$W = 35.5$

For the dew point of the distillate (top temperature) in part (b), a value of 67°C will be estimated for the first trial. The K values are read from Fig. 11.7-2 and the α values calculated. Using Eqs. (11.7-7) and (11.7-8), the following values are calculated:

Comp.	y_{iD}	$K_i(67°C)$	α_i	y_i/α_i	x_i
A	0.620	1.75	6.73	0.0921	0.351
B (L)	0.349	0.65	2.50	0.1396	0.531
C (H)	0.031	0.26	1.00	0.0310	0.118
D	0	0.10	0.385	0	0
	1.000			$\sum y_i/\alpha_i = 0.2627$	1.000

$$K_C = \sum y_i/\alpha_i = 0.2627$$

The calculated value of K_C is 0.2627, which corresponds very closely to 67°C, which is the final temperature of the dew point.

For the bubble point of the bottoms, a temperature of 135°C is assumed for trial 1 and Eqs. (11.7-5) and (11.7-6) used for the calculations. A second trial using 132°C gives the final temperature as shown below:

Comp.	x_{iW}	K_i	α_i	$\alpha_i x_i$	y_i
A	0	5.00	4.348	0	0
B (L)	0.070	2.35	2.043	0.1430	0.164
C (H)	0.507	1.15	1.000	0.5070	0.580
D	0.423	0.61	0.530	0.2242	0.256
	1.000			$\Sigma \alpha_i x_i = 0.8742$	1.000
		$K_C = 1/0.8742 = 1.144$			

The calculated value of K_C is 1.144, which is close to the value at 132°C.

For part (c) the proper α values of the light key L (n-pentane) to use in Eq. (11.7-13) are as follows:

$$\alpha_{LD} = 2.50 \qquad (t = 67°C \text{ at the column top})$$

$$\alpha_{LW} = 2.04 \qquad (t = 132°C \text{ at the column bottom})$$

$$\alpha_{L,av} = \sqrt{\alpha_{LD}\alpha_{LW}} = \sqrt{2.50(2.04)} = 2.258 \qquad \textbf{(11.7-13)}$$

Substituting into Eq. (11.7-12),

$$N_m = \frac{\log[(0.349 \times 64.5/0.031 \times 64.5)(0.507 \times 35.5/0.070 \times 35.5)]}{\log(2.258)}$$

$$= 5.404 \text{ theoretical stages (4.404 theoretical trays)}$$

The distribution or compositions of the other components can be calculated using Eq. (11.7-14). For component A, the average α value to use is

$$\alpha_{A,av} = \sqrt{\alpha_{AD}\alpha_{AW}} = \sqrt{6.73 \times 4.348} = 5.409$$

$$\frac{x_{AD}D}{x_{AW}W} = (\alpha_{A,av})^{N_m} \frac{x_{HD}D}{x_{HW}W} = (5.409)^{5.404} \frac{0.031(64.5)}{0.507(35.5)} = 1017 \quad \textbf{(11.7-14)}$$

Making an overall balance on A,

$$x_{AF}F = 40.0 = x_{AD}D + x_{AW}W \qquad \textbf{(11.7-18)}$$

Substituting $x_{AD}D = 1017 x_{AW}W$ from Eq. (11.7-14) into (11.7-18) and solving,

$$x_{AW}W = 0.039, \qquad x_{AD}D = 39.961$$

For the distribution of component D, $\alpha_{D,av} = \sqrt{0.385 \times 0.530} = 0.452$.

$$\frac{x_{DD}D}{x_{DW}W} = (\alpha_{D,av})^{N_m} \frac{x_{HD}D}{x_{HW}W} = (0.452)^{5.404} \frac{0.031(645)}{0.507(355)} = 0.001521$$

$$x_{DF}F = 15.0 = x_{DD}D + x_{DW}W$$

Solving, $x_{DD}D = 0.023$, $x_{DW}W = 14.977$.

The revised distillate and bottoms compositions are as follows:

Comp.	Distillate, D $y_D = x_D$	Distillate, D $x_D D$	Bottoms, W x_W	Bottoms, W $x_W W$
A	0.6197	39.961	0.0011	0.039
B (L)	0.3489	22.500	0.0704	2.500
C (H)	0.0310	2.000	0.5068	18.000
D	0.0004	0.023	0.4217	14.977
	1.0000	D = 64.484	1.0000	W = 35.516

Hence, the number of moles of D in the distillate is quite small, as is the number of moles of A in the bottoms.

Using the new distillate composition, a recalculation of the dew point assuming 67°C gives a calculated value of $K_C = 0.2637$. This is very close to that of 0.2627 obtained when the trace amount of D in the distillate was assumed as zero. Hence, the dew point is 67°C. Repeating the bubble-point calculation for the bottoms assuming 132°C, a calculated value of $K_C = 1.138$, which is close to the value at 132°C. Hence, the bubble point remains at 132°C. If either the bubble- or dew-point temperatures had changed, the new values would then be used in a recalculation of N_m.

11.7F Shortcut Method for Minimum Reflux Ratio for Multicomponent Distillation

As in the case of binary distillation, the minimum reflux ratio R_m is that reflux ratio which will require an infinite number of trays for the given separation of the key components.

For binary distillation, only one "pinch point" occurs where the number of steps becomes infinite, and that is usually at the feed tray. For multicomponent distillation, two pinch points or zones of constant composition occur: one in the section above the feed plate and another below the feed tray. The rigorous plate-by-plate stepwise procedure for calculating R_{ri} is trial and error and can be extremely tedious for hand calculations.

Underwood's shortcut method for calculating R_m (U1, U2) uses constant average α values and assumes constant flows in both sections of the tower. This method provides a reasonably accurate value. The two equations to be solved in order to determine the minimum reflux ratio are

$$1 - q = \sum \frac{\alpha_i x_{iF}}{\alpha_i - \theta} \tag{11.7-19}$$

$$R_m + 1 = \sum \frac{\alpha_i x_{iD}}{\alpha_i - \theta} \tag{11.7-20}$$

The values of x_{iD} for each component in the distillate in Eq. (11.7-20) are supposed to be the values at the minimum reflex. However, as an approximation, the values obtained using the Fenski total reflux equation are used. Since each α_i may vary with temperature, the average value of α_i to use in the preceding equations is approximated by using α_i at the average temperature of the top and bottom of the tower. Some (P1, S1) have used the average α which is used in the Fenske equation or the α at the entering feed temperature. To solve for R_m, the value of θ in Eq. (11.7-19) is first obtained by trial and error. This value of θ lies between the α value of the light key and the α value of the heavy key, which is 1.0. Using this value of θ in Eq. (11.7-20), the value of R_m is obtained directly. When distributed components appear between the key components, modified methods described by others (S1, T2, V1) can be used.

11.7G Shortcut Method for Number of Stages at Operating Reflux Ratio

1. Number of stages at operating reflux ratio. The determination of the minimum number of stages for total reflux presented in Section 11.7E and the minimum reflux ratio presented in Section 11.7F are useful for setting the allowable ranges for number of stages and flow conditions. These ranges are helpful in selecting the particular operating conditions for a design calculation. The relatively complex rigorous procedures for doing a stage-by-stage calculation at any operating reflux ratio have been discussed in Section 11.7A.

An important shortcut method for determining the theoretical number of stages required for an operating reflux ratio R is the empirical correlation of Erbar and Maddox (E1) given in Fig. 11.7-3. This correlation is somewhat similar to a correlation by Gilliland (G1) and should be considered as an approximate method. In Fig. 11.7-3 the operating reflux ratio R (for flow rates at the column top) is correlated with the minimum R_m obtained using the Underwood method, the minimum number of stages N_m obtained by the Fenske method, and the number of stages N at the operating R.

FIGURE 11.7-3. *Erbar–Maddox correlation between reflux ratio and number of stages (R_m based on Underwood method). [From J. H. Erbar and R. N. Maddox, Petrol. Refiner, **40**(5), 183 (1961). With permission.]*

2. *Estimate of feed-plate location.* Kirkbride (K1) has devised an approximate method to estimate the number of theoretical stages above and below the feed which can be used to estimate the feed-stage location. This empirical relation is as follows:

$$\log \frac{N_e}{N_s} = 0.206 \log \left[\left(\frac{x_{HF}}{x_{LF}} \right) \frac{W}{D} \left(\frac{x_{LW}}{x_{HD}} \right)^2 \right] \tag{11.7-21}$$

where N_e is the number of theoretical stages above the feed plate and N_s the number of theoretical stages below the feed plate.

EXAMPLE 11.7-3. Minimum Reflux Ratio and Number of Stages at Operating Reflux Ratio

Using the conditions and results given in Example 11.7-2, calculate the following:
- (a) Minimum reflux ratio using the Underwood method.
- (b) Number of theoretical stages at an operating reflux ratio R of $1.5R_m$ using the Erbar–Maddox correlation.
- (c) Location of feed tray using the method of Kirkbride.

Solution: For part (a), the temperature to use for determining the values of α_i is the average between the top of 67°C and the bottom of 132°C (from Example 11.7-2) and is $(67 + 132)/2$, or 99.5°C. The K_i values obtained from Fig. 11.7-2 and the α_i values and distillate and feed compositions to use in Eqs. (11.7-19) and (11.7-20) are as follows:

Comp.	x_{iF}	x_{iD}	K_i (99.5°C)	α_i (99.5°C)	x_{iW}
A	0.40	0.6197	3.12	5.20	0.0011
B (L)	0.25	0.3489	1.38	2.30	0.0704
C (H)	0.20	0.0310	0.60	1.00	0.5068
D	0.15	0.0004	0.28	0.467	0.4217
	1.00	1.0000			1.0000

Substituting into Eq. (11.7-19) with $q = 1.0$ for feed at the boiling point,

$$1 - q = 1 - 1 = 0 = \frac{5.20(0.40)}{5.20 - \theta} + \frac{2.30(0.25)}{2.30 - \theta} + \frac{1.00(0.20)}{1.00 - \theta} + \frac{0.467(0.15)}{0.467 - \theta}$$
$$\tag{11.7-22}$$

This is trial and error, so a value of $\theta = 1.210$ will be used for the first trial (θ must be between 2.30 and 1.00). This and other trials are shown below:

	2.08	0.575	0.200	0.070	
	—	—	—	—	
θ (Assumed)	$5.2 - \theta$	$2.3 - \theta$	$1.0 - \theta$	$0.467 - \theta$	Σ (Sum)
1.210	0.5213	0.5275	−0.9524	−0.0942	+0.0022
1.200	0.5200	0.5227	−1.0000	−0.0955	−0.0528
1.2096	0.5213	0.5273	−0.9542	−0.0943	+0.0001

The final value of $\theta = 1.2096$ is substituted into Eq. (11.7-20) to solve for R_m:

$$R_m + 1 = \frac{5.20(0.6197)}{5.20 - 1.2096} + \frac{2.30(0.3489)}{2.30 - 1.2096} + \frac{1.00(0.031)}{1.00 - 1.2096} + \frac{0.467(0.0004)}{0.467 - 1.2096}$$

Solving, $R_m = 0.395$.

For part (b), the following values are calculated: $R = 1.5R_m = 1.5(0.395) = 0.593$, $R/(R + 1) = 0.593/(0.593 + 1.0) = 0.3723$, $R_m/(R_m + 1) = 0.395/(0.395 + 1.0) = 0.2832$. From Fig. 11.7-3, $N_m/N = 0.49$. Hence, $N_m/N = 0.49 = 5.40/N$. Solving, $N = 11.0$ theoretical stages in the tower. This gives $11.0 - 1.0$ (reboiler), or 10.0 theoretical trays.

For the location of the feed tray in part (c), using Eq. (11.7-21),

$$\log \frac{N_e}{N_s} = 0.206 \log \left[\left(\frac{0.20}{0.25} \right) \frac{35.516}{64.484} \left(\frac{0.0704}{0.0310} \right)^2 \right] = 0.07344$$

Hence, $N_e/N_s = 1.184$. Also, $N_e + N_s = 1.184N_s + N_s = N = 11.0$ stages.
Solving, $N_s = 5.0$ and $N_e = 6.0$. This means that the feed tray is 6.0 trays from the top.

PROBLEMS

11.1-1. *Phase Rule for a Vapor System.* For the system NH_3–water and only a vapor phase present, calculate the number of degrees of freedom. What variables can be fixed?
                                               Ans. $F = 3$ degrees of freedom; variables T, P, y_A

11.1-2. *Boiling Point and Raoult's Law.* For the system benzene–toluene, do as follows, using the data from Table 11.1-1:
(a) At 378.2 K, calculate y_A and x_A using Raoult's law.
(b) If a mixture has a composition of $x_A = 0.40$ and is at 358.2 K and 101.32 kPa pressure, will it boil? If not, at what temperature will it boil and what will be the composition of the vapor first coming off?

11.1-3. *Boiling-Point-Diagram Calculation.* The vapor-pressure data are given below for the system hexane–octane:

		Vapor Pressure			
		n-Hexane		n-Octane	
$T(°F)$	$T(°C)$	kPa	mm Hg	kPa	mm Hg
155.7	68.7	101.3	760	16.1	121
175	79.4	136.7	1025	23.1	173
200	93.3	197.3	1480	37.1	278
225	107.2	284.0	2130	57.9	434
258.2	125.7	456.0	3420	101.3	760

(a) Using Raoult's law, calculate and plot the *x-y* data at a total pressure of 101.32 kPa.

(b) Plot the boiling-point diagram.

11.2-1. Single-Stage Contact of Vapor–Liquid System. A mixture of 100 mol containing 60 mol % *n*-pentane and 40 mol % *n*-heptane is vaporized at 101.32 kPa abs pressure until 40 mol of vapor and 60 mol of liquid in equilibrium with each other are produced. This occurs in a single-stage system, and the vapor and liquid are kept in contact with each other until vaporization is complete. The equilibrium data are given in Example 11.3-2. Calculate the composition of the vapor and the liquid.

11.3-1. Relative Volatility of a Binary System. Using the equilibrium data for the *n*-pentane–*n*-heptane system given in Example 11.3-2, calculate the relative volatility for each concentration and plot α versus the liquid composition x_A.

11.3-2. Comparison of Differential and Flash Distillation. A mixture of 100 kg mol which contains 60 mol % *n*-pentane (A) and 40 mol % *n*-heptane (B) is vaporized at 101.32 kPa pressure under differential conditions until 40 kg mol are distilled. Use equilibrium data from Example 11.3-2.

(a) What is the average composition of the total vapor distilled and the composition of the remaining liquid?

(b) If this same vaporization is done in an equilibrium or flash distillation and 40 kg mol are distilled, what is the composition of the vapor distilled and of the remaining liquid?

Ans. (a) $x_2 = 0.405$, $y_{av} = 0.892$; (b) $x_2 = 0.430$, $y_2 = 0.854$

11.3-3. Differential Distillation of Benzene–Toluene. A mixture containing 70 mol % benzene and 30 mol % toluene is distilled under differential conditions at 101.32 kPa (1 atm). A total of one-third of the moles in the feed is vaporized. Calculate the average composition of the distillate and the composition of the remaining liquid. Use equilibrium data from Table 11.1-1.

11.3-4. Steam Distillation of Ethylaniline. A mixture contains 100 kg of H_2O and 100 kg of ethylaniline (mol wt = 121.1 kg/kg mol), which is immiscible with water. A very slight amount of nonvolatile impurity is dissolved in the organic. To purify the ethylaniline, it is steam-distilled by bubbling saturated steam into the mixture at a total pressure of 101.32 kPa (1 atm). Determine the boiling point of the mixture and the composition of the vapor. The vapor pressure of each of the pure compounds is as follows (T1):

Temperature		P_A (water) (kPa)	P_B (ethylaniline) (kPa)
K	°C		
353.8	80.6	48.5	1.33
369.2	96.0	87.7	2.67
372.3	99.15	98.3	3.04
386.4	113.2	163.3	5.33

11.3-5. Steam Distillation of Benzene. A mixture of 50 g mol of liquid benzene and 50 g mol of water is boiling at 101.32 kPa pressure. Liquid benzene is immiscible in water. Determine the boiling point of the mixture and the composition of the vapor. Which component will first be removed completely from the still? Vapor-pressure data for the pure components are as follows:

Temperature		P_{water}	$P_{benzene}$
K	°C	(mm Hg)	(mm Hg)
308.5	35.3	43	150
325.9	52.7	106	300
345.8	72.6	261	600
353.3	80.1	356	760

11.4-1. Distillation Using McCabe–Thiele Method. A rectification column is fed 100 kg mol/h of a mixture of 50 mol % benzene and 50 mol % toluene at 101.32 kPa abs pressure. The feed is liquid at the boiling point. The distillate is to contain 90 mol % benzene and the bottoms 10 mol % benzene. The reflux ratio is 4.52:1. Calculate the kg mol/h distillate, kg mol/h bottoms, and the number of theoretical trays needed using the McCabe–Thiele method.

Ans. $D = 50$ kg mol/h, $W = 50$ kg mol/h, 4.9 theoretical trays plus reboiler

11.4-2. Rectification of a Heptane–Ethyl Benzene Mixture. A saturated liquid feed of 200 mol/h at the boiling point containing 42 mol % heptane and 58% ethyl benzene is to be fractionated at 101.32 kPa abs to give a distillate containing 97 mol % heptane and a bottoms containing 1.1 mol % heptane. The reflux ratio used is 2.5:1. Calculate the mol/h distillate, mol/h bottoms, theoretical number of trays, and the feed tray number. Equilibrium data are given below at 101.32 kPa abs pressure for the mole fraction n-heptane x_H and y_H:

Temperature				Temperature			
K	°C	x_H	y_H	K	°C	x_H	y_H
409.3	136.1	0	0	383.8	110.6	0.485	0.730
402.6	129.4	0.08	0.230	376.0	102.8	0.790	0.904
392.6	119.4	0.250	0.514	371.5	98.3	1.000	1.000

Ans. $D = 85.3$ mol/h, $W = 114.7$ mol/h, 9.5 trays + reboiler, feed on tray 6 from top

11.4-3. Graphical Solution for Minimum Reflux Ratio and Total Reflux. For the rectification given in Problem 11.4-1, where an equimolar liquid feed of benzene and toluene is being distilled to give a distillate of composition $x_D = 0.90$ and a bottoms of composition $x_W = 0.10$, calculate the following using graphical methods:
(a) Minimum reflux ratio R_m.
(b) Minimum number of theoretical plates at total reflux.

Ans. (a) $R_m = 0.91$; (b) 4.0 theoretical trays plus a reboiler

11.4-4. *Minimum Number of Theoretical Plates and Minimum Reflux Ratio.* Determine the minimum reflux ratio R_m and the minimum number of theoretical plates at total reflux for the rectification of a mixture of heptane and ethyl benzene as given in Problem 11.4-2. Do this by using the graphical methods of McCabe–Thiele.

11.4-5. *Rectification Using a Partially Vaporized Feed.* A total feed of 200 mol/h having an overall composition of 42 mol % heptane and 58 mol % ethyl benzene is to be fractionated at 101.3 kPa pressure to give a distillate containing 97 mol % heptane and a bottoms containing 1.1 mol % heptane. The feed enters the tower partially vaporized so that 40 mol % is liquid and 60 mol % vapor. Equilibrium data are given in Problem 11.4-2. Calculate the following:
   (a) Moles per hour distillate and bottoms.
   (b) Minimum reflux ratio R_m.
   (c) Minimum steps and theoretical trays at total reflux.
   (d) Theoretical number of trays required for an operating reflux ratio of 2.5:1.
       Compare with the results of Problem 11.4-2, which uses a saturated liquid feed.

11.4-6. *Distillation Using a Vapor Feed.* Repeat Problem 11.4-1 but use a feed that is saturated vapor at the dew point. Calculate the following:
   (a) Minimum reflux ratio R_m.
   (b) Minimum number of theoretical plates at total reflux.
   (c) Theoretical number of trays at an operating reflux ratio of $1.5(R_m)$.

11.4-7. *Enriching Tower for Benzene–Toluene.* An enriching tower is fed 100 kg mol/h of a saturated vapor feed containing 40 mol % benzene (A) and 60 mol % toluene (B) at 101.32 kPa abs. The distillate is to contain 90 mol % benzene. The reflux ratio is set at 4.0:1. Calculate the kg mol/h distillate D and bottoms W and their compositions. Also, calculate the number of theoretical plates required.
   Ans. $D = 20$ kg mol/h, $W = 80$ kg mol/h, $x_W = 0.275$

11.4-8. *Stripping Tower.* A liquid mixture containing 10 mol % n-heptane and 90 mol % n-octane is fed at its boiling point to the top of a stripping tower at 101.32 kPa abs. The bottoms are to contain 98 mol % n-octane. For every 3 mol of feed, 2 mol of vapor is withdrawn as product. Calculate the composition of the vapor and the number of theoretical plates required. The equilibrium data below are given as mole fraction n-heptane.

x	y	x	y
0.284	0.459	0.039	0.078
0.097	0.184	0.012	0.025
0.067	0.131		

11.4-9. *Stripping Tower and Direct Steam Injection.* A liquid feed at the boiling point contains 3.3 mol % ethanol and 96.7 mol % water and enters the top tray of a stripping tower. Saturated steam is injected directly into liquid in the bottom of the tower. The overhead vapor which is withdrawn contains 99% of the alcohol in the feed. Assume equimolar overflow for this problem. Equilibrium data for mole fraction of alcohol are as follows at 101.32 kPa abs pressure (1 atm abs):

x	y	x	y
0	0	0.0296	0.250
0.0080	0.0750	0.033	0.270
0.020	0.175		

(a) For an infinite number of theoretical steps, calculate the minimum moles of steam needed per mole of feed. (*Note:* Be sure to plot the q line.)

(b) Using twice the minimum moles of steam, calculate the number of theoretical steps needed, the composition of the overhead vapor, and the bottoms composition.

Ans. (a) 0.121 mol steam/mol feed;
(b) 5.0 theoretical steps, $x_D = 0.135$, $x_W = 0.00033$

11.5-1. Murphree Efficiency and Actual Number of Trays. For the distillation of heptane and ethyl benzene in Problem 11.4-2, the Murphree tray efficiency is estimated as 0.55. Determine the actual number of trays needed by stepping off the trays using the tray efficiency of 0.55. Also, calculate the overall tray efficiency E_O.

11.5-2. Packing and Tray Efficiencies for Absorption Tower. An absorber in a petroleum refinery uses a lean oil to absorb butane from a natural gas stream. The composition of the key component butane in the gas phase is related to its composition in the liquid phase at equilibrium by $y = mx = 0.7x$. At the tower bottom, where the flows are largest, $\rho_L = 57.9$ lb$_m$/ft^3 (927 kg/m^3). At the average tower temperature, $\mu_L = 1.4$ cp and the average molecular weight of the liquid is $M_L = 245$. Estimate the efficiency for a valve-tray tower and the HETP for Norton Intalox 2T structured packing.

11.5-3. Estimation of Tower Diameter of Sieve Tray. A distillation sieve-tray tower is being used to distill a hydrocarbon feed. The vapor flow rate at the tower bottom is 21 000 kg/hr and the liquid flow rate is 19 500 kg/hr. The density of the liquid $\rho_L = 673$ kg/m^3 and $\rho_V = 3.68$ kg/m^3. Assume a tray spacing of 24 in. (0.610 m). Calculate the tower diameter assuming the tower operates at 80% of flooding. Assume $\sigma = 22.5$ dyn/cm.

Ans. $K_v = 0.35$, $D = 1.372$ m (4.50 ft)

11.6-1. Use of Enthalpy–Concentration Method to Distill an Ethanol–Water Solution. A mixture of 50 wt % ethanol and 50 wt % water which is saturated liquid at the boiling point is to be distilled at 101.3 kPa pressure to give a distillate containing 85 wt % ethanol and a bottoms containing 3 wt % ethanol. The feed rate is 453.6 kg/h and a reflux ratio of 1.5 is to be used. Use equilibrium and enthalpy data from Appendix A.3. Note that the data are given in wt fraction and kJ/kg. Use these consistent units in plotting the enthalpy–concentration data and equilibrium data. Do as follows:

(a) Calculate the amount of distillate and bottoms.

(b) Calculate the number of theoretical trays needed.

(c) Calculate the condenser and reboiler loads.

Ans. (a) $D = 260.0$ kg/h, $W = 193.6$ kg/h (b) 3.9 trays plus a reboiler
(c) $q_c = 698\,750$ kJ/h, $q_R = 704\,770$ kJ/h

11.6-2. Distillation of Ethanol–Water Solution Using Enthalpy–Concentration Method. Repeat Problem 11.6-1 but use a reflux ratio of 2.0 instead of 1.5.

Ans. 3.6 theoretical trays plus reboiler

11.6-3. Minimum Reflux and Theoretical Number of Trays. A feed of ethanol–water containing 60 wt % ethanol is to be distilled at 101.32 kPa pressure to give a distillate containing 85 wt % ethanol and a bottoms containing 2 wt % ethanol. The feed rate is 10 000 kg/h and its enthalpy is 116.3 kJ/kg (50 btu/lb$_m$). Use consistent units of kg/h, weight fraction, and kJ/kg.

(a) Calculate the amount of distillate and bottoms.

(b) Determine the minimum reflux ratio using enthalpy–concentration data from Appendix A.3.

(c) Using 2.0 times the minimum reflux ratio, determine the theoretical number of trays needed.

(d) Calculate the condenser and reboiler heat loads.

(e) Determine the minimum number of theoretical plates at total reflux.

Ans. (b) $R_m = 0.373$ (c) 4.4 theoretical trays plus reboiler (d) $q_c = 3634$ kW, $q_R = 4096$ kW (e) 2.8 theoretical trays plus reboiler

11.6-4. Distillation of Benzene–Toluene Feed Using Enthalpy–Concentration Method. A liquid feed of 100 kg mol/h of benzene–toluene at the boiling point contains 55 mol % benzene and 45 mol % toluene. It is being distilled at 101.32 kPa pressure to give a distillate with $x_D = 0.98$ and a bottoms of $x_W = 0.04$. Using a reflux ratio of 1.3 times the minimum and the enthalpy-concentration method, do as follows:

(a) Determine the theoretical number of trays needed.

(b) Calculate the condenser and reboiler heat loads.

(c) Determine the minimum number of theoretical trays at total reflux.

11.6-5. Use of Enthalpy–Concentration Plot. For the system benzene–toluene do as follows:

(a) Plot the enthalpy–concentration data using values from Table 11.6-2. For a value of $x = 0.60 = y$, calculate the saturated liquid enthalpy h and the saturated vapor enthalpy H and plot these data on the graph.

(b) A mixture contains 60 mol of benzene and 40 mol of toluene. This mixture is heated so that 30 mol of vapor are produced. The mixture is in equilibrium. Determine the enthalpy of this overall mixture and plot this point on the enthalpy–concentration diagram.

11.7-1. Flash Vaporization of Multicomponent Feed. For the feed to the distillation tower of Example 11.7-1, calculate the following:

(a) Dew point of feed and composition of liquid in equilibrium. (*Note:* The boiling point of 70°C has already been calculated.)

(b) The temperature and composition of both phases when 40% of the feed is vaporized in a flash distillation.

Ans. (a) 107°C, $x_A = 0.114$, $x_B = 0.158$, $x_C = 0.281$, $x_D = 0.447$;
(b) 82°C, $x_A = 0.260$, $x_B = 0.254$, $x_C = 0.262$, $x_D = 0.224$;
$y_A = 0.610$, $y_B = 0.244$, $y_C = 0.107$, $y_D = 0.039$

11.7-2. Boiling Point, Dew Point, and Flash Vaporization. Following is the composition of a liquid feed in mole fraction: n-butane ($x_A = 0.35$), n-pentane ($x_B = 0.20$), n-hexane ($x_C = 0.25$), n-heptane ($x_D = 0.20$). At a pressure of 405.3 kPa calculate the following.

(a) Boiling point and composition of the vapor in equilibrium.

(b) Dew point and composition of the liquid in equilibrium.

(c) The temperature and composition of both phases when 60% of the feed is vaporized in a flash distillation.

11.7-3. *Vaporization of Multicomponent Alcohol Mixture.* The vapor-pressure data are given below for the following alcohols:

	Vapor Pressure (mm Hg)			
$T(°C)$	Methanol	Ethanol	n-Propanol	n-Butanol
50	415	220.0	88.9	33.7
60	629	351.5	148.9	59.2
65	767	438	190.1	77.7
70	929	542	240.6	99.6
75	1119	665	301.9	131.3
80	1339	812	376.0	165.0
85	1593	984	465	206.1
90	1884	1185	571	225.9
100	2598	1706	843	387.6

Following is the composition of a liquid alcohol mixture to be fed to a distillation tower at 101.32 kPa: methyl alcohol ($x_A = 0.30$), ethyl alcohol ($x_B = 0.20$) n-propyl alcohol ($x_C = 0.15$), and n-butyl alcohol ($x_D = 0.35$). Calculate the following assuming that the mixture follows Raoult's law:

(a) Boiling point and composition of vapor in equilibrium.
(b) Dew point and composition of liquid in equilibrium.
(c) The temperature and composition of both phases when 40% of the feed is vaporized in a flash distillation.

  Ans. (a) 83°C, $y_A = 0.589$, $y_B = 0.241$, $y_C = 0.084$, $y_D = 0.086$;
      (b) 100°C, $x_A = 0.088$, $x_B = 0.089$, $x_C = 0.136$, $x_D = 0.687$

11.7-4. *Total Reflux, Minimum Reflux, Number of Stages.* The following feed of 100 mol/h at the boiling point and 405.3 kPa pressure is fed to a fractionating tower: n-butane ($x_A = 0.40$), n-pentane ($x_B = 0.25$), n-hexane ($x_C = 0.20$), n-heptane ($x_D = 0.15$). This feed is distilled so that 95% of the n-pentane is recovered in the distillate and 95% of the n-hexane in the bottoms. Calculate the following:

(a) Moles per hour and composition of distillate and bottoms.
(b) Top and bottom temperature of tower.
(c) Minimum stages for total reflux and distribution of other components (trace components) in the distillate and bottoms, that is, moles and mole fractions. [Also correct the compositions and moles in part (a) for the traces.]
(d) Minimum reflux ratio using the Underwood method.
(e) Number of theoretical stages at an operating reflux ratio of 1.3 times the minimum using the Erbar–Maddox correlation.
(f) Location of the feed tray using the Kirkbride method.

  Ans. (a) $D = 64.75$ mol/h, $x_{AD} = 0.6178$, $x_{BD} = 0.3668$, $x_{CD} = 0.0154$, $x_{DD} = 0$;
      $W = 35.25$ mol/h, $x_{AW} = 0$, $x_{BW} = 0.0355$, $x_{CW} = 0.5390$, $x_{DW} = 0.4255$;
      (b) top, 66°C; bottom, 134°C; (c) $N_m = 7.14$ stages; trace compositions,
        $x_{AW} = 1.2 \times 10^{-4}$, $x_{DD} = 4.0 \times 10^{-5}$; (d) $R_m = 0.504$;

(e) $N = 16.8$ stages; (f) $N_e = 9.1$ stages, $N_s = 7.7$ stages, feed 9.1 stages from top

11.7-5. Shortcut Design of Multicomponent Distillation Tower. A feed of part liquid and part vapor ($q = 0.30$) at 405.4 kPa is fed at the rate of 1000 mol/h to a distillation tower. The overall composition of the feed is n-butane ($x_A = 0.35$), n-pentane ($x_B = 0.30$), n-hexane ($x_C = 0.20$), and n-heptane ($x_D = 0.15$). The feed is distilled so that 97% of the n-pentane is recovered in the distillate and 85% of the n-hexane in the bottoms. Calculate the following:

(a) Amount and composition of products and top and bottom tower temperatures.

(b) Number of stages at total reflux and distribution of other components in the products.

(c) Minimum reflux ratio, number of stages at $1.2R_m$, and feed-tray location.

11.7-6. Distillation of Multicomponent Alcohol Mixture. A feed of 30 mol % methanol (A), 20% ethanol (B), 15% n-propanol (C), and 35% n-butanol (D) is distilled at 101.32 kPa abs pressure to give a distillate composition containing 95.0 mol % methanol and a residue composition containing 5.0% methanol and the other components as calculated. The feed is below the boiling point, so that $q = 1.1$. The operating reflux ratio is 3.0. Assume that Raoult's law applies and use vapor-pressure data from Problem 11.7-3. Calculate the following:

(a) Composition and amounts of distillate and bottoms for a feed of 100 mol/h.

(b) Top and bottom temperatures and number of stages at total reflux. (Also, calculate the distribution of the other components.)

(c) Minimum reflux ratio, number of stages at $R = 3.00$, and feed-tray location.

Ans. (a) $D = 27.778$ mol/h, $x_{AD} = 0.95$, $x_{BD} = 0.05$, $x_{CD} = 0$, $x_{DD} = 0$; $W = 72.222$ mol/h, $x_{AW} = 0.0500$, $x_{BW} = 0.2577$, $x_{CW} = 0.2077$, $x_{DW} = 0.4846$; (b) 65.5°C top temperature, 94.3°C bottom, $N_m = 9.21$ stages, $x_{CD} = 3.04 \times 10^{-5}$, $x_{DD} = 8.79 \times 10^{-7}$ (trace compositions); (c) $R_m = 2.20$, $N = 16.2$ stages, $N_s = 7.6$, $N_e = 8.6$, feed on stage 8.6 from top

11.7-7. Shortcut Design Method for Distillation of Ternary Mixture. A liquid feed at its bubble point is to be distilled in a tray tower to produce the distillate and bottoms as follows: Feed, $x_{AF} = 0.047$, $x_{BF} = 0.072$, $x_{CF} = 0.881$; distillate, $x_{AD} = 0.1260$, $x_{BD} = 0.1913$, $x_{CD} = 0.6827$; bottoms, $x_{AW} = 0$, $x_{BW} = 0.001$, $x_{CW} = 0.999$. Average α values to use are $\alpha_A = 4.19$, $\alpha_B = 1.58$, $\alpha_C = 1.00$.

(a) For a feed rate of 100 mol/h, calculate D and W, number of stages at total reflux, and distribution (concentration) of A in the bottoms.

(b) Calculate R_m and the number of stages at $1.25R_m$.

REFERENCES

(D1) DePriester, C. L. *Chem. Eng. Progr. Symp. Ser.,* **49**(7), 1 (1953).

(E1) Erbar, J. H., and Maddox, R. N. *Petrol. Refiner,* **40**(5), 183 (1961).

(F1) Fair, J. R. *Petro/Chem. Eng.,* **33**(10), 45 (1961).

(G1) Gilliland, E. R. *Ind. Eng. Chem.,* **32,** 1220 (1940).

(H1) Hadden, S. T., and Grayson, H. G. *Petrol. Refiner,* **40**(9), 207 (1961).

(H2)   HOLLAND, C. D. *Multicomponent Distillation.* Englewood Cliffs, N.J.: Prentice-Hall, 1963.

(K1)   KIRKBRIDE, C. G. *Petrol. Refiner,* **23**(9), 321 (1944).

(K2)   KWAUK, M. *A.I.Ch.E. J.,* **2,** 240 (1956).

(K3)   KING, C. J. *Separation Processes,* 2nd ed. New York: McGraw-Hill Book Company, 1980.

(K4)   KISTER, H. Z. *Distillation Design.* New York: McGraw-Hill Book Company, 1992.

(L1)   LOCKETT, M. J. *Chem. Eng. Progr.,* **86** (Jan.), 19 (1990).

(O1)   O'CONNELL, H. E. *Trans. A.I.Ch.E.,* **42,** 741 (1946).

(P1)   PERRY, R. H., and GREEN, D. *Perry's Chemical Engineers' Handbook,* 6th ed. New York: McGraw-Hill Book Company, 1984.

(R1)   ROBINSON, C. S., and GILLILAND, E. R. *Elements of Fractional Distillation,* 4th ed. New York: McGraw-Hill Book Company, 1950.

(S1)   SMITH, B. D. *Design of Equilibrium Stage Processes.* New York: McGraw-Hill Book Company, 1963.

(S2)   SCHWEITZER, P. A. *Handbook of Separation Techniques for Chemical Engineers.* New York: McGraw-Hill Book Company, 1997.

(S3)   SEADER, J. D., and HENLEY, E. J. *Separation Process Principles.* New York: John Wiley & Sons, Inc., 1998.

(T1)   THIELE, E. W., and GEDDES, R. L. *Ind. Eng. Chem.,* **25,** 289 (1933).

(T2)   TREYBAL, R. E. *Mass Transfer Operations,* 3rd ed. New York: McGraw-Hill Book Company, 1980.

(U1)   UNDERWOOD, A. J. V. *Chem. Eng. Progr.,* **44,** 603 (1948); **45,** 609 (1949).

(U2)   UNDERWOOD, A. J. V. *J. Inst. Petrol.,* **32,** 614 (1946).

(V1)   VAN WINKLE, M. *Distillation.* New York: McGraw-Hill Book Company, 1967.

CHAPTER 12
Liquid–Liquid and Fluid–Solid Separation Processes

12.1 INTRODUCTION TO ADSORPTION PROCESSES

12.1A Introduction

In adsorption processes one or more components of a gas or liquid stream are adsorbed on the surface of a solid adsorbent and a separation is accomplished. In commercial processes, the adsorbent is usually in the form of small particles in a fixed bed. The fluid is passed through the bed and the solid particles adsorb components from the fluid. When the bed is almost saturated, the flow in this bed is stopped and the bed is regenerated thermally or by other methods so that desorption occurs. The adsorbed material (adsorbate) is thereby recovered and the solid adsorbent is ready for another cycle of adsorption.

Applications of liquid-phase adsorption include removal of organic compounds from water or organic solutions, colored impurities from organics, and various fermentation products from fermentor effluents. Separations include paraffins from aromatics and fructose from glucose using zeolites.

Applications of gas-phase adsorption include removal of water from hydrocarbon gases, sulfur compounds from natural gas, solvents from air and other gases, and odors from air.

12.1B Physical Properties of Adsorbents

Many adsorbents have been developed for a wide range of separations. Typically, the adsorbents are in the form of small pellets, beads, or granules ranging from about 0.1 mm to 12 mm in size, with the larger particles being used in packed beds. A particle of adsorbent has a very porous structure, with many fine pores and pore volumes up to 50% of total particle volume. The adsorption often occurs as a monolayer on the surface of the fine pores, although several layers sometimes occur. Physical adsorption, or van der Waals adsorption, usually occurs between the adsorbed molecules and the solid internal pore surface and is readily reversible.

The overall adsorption process consists of a series of steps in series. When the fluid is flowing past the particle in a fixed bed, the solute first diffuses from the bulk fluid to the gross exterior surface of the particle. Then the solute diffuses inside the pore to the surface of the pore. Finally, the solute is adsorbed on the surface. Hence, the overall adsorption process is a series of steps.

There are a number of commercial adsorbents and some of the main ones are described below. All are characterized by very large pore surface areas of 100 to over 2000 m²/g.

1. *Activated carbon.* This is a microcrystalline material made by thermal decomposition of wood, vegetable shells, coal, and so on, and has surface areas of 300 to 1200 m²/g with average pore diameters of 10 to 60 Å. Organics are generally adsorbed by activated carbon.

2. *Silica gel.* This adsorbent is made by acid treatment of sodium silicate solution and then drying. It has a surface area of 600 to 800 m²/g and average pore diameters of 20 to 50 Å. It is primarily used to dehydrate gases and liquids and to fractionate hydrocarbons.

3. *Activated alumina.* To prepare this material, hydrated aluminum oxide is activated by heating to drive off the water. It is used mainly to dry gases and liquids. Surface areas range from 200 to 500 m²/g, with average pore diameters of 20 to 140 Å.

4. *Molecular sieve zeolites.* These zeolites are porous crystalline aluminosilicates that form an open crystal lattice containing precisely uniform pores, which makes it different from other types of adsorbents, which have a range of pore sizes. Different zeolites have pore sizes from about 3 to 10 Å. Zeolites are used for drying, separation of hydrocarbons, mixtures, and many other applications.

5. *Synthetic polymers or resins.* These are made by polymerizing two major types of monomers. Those made from aromatics such as styrene and divinylbenzene are used to adsorb nonpolar organics from aqueous solutions. Those made from acrylic esters are usable with more-polar solutes in aqueous solutions.

12.1C Equilibrium Relations for Adsorbents

The equilibrium between the concentration of a solute in the fluid phase and its concentration on the solid resembles somewhat the equilibrium solubility of a gas in a liquid. Data are plotted as adsorption isotherms as shown in Fig. 12.1-1. The concentration in the solid phase is expressed as q, kg adsorbate (solute)/kg adsorbent (solid), and in the fluid phase (gas or liquid) as c, kg adsorbate/m³ fluid.

FIGURE 12.1-1. *Some common types of adsorption isotherms.*

Data that follow a linear law can be expressed by an equation similar to Henry's law:

$$q = Kc \qquad \text{(12.1-1)}$$

where K is a constant determined experimentally, m^3/kg adsorbent. This linear isotherm is not common, but in the dilute region it can be used to approximate data for many systems.

The Freundlich isotherm equation, which is empirical, often approximates data for many physical adsorption systems and is particularly useful for liquids:

$$q = Kc^n \qquad \text{(12.1-2)}$$

where K and n are constants and must be determined experimentally. If a log–log plot is made for q versus c, the slope is the dimensionless exponent n. The dimensions of K depend on the value of n. This equation is sometimes used to correlate data for hydrocarbon gases on activated carbon.

The Langmuir isotherm has a theoretical basis and is given by the following, where q_o and K are empirical constants:

$$q = \frac{q_o c}{K + c} \qquad \text{(12.1-3)}$$

where q_o is kg adsorbate/kg solid and K is kg/m^3. The equation was derived assuming that there are only a fixed number of active sites available for adsorption, that only a monolayer is formed, and that the adsorption is reversible and reaches an equilibrium condition. By plotting $1/q$ versus $1/c$, the slope is K/q_o and the intercept is $1/q_o$.

Almost all adsorption systems show that as temperature is increased, the amount adsorbed by the adsorbent decreases strongly. This is useful since adsorption is normally at room temperatures and desorption can be attained by raising the temperature.

EXAMPLE 12.1-1. Adsorption Isotherm for Phenol in Wastewater

Batch tests were performed in the laboratory using solutions of phenol in water and particles of granular activated carbon (R5). The equilibrium data at room temperature are shown in Table 12.1-1. Determine the isotherm that fits the data.

Solution: Plotting the data as $1/q$ versus $1/c$, the results are not a straight line and do not follow the Langmuir equation (12.1-3). A plot of log q versus log c in

TABLE 12.1-1. *Equilibrium Data for Example 12.1-1 (R5)*

c, $\left(\dfrac{kg\ phenol}{m^3\ solution}\right)$	q, $\left(\dfrac{kg\ phenol}{kg\ carbon}\right)$
0.322	0.150
0.117	0.122
0.039	0.094
0.0061	0.059
0.0011	0.045

FIGURE 12.1-2. *Plot of data for Example 12.1-1.*

Fig. 12.1-2 gives a straight line and, hence, follows the Freundlich isotherm, Eq. (12.1-2). The slope n is 0.229 and the constant K is 0.199, to give

$$q = 0.199c^{0.229}$$

12.2 BATCH ADSORPTION

Batch adsorption is often used to adsorb solutes from liquid solutions when the quantities treated are small in amount, as in the pharmaceutical or other industries. As with many other processes, an equilibrium relation such as the Freundlich or Langmuir isotherm and a material balance are needed. The initial feed concentration is c_F and the final equilibrium concentration is c. Also, the initial concentration of the solute adsorbed on the solid is q_F and the final equilibrium value is q. The material balance on the adsorbate is

$$q_F M + c_F S = qM + cS \tag{12.2-1}$$

where M is the amount of adsorbent, kg; and S is the volume of feed solution, m^3.
When the variable q in Eq. (12.2-1) is plotted versus c, the result is a straight line. If the equilibrium isotherm is also plotted on the same graph, the intersection of both lines gives the final equilibrium values of q and c.

EXAMPLE 12.2-1. *Batch Adsorption on Activated Carbon*
A wastewater solution having a volume of 1.0 m^3 contains 0.21 kg phenol/m^3 of solution (0.21 g/L). A total of 1.40 kg of fresh granular activated carbon is added to the solution, which is then mixed thoroughly to reach equilibrium. Using the isotherm from Example 12.1-1, what are the final equilibrium values, and what percent of phenol is extracted?

Solution: The given values are $c_F = 0.21$ kg phenol/m^3, $S = 1.0$ m^3, $M = 1.40$ kg carbon, and q_F is assumed as zero. Substituting into Eq. (12.2-1),

$$0(1.40) + 0.21(1.0) = q(1.40) + c(1.0)$$

FIGURE 12.2-1. *Solution to Example 12.2-1.*

This straight-line equation is plotted in Fig. 12.2-1. The isotherm from Example 12.1-1 is also plotted in Fig. 12.2-1. At the intersection, $q = 0.106$ kg phenol/kg carbon and $c = 0.062$ kg phenol/m^3. The percent of phenol extracted is

$$\% \text{ extracted} = \frac{c_F - c}{c_F}(100) = \frac{0.210 - 0.062}{0.210}(100) = 70.5$$

12.3 DESIGN OF FIXED-BED ADSORPTION COLUMNS

12.3A Introduction and Concentration Profiles

A widely used method for adsorption of solutes from liquid or gases employs a fixed bed of granular particles. The fluid to be treated is usually passed down through the packed bed at a constant flow rate. The situation is more complex than that for a simple stirred-tank batch process which reaches equilibrium. Mass-transfer resistances are important in the fixed-bed process, and the process is unsteady state. The overall dynamics of the system determine the efficiency of the process, rather than just the equilibrium considerations.

The concentrations of the solute in the fluid phase and of the solid adsorbent phase change with time and with position in the fixed bed as adsorption proceeds. At the inlet to the bed, the solid is assumed to contain no solute at the start of the process. As the fluid first comes in contact with the inlet of the bed, most of the mass transfer and adsorption takes place here. As the fluid passes through the bed, the concentration in this fluid drops very rapidly with distance in the bed and reaches zero well before the end of the bed is reached. The concentration profile at the start at time t_1 is shown in Fig. 12.3-1a, where the concentration ratio c/c_o is plotted versus bed length. The fluid concentration c_o is the feed concentration and c is the fluid concentration at a point in the bed.

After a short time, the solid near the entrance to the tower is almost saturated, and most of the mass transfer and adsorption now takes place at a point slightly farther from the inlet. At a later time t_2, the profile or mass-transfer zone where most of the concentration change

Chapter 12   Liquid–Liquid and Fluid–Solid Separation Processes

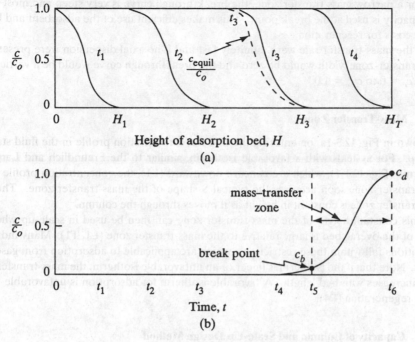

FIGURE 12.3-1. *Concentration profiles for adsorption in a fixed bed: (a) profiles at various positions and times in the bed, (b) breakthrough concentration profile in the fluid at outlet of bed.*

takes place has moved farther down the bed. The concentration profiles shown are for the fluid phase. Concentration profiles for the concentration of adsorbates on the solid would be similar. The solid at the entrance would be nearly saturated, and this concentration would remain almost constant down to the mass-transfer zone, where it would drop off rapidly to almost zero. The dashed line for time t_3 shows the concentration in the fluid phase in equilibrium with the solid. The difference in concentrations is the driving force for mass transfer.

12.3B Breakthrough Concentration Curve

As seen in Fig. 12.3-1a, the major part of the adsorption at any time takes place in a relatively narrow adsorption or *mass-transfer zone*. As the solution continues to flow, this mass-transfer zone, which is S-shaped, moves down the column. At a given time t_3 in Fig. 12.3-1a, when almost half of the bed is saturated with solute, the outlet concentration is still approximately zero, as shown in Fig. 12.3-1b. This outlet concentration remains near zero until the mass-transfer zone starts to reach the tower outlet at time t_4. Then the outlet concentration starts to rise, and at t_5 the outlet concentration has risen to c_b, which is called the *break point*.

After the break-point time is reached, the concentration c rises very rapidly up to point c_d, which is the end of the breakthrough curve, where the bed is judged ineffective. The break-point concentration represents the maximum that can be discarded and is often taken as 0.01 to 0.05 for c_b/c_o. The value c_d/c_o is taken as the point where c_d is approximately equal to c_o.

For a narrow mass-transfer zone, the breakthrough curve is very steep and most of the bed capacity is used at the break point. This makes efficient use of the adsorbent and lowers energy costs for regeneration.

If the mass-transfer rate were infinitely fast and if no axial dispersion were present, the mass-transfer-zone width would be zero and the breakthrough curve would be a vertical line from $c/c_o = 0$ to $c/c_o = 1.0$.

12.3C Mass-Transfer Zone

As shown in Fig. 12.3-1a, on entering the bed the concentration profile in the fluid starts to develop. For systems with a favorable isotherm, similar to the Freundlich and Langmuir isotherms (Fig. 12.1-1), which are concave downward (L1), the concentration profile in the mass-transfer zone soon acquires the typical S shape of the mass-transfer zone. Then the mass-transfer zone is constant in height as it moves through the column.

This constant height of the mass-transfer zone can then be used in scale-up when the height of the overall bed is large relative to the mass-transfer zone (L1, T1). Many industrial applications fall within these restrictions, which are applicable to adsorption from gases and liquids. Note that if the isotherm is linear or an unfavorable isotherm, the mass-transfer-zone width increases with bed length. A favorable isotherm for adsorption is unfavorable for effective regeneration (P4).

12.3D Capacity of Column and Scale-Up Design Method

The mass-transfer-zone width and shape depend on the adsorption isotherm, flow rate, mass-transfer rate to the particles, and diffusion in the pores. A number of theoretical methods have been published which predict the mass-transfer zone and concentration profiles in the bed. The predicted results may be inaccurate because of many uncertainties due to flow patterns and correlations for predicting diffusion and mass transfer. Hence, experiments in laboratory scale are needed in order to scale up the results.

The total or stoichiometric capacity of the packed-bed tower, if the entire bed comes to equilibrium with the feed, can be shown to be proportional to the area between the curve and a line at $c/c_o = 1.0$, as shown in Fig. 12.3-2. The total shaded area represents the total or stoichiometric capacity of the bed as follows (R6):

$$t_t = \int_0^\infty \left(1 - \frac{c}{c_o}\right) dt \tag{12.3-1}$$

where t_t is the time equivalent to the total or stoichiometric capacity. The usable capacity of the bed up to the break-point time t_b is the crosshatched area:

$$t_u = \int_0^{t_b} \left(1 - \frac{c}{c_o}\right) dt \tag{12.3-2}$$

where t_u is the time equivalent to the usable capacity or the time at which the effluent concentration reaches its maximum permissible level. The value of t_u is usually very close to that of t_b. Numerical integration of Eqs. (12.3-1) and (12.3-2) can be done using a spreadsheet.

The ratio t_u/t_t is the fraction of the total bed capacity or length utilized up to the break point (C3, L1, M1). Hence, for a total bed length of H_T m, H_B is the length of bed used up to the break point,

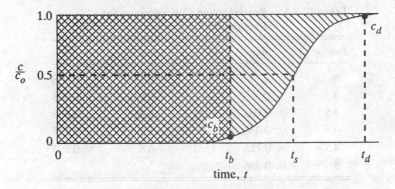

FIGURE 12.3-2. *Determination of capacity of column from breakthrough curve.*

$$H_B = \frac{t_u}{t_t} H_T \tag{12.3-3}$$

The length of unused bed H_{UNB} in m is then the unused fraction times the total length:

$$H_{UNB} = \left(1 - \frac{t_u}{t_t}\right) H_T \tag{12.3-4}$$

The H_{UNB} represents the mass-transfer section or zone. It depends on the fluid velocity and is essentially independent of total length of the column. The value of H_{UNB} may, therefore, be measured at the design velocity in a small-diameter laboratory column packed with the desired adsorbent. Then the full-scale adsorber bed can be designed simply by first calculating the length of bed needed to achieve the required usable capacity, H_B, at the break point. The value of H_B is directly proportional to t_b. Then the length H_{UNB} of the mass-transfer section is simply added to the length H_B needed to obtain the total length, H_T:

$$H_T = H_{UNB} + H_B \tag{12.3-5}$$

This design procedure is widely used; its validity depends on the conditions in the laboratory column being similar to those for the full-scale unit. The small-diameter unit must be well insulated to be similar to the large-diameter tower, which operates adiabatically. The mass velocity in both units must be the same and the bed must be of sufficient length to contain a steady-state mass-transfer zone (L1). Axial dispersion or axial mixing may not be exactly the same in both towers, but if caution is exercised, this is a useful design method.

An approximate alternative procedure to use instead of integrating and obtaining areas is to assume that the breakthrough curve in Fig. 12.3-2 is symmetrical at $c/c_o = 0.5$ and t_s. Then the value of t_t in Eq. (12.3-1) is simply t_s. This assumes that the area below the curve between t_b and t_s is equal to the area above the curve between t_s and t_d.

EXAMPLE 12.3-1. *Scale-Up of Laboratory Adsorption Column*
A waste stream of alcohol vapor in air from a process was adsorbed by activated carbon particles in a packed bed having a diameter of 4 cm and length of 14 cm containing 79.2 g of carbon. The inlet gas stream having a concentration c_o of 600 ppm and a density of 0.00115 g/cm^3 entered the bed at a flow rate of 754

TABLE 12.3-1. *Breakthrough Concentration for Example 12.3-1*

Time, h	c/c_o	Time, h	c/c_o
0	0	5.5	0.658
3	0	6.0	0.903
3.5	0.002	6.2	0.933
4	0.030	6.5	0.975
4.5	0.155	6.8	0.993
5	0.396		

cm^3/s. Data in Table 12.3-1 give the concentrations of the breakthrough curve. The break-point concentration is set at $c/c_o = 0.01$. Do as follows:

(a) Determine the break-point time, the fraction of total capacity used up to the break point, and the length of the unused bed. Also determine the saturation loading capacity of the carbon.

(b) If the break-point time required for a new column is 6.0 h, what is the new total length of the column required?

Solution: The data from Table 12.3-1 are plotted in Fig. 12.3-3. For part (a), for $c/c_o = 0.01$, the break-point time is $t_b = 3.65$ h from the graph. The value of t_d is approximately 6.95 h. Numerically or graphically integrating, the areas are

FIGURE 12.3-3. *Breakthrough curve for Example 12.3-1.*

$A_1 = 3.65$ h and $A_2 = 1.51$ h. Then from Eq. (12.3-1), the time equivalent to the total or stoichiometric capacity of the bed is

$$t_t = \int_0^\infty \left(1 - \frac{c}{c_o}\right) dt = A_1 + A_2 = 3.65 + 1.51 = 5.16 \text{ h}$$

The time equivalent to the usable capacity of the bed up to the break-point time is, using Eq. (12.3-2),

$$t_u = \int_0^{t_b = 3.65} \left(1 - \frac{c}{c_o}\right) dt = A_1 = 3.65 \text{ h}$$

Hence, the fraction of total capacity used up to the break point is $t_u/t_t = 3.65/5.16 = 0.707$. From Eq. (12.3-3) the length of the used bed is $H_B = 0.707(14) = 9.9$ cm. To calculate the length of the unused bed from Eq. (12.3-4),

$$H_{UNB} = \left(1 - \frac{t_u}{t_t}\right)H_T = (1 - 0.707)14 = 4.1 \text{ cm}$$

For part (b), for a new t_b of 6.0 h, the new H_B is obtained simply from the ratio of the break-point times multiplied by the old H_B:

$$H_B = \frac{6.0}{3.65}(9.9) = 16.3 \text{ cm}$$

$$H_T = H_B + H_{UNB} = 16.3 + 4.1 = 20.4 \text{ cm}$$

We determine the saturation capacity of the carbon:

$$\text{Air flow rate} = (754 \text{ cm}^3/\text{s})(3600 \text{ s})(0.00115 \text{ g/cm}^3) - 3122 \text{ g air/h}$$

$$\text{Total alcohol adsorbed} = \left(\frac{600 \text{ g alcohol}}{10^6 \text{ g air}}\right)(3122 \text{ g air/h})(5.16 \text{ h})$$

$$= 9.67 \text{ g alcohol}$$

$$\text{Saturation capacity} = 9.67 \text{ g alcohol}/79.2 \text{ g carbon}$$

$$= 0.1220 \text{ g alcohol/g carbon}$$

The fraction of the new bed used up to the break point is now 16.3/20.4, or 0.799.

In the scale-up, not only may it be necessary to change the column height, but also the actual throughput of fluid might be different from that used in the experimental laboratory unit. Since the mass velocity in the bed must remain constant for scale-up, the diameter of the bed should be adjusted to keep it constant.

Typical gas adsorption systems use heights of fixed beds of about 0.3 to 1.5 m with downflow of the gas. Low superficial gas velocities of 15–50 cm/s (0.5–1.7 ft/s) are used. Adsorbent particle sizes range from about 4 to 50 mesh (0.3 to 5 mm). Pressure drops are low, only a few inches of water per foot of bed. The adsorption time is about 0.5 h up to 8 h. For liquids the superficial velocity of the liquid in the bed is about 0.3 to 0.7 cm/s (4 to 10 gpm/ft²).

Practical bed depths usually need to be 5–10 times the length of bed of the mass-transfer zone to be economical (W1). The adsorption step usually uses downward flow in the bed. For desorption the flow is usually upward for greater efficiency (S3).

12.3E   Basic Models for Predicting Adsorption

Adsorption in fixed beds is the most important method used for this process. A fixed or packed bed consists of a vertical cylindrical pipe filled or packed with the adsorbent particles. Adsorbers are mainly designed using laboratory data and the methods described in Section 12.3D. In this section, the basic equations for isothermal adsorption are described so that the fundamentals involved in this process can be better understood.

An unsteady-state solute material balance in the fluid is as follows for a section dz length of bed:

$$\varepsilon \frac{\partial c}{\partial t} + (1 - \varepsilon)\rho_p \frac{\partial q}{\partial t} = -v \frac{\partial c}{\partial z} + E \frac{\partial^2 c}{\partial z^2} \tag{12.3-6}$$

where ε is the external void fraction of the bed; v is superficial velocity in the empty bed, m/s; ρ_p is density of particle, kg/m^3; and E is an axial dispersion coefficient, m^2/s. The first term represents accumulation of solute in the liquid. The second term is accumulation of solute in the solid. The third term represents the amount of solute flowing in by convection to the section dz of the bed minus that flowing out. The last term represents axial dispersion of solute in the bed, which leads to mixing of the solute and solvent.

The second differential equation needed to describe this process relates the second term of Eq. (12.3-6) for accumulation of solute in the solid to the rate of external mass transfer of the solute from the bulk solution to the particle and the diffusion and adsorption on the internal surface area. The actual physical adsorption is very rapid. The third equation is the equilibrium isotherm.

There are many solutions for these three equations which are nonlinear and coupled. These solutions frequently do not fit experimental results very well and will not be discussed here.

12.3F   Processing Variables and Adsorption Cycles

Large-scale adsorption processes can be divided into two broad classes. The first and most important is the cyclic batch system, in which the adsorption fixed bed is alternately saturated and then regenerated in a cyclic manner. The second is a continuous flow system, which involves a continuous flow of adsorbent countercurrent to a flow of feed.

There are four basic methods in common use for the cyclic batch adsorption system using fixed beds. These methods differ from each other mainly in the means used to regenerate the adsorbent after the adsorption cycle. In general, these four basic methods operate with two or sometimes three fixed beds in parallel, one in the adsorption cycle and the other one or two in a desorbing cycle, to provide continuity of flow. After a bed has completed the adsorption cycle, the flow is switched to the second newly regenerated bed for adsorption. The first bed is then regenerated by any of the following methods.

1. *Temperature-swing cycle.* This is also called the thermal-swing cycle. The spent adsorption bed is regenerated by heating it with embedded stream coils or with a hot purge gas stream to remove the adsorbate. The elevation in temperature is used to shift the adsorption equilibrium curve and affect regeneration of the adsorbent. Finally, the bed must be cooled so that it can be used for adsorption in the next cycle. The time for regeneration is generally a few hours or more.

2. *Pressure-swing cycle.* In this case the bed is desorbed by reducing the pressure at essentially constant temperature and then purging the bed at this low pressure with a small frac-

tion of the product stream. Reduction in pressure shifts the adsorption equilibrium and affects the regeneration of the adsorbent. This process for gases uses a very short cycle time for regeneration compared to that for the temperature-swing cycle.

3. *Inert-purge gas stripping cycle.* In this cycle the adsorbate is removed by passing a non-adsorbing or inert gas through the bed. This lowers the partial pressure or concentration around the particles and desorption occurs. Regeneration cycle times are usually only a few minutes.

4. *Displacement-purge cycle.* The pressure and temperature are kept essentially constant as in purge-gas stripping, but a gas or liquid is used that is adsorbed more strongly than the adsorbate and displaces the adsorbate. Again, cycle times are usually only a few minutes.

Steam stripping is often used in regeneration of solvent-recovery systems using activated-carbon adsorbent. This can be considered a combination of the temperature-swing cycle and the displacement-purge cycle.

12.4 ION-EXCHANGE PROCESSES

12.4A Introduction and Ion-Exchange Materials

Ion-exchange processes are basically chemical reactions between ions in solution and ions in an insoluble solid phase. The techniques used in ion exchange so closely resemble those used in adsorption that for the majority of engineering purposes ion exchange can be considered as a special case of adsorption.

In ion exchange, certain ions are removed by the ion-exchange solid. Since electroneutrality must be maintained, the solid releases replacement ions to the solution. The first ion-exchange materials were natural-occurring porous sands called zeolites, which are cation exchangers. Positively charged ions in solution such as Ca^{2+} diffuse into the pores of the solid and exchange with the Na^+ ions in the mineral:

$$Ca^{2+} + Na_2R \rightleftharpoons CaR + 2Na^+ \qquad \text{(12.4-1)}$$
$$\text{(solution)} \quad \text{(solid)} \qquad \text{(solid)} \quad \text{(solution)}$$

where R represents the solid. This is the basis for "softening" water. To regenerate, a solution of NaCl is added, which drives the reversible reaction above to the left. Almost all of these inorganic ion-exchange solids exchange only cations.

Most present-day ion-exchange solids are synthetic resins or polymers. Certain synthetic polymeric resins contain sulfonic, carboxylic, or phenolic groups. These anionic groups can exchange cations:

$$Na^+ + HR \rightleftharpoons NaR + H^+ \qquad \text{(12.4-2)}$$
$$\text{(solution)} \quad \text{(solid)} \qquad \text{(solid)} \quad \text{(solution)}$$

Here R represents the solid resin. The Na^+ in the solid resin can be exchanged with H^+ or other cations.

Similar synthetic resins containing amine groups can be used to exchange anions and OH^- in solution:

$$Cl^- + RNH_3OH \rightleftharpoons RNH_3Cl + OH^-$$
$$\text{(solution)} \qquad \text{(solid)} \qquad \text{(solid)} \quad \text{(solution)} \qquad \text{(12.4-3)}$$

12.4B Equilibrium Relations in Ion Exchange

The ion-exchange isotherms have been developed using the law of mass action. For example, for the case of a simple ion-exchange reaction such as Eq. (12.4-2), HR and NaR represent the ion-exchange sites on the resin filled with a proton H^+ and a sodium ion Na^+. It is assumed that all of the fixed number of sites are filled with H^+ or Na^+. At equilibrium,

$$K = \frac{[NaR][H^+]}{[Na^+][HR]} \quad (12.4\text{-}4)$$

Since the total concentration of the ionic groups $[\overline{R}]$ on the resin is fixed (B7),

$$[\overline{R}] = \text{constant} = [NaR] + [HR] \quad (12.4\text{-}5)$$

Combining Eqs. (12.4-4) and (12.4-5),

$$[NaR] = \frac{K[\overline{R}][Na^+]}{[H^+] + K[Na^+]} \quad (12.4\text{-}6)$$

If the solution is buffered, so that $[H^+]$ is constant, the above equation for sodium exchange or adsorption is similar to the Langmuir isotherm.

The ion-exchange process functions for strong acid or strong base exchangers by replacing the ions of a solution with ions such as H^+ or OH^-. These replaced ions from the solution are taken up by the resin. Then, to regenerate the resin, a small amount of solution with a high concentration of H^+ is used for cation exchangers or a high concentration of OH^- ions for anion exchangers. These high concentrations of H^+ or OH^- for regeneration shift the equilibrium to the left, making the regeneration process more favorable.

A typical ion-exchange process for removal of metals from solution is shown for copper cation being removed from a stream containing dilute $CuSO_4$ and H_2SO_4:

$$Cu^{2+} \; + \; 2HR \; \rightleftharpoons \; CuR_2 \; + \; 2H^+$$

$$\text{(solution)} \quad \text{(solid)} \qquad \text{(solid)} \quad \text{(solution)} \quad (12.4\text{-}7)$$

For regeneration, the bed of resin is contacted with a high concentration of H_2SO_4 to shift the equilibrium to the left.

12.4C Use of Equilibrium Relations and Relative-Molar-Selectivity Coefficients

Convenient tables for relative-molar-selectivity coefficients K have been prepared for various types of ion-exchange resins. Data are given in Table 12.4-1 for a polystyrene resin with 8% divinylbenzene (DVB) cross-linking (B8, P4) for strong-acid and strong-base resins. For cation exchangers, values are given for cation A entering the resin and displacing the cation Li^+, and for anion exchangers, values for anion A replacing Cl^-.

The equilibrium constant or selectivity coefficient for exchange of any two ions A and B can be approximated from Table 12.4-1 using values of K_A and K_B:

$$K_{A,B} = K_A/K_B \quad (12.4\text{-}8)$$

For example, for the reaction of cation K^+ (A) displacing cation H^+ (B),

$$A + BR \; \rightleftharpoons \; AR + B \quad (12.4\text{-}9)$$

$$K^+ + HR \; \rightleftharpoons \; KR + H^+$$

TABLE 12.4-1. *Relative-Molar-Selectivity Coefficients K for Polystyrene Cation and Anion Exchangers with 8% DVB Cross-Linking (B8, P4)*

Strong-Base Anion Exchanger (Relative to Cl^- as 1.0)		Strong-Acid Cation Exchanger (Relative to Li^+ as 1.0)	
Cl^-	1.0	Li^+	1.0
Iodide	8.7	H^+	1.27
Nitrate	3.8	Na^+	1.98
Acetate	0.2	NH_4^+	2.55
Sulfate	0.15	K^+	2.90
Hydroxide	0.05–0.07	Mg^{2+}	3.29
		Cu^{2+}	3.85
		Ca^{2+}	5.16

Substituting into Eq. (12.4-8), $K_{A,B} = K_A/K_B = 2.90/1.27 = 2.28$.

For dilute solutions, activity coefficients are relatively constant and simple concentration units are used. For Eq. (12.4-9), the equilibrium constant is as follows:

$$K_{A,B} = \frac{c_B q_{AR}}{c_A q_{BR}} = \frac{(c_{H^+})(q_{KR})}{(c_{K^+})(q_{HR})} \tag{12.4-10}$$

where, for the resin phase, concentrations q_{KR} and q_{HR} are in equivalents/L of bulk bed volume of water-swelled resin, and for the liquid phase, concentrations c_{H^+} and c_{K^+} are in equivalents/L of volume of solution.

The total concentration C in the liquid solution and the total concentration Q in the resin remain constant during the exchange process because of electroneutrality in Eq. (12.4-9). Then,

$$C = c_A + c_B, \qquad Q = q_{AR} + q_{BR} \tag{12.4-11}$$

In the case of Eq. (12.4-7), where the ion Cu^{2+} (A) replaces H^+ (B) and the charges are unequal,

$$K_{A,B} = \frac{(c_B)^2(q_{AR_2})}{(c_A)(q_{BR})^2} = \frac{(c_{H^+})^2(q_{CuR_2})}{(c_{Cu^{2+}})(q_{HR})^2} \tag{12.4-12}$$

EXAMPLE 12.4-1. *Removal of Cu^{2+} Ion from Acid Solution by an Ion-Exchange Resin*

A waste acidic stream contains copper in solution which is being removed by a strong acid–cation resin. The cation Cu^{2+} (A) is displacing the cation H^+ (B) in the resin. A polystyrene resin similar to that in Table 12.4-1 is being used. The total resin capacity Q is approximately 1.9 equivalents/L of wet bed volume. For a total concentration C of 0.10 N (0.10 equivalents/L) in the solution, calculate at equilibrium the total equivalents of Cu^{2+} in the resin when the concentration of Cu^{2+} in solution is 0.02 M (0.04 N).

Solution: The known values are $C = 0.10$ N or equivalents/L of Cu^{2+} (*A*) and H^+ (*B*) in solution and $Q = 1.9$ equivalents/L of *A* and *B* in the resin. The equilibrium relation is Eq. (12.4-7):

$$Cu^{2+} + 2HR \rightleftharpoons CuR_2 + 2H^+$$

$$\text{(solution)} \quad \text{(solid)} \qquad \text{(solid)} \quad \text{(solution)}$$

or,

$$A + 2BR \rightleftharpoons AR_2 + 2B$$

From Table 12.4-1, $K_A = K_{Cu^{2+}} = 3.85$ and $K_B = K_{H^+} = 1.27$. Then, from Eq. (12.4-8),

$$K_{A,B} = K_A/K_B = 3.85/1.27 = 3.03$$

Using Eq. (12.4-12),

$$K_{A,B} = \frac{(c_B)^2(q_{AR_2})}{(c_A)(q_{BR})^2} = \frac{(c_{H^+})^2(q_{CuR_2})}{(c_{Cu^{2+}})(q_{HR})^2}$$

From Eq. (12.4-11), $C = 0.10$ equivalents/L $= 2c_{Cu^{2+}} + c_{H^+}$. Also, $Q = 1.9 = q_{HR} + 2q_{CuR_2}$. The values to substitute into Eq. (12.4-12) are $K_{A,B} = 3.03$, $q_{CuR_2} = 1.9/2 - q_{HR}/2$, $c_{Cu^{2+}} = 0.02$, and $c_{H^+} = 0.10 - 2c_{Cu^+} = 0.10 - 0.04 = 0.06$.

$$3.03 = \frac{(0.06)^2(1.9/2 - q_{HR}/2)}{(0.02)(q_{HR})^2}$$

Rearranging,

$$(q_{HR})^2 + 0.02970 q_{HR} - 0.05644 = 0$$

Solving this quadratic equation, $q_{HR} = 0.2232$. Then $q_{CuR_2} = 1.9/2 - 0.2232/2 = 0.8384$. Hence, the equivalents of Cu^{2+} in the resin is $2(0.8384) = 1.677$ compared to a value of 1.9 when fully loaded with copper. The result shows that the removal of Cu^{2+} from the solution by the resin is highly favored.

12.4D Concentration Profiles and Breakthrough Curves

1. Basic models in ion exchange. The rate of ion exchange depends on mass transfer of ions from the bulk solution to the particle surface, diffusion of the ions in the pores of the solid to the surface, exchange of the ions at the surface, and diffusion of the exchange ions back to the bulk solution. This is similar to adsorption. The differential equations derived are also very similar to those for adsorption. The design methods used for ion exchange and adsorption are similar.

2. Concentration profiles in packed beds. Concentration profiles in packed beds for ion exchangers are very similar to those given in Fig. 12.3-1a for adsorption. The typical S-shaped curves occur and pass through the bed. The major part of the ion exchange at any time takes place in a relatively narrow mass-transfer zone. This mass-transfer zone moves down the column. In Fig. 12.3-1b the breakthrough curve is shown, which is similar for adsorption and ion exchange.

3. Mass-transfer zone. As the mass-transfer zone travels down the column, the height of this zone becomes constant. This behavior is generally characteristic in cases where the ion to be removed from the feed stream has a greater affinity for the solid resin than the ion originally present in the solid. The majority of industrial ion-exchange processes fall in this category (M1). This constant height of the mass-transfer zone can then be used for scale-up, similar to adsorption scale-up.

12.4E   Capacity of Columns and Scale-Up Design Method

1. Capacity of column. The design method for fixed-bed ion exchangers is quite similar to that used for adsorption processes. Theoretical predictions of concentration profiles, the mass-transfer zone, and mass transfer may be inaccurate because of uncertainties due to flow patterns, and so forth. Hence, experiments using small packed-bed laboratory-scale columns are needed for scale-up.

The total stoichiometric capacity of the packed bed is the total shaded area in the breakthrough curve in Fig. 12.3-2. The time t_t is the time equivalent to the total capacity:

$$t_t = \int_0^\infty (1 - c/c_o) \, dt \tag{12.3-1}$$

The usable capacity up to the break-point time t_b is the cross-hatched area from $t = 0$ to t_b. Then t_u, the time equivalent to the usable capacity, is

$$t_u = \int_0^{t_b} (1 - c/c_o) \, dt \tag{12.3-2}$$

Numerical integration of Eqs. (12.3-1) and (12.3-2) can also be done using spreadsheets. Then the fraction of the total bed length or capacity utilized up to the break point is t_u/t_t. For a total bed length of H_T m, H_B is the length of the bed used up to the break point:

$$H_B = (t_u/t_t)H_T \tag{12.3-3}$$

The length of the mass-transfer section or unused bed H_{UNB} in m is then

$$H_{UNB} = (1 - t_u/t_t)H_T \tag{12.3-4}$$

This H_{UNB} is essentially independent of the total column length. The experimental value of H_{UNB} is measured at the desired velocity in a small-diameter laboratory column. To design the full-scale column, the length of the bed H_B is calculated to achieve the desired capacity at the break point. Then the total column length is

$$H_T = H_{UNB} + H_B \tag{12.3-5}$$

The mass velocity of both the laboratory- and full-scale columns must be the same. The diameter of the large-scale column is calculated using the same given mass velocity.

2. Typical process variables. Some typical operating process variables are as follows. The laboratory column should be at least 2.5 cm in diameter and 0.3 m in length. Liquid flow rates commercially (W1) can be from 1 to 12 gpm/ft^2 (0.041–0.489 m/min) but are usually 6–8 gpm/ft^2 (0.244–0.326 m/min). Commercial columns are usually 1–3 m in height. Usually a freeboard of 50% or more open space is needed to accommodate bed expansion when regenerant flow is upward.

The resin gel can swell due to exchange by about 10 to 20%. Particle sizes used range from 0.2 mm to 1.0 mm. Typical moisture contents of the resins vary from 50 to 70%. The equilibrium exchange capacities of strong-acid or -base exchange resins are typically 3–5 meq/g of dry resin and 1–2 meq/ml of wet resin bed.

Regeneration flow rates are typically quite low, in the range of 0.5 to 5.0 bed volumes/h, in order to attain equilibrium while using minimum amounts of solution (W1). A bed volume is the total volume of the packed bed of resin as calculated from the column diameter and height of the packed bed.

Pressure drop can be predicted by using the equations for flow in packed beds. Typical pressure drops for beds are about 0.6 to 0.9 psi/ft height (13.6–20.4 kPa/m height) for flow rates of 6 to 8 gpm/ft^2. Excessive pressure drops should be avoided, since the gel-resin particles can be deformed.

A useful method for correlating experimental breakthrough curves at different flow velocities and the mass-transfer zone is as follows: Instead of plotting c/c_o versus time t, as in Fig. 12.3-1b, a plot of c/c_o versus the number of bed volumes (BV) is made. Data for different flow velocities will then tend to fall on the same curve.

3. Operating cycles. The operating cycles for ion-exchange processes in a packed bed are more complicated than those for gas adsorption. These usually consist of the following four steps, with experimental data usually needed to define each operating time (S3, W1). (1) Downflow loading of the process feed for a proper time. At the end of loading, the bed voids are filled with feed solution. (2) Displacement of the feed solution with upward flow of the regeneration solution. Thus, displacement of the occluded feed solution first occurs as a wave front. (3) Regeneration of the bed with continued upward flow of the regeneration solution. This occurs as a second wavefront. (4) Rinse upward to remove occluded regenerant from the bed. A rinse can be used instead of step (2) for recovering possibly valuable occluded process solution (W1).

For the actual design and for continuous feed flow, at least two columns are needed, so that one column is used to process the feed while the other is used for regeneration. When breakthrough occurs, the towers are switched. The total number of beds depends on the loading and regeneration times. Alternatively, a three-column system can be used for better utilization of the columns. The feed enters column 2 and then column 3 in series while column 1 is being regenerated. When breakthrough occurs in column 3, column 2 is removed for regeneration. The feed is then rerouted and goes to column 3 and then to column 1.

12.5   SINGLE-STAGE LIQUID–LIQUID EXTRACTION PROCESSES

12.5A   Introduction to Extraction Processes

In order to separate one or more of the components in a mixture, the mixture is brought into contact with another phase. The two-phase pair can be gas–liquid, which was discussed in Chapter 10; vapor–liquid, which was covered in Chapter 11; liquid–liquid; or fluid–solid. In this section *liquid–liquid extraction separation processes* are considered first. Alternative terms for the same process are *liquid extraction* or *solvent extraction*.

In distillation, the liquid is partially vaporized to create another phase, which is a vapor. The separation of the components depends on the relative vapor pressures of the substances. The vapor and liquid phases are similar chemically. In liquid–liquid extraction, the two phases are chemically quite different, which leads to a separation of the components according to physical and chemical properties.

Solvent extraction can sometimes be used as an alternative to separation by distillation or evaporation. For example, acetic acid can be removed from water by distillation or by solvent extraction using an organic solvent. The resulting organic solvent–acetic acid solution is then distilled. Choice of distillation or solvent extraction would depend on relative costs (C7). In another example, high-molecular-weight fatty acids can be separated from vegetable oils by extraction with liquid propane or by high-vacuum distillation, which is more expensive.

In the pharmaceutical industry, products such as penicillin occur in fermentation mixtures that are quite complex, and liquid extraction can be used to separate the penicillin. Many metal separations are being done commercially by extraction of aqueous solutions, such as copper–iron, uranium–vanadium, and tantalum–columbium.

12.5B Equilibrium Relations in Extraction

1. Phase rule. Generally in a liquid–liquid system we have three components, A, B, and C, and two phases in equilibrium. Substituting into the phase rule, Eq. (10.2-1), the number of degrees of freedom is 3. The variables are temperature, pressure, and four concentrations. Four concentrations occur because only two of the three mass-fraction concentrations in a phase can be specified. The third must make the total mass fractions equal to 1.0: $x_A + x_B + x_C = 1.0$. If pressure and temperature are set, which is the usual case, then, at equilibrium, setting one concentration in either phase fixes the system.

2. Triangular coordinates and equilibrium data. Equilateral triangular coordinates are often used to represent the equilibrium data for a three-component system, since there are three axes. This is shown in Fig. 12.5-1. Each of the three corners represents a pure component, A, B, or C. The point M represents a mixture of A, B, and C. The perpendicular distance from the point M to the base AB represents the mass fraction x_C of C in the mixture at M, the distance to base CB the mass fraction x_A of A, and the distance to base AC the mass fraction x_B of B. Thus,

$$x_A + x_B + x_C = 0.40 + 0.20 + 0.40 = 1.0 \tag{12.5-1}$$

A common phase diagram where a pair of components A and B are partially miscible is shown in Fig. 12.5-2. Typical examples are methyl isobutyl ketone (A)–water (B)–acetone (C), water (A)–chloroform (B)–acetone (C), and benzene (A)–water (B)–acetic acid (C). Referring to Fig. 12.5-2, liquid C dissolves completely in A or in B. Liquid A is only slightly soluble in B and B slightly soluble in A. The two-phase region is included inside below the curved envelope. An original mixture of composition M will separate into two phases a and b which are on the equilibrium tie line through point M. Other tie lines are also shown. The two phases are identical at point P, the *Plait point*.

3. Equilibrium data on rectangular coordinates. Since triangular diagrams have some disadvantages due to the special coordinates, a more useful method of plotting the three-component data is to use rectangular coordinates. This is shown in Fig. 12.5-3 for the system acetic acid (A)–water (B)–isopropyl ether solvent (C). Data for this system are from Appendix A.3. The solvent pair B and C are partially miscible. The concentration of component C is plotted

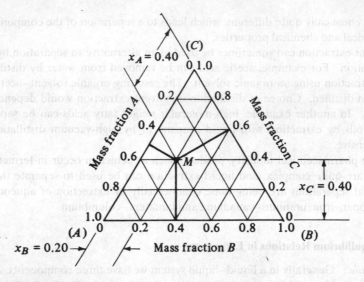

FIGURE 12.5-1. *Coordinates for a triangular diagram.*

FIGURE 12.5-2. *Liquid–liquid phase diagram where components A and B are partially miscible.*

on the vertical axis and that of A on the horizontal axis. The concentration of component B is obtained by difference from Eq. (12.5-2) or (12.5-3):

$$x_B = 1.0 - x_A - x_C \qquad (12.5\text{-}2)$$

$$y_B = 1.0 - y_A - y_C \qquad (12.5\text{-}3)$$

The two-phase region in Fig. 12.5-3 is inside the envelope and the one-phase region outside. A tie line gi is shown connecting the water-rich layer i, called the *raffinate layer,* and the ether-rich solvent layer g, called the *extract layer.* The raffinate composition is designated by x and the extract by y. Hence, the mass fraction of C is designated as y_C in the extract layer and

C (ether)

tie line

extract layer, y_C vs. y_A

two-phase region

one-phase region

raffinate layer, x_C vs. x_A

Mass fraction C (x_C, y_C)

B (water)

A (acetic acid)

Mass fraction A (x_A, y_A)

Ether layer (extract) composition, y_A

45° line

equilibrium line

Water layer (raffinate) composition, x_A

FIGURE 12.5-3.   *Acetic acid (A)–water (B)–isopropyl ether (C) liquid–liquid phase diagram at 293 K (20°C).*

as x_C in the raffinate layer. To construct the tie line *gi* using the equilibrium $y_A - x_A$ plot below the phase diagram, vertical lines to *g* and *i* are drawn.

EXAMPLE 12.5-1.   *Material Balance for Equilibrium Layers*
An original mixture weighing 100 kg and containing 30 kg of isopropyl ether (*C*), 10 kg of acetic acid (*A*), and 60 kg water (*B*) is equilibrated and the equilibrium phases separated. What are the compositions of the two equilibrium phases?

Solution: The composition of the original mixture is $x_C = 0.30$, $x_A = 0.10$, and $x_B = 0.60$. This composition of $x_C = 0.30$ and $x_A = 0.10$ is plotted as point *h* on Fig. 12.5-3. The tie line *gi* is drawn through point *h* by trial and error. The composition of the extract (ether) layer at *g* is $y_A = 0.04$, $y_C = 0.94$, and $y_B = 1.00 - 0.04 - 0.94 = 0.02$ mass fraction. The raffinate (water)-layer composition at *i* is $x_A = 0.12$, $x_C = 0.02$, and $x_B = 1.00 - 0.12 - 0.02 = 0.86$.

Another common type of phase diagram is shown in Fig. 12.5-4, where the solvent pairs *B* and *C* and *A* and *C* are partially miscible. Examples are the system styrene (*A*)–

FIGURE 12.5-4. *Phase diagram where the solvent pairs B–C and A–C are partially miscible.*

ethylbenzene (*B*)–diethylene glycol (*C*) and the system chlorobenzene (*A*)–methyl ethyl ketone (*B*)–water (*C*).

12.5C   Single-Stage Equilibrium Extraction

1. Derivation of lever-arm rule for graphical addition.   This will be derived for use with the rectangular extraction-phase-diagram charts. In Fig. 12.5-5a two streams, *L* kg and *V* kg, containing components *A*, *B*, and *C*, are mixed (added) to give a resulting mixture stream *M* kg total mass. Writing an overall mass balance and a balance on *A*,

$$V + L = M \tag{12.5-4}$$

$$V y_A + L x_A = M x_{AM} \tag{12.5-5}$$

where x_{AM} is the mass fraction of *A* in the *M* stream. Writing a balance for component *C*,

$$V y_C + L x_C = M x_{CM} \tag{12.5-6}$$

Combining Eqs. (12.5-4) and (12.5-5),

$$\frac{L}{V} = \frac{y_A - x_{AM}}{x_{AM} - x_A} \tag{12.5-7}$$

FIGURE 12.5-5.   *Graphical addition and lever-arm rule: (a) process flow, (b) graphical addition.*

Combining Eqs. (12.5-4) and (12.5-6),

$$\frac{L}{V} = \frac{y_C - x_{CM}}{x_{CM} - x_C} \tag{12.5-8}$$

Equating Eqs. (12.5-7) and (12.5-8) and rearranging,

$$\frac{x_C - x_{CM}}{x_A - x_{AM}} = \frac{x_{CM} - y_C}{x_{AM} - y_A} \tag{12.5-9}$$

This shows that points L, M, and V must lie on a straight line. By using the properties of similar right triangles,

$$\frac{L\,(\text{kg})}{V\,(\text{kg})} = \frac{\overline{VM}}{\overline{LM}} \tag{12.5-10}$$

This is the lever-arm rule, which states that kg L/kg V is equal to the length of line $\overline{VM}$/length of line $\overline{LM}$. Also,

$$\frac{L\,(\text{kg})}{M\,(\text{kg})} = \frac{\overline{VM}}{\overline{LV}} \tag{12.5-11}$$

These same equations also hold for kg mol and mol frac, lb_m, and so on.

EXAMPLE 12.5-2. Amounts of Phases in Solvent Extraction

The compositions of the two equilibrium layers in Example 12.5-1 are for the extract layer (V), $y_A = 0.04$, $y_B = 0.02$, and $y_C = 0.94$, and for the raffinate layer (L), $x_A = 0.12$, $x_B = 0.86$, and $x_C = 0.02$. The original mixture contained 100 kg and $x_{AM} = 0.10$. Determine the amounts of V and L.

Solution: Substituting into Eq. (12.5-4),

$$V + L = M = 100$$

Substituting into Eq. (12.5-5), where $M = 100$ kg and $x_{AM} = 0.10$,

$$V(0.04) + L(0.12) = 100(0.10)$$

Solving the two equations simultaneously, $L = 75.0$ and $V = 25.0$. Alternatively, using the lever-arm rule, the distance hg in Fig. 12.5-3 is measured as 4.2 units and gi as 5.8 units. Then, by Eq. (12.5-11),

$$\frac{L}{M} = \frac{L}{100} = \frac{hg}{gi} = \frac{4.2}{5.8}$$

Solving, $L = 72.5$ kg and $V = 27.5$ kg, which is in reasonably close agreement with the material-balance method.

2. *Single-stage equilibrium extraction.* We now study the separation of A from a mixture of A and B by a solvent C in a single equilibrium stage. The process is shown in Fig. 12.5-6a, where the solvent, as stream V_2, enters together with the stream L_0. The streams are mixed and equilibrated and the exit streams L_1 and V_1 leave in equilibrium with each other.

FIGURE 12.5-6. *Single-stage equilibrium liquid–liquid extraction: (a) process flow diagram, (b) plot on phase diagram.*

The equations for this process are the same as those given in Section 10.3 for a single equilibrium stage, where y represents the composition of the V streams and x the L streams:

$$L_0 + V_2 = L_1 + V_1 = M \tag{12.5-12}$$

$$L_0 x_{A0} + V_2 y_{A2} = L_1 x_{A1} + V_1 y_{A1} = M x_{AM} \tag{12.5-13}$$

$$L_0 x_{C0} + V_2 y_{C2} = L_1 x_{C1} + V_1 y_{C1} = M x_{CM} \tag{12.5-14}$$

Since $x_A + x_B + x_C = 1.0$, an equation for B is not needed. To solve the three equations, the equilibrium-phase diagram in Fig. 12.5-6b is used. Since the amounts and compositions of L_0 and V_2 are known, we can calculate values of M, x_{AM}, and x_{CM} from Eqs. (12.5-12)–(12.5-14). The points L_0, V_2, and M can be plotted as shown in Fig. 12.5-6b. Then, using trial and error, a tie line is drawn through point M, which locates the compositions of L_1 and V_1. The amounts of L_1 and V_1 can be determined by substitution into Eqs. (12.5-12)–(12.5-14) or by using the lever-arm rule.

12.6 TYPES OF EQUIPMENT AND DESIGN FOR LIQUID–LIQUID EXTRACTION

12.6A Introduction and Equipment Types

As in the separation processes of absorption and distillation, the two phases in liquid–liquid extraction must be brought into intimate contact with a high degree of turbulence in order to obtain high mass-transfer rates. After this contact of the two phases, they must be separated. In both absorption and distillation, this separation is rapid and easy because of the large difference in density between the gas or vapor phase and the liquid phase. In solvent extraction, the density difference between the two phases is not large and separation is more difficult.

There are two main classes of solvent-extraction equipment; vessels in which mechanical agitation is provided for mixing, and vessels in which the mixing is done by the flow of the fluids themselves. The extraction equipment can be operated batchwise or continuously as in absorption and in distillation.

12.6B Mixer–Settlers for Extraction

To provide efficient mass transfer, a mechanical mixer is often used to provide intimate contact between the two liquid phases. One phase is usually dispersed into the other in the form of small droplets. Sufficient time of contact should be provided for the extraction to take place. Small droplets produce large interfacial areas and faster extraction. However, the droplets must not be so small that the subsequent settling time in the settler is too large.

The design and power requirements for baffled agitators or mixers have been discussed in detail in Section 3.4. In Fig. 12.6-1a a typical mixer–settler is shown, where the mixer or agitator is entirely separate from the settler. The feed of aqueous phase and organic phase are mixed in the mixer, and then the mixed phases are separated in the settler. In Fig. 12.6-1b a combined mixer–settler is shown, which is sometimes used in the extraction of uranium salts or copper salts from aqueous solutions. Both types of mixer–settlers can be used in series for countercurrent or multiple-stage extraction. Typical stage efficiencies for a mixer–settler are 75–100%.

12.6C Spray Extraction Towers

Packed and spray-tower extractors give differential contact, where mixing and settling proceed continuously and simultaneously (C8). In the plate-type towers or mixer–settler contactors, the extraction and settling proceeds in discrete stages. In Fig. 12.6-2 the heavy liquid enters at the top of the spray tower, fills the tower as the continuous phase, and flows out through the bottom. The light liquid enters through a nozzle distributor at the bottom, which disperses or sprays the droplets upward. The light liquid coalesces at the top and flows out. In some cases the heavy liquid is sprayed downward into a rising, light continuous phase.

The spray tower has a very large axial dispersion (back-mixing) in the continuous phase. Hence, only one or two stages are usually present in such a tower. Typical performance parameters for a spray tower are given in Table 12.6-1. Despite its very low cost, this type of tower is rarely used. It can be used when a rapid, irreversible chemical reaction occurs, as in neutralization of waste acids (W1).

FIGURE 12.6-1. *Typical mixer–settlers for extraction: (a) separate mixer–settler, (b) combined mixer–settler.*

heavy liquid

light liquid outlet

coalesced interface

rising droplets

spray nozzle

light liquid

heavy liquid outlet

FIGURE 12.6-2. *Spray-type extraction tower.*

12.6D Packed Extraction Towers

A more effective type of tower is made by packing the column with random packing such as Raschig rings, Berl saddles, Pall rings, and so on, which cause the droplets to coalesce and redisperse at frequent intervals throughout the tower. The axial mixing is reduced considerably. A packed tower is more efficient than a spray tower, but back-mixing still occurs and the HETS (height equivalent to a theoretical stage) is generally greater than for the pulsed and mechanically agitated towers discussed later in Sections 12.6F and G.

Packed towers are used where only a few stages are needed (S3) and generally with low-interfacial-tension systems of about 10 dyn/cm or so (W1). When using random packings, it is preferable to choose a material that is preferentially wetted by the continuous phase. For example, stoneware Raschig rings or Berl saddles are used for water as the continuous phase and carbon rings or saddles for toluene as the continuous phase (T2). Packed towers more often use random packing and less often structured packing. Some typical performance values for packed towers are given in Table 12.6-1.

The few data available for structured packing have similar HETS values as packed or sieve-tray towers but give higher capacities (H4). The structured packings used for extraction are similar to those used for distillation.

In packed absorption towers, flooding occurs when the gas velocity is increased until the liquid cannot flow downward and is carried up by the gas out of the tower. In packed liquid-extraction towers, flooding occurs when increasing the dispersed or continuous flow rates causes both phases to leave at the outlet of the continuous phase.

A *flooding correlation* by Crawford and Wilke (C9) is given in Fig. 12.6-3, where V_C and V_D are superficial velocities of continuous and dispersed phases in ft/h, ρ_C and ρ_D are densities of continuous and dispersed phases in lb_m/ft^3, $\Delta\rho$ is $|\rho_C - \rho_D|$, μ_C is viscosity of continuous phase in $lb_m/ft \cdot h$, a is specific surface area of packing in ft^2/ft^3 (Table 10.6-1), ε is void fraction of packed section (Table 10.6-1), and σ is interfacial tension between phases in

TABLE 12.6-1. *Typical Performance for Several Types of Commercial Extraction Towers*

Type	Capacity of Combined Streams, $(V_D + V_C)$, $m^3/m^2 \cdot h$	Approximate Flooding, $(V_D + V_C)$, $m^3/m^2 \cdot h$	Spacing between Stages, T, cm	Overall Height of Transfer Unit, H_{OL}, m	Plate Efficiency, E_O, %	Height of Equilibrium Stage, HETS, m	Ref.
Spray Tower	15–75			3–6		3–6	M4, S5
Packed Tower	12–30			0.9–1.7		0.4–1.5	S4, S5, W1
Structured Packing Tower	65–90					0.5–1.6	H4
Sieve-Tray Tower	27–60		10–25		8–30	0.8–1.2	M4, P4, S4
Pulsed Packed Tower	17–23	40				0.15–0.3	P4, S4, W1
Pulsed Sieve-Tray Tower	25–35	60	5.1			0.15–0.3	S4, W1
Scheibel Tower	10–14*	40	2.5–20			0.1–0.3	P4, S2, S3, W1
Karr Tower	30–40	80–100	5–15			0.2–0.6	S2, S4

*Throughput for diameter $D_1 = 7.6$ cm. For larger towers of D_2 diameter see Eq. (12.6-3).

lb_m/h^2. Note: 1.0 dyn/cm = 28 572 lb_m/h^2. It is recommended that the design flow rates be set at 50% of flooding due to uncertainties in the correlation.

EXAMPLE 12.6.1. *Prediction of Flooding and Packed-Tower Diameter*

Toluene as the dispersed phase is being used to extract diethylamine from a dilute water solution in a packed tower of 1-in. Pall rings at 26.7°C. The flow rate of toluene $V = 84$ ft^3/h and of water solution $L = 56$ ft^3/h. The physical properties of the dilute solutions are: for the aqueous continuous phase (C), $\rho_C = 62.2$ lb_m/ft^3, $\mu_C = 0.860$ cp = 0.860(2.4191) = 2.080 $lb_m/ft \cdot h$; for the dispersed phase, $\rho_D = 54.0$ lb_m/ft^3. The interfacial tension $\sigma = 25$ dyn/cm (T2). Do as follows:

(a) Predict the flooding velocity.
(b) Using 50% of flooding, determine the tower diameter.

$$\left(\frac{\sigma}{\rho_C}\right)^{0.2}\left(\frac{\mu_C}{\Delta\rho}\right)\left(\frac{a}{\varepsilon}\right)^{1.5}$$

$$\frac{\left(V_C^{0.5} + V_D^{0.5}\right)^2 \rho_C}{a\mu_C}$$

FIGURE 12.6-3.   *Flooding correlation for packed extraction towers. [From J. W. Crawford and C. R. Wilke, Chem. Eng. Prog., 47, 423 (1951). With permission.]*

(c) If the separation requires 5.0 theoretical stages, calculate the tower height.

Solution: For part (a), from Table 10.6-1 for 1-in. Pall rings, the surface area $a = 63$ ft^2/ft^3 and $\varepsilon = 0.94$ void fraction. Also, $\sigma = (25$ dyn/cm)(28 572 lb$_m$/h^2)/(dyn/cm) = 714 300 lb$_m$/h^2. Then, for the ordinate in Fig. 12.6-3,

$$\left(\frac{\sigma}{\rho_C}\right)^{0.2}\left(\frac{\mu_C}{\Delta\rho}\right)\left(\frac{a}{\varepsilon}\right)^{1.5} = \left(\frac{714\,300}{62.2}\right)^{0.2}\left(\frac{2.080}{62.2 - 54.0}\right)\left(\frac{63}{0.94}\right)^{1.5}$$

$$= 902.8$$

From Fig. 12.6-3, the abscissa value is 170. Hence,

$$170 = \frac{\left(V_C^{0.5} + V_D^{0.5}\right)^2\rho_C}{a\mu_C} = \frac{\left(V_C^{0.5} + V_D^{0.5}\right)^2(62.2)}{(63)(2.080)}$$

Solving, $(V_C^{0.5} + V_D^{0.5}) = 18.92$. Also, since $V_D/V_C = V/L = 84/56 = 1.5$, the final result gives $V_D = 108.45$ ft/h and $V_C = 72.30$ ft/h for the flooding velocity.

For part (b), using 50% of flooding, $V_D = 54.2$, $V_C = 36.15$ ft/h, and $V_C + V_D = 90.35$ ft/h $= 90.35/3.2808 = 27.54$ m/h. This is still in the typical range given for packed towers in Table 12.6-1 of 12–30 m/h.

The tower cross-sectional area $= L/V_C = (56 \text{ ft}^3/\text{h})/(36.15 \text{ ft}/\text{h}) = 1.549 \text{ ft}^2$. Then, $\pi D^2/4 = 1.549$ and $D = 1.404$ ft (0.428 m).

For part (c), use the average HETS for packed towers from Table 12.6-1 of $(0.4 + 1.5)/2$, or 0.95 m (3.117 ft). Then the tower height is (HETS ft/stage) (number of stages) or 3.117(5.0) = 15.58 ft (4.75 m). Adding about 2 ft to the top and bottom for inlet nozzles and settling zones, the total height = 15.58 + 2 + 2 = 19.58 ft (5.97 m).

To use Fig. 12.6-3, the value of the interfacial tension σ is needed. This is a very important variable for extraction and can vary from about 5 to 50 dyn/cm. The interfacial tension between immiscible phases that must be settled must be sufficiently high for rapid coalescence. Also, high values of σ mean that often extra energy or agitation must be used in the tower for dispersion of one phase in the other. However, too low a value may result in too-slow coalescence or stable emulsions.

To estimate the *interfacial tension* of a two-phase system when experimental data are not available, Eq. (12.6-1) can be used for type one ternary systems, with an average deviation of about ±15% (T2):

$$\sigma = -7.34 \ln[x_{AB} + x_{BA} + (x_{CA} + x_{CB})/2] - 4.90 \qquad \text{(12.6-1)}$$

where σ is the interfacial tension in dyn/cm, x_{AB} is the mole fraction of solvent A in the saturated solvent-rich B layer, x_{BA} is the mole fraction of B in the saturated solvent-rich A layer, x_{CA} is the mole fraction of the distributed solute C in A, and x_{CB} is the mole fraction of solute C in B. This equation holds only for a range of values for $[x_{AB} + x_{BA} + (x_{CA} + x_{CB})/2]$ between 0.0004 and 0.30. A value of 1.0 indicates complete solution of the phases at the plait point. The range of σ values is 4–52.5 dyn/cm.

EXAMPLE 12.6-2. *Estimation of Interfacial Tension*
Equilibrium data for the system water (A)–acetic acid (C)–methylisobutyl ketone (MIBK) (B) are as follows in wt %, where the acetic acid concentration is dilute (P4):

Water-rich (A) phase			MIBK-rich (B) phase		
Water (A)	Acid (C)	MIBK (B)	Water (A)	Acid (C)	MIBK (B)
98.45	0	1.55	2.12	0	97.88
95.46	2.85	1.7	2.80	1.87	95.33

Estimate the interfacial tension for the data point containing some acetic acid.

Solution: The molecular weight for A is 18.02, for B is 100.16, and for C is 60.05. Converting 1.7 wt % (B) to mole fraction x_{BA} in the (A)-rich layer,

$$x_{BA} = \frac{1.7/100.16}{95.46/18.02 + 2.85/60.05 + 1.7/100.16} = 0.003163$$

Also, 2.85 wt % (C) in the (A)-rich layer becomes $x_{CA} = 0.00885$. Similarly, 2.80 wt % (C) becomes $x_{AB} = 0.1365$, and 1.87 wt % (C) becomes $x_{CB} = 0.02736$.

Substituting into Eq. (12.6-1),

$$\sigma = -7.34 \ln[0.1365 + 0.003163 + (0.00885 + 0.02736)/2] - 4.90$$

$$= 8.65 \text{ dyn/cm}$$

For the binary liquid system, water (A)–MIBK (B), the calculated mole fractions are $x_{BA} = 0.002825$ and $x_{AB} = 0.1074$. Then using Eq. (12.6-1), $\sigma = 11.49$ dyn/cm.

12.6E Perforated-Plate (Sieve-Tray) Extraction Towers

Perforated plates or sieve trays are also used for dispersion of liquid drops and coalescence on each tray, as shown in Fig. 12.6-4. This is similar to the sieve trays described in Fig. 10.6-1a for distillation and absorption. The downcomers carry the heavier continuous liquid phase from one tray to the next. The light dispersed phase coalesces below the tray, jets up to the tray above, and then coalesces on the tray above. Overflow weirs are not used on downcomers (S3).

The holes in the tray are 0.32–0.64 cm in diameter, and the % of open tray area is 15–25% of the column cross-sectional area. Tray spacings of 10–25 cm are used.

The following equation can be used to estimate the fractional tray efficiency E_o in a tray tower (P4):

$$E_o = \frac{0.352 T^{0.5}}{\sigma d_o^{0.35}} (V_D/V_C)^{0.42} \tag{12.6-2}$$

where σ is interfacial tension in dyn/cm, T is tray spacing in ft, d_o is hole diameter in ft, and V_D and V_C are superficial velocities in ft/s. For systems with high interfacial tensions, heights of transfer units are relatively high and stage efficiencies low.

Some typical operating conditions in tray towers are given in Table 12.6-1. To scale-up towers from small to larger sizes, the same sum of superficial velocities $V_C + V_D$ should be used (S3). A throughput design value of about 50% of flooding also should be used for all types of extraction towers.

FIGURE 12.6-4. *Perforated-plate or sieve-tray extraction tower.*

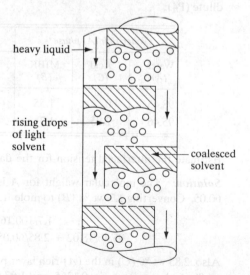

heavy liquid

rising drops of light solvent

coalesced solvent

EXAMPLE 12.6-3. Tray Efficiency for Perforated-Plate Tower

Acetic acid is being extracted from water by the solvent methylisobutyl ketone in a perforated-plate tower at 25°C. The flow rate of the continuous aqueous phase is 120 ft³/h and that of the dispersed solvent phase is 240 ft³/h. The interfacial tension is 9.1 dyn/cm. The tray spacing is 1.0 ft and the hole size on the tray is 0.25 in. Estimate the fraction tray efficiency E_o.

Solution: $V_D/V_C = 240/120$, $\sigma = 9.1$ dyn/cm, $T = 1.0$ ft, and $d_o = 0.25/12 = 0.02083$ ft. Substituting into Eq. (12.6-2),

$$E_o = \frac{0.352T^{0.5}(V_D/V_C)^{0.42}}{\sigma d_o^{0.35}} = \frac{0.35(1.0)^{0.5}(240/120)^{0.42}}{9.1(0.02083)^{0.35}}$$

$$E_o = 0.201$$

12.6F Pulsed Packed and Sieve-Tray Towers

There are many types of towers that are mechanically agitated to increase the mass-transfer efficiency and/or the throughput. An ordinary packed tower or one with special sieve plates can be pulsed by applying a rapid reciprocating motion of relatively short amplitude to the liquid contents. A reciprocating plunger pump, bellows pump, or high-pressure air pulse is externally connected to the space containing the continuous fluid so that the entire contents of the tower move up or down. Continuous inlet flows of continuous and dispersed phases enter and exit the tower.

1. Pulsed packed towers. Pulsing packed towers reduces the HETS considerably, by about a factor of 2 or so. Pulsing is also useful in handling liquids with high interfacial tensions, up to 30–40 dyn/cm (W1). Typical values for HETS of 0.15–0.3 m are given in Table 12.6-1. Since pulsing is uniform across the cross section, scale-up of tower size can be accomplished by using the same value of $V_D + V_C$ (W1).

2. Pulsed sieve-tray towers. Typical amplitudes used are from 0.6 to 2.5 cm and frequencies from 100 to 250 cycles/min (P4). Typical hole size is 0.32 cm diameter, with 20–25% free space on the tray and 5.1 cm (2 in.) tray spacing. The trays occupy the entire cross section of the tower and there are no downspouts. During upward pulsing, the light liquid is forced through the holes and droplets rise to the tray above. During downward pulsing, the heavy liquid behaves in a similar manner. Typical operating values are given in Table 12.6-1. Pulsing the tower markedly reduces the HETS.

12.6G Mechanically Agitated Extraction Towers

There are many types of mechanically agitated towers, two of the most important of which are the Scheibel tower shown in Fig. 12.6-5a and the Karr tower shown in Fig. 12.6-5b.

1. Scheibel tower. In the Scheibel tower, a series of rotating turbine agitators form dispersions which coalesce in passing through the knitted mesh. The mixture then passes through the outer settling zone. The tower thus operates as a series of mixer–settler extraction units.

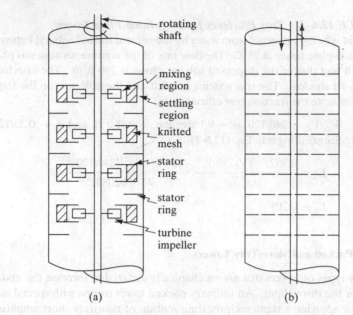

rotating shaft

mixing region

settling region

knitted mesh

stator ring

stator ring

turbine impeller

(a)   (b)

FIGURE 12.6-5. *Mechanically agitated extraction towers: (a) Scheibel rotating-agitator tower, (b) Karr reciprocating-plate tower.*

The tower operates with high efficiencies, as shown in Table 12.6-1. In scaling up from a total combined flow rate Q_1 for both phases in m³/s to Q_2, the diameter D_2 is approximately related to D_1 by (L4, S2)

$$\frac{D_2}{D_1} = \left(\frac{Q_2}{Q_1}\right)^{0.4}$$
(12.6-3)

Also, in scaling up from diameter D_1 to D_2, the HETS varies as follows:

$$(HETS)_2/(HETS)_1 = (D_2/D_1)^{0.5}$$
(12.6-4)

Equations for scale-up of the column internals are available (L4, S6).

2. Karr reciprocating-plate tower. As shown in Fig. 12.6-5b for the Karr column, the perforated trays are moved up and down to increase agitation and to pulse the liquids. This results in a more uniform drop-size distribution because the shear forces are more uniform over the tower cross section (K4, P4).

Typical parameters are an amplitude of plate movement of 2.5 cm (1 in.), 100–150 strokes/min, and plate spacing of 5–15 cm. Trays contain holes 1.4 cm in diameter and open space of 50–60% (W1). Scale-up procedures for the Karr column are relatively accurate. In scaling up a small tower with diameter D_1 to a larger size D_2, the total throughput per unit area $(V_C + V_D)$, plate spacing, and amplitude are kept constant. Then the HETS in m and the strokes per minute (SPM) are scaled up by (K4, P4)

$$(HETS_2)/(HETS_1) = (D_2/D_1)^{0.38}$$
(12.6-5)

$$(SPM_2)/(SPM_1) = (D_1/D_2)^{0.14}$$
(12.6-6)

Typical performance values are given in Table 12.6-1.

12.7 CONTINUOUS MULTISTAGE COUNTERCURRENT EXTRACTION

12.7A Introduction

In Section 12.5 single-stage equilibrium contact was used to transfer solute A from one liquid to another liquid phase. To transfer more solute, single-stage contact can be repeated by bringing the exit L_1 stream into contact with fresh solvent V_2, as shown in Fig. 12.5-6. In this way a greater percentage removal of solute A is obtained. However, this is wasteful of the solvent stream as well as giving a dilute product of A in the outlet solvent extract streams. In order to use less solvent and to obtain a more concentrated exit extract stream, countercurrent multistage contacting is often employed.

Many of the fundamental equations for countercurrent gas absorption and rectification are the same as or similar to those used in countercurrent extraction. Because of the frequently high solubility of the two liquid phases in each other, the equilibrium relationships in extraction are more complicated than in absorption and distillation.

12.7B Continuous Multistage Countercurrent Extraction

1. Countercurrent process and overall balance. The process flow for this extraction process is the same as given previously in Fig. 10.3-2 and is shown in Fig. 12.7-1. The feed stream containing the solute A to be extracted enters at one end of the process and the solvent stream enters at the other end. The extract and raffinate streams flow countercurrently from stage to stage, and the final products are the extract stream V_1 leaving stage 1 and the raffinate stream L_N leaving stage N.

Making an overall balance on all N stages,

$$L_0 + V_{N+1} = L_N + V_1 = M \tag{12.7-1}$$

where M represents total kg/h (lb$_m$/h) and is a constant, L_0 the inlet feed flow rate in kg/h, V_{N+1} the inlet solvent flow rate in kg/h, V_1 the exit extract stream, and L_N the exit raffinate stream. Making an overall component balance on component C,

$$L_0 x_{C0} + V_{N+1} y_{CN+1} = L_N x_{CN} + V_1 y_{C1} = M x_{CM} \tag{12.7-2}$$

Combining Eqs. (12.7-1) and (12.7-2) and rearranging,

$$x_{CM} = \frac{L_0 x_{C0} + V_{N+1} y_{CN+1}}{L_0 + V_{N+1}} = \frac{L_N x_{CN} + V_1 y_{C1}}{L_N + V_1} \tag{12.7-3}$$

A similar balance on component A gives

$$x_{AM} = \frac{L_0 x_{A0} + V_{N+1} y_{AN+1}}{L_0 + V_{N+1}} = \frac{L_N x_{AN} + V_1 y_{A1}}{L_N + V_1} \tag{12.7-4}$$

extract V_1 ... solvent V_{N+1}

L_0 feed ... L_N raffinate

FIGURE 12.7-1. *Countercurrent-multistage-extraction-process flow diagram.*

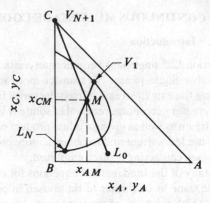

FIGURE 12.7-2. *Use of the mixture point M for overall material balance in countercurrent solvent extraction.*

Equations (12.7-3) and (12.7-4) can be used to calculate the coordinates of point M on the phase diagram, which ties together the two entering streams L_0 and V_{N+1} and the two exit streams V_1 and L_N. Usually, the flows and compositions of L_0 and V_{N+1} are known and the desired exit composition x_{AN} is set. If we plot points L_0, V_{N+1}, and M as in Fig. 12.7-2, a straight line must connect these three points. Then L_N, M, and V_1 must lie on one line. Moreover, L_N and V_1 must also lie on the phase envelope, as shown. These balances also hold for lb_m and mass fraction, kg mol and mol fractions, and so on.

EXAMPLE 12.7-1. Material Balance for Countercurrent Stage Process

Pure solvent isopropyl ether at the rate of $V_{N+1} = 600$ kg/h is being used to extract an aqueous solution of $L_0 = 200$ kg/h containing 30 wt % acetic acid (A) by countercurrent multistage extraction. The desired exit acetic acid concentration in the aqueous phase is 4%. Calculate the compositions and amounts of the ether extract V_1 and the aqueous raffinate L_N. Use equilibrium data from Appendix A.3.

Solution: The given values are $V_{N+1} = 600$, $y_{AN+1} = 0$, $y_{CN+1} = 1.0$, $L_0 = 200$, $x_{A0} = 0.30$, $x_{B0} = 0.70$, $x_{C0} = 0$, and $x_{AN} = 0.04$. In Fig. 12.7-3, V_{N+1} and L_0 are plotted. Also, since L_N is on the phase boundary, it can be plotted at $x_{AN} = 0.04$. For the mixture point M, substituting into Eqs. (12.7-3) and (12.7-4),

$$x_{CM} = \frac{L_0 x_{C0} + V_{N+1} y_{CN+1}}{L_0 + V_{N+1}} = \frac{200(0) + 600(1.0)}{200 + 600} = 0.75 \qquad \textbf{(12.7-3)}$$

$$x_{AM} = \frac{L_0 x_{A0} + V_{N+1} y_{AN+1}}{L_0 + V_{N+1}} = \frac{200(0.30) + 600(0)}{200 + 600} = 0.075 \qquad \textbf{(12.7-4)}$$

Using these coordinates, the point M is plotted in Fig. 12.7-3. We locate V_1 by drawing a line from L_N through M and extending it until it intersects the phase boundary. This gives $y_{A1} = 0.08$ and $y_{C1} = 0.90$. For L_N a value of $x_{CN} = 0.017$ is obtained. By substituting into Eqs. (12.7-1) and (12.7-2) and solving, $L_N = 136$ kg/h and $V_1 = 664$ kg/h.

2. Stage-to-stage calculations for countercurrent extraction. The next step after an overall balance has been made is to go stage by stage to determine the concentrations at each stage and the total number of stages N needed to reach L_N in Fig. 12.7-1.

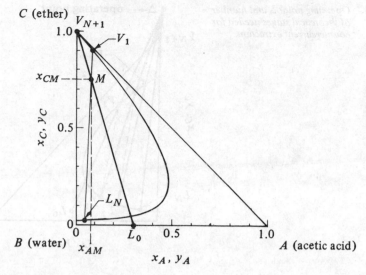

FIGURE 12.7-3. *Method to perform overall material balance for Example 12.7-1.*

Making a total balance on stage 1,

$$L_0 + V_2 = L_1 + V_1 \qquad \text{(12.7-5)}$$

Making a similar balance on stage n,

$$L_{n-1} + V_{n+1} = L_n + V_n \qquad \text{(12.7-6)}$$

Rearranging Eq. (12.7-5) to obtain the difference Δ in flows,

$$L_0 - V_1 = L_1 - V_2 = \Delta \qquad \text{(12.7-7)}$$

This value of Δ in kg/h is constant, and for all stages,

$$\Delta = L_0 - V_1 = L_n - V_{n+1} = L_N - V_{N+1} = \cdots \qquad \text{(12.7-8)}$$

This also holds for a balance on component A, B, or C:

$$\Delta x_\Delta = L_0 x_0 - V_1 y_1 = L_n x_n - V_{n+1} y_{n+1} = L_N x_N - V_{N+1} y_{N+1} = \cdots \qquad \text{(12.7-9)}$$

Combining Eqs. (12.7-8) and (12.7-9) and solving for x_Δ,

$$x_\Delta = \frac{L_0 x_0 - V_1 y_1}{L_0 - V_1} = \frac{L_n x_n - V_{n+1} y_{n+1}}{L_n - V_{n+1}} = \frac{L_N x_N - V_{N+1} y_{N+1}}{L_N - V_{N+1}} \qquad \text{(12.7-10)}$$

where x_Δ is the x coordinate of point Δ.

Equations (12.7-7) and (12.7-8) can be written as

$$L_0 = \Delta + V_1 \qquad L_n = \Delta + V_{n+1} \qquad L_N = \Delta + V_{N+1} \qquad \text{(12.7-11)}$$

From Eq. (12.7-11), we see that L_0 is on a line through Δ and V_1, L_n is on a line through Δ and V_{n+1}, and so on. This means Δ is a point common to all streams passing each other, such as L_0 and V_1, L_n and V_{n+1}, L_N and V_{N+1}, and so on. The coordinates for locating this Δ

FIGURE 12.7-4. *Operating point Δ and number of theoretical stages needed for countercurrent extraction.*

$\Delta \leftarrow$ operating point

operating point are given for $x_{C\Delta}$ and $x_{A\Delta}$ in Eq. (12.7-10). Since the end points V_{N+1}, L_N or V_1, and L_0 are known, x_Δ can be calculated and point Δ located. Alternatively, the Δ point is located graphically in Fig. 12.7-4 as the intersection of lines L_0V_1 and L_NV_{N+1}.

In order to step off the number of stages using Eq. (12.7-11) we start at L_0 and draw the line $L_0\Delta$, which locates V_1 on the phase boundary. Next a tie line through V_1 locates L_1, which is in equilibrium with V_1. Then line $L_1\Delta$ is drawn giving V_2. The tie line V_2L_2 is drawn. This stepwise procedure is repeated until the desired raffinate composition L_N is reached. The number of stages N required to perform the extraction is thus obtained.

EXAMPLE 12.7-2. Number of Stages in Countercurrent Extraction

Pure isopropyl ether of 450 kg/h is being used to extract an aqueous solution of 150 kg/h with 30 wt % acetic acid (A) by countercurrent multistage extraction. The exit acid concentration in the aqueous phase is 10 wt %. Calculate the number of stages required.

Solution: The known values are $V_{N+1} = 450$, $y_{AN+1} = 0$, $y_{CN+1} = 1.0$, $L_0 = 150$, $x_{A0} = 0.30$, $x_{B0} = 0.70$, $x_{C0} = 0$, and $x_{AN} = 0.10$. The points V_{N+1}, L_0, and L_N are plotted in Fig. 12.7-5. For the mixture point M, substituting into Eqs. (12.7-3) and (12.7-4), $x_{CM} = 0.75$ and $x_{AM} = 0.075$. The point M is plotted and V_1 is located at the intersection of line L_NM with the phase boundary to give $y_{A1} = 0.072$ and $y_{C1} = 0.895$. (This construction is not shown. See Example 12.7-1 for construction of lines.)

The lines L_0V_1 and L_NV_{N+1} are drawn and the intersection is the operating point Δ as shown. Alternatively, the coordinates of Δ can be calculated from Eq. (12.7-10) to locate point Δ. Starting at L_0 we draw line $L_0\Delta$, which locates V_1. Then a tie line through V_1 locates L_1 in equilibrium with V_1. (The tie-line data are obtained from an enlarged plot such as the bottom of Fig. 12.5-3.) Line $L_1\Delta$ is next drawn locating V_2. A tie line through V_2 gives L_2. A line $L_2\Delta$ gives V_3. A final tie line gives L_3, which has gone beyond the desired L_N. Hence, about 2.5 theoretical stages are needed.

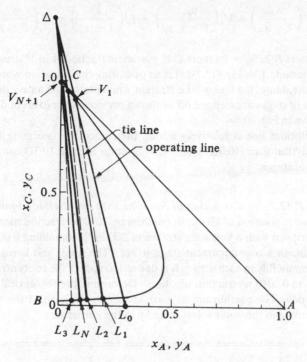

FIGURE 12.7-5. *Graphical solution for countercurrent extraction in Example 12.7-2.*

3. Minimum solvent rate. If a solvent rate V_{N+1} is selected at too low a value, a limiting case will be reached, with a line through Δ and a tie line being the same. Then an infinite number of stages will be needed to reach the desired separation. The minimum amount of solvent has been reached. For actual operation a greater amount of solvent must be used.

The procedure for obtaining this minimum is as follows. A tie line is drawn through point L_0 (Fig. 12.7-4) to intersect the extension of line $L_N V_{N+1}$. Other tie lines to the left of this tie line are drawn, including one through L_N to intersect the line $L_N V_{N+1}$. The intersection of a tie line on line $L_N V_{N+1}$ which is nearest to V_{N+1} represents the Δ_{min} point for minimum solvent. The actual position of Δ used must be closer to V_{N+1} than Δ_{min} for a finite number of stages. This means that more solvent must be used. Usually, the tie line through L_0 represents the Δ_{min}.

12.7C Countercurrent-Stage Extraction with Immiscible Liquids

If the solvent stream V_{N+1} contains components A and C and the feed stream L_0 contains A and B, and if components B and C are relatively immiscible in each other, the stage calculations may be made more easily. The solute A is relatively dilute and is being transferred from L_0 to V_{N+1}.

Referring to Fig. 12.7-1 and making an overall balance for A over the whole system and then over the first n stages,

$$L'\left(\frac{x_0}{1-x_0}\right) + V'\left(\frac{y_{N+1}}{1-y_{N+1}}\right) = L'\left(\frac{x_N}{1-x_N}\right) + V'\left(\frac{y_1}{1-y_1}\right) \qquad \textbf{(12.7-12)}$$

$$L'\left(\frac{x_0}{1-x_0}\right) + V'\left(\frac{y_{n+1}}{1-y_{n+1}}\right) = L'\left(\frac{x_n}{1-x_n}\right) + V'\left(\frac{y_1}{1-y_1}\right) \qquad \textbf{(12.7-13)}$$

where $L' = $ kg inert B/h, $V' = $ kg inert C/h, $y = $ mass fraction A in V stream, and $x = $ mass fraction A in L stream. This Eq. (12.7-13) is an operating-line equation whose slope $\cong L'/V'$. If y and x are quite dilute, the line will be straight when plotted on an x-y diagram.

The number of stages are stepped off as shown previously for cases of distillation and absorption, as shown in Fig. 10.3-4.

If the equilibrium line is relatively dilute, then since the operating line is essentially straight, the analytical Eqs. (10.3-21)–(10.3-26) given in Section 10.3D can be used to calculate the number of stages.

EXAMPLE 12.7-3. *Extraction of Nicotine with Immiscible Liquids.*

An inlet water solution of 100 kg/h containing 0.010 wt fraction nicotine (A) in water is stripped with a kerosene stream of 200 kg/h containing 0.0005 wt fraction nicotine in a countercurrent-stage tower. The water and kerosene are essentially immiscible in each other. It is desired to reduce the concentration of the exit water to 0.0010 wt fraction nicotine. Determine the theoretical number of stages needed. The equilibrium data are as follows (C5), with x the weight fraction of nicotine in the water solution and y in the kerosene:

x	y	x	y
0.001010	0.000806	0.00746	0.00682
0.00246	0.001959	0.00988	0.00904
0.00500	0.00454	0.0202	0.0185

(a) Plot the equilibrium data and graphically determine the number of theoretical steps.

(b) Use the Kremser equation (10.3-21) and calculate the number of theoretical steps.

Solution: The given values are $L_0 = 100$ kg/h, $x_0 = 0.010$, $V_{N+1} = 200$ kg/h, $y_{N+1} = 0.0005$, $x_N = 0.0010$. The inert streams are

$$L' = L(1-x) = L_0(1-x_0) = 100(1-0.010)$$
$$= 99.00 \text{ kg water/h}$$
$$V' = V(1-y) = V_{N+1}(1-y_{N+1}) = 200(1-0.0005)$$
$$= 199.9 \text{ kg kerosene/h}$$

Making an overall balance on A using Eq. (12.7-12) and solving, $y_1 = 0.00498$. These points on the operating line are plotted in Fig. 12.7-6.

Since the operating-line equation is for dilute solutions, a straight line is drawn. The equilibrium data are plotted and the line is slightly curved.

For part (a), the number of stages are stepped off, giving $N = 4.5$ theoretical stages.

FIGURE 12.7-6. *Solution for extraction with immiscible liquids in Example 12.7-3.*

For part (b), to calculate the total flow rates L_N and V_1, the following equations can be solved:

$$L' = 99.0 = L_N(1 - x_N) = L_N(1 - 0.0010).$$

$$L_N = 99.10 \text{ kg/h}$$

$$V' - 199.9 - V_1(1 - y_1) = V_1(1 - 0.00497).$$

$$V_1 = 200.9 \text{ kg/h}$$

Also, $L_0 = 100$ and $V_{N+1} = 200$ kg/h. To use Eq. (10.3-21) the slope of the equilibrium curve must be calculated at the top and bottom of the tower, since the line is not straight. At the top on the equilibrium curve, at the point $y_1 = 0.00498$, the tangent or slope at this point is determined to be $m_1 = 0.91$. At the bottom or dilute end, at $x_N = 0.0010$ on the equilibrium curve, the line is straight and m_2 can be calculated from the equilibrium data as $m_2 = 0.000806/0.001010 = 0.798$. Then $A_1 = L/(mV) = L_0/(m_1V_1) = 100/(0.91 \times 200.9) = 0.547$. Also, $A_2 = L_N/(m_2V_{N+1}) = 99.1/(0.798 \times 200) = 0.621$. The average value of $A = \sqrt{0.547 \times 0.621} = 0.583$.

Substituting into Eq. (10.3-22) using $m = m_2 = 0.798$,

$$N = \frac{\ln\left[\dfrac{x_0 - (y_{N+1}/m)}{x_N - (y_{N+1}/m)}(1 - A) + A\right]}{\ln(1/A)}$$

$$= \frac{\ln\left[\dfrac{0.010 - 0.0005/0.798}{0.001 - 0.0005/0.798}(1 - 0.583) + 0.583\right]}{\ln(1/0.583)}$$

$N = 4.45$ theoretical stages. This compares closely with the graphical-method result of 4.5 theoretical stages.

12.7D Design of Towers for Extraction

1. Operating-line equation for relatively immiscible liquids. In this case, in Fig. 12.7-7a the liquid feed stream L and the solvent stream V are relatively immiscible in each other and solute A is relatively dilute in both streams. The outlet feed stream is commonly called the raffinate and the outlet solvent stream the extract. For the countercurrent extraction of A from the feed stream L to the solvent stream V, an overall material balance around the dashed-line box gives the following operating line equation:

$$L'\left(\frac{x}{1-x}\right) + V'\left(\frac{y_1}{1-y_1}\right) = L'\left(\frac{x_1}{1-x_1}\right) + V'\left(\frac{y}{1-y}\right) \qquad \textbf{(12.7-14)}$$

where L' = kg feed B/h, V' = kg solvent/h, y = mass fraction A in solvent V stream, and x = mass fraction A in feed L stream.

This operating-line equation will be slightly curved when plotted on an x-y diagram as in Fig. 12.7-7b. Note that units of mole fraction and molar flow rates can also be used. The number of theoretical steps are stepped off as previously shown in Fig. 12.7-6. If the two liquid solvent and feed streams are immiscible in each other, L' and V' are constant.

2. Limiting solvent flows and optimum L'/V' ratios. In an extraction process, the inlet feed flow L_2 and its composition x_2 are usually set. The exit concentration x_1 in the raffinate (L_1 stream) is often set by the designer. The inlet concentration y_1 of the solvent (V_1 stream) is

FIGURE 12.7-7. *Extraction-tower flows: (a) process flow and material balance for countercurrent extraction tower, (b) operating line for minimum solvent flow for tower and actual operating line.*

generally fixed by process requirements in regenerating the solvent for recycle back to the tower. Hence, the amount of the entering solvent flow V_1 or V' is open to choice.

In Fig. 12.7-7b, the concentrations x_1, x_2, and y_1 are set. When the operating line has a maximum slope and touches the equilibrium line at point P, then the solvent flow is at a minimum at V'_{min}. The value of y_2 is at a maximum of $y_{2,max}$. As in absorption and stripping, the optimum flow rate is taken as 1.2–1.5 times V'_{min}, with 1.5 normally used (S6). Note that if the equilibrium line is curved and highly concave upward, then, for the minimum value V'_{min}, the operating line is tangent to the equilibrium line instead of intersecting it. Then the optimum is taken as 1.2–1.5 times V'_{min}.

3. Analytical equations for number of trays. The analytical equation to calculate the number of theoretical trays N for extraction is the same as Eq. (10.6-8) for stripping in gas–liquid separations and is given as

$$N = \frac{\ln\left[\dfrac{(x_2 - y_1/m)}{(x_1 - y_1/m)}(1 - A) + A\right]}{\ln(1/A)}$$ (12.7-15)

where $A = L/mV$. The value of A may vary in the tower if the operating and equilibrium lines are curved somewhat. Referring to Fig. 12.7-7b, at the concentrated top of the tower, the slope m_2 or tangent at point y_2 on the equilibrium line is used. At the bottom or dilute end, the slope m_1 at point x_1 on the equilibrium line is used. Then $A_1 = L_1/m_1V_1$, $A_2 = L_2/m_2 V_2$, and $A = \sqrt{A_1 A_2}$. Also, the dilute m_1 is used in Eq. (12.7-15). A useful equation is Eq. (12.7-16), which allows one to calculate the performance of an existing tower when the number of theoretical steps N are known:

$$\frac{x_2 - x_1}{x_2 - y_1/m} = \frac{(1/A)^{N+1} - (1/A)}{(1/A)^{N+1} - 1}$$ (12.7-16)

12.7E Design of Packed Towers for Extraction Using Mass-Transfer Coefficients

The use of mass-transfer coefficients in extraction is similar to their use in stripping in absorption. The equations for dilute solutions and essentially immiscible solvents using overall coefficients are essentially identical to those for stripping with dilute solutions as given previously in Section 10.6G as Eqs. (10.6-46) and (10.6-47). For extraction,

$$z = H_{OL} N_{OL} = H_{OL} \int_{x_2}^{x_1} \frac{dx}{x^* - x}$$ (12.7-17)

$$H_{OL} = \frac{L}{K'_x aS}$$ (12.7-18)

If both the operating and equilibrium lines are straight and dilute, the integral in Eq. (12.7-17) can be integrated to give

$$N_{OL} = \frac{(x_1 - x_2)}{(x^* - x)_M}$$ (12.7-19)

where

$$(x^* - x)_M = \frac{(x_1^* - x_1) - (x_2^* - x_2)}{\ln[(x_1^* - x_1)/(x_2^* - x_2)]}$$ (12.7-20)

In terms of the V phase,

$$N_{OV} = \frac{(y_1 - y_2)}{(y - y^*)_M}$$ (12.7-21)

where $(y - y^*)_M$ is defined in Eq. (10.6-28). The value of the overall number of transfer units N_{OL} can also be determined using Eq. (10.6-53) as

$$N_{OL} = \frac{1}{(1 - A)} \ln\left[(1 - A)\left(\frac{x_2 - y_1/m}{x_1 - y_1/m}\right) + A\right]$$ (12.7-22)

EXAMPLE 12.7-4. Extraction of Acetone from Water with Trichloroethane in a Tower

An inlet water solution of 800 kg/h containing 12.0 wt % acetone is extracted with the solvent trichloroethane containing 0.5 wt % acetone in a countercurrent tray tower at 25°C. The solvents water and trichloroethane are essentially immiscible in each other up to a concentration of acetone in water of 27 wt %. The exit concentration in the water (raffinate) stream is set at 1.0 wt % acetone. The equilibrium data are as follows (T3), where x is the weight fraction of acetone in the water solution and y in the trichloroethane solution:

x	y	x	y
0.0120	0.0196	0.0833	0.1304
0.0294	0.0476	0.1081	0.1666
0.0462	0.0741	0.1316	0.2000
0.0571	0.0909		

(a) Determine the minimum solvent rate needed.
(b) Using 1.3 times the minimum rate, graphically determine the number of theoretical steps needed.
(c) Calculate the number of steps using the analytical equation.
(d) Using a packed tower, the height of a transfer unit H_{OL} is estimated to be 1.2 m. Calculate the number of transfer units N_{OL} and the tower height.

Solution: For part (a), the given values are $L_2 = 800$ kg/h, $x_2 = 0.12$, $x_1 = 0.01$, $y_1 = 0.005$. The inlet stream is

$$L' = L_2(1 - x_2) = 800(1 - 0.12) = 704.0 \text{ kg water/h}$$

The equilibrium data are plotted in Fig. 12.7-8, and the line is curved somewhat. The operating line for minimum solvent flow is plotted from point x_1, y_1 to point P, where $x_2 = 0.12$ on the equilibrium line and $y_{2,max} = 0.184$.

Rewriting Eq. (12.7-14) for an overall balance, and substituting the known values,

$$L'\left(\frac{x_2}{1-x_2}\right) + V'\left(\frac{y_1}{1-y_1}\right) = L'\left(\frac{x_1}{1-x_1}\right) + V'\left(\frac{y_{2,max}}{1-y_{2,max}}\right)$$

$$704\left(\frac{0.12}{1-0.12}\right) + V'\left(\frac{0.005}{1-0.005}\right) = 704\left(\frac{0.01}{1-0.01}\right) + V'\left(\frac{0.184}{1-0.184}\right)$$

Solving, $V' = V'_{min} = 403.2$ kg solvent/h. Setting $x = 0.07$ in Eq. (12.7-14) and solving, $y = 0.1062$. Repeating this for several other x values, these points on the operating line are plotted in Fig. 12.7-8. This operating line for minimum solvent flow (dashed line) is slightly curved and does not intersect or become tangent to the equilibrium line at any point other than P.

For part (b), $V' = 1.3V'_{min} = 1.3(403.2) = 524.2$ kg solvent/h. Substituting into the operating-line Eq. (12.7-14) and solving for y_2,

$$L'\left(\frac{x_2}{1-x_2}\right) + V'\left(\frac{y_1}{1-y_1}\right) = L'\left(\frac{x_1}{1-x_1}\right) + V'\left(\frac{y_2}{1-y_2}\right)$$

$$704\left(\frac{0.12}{1-0.12}\right) + 524.2\left(\frac{0.005}{1-0.005}\right) = 704\left(\frac{0.01}{1-0.01}\right) + 524.2\left(\frac{y_2}{1-y_2}\right)$$

Then, $y_2 = 0.1486$. As before, calculating several points on the operating line, which is curved, for $x = 0.04$, $y = 0.0453$; for $x = 0.08$, $y = 0.0977$. Plotting these points shows a curved operating line. Stepping off the trays, a total of 7.4 steps are obtained.

For part (c), the total flows are first calculated as

$$L_1 = \frac{L'}{1-x_1} = \frac{704}{1-0.01} - 711.1, \qquad V_1 = \frac{V'}{1-y_1} = \frac{524.2}{1-0.005} = 526.8$$

$$L_2 = 800, \qquad V_2 = \frac{V'}{1-y_2} = \frac{524.2}{1-0.1486} = 615.7$$

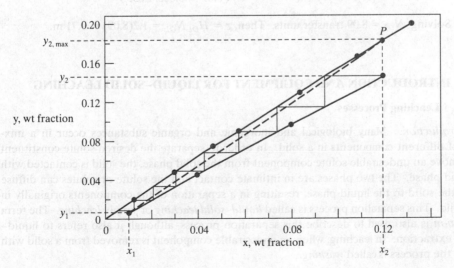

FIGURE 12.7-8. *Operating and equilibrium line for Example 12.7-4.*

The value of m_2 is the slope or tangent at point y_2 on the equilibrium line, which gives $m_2 = 1.49$. The value of m_1 at point x_1 at the dilute end on the equilibrium line is, from the first ·set of equilibrium data points, equal to $y/x = 0.0196/0.0120 = 1.633 = m_1$. Then

$$A_1 = \frac{L_1}{m_1 V_1} = \frac{711.1}{1.633(526.8)} = 0.827$$

$$A_2 = \frac{L_2}{m_2 V_2} = \frac{800}{1.49(615.7)} = 0.872$$

$$A = \sqrt{A_1 A_2} = \sqrt{0.827(0.872)} = 0.849$$

Using Eq. (12.7-15),

$$N = \frac{\ln\left[\dfrac{x_2 - (y_1/m)}{x_1 - (y_1/m)}(1 - A) + A\right]}{\ln(1/A)}$$

$$= \frac{\ln\left[\dfrac{0.12 - 0.0005/1.633}{0.01 - 0.0005/1.633}(1 - 0.849) + 0.849\right]}{\ln(1/0.849)}$$

Then, $N = 7.46$ theoretical steps. This agrees closely with the graphical value of 7.4.

For part (d), Eq. (12.7-19) will not be used, because the operating and equilibrium lines are slightly curved. Using Eq. (12.7-22),

$$N_{OL} = \frac{1}{(1 - A)} \ln\left[(1 - A)\left(\frac{x_2 - y_1/m}{x_1 - y_1/m}\right) + A\right]$$

$$= \frac{1}{(1 - 0.849)} \ln\left[(1 - 0.849)\left(\frac{0.12 - 0.005/1.633}{0.01 - 0.005/1.633}\right) + 0.849\right]$$

Solving, $N_{OL} = 8.09$ transfer units. Then, $z = H_{OL} N_{OL} = 1.2(8.09) = 9.71$ m.

12.8 INTRODUCTION AND EQUIPMENT FOR LIQUID–SOLID LEACHING

12.8A Leaching Processes

1. Introduction.   Many biological and inorganic and organic substances occur in a mixture of different components in a solid. In order to separate the desired solute constituent or remove an undesirable solute component from the solid phase, the solid is contacted with a liquid phase. The two phases are in intimate contact and the solute or solutes can diffuse from the solid to the liquid phase, resulting in a separation of the components originally in the solid. This separation process is called *liquid–solid leaching* or simply *leaching*. The term *extraction* is also used to describe this separation process, although it also refers to liquid–liquid extraction. In leaching, when an undesirable component is removed from a solid with water, the process is called *washing*.

2. *Leaching processes for biological substances.* In the biological and food processing industries, many products are separated from their original natural structure by liquid–solid leaching. An important process, for example, is the leaching of sugar from sugar beets with hot water. In the production of vegetable oils, organic solvents such as hexane, acetone, and ether are used to extract the oil from peanuts, soybeans, flax seeds, castor beans, sunflower seeds, cotton seeds, tung meal, and halibut livers. In the pharmaceutical industry, many different pharmaceutical products are obtained by leaching plant roots, leaves, and stems. For the production of soluble "instant" coffee, ground roasted coffee is leached with fresh water. Soluble tea is produced by water leaching of tea leaves. Tannin is removed from tree barks by leaching with water.

3. *Leaching processes for inorganic and organic materials.* Leaching processes are used extensively in the metals processing industries. The useful metals usually occur in mixtures with very large amounts of undesirable constituents, and leaching is used to remove the metals as soluble salts. Copper salts are dissolved or leached from ground ores containing other minerals by sulfuric acid or ammoniacal solutions. Cobalt and nickel salts are leached from their ores by sulfuric acid–ammonia–oxygen mixtures. Gold is leached from its ore using an aqueous sodium cyanide solution. Sodium hydroxide is leached from a slurry of calcium carbonate and sodium hydroxide prepared by reacting Na_2CO_3 with $Ca(OH)_2$.

12.8B Preparation of Solids for Leaching

1. Inorganic and organic materials. The method of preparation of the solid depends to a large extent upon the proportion of the soluble constituent present, its distribution throughout the original solid, the nature of the solid — that is, whether it is composed of plant cells or whether the soluble material is completely surrounded by a matrix of insoluble matter — and the original particle size.

If the soluble material is surrounded by a matrix of insoluble matter, the solvent must diffuse inside to contact and dissolve the soluble material and then diffuse out. This occurs in many hydrometallurgical processes where metal salts are leached from mineral ores. In these cases crushing and grinding of the ores is used to increase the rate of leaching, since the soluble portions are made more accessible to the solvent. If the soluble substance is in solid solution in the solid or is widely distributed throughout the whole solid, the solvent leaching action may form small channels. The passage of additional solvent is then made easier, and grinding to very small sizes may not be needed. Grinding of the particles is not necessary if the soluble material is dissolved in solution adhering to the solid. Then simple washing can be used, as in washing of chemical precipitates.

2. Animal and vegetable materials. Biological materials are cellular in structure and the soluble constituents are generally found inside the cells. The rate of leaching may be comparatively slow because the cell walls provide another resistance to diffusion. However, to grind the biological material sufficiently small to expose the contents of individual cells is impractical. Sugar beets are cut into thin, wedge-shaped slices for leaching so that the distance required for the water solvent to diffuse in order to reach individual cells is reduced. The cells of the sugar beet are kept essentially intact so that sugar will diffuse through the semipermeable cell walls, while the undesirable albuminous and colloidal components cannot pass through the walls.

For the leaching of pharmaceutical products from leaves, stems, and roots, drying of the material before extraction helps rupture the cell walls. Thus, the solvent can directly dissolve the solute. The cell walls of soybeans and many vegetable seeds are largely ruptured when the original materials are reduced in size to about 0.1 mm to 0.5 mm by rolling or flaking. Cells are smaller in size, but the walls are ruptured and the vegetable oil is easily accessible to the solvent.

12.8C   Rates of Leaching

1. Introduction and general steps.   In the leaching of soluble materials from inside a particle by means of a solvent, the following general steps can occur in the overall process. The solvent must be transferred from the bulk solvent solution to the surface of the solid. Next, the solvent must penetrate or diffuse into the solid. The solute dissolves into the solvent. The solute then diffuses through the solid solvent mixture to the surface of the particle. Finally, the solute is transferred to the bulk solution. The many different phenomena encountered make it virtually impracticable if not impossible to apply any one theory to the leaching action.

In general, the rate of transfer of the solvent from the bulk solution to the solid surface is quite rapid, while the rate of transfer of the solvent into the solid may be somewhat rapid or slow. These are not, in many cases, the rate-limiting steps in the overall leaching process. This solvent transfer usually occurs initially, when the particles are first contacted with the solvent. The dissolving of the solute into the solvent inside the solid may be a simple physical dissolution process or an actual chemical reaction that frees the solute for dissolution. Our knowledge of the dissolution process is limited and the mechanism may be different for each solid (K1).

The rate of diffusion of the solute through the solid and solvent to the surface of the solid is often the controlling resistance in the overall leaching process and may depend on a number of different factors. If the solid is made up of an inert porous solid structure, with the solute and solvent in the pores in the solid, the diffusion through the porous solid can be described by an effective diffusivity. The void fraction and tortuosity are needed. This is described in Section 6.5C for diffusion in porous solids.

In biological or natural substances, additional complexity occurs because of the cells present. In the leaching of thin sugar beet slices, about one-fifth of the cells are ruptured in the slicing of the beets. The leaching of the sugar is then similar to a washing process (Y1). In the remaining cells, sugar must diffuse out through the cell walls. The net result of the two transfer processes does not follow the simple diffusion law with a constant effective diffusivity.

With soybeans, whole beans cannot be leached effectively. The rolling and flaking of the soybeans ruptures cell walls so that the solvent can more easily penetrate by capillary action. The rate of diffusion of the soybean oil solute from the soybean flakes does not permit simple interpretation. A method for designing large-scale extractors involves using small-scale laboratory experiments (O2) with flakes.

The resistance to mass transfer of the solute from the solid surface to the bulk solvent is in general quite small compared to the resistance to diffusion within the solid (O1) itself. This has been found for leaching soybeans, where the degree of agitation of the external solvent has no appreciable effect on the extraction rate (O3, Y1).

2. Rate of leaching when dissolving a solid.   When a material is being dissolved from the solid to the solvent solution, however, the rate of mass transfer from the solid surface to the liquid is the controlling factor. There is essentially no resistance in the solid phase if it is a pure material. The equation for this can be derived as follows for a batch system. The following can also be used for the case when diffusion in the solid is very rapid compared to diffusion from the particle.

The rate of mass transfer of solute A being dissolved to the solution of volume V m³ is

$$\frac{\overline{N}_A}{A} = k_L(c_{AS} - c_A) \tag{12.8-1}$$

where $\overline{N}_A$ is kg mol of A dissolving to the solution/s. A is surface area of particles in m², k_L is a mass-transfer coefficient in m/s, c_{AS} is the saturation solubility of the solid solute A in the solution in kg mol/m³, and c_A is the concentration of A in the solution at time t sec in kg mol/m³. By a material balance, the rate of accumulation of A in the solution is equal to Eq. (12.8-1) times the area A:

$$\frac{V dc_A}{dt} = \overline{N}_A = Ak_L(c_{AS} - c_A) \tag{12.8-2}$$

Integrating from $t = 0$ and $c_A = c_{A0}$ to $t = t$ and $c_A = c_A$,

$$\int_{c_{A0}}^{c_A} \frac{dc_A}{c_{AS} - c_A} = \frac{Ak_L}{V} \int_{t=0}^{t} dt \tag{12.8-3}$$

$$\frac{c_{AS} - c_A}{c_{AS} - c_{A0}} = e^{-(k_L A/V)t} \tag{12.8-4}$$

The solution approaches a saturated condition exponentially. Often the interfacial area A will increase during the extraction if the external surface becomes very irregular. If the soluble material forms a high proportion of the total solid, disintegration of the particles may occur. If the solid is completely dissolving, the interfacial area changes markedly. Also, the mass-transfer coefficient may then change.

If the particles are very small, the mass-transfer coefficient to the particle in an agitated system can be predicted by using equations given in Section 7.4. For larger particles, which are usually present in leaching, equations for predicting the mass-transfer coefficient k_L in agitated mixing vessels are given in Section 7.4 and reference (B1).

3. Rate of leaching when diffusion in solid controls. In the case where unsteady-state diffusion in the solid is the controlling resistance in the leaching of the solute by an external solvent, the following approximations can be used. If the average diffusivity $D_{A\,\text{eff}}$ of solute A is approximately constant, then for extraction in a batch process, unsteady-state mass-transfer equations can be used, as discussed in Section 7.1. If the particle is approximately spherical, Fig. 5.3-13 can be used.

EXAMPLE 12.8-1. Prediction of Time for Batch Leaching
Particles having an average diameter of approximately 2.0 mm are leached in a batch-type apparatus with a large volume of solvent. The concentration of the solute A in the solvent is kept approximately constant. A time of 3.11 h is needed to leach 80% of the available solute from the solid. Assuming that diffu-

sion in the solid is controlling and the effective diffusivity is constant, calculate the time of leaching if the particle size is reduced to 1.5 mm.

Solution: For 80% extraction, the fraction unextracted E_s is 0.20. Using Fig. 5.3-13 for a sphere, for $E_s = 0.20$, a value of $D_{A\,\text{eff}}\, t/a^2 = 0.112$ is obtained, where $D_{A\,\text{eff}}$ is the effective diffusivity in mm^2/s, t is time in s, and a is radius in mm. For the same fraction E_s, the value of $D_{A\,\text{eff}}\, t/a^2$ is constant for a different size. Hence,

$$t_2 = \frac{t_1 a_2^2}{a_1^2} \tag{12.8-5}$$

where t_2 is time for leaching with a particle size a_2. Substituting into Eq. (12.8-5),

$$t_2 = (3.11)\frac{(1.5/2)^2}{(2.0/2)^2} = 1.75\ \text{h}$$

4. Methods of operation in leaching. There are a number of general methods of operation in the leaching of solids. The operations can be carried out under batch or unsteady-state conditions as well as under continuous or steady-state conditions. Both continuous and stage-wise types of equipment are used in steady or unsteady-state operation.

In unsteady-state leaching, a method commonly used in the mineral industries is *in-place leaching,* where the solvent is allowed to percolate through the actual ore body. In other cases the leach liquor is pumped over a pile of crushed ore and collected at the ground level as it drains from the heap. Copper is leached by sulfuric acid solutions from sulfide ores in this manner.

Crushed solids are often leached by percolation through stationary solid beds in a vessel with a perforated bottom to permit drainage of the solvent. The solids should not be too fine, or a high resistance to flow will be encountered. Sometimes a number of tanks are used in series, called an *extraction battery,* and fresh solvent is fed to the solid that is most nearly extracted. The tanks can be open tanks or closed tanks called *diffusers.* The solvent flows through the tanks in series, being withdrawn from the freshly charged tank. This simulates a continuous countercurrent stage operation. As a tank is completely leached, a fresh charge is added to the tank at the other end. Multiple piping is used so that tanks do not have to be moved for countercurrent operation. This is often called the *Shanks system.* It is used widely in leaching sodium nitrate from ore, recovering tannins from barks and woods, in the mineral industries, in the sugar industry, and in other processes.

In some processes the crushed solid particles are moved continuously by bucket-type conveyors or a screw conveyor. The solvent flows countercurrent to the moving bed.

Finely ground solids may be leached in agitated vessels or in thickeners. The process can be unsteady-state batch or the vessels can be arranged in a series to obtain a countercurrent stage process.

12.8D Types of Equipment for Leaching

1. Fixed-bed leaching. Fixed-bed leaching is used in the beet sugar industry and is also used for the extraction of tanning extracts from tanbark, for the extraction of pharmaceuticals from barks and seeds, and in other processes. In Fig. 12.8-1 a typical sugar beet diffuser or extractor is shown. The cover is removable so that sugar beet slices called *cossettes* can be

FIGURE 12.8-1. *Typical fixed-bed apparatus for sugar beet leaching.*

dumped into the bed. Heated water at 344 K (71°C) to 350 K (77°C) flows into the bed to leach out the sugar. The leached sugar solution flows out the bottom onto the next tank in series. Countercurrent operation is used in the Shanks system. The top and bottom covers are removable so that the leached beets can be removed and a fresh charge added. About 95% of the sugar in the beets is leached to yield an outlet solution from the system of about 12 wt %.

2. Moving-bed leaching. There are a number of devices for stagewise countercurrent leaching where the bed or stage moves instead of being stationary. These are used widely in extracting oil from vegetable seeds such as cottonseeds, peanuts, and soybeans. The seeds are usually dehulled first, sometimes precooked, often partially dried, and rolled or flaked. Sometimes preliminary removal of oil is accomplished by expression. The solvents are usually petroleum products, such as hexane. The final solvent–vegetable solution, called *miscella,* may contain some finely divided solids.

In Fig. 12.8-2a an enclosed moving-bed bucket elevator device is shown. This is called the *Bollman extractor.* Dry flakes or solids are added at the upper right side to a perforated basket or bucket. As the buckets on the right side descend, they are leached by a dilute solution of oil in solvent called *half miscella.* This liquid percolates downward through the moving buckets and is collected at the bottom as the strong solution or *full miscella.* The buckets moving upward on the left are leached countercurrently by fresh solvent sprayed on the top bucket. The wet flakes are dumped as shown and removed continuously.

The *Hildebrandt extractor* in Fig. 12.8-2b consists of three screw conveyors arranged in a U shape. The solids are charged at the top right, conveyed downward, across the bottom, and then up the other leg. The solvent flows countercurrently.

3. Agitated solid leaching. When the solid can be ground fine to about 200 mesh (0.074 mm), it can be kept in suspension by small amounts of agitation. Continuous countercurrent leaching can be accomplished by placing a number of agitators in series, with settling tanks or thickeners between each agitator.

Sometimes the thickeners themselves are used as combination contactor-agitators and settlers, as shown in Fig. 12.8-3. In this countercurrent-stage system, fresh solvent enters the

FIGURE 12.8-2. *Equipment for moving-bed leaching: (a) Bollman bucket-type extractor, (b) Hilde-brandt screw-conveyor extractor.*

FIGURE 12.8-3. *Countercurrent leaching using thickeners.*

first stage thickener as shown. The clear, settled liquid leaves and flows from stage to stage. The feed solids enter the last stage, where they are contacted with solvent from the previous stage and then enter the settler. The slowly rotating rake moves the solids to the bottom discharge. The solids together with some liquid are pumped as a slurry to the next tank. If the contact is insufficient, a mixer can be installed between the settlers.

12.9 EQUILIBRIUM RELATIONS AND SINGLE-STAGE LEACHING

12.9A Equilibrium Relations in Leaching

1. Introduction. To analyze single-stage and countercurrent-stage leaching, an operating-line equation or material-balance relation and the equilibrium relations between the two streams are needed, as in liquid–liquid extraction. It is assumed that the solute-free solid is insoluble in the solvent. In leaching, assuming there is sufficient solvent present so that all the solute in the entering solid can be dissolved into the liquid, equilibrium is reached when the solute is dissolved. Hence, all the solute is completely dissolved in the first stage. There usually is sufficient time for this to occur in the first stage.

It is also assumed that there is no adsorption of the solute by the solid in the leaching. This means that the solution in the liquid phase leaving a stage is the same as the solution that remains with the solid matrix in the settled slurry leaving the stage. In the settler in a stage it is not possible or feasible to separate all the liquid from the solid. Hence, the settled solid leaving a stage always contains some liquid in which dissolved solute is present. This solid–liquid stream is called the *underflow* or *slurry stream.* Consequently, the concentration of oil or solute in the liquid or *overflow stream* is equal to the concentration of solute in the liquid solution accompanying the slurry or underflow stream. Hence, on an *x-y* plot the equilibrium line is on the 45° line.

The amount of solution retained with the solids in the settling portion of each stage may depend upon the viscosity and density of the liquid in which the solid is suspended. This, in turn, depends upon the concentration of the solute in the solution. Hence, experimental data showing the variation of the amount and composition of solution retained in the solids as a function of the solute composition must be obtained. These data should be obtained under conditions of concentrations, time, and temperature similar to those in the process for which the stage calculations are to be made.

2. Equilibrium diagrams for leaching. The equilibrium data can be plotted on the rectangular diagram as wt fraction for the three components: solute (*A*), inert or leached solid (*B*), and solvent (*C*). The two phases are the overflow (liquid) phase and the underflow (slurry) phase. This method is discussed elsewhere (B2). Another convenient method of plotting the equilibrium data will be used, instead, which is similar to the method discussed in the enthalpy–concentration plots in Section 11.6.

The concentration of inert or insoluble solid *B* in the solution mixture or the slurry mixture can be expressed in kg (lb_m) units:

$$N = \frac{kg\ B}{kg\ A + kg\ C} = \frac{kg\ solid}{kg\ solution} = \frac{lb\ solid}{lb\ solution} \quad \textbf{(12.9-1)}$$

There will be a value of *N* for the overflow where *N* = 0, and for the underflow *N* will have different values, depending on the solute concentration in the liquid. The compositions of solute *A* in the liquid will be expressed as wt fractions:

$$x_A = \frac{kg\ A}{kg\ A + kg\ C} = \frac{kg\ solute}{kg\ solution} \quad (overflow\ liquid) \quad \textbf{(12.9-2)}$$

$$y_A = \frac{kg\ A}{kg\ A + kg\ C} = \frac{kg\ solute}{kg\ solution} \quad (liquid\ in\ slurry) \quad \textbf{(12.9-3)}$$

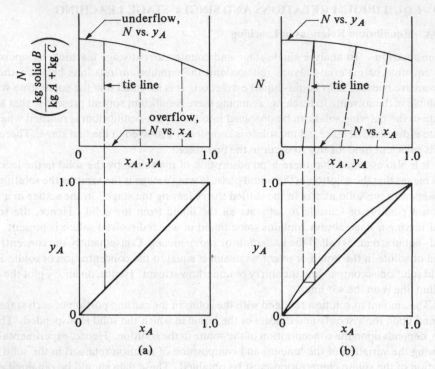

FIGURE 12.9-1. *Several typical equilibrium diagrams: (a) case for vertical tie lines and $y_A = x_A$, (b) case where $y_A \neq x_A$ for tie lines.*

where x_A is the wt fraction of solute A in the overflow liquid and y_A is the wt fraction of A on a solid-B-free basis in the liquid associated with the slurry or underflow. For the entering solid feed to be leached, N is kg inert solid/kg solute A and $y_A = 1.0$. For pure entering solvent $N = 0$ and $x_A = 0$.

In Fig. 12.9-1a a typical equilibrium diagram is shown, where solute A is infinitely soluble in solvent C, which would occur, for example, in the system soybean oil (A)–soybean inert solid meal (B)–hexane solvent (C). The upper curve of N versus y_A for the slurry underflow represents the separated solid under experimental conditions similar to the actual stage process. The bottom line of N versus x_A, where $N = 0$ on the axis, represents the overflow liquid composition where all the solid has been removed. In some cases small amounts of solid may remain in the overflow. The tie lines are vertical, and on a y-x diagram, the equilibrium line is $y_A = x_A$ on the 45° line. In Fig. 12.9-1b the tie lines are not vertical, which can result from insufficient contact time, so that all the solute is not dissolved; adsorption of solute A on the solid; or the solute being soluble in the solid B.

If the underflow line of N versus y is straight and horizontal, the amount of liquid associated with the solid in the slurry is constant for all concentrations. This would mean that the underflow liquid rate is constant throughout the various stages as well as the overflow stream. This is a special case which is sometimes approximated in practice.

12.9B Single-Stage Leaching

In Fig. 12.9-2a a single-stage leaching process is shown where V is kg/h (lb_m/h) of overflow solution with composition x_A and L is kg/h of liquid in the slurry solution with composition y_A based on a given flow rate B kg/h of dry, solute-free solid. The material-balance equations are almost identical to Eqs. (12.5-12)–(12.5-14) for single-stage liquid–liquid extraction and are as follows for a total solution balance (solute A + solvent C), a component balance on A, and a solids balance on B, respectively:

$$L_0 + V_2 = L_1 + V_1 = M \tag{12.9-4}$$

$$L_0 y_{A0} + V_2 x_{A2} = L_1 y_{A1} + V_1 x_{A1} = M x_{AM} \tag{12.9-5}$$

$$B = N_0 L_0 + 0 = N_1 L_1 + 0 = N_M M \tag{12.9-6}$$

where M is the total flow rate in kg $A + C$/h and x_{AM} and N_M are the coordinates of this point M. A balance on C is not needed, since $x_A + x_C = 1.0$ and $y_A + y_C = 1.0$. As shown before, $L_1 M V_1$ must lie on a straight line and $L_0 M V_2$ must also lie on a straight line. This is shown in Fig. 12.9-2b. Also, L_1 and V_1 must lie on the vertical tie line. The point M is the intersection of the two lines. If L_0 entering is the fresh solid feed to be leached with no solvent C present, it will be located above the N-versus-y line in Fig. 12.9-2b.

EXAMPLE 12.9-1. Single-Stage Leaching of Flaked Soybeans

In a single-stage leaching of soybean oil from flaked soybeans with hexane, 100 kg of soybeans containing 20 wt % oil is leached with 100 kg of fresh hexane solvent. The value of N for the slurry underflow is essentially constant at 1.5 kg insoluble solid/kg solution retained. Calculate the amounts and compositions of the overflow V_1 and the underflow slurry L_1 leaving the stage.

Solution: The process flow diagram is the same as given in Fig. 12.9-2a. The known process variables are as follows: for the entering solvent flow, $V_2 = 100$ kg, $x_{A2} = 0$, $x_{C2} = 1.0$; for the entering slurry stream, $B = 100(1.0 - 0.2) = 80$ kg in-

FIGURE 12.9-2. *Process flow and material balance for single-stage leaching: (a) process flow, (b) material balance.*

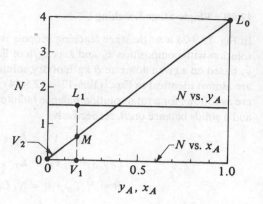

FIGURE 12.9-3. *Graphical solution of single-stage leaching for Example 12.9-1.*

soluble solid, $L_0 = 100(1.0 - 0.8) = 20$ kg A, $N_0 = 80/20 = 4.0$ kg solid/kg solution, $y_{A0} = 1.0$.

To calculate the location of M, substituting into Eqs. (12.9-4), (12.9-5), and (12.9-6) and solving,

$$L_0 + V_2 = 20 + 100 = 120 \text{ kg} = M$$

$$L_0 y_{A0} + V_2 x_{A2} = 20(1.0) + 100(0) = 120 x_{AM}$$

Hence, $x_{AM} = 0.167$.

$$B = N_0 L_0 = 4.0(20) = 80 = N_M(120)$$

$$N_M = 0.667$$

The point M is plotted in Fig. 12.9-3 along with V_2 and L_0. The vertical tie line is drawn locating L_1 and V_1 in equilibrium with each other. Then $N_1 = 1.5$, $y_{A1} = 0.167$, $x_{A1} = 0.167$. Substituting into Eqs. (12.9-4) and (12.9-6) and solving or using the lever-arm rule, $L_1 = 53.3$ kg and $V_1 = 66.7$ kg.

12.10 COUNTERCURRENT MULTISTAGE LEACHING

12.10A Introduction and Operating Line for Countercurrent Leaching

A process flow diagram for countercurrent multistage leaching is shown in Fig. 12.10-1 and is similar to Fig. 12.7-1 for liquid–liquid extraction. The ideal stages are numbered in the direction of the solids or underflow stream. The solvent (C)–solute (A) phase or V phase is the liquid phase that overflows continuously from stage to stage countercurrent to the solid phase, dissolving solute as it moves along. The slurry phase L composed of inert solids (B) and a liquid phase of A and C is the continuous underflow from each stage. Note that the composition of the V phase is denoted by x and the composition of the L phase by y, which is the reverse of that for liquid–liquid extraction.

It is assumed that solid B is insoluble and is not lost in the liquid V phase. The flow rate of the solids is constant throughout the cascade of stages. As in single-stage leaching, V is kg/h (lb$_m$/h) of overflow solution and L is kg/h of liquid solution in the slurry retained by the solid.

V_1
x_1

V_2

V_3

V_n

V_{n+1}

V_N

V_{N+1}
x_{N+1}

y_0, N_0
L_0, B_0

1

2

n

N

y_N, N_N
L_N, B

L_1

L_2

L_{n-1}

L_n

L_{N-1}

feed
solids

underflow
stream

leached
solids

FIGURE 12.10-1. *Process flow for countercurrent multistage leaching.*

In order to derive the operating-line equation, an overall balance and a component balance on solute A is made over the first n stages:

$$V_{n+1} + L_0 = V_1 + L_n \qquad (12.10\text{-}1)$$

$$V_{n+1}x_{n+1} + L_0 y_0 = V_1 x_1 + L_n y_n \qquad (12.10\text{-}2)$$

Solving for x_{n+1} and eliminating V_{n+1},

$$x_{n+1} = \frac{1}{1 + (V_1 - L_0)/L_n} y_n + \frac{V_1 x_1 - L_0 x_0}{L_n + V_1 - L_0} \qquad (12.10\text{-}3)$$

The operating-line equation (12.10-3), when plotted on an x-y plot, passes through the terminal points x_1, y_0 and x_{N+1}, y_N.

In the leaching process, if the viscosity and density of the solution change appreciably with the solute (A) concentration, the solids from the lower-numbered stages where solute concentrations are high may retain more liquid solution than the solids from the higher-numbered stages, where the solute concentration is dilute. Then L_n, the liquid retained in the solids underflow, will vary, and the slope of Eq. (12.10-3) will vary from stage to stage. This condition of variable underflow will be considered first. The overflow will also vary. If the amount of solution L_n retained by the solid is constant and independent of concentration, then constant underflow occurs. This simplifies somewhat the stage-to-stage calculations. This case will be considered later.

12.10B Variable Underflow in Countercurrent Multistage Leaching

The methods in this section are very similar to those used in Section 12.7B for countercurrent solvent extraction, where the L and V flow rates varied from stage to stage. Making an overall total solution (solute A + solvent C) balance on the process shown in Fig. 12.10-1,

$$L_0 + V_{N+1} = L_N + V_1 = M \qquad (12.10\text{-}4)$$

where M is the total mixture flow rate in kg $A + C$/h. Next, making a component balance on A,

$$L_0 y_{A0} + V_{N+1} x_{AN+1} = L_N y_{AN} + V_1 x_{A1} = M x_{AM} \qquad (12.10\text{-}5)$$

Making a total solids balance on B,

$$B = N_0 L_0 = N_N L_N = N_M M \qquad (12.10\text{-}6)$$

where N_M and x_{AM} are the coordinates of point M shown in Fig. 12.10-2, which is the operating diagram for the process. As demonstrated previously, $L_0 M V_{N+1}$ must lie on a straight line and $V_1 M L_N'$ must also lie on a straight line. Usually the flows and compositions of L_0 and V_{N+1} are known and the desired exit concentration y_{AN} is set. Then the coordinates N_M and x_{AM} can be calculated from Eqs. (12.10-4)–(12.10-6) and point M plotted. Then L_N, M, and V_1 must lie on one line, as shown in Fig. 12.10-2.

In order to go stage by stage on Fig. 12.10-2, we must derive the operating-point equation. Making a total balance on stage 1 and then on stage n,

$$L_0 + V_2 = L_1 + V_1 \tag{12.10-7}$$

$$L_{n-1} + V_{n+1} = L_n + V_n \tag{12.10-8}$$

Rearranging Eq. (12.10-7) for the difference flows Δ in kg/h,

$$L_0 - V_1 = L_1 - V_2 = \Delta \tag{12.10-9}$$

This value Δ is constant and also holds for Eq. (12.10-8) rearranged and for all stages:

$$\Delta = L_0 - V_1 = L_n - V_{n+1} = L_N - V_{N+1} = \cdots \tag{12.10-10}$$

This can also be written for a balance on solute A to give

$$x_{A\Delta} = \frac{L_0 y_{A0} - V_1 x_{A1}}{L_0 - V_1} = \frac{L_N y_{AN} - V_{N+1} x_{AN+1}}{L_N - V_{N+1}} \tag{12.10-11}$$

FIGURE 12.10-2. *Number of stages for multistage countercurrent leaching.*

where $x_{A\Delta}$ is the x coordinate of the operating point Δ. A balance made on solids gives

$$N_\Delta = \frac{B}{L_0 - V_1} = \frac{N_0 L_0}{L_0 - V_1} \qquad (12.10\text{-}12)$$

where N_Δ is the N coordinate of the operating point Δ.

As shown in Section 12.7B, Δ is the operating point. This point Δ is located graphically in Fig. 12.10-2 as the intersection of lines $L_0 V_1$ and $L_N V_{N+1}$. From Eq. (12.10-10) we see that V_1 is on a line between L_0 and Δ, V_2 is on a line between L_1 and Δ, V_{n+1} is on a line between L_n and Δ, and so on.

To graphically determine the number of stages, we start at L_0 and draw line $L_0\Delta$ to locate V_1. A tie line through V_1 locates L_1. Line $L_1\Delta$ is drawn given V_2. A tie line gives L_2. This is continued until the desired L_N is reached. In Fig. 12.10-2, about 3.5 stages are required.

EXAMPLE 12.10-1. Countercurrent Leaching of Oil from Meal

A continuous countercurrent multistage system is to be used to leach oil from meal by benzene solvent (B3). The process is to treat 2000 kg/h of inert solid meal (B) containing 800 kg oil (A) and also 50 kg benzene (C). The inlet flow per hour of fresh solvent mixture contains 1310 kg benzene and 20 kg oil. The leached solids are to contain 120 kg oil. Settling experiments similar to those in the actual extractor show that the solution retained depends upon the concentration of oil in the solution. The data (B3) are tabulated below as N kg inert solid B/kg solution and y_A kg oil A/kg solution:

N	y_A	N	y_A
2.00	0	1.82	0.4
1.98	0.1	1.75	0.5
1.94	0.2	1.68	0.6
1.89	0.3	1.61	0.7

Calculate the amounts and concentrations of the stream leaving the process and the number of stages required.

Solution: The underflow data from the table are plotted in Fig. 12.10-3 as N versus y_A. For the inlet solution with the untreated solid, $L_0 = 800 + 50 = 850$ kg/h, $y_{A0} = 800/(800 + 50) = 0.941$, $B = 2000$ kg/h, $N_0 = 2000/(800 + 50) = 2.36$. For the inlet leaching solvent, $V_{N+1} = 1310 + 20 = 1330$ kg/h and $x_{AN+1} = 20/1330 = 0.015$. The points V_{N+1} and L_0 are plotted.

The point L_N lies on the N-versus-y_A line in Fig. 12.10-3. Also for this point, the ratio N_N/y_{AN} = (kg solid/kg solution)/(kg oil/kg solution) = kg solid/kg oil = 2000/120 = 16.67. Hence, a dashed line through the origin at $y_A = 0$ and $N = 0$ is plotted with a slope of 16.67 and intersects the N-versus-y_A line at L_N. The coordinates of L_N at this intersection are $N_N = 1.95$ kg solid/kg solution and $y_{AN} = 0.118$ kg oil/kg solution.

Making an overall balance by substituting into Eq. (12.10-4) to determine point M,

$$L_0 + V_{N+1} = 850 + 1330 = 2180 \text{ kg/h} = M$$

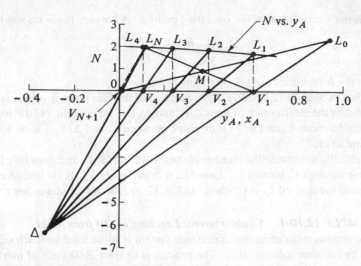

FIGURE 12.10-3. *Graphical construction for number of stages for Example 12.10-1.*

Substituting into Eq. (12.10-5) and solving,

$$L_0 y_{A0} + V_{N+1} x_{AN+1} = 850(0.941) + 1330(0.015) = 2180 x_{AM}$$

$$x_{AM} = 0.376$$

Substituting into Eq. (12.10-6) and solving,

$$B = 2000 = N_M M = N_M(2180) \qquad N_M = 0.918$$

The point M is plotted with the coordinates $x_{AM} = 0.376$ and $N_M = 0.918$ in Fig. 12.10-3. The line $V_{N+1} M L_0$ is drawn, as is line $L_N M$, which intersects the abscissa at point V_1 where $x_{A1} = 0.600$.

The amounts of streams V_1 and L_N are calculated by substituting into Eqs. (12.10-4) and (12.10-5), and solving simultaneously:

$$L_N + V_1 = M = 2180$$

$$L_N y_{AN} + V_1 x_{A1} = L_N(0.118) + V_1(0.600) = 2180(0.376)$$

Hence, $L_N = 1016$ kg solution/h in the outlet underflow stream and $V_1 = 1164$ kg solution/h in the exit overflow stream. Alternatively, the amounts could have been calculated using the lever-arm rule.

The operating point Δ is obtained as the intersection of lines $L_0 V_1$ and $L_N V_{N+1}$ in Fig. 12.10-3. Its coordinates can also be calculated from Eqs. (12.10-11) and (12.10-12). The stages are stepped off as shown. The fourth stage for L_4 is slightly past the desired L_N. Hence, about 3.9 stages are required.

12.10C Constant Underflow in Countercurrent Multistage Leaching

In this case the liquid L_n retained in the underflow solids is constant from stage to stage. This means that a plot of N versus y_A is a horizontal straight line and N is constant. Then the operating-line equation (12.10-3) is a straight line when plotted as y_A versus x_A. The equilibrium line can also be plotted on the same diagram. In many cases the equilibrium line may also be straight, with $y_A = x_A$. Special treatment must be given the first stage, however, as L_0 is generally not equal to L_n, since it contains little or no solvent. A separate material and equilibrium balance is made on stage 1 to obtain L_1 and V_2 (see Fig. 12.10-1). Then the straight operating line can be used and the McCabe–Thiele method used to step off the number of stages.

Since this procedure for constant underflow requires almost as many calculations as the general case for variable underflow, the general procedure can be used for constant underflow by simply using a horizontal line of N versus y_A in Fig. 12.10-2 and stepping off the stages with the Δ point.

12.11 INTRODUCTION AND EQUIPMENT FOR CRYSTALLIZATION

12.11A Crystallization and Types of Crystals

1. Introduction. Separation processes for gas–liquid and liquid–liquid systems have been treated in this and previous chapters. Also, the separation process of leaching was discussed for a solid–liquid system. Crystallization is another solid–liquid separation process, in which mass transfer of a solute from the liquid solution to a pure solid crystalline phase occurs. An important example is in the production of sucrose from sugar beet, where the sucrose is crystallized out from an aqueous solution.

Crystallization is a process where solid particles are formed from a homogeneous phase. This process can occur in the freezing of water to form ice, in the formation of snow particles from a vapor, in the formation of solid particles from a liquid melt, or in the formation of solid crystals from a liquid solution. The last process mentioned, crystallization from a solution, is the most important one commercially and will be treated in the present discussion. In crystallization the solution is concentrated and usually cooled until the solute concentration becomes greater than its solubility at that temperature. Then the solute comes out of the solution, forming crystals of approximately pure solute.

In commercial crystallization not only are the yield and purity of the crystals important but also the sizes and shapes of the crystals. It is often desirable that crystals be uniform in size. Size uniformity is desirable to minimize caking in the package, for ease of pouring, for ease in washing and filtering, and for uniform behavior when used. Sometimes large crystals are requested by the purchaser, even though smaller crystals are just as useful. Also, crystals of a certain shape are sometimes required, such as needles rather than cubes.

2. Types of crystal geometry. A crystal can be defined as a solid composed of atoms, ions, or molecules which are arranged in an orderly and repetitive manner. It is a highly organized type of matter. The atoms, ions, or molecules are located in three-dimensional arrays or space lattices. The interatomic distances between these imaginary planes or space lattices in a crystal are measured by X-ray diffraction, as are the angles between these planes. The pattern or arrangement of these space lattices is repeated in all directions.

Crystals appear as polyhedrons having flat faces and sharp corners. The relative sizes of the faces and edges of different crystals of the same material may differ greatly. However, the angles between the corresponding faces of all crystals of the same material are equal and are characteristic of that particular material. Therefore, crystals are classified on the basis of these interfacial angles.

There are seven classes of crystals, depending upon the arrangement of the axes to which the angles are referred:

1. **Cubic system.** Three equal axes at right angles to each other.
2. **Tetragonal system.** Three axes at right angles to each other, one axis longer than the other two.
3. **Orthorhombic system.** Three axes at right angles to each other, all of different lengths.
4. **Hexagonal system.** Three equal axes in one plane at 60° to each other, and a fourth axis at right angles to this plane and not necessarily the same length.
5. **Monoclinic system.** Three unequal axes, two at right angles in a plane and a third at some angle to this plane.
6. **Triclinic system.** Three unequal axes at unequal angles to each other and not 30, 60, or 90°.
7. **Trigonal system.** Three equal and equally inclined axes.

The relative development of different types of faces of a crystal may differ depending on the solute crystallizing. Sodium chloride crystallizes from aqueous solutions with cubic faces only. But if sodium chloride crystallizes from an aqueous solution with a given slight impurity present, the crystals will have octahedral faces. Both types of crystals, however, are in the cubic system. The crystallization in overall shapes of plates or needles has no relation to the type of crystal system and usually depends upon the process conditions under which the crystals are grown.

12.11B Equilibrium Solubility in Crystallization

In crystallization equilibrium is attained when the solution or mother liquor is saturated. This is represented by a *solubility curve*. Solubility is dependent mainly upon temperature. Pressure has a negligible effect on solubility. Solubility data are given in the form of curves where solubilities in some convenient units are plotted versus temperature. Tables of solubilities are given in many chemical handbooks (P1). Solubility curves for some typical salts in water were given in Fig. 8.1-1. In general, the solubilities of most salts increase slightly or markedly with increasing temperature.

A very common type of curve is shown in Fig. 8.1-1 for KNO_3, where the solubility increases markedly with temperature and there are no hydrates. Over the whole range of temperatures, the solid phase is KNO_3. The solubility of NaCl is marked by its small change with temperature. In solubility plots the solubility data are ordinarily given as parts by weight of anhydrous material per 100 parts by weight of total solvent (i.e., water in many cases).

In Fig. 12.11-1 the solubility curve is shown for sodium thiosulfate, $Na_2S_2O_3$. The solubility increases rapidly with temperature, but there are definite breaks in the curve which indicate different hydrates. The stable phase up to 48.2°C is the pentahydrate $Na_2S_2O_3 \cdot 5H_2O$. This means that at concentrations above the solubility line (up to 48.2°C), the solid crystals formed are $Na_2S_2O_3 \cdot 5H_2O$. At concentrations below the solubility line, only a solution exists. From 48.2 to about 65°C, the stable phase is $Na_2S_2O_3 \cdot 2H_2O$. A half-hydrate is present between 65 to 70°C, and the anhydrous salt is the stable phase above 70°C.

12.11C Yields and Heat and Material Balances in Crystallization

1. Yields and material balances in crystallization. In most of the industrial crystallization processes, the solution (mother liquor) and the solid crystals are in contact for enough time to reach equilibrium. Hence, the mother liquor is saturated at the final temperature of the

FIGURE 12.11-1. *Solubility of sodium thiosulfate, Na₂S₂O₃, in water.*

process, and the final concentration of the solute in the solution can be obtained from the solubility curve. The yield of crystals from a crystallization process can then be calculated knowing the initial concentration of solute, the final temperature, and the solubility at this temperature.

In some instances in commercial crystallization, the rate of crystal growth may be quite slow, due to a very viscous solution or a small surface of crystals exposed to the solution. Hence, some supersaturation may still exist, giving a lower yield of crystals than predicted.

In making the material balances, the calculations are straightforward when the solute crystals are anhydrous. Simple water and solute material balances are made. When the crystals are hydrated, some of the water in the solution is removed with the crystals as a hydrate.

EXAMPLE 12.11-1. Yield of a Crystallization Process
A salt solution weighing 10000 kg with 30 wt % Na_2CO_3 is cooled to 293 K (20°C). The salt crystallizes as the decahydrate. What will be the yield of $Na_2CO_3 \cdot 10H_2O$ crystals if the solubility is 21.5 kg anhydrous Na_2CO_3/100 kg of total water? Do this for the following cases:

(a) Assume that no water is evaporated.
(b) Assume that 3% of the total weight of the solution is lost by evaporation of water in cooling.

Solution: The molecular weights are 106.0 for Na_2CO_3, 180.2 for $10H_2O$, and 286.2 for $Na_2CO_3 \cdot 10H_2O$. The process flow diagram is shown in Fig. 12.11-2, with W being kg H_2O evaporated, S kg solution (mother liquor), and C kg crystals of $Na_2CO_3 \cdot 10H_2O$. Making a material balance around the dashed-line box for water for part (a), where $W = 0$,

$$0.70(10\,000) = \frac{100}{100 + 21.5}(S) + \frac{180.2}{286.2}(C) + 0 \qquad \textbf{(12.11-1)}$$

where $(180.2)/(286.2)$ is wt fraction of water in the crystals. Making a balance for Na_2CO_3,

$$0.30(10\,000) = \frac{21.5}{100 + 21.5}(S) + \frac{106.0}{286.2}(C) + 0 \qquad \textbf{(12.11-2)}$$

FIGURE 12.11-2. *Process flow for crystallization in Example 12.11-1.*

Solving the two equations simultaneously, $C = 6370$ kg of $Na_2CO_3 \cdot 10H_2O$ crystals and $S = 3630$ kg solution.

For part (b), $W = 0.03(10\ 000) = 300$ kg H_2O. Equation (12.11-1) becomes

$$0.70(10\ 000) = \frac{100}{100 + 21.5}(S) + \frac{180.2}{286.2}(C) + 300 \qquad \textbf{(12.11-3)}$$

Equation (12.11-2) does not change, since no salt is in the W stream. Solving Eqs. (12.11-2) and (12.11-3) simultaneously, $C = 6630$ kg of $Na_2CO_3 \cdot 10H_2O$ crystals and $S = 3070$ kg solution.

2. Heat effects and heat balances in crystallization. When a compound whose solubility increases as temperature increases dissolves, there is an absorption of heat, called the *heat of solution.* An evolution of heat occurs when a compound dissolves whose solubility decreases as temperature increases. For compounds dissolving whose solubility does not change with temperature, there is no heat evolution on dissolution. Most data on heats of solution are given as the change in enthalpy in kJ/kg mol (kcal/g mol) of solute occurring with the dissolution of 1 kg mol of the solid in a large amount of solvent at essentially infinite dilution.

In crystallization the opposite of dissolution occurs. At equilibrium the heat of crystallization is equal to the negative of the heat of solution at the same concentration in solution. If the heat of dilution from saturation in the solution to infinite dilution is small, this can be neglected, and the negative of the heat of solution at infinite dilution can be used for the heat of crystallization. With many materials this heat of dilution is small compared with the heat of solution, and this approximation is reasonably accurate. Heat-of-solution data are available in several references (P1, N1).

Probably the most satisfactory method for calculating heat effects during a crystallization process is to use the enthalpy–concentration chart for the solution and the various solid phases which are present for the system. However, only a few such charts are available, including the following systems: calcium chloride–water (H1), magnesium sulfate–water (P2), and ferrous sulfate–water (K2). When such a chart is available, the following procedure is used. The enthalpy H_1 of the entering solution at the initial temperature is read off the chart, where H_1 is kJ (btu) for the total feed. The enthalpy H_2 of the final mixture of crystals and mother liquor at the final temperature is also read off the chart. If some evaporation occurs, the enthalpy H_v of the water vapor is obtained from the steam tables. Then the total heat absorbed q in kJ is

$$q = (H_2 + H_V) - H_1 \qquad \textbf{(12.11-4)}$$

If q is positive, heat must be added to the system. If it is negative, heat is evolved or given off.

EXAMPLE 12.11-2. Heat Balance in Crystallization

A feed solution of 2268 kg at 327.6 K (54.4°C) containing 48.2 kg MgSO$_4$/100 kg total water is cooled to 293.2 K (20°C), where MgSO$_4 \cdot$ 7H$_2$O crystals are removed. The solubility of the salt is 35.5 kg MgSO$_4$/100 kg total water (P1). The average heat capacity of the feed solution can be assumed as 2.93 kJ/kg $\cdot$ K (H1). The heat of solution at 291.2 K (18°C) is -13.31×10^3 kJ/kg mol MgSO$_4 \cdot$ 7H$_2$O (P1). Calculate the yield of crystals and make a heat balance to determine the total heat absorbed, q, assuming that no water is vaporized.

Solution: Making a water balance and a balance for MgSO$_4$ using equations similar to (12.11-1) and (12.11-2) in Example 12.11-1, $C = 616.9$ kg MgSO$_4 \cdot$ 7H$_2$O crystals and $S = 1651.1$ kg solution.

To make a heat balance, a datum of 293.2 K (20°C) will be used. The molecular weight of MgSO$_4 \cdot$ 7H$_2$O is 246.49. The enthalpy of the feed is H_1:

$$H_1 = 2268(327.6 - 293.2)(2.93) = 228\,600 \text{ kJ}$$

The heat of solution is $-(13.31 \times 10^3)/246.49 = -54.0$ kJ/kg crystals. Then the heat of crystallization is $-(-54.0) = +54.0$ kJ/kg crystals, or $54.0(616.9) = 33\,312$ kJ. This assumes that the value at 291.2 K is the same as at 293.2 K. The total heat absorbed, q, is

$$q = -228\,600 - 33\,312 = -261\,912 \text{ kJ}(-248\,240 \text{ btu})$$

Since q is negative, heat is given off and must be removed.

12.11D Equipment for Crystallization

1. Introduction and classification of crystallizers. Crystallizers may be classified according to whether they are batch or continuous in operation. Batch operation is done for certain special applications. Continuous operation of crystallizers is generally preferred.

Crystallization cannot occur without *supersaturation*. A main function of any crystallizer is to cause a supersaturated solution to form. Crystallizing equipment can be classified according to the methods used to bring about supersaturation as follows: (1) supersaturation produced by cooling the solution with negligible evaporation—tank and batch-type crystallizers; (2) supersaturation produced by evaporation of the solvent with little or no cooling—evaporator–crystallizers and crystallizing evaporators; (3) supersaturation by combined cooling and evaporation in an adiabatic evaporator—vacuum crystallizers.

In crystallizers producing supersaturation by cooling, the substances must have a solubility curve that decreases markedly with temperature. This occurs for many substances, and this method is commonly used. When the solubility curve changes little with temperature, as for common salt, evaporation of the solvent to produce supersaturation is often used. Sometimes evaporation with some cooling may be used. In the method of cooling adiabatically in a vacuum, a hot solution is introduced into a vacuum, where the solvent flashes or evaporates and the solution is cooled adiabatically. This method for producing supersaturation is the most important one for large-scale production.

In another method of classification of crystallizers, the equipment is classified according to the method of suspending the growing product crystals. Examples are crystallizers where the suspension is agitated in a tank, is circulated by a heat exchanger, or is circulated in a scraped surface exchanger.

An important difference between many commercial crystallizers is the manner in which the supersaturated liquid contacts the growing crystals. In one method, called the *circulating magma method,* the entire magma of crystals and supersaturated liquid is circulated through both the supersaturation and crystallization steps without separating the solid from the liquid into two streams. Crystallization and supersaturation are occurring together in the presence of the crystals. In the second method, called the *circulating liquid method,* a separate stream of supersaturated liquid is passed through a fluidized bed of crystals, where the crystals grow and new ones form by nucleation. Then the saturated liquid is passed through an evaporating or cooling region to produce supersaturation again for recycling.

2. Tank crystallizers. In tank crystallization, which is an old method still used in some specialized cases, hot saturated solutions are allowed to cool in open tanks. After a period of time the mother liquor is drained and the crystals removed. Nucleation and the size of crystals are difficult to control. Crystals contain considerable amounts of occluded mother liquor. Labor costs are very high. In some cases the tank is cooled by coils or a jacket and an agitator used to improve the heat-transfer rate. However, crystals often build up on these surfaces. This type of crystallizer has limited application; it is sometimes used to produce certain fine chemicals and pharmaceutical products.

3. Scraped surface crystallizers. One type of scraped surface crystallizer is the Swenson–Walker crystallizer, which consists of an open trough 0.6 m wide with a semicircular bottom having a cooling jacket outside. A slow-speed spiral agitator rotates and suspends the growing crystals on turning. The blades pass close to the wall and break off any deposits of crystals on the cooled wall. The product generally has a somewhat wide crystal-size distribution.

In the double-pipe scraped surface crystallizer, cooling water passes in the annular space. An internal agitator is fitted with spring-loaded scrapers that wipe the wall and provide good heat-transfer coefficients. This type is called a *votator* and is used in crystallizing ice cream and plasticizing margarine. A sketch is given in Fig. 4.13-2.

4. Circulating-liquid evaporator–crystallizer. In a combination evaporator–crystallizer, shown in Fig. 12.11-3a, supersaturation is generated by evaporation. The circulating liquid is drawn by the screw pump down inside the tube side of the condensing steam heater. The heated liquid then flows into the vapor space, where flash evaporation occurs, giving some supersaturation. The vapor leaving is condensed. The supersaturated liquid flows down the downflow tube and then up through the bed of fluidized and agitated crystals, which are growing in size. The leaving saturated liquid then goes back as a recycle stream to the heater, where it is joined by the entering feed. The larger crystals settle out and a slurry of crystals and mother liquor is withdrawn as product. This type is also called the *Oslo crystallizer.*

5. Circulating-magma vacuum crystallizer. In the circulating-magma vacuum-type crystallizer shown in Fig. 12.11-3b, the magma or suspension of crystals is circulated out of the main body through a circulating pipe by a screw pump. The magma flows through a heater, where its temperature is raised 2–6 K. The heated liquor then mixes with body slurry and boiling occurs at the liquid surface. This causes supersaturation in the swirling liquid near the sur-

FIGURE 12.11-3. *Types of crystallizers: (a) circulating-liquid evaporator-crystallizer, (b) circulating-magma vacuum crystallizer.*

face, which results in deposits on the swirling suspended crystals until they leave again via the circulating pipe. The vapors leave through the top. A steam-jet ejector provides the vacuum.

12.12 CRYSTALLIZATION THEORY

12.12A Introduction

When crystallization occurs in a homogeneous mixture, a new solid phase is created. An understanding of the mechanisms by which crystals form and then grow is helpful in designing and operating crystallizers. Much experimental and theoretical work has been done to help understand crystallization.

The overall process of crystallization from a supersaturated solution is considered to consist of the basic steps of nucleus formation or nucleation and of crystal growth. If the solution is free of all solid particles, whether foreign or of the crystallizing substance, then nucleus formation must first occur, before crystal growth starts. New nuclei may continue to form while the nuclei present are growing. The driving force for the nucleation step as well as the growth step is supersaturation. These two steps do not occur in a saturated or undersaturated solution.

12.12B Nucleation Theories

1. Solubility and crystal size. In a solution at a given temperature, the thermodynamic difference between small and large particles or crystals is that the small particle has a significant amount of surface energy per unit mass, whereas the large particle does not. As a result, the solubility of a small crystal, of less than micrometer size, is greater than that of a larger-size crystal.

The ordinary solubility applies only to moderately large crystals. Hence, in a supersaturated solution a small crystal can be in equilibrium. If a larger crystal is also present, the larger crystal will grow and the smaller crystal will dissolve. This effect of particle size is an important factor in nucleation.

2. Homogeneous nucleation. As a result of rapid random fluctuations of molecules in a homogeneous solution, the molecules may come together and associate into a cluster. This loose aggregate may quickly disappear. However, if the supersaturation is large enough, then enough particles may associate to form a nucleus which can grow and become oriented into a fixed lattice to form a crystal. The number of particles needed to form a stable nucleus ranges up to a few hundred. In solutions with high supersaturation and no agitation, homogeneous nucleation may be important.

3. Contact nucleation. This is due to two types of contact nucleation. In the first type, the formation of new nuclei by contact nucleation is due to interference of the contacting agent (walls of a container or agitator blades) with clusters of solute molecules becoming organized into the existing crystals and by actual breakage of microscopic growths on the surface of the growing crystals. In the second type, the formation of new nuclei occurs in collisions between crystals. The intensity of agitation is an important factor in contact nucleation.

This phenomenon of contact nucleation has been isolated and studied experimentally (B9, C4) and a correlation has been developed. In practice, experimental data from an actual crystallizer are required for design.

4. Nucleation in commercial crystallizers. In commercial crystallizers, supersaturation is low and agitation is used to keep the crystals suspended. At low supersaturation the crystal growth rate is at the optimum for more-uniform crystals. The predominant mechanism is contact nucleation. Homogeneous nucleation is largely absent because of the agitation and low supersaturation.

12.12C Rate of Crystal Growth and ΔL Law

1. Rate of crystal growth and growth coefficients. The rate of growth of a crystal face is the distance moved per unit time in a direction that is perpendicular to the face. Crystal growth is a layer-by-layer process, and since growth can occur only at the outer face of the crystal, the solute material must be transported to that face from the bulk of the solution. The solute molecules reach the face by diffusion through the liquid phase. The usual mass-transfer coefficient k_y applies in this case. At the surface the resistance to integration of the molecules into the space lattice at the face must be considered. This reaction at the surface occurs at a finite rate, and the overall process consists of two resistances in series. The solution must be supersaturated for the diffusion and interfacial steps to proceed.

The equation for mass transfer of solute A from the bulk solution of supersaturation concentration y_A, mole fraction of A, to the surface where the concentration is y'_A, is

$$\frac{\overline{N}_A}{A_i} = k_y(y_A - y'_A) \tag{12.12-1}$$

where k_y is the mass-transfer coefficient in kg mol/s · m² · mol frac, $\overline{N}_A$ is rate in kg mol A/s, and A_i is area in m² of surface i. Assuming that the rate of reaction at the crystal surface is also dependent on the concentration difference,

$$\frac{\overline{N}_A}{A_i} = k_s(y'_A - y_{Ae}) \tag{12.12-2}$$

where k_s is a surface-reaction coefficient in kg mol/s $\cdot$ m$^2 \cdot$ mol frac and y_{Ae} is the saturation concentration. Combining Eqs. (12.12-1) and (12.12-2),

$$\frac{\overline{N}_A}{A_i} = \frac{y_A - y_{Ae}}{1/k_y + 1/k_s} = K(y_A - y_{Ae}) \tag{12.12-3}$$

where K is the overall transfer coefficient.

The mass-transfer coefficient k_y can be predicted by methods given in Section 7.4 for convective mass-transfer coefficients. When the mass-transfer coefficient k_y is very large, the surface reaction is controlling and $1/k_y$ is negligible. Conversely, when the mass-transfer coefficient is very small, diffusional resistance is controlling. Surface-reaction coefficients and overall transfer coefficients have been measured and reported for a number of systems (B4, H2, P3, V1). Much of the information in the literature is not directly applicable, because the conditions of measurement differ greatly from those in a commercial crystallizer. Also, the velocities and the level of supersaturation in a system are difficult to determine, and vary with position of the circulating magma in the crystallizer.

2. The ΔL law of crystal growth. McCabe (M1) has shown that all crystals that are geometrically similar and of the same material in the same solution grow at the same rate. Growth is measured as the increase in length ΔL, in mm, in linear dimension of one crystal. This increase in length is for geometrically corresponding distances on all crystals. This increase is independent of the initial size of the initial crystals, provided that all the crystals are subject to the same environmental conditions. This law follows from Eq. (12.12-3), where the overall transfer coefficient is the same for each face of all crystals.

Mathematically, this can be written

$$\frac{\Delta L}{\Delta t} = G \tag{12.12-4}$$

where Δt is time in h and growth rate G is a constant in mm/h. Hence, if D_1 is the linear dimension of a given crystal at time t_1 and D_2 at time t_2,

$$\Delta L = D_2 - D_1 = G(t_2 - t_1) \tag{12.12-5}$$

The total growth $(D_2 - D_1)$ or ΔL is the same for all crystals.

The ΔL law fails in cases where the crystals are given any different treatment based on size. It has been found to hold for many materials, particularly when the crystals are under 50 mesh in size (0.3 mm). Even though this law is not applicable in all cases, it is reasonably accurate in many situations.

12.12D Particle-Size Distribution of Crystals

An important factor in the design of crystallization equipment is the expected particle-size distribution of the crystals obtained. Usually, the dried crystals are screened to determine the particle sizes. The percent retained on different-sized screens is recorded. The screens or sieves used are the Tyler standard screens, whose sieve or clear openings in mm are given in Appendix A.5-3.

FIGURE 12.12-1. *Typical particle-size distribution from a crystallizer. [From R. C. Bennett and M. Van Buren, Chem. Eng. Progr. Symp., 65(95), 46 (1969).]*

The data are plotted as particle diameter (sieve opening in screen) in mm versus the cumulative percent retained at that size on arithmetic probability paper. Data for urea particles from a typical crystallizer (B5) are shown in Fig. 12.12-1. Many types of such data will show an approximate straight line for a large portion of the plot.

A common parameter used to characterize the size distribution is the coefficient of variation, CV, as a percent:

$$CV = 100 \frac{PD_{16\%} - PD_{84\%}}{2PD_{50\%}} \tag{12.12-6}$$

where $PD_{16\%}$ is the particle diameter at 16 percent retained. By giving the coefficient of variation and mean particle diameter, a description of the particle-size distribution is obtained if the line is approximately straight between 90 and 10%. For a product removed from a mixed-suspension crystallizer, the CV value is about 50% (R1). In a mixed-suspension system, the crystallizer is at steady state and contains a well-mixed-suspension magma with no product classification and no solids entering with the feed.

12.12E   Model for Mixed Suspension–Mixed Product Removal Crystallizer

1. Introduction and model assumptions. This model will be derived for a mixed suspension–mixed product removal (MSMPR) crystallizer, which is by far the most important type of crystallizer in use in industry today. Conditions assumed are as follows: steady state, suspension completely mixed, no product classification, uniform concentration, no crystals in feed, and the ΔL law of crystal growth applies. All continuous crystallizers have mixing by an agitator or by pump around. In ideal mixing, the effluent composition is the same as in the vessel. This is similar to a CSTR continuous-stirred tank reactor.

2. Crystal population-density function n. To analyze data from a crystallizer, an overall theory must consider combining the effects of nucleation rate, growth rate, and material balance. Randolph and Larson (R1, R2, R3) derived such a model. They plotted the total cumulative number of crystals N per unit volume of suspension (usually 1 L) of size L and smaller versus this size L, as in Fig. 12.12-2. The slope dN/dL of this line is defined as the crystal population density n:

$$n = dN/dL \tag{12.12-7}$$

slope $dN/dL = n$

N,
Cumulative
number of
crystals/Liter

Crystal size, L, mm

FIGURE 12.12-2. *Determination of population density n of crystals.*

where n is the number of crystals/$(L \cdot mm)$. This characterizes the nuclear growth rate of this crystallizer. For this model a relation between population density n and size L is desired.

This population density is obtained experimentally by screen analysis of the total crystal content of a given volume, such as 1.0 L of magma suspension. Each sieve fraction by weight is obtained by collection between two closely spaced and adjacent screens. Then, $L_{av} = (L_1 + L_2)/2$, where L_1 and L_2 are the openings in mm in the two adjacent screens. Also, $\Delta L = (L_1 - L_2)$, where L_1 is the size opening of the upper screen. Then the volume of a particle v_p is

$$v_p = aL_{av}^3 \qquad (12.12\text{-}8)$$

where v_p is mm^3/particle and a is a constant shape factor. Knowing the total weight of the crystals in this fraction, the density ρ in g/mm^3, and the weight of each crystal, which is ρv_p, the total number of crystals ΔN is obtained for the size range ΔL.
Then, rewriting Eq. (12.12-7) for this ΔL size,

$$n = \frac{dN}{dL} \cong \frac{\Delta N}{\Delta L} \qquad (12.12\text{-}9)$$

This method permits the calculation of n for each fraction collected in the screen analysis with an average size of L_{av} mm.

3. Population material balance. To make a population material balance, in Δt time, $\Delta n \, \Delta L$ crystals are withdrawn. Since the effluent composition in the outflow of Q L/h is the same as that in the crystallizer, then the ratio $(\Delta n \, \Delta L)/(n \, \Delta L)$, or fraction of particles withdrawn during Δt time, is the same as the volume ratio $Q \, \Delta t$ withdrawn divided by the total volume V of the crystallizer. Hence,

$$\frac{-\Delta n \, \Delta L}{n \, \Delta L} = \frac{Q \, \Delta t}{V} \qquad (12.12\text{-}10)$$

During this time period Δt, the growth ΔL of a crystal is

$$\Delta L = G \, \Delta t \qquad (12.12\text{-}11)$$

where G is growth rate in mm/h. Combining Eqs. (12.12-10) and (12.12-11),

$$\frac{-\Delta n}{n} = \frac{Q\ \Delta L}{VG} \tag{12.12-12}$$

Letting $\Delta L \to 0$, $\Delta n \to 0$, and integrating,

$$\int_{n^0}^{n} \frac{dn}{n} = -\frac{1}{G\tau} \int_{0}^{L} dL \tag{12.12-13}$$

$$\ln n = -\frac{L}{G\tau} + \ln n^0 \tag{12.12-14}$$

where n^0 is population of nuclei when $L = 0$, n is population when the size is L, and V/Q is τ the total retention or holdup time in h in the crystallizer. A plot of Eq. (12.12-14) of $\ln n$ versus L is a straight line with intercept n^0 and slope $-1/G\tau$. If the line is not straight, this could be an indication of the violation of the ΔL law. These calculations are well suited for being done with a computer spreadsheet.

4. *Average particle size and nucleation rate.* Further derivation of the population approach results in the equation for the average size L_a in mm of the mass distribution:

$$L_a = 3.67 G\tau \tag{12.12-15}$$

Here, 50% of the mass of the product is smaller or larger in size than this value. Also, the predominant particle size is given as

$$L_d = 3.00 G\tau \tag{12.12-16}$$

This predominant particle size means more of the mass is in this differential size interval than in any other size interval.

Another relation can be obtained from this model, which relates the nucleation rate B^0 to the value of the zero-size particle population density n^0 and the growth rate G. For the condition $L \to 0$, the limit of dN/dt (nucleation rate) can be written as

$$\lim_{L \to 0} \frac{dN}{dt} = \lim_{L \to 0} \frac{dN}{dL}\frac{dL}{dt} \tag{12.12-17}$$

However, when $L \to 0$, the slope $dL/dt = G$, the slope $dN/dL = n^0$, and $B^0 = dN/dt$. Hence,

$$B^0 = Gn^0 \tag{12.12-18}$$

where B^0 is nucleation rate in number of nuclei/h $\cdot$ L.

5. *Prediction of cumulative weight fraction obtained.* The population equation can be used to perform a reverse calculation when only values of G and τ are known. The following equation has been derived from the population density function (L4):

$$(1 - W_f) = e^{-x}(1 + x + x^2/2 + x^3/6) \tag{12.12-19}$$

where $x = L/G\tau$, and $(1 - W_f)$ is the cumulative wt fraction at opening L mm, which is in the same form of results as from a screen analysis.

6. *Use of population-model approach for process design.* The data for experimental crystal growth rate G and nucleation rate B^0 obtained by means of the population material balance

are for one given set of conditions in the crystallizer. Then additional experiments can be conducted to determine the effect of residence time τ (production rate) and, possibly, pump-around rate (mixing) on B^0 and G. This is done until the desired distribution W_f from Eq. (12.12-19) is achieved. Or, in some cases, the goal may be for a desired dominant size L_d to be obtained. In many cases, as the residence time τ is increased, the experimental growth rate G decreases. Additional useful references are (B6, C2, C4, L5, M2, P1, R4, S2).

EXAMPLE 12.12-1. *Growth and Nucleation Rates in MSMPR Crystallizer*
Calculate the population density and nucleation growth rates for crystal samples of urea from a screen analysis. The slurry density (g of crystals) is 450 g/liter, the crystal shape factor a is 1.00, the crystal density ρ is 1.335 g/cm^3, and the residence time τ is 3.38 h. The screen analysis from reference (B5) is as follows:

Mesh	Wt %	Mesh	Wt %
−14, +20	4.4	−48, +65	15.5
−20, +28	14.4	−65, +100	7.4
−28, +35	24.2	−100	2.5
−35, +48	31.6		

Solution: The data above are tabulated in Table 12.12-1 using data from Appendix A.5-3. The value of L is the screen opening. For the 14–20 mesh portion, $L_{av} = (1.168 + 0.833)/2 = 1.001$ mm and $\Delta L = 1.168 - 0.833 = 0.335$ mm. For $L_{av} = 1.001$ mm, using Eq. (12.12-8), $v_p = aL_{av}^3 = 1.00(1.001)^3 = 1.003$ mm^3/particle. The density $\rho = 1.335$ g/cm^3 = 1.335×10^{-3} g/mm^3 and the mass/particle = $\rho v_p = 1.335 \times 10^{-3}(1.003) = 1.339 \times 10^{-3}$ g. The total mass of crystals = (450 g/L)(0.044 wt frac).

Using Eq. (12.12-9) to calculate n for the 14–20 mesh size range,

$$n = \frac{\Delta N}{\Delta L} = \frac{(450 \text{ g/L})(\text{wt frac})}{\rho(aL^3)\,\Delta L}$$

$$= \frac{(450 \text{ g/L})(0.044)}{(1.335 \times 10^{-3} \text{ g/mm}^3)(1.00)(1.001 \text{ mm})^3(0.335 \text{ mm})}$$

$$= 4.414 \times 10^4 \quad \text{number of crystals/L} \cdot \text{mm}$$

Then $\ln n = \ln 4.414 \times 10^4 = 10.695$. For the 20–28 mesh size range, $L_{av} = 0.711$/mm, and $\Delta L = 0.244$. Then,

$$n = \frac{(450)(0.144)}{(1.335 \times 10^{-3})(1.00)(0.711)^3(0.244)} = 5.535 \times 10^5$$

Then $\ln n = 13.224$. Other values are calculated in a similar manner using a computer spreadsheet and are given in Table 12.12-1.

The $\ln n$ is plotted versus L in Fig. 12.12-3. The equation of this line is Eq. (12.12-14), where the slope is −9.12 and the intercept = 19.79:

$$\ln n = -9.12L + 19.79 = \frac{-L}{G\tau} + \ln n^0$$

TABLE 12.12-1. Data and Calculations for Example 12.12-1

Mesh	L (mm)	Mesh	L (mm)	L_{av} (mm)	ΔL (mm)	ln n	wt %
14	1.168	20	0.833	1.001	0.335	10.695	4.4
20	0.833	28	0.589	0.711	0.244	13.224	14.4
28	0.589	35	0.417	0.503	0.172	15.131	24.2
35	0.417	48	0.295	0.356	0.122	16.778	31.6
48	0.295	65	0.208	0.252	0.087	17.441	15.5
65	0.208	100	0.147	0.178	0.061	18.099	7.4

FIGURE 12.12-3. Plot of population density n versus length for Example 12.12-1.

The slope $-9.12 = -1/G\tau = -1/(G)(3.38)$. Hence, $G = 0.03244$ mm/h. The intercept $\ln n^0 = 19.79$. Hence, $n^0 = 3.933 \times 10^8$. From Eq. (12.12-18), the nucleation rate B^0 is

$$B^0 = Gn^0 = 0.03244(3.933 \times 10^8) = 1.276 \times 10^7 \text{ nuclei/h} \cdot \text{L}$$

The average size is, from Eq. (12.12-15), $L_a = 3.67G\tau = 3.67(0.03244)(3.38) = 0.402$ mm. The predominant size, from Eq. (12.12-16), is $L_d = 3.00G\tau = 3.00(0.03244)(3.38) = 0.329$ mm.

PROBLEMS

12.1-1. Equilibrium Isotherm for Glucose Adsorption. Equilibrium isotherm data for adsorption of glucose from an aqueous solution to activated alumina are as follows (H3):

c (g/cm^3)	0.0040	0.0087	0.019	0.027	0.094	0.195
q (g solute/g alumina)	0.026	0.053	0.075	0.082	0.123	0.129

Determine the isotherm that fits the data and give the constants of the equation using the given units.

Ans. Langmuir isotherm, $q = 0.145c/(0.0174 + c)$

12.2-1. Batch Adsorption for Phenol Solution. A wastewater solution having a volume of $2.5\ m^3$ contains 0.25 kg phenol/m^3 of solution. This solution is mixed thoroughly in a batch process with 3.0 kg of granular activated carbon until equilibrium is reached. Use the isotherm from Example 12.2-1 and calculate the final equilibrium values and the percent phenol extracted.

12.3-1. Scale-Up of Laboratory Adsorption-Column Data. Using the break-point time and other results from Example 12.3-1, do as follows:

(a) The break-point time for a new column is to be 8.5 h. Calculate the new total length of the column required, column diameter, and the fraction of total capacity used up to the break point. The flow rate is to remain constant at 754 cm^3/s.

(b) Use the same conditions as in part (a), but the flow rate is to be increased to 2000 cm^3/s.

Ans. (a) $H_T = 27.2$ cm, 0.849 fraction; (b) $D = 6.52$ cm

12.3-2. Drying of Nitrogen and Scale-Up of Column. Using molecular sieves, water vapor was removed from nitrogen gas in a packed bed (C3) at 28.3°C. The column height was 0.268 m, with the bulk density of the solid bed being equal to 712.8 kg/m^3. The initial water concentration in the solid was 0.01 kg water/kg solid and the mass velocity of the nitrogen gas was 4052 kg/$m^2 \cdot$ h. The initial water concentration in the gas was $c_o = 926 \times 10^{-6}$ kg water/kg nitrogen. The breakthrough data are as follows:

t (h)	0	9	9.2	9.6	10	10.4
c (kg H_2O/kg $N_2 \times 10^6$)	<0.6	0.6	2.6	21	91	235
t (h)	10.8	11.25	11.5	12.0	12.5	12.8
c (kg H_2O/kg $N_2 \times 10^6$)	418	630	717	855	906	926

A value of $c/c_o = 0.02$ is desired at the break point. Do as follows:

(a) Determine the break-point time, the fraction of total capacity used up to the break point, the length of the unused bed, and the saturation loading capacity of the solid.

(b) For a proposed column length $H_T = 0.40$ m, calculate the break-point time and fraction of total capacity used.

Ans. (a) $t_b = 9.58$ h, fraction used = 0.878

12.4-1. Scale-Up of Ion-Exchange Column. An ion-exchange process using a resin to remove copper ions from aqueous solution is conducted in a 1.0-in.-diameter column 1.2 ft high. The flow rate is 1.5 gph and the break point occurred at 7.0 min. Integrating the breakthrough curve gives a ratio of usable capacity to total capacity of 0.60. Design a new tower that will be 3.0 ft high and operate at 4.5 gph. Calculate the new tower size and break-point time.

Ans. $t_b = 24.5$ min, $D = 1.732$ in.

12.4-2. Height of Tower in Ion Exchange. In a given run using a flow rate of 0.2 m^3/h in an ion-exchange tower with a column height of 0.40 m, the break point occurred at 8.0 min. The ratio of usable capacity to total equilibrium capacity is 0.65. What is the height of a similar column operating for 13.0 min to the break point at the same flow rate?

12.4-3. Ion Exchange of Copper in Column. An ion-exchange column containing 99.3 g of amberlite ion-exchange resin was used to remove Cu^{2+} from a solution where $c_o = 0.18$ M $CuSO_4$. The tower height = 30.5 cm and the diameter = 2.59 cm. The flow rate was 1.37 cm^3 solution/s to the tower. The breakthrough data are shown below:

t (s)	420	480	510	540	600	660
c (g mol Cu/L)	0	0.0033	0.0075	0.0157	0.0527	0.1063

t (s)	720	780	810	870	900	
c (g mol Cu/L)	0.1433	0.1634	0.1722	0.1763	0.180	

The concentration desired at the break point is $c/c_o = 0.010$. Determine the break-point time, fraction of total capacity used up to the break point, length of unused bed, and the saturation loading capacity of the solid.

12.4-4. *Effect of Total Concentration on Loading of Ion-Exchange Resin.* Use the conditions of Example 12.4-1 for ion exchange of Cu^{2+} with H^+. However, determine the effect of total concentration in the solution on the loading of Cu^{2+} on the resin. Do this for a total concentration C of 0.010 N in the solution at equilibrium instead of 0.10 N. Also, the concentration of Cu^{2+} in the solution is 0.002 M (0.004 N) instead of 0.02 M.

Ans. $q_{CuR_2} = 0.9132$ equiv/L

12.4-5. *Equilibrium in Ion Exchange of NH_4^+ for H^+.* For the case where the cation NH_4^+ (*A*) replaces H^+ (*B*) in a polystyrene resin with 8% DVB, calculate the equilibrium constant $K_{A,B}$. The total resin capacity $Q = 2.0$ equiv/L wet bed volume. The total concentration $C = 0.20$ N in the solution. Calculate at equilibrium the equivalents of NH_4^+ in the resin when the concentration of NH_4^+ in solution is 0.04 N.

Ans. $q_{NH_4R} = 0.6684$ equiv/L

12.5-1. *Composition of Two Liquid Phases in Equilibrium.* An original mixture weighing 200 kg and containing 50 kg of isopropyl ether, 20 kg of acetic acid, and 130 kg of water is equilibrated in a mixer–settler and the phases separated. Determine the amounts and compositions of the raffinate and extract layers. Use equilibrium data from Appendix A.3.

12.5-2. *Single-Stage Extraction.* A single-stage extraction is performed in which 400 kg of a solution containing 35 wt % acetic acid in water is contacted with 400 kg of pure isopropyl ether. Calculate the amounts and compositions of the extract and raffinate layers. Solve for the amounts both algebraically and by the lever-arm rule. What percent of the acetic acid is removed? Use equilibrium data from Appendix A.3.

Ans. $L_1 = 358$ kg, $x_{B1} = 0.715$, $x_{C1} = 0.03$, $V_1 = 442$ kg, $y_{A1} = 0.11$, $y_{C1} = 0.86$, 34.7% removed.

12.5-3. *Single-Stage Extraction with Unknown Composition.* A feed mixture weighing 200 kg of unknown composition containing water, acetic acid, and isopropyl ether is contacted in a single stage with 280 kg of a mixture containing 40 wt % acetic acid, 10 wt % water, and 50 wt % isopropyl ether. The resulting raffinate layer weighs 320 kg and contains 29.5 wt % acetic acid, 66.5 wt % water, and 4.0 wt % isopropyl ether. Determine the original composition of the feed mixture and the composition of the resulting extract layer. Use equilibrium data from Appendix A.3.

Ans. $x_{A0} = 0.032$, $x_{B0} = 0.948$, $y_{A1} = 0.15$

12.5-4. *Extraction of Acetone in a Single Stage.* A mixture weighing 1000 kg contains 23.5 wt % acetone and 76.5 wt % water and is to be extracted by 500 kg methyl-isobutyl ketone in a single-stage extraction. Determine the amounts and compositions of the extract and raffinate phases. Use equilibrium data from Appendix A.3.

Chapter 12   Liquid–Liquid and Fluid–Solid Separation Processes

12.6-1. Flooding Velocity and Tower Diameter. Using the same flow rates for each stream and feed conditions as in Ex. 12.6-1, with 1-in. Pall rings, design a tower for 50% of flooding with the aqueous phase dispersed instead of the toluene phase. Compare results.

Ans. Diameter = 1.274 ft

12.6-2. Interfacial Tension in Extraction System. Equilibrium data for the system water (A)–acetic acid (C)–isopropyl ether (B) are given in the Appendix, Table A.3-24. Using the data in dilute solution, where the wt fraction of acetic acid in the water-rich phase is 0.69%, calculate the interfacial tension.

Ans. $\sigma = 20.28$ dyn/cm

12.6-3. Perforated-Plate Tray Efficiency. An organic solvent is extracting an acid from a water solution in a perforated plate tower. The dispersed organic solvent flow rate is 600 ft³/h and the continuous aqueous flow rate is 400 ft³/h. The interfacial tension is 15 dyn/cm and the tray spacing is 1.1 ft. The hole size is 0.40 cm. Estimate the tray efficiency. What happens if the solvent flow rate is reduced to 400 ft³/h?

Ans. $E_o = 0.133$ (solvent 600 ft³/h)

12.7-1. Multiple-Stage Extraction with Fresh Solvent in Each Stage. Pure water is to be used to extract acetic acid from 400 kg of a feed solution containing 25 wt % acetic acid in isopropyl ether. Use equilibrium data from Appendix A.3.

(a) If 400 kg of water is used, calculate the percent recovery in the water solution in a one-stage process.

(b) If a multiple three-stage system is used and 133.3 kg fresh water is used in each stage, calculate the overall percent recovery of the acid in the total outlet water. (*Hint:* First, calculate the outlet extract and raffinate streams for the first stage using 400 kg of feed solution and 133 kg of water. For the second stage, 133 kg of water contacts the outlet organic phase from the first stage. For the third stage, 133.3 kg of water contacts the outlet organic phase from the second stage, and so on.)

12.7-2. Overall Balance in Countercurrent Stage Extraction. An aqueous feed of 200 kg/h containing 25 wt % acetic acid is being extracted by pure isopropyl ether at the rate of 600 kg/h in a countercurrent multistage system. The exit acid concentration in the aqueous phase is to contain 3.0 wt % acetic acid. Calculate the compositions and amounts of the exit extract and raffinate streams. Use equilibrium data from Appendix A.3.

12.7-3. Minimum Solvent and Countercurrent Extraction of Acetone. An aqueous feed solution of 1000 kg/h containing 23.5 wt % acetone and 76.5 wt % water is being extracted in a countercurrent multistage extraction system using pure methylisobutyl ketone solvent at 298–299 K. The outlet water raffinate will contain 2.5 wt % acetone. Use equilibrium data from Appendix A.3.

(a) Calculate the minimum solvent that can be used. [*Hint*: In this case the tie line through the feed L_0 represents the condition for minimum solvent flow rate. This gives $V_{1\,\text{min}}$. Then draw lines $L_N V_{1\,\text{min}}$ and $L_0 V_{N+1}$ to give the mixture point M_{min} and the coordinate $x_{AM\,\text{min}}$. Using Eq. (12.7-4), solve for $V_{N+1\,\text{min}}$, the minimum value of the solvent flow rate V_{N+1}.]

(b) Using a solvent flow rate of 1.5 times the minimum, calculate the number of theoretical stages.

12.7-4. Countercurrent Extraction of Acetic Acid and Minimum Solvent. An aqueous feed solution of 1000 kg/h of acetic acid–water solution contains 30.0 wt % acetic acid and is to be extracted in a countercurrent multistage process with pure isopropyl ether to reduce the acid concentration to 2.0 wt % acid in the final raffinate. Use equilibrium data from Appendix A.3.

(a) Calculate the minimum solvent flow rate that can be used. (*Hint:* See Problem 12.7-3 for the method to use.)

(b) If 2500 kg/h of ether solvent is used, determine the number of theoretical stages required. (*Note:* It may be necessary to replot on an expanded scale the concentrations at the dilute end.)

Ans. (a) Minimum solvent flow rate $V_{N+1} = 1630$ kg/h; (b) 7.5 stages

12.7-5. *Number of Stages in Countercurrent Extraction.* Repeat Example 12.7-2 but use an exit acid concentration in the aqueous phase of 4.0 wt %.

12.7-6. *Extraction with Immiscible Solvents.* A water solution of 1000 kg/h containing 1.5 wt % nicotine in water is stripped with a kerosene stream of 2000 kg/h containing 0.05 wt % nicotine in a countercurrent stage tower. The exit water is to contain only 10% of the original nicotine, that is, 90% is removed. Use equilibrium data from Example 12.7-3. Calculate the number of theoretical stages needed.

Ans. 3.7 stages

12.7-7. *Numbers of Transfer Units for Extraction of Nicotine.* Using the data from Example 12.7-3 for nicotine extraction, replot the equilibrium and operating lines. For this system using a packed tower, the height of a transfer unit has been estimated as $H_{OL} = 1.1$ m. Calculate the number of transfer units by two different methods and compare the values. Also calculate the tower height.

Ans. $N_{OL} = 5.76$ transfer units (Eq. 12.7-22), $z = 6.34$ m

12.7-8. *Minimum Solvent Rate with Immiscible Solvents.* Determine the minimum solvent kerosene rate to perform the desired extraction in Example 12.7-3. Using 1.50 times this minimum rate, determine the number of theoretical stages needed graphically and also by using the analytical equation.

Ans. $V' = 153.8$ kg/h, $N = 6.86$ analytically

12.7-9. *Stripping Nicotine from Kerosene.* A kerosene flow of 100 kg/h contains 1.4 wt % nicotine and is to be stripped with pure water in a countercurrent multistage tower. It is desired to remove 90% of the nicotine. Using a water rate of 1.50 times the minimum, determine the number of theoretical stages required. (Use the equilibrium data from Example 12.7-3.)

12.7-10. *Extraction of Acetone from Water and Number of Transfer Units.* Repeat Example 12.7-4 for the extraction of acetone from water using 1.5 times the minimum solvent flow rate. Do as follows:

(a) Graphically determine the number of theoretical steps needed.

(b) Calculate the number of steps using the analytical equation.

(c) For a packed tower with this system, the height of the transfer unit H_{OL} has been estimated as 0.9 m. Calculate the number of transfer units N_{OL} and the tower height.

Ans. (b) $N = 5.34$ steps analytically; (c) $N_{OL} = 6.21$ transfer units

12.7-11. *Predicting Extraction for Existing Tower with a Given Number of Steps.* An existing tower contains 5.0 theoretical steps. It is desired to predict its performance under the following conditions using the system water–acetone–trichloroethane given in Example 12.7-4. An inlet water stream of 1000 kg/h containing 8.0 wt % acetone is extracted with 750 kg/h trichloroethane containing 1.0 wt % acetone in this countercurrent tower at 25°C. Determine the outlet concentration x_1 in the water solution and in the trichloroethane solution using an analytical equation. Also plot the equilibrium and operating lines and step off 5.0 steps. Assume dilute solutions.

Ans. $x_1 = 0.01205$, $y_2 = 0.0932$

12.8-1. *Effective Diffusivity in Leaching Particles.* In Example 12.8-1 a time of leaching of the solid particle of 3.11 h is needed to remove 80% of the solute. Perform the following calculations:

(a) Using the experimental data, calculate the effective diffusivity, $D_{A\,eff}$.

(b) Predict the time to leach 90% of the solute from the 2.0 mm particle.

Ans. (a) $D_{A\,eff} = 1.0 \times 10^{-5}$ mm^2/s; (b) $t = 5.00$ h

12.9-1. *Leaching of Oil from Soybeans in a Single Stage.* Repeat Example 12.9-1 for single-stage leaching of oil from soybeans. The 100 kg of soybeans contains 22 wt % oil and the solvent feed is 80 kg of solvent containing 3 wt % soybean oil.

Ans. $L_1 = 52.0$ kg, $y_{A1} = 0.239$, $V_1 = 50.0$ kg, $x_{A1} = 0.239$, $N_1 = 1.5$

12.9-2. *Leaching a Soybean Slurry in a Single Stage.* A slurry of flaked soybeans weighing a total of 100 kg contains 75 kg of inert solids and 25 kg of solution with 10 wt % oil and 90 wt % solvent hexane. This slurry is contacted with 100 kg of pure hexane in a single stage so that the value of N for the outlet underflow is 1.5 kg insoluble solid/kg solution retained. Calculate the amounts and compositions of the overflow V_1 and the underflow L_1 leaving the stage.

12.10-1. *Constant Underflow in Leaching Oil from Meal.* Use the same conditions as given in Example 12.10-1, but assume constant underflow of $N = 1.85$ kg solid/kg solution. Calculate the exit flows and compositions and the number of stages required. Compare with Example 12.10-1.

Ans. $y_{AN} = 0.111$, $x_{A1} = 0.623$, 4.3 stages

12.10-2. *Effect of Less Solvent Flow in Leaching Oil from Meal.* Use the same conditions as given in Example 12.10-1, but the inlet fresh-solvent-mixture flow rate per hour is decreased by 10%, to 1179 kg of benzene and 18 kg of oil. Calculate the number of stages needed.

12.10-3. *Countercurrent Multistage Washing of Ore.* A treated ore containing inert solid gangue and copper sulfate is to be leached in a countercurrent multistage extractor using pure water to leach the CuSO$_4$. The solid charge rate per hour consists of 10 000 kg of inert gangue (B), 1200 kg of CuSO$_4$ (solute A), and 400 kg of water (C). The exit wash solution is to contain 92 wt % water and 8 wt % CuSO$_4$. A total of 95% of the CuSO$_4$ in the inlet ore is to be recovered. The underflow is constant at $N = 0.5$ kg inert gangue solid/kg aqueous solution. Calculate the number of stages required.

Ans. 9 stages, $L_N = 20\,000$ kg/h, $y_{AN} = 0.0030$, $V_1 = 14\,250$ kg/h

12.10-4. *Countercurrent Multistage Leaching of Halibut Livers.* Fresh halibut livers containing 25.7 wt % oil are to be extracted with pure ethyl ether to remove 95% of the oil in a countercurrent multistage leaching process. The feed rate is 1000 kg of fresh livers per hour. The final exit overflow solution is to contain 70 wt % oil. The retention of solution by the inert solids (oil-free liver) of the liver varies as follows (C1), where N is kg inert solid/kg solution retained and y_A is kg oil/kg solution:

N	y_A	N	y_A	N	y_A
4.88	0	2.47	0.4	1.39	0.81
3.50	0.2	1.67	0.6		

Calculate the amounts and compositions of the exit streams and the total number of theoretical stages.

12.10-5. *Countercurrent Leaching of Flaked Soybeans.* Soybean flakes containing 22 wt % oil are to be leached in a countercurrent multistage process to contain 0.8 kg oil/100 kg inert solid using fresh and pure hexane solvent. For every 1000 kg soybeans, 1000 kg hexane is used. Experiments (S1) give the following retention of solution with the solids in the underflow, where N is kg inert solid/kg solution retained and y_A is wt fraction of oil in solution:

N	y_A
1.73	0
1.52	0.20
1.43	0.30

Calculate the exit flows and compositions and the number of theoretical stages needed.

12.11-1. *Crystallization of Ba(NO₃)₂.* A hot solution of $Ba(NO_3)_2$ from an evaporator contains 30.6 kg $Ba(NO_3)_2$/100 kg H_2O and goes to a crystallizer, where the solution is cooled and $Ba(NO_3)_2$ crystallizes. On cooling, 10% of the original water present evaporates. For a feed solution of 100 kg total, calculate the following:
(a) The yield of crystals if the solution is cooled to 290 K (17°C), where the solubility is 8.6 kg $Ba(NO_3)_2$/100 kg total water.
(b) The yield if cooled instead to 283 K, where the solubility is 7.0 kg $Ba(NO_3)_2$/100 kg total water.
           Ans. (a) 17.47 kg $Ba(NO_3)_2$ crystals

12.11-2. *Dissolving and Subsequent Crystallization.* A batch of 1000 kg of KCl is dissolved in sufficient water to make a saturated solution at 363 K, where the solubility is 35 wt % KCl in water. The solution is cooled to 293 K, at which temperature its solubility is 25.4 wt %.
(a) What is the weight of water required for solution and the weight of crystals of KCl obtained?
(b) What is the weight of crystals obtained if 5% of the original water evaporates on cooling?
      Ans. (a) 1857 kg water, 368 kg crystals; (b) 399 kg crystals

12.11-3. *Crystallization of MgSO₄·7H₂O.* A hot solution containing 1000 kg of $MgSO_4$ and water having a concentration of 30 wt % $MgSO_4$ is cooled to 288.8 K, where crystals of $MgSO_4·7H_2O$ are precipitated. The solubility at 288.8 K is 24.5 wt % anhydrous $MgSO_4$ in the solution. Calculate the yield of crystals obtained if 5% of the original water in the system evaporates on cooling.

12.11-4. *Heat Balance in Crystallization.* A feed solution of 10 000 lb$_m$ at 130°F containing 47.0 lb $FeSO_4$/100 lb total water is cooled to 80°F, where $FeSO_4·7H_2O$ crystals are removed. The solubility of the salt is 30.5 lb $FeSO_4$/100 lb total water (P1). The average heat capacity of the feed solution is 0.70 btu/lb$_m$·°F. The heat of solution at 18°C is -4.4 kcal/g mol (-18.4 kJ/g mol) $FeSO_4·7H_2O$ (P1). Calculate the yield of crystals and make a heat balance. Assume that no water is vaporized.
      Ans. 2750 lb$_m$ $FeSO_4·7H_2O$ crystals, $q = -428\,300$ btu ($-451\,900$ kJ)

12.11-5. *Effect of Temperature on Yield and Heat Balance in Crystallization.* Use the conditions given in Example 12.11-2, but the solution is cooled instead to 283.2 K, where the solubility is 30.9 kg $MgSO_4$/100 kg total water (P1). Calculate the effect on yield and the heat absorbed by using 283.2 K instead of 293.2 K for the crystallization.

12.12-1. *Growth and Nucleation Rate in MSMPR Crystallizer.* Experimental data were obtained for an MSMPR crystallizer (S2). The slurry density is 169 g/L, the crystal density ρ is 1.65 g/m³, the residence time τ is 6.57 h, and the shape factor a is 0.98. The screen analysis of the crystals is as follows:

Mesh	Wt %	Mesh	Wt %
−14, +20	4.5	−35, +48	31.5
−20, +28	14.5	−48, +65	15.5
−28, +35	24.0	−65, +100	7.5
		−100	2.5

Using these data, do as follows:
(a) Calculate the population density, growth rate, and nucleation rate. Also calculate the average size L_a.
(b) Using these calculated values, predict the cumulative weight fraction versus size L from the experimental value of G and τ. Compare the predicted and experimental values.
    Ans. (a) $G = 0.01673$ mm/h; (b) For $L = 0.589$ mm, $(1 - W_f) = 0.218$

12.12-2. *Prediction of Cumulative Weight Fraction of Crystals from Growth Rate.* In Example 12.12-1, the growth rate G was determined to be 0.03244 mm/h for a residence time τ of 3.38 h. Using these values, predict the cumulative weight fraction versus size L. Compare the predicted values with the experimental values.
    Ans. $L = 0.589$ mm, $(1 - W_f) = 0.217$; $L = 0.417$ mm, $(1 - W_f) = 0.473$

REFERENCES

(B1) BLAKEBROUGH, N. *Biochemical and Biological Engineering Science,* Vol. 1. New York: Academic Press, Inc., 1968.

(B2) BADGER, W. L., and BANCHERO, J. T. *Introduction to Chemical Engineering.* New York: McGraw-Hill Book Company, 1955.

(B3) BADGER, W. L., and McCABE, W. L. *Elements of Chemical Engineering.* New York: McGraw-Hill Book Company, 1936.

(B4) BUCKLEY, H. E. *Crystal Growth.* New York: John Wiley & Sons, Inc., 1951.

(B5) BENNETT, R. C., and VAN BUREN, M. *Chem. Eng. Progr. Symp.,* **65**(95), 46 (1969).

(B6) BENNETT, R. C., FIELDELMAN, H., and RANDOLPH, A. D. *Chem. Eng. Progr.,* **69**(7), 86 (1972).

(B7) BELTER, P. A., CUSSLER, E. L., and HU, W. S. *Bioseparations.* New York: John Wiley & Sons, Inc., 1988.

(B8) BONNER, O. D., and SMITH, L. L. *J. Phys. Chem.,* **61,** 236 (1957).

(B9) BENNETT, R. C., FIEDELMAN, H., and RANDOLPH, A. D. *Chem. Eng. Progr.,* **69**(7), 86 (1973).

(C1) CHARM, S. E. *The Fundamentals of Food Engineering,* 2nd ed. Westport, Conn.: Avi Publishing Co., Inc., 1971.

| (C2) | Crystallization from Solutions and Melts, *Chem. Eng. Progr. Symp.*, **65**(95), (1969). |

(C2)   Crystallization from Solutions and Melts, *Chem. Eng. Progr. Symp.*, **65**(95), (1969).

(C3)   COLLINS, J. J. *Chem. Eng. Progr. Symp. Series,* **63**(74), 31 (1967).

(C4)   CLONTZ, N. A., and McCABE, W. L. *A.I.Ch.E. Symp. Ser. No. 110,* **67,** 6 (1971).

(C5)   CLAFFEY, J. B., BADGETT, C. O., SKALAMERA, C. D., and PHILLIPS, G. W. *Ind. Eng. Chem.,* **42,** 166 (1950).

(C6)   CUSACK, R. W., and KARR, A. E. *Chem. Eng.,* **98**(4), 112 (1991).

(C7)   CUSACK, R. W., FREMEAUX, P., and GLATZ, D. *Chem. Eng.,* **98**(2), 66 (1991).

(C8)   CUSACK, R. W., and FREMEAUX, P. *Chem. Eng.,* **98**(3), 132 (1991).

(C9)   CRAWFORD, J. W., and WILKE, C. R. *Chem. Eng. Prog.,* **47,** 423 (1951).

(H1)   HOUGEN, O. A., WATSON, K. M., and RAGATZ, R. A. *Chemical Process Principles,* Part I, 2nd ed. New York: John Wiley & Sons, Inc., 1954.

(H2)   HIXSON, A. W., and KNOX, K. L. *Ind. Eng. Chem.,* **43,** 2144 (1951).

(H3)   HU, M. C., HAERING, E. R., and GEANKOPLIS, C. J. *Chem. Eng. Sci.,* **40,** 2241 (1985).

(H4)   HUMPHRY, J. L., and KELLER, G. E. *Separation Process Technology.* New York: McGraw-Hill Book Company, 1997.

(K1)   KARNOFSKY, G. J. *Am. Oil Chemist's Soc.,* **26,** 564 (1949).

(K2)   KOBE, K. A., and COUCH, E. J., JR. *Ind. Eng. Chem.,* **46,** 377 (1954).

(K3)   KARR, A. E. and LO, T. C. *Proc. Int. Solv. Ext. Conf. (ISEC),* **1,** 299 (1971).

(K4)   KARR, A. E. *Sepn. Sci. Tech.,* **15**(No. 4), 877 (1980).

(L1)   LUKCHIS, G. M. *Chem. Eng.,* **80** (June 11), 111 (1973).

(L2)   LARSON, M. A. *Chem. Eng.,* **85** (Feb. 13), 90 (1978).

(L3)   LO, T. C., and KARR, A. E. *I.E.C. Proc. Des. Dev.,* **11**(4), 495 (1972).

(L4)   LO, T. C., BAIRD, M. H. I., and HANSON, C. *Handbook of Solvent Extraction.* New York: John Wiley & Sons, Inc., 1983.

(L5)   LARSON, M. A., and RANDOLPH, A. D. *Chem. Eng. Progr. Symp.,* **65**(95), 1 (1969).

(M1)   MICHAELS, A. S. *Ind. Eng. Chem.,* **44**(8), 1922 (1952).

(M2)   MURRAY, D. C., and LARSON, M. A. *A.I.Ch.E. J.,* **11,** 728 (1965).

(M3)   McCABE, W. L., SMITH, J. C., and HARRIOTT, P. *Unit Operations of Chemical Engineering,* 4th ed. New York: McGraw-Hill Book Company, 1985.

(M4)   McCABE, W. L., SMITH, J. C., and HARRIOTT, P. *Unit Operations of Chemical Engineering,* 5th ed. New York: McGraw-Hill Book Company, 1992.

(N1)   NATIONAL RESEARCH COUNCIL. *International Critical Tables,* Vol. 5. New York: McGraw-Hill Book Company, 1929.

(O1)   OSBURN, J. Q., and KATZ, D. L. *Trans. A.I.Ch.E.,* **40,** 511 (1944).

(O2)   OTHMER, D. F., and JAATINEN, W. A. *Ind. Eng. Chem.,* **51,** 543 (1959).

(O3)   OTHMER, D. F., and AGARWAL, J. C. *Ind. Eng. Chem.,* **51,** 372 (1955).

(P1)   PERRY, R. H., and GREEN, D. *Perry's Chemical Engineers' Handbook,* 6th ed. New York: McGraw-Hill Book Company, 1984.

(P2)   PERRY, J. H. *Chemical Engineers' Handbook,* 4th ed. New York: McGraw-Hill Book Company, 1963.

(P3)   PERRY, R. H., and CHILTON, C. H. *Chemical Engineers' Handbook,* 5th ed. New York: McGraw-Hill Book Company, 1973.

(P4)   PERRY, R. H., and GREEN, D. *Perry's Chemical Engineers' Handbook,* 7th ed. New York: McGraw-Hill Book Company, 1997.

(R1)   RANDOLPH, A. D., and LARSON, M. A. *Theory of Particulate Systems.* New York: Academic Press, Inc., 1971.

(R2)   RANDOLPH, A. D., and LARSON, M. A. *A.I.Ch.E. J.,* **8,** 639 (1962).

(R3)   RANDOLPH, A. D. *A.I.Ch.E. J.,* **11,** 424 (1965).

(R4) ROUSSEAU, R. W. (ed.). *Handbook of Separation Process Technology*. New York: John Wiley & Sons, Inc., 1987.

(R5) REYNOLDS, T. D. *Unit Operations and Processes in Environmental Engineering*. Boston: PWS Publishers, 1982.

(R6) RUTHVEN, D. M. *Principles of Adsorption and Adsorption Processes*. New York: John Wiley & Sons, Inc., 1984.

(S1) SMITH, C. T. *J. Am. Oil Chemists' Soc.*, **28,** 274 (1951).

(S2) SCHWEITZER, P. A. *Handbook of Separation Techniques for Chemical Engineers*. New York: McGraw-Hill Book Company, 1997.

(S3) SEADER, J. D., and HENLEY, E. J. *Separation Process Principles*. New York: John Wiley & Sons, Inc., 1998.

(S4) STICHLMAIR, J. *Chemie Ingeniur Technik*, **52,** 253 (1980).

(S5) STRIGLE, R. F. *Packed Tower Design and Applications*. Houston: Gulf Publishing Company, 1994.

(T1) TREYBAL, R. E. *Mass Transfer Operations*, 3rd ed. New York: McGraw-Hill Book Company, 1980.

(T2) TREYBAL, R. E. *Liquid Extraction*, 2nd ed. New York: McGraw-Hill Book Company, 1963.

(T3) TREYBAL, R. E. LAWRENCE, D. W., and DALEY, F. *Ind. Eng. Chem.*, **38,** 817 (1946).

(V1) VAN HOOK, A. *Crystallization, Theory and Practice*. New York: John Wiley & Sons, Inc., 1951.

(W1) WALAS, S. M. *Chemical Process Equipment*. Boston: Butterworth-Heinemann, 1990.

(Y1) YANG, H. H., and BRIER, J. C. *A.I.Ch.E. J.*, **4,** 453 (1958).

CHAPTER 13
Membrane Separation Processes

13.1 INTRODUCTION AND TYPES OF MEMBRANE SEPARATION PROCESSES

13.1A Introduction

Separations by the use of membranes are becoming increasingly important in the process industries. In this relatively new separation process, the membrane acts as a semipermeable barrier and separation occurs by the membrane controlling the rate of movement of various molecules between two liquid phases, two gas phases, or a liquid and a gas phase. The two fluid phases are usually miscible and the membrane barrier prevents actual, ordinary hydrodynamic flow. A classification of the main types of membrane separation follows.

13.1B Classification of Membrane Processes

1. Gas diffusion in porous solid.   In this type a gas phase is present on both sides of the membrane, which is a microporous solid. The rates of molecular diffusion of the various gas molecules depend on the pore sizes and the molecular weights. This type of diffusion in the molecular, transition, and Knudsen regions was discussed in detail in Section 7.6.

2. Liquid permeation or dialysis.   In this case, the small solutes in one liquid phase diffuse readily because of concentration differences through a porous membrane to the second liquid (or vapor) phase. Passage of large molecules through the membrane is more difficult. This membrane process has been applied in chemical processing separations such as separation of H_2SO_4 from nickel and copper sulfates in aqueous solutions, food processing, and artificial kidneys, and will be covered in detail in Section 13.2. In electrodialysis, separation of ions occurs by imposing an emf difference across the membrane.

3. Gas permeation in a membrane.   The membrane in this process is usually a polymer such as rubber, polyamide, and so on, and is not a porous solid. The solute gas first dissolves in the membrane and then diffuses in the solid to the other gas phase. This was discussed in detail in Section 6.5 for solutes following Fick's law and will be considered again, for the case where resistances are present, in Section 13.3A. In Sections 13.3 to 13.8, different process flow patterns are considered. Examples of membrane separations are helium being separated from natural gas and nitrogen from air. Separation of a gas mixture occurs because each type of molecule diffuses at a different rate through the membrane.

4. Reverse osmosis. A membrane, which impedes the passage of a low-molecular-weight solute, is placed between a solute–solvent solution and a pure solvent. The solvent diffuses into the solution by osmosis. In reverse osmosis, a reverse pressure difference is imposed which causes the flow of solvent to reverse, as in the desalination of seawater. This process is also used to separate other low-molecular-weight solutes, such as salts, sugars, and simple acids from a solvent (usually water). This process will be covered in detail in Sections 13.9 and 13.10.

5. Ultrafiltration membrane process. In this process, pressure is used to obtain a separation of molecules by means of a semipermeable polymeric membrane (M2). The membrane discriminates on the basis of molecular size, shape, or chemical structure and separates relatively high-molecular-weight solutes such as proteins, polymers, colloidal materials such as minerals, and so on. The osmotic pressure is usually negligible because of the high molecular weights. This will be covered in Section 13.11.

6. Microfiltration membrane process. In microfiltration, pressure-driven flow through the membrane is used to separate micron-size particles from fluids. The particles are usually larger than those in ultrafiltration. Examples are separation of bacteria, paint pigment, yeast cells, and so on from solutions. This process will be covered in Section 13.12.

7. Gel permeation chromotography. The porous gel retards diffusion of the high-molecular-weight solutes. The driving force is concentration. This process is quite useful in analyzing complex chemical solutions and in the purification of very specialized and/or valuable components.

13.2 LIQUID PERMEATION MEMBRANE PROCESSES OR DIALYSIS

13.2A Series Resistances in Membrane Processes

In membrane processes with liquids, the solute molecules must first be transported or diffuse through the liquid film of the first liquid phase on one side of the solid membrane, then through the membrane itself, and finally through the film of the second liquid phase. This is shown in Fig. 13.2-1a, where c_1 is the bulk liquid-phase concentration of the diffusing solute A in kg mol A/m^3, c_{1i} is the concentration of A in the fluid just adjacent to the solid, and c_{1iS} is the concentration of A in the solid at the surface and is in equilibrium with C_{1i}. The mass-transfer coefficients are k_{c1} and k_{c2} in m/s. The equilibrium distribution coefficient K' is defined as

$$K' = \frac{c_S}{c_L} = \frac{c_{1iS}}{c_{1i}} = \frac{c_{2iS}}{c_{2i}} \tag{13.2-1}$$

Note that K' is the inverse of K defined in Eq. (7.1-16).

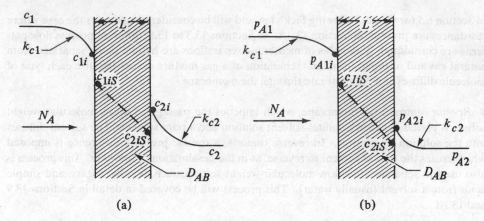

(a)   (b)

FIGURE 13.2-1.   *Concentration profiles for membrane processes: (a) two liquid films and a solid,*
                 (b) two gas films and a solid.

The flux equations through each phase are all equal to each other at steady state and are as follows:

$$N_A = k_{c1}(c_1 - c_{1i}) = \frac{D_{AB}}{L}(c_{1iS} - c_{2iS}) = k_{c2}(c_{2i} - c_2) \qquad (13.2-2)$$

Substituting $c_{1iS} = K'c_{1i}$ and $c_{2iS} = K'c_{2i}$ into Eq. (13.2-2),

$$N_A = k_{c1}(c_1 - c_{1i}) = \frac{D_{AB}K'}{L}(c_{1i} - c_{2i}) = p_M(c_{1i} - c_{2i}) = k_{c2}(c_{2i} - c_2) \qquad (13.2-3)$$

$$p_M = \frac{D_{AB}K'}{L} \qquad (13.2-4)$$

where p_M is the permeance in the solid in m/s, L is the thickness in m, and D_{AB} is the diffusivity of A in the solid in m²/s. Note that the permeance p_M in Eq. (13.2-4) is different from the permeability P_M defined in Eq. (6.5-9). Also, the value of p_M is inversely proportional to the thickness L. Instead of determining D_{AB} and K' in two separate experiments, it is more convenient to determine p_M in one separate diffusion experiment. Solving each of the parts of Eq. (13.2-3) for the concentration difference,

$$c_1 - c_{1i} = \frac{N_A}{k_{c1}} \qquad c_{1i} - c_{2i} = \frac{N_A}{p_M} \qquad c_{2i} - c_2 = \frac{N_A}{k_{c2}} \qquad (13.2-5)$$

Adding the equations, the internal concentrations c_{1i} and c_{2i} drop out, and the final equation is

$$N_A = \frac{c_1 - c_2}{1/k_{c1} + 1/p_M + 1/k_{c2}} \qquad (13.2-6)$$

In some cases, the resistances in the two liquid films are quite small compared to the membrane resistance, which controls the permeation rate.

EXAMPLE 13.2-1.   *Membrane Diffusion and Liquid Film Resistances*
A liquid containing dilute solute A at a concentration $c_1 = 3 \times 10^{-2}$ kg mol/m³ is flowing rapidly past a membrane of thickness $L = 3.0 \times 10^{-5}$ m. The distribution

FIGURE 13.2-2. *Concentrations for Example 13.2-1.*

coefficient $K' = 1.5$ and $D_{AB} = 7.0 \times 10^{-11}$ m^2/s in the membrane. The solute diffuses through the membrane, and its concentration on the other side is $c_2 = 0.50 \times 10^{-2}$ kg mol/m^3. The mass-transfer coefficient k_{c1} is large and can be considered as infinite, and $k_{c2} = 2.02 \times 10^{-5}$ m/s.

(a) Derive the equation to calculate the steady-state flux N_A and make a sketch.

(b) Calculate the flux and the concentrations at the membrane interfaces.

Solution: For part (a), the sketch is shown in Fig. 13.2-2. Note that the concentration profile on the left side is flat ($k_{c1} = \infty$) and $c_1 = c_{1i}$. The derivation is the same as for Eq. (13.2-6), but $1/k_{c1} = 0$ to give

$$N_A = \frac{c_1 - c_2}{1/p_M + 1/k_{c2}} \qquad (13.2\text{-}7)$$

For part (b), to calculate the flux using Eqs. (13.2-4) and (13.2-7),

$$p_M = \frac{D_{AB}K'}{L} = \frac{7.0 \times 10^{-11}(1.5)}{3.0 \times 10^{-5}} = 3.5 \times 10^{-6} \text{ m/s}$$

$$N_A = \frac{c_1 - c_2}{1/p_M + 1/k_{c2}} = \frac{3.0 \times 10^{-2} - 0.5 \times 10^{-2}}{1/3.5 \times 10^{-6} + 1/2.02 \times 10^{-5}}$$

$$= 7.458 \times 10^{-8} \text{ kg mol/s} \cdot \text{m}^2$$

To calculate c_{2i},

$$N_A = 7.458 \times 10^{-8} = k_{c2}(c_{2i} - c_2) = 2.02 \times 10^{-5}(c_{2i} - 0.5 \times 10^{-2})$$

Solving, $c_{2i} = 0.869 \times 10^{-2}$ kg mol/m^3. Also, using Eq. (13.2-1),

$$K' = 1.5 = \frac{c_{2iS}}{c_{2i}} = \frac{c_{2iS}}{0.869 \times 10^{-2}}$$

Solving, $c_{2iS} = 1.304 \times 10^{-2}$ kg mol/m^3.

13.2B Dialysis Processes

Dialysis uses a semipermeable membrane to separate species by virtue of their different diffusion rates in the membrane. The feed solution or dialyzate, which contains the solutes to be separated, flows on one side of the membrane and the solvent or diffusate stream on the other side. Some solvent may also diffuse across the membrane in the opposite direction, which reduces performance by diluting the dialyzate.

In practice dialysis is used to separate species which differ appreciably in size and thus have a reasonably large difference in diffusion rates. Solute fluxes depend on the concentration gradient in the membrane. Hence, dialysis is characterized by low flux rates in comparison to other membrane processes, such as reverse osmosis and ultrafiltration, which depend on applied pressure.

In general, dialysis is used with aqueous solutions on both sides of the membrane. The film resistances can be appreciable compared to the membrane resistance. Applications include recovery of sodium hydroxide in cellulose processing, recovery of acids from metallurgical liquors, removal of products from a culture solution in fermentation, desalting of cheese whey solids, and reduction of alcohol content of beer. Many small-scale applications occur in the pharmaceutical industry.

13.2C   Types of Equipment for Dialysis

Various geometrical configurations are used in liquid membrane processes. A common one is similar to a filter press, where the membrane is a flat plate. Vertical solid membranes are placed in between alternating liquor and solvent feed frames, with the liquor to be dialyzed being fed to the bottom and the solvent to the top of these frames. The dialyzate and the diffusate are removed through channels located at the top and bottom of the frames, respectively. The most important type consists of many small tubes or very fine hollow fibers arranged in a bundle, like a heat exchanger. This type of unit has a very high ratio of membrane area to volume of the unit.

13.2D   Hemodialysis in Artificial Kidney

An important example of the liquid permeation process is dialysis with an artificial kidney in the biomedical field. In this application for purifying human blood, the principal solutes removed are the small solutes urea, uric acid, creatinine, phosphates, and excess amounts of chloride. A typical membrane used is cellophane about 0.025 mm thick, which allows small solutes to diffuse but retains the large proteins in the blood. During the hemodialysis, blood is passed on one side of the membrane while an aqueous dialyzing fluid flows on the other side. Solutes such as urea, uric acid, NaCl, and so on, which have elevated concentrations in the blood, diffuse across the membrane to the dialyzing aqueous solution, which contains certain concentrations of solutes such as potassium salts, and so on, to ensure that concentrations in the blood do not drop below certain levels. In one configuration the membranes are stacked in the form of a multilayered sandwich, with blood flowing past one side of the membrane and dialyzing fluid past the other side. The hollow fiber type is used quite often.

> ### EXAMPLE 13.2-2.   Dialysis to Remove Urea from Blood
> Calculate the flux and the rate of removal of urea at steady state in g/h from blood in a cuprophane (cellophane) membrane dialyzer at 37°C. The membrane is 0.025 mm thick and has an area of 2.0 m^2. The mass-transfer coefficient on the blood side is estimated as $k_{c1} = 1.25 \times 10^{-5}$ m/s and that on the aqueous side is 3.33×10^{-5} m/s. The permeance of the membrane is 8.73×10^{-6} m/s (B2). The concentration of urea in the blood is 0.02 g urea/100 mL and that in the dialyzing fluid will be assumed as 0.

Solution: The concentration $c_1 = 0.02/100 = 2.0 \times 10^{-4}$ g/mL = 200 g/m^3 and $c_2 = 0$. Substituting into Eq. (13.2-6),

$$N_A = \frac{c_1 - c_2}{1/k_{c1} + 1/p_M + 1/k_{c2}}$$

$$= \frac{200 - 0}{1/1.25 \times 10^{-5} + 1/8.73 \times 10^{-6} + 1/3.33 \times 10^{-5}}$$

$$= 8.91 \times 10^{-4} \text{ g/s} \cdot \text{m}^2$$

For a time of 1 h and an area of 2.0 m^2,

$$\text{rate of removal} = 8.91 \times 10^{-4}(3600)(2.0) = 6.42 \text{ g urea/h}$$

13.3   GAS PERMEATION MEMBRANE PROCESSES

13.3A   Series Resistances in Membrane Processes

In membrane processes with two gas phases and a solid membrane, similar equations can be written for the case illustrated in Fig. 13.2-1b. The equilibrium relation between the solid and gas phases is given by

$$H = \frac{S}{22.414} = \frac{c_S}{p_A} = \frac{c_{1iS}}{p_{A1i}} = \frac{c_{2iS}}{p_{A2i}} \tag{13.3-1}$$

where S is the solubility of A in m^3 (STP)/atm $\cdot$ m^3 solid, as shown in Eq. (6.5-5), and H is the equilibrium relation in kg mol/m$^2 \cdot$ atm. This is similar to Henry's law. The flux equations in each phase are as follows:

$$N_A = \frac{k_{c1}}{RT}(p_{A1} - p_{A1i}) = \frac{D_{AB}}{L}(c_{1iS} - c_{2iS}) \tag{13.3-2}$$

$$= \frac{D_{AB}S}{L(22.414)}(p_{A1i} - p_{A2i}) \tag{13.3-3}$$

$$= \frac{k_{c2}}{RT}(p_{A2i} - p_{A2}) \tag{13.3-4}$$

The permeability P_M given previously is

$$P_M = D_{AB}S \qquad \frac{\text{m}^3\,(\text{STP}) \cdot \text{m}}{\text{s} \cdot \text{m}^2\text{C.S.} \cdot \text{atm}} \tag{6.5-9}$$

The permeability P_M is given in kg mol units by dividing Eq. (6.5-9) by 22.414 m^3/kg mol:

$$1.00 \frac{\text{kg mol} \cdot \text{m}}{\text{s} \cdot \text{m}^2\text{C.S.} \cdot \text{atm}} = \frac{1}{22.414} \frac{\text{m}^3\,(\text{STP}) \cdot \text{m}}{\text{s} \cdot \text{m}^2\text{C.S.} \cdot \text{atm}} \tag{13.3-5}$$

Then the flux N_A through the membrane given by Eq. (13.3-3) becomes

$$N_A = \frac{P_M}{L}(p_{A1i} - p_{A2i}) \tag{13.3-6}$$

Eliminating the interfacial concentrations as before,

$$N_A = \frac{(p_{A1} - p_{A2})}{1/(k_{c1}/RT) + 1/(P_M/L) + 1/(k_{c2}/RT)} \qquad \text{(13.3-7)}$$

In the case where pure A (p_{A1}) is on the left side of the membrane, there is no diffusional resistance in the gas phase, and k_{c1} can be considered to be infinite. Note that $k_{G1} = k_{c1}/RT$.

An example of gas permeation in a membrane is the use of a polymeric membrane as an oxygenator for a heart–lung machine to oxygenate blood. In this biomedical application, pure O_2 gas is on one side of a thin membrane and blood is on the other side. Oxygen diffuses through the membrane into the blood and CO_2 diffuses in a reverse direction into the gas stream.

13.3B Types of Membranes and Permeabilities for Separation of Gases

1. Types of dense-phase symmetric membranes. Early membranes were limited in their use because of low selectivities in separating two gases and quite low permeation fluxes. This low-flux problem was due to the fact that the membranes had to be relatively thick (1 mil or 1/1000 of an inch or greater) in order to avoid tiny holes, which reduced the separation by allowing viscous or Knudsen flow of the feed. Development of silicone polymers (1 mil thickness) increased the permeability by factors of 10–20 or so. These are called dense-phase symmetric membranes.

2. Types of asymmetric membranes. Newer asymmetric membranes include a very thin but dense skin on one side of the membrane supported by a porous substructure (R1). The dense skin has a thickness of about 1000 Å and the porous support thickness is about 25–100 μm. The flux increase of these membranes is thousands of time higher than the 1-mil-thick original membranes. Some typical materials currently used for asymmetric membranes are a composite of polysulfone coated with silicone rubber, cellulose acetate and modified cellulose acetates, aromatic polyamides or aromatic polyimides, and silicone–polycarbonate copolymer on a porous support.

3. Permeability of membranes. The permeability P_M in Eqs. (6.5-9) and (13.3-6) is defined as $D_{AB}S$ in m^3 (STP)/s $\cdot$ m^2C.S. $\cdot$ atm/m. Since mixtures of gases are often present, P'_A for gas A and P'_B for gas B will be used instead of P_M. The different sets of units used and their conversion factors are given in Table 13.3-1. Sometimes units are given in terms of Barrers, as also defined in Table 13.3-1.

The accurate prediction of permeabilities of gases in membranes is generally not possible, and experimental values are needed. Experimental data for common gases in some typical dense-phase membranes are given in Table 13.3-2. Note that there are wide differences among the permeabilities of various gases in a given membrane. Silicone rubber exhibits very high permeabilities for the gases in the table.

For the effect of temperature T in K, ln P'_A is approximately a linear function of $1/T$ and increases with T. However, operation at high temperatures can often degrade the membranes. When a mixture of gases is present, reductions of permeability of an individual component of up to 10% or so can often occur. In a few cases, much larger reductions have been observed (R1). Hence, when using a mixture of gases, experimental data should be obtained to determine if there is any interaction between the gases. The presence of water vapor can have similar effects on the permeabilities and can also possibly damage the membranes.

TABLE 13.3-1. *Conversion Factors for Permeability P'_A and Permeance P'_A/t*

Permeability, P'_A	Permeance, P'_A/t
$$\dfrac{1.00\ cm^3\ (STP)\cdot cm}{s\cdot cm^2\cdot cm\ Hg} = 7.501\times 10^{-8}\dfrac{m^3\ (STP)\cdot m}{s\cdot m^2\cdot Pa}$$	$$\dfrac{1.00\ cm^3\ (STP)}{s\cdot cm^2\cdot cm\ Hg} = 7.501\times 10^{-6}\dfrac{m^3\ (STP)}{s\cdot m^2\cdot Pa}$$
$$1.00\ Barrer = 10^{-10}\dfrac{cm^3\ (STP)\cdot cm}{s\cdot cm^2\cdot cm\ Hg}$$	$$1.00\ Barrer/cm = 10^{-10}\dfrac{cm^3\ (STP)}{s\cdot cm^2\cdot cm\ Hg}$$
$$\dfrac{1.00\ cm^3\ (STP)\cdot cm}{s\cdot cm^2\cdot cm\ Hg} = 480.9\dfrac{ft^3\ (STP)\cdot ft}{day\cdot ft^2\cdot psi}$$	$$\dfrac{1.00\ cm^3\ (STP)}{s\cdot cm^2\cdot cm\ Hg} = 1.4659\times 10^4\dfrac{ft^3\ (STP)}{day\cdot ft^2\cdot psi}$$
$$\dfrac{1.00\ cm^3\ (STP)\cdot cm}{s\cdot cm^2\cdot cm\ Hg} = 20.04\dfrac{ft^3\ (STP)\cdot ft}{hr\cdot ft^2\cdot psi}$$	$$\dfrac{1.00\ cm^3\ (STP)}{s\cdot cm^2\cdot cm\ Hg} = 610.8\dfrac{ft^3\ (STP)}{hr\cdot ft^2\cdot psi}$$

TABLE 13.3-2. *Permeabilities of Various Gases in Dense-Phase Symmetric Membranes*

Material	Temp. (°C)	He	H_2	CH_4	CO_2	O_2	N_2	Ref.
			Permeability, P'_A, $\dfrac{cm^3(STP)\cdot cm}{s\cdot cm^2\cdot cm\ Hg}\times 10^{10}$					
Silicone rubber	25	300	550	800	2700	500	250	(S2)
Natural rubber	25	31	49	30	131	24	8.1	(S2)
Polycarbonate (Lexane)	25–30	15	12		5.6,10	1.4		(S2)
Nylon 66	25	1.0			0.17	0.034	0.008	(S2)
Polyester (Permasep)	—		1.65	0.035	0.31		0.031	(H1)
Silicone-polycarbonate copolymer (57% silicone)	25		210		970	160	70	(W2)
Teflon FEP	30	62		1.4			2.5	(S1)
Ethyl cellulose	30	35.7	49.2	7.47	47.5	11.2	3.29	(W3)
Polystyrene	30	40.8	56.0	2.72	23.3	7.47	2.55	(W3)

4. Permeance of membranes. In many cases, especially in asymmetric membranes, the thickness t is not measured and only experimental values of permeance P'_A/t are given. Conversion factors are also given in Table 13.3-1.

13.3C Types of Equipment for Gas Permeation Membrane Processes

1. Flat membranes. Flat membranes are mainly used in experiments to characterize the permeability of the membrane. The modules are easy to fabricate and use and the areas of the membranes are well defined. In some cases modules are stacked together like a multi-

FIGURE 13.3-1. *Spiral-wound elements and assembly. [From R. I. Berry,* Chem. Eng., **88** *(July 13), 63 (1981). With permission.]*

layer sandwich or plate-and-frame filter press. The major drawback of this type is the very small membrane area per unit separator volume. Small commercial flat membranes are used for producing oxygen-enriched air for individual medical applications.

2. Spiral-wound membranes. This configuration retains the simplicity of fabricating flat membranes while increasing markedly the membrane area per unit separator volume up to 100 ft^2/ft^3 (328 m^2/m^3) and decreasing pressure drops (R1). The assembly consists of a sand-wich of four sheets wrapped around a central core of a perforated collecting tube. The four sheets consist of a top sheet of an open separator grid for the feed channel, a membrane, a porous felt backing for the permeate channel, and another membrane, as shown in Fig. 13.3-1. The spiral-wound element is 100 to 200 mm in diameter and is about 1 to 1.5 m long in the ax-ial direction. The flat sheets before rolling are about 1–1.5 m by about 2–2.5 m. The space between the membranes (open grid for feed) is about 1 mm and the thickness of the porous backing (for permeate) is about 0.2 mm.

The whole spiral-wound element is located inside a metal shell. The feed gas enters at the left end of the shell, enters the feed channel, and flows through this channel in the axial direction of the spiral to the right end of the assembly (Fig. 13.3-1). Then the exit residue gas leaves the shell at this point. The feed stream, which is in the feed channel, permeates per-pendicularly through the membrane. This permeate then flows through the permeate chan-nel in a direction perpendicular to the feed stream toward the perforated collecting tube, where it leaves the apparatus at one end. This is illustrated in Fig. 13.3-2, where the local gas flow paths are shown for a small element of the assembly.

3. Hollow-fiber membranes. The membranes are in the shape of very-small-diameter hol-low fibers. The inside diameter of the fibers is in the range of 100–500 μm and the outside 200–1000 μm, with the length up to 3–5 m. The module resembles a shell-and-tube heat ex-

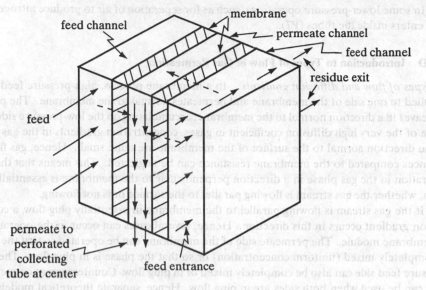

FIGURE 13.3-2. *Local gas flow paths for spiral-wound separator.*

FIGURE 13.3-3. *Hollow-fiber separator assembly.*

changer. Thousands of fine tubes are bound together at each end into a tube sheet that is surrounded by a metal shell having a diameter of 0.1–0.2 m, so that the membrane area per unit volume is up to 10 000 m^2/m^3, as in Fig. 13.3-3. A typical large industrial permeator has fibers of 200 μm ID and 400 μm OD in a shell 6 in. in diameter and 10 ft long (P7).

Typically, the high-pressure feed enters the shell side at one end and leaves at the other end. The hollow fibers are closed at one end of the tube bundles. The permeate gas inside the fibers flows countercurrent to the shell-side flow and is collected in a chamber where the open ends of the fibers terminate. Then the permeate exits the device.

In some lower-pressure operations, such as for separation of air to produce nitrogen, the feed enters inside the tubes (P7).

13.3D Introduction to Types of Flow in Gas Permeation

1. Types of flow and diffusion gradients. In a membrane process, high-pressure feed gas is supplied to one side of the membrane and permeates normal to the membrane. The permeate leaves in a direction normal to the membrane, accumulating on the low-pressure side. Because of the very high diffusion coefficient in gases, concentration gradients in the gas phase in the direction normal to the surface of the membrane are quite small. Hence, gas film resistances compared to the membrane resistance can be neglected. This means that the concentration in the gas phase in a direction perpendicular to the membrane is essentially uniform, whether the gas stream is flowing parallel to the surface or is not flowing.

If the gas stream is flowing parallel to the membrane in essentially plug flow, a concentration gradient occurs in this direction. Hence, several cases can occur in the operation of a membrane module. The permeate side of the membrane can be operated so that the phase is completely mixed (uniform concentration) or so that the phase is in plug flow. The high-pressure feed side can also be completely mixed or in plug flow. Countercurrent or cocurrent flow can be used when both sides are in plug flow. Hence, separate theoretical models must be derived for these different types of operation, as given in Sections 13.4–13.8.

2. Assumptions used and ideal flow patterns. In deriving theoretical models for gas separation by membranes, isothermal conditions and negligible pressure drop in the feed stream and permeate stream are generally assumed. It is also assumed that the effects of total pressure and/or composition of the gas are negligible and that the permeability of each component is constant (i.e., no interactions between different components).

Since there are a number of idealized flow patterns, the important types are summarized in Fig. 13.3-4. In Fig. 13.3-4a, complete mixing is assumed for the feed chamber and the per-

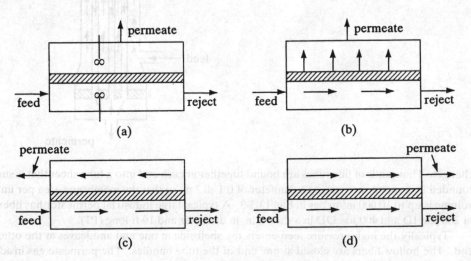

FIGURE 13.3-4. *Ideal flow patterns in a membrane separator for gases: (a) complete mixing, (b) cross-flow, (c) countercurrent flow, (d) cocurrent flow.*

meate chamber. Similar to a continuous-stirred tank, the reject or residue and the product or permeate compositions are equal to their respective uniform compositions in the chambers.

An ideal cross-flow pattern is given in Fig. 13.3-4b, where the feed stream is in plug flow and the permeate flows in a normal direction away from the membrane without mixing. Since the feed composition varies along its flow path, the local permeate concentration also varies along the membrane path.

In Fig. 13.3-4c, both the feed stream and permeate stream are in plug flow countercurrent to each other. The composition of each stream varies along its flow path. Cocurrent flow of the feed and permeate streams is shown in Fig. 13.3-4d.

13.4 COMPLETE-MIXING MODEL FOR GAS SEPARATION BY MEMBRANES

13.4A Basic Equations Used

In Fig. 13.4-1, a detailed process flow diagram is shown for complete mixing. When a separator element is operated at a low recovery (i.e., where the permeate flow rate is a small fraction of the entering feed rate), there is a minimal change in composition. Then the results derived using the complete-mixing model provide reasonable estimates of permeate purity. This case was derived by Weller and Steiner (W4).

Using nomenclature similar to that for distillation (P7), using the feed and nonpermeate flow rate as L and composition x mole fraction and the permeate flow rate as V and composition y.

The overall material balance (Fig. 13.4-1) is as follows:

$$L_f = L_o + V_p \tag{13.4-1}$$

where L_f is total feed flow rate in cm^3 (STP)/s; L_o is outlet reject flow rate, cm^3 (STP)/s; and V_p is outlet permeate flow rate, cm^3 (STP)/s. The cut or fraction of feed permeated, θ, is given as

$$\theta = \frac{V_p}{L_f} \tag{13.4-2}$$

The rate of diffusion or permeation of species A (in a binary of A and B) is given below by an equation similar to Eq. (13.3-6) but using cm^3 (STP)/s as rate of permeation rather than flux in kg mol/s $\cdot$ cm^2:

$$\frac{V_A}{A_m} = \frac{V_p y_p}{A_m} = \left(\frac{P_A'}{t}\right)(p_h x_o - p_l y_p) \tag{13.4-3}$$

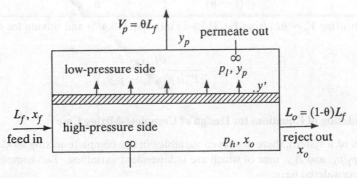

FIGURE 13.4-1. *Process flow for complete mixing case.*

where P'_A is permeability of A in the membrane, $\text{cm}^3\ (\text{STP}) \cdot \text{cm}/(\text{s} \cdot \text{cm}^2 \cdot \text{cm Hg})$; V_A is flow rate of A in permeate, $\text{cm}^3\ (\text{STP})/\text{s}$; A_m is membrane area, cm^2; t is membrane thickness, cm; p_h is total pressure in the high-pressure (feed) side, cm Hg; p_l is total pressure in the low-pressure or permeate side, cm Hg; x_o is mole fraction of A in reject side; x_f is mole fraction of A in feed; and y_p is mole fraction of A in permeate. Note that $p_h x_o$ is the partial pressure of A in the reject gas phase and $p_l y_p$ is the partial pressure in the permeate side. A similar equation can be written for component B.

$$\frac{V_B}{A_m} = \frac{V_p(1 - y_p)}{A_m} = \left(\frac{P'_B}{t}\right)[p_h(1 - x_o) - p_l(1 - y_p)] \tag{13.4-4}$$

Where P'_B is permeability of B, $\text{cm}^3\ (\text{STP}) \cdot \text{cm}/(\text{s} \cdot \text{cm}^2 \cdot \text{cm Hg})$. The ideal separation factor α^* is

$$\alpha^* = P'_A/P'_B \tag{13.4-5}$$

Dividing Eq. (13.4-3) by (13.4-4),

$$\frac{y_p}{1 - y_p} = \frac{\alpha^*[x_o - (p_l/p_h)y_p]}{(1 - x_o) - (p_l/p_h)(1 - y_p)} \tag{13.4-6}$$

This equation relates the reject concentration x_o to the permeate concentration y_p. The concentration in the bulk or reject gas phase is x_o. The permeate concentration y_p in the bulk gas phase is the same as the gas concentration y' on the lower-pressure side immediately adjacent to the dense-phase membrane or on the low-pressure side of the dense skin layer of the asymmetric membrane, which is called the interface or local concentration.

Equation (13.4-6) is a quadratic equation and its solution is

$$y_p = \frac{-b + \sqrt{b^2 - 4ac}}{2a} \tag{13.4-7}$$

where

$$a = 1 - \alpha^*, \quad b = -1 + \alpha^* + \frac{1}{r} + \frac{x_o}{r}(\alpha^* - 1), \quad c = \frac{-\alpha^* x_o}{r}, \quad r = p_l/p_h$$

Making an overall material balance on component A,

$$L_f x_f = L_o x_o + V_p y_p \tag{13.4-8}$$

Dividing by L_f and solving for the outlet reject composition,

$$x_o = \frac{x_f - \theta y_p}{(1 - \theta)} \quad \text{or} \quad y_p = \frac{x_f - x_o(1 - \theta)}{\theta} \tag{13.4-9}$$

Substituting $V_p = \theta L_f$ from Eq. (13.4-2) into Eq. (13.4-3) and solving for the membrane area, A_m,

$$A_m = \frac{\theta L_f y_p}{(P'_A/t)(p_h x_o - p_l y_p)} \tag{13.4-10}$$

13.4B Solution of Equations for Design of Complete-Mixing Case

For design of a system, there are seven variables in the complete-mixing model (H1), x_f, x_o, y_p, θ, α^*, p_l/p_h, and A_m, four of which are independent variables. Two commonly occurring cases are considered here.

Case 1. This is the simplest case, where x_f, x_o, α^*, and p_l/p_h are given and y_p, θ, and A_m are to be determined by solution of the equations. By use of the quadratic equation, Eq. (13.4-7) is solved for the permeate composition y_p in terms of x_o. Hence, to solve this case, y_p is first calculated using Eq. (13.4-7). Then the fraction of feed permeated, θ, is calculated using Eq. (13.4-9) and the membrane area, A_m, using Eq. (13.4-10).

EXAMPLE 13.4-1. Design of a Membrane Unit for Complete Mixing

A membrane is to be used to separate a gaseous mixture of A and B whose feed flow rate is $L_f = 1 \times 10^4$ cm³ (STP)/s and feed composition of A is $x_f = 0.50$ mole fraction. The desired composition of the reject is $x_o = 0.25$. The membrane thickness $t = 2.54 \times 10^{-3}$ cm, the pressure on the feed side is $p_h = 80$ cm Hg, and on the permeate side it is $p_l = 20$ cm Hg. The permeabilities are $P'_A = 50 \times 10^{-10}$ cm³ (STP)·cm/(s·cm²·cm Hg) and $P'_B = 5 \times 10^{-10}$. Assuming the complete-mixing model, calculate the permeate composition, y_p, the fraction permeated, θ, and the membrane area, A_m.

Solution: Substituting into Eq. (13.4-5),

$$\alpha^* = \frac{P'_A}{P'_B} = \frac{50 \times 10^{-10}}{(5 \times 10^{-10})} = 10$$

Using Eq. (13.4-7),

$$r = p_l/p_h = 20/80 = 0.25$$

$$a = 1 - \alpha^* = 1 - 10 = -9$$

$$b = -1 + \alpha^* + \frac{1}{r} + \frac{x_o}{r}(\alpha^* - 1)$$

$$= -1 + 10 + \frac{1}{0.25} + \frac{0.25}{0.25}(10 - 1) = 22.0$$

$$c = \frac{-\alpha^* x_o}{r} = \frac{-10}{0.25}(0.25) = -10$$

$$y_p = \frac{-b + \sqrt{b^2 - 4ac}}{2a}$$

$$= \frac{-22.0 + \sqrt{(22.0)^2 - 4(-9)(-10)}}{2(-9)} = 0.604$$

Using the material-balance equation (13.4-9),

$$x_o = \frac{x_f - \theta y_p}{1 - \theta}; \qquad 0.25 = \frac{0.50 - \theta(0.604)}{1 - \theta}$$

Solving, $\theta = 0.706$. Also, using Eq. (13.4-10),

$$A_m = \frac{\theta L_f y_p}{(P'_A/t)(p_h x_o - p_l y_p)}$$

$$= \frac{0.706(1 \times 10^4)(0.604)}{[50 \times 10^{-10}/(2.54 \times 10^{-3})](80 \times 0.25 - 20 \times 0.604)}$$

$$= 2.735 \times 10^8 \text{ cm}^2 \ (2.735 \times 10^4 \text{ m}^2)$$

Case 2. In this case x_f, θ, α^*, and p_l/p_h are given and y_p, x_o, and A_m are to be determined. Equation (13.4-7) cannot be solved for y_p since x_o is unknown. Hence, x_o from Eq. (13.4-9) is substituted into Eq. (13.4-7) and the resulting equation solved for y_p using the quadratic equation, to give

$$y_p = \frac{-b_1 + \sqrt{b_1^2 - 4a_1c_1}}{2a_1} \tag{13.4-11}$$

where

$$a_1 = \theta + \frac{p_l}{p_h} - \frac{p_l}{p_h}\theta - \alpha^*\theta - \alpha^*\frac{p_l}{p_h} + \alpha^*\frac{p_l}{p_h}\theta$$

$$b_1 = 1 - \theta - x_f - \frac{p_l}{p_h} + \frac{p_l}{p_h}\theta + \alpha^*\theta + \alpha^*\frac{p_l}{p_h} - \alpha^*\frac{p_l}{p_h}\theta + \alpha^*x_f$$

$$c_1 = -\alpha^*x_f$$

After solving for y_p, the value of x_o is calculated from Eq. (13.4-9) and A_m from Eq. (13.4-10).

EXAMPLE 13.4-2. Membrane Design for Separation of Air

It is desired to determine the membrane area needed to separate an air stream using a membrane 1 mil thick with an oxygen permeability of $P'_A = 500 \times 10^{-10}$ cm^3 (STP) $\cdot$ cm/(s $\cdot$ cm^2 $\cdot$ cm Hg). An $\alpha^* = 10$ for oxygen permeability divided by nitrogen permeability (S6) will be used. The feed rate is $L_f = 1 \times 10^6$ cm^3 (STP)/s and the fraction cut $\theta = 0.20$. The pressures selected for use are $p_h = 190$ cm Hg and $p_l = 19$ cm Hg. Again, assuming the complete-mixing model, calculate the permeate composition, the reject composition, and the area.

Solution: Using Eq. (13.4-11) for a feed composition of $x_f = 0.209$,

$$a_1 = \theta + \frac{p_l}{p_h} - \frac{p_l}{p_h}\theta - \alpha^*\theta - \alpha^*\frac{p_l}{p_h} + \alpha^*\frac{p_l}{p_h}\theta$$

$$= 0.2 + \frac{19}{190} - \frac{19}{190}(0.2) - 10(0.2) - 10\frac{(19)}{190} + 10\left(\frac{19}{190}\right)(0.2) = -2.52$$

$$b_1 = 1 - \theta - x_f - \frac{p_l}{p_h} + \frac{p_l}{p_h}\theta + \alpha^*\theta + \alpha^*\frac{p_l}{p_h} - \alpha^*\frac{p_l}{p_h}\theta + \alpha^*x_f$$

$$= 1 - 0.2 - 0.209 - \frac{19}{190} + \frac{19}{190}(0.2) + 10(0.2)$$

$$+ 10\left(\frac{19}{190}\right) - 10\left(\frac{19}{190}\right)(0.2) + 10(0.209) = 5.401$$

$$c_1 = -\alpha^*x_f = -10(0.209) = -2.09$$

$$y_p = \frac{-b_1 + \sqrt{b_1^2 - 4a_1c_1}}{2a_1}$$

$$= \frac{-5.401 + \sqrt{(5.401)^2 - 4(-2.52)(-2.09)}}{2(-2.52)}$$

$$= 0.5067$$

Substituting into Eq. (13.4-9),

$$x_o = \frac{x_f - \theta y_p}{(1 - \theta)} = \frac{0.209 - 0.2(0.5067)}{(1 - 0.2)} = 0.1346$$

Finally, using Eq. (13.4-10) to find the area,

$$A_m = \frac{\theta L_f y_p}{(P_A'/t)(p_h x_o - p_l y_p)}$$

$$= \frac{0.2(1 \times 10^6)(0.5067)}{(500 \times 10^{-10}/2.54 \times 10^{-3})(190 \times 0.1346 - 19 \times 0.5067)}$$

$$= 3.228 \times 10^8 \text{ cm}^2$$

13.4C Minimum Concentration of Reject Stream

If all of the feed is permeated, then $\theta = 1$ and the feed composition $x_f = y_p$. For all values of $\theta < 1$, the permeate composition $y_p > x_f$ (H1). Substituting the value $x_f = y_p$ into Eq. (13.4-7) and solving, the minimum reject composition x_{oM} for a given x_f value is obtained as

$$x_{oM} = \frac{x_f \left[1 + (\alpha^* - 1)\dfrac{p_l}{p_h}(1 - x_f) \right]}{\alpha^*(1 - x_f) + x_f} \tag{13.4-12}$$

Hence, a feed of x_f concentration cannot be stripped lower than a value of x_{oM} even with an infinitely large membrane area for a completely mixed system. To strip beyond this limiting value, a cascade-type system could be used. However, a single unit which is not completely mixed but is designed for plug flow could also be used.

EXAMPLE 13.4-3.   Effect of Feed Composition on Minimum Reject Concentration

Calculate the minimum reject concentration for Example 13.4-1 where the feed concentration is $x_f = 0.50$. Also, what is the effect of raising the feed purity to $x_f = 0.65$?

Solution: Substituting $x_f = 0.50$ into Eq. (13.4-12),

$$x_{oM} = \frac{x_f \left[1 + (\alpha^* - 1)\dfrac{p_l}{p_h}(1 - x_f) \right]}{\alpha^*(1 - x_f) + x_f}$$

$$= \frac{0.50 \left[1 + (10 - 1)\left(\dfrac{20}{80}\right)(1 - 0.50) \right]}{10(1 - 0.50) + 0.50}$$

$$= 0.1932$$

For $x_f = 0.65$,

$$x_{oM} = \frac{0.65 \left[1 + (10 - 1)\left(\dfrac{20}{80}\right)(1 - 0.65) \right]}{10(1 - 0.65) + 0.65} = 0.2780$$

13.5 COMPLETE-MIXING MODEL FOR MULTICOMPONENT MIXTURES

13.5A Derivation of Equations

When multicomponent mixtures are present, the iteration method of Stern et al. (S1) is quite useful. This method will be derived for a ternary mixture of components A, B, and C. The process flow diagram is the same as Fig. 13.4-1, where the feed composition x_f is x_{fA}, x_{fB}, and x_{fC}. The known values are

$$x_{fA}, x_{fB}, x_{fC}; L_f; \theta; p_h, p_l; P'_A, P'_B, P'_C; \text{ and } t$$

The unknown values to be determined are

$$y_{pA}, y_{pB}, y_{pC}; x_{oA}, x_{oB}, x_{oC}; V_p \text{ or } L_o; \text{ and } A_m$$

These eight unknowns can be obtained by solving a set of eight simultaneous equations using an iteration method. Three rate-of-permeation equations similar to Eq. (13.4-3) are as follows for components A, B, and C:

$$V_p y_{pA} = \frac{P'_A}{t} A_m (p_h x_{oA} - p_l y_{pA}) \tag{13.5-1}$$

$$V_p y_{pB} = \frac{P'_B}{t} A_m (p_h x_{oB} - p_l y_{pB}) \tag{13.5-2}$$

$$V_p y_{pC} = \frac{P'_C}{t} A_m (p_h x_{oC} - p_l y_{pC}) \tag{13.5-3}$$

The three material-balance equations similar to Eq. (13.4-9) are written for components A, B, and C:

$$x_{oA} = \frac{1}{1 - \theta} x_{fA} - \frac{\theta}{1 - \theta} y_{pA} \tag{13.5-4}$$

$$x_{oB} = \frac{1}{1 - \theta} x_{fB} - \frac{\theta}{1 - \theta} y_{pB} \tag{13.5-5}$$

$$x_{oC} = \frac{1}{1 - \theta} x_{fC} - \frac{\theta}{1 - \theta} y_{pC} \tag{13.5-6}$$

Also, two final equations can be written as

$$\sum_n y_{pn} = y_{pA} + y_{pB} + y_{pC} = 1.0 \tag{13.5-7}$$

$$\sum_n x_{on} = x_{oA} + x_{oB} + x_{oC} = 1.0 \tag{13.5-8}$$

Substituting x_{oA} from Eq. (13.5-4) into Eq. (13.5-1) and solving for A_m,

$$A_m = \frac{V_p y_{pA} t}{P'_A \left[\dfrac{p_h}{1 - \theta}(x_{fA} - \theta y_{pA}) - p_l y_{pA} \right]} \tag{13.5-9}$$

For component B, Eq. (13.5-5) is substituted into Eq. (13.5-2), giving

$$A_m = \frac{V_p y_{pB} t}{P'_B \left[\dfrac{p_h}{1 - \theta}(x_{fB} - \theta y_{pB}) - p_l y_{pB} \right]} \tag{13.5-10}$$

Rearranging Eq. (13.5-10) and solving for y_{pB},

$$y_{pB} = \frac{p_h x_{fB}/(1-\theta)}{V_p t/(P_B' A_m) + \theta p_h/(1-\theta) + p_l} \qquad \textbf{(13.5-11)}$$

In a similar manner Eq. (13.5-12) is derived for y_{pC}:

$$y_{pC} = \frac{p_h x_{fC}/(1-\theta)}{V_p t/(P_C' A_m) + \theta p_h/(1-\theta) + p_l} \qquad \textbf{(13.5-12)}$$

13.5B Iteration Solution Procedure for Multicomponent Mixtures

The following iteration or trial-and-error procedure can be used to solve the equations above:

1. A value of y_{pA} is assumed where $y_{pA} > x_{fA}$.
2. Using Eq. (13.4-2) and the known value of θ, V_p is calculated.
3. The membrane area is calculated from Eq. (13.5-9).
4. Values of y_{pB} and y_{pC} are calculated from Eqs. (13.5-11) and (13.5-12).
5. The sum $\sum_n y_{pn}$ is calculated from Eq. (13.5-7). If this sum is not equal to 1.0. steps 1 through 5 are repeated until the sum is 1.0.
6. Finally, x_{oA}, x_{oB}, and x_{oC} are calculated from Eqs. (13.5-4), (13.5-5), and (13.5-6).

EXAMPLE 13.5-1. Design of Membrane Unit for Multicomponent Mixture
A multicomponent gaseous mixture having a composition of $x_{fA} = 0.25$, $x_{fB} = 0.55$, and $x_{fC} = 0.20$ is to be separated by a membrane with a thickness of 2.54×10^{-3} cm using the complete-mixing model. The feed flow rate is 1.0×10^4 cm^3 (STP)/s and the permeabilities are $P_A' = 200 \times 10^{-10}$ cm^3 (STP) $\cdot$ cm/(s $\cdot$ cm$^2 \cdot$ cm Hg), $P_B' = 50 \times 10^{-10}$, and $P_C' = 25 \times 10^{-10}$. The pressure on the feed side is 300 cm Hg and 30 cm Hg on the permeate side. The fraction permeated will be 0.25. Calculate the permeate composition, reject composition, and membrane area using the complete-mixing model.

Solution: Following the iteration procedure, a value of $y_{pA} = 0.50$ is assumed. Substituting into Eq. (13.4-2) for step 2,

$$V_p = \theta L_f = 0.25 \times 1.0 \times 10^4 = 0.25 \times 10^4 \text{ cm}^3 \text{ (STP)/s}$$

Using Eq. (13.5-9), the membrane area for step (3) is

$$A_m = \frac{V_p y_{pA} t}{P_A' \left[\dfrac{p_h}{1-\theta}(x_{fA} - \theta y_{pA}) - p_l y_{pA} \right]}$$

$$= \frac{0.25 \times 10^4 (0.50)(2.54 \times 10^{-3})}{200 \times 10^{-10}} \Bigg/ \left[\frac{300}{1-0.25}(0.25 - 0.25 \times 0.50) - 30(0.50) \right]$$

$$= 4.536 \times 10^6 \text{ cm}^2$$

Following step 4, the values y_{pB} and y_{pC} are calculated using Eqs. (13.5-11) and (13.5-12):

$$y_{pB} = \frac{p_h x_{fB}/(1 - \theta)}{V_p t/(P'_B A_m) + \theta p_h/(1 - \theta) + p_l}$$

$$= \frac{300 \times 0.55/(1 - 0.25)}{0.25 \times 10^4 \times 2.54 \times 10^{-3}/(50 \times 10^{-10} \times 4.536 \times 10^6) + 0.25 \times 300/(1 - 0.25) + 30}$$

$$= 0.5366$$

$$y_{pC} = \frac{p_h x_{fC}/(1 - \theta)}{V_p t/(P'_C A_m) + \theta p_h/(1 - \theta) + p_l}$$

$$= \frac{300 \times 0.20/(1 - 0.25)}{0.25 \times 10^4 \times 2.54 \times 10^{-3}/(25 \times 10^{-10} \times 4.536 \times 10^6) + 0.25 \times 300/(1 - 0.25) + 30}$$

$$= 0.1159$$

Substituting into Eq. (13.5-7),

$$\sum_n y_{pn} = y_{pA} + y_{pB} + y_{pC} = 0.5000 + 0.5366 + 0.1159 = 1.1525$$

For the second iteration, assuming that $y_{pA} = 0.45$, the following values are calculated:

$$A_m = 3.546 \times 10^6 \text{ cm}^2 \qquad y_{pB} = 0.4410 \qquad y_{pC} = 0.0922$$

$$\sum_n y_{pn} = 0.9832$$

The final iteration values are $A_m = 3.536 \times 10^6 \text{ cm}^2$; $y_{pA} = 0.4555$, $y_{pB} = 0.4502$, and $y_{pC} = 0.0943$. Substituting into Eqs. (13.5-4), (13.5-5), and (13.5-6),

$$x_{oA} = \frac{1}{1 - \theta} x_{fA} - \frac{\theta}{1 - \theta} y_{pA} = \frac{1}{1 - 0.25}(0.25)$$

$$- \frac{0.25}{1 - 0.25}(0.4555) = 0.1815$$

$$x_{oB} = \frac{1}{1 - \theta} x_{fB} - \frac{\theta}{1 - \theta} y_{pB} = \frac{1}{1 - 0.25}(0.55)$$

$$- \frac{0.25}{1 - 0.25}(0.4502) = 0.5833$$

$$x_{oC} = \frac{1}{1 - \theta} x_{fC} - \frac{\theta}{1 - \theta} y_{pC} = \frac{1}{1 - 0.25}(0.20)$$

$$- \frac{0.25}{1 - 0.25}(0.0943) = 0.2352$$

13.6. CROSS-FLOW MODEL FOR GAS SEPARATION BY MEMBRANES

13.6A   Derivation of Basic Equations

A detailed flow diagram for the cross-flow model derived by Weller and Steiner (W3, W4) is shown in Fig. 13.6-1. In this case the longitudinal velocity of the high-pressure or reject stream is large enough that this gas stream is in plug flow and flows parallel to the membrane.

FIGURE 13.6-1. *Process flow diagram for cross-flow model.*

On the low-pressure side the permeate stream is almost pulled into vacuum, so that the flow is essentially perpendicular to the membrane.

This model assumes no mixing in the permeate side as well as no mixing on the high-pressure side. Hence, the permeate composition at any point along the membrane is determined by the relative rates of permeation of the feed components at that point. This cross-flow pattern approximates that in an actual spiral-wound membrane separator (Fig. 13.3-1) with a high-flux asymmetric membrane resting on a porous felt support (P2, R1).

Referring to Fig. 13.6-1, the local permeation rate over a differential membrane area dA_m at any point in the stage is

$$y \, dV = \frac{P'_A}{t} [p_h x - p_l y] \, dA_m \qquad \text{(13.6-1)}$$

$$(1 - y) \, dV = \frac{P'_B}{t} [p_h (1 - x) - p_l (1 - y)] \, dA_m \qquad \text{(13.6-2)}$$

where $dL = dV$ and is the total flow rate permeating through the area dA_m. Dividing Eq. (13.6-1) by (13.6-2) gives

$$\frac{y}{1 - y} = \frac{\alpha^*[x - (p_l/p_h)y]}{(1 - x) - (p_l/p_h)(1 - y)} \qquad \text{(13.6-3)}$$

This equation relates the permeate composition y to the reject composition x at a point along the path. It is similar to Eq. (13.4-6) for complete mixing. Hwang and Kammermeyer (H1) give a computer program for the solution of the above system of differential equations by numerical methods.

Weller and Steiner (W3, W4) used some ingenious transformations and were able to obtain an analytical solution to the three equations as follows:

$$\frac{(1 - \theta^*)(1 - x)}{(1 - x_f)} = \left(\frac{u_f - E/D}{u - E/D} \right)^R \left(\frac{u_f - \alpha^* + F}{u - \alpha^* + F} \right)^S \left(\frac{u_f - F}{u - F} \right)^T \qquad \text{(13.6-4)}$$

where

$$\theta^* = 1 - \frac{L}{L_f}$$

$$i = \frac{x}{1 - x}$$

$$u = -Di + (D^2i^2 + 2Ei + F^2)^{0.5}$$

$$D = 0.5\left[\frac{(1 - \alpha^*)p_l}{p_h} + \alpha^*\right]$$

$$E = \frac{\alpha^*}{2} - DF$$

$$F = -0.5\left[\frac{(1 - \alpha^*)p_l}{p_h} - 1\right]$$

$$R = \frac{1}{2D - 1}$$

$$S = \frac{\alpha^*(D - 1) + F}{(2D - 1)(\alpha^*/2 - F)}$$

$$T = \frac{1}{1 - D - (E/F)}$$

The term u_f is the value of u at $i = i_f = x_f/(1 - x_f)$. The value of θ^* is the fraction permeated up to the value of x in Fig. 13.6-1. At the outlet where $x = x_o$, the value of θ^* is equal to θ, the total fraction permeated. The composition of the exit permeate stream is y_p and is calculated from the overall material balance, Eq. (13.4-9).

The total membrane area was obtained by Weller and Steiner (W3, W4) using some additional transformations of Eqs. (13.6-1)–(13.6-3) to give

$$A_m = \frac{tL_f}{p_h P'_B} \int_{i_0}^{i_f} \frac{(1 - \theta^*)(1 - x)\, di}{(f_i - i)\left[\dfrac{1}{1 + i} - \dfrac{p_l}{p_h}\left(\dfrac{1}{1 + f_i}\right)\right]} \tag{13.6-5}$$

where

$$f_i = (Di - F) + (D^2i^2 + 2Ei + F^2)^{0.5}$$

Values of θ^* in the integral can be obtained from Eq. (13.6-4). The integral can be calculated numerically. The term i_f is the value of i at the feed x_f, and i_o is the value of i at the outlet x_o. A shortcut approximation of the area without using a numerical integration, available from Weller and Steiner (W3), has a maximum error of about 20%.

13.6B Procedure for Design of Cross-Flow Case

In the design for the complete-mixing model there are seven variables, and two of the most common cases were discussed in Section 13.4B. Similarly, for the cross-flow model these same common cases occur.

Case 1. The values of x_f, x_o, α^*, and p_l/p_h are given and y_p, θ and A_m are to be determined. The value of θ^* or θ can be calculated directly from Eq. (13.6-4) since all other values in this equation are known. Then y_p is calculated from Eq. (13.4-9). To calculate the area A_m, a series of values of x less than the feed x_f and greater than the reject outlet x_o are substituted into Eq. (13.6-4) to give a series of θ^* values. These values are then used to numerically or graphically integrate Eq. (13.6-5) to obtain the area A_m.

Case 2. In this case the values of x_f, θ, α^*, and p_l/p_h are given and y_p, x_o, and A_m are to be determined. This is trial and error, where values of x_o are substituted into Eq. (13.6-4) to solve the equation. The membrane area is calculated as in Case 1.

EXAMPLE 13.6-1. *Design of a Membrane Unit Using Cross-Flow*
The same conditions for the separation of an air stream as given in Example 13.4-2 for complete mixing are to be used in this example. The process flow streams will be in cross-flow. The given values are $x_f = 0.209$, $\theta = 0.20$, $\alpha^* = 10$, $p_h = 190$ cm Hg, $p_l = 19$ cm Hg, $L_f = 1 \times 10^6$ cm³ (STP)/s, $P'_A = 500 \times 10^{-10}$ cm³ (STP)·cm/(s·cm²·cm Hg), and $t = 2.54 \times 10^{-3}$ cm. Do as follows:
   (a) Calculate y_p, x_o, and A_m.
   (b) Compare the results with Example 13.4-2.

Solution: Since this is the same as Case 2, a value of $x_o = 0.1642$ will be used for the first trial for part (a). Substituting into Eq. (13.6-4),

$$i = i_f = \frac{x_f}{1 - x_f} = \frac{0.209}{1 - 0.209} = 0.2642$$

$$i = \frac{0.1642}{1 - 0.1642} = 0.1965$$

$$D = 0.5\left[\frac{(1 - \alpha^*)p_l}{p_h} + \alpha^*\right]$$

$$= 0.5\left[\frac{(1 - 10)19}{190} + 10\right] = 4.550$$

$$F = -0.5\left[\frac{(1 - \alpha^*)p_l}{p_h} - 1\right]$$

$$= -0.5\left[\frac{(1 - 10)19}{190} - 1\right] = 0.950$$

$$E = \frac{\alpha^*}{2} - DF = \frac{10}{2} - 4.550(0.950) = 0.6775$$

$$R = \frac{1}{2D - 1} = \frac{1}{2(4.550) - 1} = 0.12346$$

$$S = \frac{\alpha^*(D - 1) + F}{(2D - 1)(\alpha^*/2 - F)}$$

$$= \frac{10(4.550 - 1) + 0.950}{(2 \times 4.550 - 1)(10/2 - 0.950)} = 1.1111$$

$$T = \frac{1}{1 - D - (E/F)}$$

$$= \frac{1}{1 - 4.550 - 0.6775/0.950} = -0.2346$$

$$u_f = -Di + (D^2i^2 + 2Ei + F^2)^{0.5}$$

$$= -(4.550)(0.2642) + [(4.550)^2(0.2642)^2$$
$$+ 2(0.6775)(0.2642) + (0.950)^2]^{0.5}$$

$$= 0.4427$$

$$u = -(4.550)(0.1965) + [(4.550)^2(0.1965)^2$$
$$+ 2(0.6775)(0.1965) + (0.950)^2]^{0.5}$$

$$= 0.5089$$

$$\frac{(1 - \theta^*)(1 - x)}{(1 - x_f)} = \frac{(1 - \theta^*)(1 - 0.1642)}{(1 - 0.209)}$$

$$= \left(\frac{0.4427 - 0.6775/4.550}{0.5089 - 0.6775/4.550}\right)^{0.12346}$$

$$\times \left(\frac{0.4427 - 10 + 0.950}{0.5089 - 10 + 0.950}\right)^{1.1111}$$

$$\times \left(\frac{0.4427 - 0.950}{0.5089 - 0.950}\right)^{-0.2346}$$

Solving, $\theta^* = 0.0992$. This value of 0.0992 does not agree with the given value of $\theta = 0.200$. However, these values can be used later to solve Eq. (13.6-5).

For the second iteration, a value of $x_o = 0.142$ is assumed and is used again to solve for θ^* in Eq. (13.6-4), which results in $\theta^* = 0.1482$. For the final iteration, $x_o = 0.1190$ and $\theta^* = \theta = 0.2000$. Several more values are calculated for later use and are: for $x_o = 0.187$, $\theta^* = 0.04876$, and for $x_o = 0.209$, $\theta^* = 0$. These values are tabulated in Table 13.6-1.

Using the material-balance equation (13.4-9) to calculate y_p,

$$y_p = \frac{x_f - x_o(1 - \theta)}{\theta} = \frac{0.209 - 0.1190(1 - 0.2000)}{0.2000} = 0.5690$$

TABLE 13.6-1. *Calculated Values for Example 13.6-1*

θ^*	x	y_p	F_i
0	0.209	0.6550	0.6404
0.04876	0.1870	0.6383	0.7192
0.0992	0.1642	0.6158	0.8246
0.1482	0.1420	0.5940	0.9603
0.2000	0.1190	0.5690	1.1520

To calculate y_p at $\theta^* = 0$, Eqs. (13.6-3) and (13.4-17) must be used, giving $y_p = 0.6550$.

To solve for the area, Eq. (13.6-5) can be written as

$$A_m = \frac{tL_f}{p_h P'_B} \int_{i_o}^{i_f} \left[\frac{(1 - \theta^*)(1 - x)}{(f_i - i)\left[\dfrac{1}{1 + i} - \dfrac{p_l}{p_h}\left(\dfrac{1}{1 + f_i}\right)\right]} \right] di = \frac{tL_f}{p_h P'_B} \int_{i_o}^{i_f} F_i \, di$$

(13.6-6)

where the function F_i is defined as above. Values of F_i will be calculated for different values of i in order to integrate the equation. For $\theta^* = 0.200$, $x_o = 0.119$, and from Eq. (13.6-4),

$$i = i_o = \frac{x}{(1 - x)} = \frac{0.119}{(1 - 0.119)} = 0.1351$$

From Eq. (13.6-5),

$$f_i = (Di - F) + (D^2 i^2 + 2Ei + F^2)^{0.5}$$

$$= (4.55 \times 0.1351 - 0.950) + [(4.55)^2 (0.1351)^2$$

$$+ 2(0.6775)(0.1351) + (0.95)^2]^{0.5}$$

$$= 0.8744$$

Using the definition of F_i from Eq. (13.6-6),

$$F_i = \frac{(1 - \theta^*)(1 - x)}{(f_i - i)\left[\dfrac{1}{1 + i} - \dfrac{p_l}{p_h}\left(\dfrac{1}{1 + f_i}\right)\right]}$$

$$= \frac{(1 - 0.200)(1 - 0.119)}{(0.8744 - 0.1351)\left[\dfrac{1}{1 + 0.1351} - \dfrac{19}{190}\left(\dfrac{1}{1 + 0.8744}\right)\right]}$$

$$= 1.1520$$

Other values of F_i are calculated for the remaining values of θ^* and are tabulated in Table 13.6-1. The integral of Eq. (13.6-6) is obtained by using the values from Table 13.6-1 and numerically integrating F_i versus i to give an area of 0.1082. Finally, substituting into Eq. (13.6-6),

$$A_m = \frac{tL_f}{p_h P'_R} \int_{i_o}^{i_f} F_i \, di = \frac{2.54 \times 10^{-3}(1 \times 10^6)}{190(50 \times 10^{-10})/10}(0.1082)$$

$$= 2.893 \times 10^8 \text{ cm}^2$$

For part (b), from Example 13.4-2, $y_p = 0.5067$ and $A_m = 3.228 \times 10^8$ cm^2. Hence, the cross-flow model yields a higher y_p of 0.5690, compared to 0.5067 for the complete-mixing model. Also, the area for the cross-flow model is 10% less than for the complete-mixing model.

13.7 DERIVATION OF EQUATIONS FOR COUNTERCURRENT AND COCURRENT FLOW FOR GAS SEPARATION FOR MEMBRANES

13.7A Concentration Gradients in Membranes

1. Dense-phase membrane. In gas separation using a dense-phase symmetrical polymer membrane, the solute diffuses through the high-pressure-side gas film to the membrane surface. Then it dissolves in the membrane. At the interface equilibrium occurs. The solute then diffuses through the solid membrane, and finally diffuses through the gas film. The gas film resistances are quite small and can be neglected (N1). In Fig. 13.7-1a the concentration profiles are shown. The concentration y in the flowing bulk gas phase is the same as y at the interface of the dense polymer and depends on the flow pattern of the permeate phase.

2. Asymmetric membrane. As shown in Fig. 13.7-1b, the membrane includes a very thin, dense polymer membrane which is about 0.1 to 1 μm thick (M5, P7) and a very thick porous layer 50–200 μm thick. A typical hollow-fiber membrane for air separation has an ID of 95 μm and an OD of 135 μm, with a wall thickness of 20 μm.

The concentration gradient in the thin dense polymer phase is similar to that for the symmetrical membrane. However, the concentration y of component A in the bulk permeate gas phase is not the same as y' at the surface of the thin dense polymer layer. The concentration y of the bulk gas permeate stream depends on the flow pattern and material balances. Also, the value of y can be greater or less than y'.

The porous layer is so open that there is assumed to be little or no resistance to the flow and y' is constant along this path. Hence, it is assumed that there is no penetration or mixing of the bulk gas phase y inside the porous layer.

13.7B Derivation of Equations for Countercurrent Flow in Dense-Phase Symmetric Membranes

A flow diagram for this countercurrent-flow model is given in Fig. 13.7-2, where both streams are in plug flow. The derivation follows that given by others (B1, N1, P4, W5).

FIGURE 13.7-1. *Concentration profiles in membranes. (a) dense-phase symmetrical membranes, (b) asymmetric membrane.*

FIGURE 13.7-2. *Flow diagram for the countercurrent-flow model with dense-phase symmetric membrane.*

Making a total material balance,

$$L_f = L_o + V_p \tag{13.7-1}$$

where L_f is total feed flow rate, cm³ (STP)/s, L_o is outlet nonpermeate (reject) flow rate, cm³ (STP)/s, and V_p is outlet permeate flow rate, cm³ (STP)/s. The rates of permeation of A and in B in a binary mixture are similar to Eqs. (13.4-3) and (13.4-4):

$$V_A/A_m = Vy/A_m = (P'_A/t)(p_h x - p_l y) \tag{13.7-2}$$

$$V_B/A_m = V(1 - y)/A_m = (P'_B/t)[p_h(1 - x) - p_l(1 - y)] \tag{13.7-3}$$

where P'_A is permeability of A, cm³ (STP) · cm/(s · cm² · cm Hg); V_A is flow rate of A in permeate, cm³ (STP)/s; A_m is membrane area, cm²; p_h is total pressure in the high-pressure side, cm Hg; and p_l is total pressure in low-pressure side, cm Hg.

The flux of A out of the element with area dA_m is

$$dL_A = y\, dL = (P'_A/t)[p_h x - p_l y]\, dA_m \tag{13.7-4}$$

The flux of B is

$$dL_B = (1 - y)\, dL = (P'_B/t)[p_h(1 - x) - p_l(1 - y)]\, dA_m \tag{13.7-5}$$

Making a total balance on the reject stream for area dA_m,

$$L = L - dL + dL_A + dL_B \tag{13.7-6}$$

This gives

$$dL = dL_A + dL_B \tag{13.7-7}$$

Making a balance on A for area dA_m,

$$Lx = (L - dL)(x - dx) + dL_A \tag{13.7-8}$$

Rearranging,

$$dL_A = L\, dx + x\, dL \tag{13.7-9}$$

Substituting Eq. (13.7-7) into (13.7-9),

$$L\, dx = (1 - x)\, dL_A - x\, dL_B \tag{13.7-10}$$

Making a total balance on permeate stream for area dA_m,

$$V = V - dV + dL_A + dL_B \tag{13.7-11}$$

This gives

$$dV = dL_A + dL_B \tag{13.7-12}$$

Making a balance on A for area dA_m,

$$Vy = (V - dV)(y - dy) + dL_A \tag{13.7-13}$$

Rearranging,

$$dL_A = V\,dy + y\,dV \tag{13.7-14}$$

Substituting Eq. (13.7-12) into (13.7-14),

$$V\,dy = (1 - y)\,dL_A - y\,dL_B \tag{13.7-15}$$

To eliminate the variables L and V, an overall balance is made for the area dA_m and the reject outlet stream:

$$L = L_o + V \tag{13.7-16}$$

$$Lx = L_o x_o + Vy \tag{13.7-17}$$

To eliminate V, V from Eq. (13.7-16) is substituted into (13.7-17) and solved for L:

$$L = L_o(x_o - y)/(x - y) \tag{13.7-18}$$

To eliminate L, L from Eq. (13.7-16) is substituted into (13.7-17) and solved for V:

$$V = L_o(x_o - x)/(x - y) \tag{13.7-19}$$

Substituting Eq. (13.7-18) into (13.7-10),

$$\frac{L_o(x_o - y)\,dx}{(x - y)} = (1 - x)\,dL_A - x\,dL_B \tag{13.7-20}$$

Substituting Eqs. (13.7-4) and (13.7-5) into (13.7-20),

$$\frac{L_o(x_o - y)\,dx}{(x - y)} = (1 - x)[(P'_A/t)(p_h x - p_l y)]\,dA_m$$

$$\qquad - x(P'_B/t)[p_h(1 - x) - p_l(1 - y)]\,dA_m \tag{13.7-21}$$

Rearranging,

$$\frac{L_o}{(P'_B/t)p_h}\,\frac{dx}{dA_m} = -\left(\frac{x - y}{y - x_o}\right)\{(1 - x)\alpha^*(x - ry) - x[(1 - x) - r(1 - y)]\}$$

$$\tag{13.7-22}$$

where $r = p_l/p_h$ and $\alpha^* = (P'_A/t)/(P'_B/t)$.

In a similar manner, substituting Eq. (13.7-19) into (13.7-15),

$$\frac{L_o(x_o - x)\,dy}{(x - y)} = (1 - y)\,dL_A - y\,dL_B \tag{13.7-23}$$

Again, substituting Eqs. (13.7-4) and (13.7-5) into (13.7-23) and rearranging,

$$\frac{L_o}{(P'_B/t)p_h} \frac{dy}{dA_m} = -\left(\frac{x-y}{x-x_o}\right)\{(1-y)\alpha^*(x-ry) - y[(1-x) - r(1-y)]\}$$

(13.7-24)

Dividing Eq. (13.7-24) by (13.7-22),

$$\frac{dy}{dx} = \frac{(y-x_o)}{(x-x_o)} \frac{\{(1-y)\alpha^*(x-ry) - y[(1-x) - r(1-y)]\}}{\{(1-x)\alpha^*(x-ry) - x[(1-x) - r(1-y)]\}}$$

(13.7-25)

Inverting Eq. (13.7-22),

$$\frac{dA_m}{dx} = \frac{-L_o}{(P'_B/t)p_h} \frac{[(y-x_o)/(x-y)]}{\{(1-y)\alpha^*(x-ry) - x[(1-x) - r(1-y)]\}}$$

(13.7-26)

13.7C Solution of Countercurrent Flow Equations in Dense-Phase Symmetric Membranes

At the outlet of the residue stream of composition x_o, the permeate y' and x_o are related by Eq. (13.4-6), repeated here as Eq. (13.7-27), where $y_p = y'$:

$$\frac{y'}{1-y'} = \frac{\alpha^*[x_o - (p_l/p_h)y']}{(1-x_o) - (p_l/p_h)(1-y')}$$

(13.7-27)

The solution to this quadratic equation is given as Eq. (13.4-7).

In order to solve Eqs. (13.7-25) and (13.7-26), the following procedure can be used, where x_o is known or set:

1. Using Eq. (13.7-27), the value of y' is calculated for $x = x_o$.
2. To integrate Eq. (13.7-25), the value of (dy/dx) at $x = x_o$ must be calculated. However, this value is indeterminate since the denominator is zero. Using L'Hopital's rule (N1, P4, R1) the numerator is differentiated with respect to x and the denominator with respect to x and the value of y is set as y' to give

$$\left(\frac{dy}{dx}\right)_{x=x_o} = \frac{(y'-x_o)[\alpha^* - (\alpha^* - 1)y']}{\{\alpha^*(1-x_o)(x_o - ry') - x_o[(1-x_o) - r(1-y')] - (y'-x_o)[(\alpha^* - 1)(2ry' - x_o - r) - 1]\}}$$

(13.7-28)

3. Starting at the residual end at x_o, Eq. (13.7-25) is integrated numerically to give the y-versus-x relationship and y_p (P4, R1).
4. The relationship of y versus x is substituted into Eq. (13.7-26), which is integrated from x_f to x_o to obtain the area A_m.
5. Substituting into the material-balance Eqs. (13.4-8) and (13.4-2), the cut or fraction of feed permeated, θ, is calculated (N1, R1, W5).
6. If θ is set and x_o is unknown, the solution is trial and error. The value of x_o is assumed and the integration of Eq. (13.7-25) is performed to obtain y_p. Then x_o is calculated from Eq. (13.4-9). This is repeated until the assumed and calculated values of x_o agree.

13.7D Derivation of Equations for Countercurrent Flow in Asymmetric Membranes

The flow diagram for this countercurrent-flow model is shown in Fig. 13.7-3, where both streams are in plug flow. The permeate y' leaving the membrane differs from the symmetric-membrane case and is not the same as the bulk phase concentration y at this point. This is also shown in Fig. 13.7-1b.

The flux of A out of the element with area dA_m is

$$dL_A = y \, dL = (P'_A/t)(p_h x - p_l y') \, dA_m \tag{13.7-29}$$

where y' is given by Eq. (13.7-30), which is similar to Eqs. (13.7-27) and (13.4-6):

$$\frac{y'}{1 - y'} = \frac{\alpha^*[x - (p_l/p_h)y']}{(1 - x) - (p_l/p_h)(1 - y')} \tag{13.7-30}$$

The flux of B is

$$dL_B = (1 - y) \, dL = (P'_B/t)[p_h(1 - x) - p_l(1 - y')] \, dA_m \tag{13.7-31}$$

Equations (13.7-29) and (13.7-31) differ from Eqs. (13.7-4) and (13.7-5) for the symmetric membrane in that y' is used instead of y in the terms for concentration difference.

The rest of the derivation is identical to that for the dense-phase symmetric membrane (N1, R1). The final equations are

$$\frac{L_o}{(P'_B/t)p_h} \frac{dx}{dA_m} = \frac{-(x - y)}{(y - x_o)}\{(1 - x)\alpha^*(x - ry') - x[(1 - x) - r(1 - y')]\} \tag{13.7-32}$$

$$\frac{dx}{dy} = \frac{(y - x_o)}{(x - x_o)} \frac{\{(1 - y)\alpha^*(x - ry') - y[(1 - x) - r(1 - y')]\}}{\{(1 - x)\alpha^*(x - ry') - x[(1 - x) - r(1 - y')]\}} \tag{13.7-33}$$

Inverting Eq. (13.7-32),

$$\frac{dA_m}{dx} = \frac{-L_o}{(P'_B/t)p_h} \frac{[(y - x_o)/(x - y)]}{\{(1 - x)\alpha^*(x - ry') - x[(1 - x) - r(1 - y')]\}} \tag{13.7-34}$$

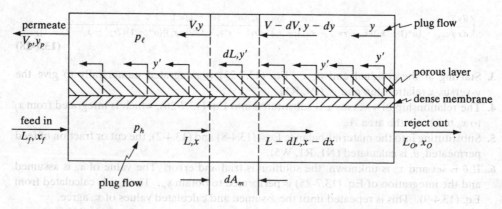

FIGURE 13.7-3. *Flow diagram for countercurrent flow with asymmetric membrane.*

Equations (13.7-27) for y' and (13.7-28) for (dy/dx) at $x = x_o$ for symmetric membranes are also applicable here for asymmetric membranes. The method of solution for the above equations is similar to that for symmetric membranes.

13.7E   Derivation of Equations for Cocurrent Flow in Asymmetric Membranes

For cocurrent flow, the cocurrent model is shown in Fig. 13.7-4. The derivation uses Eqs. (13.7-29)–(13.7-31) as before. Proceeding in a manner similar to the countercurrent case, the final equations are (N1, P4, R1):

$$\frac{dy}{dx} = \frac{(y - x_f)\,\{(1 - y)\alpha^*(x - ry') - y[(1 - x) - r(1 - y')]\}}{(x - x_f)\,\{(1 - x)\alpha^*(x - ry') - x[(1 - x) - r(1 - y')]\}} \tag{13.7-35}$$

$$\frac{dA_m}{dx} = \frac{L_f}{(P'_B/t)p_h}\,\frac{[(y - x_f)/(x - y)]}{\{(1 - x)\alpha^*(x - ry') - x[(1 - x) - r(1 - y')]\}} \tag{13.7-36}$$

The method of solution is similar to that for countercurrent flow. Integration of Eq. (13.7-35) is started at the feed inlet, where y' is determined by using x_f instead of x_o in Eq. (13.7-27). Then, using Eq. (13.7-28) with x_f instead of x_o, (dy/dx) at $x = x_f$ is calculated. This is then used to integrate Eq. (13.7-35) starting at the feed end, where $x = x_f$. Finally, Eq. (13.7-36) is integrated to obtain A_m.

13.7F   Effects of Processing Variables on Gas Separation

1. Effects of pressure ratio and separation factor on recovery. Using the Weller-Steiner Eq. (13.4-6) for the complete-mixing model, the effects of pressure ratio, p_h/p_l, and separation factor, α^*, on permeate purity can be determined for a fixed feed composition. Figure 13.7-5 is a plot of this equation for a feed concentration of 30% (S7). For symmetric and asymmetric membranes, this equation can be expected to provide estimates of product purity and trends for conditions of low to modest recovery in all types of models, including complete-mixing, cross-flow, and countercurrent.

Figure 13.7-5 shows that above an α^* of 20, the product purity is not greatly affected. Also, above a pressure ratio of about 6, this ratio has a diminishing effect on product purity.

FIGURE 13.7-4   *Flow diagram for cocurrent flow with asymmetric membrane.*

FIGURE 13.7-5. *Effects of separation factor and pressure ratio on permeate purity. (Feed $x_f = 0.30$.) [From "Membranes Separate Gases Selectively," by D. J. Stookey, C. J. Patton, and G. L. Malcolm, Chem. Eng. Progr., 82(11), 36(1986). Reproduced by permission of the American Institute of Chemical Engineers.]*

If liquids are present in the gas separation process, a liquid film can increase the membrane resistance markedly. Liquids can also damage the membrane by chemical action or by swelling or softening. If water vapor is present in the gas streams, the dew point may be reached in the residue product and liquid may condense. Condensation of hydrocarbons must also be avoided.

2. Effects of process flow patterns on separation in symmetric membranes. Detailed parametric studies have been done by various investigators (P4, P5, W5) for binary systems. They compared the four flow patterns of complete mixing, cross-flow, cocurrent, and countercurrent flow. In Fig. 13.7-6 (W5) the permeate concentration is shown plotted versus stage cut, θ, for a feed of air ($x_f = 0.209$ for oxygen) with $\alpha^* = 10$ and $p_h/p_l = 5$. It is shown that, as expected, the countercurrent flow pattern gives the best separation. The other patterns—cross-flow, cocurrent, and complete mixing—give lower separations in descending order. Note that when the stage cut $\theta = 0$, all flow patterns are equivalent to the complete mixing model and give the same permeate composition. Also, at $\theta = 1.00$, all patterns again give the same value of $y_p = 0.209$, which is also the feed composition.

The required membrane areas for the same process conditions and air feed versus stage cut were also determined (W5). The areas for all four types of flow pattern were shown to be within about 10% of each other. The countercurrent and cross-flow patterns give the lowest area required.

3. Effects of process flow patterns on separation in asymmetric membranes. Calculations using the mathematical models for asymmetric membranes give virtually identical performances for cocurrent and countercurrent flow (G1, P2, P6). The porous support prevents mixing of the bulk permeate concentration and the skin surface concentration y' as shown in Fig. 13.7-1b. Hence, the direction of the bulk flow permeate stream has no effect. Experi-

FIGURE 13.7-6. *Effect of flow pattern in symmetric membranes. Operating conditions for air are as follows: $x_f = 0.209$, $\alpha^* = 10$, $p_h/p_l = 380\ cm\ Hg/76\ cm\ Hg = 5$. $P'_A = 500 \times 10^{-10}\ cm^3\ (STP) \cdot cm/ s \cdot cm^2 \cdot cm\ Hg$. (1) countercurrent flow, (2) cross-flow, (3) cocurrent flow, (4) complete mixing (W5). [Reprinted from W. P. Walawender and S. A. Stern, Sep. Sci.,* **7**, *553 (1972). By courtesy of Marcel Dekker, Inc.]*

mental tests using helium recovery from natural gas (P2, P6), nitrogen recovery from air (G1), and helium from nitrogen (G1) show that the experimental data and the model predictions agree quite well.

4. Effect of pressure drop on separations in asymmetric membranes. In hollow-fiber membranes (N1), an appreciable pressure drop can occur for flow inside long tubes or for tubes with very small inside diameters. In the shell side the pressure drop is generally very small and is neglected. Pressure drop in the tubes is always detrimental to the separation. For feed inside the tubes, the actual average feed pressure will be less than the inlet feed pressure. If the permeate flow is inside the tubes, then the actual average permeate pressure will be higher than the permeate outlet pressure. In both of these cases, the driving force for permeation is reduced and less separation occurs.

To reduce these pressure effects, where the stage cut θ is small, giving a low permeate flow rate, it is preferable to have the large feed flow rate in the shell, where the pressure drop is small. For a high stage cut, the feed should be inside the tubes, where most of the feed permeates into the shell.

Using the model equations, the pressure drop inside the tubes can be accounted for by using the Hagen–Poisseuille equation (2.10-2) for laminar flow:

$$\frac{\Delta p}{(z_2 - z_1)} = \frac{32 \mu v}{D^2} \tag{2.10-2}$$

where $z_2 - z_1$ is total length. Writing this for a differential length dz cm and a dp_h in Pascals,

$$\frac{dp_h}{dz} = \frac{-32 \mu v}{D^2} \tag{13.7-37}$$

Converting the feed flow rate L cm³/s at T_S and p_S (STP) to the actual velocity v at T and p_h,

$$\frac{dp_h}{dz} = \frac{-128\mu}{\pi D^4 N_T}\left(L\frac{T}{T_S}\frac{p_S}{p_h}\right) \tag{13.7-38}$$

where N_T is the number of tubes in parallel. The average viscosity μ can be approximated by using the average mole fraction of the feed and the residual outlet. The average μ is then the sum of the mole fractions of each component times the viscosity of the pure gases. The final equation is (G1, N1, P2)

$$\frac{dp_h^2}{dz} = \frac{-256\mu L T p_S}{\pi D^4 N_T T_S} \tag{13.7-39}$$

The area A_m can be related to z by $dA_m = \pi D N_T\, dz$. This then relates dA_m to dp_h. In integrating the model equations, a constant (uniform) p_h is first assumed (G1, P2, P7). This gives the relation between y and x and A_m. Then, using the material-balance equation (13.7-18) between L and y and x, equation (13.7-39) is used to generate a new pressure profile. This process is then repeated.

13.8   DERIVATION OF FINITE-DIFFERENCE NUMERICAL METHOD FOR ASYMMETRIC MEMBRANES

13.8A   Countercurrent Flow

The flow diagram for the numerical method is shown in Fig. 13.8-1. Using the method derived by McCabe et al. (M5) and taking an area ΔA_m, the mass balances on both streams can be written as

$$\Delta V = L_{in} - L_{out} \tag{13.8-1}$$

The value of y'_{in} can be calculated from Eq. (13.7-27) using x_{in} for x and y'_{in} for y'. Also, y'_{out} can be calculated similarly from x_{out}. Then, writing a balance on A,

$$\Delta V y'_{av} = L_{in} x_{in} - L_{out} x_{out} \tag{13.8-2}$$

FIGURE 13.8-1.   *Flow diagram for countercurrent flow with asymmetric membrane using finite difference method.*

where $y'_{av} = (y'_{in} + y'_{out})/2$. Substituting L_{out} from Eq. (13.8-1) into (13.8-2),

$$\Delta V = L_{in} \frac{(x_{in} - x_{out})}{(y'_{av} - x_{out})} \qquad \textbf{(13.8-3)}$$

Equations (13.7-27), (13.8-2), and (13.8-3) can be solved numerically starting at the feed $x_f = x_{in}$ to determine the permeate ΔV and y'_{av} for each ΔA_m and increments of x to x_o at the outlet reject. Usually 10 or so increments of x from x_f to x_o are sufficient.

Then, to obtain the values of V and the bulk composition y as a function of x, the calculation is started at x_o. Using Equations (13.8-4) and (13.8-5), the increments of ΔV are added to get V, and y is calculated for each ΔA_m increment up to x_f at the feed inlet:

$$V = \sum \Delta V \qquad \textbf{(13.8-4)}$$

$$y = \frac{\sum y'_{av} \Delta V}{V} \qquad \textbf{(13.8-5)}$$

For cocurrent or parallel flow, the only difference is in calculating V. Starting at x_f inlet and using Eqs. (13.8-4) and (13.8-5), the increments of ΔV are added to get V up to x_o.

To calculate the area for countercurrent or cocurrent flow, rewriting Eq. (13.7-4),

$$\frac{\Delta V y'_{av}}{\Delta A_m} = \frac{\Delta V_A}{\Delta A_m} = (P'_A/t)p_h(x - ry')_{av} \qquad \textbf{(13.8-6)}$$

where $r = p_l/p_h$. The average driving force is

$$(x - ry')_{av} = [(x_{in} - ry'_{in}) + (x_{out} - ry'_{out})]/2 \qquad \textbf{(13.8-7)}$$

Solving for ΔA_m,

$$\Delta A_m = \frac{\Delta V y'_{av}}{(P'_A/t)p_h(x - ry')_{av}} \qquad \textbf{(13.8-8)}$$

Starting at x_f, ΔA_m is calculated for each increment to obtain $\sum \Delta A_m$ versus x.

13.8B Short-Cut Numerical Method

Making an approximate material balance to obtain a y'_{av} or y_p for the total area from y'_f to y'_o (M5),

$$y_p = y'_{av} = (y'_f + y'_o)/2 \qquad \textbf{(13.8-9)}$$

An overall and component material balance gives

$$L_f = L_o + V_p \qquad \textbf{(13.8-10)}$$

$$L_f x_f = L_o x_o + V_p y_p \qquad \textbf{(13.8-11)}$$

Substituting Eq. (13.8-10) into (13.8-11),

$$L_f x_f = (L_f - V_p)x_o + V_p y_p \qquad \textbf{(13.8-12)}$$

Equation (13.8-12) can be solved for V_p and (13.8-10) solved for L_o.

To calculate the approximate area for countercurrent or cocurrent flow, Eq. (13.8-8) is rewritten for the total area A_m:

$$A_m = \frac{V_p y'_{av}}{(P'_A/t)p_h(x - ry')_{lm}} \tag{13.8-13}$$

where $(x - ry')_{lm}$ is the ln mean of $(x_f - ry'_f)$ and $(x_o - ry'_o)$. Since plots of x and y' versus A_m are approximately straight lines, this approximate area is within about 15% of the A_m calculated by the finite-difference method.

EXAMPLE 13.8-1. Air Separation Using an Asymmetric Membrane for Countercurrent Flow

It is desired to design a hollow-fiber asymmetric membrane for air separation to produce a residue which contains 97.0% N_2 using countercurrent flow. The dense polymer layer is in the inside of the tubes and the feed is in the tubes. Experimental values for commercial membranes give separation factors α^* of O_2/N_2 between 3 and 7 (H2) with a typical value of 5.0 (G1). Permeance values of P'_A/t are given (H2) of 5×10^{-6} to 250×10^{-6} cm^3 (STP)/(s·cm^2·cm Hg) with a typical value of 20×10^{-6} (G1). The typical values will be used. The feed or tube side pressure is 1034 kPa abs and the shell side or permeate is 103.4 kPa. The feed rate of air is 10.0 m^3 (STP)/h.

(a) Using the finite-difference method, calculate the permeate composition, the fraction θ of feed permeated, and the residue and permeate flows. Assume negligible pressure drop in the tubes. Calculate the composition y of the permeate as a function of the residue composition x.

(b) Calculate the membrane area needed.

(c) Using the short-cut procedure, calculate the permeate composition, θ, flows, and membrane area.

FIGURE 13.8-2. *Finite-difference elements for countercurrent flow in Example 13.8-1.*

(d) Repeat (a) for cocurrent flow. Plot x, y, and y' for countercurrent and cocurrent flow versus area.

Solution: For part (a), $L_f = 10.0$ m^3 (STP)/h, $x_f = 0.209$, $x_o = 0.03$, $p_h = 1034$ kPa, $p_l = 103.4$ kPa, $P'_A/t = 20 \times 10^{-6}$ cm^3 (STP)/(s·cm^2·cm Hg), $\alpha^* = 5.0$. Using Table 13.3-1,

$$P'_A/t = (20 \times 10^{-6})(7.501 \times 10^{-6}) = 1.500 \times 10^{-10} \text{ m}^3 \text{(STP)}/(\text{s·m}^2 \text{·Pa})$$

$$r = p_l/p_h = 103.4/1034 = 0.10$$

Starting at the feed inlet (Fig. 13.8-2), where $x_f = 0.209$, using an area ΔA_m, going from $x_f = x_1 = 0.209$ to $x_2 = 0.190$, and using Eq. (13.7-27) to calculate y',

$$\frac{y'_1}{1 - y'_1} = \frac{\alpha^*[x_1 - (p_l/p_h)y'_1]}{(1 - x_1) - (p_l/p_h)(1 - y'_1)} \tag{13.7-27}$$

The solution to this is given by the quadratic equation (13.4-7):

$$y' = \frac{-b + \sqrt{b^2 - 4ac}}{2a} \tag{13.4-7}$$

where $a = 1 - \alpha^*$, $b = -1 + \alpha^* + 1/r + x/r(\alpha^* - 1)$, and $c = -a^*x/r$. Substituting and solving for y'_1 where $x_1 = 0.209$,

$$x_1 = 0.209,$$

$$a = 1 - 5 = -4.0$$

$$b = -1 + 5.0 + \frac{1}{0.1} + \frac{x_1(5 - 1)}{0.1} = 14.0 + 40x_1 = 14.0 + 40(0.209) = 22.36$$

$$c = \frac{-\alpha^*x_1}{r} = \frac{-5x_1}{0.10} = -50x_1 = -50(0.209) = -10.45$$

$$y'_1 = \frac{-22.36 + [(22.36)^2 - 4(-4.0)(-10.45)]^{1/2}}{2(-4.0)} = 0.5148$$

Again, for $x_2 = 0.190$, $y'_2 = 0.4830$ is obtained from Eq. (13.7-27).

Then, $y'_{av} = (y'_1 + y'_2)/2 = (0.5148 + 0.4830)/2 = 0.4989$. Substituting into Eq. (13.8-3),

$$\Delta V_1 = \frac{L_1(x_1 - x_2)}{(y'_{av} - x_2)} = \frac{10.0(0.209 - 0.190)}{(0.4989 - 0.190)} = 0.6151 \text{ m}^3/\text{h}$$

Then by Eq. (13.8-1),

$$L_2 = L_1 - \Delta V_1 = 10.0 - 0.6151 = 9.3849 \text{ m}^3/\text{h}$$

$$y'_{av} \Delta V_1 = 0.4989(0.6151) = 0.3069$$

For the second increment for ΔA_{m2} in Fig. 13.8-2, solving for y'_3 with $x_3 = 0.170$,

$$a = -4.0, \quad b = 14.0 + 40(10.170) = 20.8, \quad c = -50(0.170) = -8.5$$

Using Eq. (13.4-7), $y'_3 = 0.4471$. Then $y'_{av} = (y'_2 + y'_3)/2 = (0.4830 + 0.4471)/2 = 0.4651$

TABLE 13.8-1. *Compositions and Areas for Numerical Method in Example 13.8-1*

x	Countercurrent y	Cocurrent y	Counter and Cocurrent y'	ΔA, Area (m²)	A, Area (m²)
0.209	0.3181	0.5148	0.5148	0.000	0.000
0.190	0.2983	0.4989	0.4830	3.674	3.674
0.170	0.2769	0.4817	0.4471	3.968	7.642
0.150	0.2549	0.4637	0.4084	4.117	11.759
0.130	0.2323	0.4446	0.3665	4.323	16.082
0.110	0.2090	0.4242	0.3214	4.607	20.689
0.090	0.1847	0.4021	0.2726	5.006	25.695
0.070	0.1593	0.3779	0.2198	5.592	31.287
0.050	0.1322	0.3505	0.1629	6.508	37.795
0.030	0.1014	0.3181	0.1014	8.144	**45.939**

$$\Delta V_2 = \frac{L_2(x_2 - x_3)}{(y'_{av} - x_3)} = 9.3849\frac{(0.190 - 0.170)}{(0.4651 - 0.170)} = 0.6360 \text{ m}^3/\text{h}$$

Also,

$$L_3 = L_2 - \Delta V_2 = 9.3849 - 0.6360 = 8.7489 \text{ m}^3/\text{h}$$

$$y'_{av} \Delta V_2 = 0.4651(0.6360) = 0.2958$$

This is continued, and for the eighth increment, $x_8 = 0.07$, $x_9 = 0.050$, $y'_8 = 0.2198$, $y'_9 = 0.1629$, $y'_{av} = 0.1914$, $\Delta V_8 = 0.7757$, and $L_9 = 4.7088$. For the final or ninth increment, $x_{10} = x_o = 0.030$, $x_9 = 0.050$, $y'_9 = 0.1629$, $y'_{10} = 0.1014$, $y'_{av} = 0.1322$, $\Delta V_9 = 0.9215$, and $L_{10} = L_o = 3.7873 \text{ m}^3/\text{h}$. The permeate flow rate $V_p = L_f - L_o = 10.00 - 3.7873 = 6.2127 \text{ m}^3/\text{h}$. The stage cut $\theta = 6.2127/10.00 = 0.6213$.

To calculate the bulk composition y as a function of x for countercurrent flow, it is necessary to start at x_o. Using Eq. (13.8-4),

$$V_9 = \sum \Delta V = V_{10} + \Delta V_9 = 0 + 0.9215 = 0.9215$$

For calculation of y_9 using Eq. (13.8-5),

$$y_9 = \frac{\sum y'_{av} \Delta V_9}{V_9} = \frac{0.1322(0.9215)}{0.9215} = \frac{0.1218}{0.9215} = 0.1322$$

For the eighth plus ninth increments,

$$V_8 = \sum \Delta V = V_9 + \Delta V_8 = 0.9215 + 0.7757 = 1.6972$$

$$y_8 = \frac{\sum y'_{av} \Delta V}{V} = \frac{0.1218 + 0.1914(0.7757)}{1.6972} = 0.1593$$

This calculation is continued up to the feed entrance. Values of y, x, and y' are given in Table 13.8-1.

To calculate y as a function of x for cocurrent flow, it is necessary to start at x_f. For the first increment, from Eq. (13.8-4),

$$V_1 = \sum \Delta V = 0 + \Delta V_1 = 0 + 0.6151 = 0.6151$$

$$y_1 = \frac{\sum y'_{av} \Delta V}{V} = \frac{0.4989(0.6151)}{0.6151} = \frac{0.3069}{0.6151} = 0.4989$$

For the second increment,

$$V = \sum \Delta V = V_1 + \Delta V_2 = 0.6151 + 0.6360 = 1.2511$$

$$y_2 = \frac{0.3069 + 0.4651(0.6360)}{1.2511} = 0.4817$$

This calculation is continued up to the outlet at x_o.

For part (b), Eq. (13.8-8) is used starting at x_f for both countercurrent and cocurrent flows. For the first increment, the flow rates in m³/h are converted to m³/s by multiplying by (1/3600). Also, $x_f = 0.209$, $x_2 = 0.190$, $y'_1 = 0.5148$, $y'_2 = 0.4830$, $y'_{av} = 0.4989$, $\Delta V_1 = 0.6151$ m³/h, and $p_h = 1034$ kPa. Calculating $x - ry'$ at points 1 and 2 and the average $(x - ry')$ from Eq. (13.8-7),

$$x_1 - ry'_1 = 0.209 - 0.10(0.5148) = 0.15752$$

$$x_2 - ry'_2 = 0.190 - 0.10(0.4830) = 0.14170$$

$$(x - ry')_{av} = (0.15752 + 0.14170)/2 = 0.1496$$

Using Eq. (13.8-8),

$$\Delta A_{m1} = \frac{(0.6151)(1/3600)(0.4989)}{(1.500 \times 10^{-10})(1034 \times 10^3)(0.1496)} = 3.674 \text{ m}^2$$

For the second increment, $x_3 = 0.170$, $y'_3 = 0.4471$, $y'_{av} = 0.4651$, and $\Delta V_2 = 0.6360$. Then,

$$x_2 - ry'_2 = 0.14170$$

$$x_3 - ry'_3 = 0.170 - 0.10(0.4471) = 0.12529$$

$$(x - ry')_{av} = (0.14170 + 0.12529)/2 = 0.13350$$

$$\Delta A_{m2} = \frac{(0.6360)(1/3600)(0.4651)}{(1.500 \times 10^{-10})(1034 \times 10^3)(0.13350)} = 3.968 \text{ m}^2$$

This is continued, and the results are given in Table 13.8-1. The final total area is 45.94 m².

For part (c), using the shortcut procedure, Eq. (13.8-9) gives the value of y_p:

$$y_p = y'_{av} = (y'_f + y'_o)/2 = (0.5148 + 0.1014)/2 = 0.3081$$

This value of 0.3081 compares to 0.3181 for the numerical method. Making a component balance in Eq. (13.8-12),

$$L_f x_f = (L_f - V_p)x_o + V_p y_p$$

$$10.0(0.209) = (10.0 - V_p)0.03 + V_p(0.3081)$$

FIGURE 13.8-3. *Plot of composition versus area for numerical method in Example 13.8-1.*

Solving, $V_p = 6.437$ and $L_o = (10.00 - 6.437) = 3.563$. This gives a stage cut $\theta = 6.437/10.00 = 0.6437$, as compared with 0.6213 for the numerical method. To calculate the area, the driving forces are

$$x_f - ry'_f = 0.209 - 0.10(0.5148) = 0.15752$$

$$x_o - ry'_o = 0.030 - 0.10(0.1014) = 0.01986$$

$$(x - ry')_{lm} = \frac{(0.15752 - 0.01986)}{\ln(0.15752/0.01986)} = 0.06648$$

The area from Eq. (13.8-13) is

$$A_m = \frac{6.437(1/3600)(0.3081)}{(1.500 \times 10^{-10})(1034 \times 10^3)(0.06648)} = 53.43 \text{ m}^2$$

This value of 53.43 is about 16% greater than the numerical method. A plot of these data for the numerical method is given in Fig. 13.8-3.

13.8C Use of Spreadsheet for Finite-Difference Numerical Method

The numerical method can easily be adapted so that a spreadsheet can be used to solve the problem for asymmetric membranes. Using Excel® or other programs, basic formulas can be entered into cells.

Output data from a spreadsheet are given in Table 13.8-2 for Example 13.8-1. Input data for the calculations are briefly as follows: In cells D3–D10 known values are entered. In cell D11 the equation for $r = p_l/p_h$ is given by the formula \$D\$8/\$D\$7.

Row 13 is used to keep track of the indexes used in this part of the calculation. Row 14 gives the input values of x_1, x_2, and so on. In rows 15–18 the values of a, b, c, and y' are calculated using Eqs. (13.4-7) and (13.7-27). For example, in cell B18 the formula entered

TABLE 13.8-2. *Output from Spreadsheet for Finite-Difference Method for Example 13.8-1*

Col/Row	A	B	C	D	E	F	G	H	I	J	K
1	Example 13.8-1										
2											
3	Input Variables:										
4	L_f (feed rate)			10	m**3(STP)/hr						
5	x_f (O$_2$ mole fraction—feed)			0.209							
6	x_o (O$_2$ mole fraction—outlet)			0.03							
7	Pressure (feed), p_h			1034	kPa						
8	Pressure (permeate), p_l			103.4	kPa						
9	P'_A/t			1.50E-10	m**3(STP)/s·m**2·Pa						
10	$\alpha*$(O$_2$/N$_2$ separation factor)			5							
11	$r = p_l/p_h$			0.1							
12											

TABLE 13.8-2. *Continued*

Col/Row	A	B	C	D	E	F	G	H	I	J	K
13	I	1	2	3	4	5	6	7	8	9	10
14	$x(I)$	0.2090	0.1900	0.17	0.15	0.13	0.11	0.09	0.07	0.05	0.03
15	a	-4.0000	-4.0000	-4.0000	-4.0000	-4.0000	-4.0000	-4.0000	-4.0000	-4.0000	-4.0000
16	b	22.3600	21.6000	20.8000	20.0000	19.2000	18.4000	17.6000	16.8000	16.0000	15.2000
17	c	-10.4500	-9.5000	-8.5000	-7.5000	-6.5000	-5.5000	-4.5000	-3.5000	-2.5000	-1.5000
18	$y'(I)$	0.5148	0.4830	0.4471	0.4083	0.3665	0.3214	0.2726	0.2198	0.1629	0.1014
19	$y(\text{avg})$		0.4989	0.4651	0.4277	0.3874	0.3439	0.2970	0.2462	0.1914	0.1321
20	ΔV		0.6151	0.6361	0.6300	0.6307	0.6401	0.6617	0.7022	0.7759	0.9219
21	$L(I)$	10.0000	9.3849	8.7487	8.1187	7.4880	6.8478	6.1861	5.4839	4.7081	3.7862
22											
23	I		1	2	3	4	5	6	7	8	9
24	$V(\text{counter})$	6.2138	6.2138	5.5987	4.9626	4.3326	3.7018	3.0617	2.4000	1.6978	0.9219
25	$y_{\text{avg}}*\Delta V$	1.9764	1.9764	1.6695	1.3737	1.1042	0.8599	0.6397	0.4432	0.2703	0.1218
26	$y(I)$	0.3181	0.3181	0.2982	0.2768	0.2549	0.2323	0.2089	0.1847	0.1592	0.1321
27											

Table 13.8-2. *Continued*

Col/Row	A	B	C	D	E	F	G	H	I	J	K
28	Checks:										
29	Mass(in)	10.0000									
30	Mass(out)	10.0000									
31	$[O_2]_{in}$	2.0900									
32	$[O_2]_{out}$	2.0900									
33											
34	I		1	2	3	4	5	6	7	8	9
35	V(cocurr)		0.6151	1.2513	1.8813	2.5120	3.1522	3.8139	4.5161	5.2919	6.2138
36	$y_{avg}*\Delta V$		0.3069	0.6027	0.8722	1.1166	1.3367	1.5333	1.7061	1.8546	1.9764
37	$y(I)$		0.4989	0.4817	0.4636	0.4445	0.4241	0.4020	0.3778	0.3505	0.3181
38											
39	Calculate the Areas for each increment:										
40											
41	$(x - ry')_{avg}$	0.1496	0.1335	0.1172	0.1013	0.0856	0.0703	0.0554	0.0409	0.0268	0.0099
42	$(P'_A/t)*p_h$	0.5584									
43	ΔA	3.6735	3.9690	4.1170	4.3223	4.6063	5.0061	5.5907	6.5072	8.1449	
44	Total Area	45.9370									

is =(-B16+SQRT(B16*B16-4*B15*B17))/2*B15). In row 19, $y'_{av} = (y'_1 + y'_2)/2$. In row 20, ΔV is calculated from Eq. (13.8-3). The formula in cell C20 is =B21*(B14−C14)/ (C19−C14) and in D20 is =C21*(C14−D14)/(D19−D14). In row 21, L is calculated from Eq. (13.8-1), where $L_2 = L_1 - \Delta V_1$ by using the formula in cell C21, which is =−(C20−B21), for C22, =−(D20−B21), and so on.

Row 23 is a new set of indexes for countercurrent flow. To calculate V in row 24 using Eq. (13.8-4), where $V = \sum \Delta V$, and starting at the outlet x_o, the formula in cell K24 is =K20, in J24, =J20+K24, and so on. For row 25, to calculate $\sum y'_{av} \Delta V$, the formula in cell K25 is =K19*K20, in J25, J19*J20+K25, and so on. For the bulk permeate composition, y is calculated in row 26 from Eq. (13.8-5), where $y = \sum y'_{av} \Delta V/V$. In cell B26, the formula is =B25/B24.

Rows 28–32 are optional and are used to check the mass balances for the inlet and outlet streams. In cell B29, the mass in is =$D$4; the mass out in B30 is =B24+K21. Similarly, cell B31 is =$D$4*$D$5 and B32 is =B24*B26+K21*K14.

For cocurrent flow, starting at x_f, Eq. (13.8-4), where $V = \sum \Delta V$, is calculated in row 35. In row 36, $\sum y'_{av} \Delta V$ is calculated using the formula in cell C36 of =19*C20, in D36, =D19*D20+C36, and so on. Then Eq. (13.8-5) is used to calculate the bulk composition y from $\sum y'_{av} \Delta V/V$ in row 37.

To calculate the areas, in row 41 $(x - ry')_{av}$ is calculated for each increment, using Eq. (13.8-7). The formula in cell B41 is =((B14−$D$11*B18)+(C14−$D$11*C18))/2. In cell B42 the conversion of V m³/h to m³/s and kPa to Pa is performed using =($D$9*$D$7*1000*3600). In row 43, using Eq. (13.8-8) to calculate ΔA_m, the formula in cell B43 is C19*C20/($B$42*B41). In row 44 all of the ΔA_m values in row 43 are added to get the total A_m using =SUM(B43:J43).

13.8D Calculation of Pressure-Drop Effects on Permeation

1. Estimation of number of tubes and length. In order to calculate the pressure drop inside the hollow-fiber tubes, the dimensions, number of tubes, and area A_m of the membrane must be known. The following procedure can be employed. The shortcut procedure is first used with Eqs. (13.8-9)–(13.8-13). This gives L_f, L_o, V_p, y'_{av}, and A_m. Then the average flow rate in the tubes is calculated from the equation $L_{av} = (L_f + L_o)/2$.

The number of tubes in parallel N_T must be estimated from typical laboratory or commercial data. For example, for air with a flow rate of 3 m³/h, 3.8×10^4 fibers (N_T) are used with an ID of 95 μm, and a length ($z_2 - z_1$) of 48.26 cm. For a flow rate L_f of 10.0 m³/hr in Example 13.8-1 and to keep a similar and reasonable velocity in the tubes, the N_T needed will be directly proportional to the inlet L_f. Then, knowing the A_m, an estimated total length ($z_2 - z_1$) of the tubes can be calculated from Eq. (13.8-14):

$$A_m = \pi D N_T (z_2 - z_1) \qquad (13.8\text{-}14)$$

2. Finite-difference method to include effect of pressure drop. For the finite-difference numerical method, Eq. (13.8-14) can be rewritten as

$$\Delta A_m = \pi D N_T (\Delta z) \qquad (13.8\text{-}15)$$

Also, Eq. (13.7-38) can be rewritten for a finite increment of Δz length:

$$\frac{\Delta p_h}{\Delta z} = \frac{-128\mu}{\pi D^4 N_T} \left(L \frac{T}{T_S} \frac{p_S}{p_{h\,av}} \right) \qquad (13.8\text{-}16)$$

The following steps, which may require several iterations, can be used in the finite-difference numerical method to include the effect of pressure drop in the tubes:

1. For the first increment shown in Fig. 13.8-2, a constant inlet pressure p_{h1} (p_h) is used for $p_{h\,av}$ to calculate y_1' and y_2', ΔV_1, L_2, and ΔA_{m1} from Eqs. (13.7-27), (13.8-1), (13.8-3), (13.8-7), and (13.8-8).
2. The value of N_T is obtained from typical data as discussed above in Subsection 1. Using Eq. (13.8-15), the incremental length Δz is obtained.
3. Using $L_{av} = (L_1 + L_2)/2$ and the inlet p_{h1} for $p_{h\,av}$, the Δp_h for the first increment is calculated from Eq. (13.8-16).
4. For the second iteration, the new $p_{h\,av}$ to use is calculated from $p_{h\,av} = p_{h1} - \Delta p_h/2$. A new value of the outlet $p_{h2} = p_{h1} - \Delta p_h$ is used to recalculate a new y_2' from Eq. (13.7-27). The value of y_1' remains the same. Then by repeating steps 1 through 4, a new value of Δp_h is obtained. Usually only three or so iterations are needed to obtain a constant value of Δp_h, $p_{h\,av}$, and ΔA_{m1}. Using a spreadsheet as in Ex. 13.8-1, this procedure can be repeated for each finite section.

3. Determination of effect of pressure drop using shortcut method. The values of L_{av}, N_T, A_m, and overall length $(z_2 - z_1)$ are obtained from the shortcut calculation in Subsection 1 above. The shortcut value of the overall pressure drop $(p_h - p_{ho})$ can be obtained from Eq. (13.8-16) using p_h at the inlet as $p_{h\,av}$ and the overall length $(z_2 - z_1)$. Then for a second and final iteration, the new and corrected pressures $p_{h\,av} = p_h - \Delta p_h/2$ and $p_{ho} = p_h - \Delta p_h$ are used in Eqs. (13.7-27) and (13.8-9)–(13.8-13) to recalculate y_o', y_{av}', V_p, and A_m again. This recalculated A_m will include an approximate effect of pressure drop in the tubes.

13.9   REVERSE-OSMOSIS MEMBRANE PROCESSES

13.9A   Introduction

1. Introduction. To be useful for separation of different species, a membrane must allow passage of certain molecules and exclude or greatly restrict passage of others. In osmosis, a spontaneous transport of solvent occurs from a dilute solute or salt solution to a concentrated solute or salt solution across a semipermeable membrane which allows passage of the solvent but impedes passage of the salt solutes. In Fig. 13.9-1a, the solvent water normally flows through the semipermeable membrane to the salt solution. The levels of both liquids are the same as shown. The solvent flow can be reduced by exerting a pressure on the salt-solution side and membrane, as shown in Fig. 13.9-1b, until at a certain pressure, called the osmotic pressure π of the salt solution, equilibrium is reached and the amount of the solvent passing in opposite directions is equal. The chemical potentials of the solvent on both sides of the membrane are equal. The properties of the solution determine only the value of the osmotic pressure, not the membrane, provided that it is truly semipermeable. To reverse the flow of the water so that it flows from the salt solution to the fresh solvent, as in Fig. 13.9-1c, the pressure is increased above the osmotic pressure on the solution side.

This phenomenon, called *reverse osmosis,* is used in a number of processes. An important commercial use is in the desalination of seawater or brackish water to produce fresh water. Unlike distillation and freezing processes used to remove solvents, reverse osmosis can operate at ambient temperature without phase change. This process is quite useful for the processing of thermally and chemically unstable products. Applications include concen-

solvent
flow

fresh
water
solvent

NaCl-water

membrane

(a)　　　　　　(b)　　　　　　(c)

FIGURE 13.9-1.　*Osmosis and reverse osmosis: (a) osmosis, (b) osmotic equilibrium,
(c) reverse osmosis.*

tration of fruit juices and milk, recovery of protein and sugar from cheese whey, and concentration of enzymes.

2. Osmotic pressure of solutions.　Experimental data show that the osmotic pressure π of a solution is proportional to the concentration of the solute and temperature T. Van't Hoff originally showed that the relationship is similar to that for pressure of an ideal gas. For example, for dilute water solutions,

$$\pi = \frac{n}{V_m} RT \qquad (13.9\text{-}1)$$

where n is the number of kg mol of solute, V_m the volume of pure solvent water in m^3 associated with n kg mol of solute, R the gas law constant $82.057 \times 10^{-3} \, m^3 \cdot atm/kg \, mol \cdot K$, and T is temperature in K. If a solute exists as two or more ions in solution, n represents the total number of ions. For more concentrated solutions, Eq. (13.9-1) is modified using the osmotic coefficient ϕ, which is the ratio of the actual osmotic pressure π to the ideal π calculated from the equation. For very dilute solutions, ϕ has a value of unity and usually decreases as concentration increases. In Table 13.9-1 some experimental values of π are given for NaCl solutions, sucrose solutions, and seawater solutions (S3, S5).

EXAMPLE 13.9-1.　*Calculation of Osmotic Pressure of Salt Solution*
Calculate the osmotic pressure of a solution containing 0.10 g mol NaCl/1000 g H_2O at 25°C.

Solution:　From Table A.2-3, the density of water $= 997.0 \, kg/m^3$. Then, $n = 2 \times 0.10 \times 10^{-3} = 2.00 \times 10^{-4}$ kg mol (NaCl gives two ions). Also, the volume of the pure solvent water $V_m = 1.00 \, kg/(997.0 \, kg/m^3)$. Substituting into Eq. (13.9-1),

$$\pi = \frac{n}{V_m} RT = \frac{2.00 \times 10^{-4}(82.057 \times 10^{-3})(298.15)}{1.000/997.0} = 4.88 \text{ atm}$$

This compares with the experimental value in Table 13.9-1 of 4.56 atm.

Sodium Chloride Solutions			Sea Salt Solutions		Sucrose Solutions	
$\dfrac{g\,mol\,NaCl}{kg\,H_2O}$	Density (kg/m^3)	Osmotic Pressure (atm)	Wt % Salts	Osmotic Pressure (atm)	Solute Mol. Frac. $\times 10^3$	Osmotic Pressure (atm)
0	997.0	0	0	0	0	0
0.01	997.4	0.47	1.00	7.10	1.798	2.48
0.10	1001.1	4.56	3.45*	25.02	5.375	7.48
0.50	1017.2	22.55	7.50	58.43	10.69	15.31
1.00	1036.2	45.80	10.00	82.12	17.70	26.33
2.00	1072.3	96.2				

* Value for standard seawater.

3. Types of membranes for reverse osmosis. One of the more important membranes for reverse-osmosis desalination and many other reverse-osmosis processes is the cellulose acetate membrane. The asymmetric membrane is made as a composite film in which a thin, dense layer about 0.1–10 μm thick of extremely fine pores is supported upon a much thicker (50–125 μm) layer of microporous sponge with little resistance to permeation. The thin, dense layer has the ability to block the passage of quite small solute molecules. In desalination the membrane rejects the salt solute and allows the solvent water to pass through. Solutes which are most effectively excluded by the cellulose acetate membrane are the salts NaCl, NaBr, CaCl₂, and Na₂SO₄; sucrose; and tetralkyl ammonium salts. The main limitations of the cellulose acetate membrane are that for the most part it can only be used in aqueous solutions and that it must be used below about 60°C.

Another important membrane useful for seawater, wastewater, nickel-plating rinse solutions, and other solutes is the synthetic aromatic polyamide membrane "Permasep," made in the form of very fine, hollow fibers (L1, P3). When used industrially this type of membrane withstands continued operation at pH values of 10 to 11 (S4). Many other anisotropic membranes have also been synthesized from synthetic polymers, some of which can be used in organic solvents, at higher temperatures, and at high or low pH (M2, R1).

13.9B Flux Equations for Reverse Osmosis

1. Basic models for membrane processes. There are two basic types of mass-transport mechanisms which can take place in membranes. In the first basic type, using tight membranes, which are capable of retaining solutes of about 10 Å in size or less, diffusion-type transport mainly occurs. Both the solute and the solvent migrate by molecular or Fickian diffusion in the polymer, driven by concentration gradients set up in the membrane by the applied pressure difference. In the second basic type, using loose, microporous membranes which retain particles larger than 10 Å, a sieve-type mechanism occurs, where the solvent moves through the micropores in essentially viscous flow and the solute molecules small enough to pass through the pores are carried by convection with the solvent. For details of this second type of mechanism, see (M2, W1).

2. *Diffusion-type model.* For diffusion-type membranes, the steady-state equations governing the transport of solvent and solute are to a first approximation as follows (M2, M3). For the diffusion of the solvent through the membrane, as shown in Fig. 13.9-2,

$$N_w = \frac{P_w}{L_m}(\Delta P - \Delta \pi) = A_w(\Delta P - \Delta \pi) \qquad (13.9\text{-}2)$$

$$A_w = \frac{P_w}{L_m} \qquad (13.9\text{-}3)$$

where N_w is the solvent (water) flux in $kg/s \cdot m^2$; P_w the solvent membrane permeability, kg solvent/$s \cdot m \cdot atm$; L_m the membrane thickness, m; A_w the solvent permeability constant, kg solvent/$s \cdot m^2 \cdot atm$; $\Delta P = P_1 - P_2$ (hydrostatic pressure difference with P_1 pressure exerted on feed and P_2 on product solution), atm; and $\Delta \pi = \pi_1 - \pi_2$ (osmotic pressure of feed solution − osmotic pressure of product solution), atm. Note that subscript 1 is the feed or upstream side of the membrane and 2 the product or downstream side of the membrane.

For the diffusion of the solute through the membrane, an approximation for the flux of the solute is (C1, M1)

$$N_s = \frac{D_s K_s}{L_m}(c_1 - c_2) = A_s(c_1 - c_2) \qquad (13.9\text{-}4)$$

$$A_s = \frac{D_s K_s}{L_m} \qquad (13.9\text{-}5)$$

where N_s is the solute (salt) flux in kg solute/$s \cdot m^2$; D_s the diffusivity of solute in membrane, m^2/s; $K_s = c_m/c$ (distribution coefficient), concentration of solute in membrane/concentration of solute in solution; A_s is the solute permeability constant, m/s; c_1 the solute concentration in upstream or feed (concentrate) solution, kg solute/m^3; and c_2 the solute concentration in downstream or product (permeate) solution, kg solute/m^3. The distribution coefficient K_s is approximately constant over the membrane.

Making a material balance at steady state for the solute, the solute diffusing through the membrane must equal the amount of solute leaving in the downstream or product (permeate) solution:

$$N_s = \frac{N_w c_2}{c_{w2}} \qquad (13.9\text{-}6)$$

where c_{w2} is the concentration of solvent in stream 2 (permeate), kg solvent/m^3. If the stream 2 is dilute in solute, c_{w2} is approximately the density of the solvent. In reverse osmosis, the solute rejection R is defined as the ratio concentration difference across the mem-

FIGURE 13.9-2. *Concentrations and fluxes in reverse-osmosis process.*

brane divided by the bulk concentration on the feed or concentrate side (fraction of solute remaining in the feed stream):

$$R = \frac{c_1 - c_2}{c_1} = 1 - \frac{c_2}{c_1} \tag{13.9-7}$$

This can be related to the flux equations as follows, by first substituting Eqs. (13.9-2) and (13.9-4) into (13.9-6) to eliminate N_w and N_s in Eq. (13.9-6). Then, solving for c_2/c_1 and substituting this result into Eq. (13.9-7),

$$R = \frac{B(\Delta P - \Delta \pi)}{1 + B(\Delta P - \Delta \pi)} \tag{13.9-8}$$

$$B = \frac{P_w}{D_s K_s c_{w2}} = \frac{A_w}{A_s c_{w2}} \tag{13.9-9}$$

where B is in atm^{-1}. Note that B is composed of the various physical properties P_w, D_s, and K_s of the membrane and must be determined experimentally for each membrane. Usually it is the product $D_s K_s$ that is determined, not the values of D_s and K_s separately. Also, many of the data reported in the literature give values of (P_w/L_m) or A_w in kg solvent/s $\cdot$ m² $\cdot$ atm and $(D_s K_s/L_m)$ or A_s in m/s and not separate values of L_m, P_w, and so on.

EXAMPLE 13.9-2. Experimental Determination of Membrane Permeability
Experiments at 25°C were performed to determine the permeabilities of a cellulose acetate membrane (A1, W1). The laboratory test section shown in Fig. 13.9-3 has membrane area $A = 2.00 \times 10^{-3}$ m². The inlet feed solution concentration of NaCl is $c_1 = 10.0$ kg NaCl/m³ solution (10.0 g NaCl/L, $\rho_1 = 1004$ kg solution/m³). The water recovery is assumed low so that the concentration c_1 in the entering feed solution flowing past the membrane and the concentration of the exit feed solution are essentially equal. The product solution contains $c_2 = 0.39$ kg NaCl/m³ solution ($\rho_2 = 997$ kg solution/m³) and its measured flow rate is 1.92×10^{-8} m³ solution/s. A pressure differential of 5514 kPa (54.42 atm) is used. Calculate the permeability constants of the membrane and the solute rejection R.

Solution: Since c_2 is very low (dilute solution), the value of c_{w2} can be assumed as the density of water (Table 13.9-1), or $c_{w2} = 997$ kg solvent/m³. To convert the product flow rate to water flux, N_w, using an area of 2.00×10^{-3} m²,

$$N_w = (1.92 \times 10^{-8} \text{ m}^3/\text{s})(997 \text{ kg solvent/m}^3)(1/2.00 \times 10^{-3} \text{ m}^2)$$

$$= 9.57 \times 10^{-3} \text{ kg solvent/s} \cdot \text{m}^2$$

FIGURE 13.9-3. *Process flow diagram of experimental reverse-osmosis laboratory unit.*

Substituting into Eq. (13.9-6),

$$N_s = \frac{N_w c_2}{c_{w2}} = \frac{(9.57 \times 10^{-3})(0.39)}{997}$$

$$= 3.744 \times 10^{-6} \text{ kg solute NaCl/s} \cdot \text{m}^2$$

To determine the osmotic pressures from Table 13.9-1, the concentrations are converted as follows. For c_1, 10 kg NaCl is in 1004 kg solution/m^3 ($\rho_1 = 1004$). Then, $1004 - 10 = 994$ kg H_2O in 1 m^3 solution. Hence, in the feed solution, where the molecular weight of NaCl = 58.45, $(10.00 \times 1000)/(994 \times 58.45) = 0.1721$ g mol NaCl/kg H_2O. From Table 13.9-1, $\pi_1 = 7.80$ atm by linear interpolation. Substituting into Eq. (13.9-1), the predicted $\pi_1 = 8.39$ atm, which is higher than the experimental value. For the product solution, $997 - 0.39 = 996.6$ kg H_2O. Hence, $(0.39 \times 1000)/(996.6 \times 58.45) = 0.00670$ g mol NaCl/kg H_2O. From Table 13.9-1, $\pi_2 = 0.32$ atm. Then, $\Delta \pi = \pi_1 - \pi_2 = 7.80 - 0.32 = 7.48$ atm and $\Delta P = 54.42$ atm.

Substituting into Eq. (13.9-2),

$$N_w = 9.57 \times 10^{-3} = \frac{P_w}{L_m}(\Delta P - \Delta \pi) = \frac{P_w}{L_m}(54.42 - 7.48)$$

Solving, $(P_w/L_m) = A_w = 2.039 \times 10^{-4}$ kg solvent/s $\cdot$ m$^2 \cdot$ atm. Substituting into Eq. (13.9-4),

$$N_s = 3.744 \times 10^{-6} = \frac{D_s K_s}{L_m}(c_1 - c_2) = \frac{D_s K_s}{L_m}(10.00 - 0.39)$$

Solving, $(D_s K_s/L_m) = A_s = 3.896 \times 10^{-7}$ m/s.

To calculate the solute rejection R by substituting into Eq. (13.9-7),

$$R = \frac{c_1 - c_2}{c_1} = \frac{10.00 - 0.39}{10.00} = 0.961$$

Also, substituting into Eq. (13.9-9) and then Eq. (13.9-8),

$$B = \frac{P_w/L_m}{(D_s K_s/L_m)c_{w2}} = \frac{2.039 \times 10^{-4}}{(3.896 \times 10^{-7})997} = 0.5249 \text{ atm}^{-1}$$

$$R = \frac{B(\Delta P - \Delta \pi)}{1 + B(\Delta P - \Delta \pi)} = \frac{0.5249(54.42 - 7.48)}{1 + 0.5249(54.42 - 7.48)} = 0.961$$

13.10   APPLICATIONS, EQUIPMENT, AND MODELS FOR REVERSE OSMOSIS

13.10A   Effects of Operating Variables

In many commercial units, operating pressures in reverse osmosis range from about 1035 up to 10 350 kPa (150 up to 1500 psi). Comparison of Eq. (13.9-2) for solvent flux with Eq. (13.9-4) for solute flux shows that the solvent flux N_w depends only on the net pressure difference, while the solute flux N_s depends only on the concentration difference. Hence, as the feed pressure is increased, solvent or water flow through the membrane increases and the solute flow remains approximately constant, giving lower solute concentration in the product solution.

At a constant applied pressure, increasing the feed solute concentration increases the product solute concentration. This is caused by the increase in the feed osmotic pressure, since as more solvent is extracted from the feed solution (as water recovery increases), the solute concentration becomes higher and the water flux decreases. Also, the amount of solute present in the product solution increases because of the higher feed concentration.

If a reverse-osmosis unit has a large membrane area (as in a commercial unit), and the path between the feed inlet and outlet is long, the outlet feed concentration can be considerably higher than the inlet feed c_1. Then the salt flux will be greater at the outlet feed as compared to the inlet (K2). Many manufacturers use the feed solute or salt concentration average between inlet and outlet to calculate the solute or salt rejection R in Eq. (13.9-7).

EXAMPLE 13.10-1. *Prediction of Performance in a Reverse-Osmosis Unit*
A reverse-osmosis membrane to be used at 25°C for a NaCl feed solution containing 2.5 g NaCl/L (2.5 kg NaCl/m^3, $\rho = 999$ kg/m^3) has a water permeability constant $A_w = 4.81 \times 10^{-4}$ kg/s $\cdot$ m^2 $\cdot$ atm and a solute (NaCl) permeability constant $A_s = 4.42 \times 10^{-7}$ m/s (A1). Calculate the water flux and solute flux through the membrane using $\Delta P = 27.20$ atm and the solute rejection R. Also calculate c_2 of the product solution.

Solution: In the feed solution, $c_1 = 2.5$ kg NaCl/m^3 and $\rho_1 = 999$ kg solution/m^3. Hence, for the feed, $999 - 2.5 = 996.5$ kg H$_2$O in 1.0 m^3 solution: also for the feed, $(2.50 \times 1000)/(996.5 \times 58.45) = 0.04292$ g mol NaCl/kg H$_2$O. From Table 13.9-1, $\pi_1 = 1.97$ atm. Since the product solution c_2 is unknown, a value of $c_2 = 0.1$ kg NaCl/m^3 will be assumed. Also, since this is quite dilute, $\rho_2 = 997$ kg solution/m^3 and $C_{w2} = 997$ kg solvent/m^3. Then for the product solution, $(0.10 \times 1000)/(996.9 \times 58.45) = 0.00172$ g mol NaCl/kg H$_2$O and $\pi_2 = 0.08$ atm. Also, $\Delta\pi - \pi_1$ $\pi_2 - 1.97 - 0.08 = 1.89$ atm.

Substituting into Eq. (13.9-2),

$$N_w = A_w(\Delta P - \Delta\pi) = 4.81 \times 10^{-4}(27.20 - 1.89)$$

$$= 1.217 \times 10^{-2} \text{ kg H}_2\text{O/s} \cdot \text{m}^2$$

For calculation of R, substituting first into Eq. (13.9-9),

$$B = \frac{A_w}{A_s c_{w2}} = \frac{4.81 \times 10^{-4}}{4.42 \times 10^{-7} \times 997} = 1.092 \text{ atm}^{-1}$$

Next, substituting into Eq. (13.9-8),

$$R = \frac{B(\Delta P - \Delta\pi)}{1 + B(\Delta P - \Delta\pi)} = \frac{1.092(27.20 - 1.89)}{1 + 1.092(27.20 - 1.89)} = 0.965$$

Using this value of R in Eq. (13.9-7),

$$R = 0.965 = \frac{c_1 - c_2}{c_1} = \frac{2.50 - c_2}{2.50}$$

Solving, $c_2 = 0.0875$ kg NaCl/m^3 for the product solution. This is close enough to the assumed value of $c_2 = 0.10$ that π_2 will not change significantly on a second trial. Hence, the final value of c_2 is 0.0875 kg NaCl/m^3 (0.0875 g NaCl/L).

Substituting into Eq. (13.9-4),

$$N_s = A_s(c_1 - c_2) = 4.42 \times 10^{-7}(2.50 - 0.0875)$$

$$= 1.066 \times 10^{-6} \text{ kg NaCl/s} \cdot \text{m}^2$$

13.10B Concentration Polarization in Reverse-Osmosis Diffusion Model

In desalination, localized concentrations of solute build up at the point where the solvent leaves the solution and enters the membrane. The solute accumulates in a relatively stable boundary layer (Fig. 13.9-3) next to the membrane. Concentration polarization, β, is defined as the ratio of the salt concentration at the membrane surface to the salt concentration in the bulk feed stream c_1. Concentration polarization causes the water flux to decrease, since the osmotic pressure π_1 increases as the boundary layer concentration increases and the overall driving force $(\Delta P - \Delta \pi)$ decreases. Also, the solute flux increases, since the solute concentration increases at the boundary. Hence, often the ΔP must be increased to compensate, which results in higher power costs (K2).

The effect of the concentration polarization β can be included approximately by modifying the value of $\Delta \pi$ in Eqs. (13.9-2) and (13.9-8) as follows (P6):

$$\Delta \pi = \beta \pi_1 - \pi_2 \tag{13.10-1}$$

It is assumed that the osmotic pressure π_1 is directly proportional to the concentration, which is approximately correct. Also, Eq. (13.9-4) can be modified as

$$N_s = A_s(\beta c_1 - c_2) \tag{13.10-2}$$

The usual concentration polarization ratio (K3) is 1.2 to 2.0, that is, the concentration in the boundary layer is 1.2–2.0 times c_1 in the bulk feed solution. This ratio is often difficult to predict. In desalination of seawater, using values of about 1000 psia $= \Delta P$, π_1 can be large. Increasing this π_1 by a factor of 1.2–2.0 can appreciably reduce the solvent flux. For brackish waters containing 2–10 g/L and using ΔP values of 17–55 atm abs, the value of π_1 is low and concentration polarization is not important.

The boundary layer can be reduced by increasing the turbulence by using higher feed-solution velocities. However, this extra flow results in a smaller ratio of product solution to feed. Also, screens can be put in the path to induce turbulence. Equations for predicting the mass-transfer coefficient to the surface and, hence, the concentration polarization, are given for specific geometries such as flow past plates, inside tubes, outside tubes, and so on (H2, N1). Then equations for the flux of water can be used with these mass-transfer coefficients in a manner similar to that for ultrafiltration given in Section 13.11.

13.10C Permeability Constants for Reverse-Osmosis Membranes

Permeability constants for membranes must be determined experimentally for the particular type of membrane to be used. For cellulose acetate membranes, typical water permeability constants A_w range from about 1×10^{-4} to 5×10^{-4} kg solvent/s $\cdot$ m$^2 \cdot$ atm (A1, M3, W1). Values for other types of membranes can differ widely. Generally, the water permeability constant for a particular membrane does not depend upon the solute present. For the solute permeability constants A_s of cellulose acetate membranes, some relative typical values are as follows, assuming a value of $A_s' = 4 \times 10^{-7}$ m/s for NaCl: 1.6×10^{-7} m/s (BaCl$_2$), 2.2×10^{-7} (MgCl$_2$), 2.4×10^{-7} (CaCl$_2$), 4.0×10^{-7} (Na$_2$SO$_4$), 6.0×10^{-7} (KCl), 6.0×10^{-7} (NH$_4$Cl) (A1).

13.10D Types of Equipment for Reverse Osmosis

The equipment for reverse osmosis is quite similar to that for gas permeation membrane processes described in Section 13.3C. In the plate-and-frame-type unit, thin plastic support plates with thin grooves are covered on both sides with membranes as in a filter press. Pressurized feed solution flows between the closely spaced membranes (L1). Solvent permeates through the membrane and flows in the grooves to an outlet. In the tubular-type unit, membranes in the form of tubes are inserted inside porous-tube casings, which serve as a pressure vessel. These tubes are then arranged in bundles like a heat exchanger.

In the spiral-wound type, a planar membrane is used and a flat, porous support material is sandwiched between the membranes. Then the membranes, support, and a mesh feed-side spacer are wrapped in a spiral around a tube. In the hollow-fiber type, fibers of $100-200$ μm diameter with walls about 25 μm thick are arranged in a bundle similar to a heat exchanger (L1, R1).

13.10E Complete-Mixing Model for Reverse Osmosis

The process flow diagram for the complete-mixing model is shown in Fig. 13.10-1. The model is a simplified one for use with low concentrations of salt of about 1% or so, such as occur in brackish waters. Also, a relatively low recovery of solvent occurs and the effects of concentration polarization are small. Since the concentration of the permeate is very low, the permeate side acts as though it were completely mixed.

For the overall material balance for dilute solutions,

$$q_f = q_1 + q_2 \tag{13.10-3}$$

where q_f is volumetric flow rate of feed, m^3/s; q_2 is flow rate of permeate, m^3/s; and q_1 is flow rate of residue or exit, m^3/s. Making a solute balance,

$$c_f q_f = c_1 q_1 + c_2 q_2 \tag{13.10-4}$$

Defining the cut or fraction of solvent recovered as $\theta = q_2/q_f$, Eq. (13.10-4) becomes

$$c_f = (1 - \theta)c_1 + \theta c_2 \tag{13.10-5}$$

The equations previously derived for the fluxes and rejection are useful in this case and are as follows:

$$N_w = A_2(\Delta P - \Delta \pi) \tag{13.9-2}$$

Figure 13.10-1. *Process flow for complete-mixing model for reverse osmosis.*

$$N_s = A_s(c_1 - c_2) \qquad \textbf{(13.9-4)}$$

$$R = \frac{c_1 - c_2}{c_1} \qquad \textbf{(13.9-7)}$$

$$R = \frac{B(\Delta P - \Delta \pi)}{1 + B(\Delta P - \Delta \pi)} \qquad \textbf{(13.9-8)}$$

When the cut or fraction recovered, θ, is specified, the solution is trial and error. Since the permeate and reject concentrations c_1 and c_2 are unknown, a value of c_2 is assumed. Then c_1 is calculated from Eq. (13.10-5). Next, N_w is obtained from Eq. (13.9-2) and c_2 from Eqs. (13.9-7) and (13.9-8). If the calculated value of c_2 does not equal the assumed value, the procedure is repeated.

When concentration-polarization effects are present, an estimated value of β can be used to make an approximate correction for these effects. This is used in Eq. (13.10-1) to obtain a value of $\Delta \pi$ for use in Eqs. (13.9-2) and (13.9-8). Also, Eq. (13.10-2) will replace Eq. (13.9-4). A more detailed analysis of this complete mixing model is given by others (H1, K1), in which the mass-transfer coefficient in the concentration-polarization boundary layer is used.

The cross-flow model for reverse osmosis is similar to that for gas separation by membranes which was discussed in Section 13.6. Because of the small solute concentration, the permeate side acts as if completely mixed. Hence, even if the module is designed for countercurrent or cocurrent flow, the cross-flow model is valid. This is discussed in detail elsewhere (H1).

13.11   ULTRAFILTRATION MEMBRANE PROCESSES

13.11A   Introduction

Ultrafiltration is a membrane process that is quite similar to reverse osmosis. It is a pressure-driven process where the solvent and, when present, small solute molecules pass through the membrane and are collected as a permeate. Larger solute molecules do not pass through the membrane and are recovered in a concentrated solution. The solutes or molecules to be separated generally have molecular weights greater than 500 and up to 1 000 000 or more, such as macromolecules of proteins, polymers, and starches as well as colloidal dispersions of clays, latex particles, and microorganisms.

Unlike reverse osmosis, ultrafiltration membranes are too porous to be used for desalting. The rejection R, often called retention, is also given by Eq. (13.9-7), which is defined for reverse osmosis. Ultrafiltration is also used to separate a mixture of different-molecular-weight proteins. The molecular-weight cut-off of the membrane is defined as the molecular weight of globular proteins, which are 90% retained by the membrane. A rule of thumb is that the molecular mass must differ by a factor of 10 for a good separation (P7).

Ultrafiltration is used in many different processes at the present time. Some of these are separation of oil–water emulsions, concentration of latex particles, processing of blood and plasma, fractionation or separation of proteins, recovery of whey proteins in cheese manufacturing, removal of bacteria and other particles to sterilize wine, and clarification of fruit juices.

Membranes for ultrafiltration are in general similar to those for reverse osmosis and are commonly asymmetric and more porous. The membrane consists of a very thin, dense skin supported by a relatively porous layer for strength. Membranes are made from aromatic polyamides, cellulose acetate, cellulose nitrate, polycarbonate, polyimides, polysulfone, and so forth (M2, P6, R1).

13.11B Types of Equipment for Ultrafiltration

The equipment for ultrafiltration is similar to that used for reverse osmosis and gas separation processes, described in Sections 13.3C and 13.10D. The tubular-type unit is less prone to fouling and more easily cleaned than any of the other three types; however, this type is relatively costly.

Flat sheet membranes in a plate-and-frame unit offer the greatest versatility but at the highest capital cost (P6). Membranes can easily be cleaned or replaced by disassembly of the unit. Spiral-wound modules provide relatively low costs per unit membrane area. These units are more prone to fouling than tubular units but are more resistant to fouling than hollow-fiber units. Hollow-fiber modules are the least resistant to fouling as compared to the other three types. However, the hollow-fiber configuration has the highest ratio of membrane area per unit volume.

Cross-flow filtration is the most common type of model used (P7). Spiral-wound flat sheets are used most of all, followed by hollow-fiber units. Batch processes are also quite common. Stirred tanks with a membrane are used which approximate cross-flow operation (R1).

13.11C Flux Equations for Ultrafiltration

The flux equation for diffusion of solvent through the membrane is the same as Eq. (13.9-2) for reverse osmosis:

$$N_w = A_w(\Delta P - \Delta \pi) \qquad (13.9\text{-}2)$$

In ultrafiltration the membrane does not allow passage of the solute, which is generally a macromolecule. The concentration in moles/liter of the large solute molecules is usually small. Hence, the osmotic pressure is very low and can be neglected. Then Eq. (13.9-2) becomes

$$N_w = A_w(\Delta P) \qquad (13.11\text{-}1)$$

Ultrafiltration units operate at about 5–100 psi pressure drop, compared to 400–2000 for reverse osmosis. For low-pressure drops of, say, 5–10 psi and dilute solutions of up to 1 wt % or so, Eq. (13.11-1) predicts the performance reasonably well for well-stirred systems.

Since the solute is rejected by the membrane, it accumulates and starts to build up at the surface of the membrane. As pressure drop is increased and/or concentration of the solute is increased, concentration polarization occurs, which is much more severe than in reverse osmosis. This is shown in Fig. 13.11-1a, where c_1 is the concentration of the solute in the bulk solution, kg solute/m^3, c_s is the concentration of the solute at the surface of the membrane, and c_p is the concentration in the permeate.

As the pressure drop increases, this increases the solvent flux N_w to and through the membrane. This results in a higher convective transport of the solute to the membrane, that is, the solvent carries with it more solute. The concentration c_s increases and gives a larger back molecular diffusion of solute from the membrane to the bulk solution. At steady state the convective flux equals the diffusion flux:

$$\frac{N_w c}{\rho} = -D_{AB} \frac{dc}{dx} \qquad (13.11\text{-}2)$$

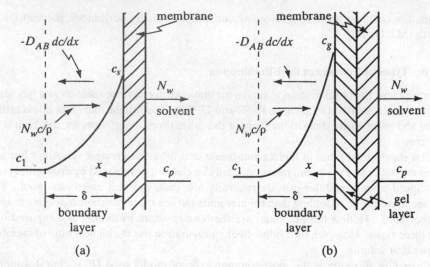

FIGURE 13.11-1. *Concentration polarization in ultrafiltration: (a) concentration profile before gel formation, (b) concentration profile with a gel layer formed at membrane surface.*

where $N_w c/\rho = [\text{kg solvent}/(\text{s} \cdot \text{m}^2)](\text{kg solute}/\text{m}^3)/(\text{kg solvent}/\text{m}^3) = \text{kg solute}/\text{s} \cdot \text{m}^2$; D_{AB} is diffusivity of solute in solvent, m^2/s; and x is distance, m. Integrating this equation between the limits of $x = 0$ and $c = c_s$ and $x = \delta$ and $c = c_1$,

$$\frac{N_w}{\rho} = \left(\frac{D_{Ab}}{\delta}\right)\ln\left(\frac{c_s - c_p}{c_1 - c_p}\right) = k_c \ln\left(\frac{c_s - c_p}{c_1 - c_p}\right) \qquad \textbf{(13.11-3)}$$

where k_c is the mass-transfer coefficient, m/s. Further increases in pressure drop increase the value of c_s to a limiting concentration, at which the accumulated solute forms a semisolid gel where $c_s = c_g$, as shown in Fig. 13.11-1b. For the usual case of almost-complete solute retention (P7), $c_p = 0$ and Eq. (13.11-3) becomes

$$\frac{N_w}{\rho} = k_c \ln(c_s/c_1) \qquad \textbf{(13.11-4)}$$

Still further increases in pressure drop do not change c_g and the membrane is said to be "gel polarized." Then Eq. (13.11-3) becomes (P1, P6, R1)

$$\frac{N_w}{\rho} = k_c \ln\left(\frac{c_g}{c_1}\right) \qquad \textbf{(13.11-5)}$$

With increases in pressure drop, the gel layer increases in thickness, causing the solvent flux to decrease because of the added gel-layer resistance. Finally, the net flux of solute by convective transfer becomes equal to the back diffusion of solute into the bulk solution because of the polarized concentration gradient, as given by Eq. (13.11-5).

The added gel-layer resistance next to the membrane causes an increased resistance to solvent flux, as given by

$$N_w = \frac{\Delta P}{1/A_w + R_g} \qquad \textbf{(13.11-6)}$$

where $1/A_w$ is the membrane resistance and R_g is the variable gel-layer resistance, $(s \cdot m^2 \cdot atm)/kg$ solvent. The solvent flux in this gel-polarized regime is independent of pressure difference and is determined by Eq. (13.11-5) for back diffusion. Experimental data confirm the use of Eq. (13.11-5) for a large number of macromolecular solutions, such as proteins and so forth as well as colloidal suspensions, such as latex particles and so forth (P1, P6).

13.11D Effects of Processing Variables in Ultrafiltration

A plot of typical experimental data for flux versus pressure difference is shown in Fig. 13.11-2 (H1, P6). At low pressure differences and/or low solute concentrations, the data typically follow Eq. (13.11-1). For a given bulk concentration, c_1, the flux approaches a constant value at high pressure differences, as shown in Eq. (13.11-5). Also, more-dilute protein concentrations give higher flux rates, as expected from Eq. (13.11-5). Most commercial applications are flux-limited by concentration polarization and operate in the region where the flux is approximately independent of pressure difference (R1).

Using experimental data, a plot of N_w/ρ versus $\ln c_1$ is a straight line with a negative slope of k_c, the mass-transfer coefficient, as shown by Eq. (13.11-5). These plots also give the value of c_g, the gel concentration. Data (P1) show that the gel concentration for many macromolecular solutions is about 25 wt %, with a range of 5 to 50%. For colloidal dispersions it is about 65 wt %, with a range of 50 to 75%.

The concentration-polarization effects for hollow fibers are often quite small, due to the low solvent flux. Hence, Eq. (13.11-1) describes the flux. In order to increase the ultrafiltration solvent flux, cross-flow of fluid past the membrane can be used to sweep away part of the polarized layer, thereby increasing k_c in Eq. (13.11-5). Higher velocities and other methods are used to increase turbulence and hence k_c. In most cases the solvent flux is too small to operate in a single-pass mode. It is necessary to recirculate the feed past the membrane, with recirculation rates of 10/1 to 100/1 often used.

Methods for predicting the mass-transfer coefficient k_c in Eq. (13.11-5) are given by others (P1, P6) for known geometries such as channels and so forth. Predictions of flux in known geometries using these methods and experimental values of c_g in Eq. (13.11-5) in the

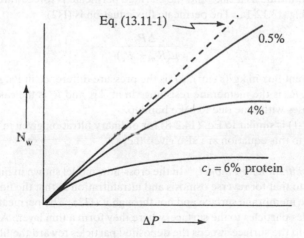

FIGURE 13.11-2. *Effect of pressure difference on solvent flux.*

gel polarization regime compare with experimental values for macromolecular solutions within about 25–30%. However, for colloidal dispersions the experimental flux is higher than the theoretical by factors of 20–30 for laminar flow and 8–10 for turbulent flow. Hence, Eq. (13.11-5) is not useful for predicting the solvent flux accurately. Generally, for design of commercial units it is necessary to obtain experimental data on single modules.

13.12   MICROFILTRATION MEMBRANE PROCESSES

13.12A   Introduction

In microfiltration, pressure-driven flow through a membrane is used to separate micron-size particles from fluids. The size range of particles ranges from 0.02 μm to 10 μm (H2). This microfiltration separates particles from solutions. The particles are usually larger than the solutes in reverse osmosis and ultrafiltration. Hence, osmotic pressure is negligible. At the very low end of the size range, very large soluble macromolecules are retained. Bacteria and other microorganisms (P7) are also retained on these membranes. Other particles in this size range are paint pigment, yeast cells, suspended matter such as cells from fermentation broth, particles in beer pasteurization, and so on. The dividing line between ultrafiltration and microfiltration is not very distinct.

The pore sizes of the membranes and the permeate flux are typically larger than for reverse osmosis and ultrafiltration. Usually the pressure drop used across the membranes varies from 1 psi to 50 psi (H2). Types of membranes are extremely varied and can be ceramics, polymers, and so on.

Many different geometries of membranes are used. These include spiral-wound, plate and frame, hollow fiber, cartridge filters with pleated membranes, and so on. Disposable cartridges are also used.

13.12B   Models for Microfiltration

1. Dead-end microfiltration flow model.   In many laboratory batch filtrations, the batch process is run in dead-end flow, with the membrane replacing the conventional filter paper. The particles build up with time as a cake and the clarified permeate is forced through the membrane, as shown in Fig. 13.12-1a. The permeate flux equation is (H2)

$$N_w = \frac{\Delta P}{\mu(R_m + R_c)} \tag{13.12-1}$$

where N_w is the solvent flux in kg/(s · m^2), ΔP is the pressure difference in Pa, μ is viscosity of the solvent in Pa · s, R_m is the membrane resistance in m^2/kg, and R_c is the cake resistance in m^2/kg, which increases with time due to cake buildup.

This Eq. (13.12-1) is similar to Eq. (14.2-8) for ordinary filtration given in Section 14.2 of this text. Solutions to this equation are also given there.

2. Cross-flow microfiltration flow model.   In the cross-flow model shown in Fig. 13.12-1b, the operation is similar to that for reverse osmosis and ultrafiltration in that the flow of bulk solution is parallel to the membrane surface and not through it (H2). The permeate flow through the membrane carries particles to the surface, where they form a thin layer. A relatively high flow rate tangential to the surface sweeps the deposited particles toward the filter exit leaving

feed

permeate

feed

reject

permeate

permeate

(a)

(b)

FIGURE 13.12-1. *Process flow for microfiltration: (a) dead-end flow, (b) cross-flow.*

a relatively thin deposited cake layer. This thin cake layer is similar to the gel layer formed in ultrafiltration. This cross-flow is effective in controlling concentration polarization and cake buildup, allowing relatively high fluxes to be maintained.

This concentration-polarization model of convection of particles to the cake layer is balanced by particle diffusion by Brownian diffusion away from the cake surface. This model is similar to the flux Eq. (13.11-3) for ultrafiltration. Other models are also given elsewhere (H2).

PROBLEMS

13.2-1. *Diffusion Through Liquids and a Membrane.* A membrane process is being designed to recover solute A from a dilute solution where $c_1 = 2.0 \times 10^{-2}$ kg mol A/m^3 by dialysis through a membrane to a solution where $c_2 = 0.3 \times 10^{-2}$. The membrane thickness is 1.59×10^{-5} m, the distribution coefficient $K' = 0.75$, $D_{AB} = 3.5 \times 10^{-11}$ m^2/s in the membrane, the mass-transfer coefficient in the dilute solution is $k_{c1} = 3.5 \times 10^{-5}$ m/s, and $k_{c2} = 2.1 \times 10^{-5}$.

(a) Calculate the individual resistances, total resistance, and total percent resistance of the two films.

(b) Calculate the flux at steady state and the total area in m^2 for a transfer of 0.01 kg mol solute/h.

(c) Increasing the velocity of both liquid phases flowing past the surface of the membrane will increase the mass-transfer coefficients, which are approximately proportional to $v^{0.6}$, where v is velocity. If the velocities are doubled, calculate the total percent resistance of the two films and the percent increase in flux.

Ans. (a) Total resistance = 6.823×10^5 s/m, 11.17% resistance;
(b) $N_A = 2.492 \times 10^{-8}$ kg mol A/s $\cdot$ m^2, area = 111.5 m^2

13.2-2. *Suitability of a Membrane for Hemodialysis.* Experiments are being conducted to determine the suitability of a cellophane membrane 0.029 mm thick for use in an artificial-kidney device. In an experiment at 37°C using NaCl as the diffusing solute, the membrane separates two components containing stirred aqueous solutions of NaCl, where $c_1 = 1.0 \times 10^{-4}$ g mol/cm³ (100 g mol/m³) and $c_2 = 5.0 \times 10^{-7}$. The mass-transfer coefficients on either side of the membrane have been estimated as $k_{c1} =$

$k_{c2} = 5.24 \times 10^{-5}$ m/s. Experimental data obtained gave a flux $N_A = 8.11 \times 10^{-4}$ g mol NaCl/s $\cdot$ m^2 at pseudo-steady-state conditions.

(a) Calculate the permeability p_M in m/s and $D_{AB}K'$ in m^2/s.

(b) Calculate the percent resistance to diffusion in the liquid films.

13.3-1. Gas-Permeation Membrane for Oxygenation. To determine the suitability of silicone rubber for its use as a membrane for a heart–lung machine to oxygenate blood, an experimental value of the permeability at 30°C of oxygen was obtained, where $P_M = 6.50 \times 10^{-7}$ cm^3 O$_2$ (STP)/(s $\cdot$ cm$^2 \cdot$ cm Hg/mm).

(a) Predict the maximum flux of O$_2$ in kg mol/s $\cdot$ m^2 with an O$_2$ pressure of 700 mm Hg on one side of the membrane and an equivalent pressure in the blood film side of 50 mm. The membrane is 0.165 mm thick. Since the gas film is pure oxygen, the gas film resistance is zero. Neglect the blood film resistance in this case.

(b) Assuming a maximum requirement for an adult of 300 cm^3 O$_2$ (STP) per minute, calculate the membrane surface area required in m^2. (*Note:* The actual area needed should be considerably larger since the blood film resistance, which must be determined by experiment, can be appreciable.)

$\qquad\qquad\qquad\qquad\qquad\qquad\qquad\qquad$ **Ans.** (b) 1.953 m^2

13.4-1. Derivation of Equation for Permeate Concentration. Derive Eq. (13.4-11) for Case 2 for complete mixing. Note that x_o from Eq. (13.4-9) must first be substituted into Eq. (13.4-6) before multiplying out the equation and solving for y_p.

13.4-2. Use of Complete-Mixing Model for Membrane Design. A membrane having a thickness of 2×10^{-3} cm, permeability $P'_A = 400 \times 10^{-10}$ cm^3 (STP) $\cdot$ cm/(s $\cdot$ cm$^2 \cdot$ cm Hg), and $\alpha^* = 10$ is to be used to separate a gas mixture of A and B. The feed flow rate is $L_f = 2 \times 10^3$ cm^3 (STP)/s and its composition is $x_f = 0.413$. The feed-side pressure is 80 cm Hg and the permeate-side pressure is 20 cm Hg. The reject composition is to be $x_o = 0.30$. Using the complete-mixing model, calculate the permeate composition, fraction of feed permeated, and membrane area.

$\qquad\qquad\qquad\qquad\qquad\qquad\qquad\qquad$ **Ans.** $y_p = 0.678$

13.4-3. Design Using Complete-Mixing Model. A gaseous feed stream having a composition $x_f = 0.50$ and a flow rate of 2×10^3 cm^3 (STP)/s is to be separated in a membrane unit. The feed-side pressure is 40 cm Hg and the permeate is 10 cm Hg. The membrane has a thickness of 1.5×10^{-3} cm, permeability $P'_A = 40 \times 10^{-10}$ cm^3 (STP) $\cdot$ cm/(s $\cdot$ cm$^2 \cdot$ cm Hg), and $\alpha^* = 10$. The fraction of feed permeated is 0.529.

(a) Use the complete-mixing model to calculate the permeate composition, reject composition, and membrane area.

(b) Calculate the minimum reject concentration.

(c) If the feed composition is increased to $x_f = 0.60$, what is this new minimum reject concentration?

$\qquad\qquad$ **Ans.** (a) $A_m = 5.153 \times 10^7$ cm^2 (c) $x_{oM} = 0.2478$

13.4-4. Effect of Permeabilities on Minimum Reject Concentration. For the conditions of Problem 13.4-2, $x_f = 0.413$, $\alpha^* = 10$, $p_l = 20$ cm Hg, $p_h = 80$ cm Hg, and $x_o = 0.30$. Calculate the minimum reject concentration for the following cases:

(a) Calculate x_{oM} for the given conditions.

(b) Calculate the effect on x_{oM} if the permeability of B increases so that α^* decreases to 5.

(c) Calculate the limiting value of x_{oM} when α^* is lowered to its minimum value of 1.0. Make a plot of x_{oM} versus α^* for these three cases.

13.4-5. Minimum Reject Concentration and Pressure Effect. For Example 13.4-2 for separation of air, do as follows:
(a) Calculate the minimum reject concentration.
(b) If the pressure on the feed side is reduced by one-half, calculate the effect on x_{oM}.

$$\textbf{Ans.} \quad \text{(b) } x_{oM} = 0.0624$$

13.5-1. Separation of Multicomponent Gas Mixtures. Using the same feed composition and flow rate, pressures, and membrane as in Example 13.5-1, do the following, using the complete-mixing model:
(a) Calculate the permeate composition, reject composition, and membrane area for a fraction permeated of 0.50 instead of 0.25.
(b) Repeat part (a) but for $\theta = 0.90$.
(c) Make a plot of permeate composition y_{pA} versus θ and also of area A_m versus θ using the calculated values for $\theta = 0.25, 0.50$, and 0.90.

13.5-2. Separation of Helium from Natural Gas. A typical composition of a natural gas (S1) is 0.5% He (A), 17.0% N_2 (B), 76.5% CH_4 (C), and 6.0% higher hydrocarbons (D). The membrane proposed to separate helium has a thickness of 2.54×10^{-3} cm, and the permeabilities are $P'_A = 60 \times 10^{-10}$ cm^3 (STP)$\cdot$cm/(s$\cdot$cm$^2 \cdot$cm Hg), $P'_B = 3.0 \times 10^{-10}$, and $P'_C = 1.5 \times 10^{-10}$. It is assumed that the higher hydrocarbons are essentially nonpermeable $(P'_D \cong 0)$. The feed flow rate is 2.0×10^5 cm^3 (STP)/s. The feed pressure $p_h = 500$ cm Hg and the permeate pressure $p_l = 20$ cm Hg.
(a) For a fraction permeated of 0.2, calculate the permeate composition, reject composition, and membrane area using the complete mixing model.
(b) Use the permeate from part (a) as feed to a completely mixed second stage. The pressure $p_h = 500$ cm Hg and $p_l = 20$ cm. For a fraction permeated of 0.20, calculate the permeate composition and membrane area.

13.6-1. Design Using Cross-Flow Model for Membrane. Use the same conditions for the separation of an air stream as given in Example 13.6-1. The given values are $x_f = 0.209$, $\alpha^* = 10$, $p_h = 190$ cm Hg, $p_l = 19$ cm Hg, $L_f = 1 \times 10^6$ cm^3 (STP)/s, $P'_A = 500 \times 10^{-10}$ cm^3 (STP)$\cdot$cm/(s$\cdot$cm$^2 \cdot$cm Hg), and $t = 2.54 \times 10^{-3}$ cm. Do as follows using the cross-flow model:
(a) Calculate y_p, x_o, and A_m for $\theta = 0.40$.
(b) Calculate y_p and x_o for $\theta = 0$.

$$\textbf{Ans.} \quad \text{(a) } y_p = 0.452, \, x_o = 0.0303, \, A_m = 6.94 \times 10^8 \text{ cm}^2 \text{ (S6);}$$
$$\text{(b) } y_p = 0.655, \, x_o = 0.209$$

13.7-1. Equations for Cocurrent and Countercurrent Flow Models. Derive the equations for the following cases:
(a) For cocurrent flow, show the detailed steps for deriving Eqs. (13.7-35) and (13.7-36).
(b) For countercurrent flow, show the detailed steps in obtaining Eq. (13.7-22) from (13.7-4) and (13.7-5). Also, show the detailed steps to derive Eq. (13.7-24).

13.7-2. Design Using Countercurrent-Flow Model for Membrane. Use the same conditions as given in Example 13.6-1 for the separation of an air stream. The given values are $x_f = 0.209$, $\alpha^* = 10$, $p_h = 190$ cm Hg, $p_l = 19$ cm Hg, $L_f = 1 \times 10^6$ cm^3 (STP)/s, $P'_A = 500 \times 10^{-10}$ cm^3 (STP)$\cdot$cm/(s$\cdot$cm$^2 \cdot$cm Hg), and $t = 2.54 \times 10^{-3}$ cm. Using the countercurrent-flow model, calculate y_p, x_o, and A_m for $\theta = 0.40$. (Note that this problem involves a trial-and-error procedure along with the numerical solution of two differential equations.)

13.8-1. *Effect of Pressure Drop on Asymmetric Membrane Calculations.* Using the same conditions as in Example 13.8-1, do as follows:
(a) Use the shortcut method to calculate the overall pressure drop Δp_h using Eq. (13.8-16) over the entire length. Use typical data for air given in Section 13.8C to calculate N_T, fiber length $z_2 - z_1$, and so forth. Assume $T = 25° + 273$ K and $p_h = 1034$ kPa, $T_s = 273$ K, $p_s = 101.325$ kPa.
(b) With the above values of p_h, use the shortcut method in a second iteration to recalculate A_m. (Be sure to correct for P_{ho} at x_o and y'_o.)
(c) Calculate the pressure drop if the number of tubes N_T in part (a) is reduced by 50%.

Ans. (a) $N_T = 1.267 \times 10^5$, $(z_2 - z_1) = 1.413$ m, $\Delta p_h = 20.74$ kPa;
(b) $A_m = 54.10$ m^2; (c) $\Delta p_h = 82.96$ kPa

13.8-2. *Spreadsheet Calculation for Asymmetric Membrane.* Using the conditions for Example 13.8-1, write the detailed spreadsheet and calculate the results. Compare these results with those in Table 13.8-2.

13.8-3. *Comparison of Experimental and Predicted Spreadsheet Results in a Pilot-Unit Asymmetric Membrane.* A pilot-size membrane used to separate air in order to obtain nitrogen has the following dimensions with the feed inside the tubes: total $N_T = 3.8 \times 10^4$ fibers, ID = 95 μm, OD = 135 μm, length of fibers = 19 in. An experimental run gave the following results. Feed rate $L_f = 1.086$ m^3/h, $L_o = 0.654$ m^3/h, $V_p = 0.450$ m^3/h, $x_o = 0.067$ mole fraction oxygen, $y_p = 0.413$, $p_h = 703.81$ kPa, $p_l = 98.10$ kPa, and $T = 25°$C. The permeances determined previously are $(P'O_2/t) = 1.50 \times 10^{-10}$ m^3 (STP)/(s $\cdot$ m$^2 \cdot$ Pa), $(P'N_2/t) = 2.47 \times 10^{-11}$. Flow is counter current. Do as follows:
(a) Predict the pressure drop in the tubes using the shortcut method.
(b) Using a spreadsheet, predict the performance of this run and compare these results with the experimental values. Note that this is trial and error, since the area is fixed but the value of x_o is not. First assume a value of x_o. Then divide the difference between $x_f = 0.209$ and x_o into nine equal parts and perform the spreadsheet calculation. If the calculated and actual areas do not agree, assume another value of x_o, and so forth. Neglect pressure drop.

Ans. (a) $\Delta p_h = 4.455$ kPa; (b) $x_o = 0.079$, $V_p = 0.442$ m^3/hr, $y_p = 0.398$

13.9-1. *Osmotic Pressure of Salt and Sugar Solutions.* Calculate the osmotic pressure of the following solutions at 25°C and compare with the experimental values:
(a) Solution of 0.50 g mol NaCl/kg H$_2$O. (See Table 13.9-1 for the experimental value.)
(b) Solution of 1.0 g sucrose/kg H$_2$O. (Experimental value = 0.0714 atm.)
(c) Solution of 1.0 g MgCl$_2$/kg H$_2$O. (Experimental value = 0.660 atm.)

Ans. (a) $\pi = 24.39$ atm; (b) $\pi = 0.0713$ atm; (c) $\pi = 0.768$ atm

13.9-2. *Determination of Permeability Constants for Reverse Osmosis.* A cellulose–acetate membrane with an area of 4.0×10^{-3} m^2 is used at 25°C to determine the permeability constants for reverse osmosis of a feed salt solution containing 12.0 kg NaCl/m^3 ($\rho = 1005.5$ kg/m^3). The product solution has a concentration of 0.468 kg NaCl/m^3

$(\rho = 997.3 \text{ kg/m}^3)$. The measured product flow rate is 3.84×10^{-8} m³/s and the pressure difference used is 56.0 atm. Calculate the permeability constants and the solute rejection R.

Ans. $A_w = 2.013 \times 10^{-4}$ kg solvent/s · m² · atm, $R = 0.961$

13.9-3. *Performance of a Laboratory Reverse-Osmosis Unit.* A feed solution at 25°C contains 3500 mg NaCl/L ($\rho = 999.5$ kg/m³). The permeability constant $A_w = 3.50 \times 10^{-4}$ kg solvent/s · m² · atm and $A_s = 2.50 \times 10^{-7}$ m/s. Using a $\Delta P = 35.50$ atm, calculate the fluxes, solute rejection R, and product solution concentration in mg NaCl/L. Repeat, but using a feed solution of 3500 mg BaCl₂/L. Use the same value of A_w, but $A_s = 1.00 \times 10^{-7}$ m/s (A1).

13.10-1. *Effect of Pressure on Performance of Reverse-Osmosis Unit.* Using the same conditions and permeability constants as in Example 13.10-1, calculate the fluxes, solute rejection R, and product concentration c_2 for ΔP pressures of 17.20, 27.20, and 37.20 atm. (*Note:* The values for 27.20 atm have already been calculated.) Plot the fluxes, R, and c_2 versus the pressure.

13.10-2. *Effect of Concentration Polarization on Reverse Osmosis.* Repeat Example 13.10-1 but use a concentration polarization of 1.5. (*Note:* The flux equations and the solute rejection R should be calculated using this new value of c_1.)

Ans. $N_w = 1.171 \times 10^{-2}$ kg solvent/s · m², $c_2 = 0.1361$ kg NaCl/m³

13.10-3. *Performance of a Complete-Mixing Model for Reverse Osmosis.* Use the same feed conditions and pressures given in Example 13.10-1. Assume that the cut or fraction recovered of the solvent water will be 0.10 instead of the very low water recovery assumed in Example 13.10-1. Hence, the concentrations of the entering feed solution and the exit feed will not be the same. The flow rate q_2 of the permeate water solution is 100 gal/h. Calculate c_1 and c_2 in kg NaCl/m³ and the membrane area in m².

Ans. $c_1 = 2.767$ kg/m³, $c_2 = 0.0973$ kg/m³, area = 8.68 m²

13.11-1. *Flux for Ultrafiltration.* A solution containing 0.9 wt % protein is to undergo ultrafiltration using a pressure difference of 5 psi. The membrane permeability is $A_w = 1.37 \times 10^{-2}$ kg/s · m² · atm. Assuming no effects of polarization, predict the flux in kg/s · m² and in units of gal/ft² · day, which are often used in industry.

Ans. 9.88 gal/ft² · day

13.11-2. *Time for Ultrafiltration Using Recirculation.* It is desired to use ultrafiltration for 800 kg of a solution containing 0.05 wt % of a protein to obtain a solution of 1.10 wt %. The feed is recirculated past the membrane with a surface area of 9.90 m². The permeability of the membrane is $A_w = 2.50 \times 10^{-2}$ kg/s · m² · atm. Neglecting the effects of concentration polarization, if any, calculate the final amount of solution and the time to achieve this, using a pressure difference of 0.50 atm.

REFERENCES

(A1) AGRAWAL, J. P., and SOURIRAJAN, S. *Ind. Eng. Chem.,* **69**(11), 62 (1969).

(B1) BLAISDELL, C. T., and KAMMERMEYER, K. *Chem. Eng. Sci.,* **28,** 1249 (1973).

(B2) BABB, A. L., MAURER, C. J., FRY, D. L., POPOVICH, R. P., and MCKEE, R. E. *Chem. Eng. Progr. Symp.,* **64**(84), 59 (1968).

(B3) BERRY, R. I. *Chem. Eng.,* **88** (July 13), 63 (1981).

(C1) CLARK, W. E. *Science,* **138,** 148 (1962).

(G1) GIGLIA, S., BIKSON, B., and PERRIN, J. E. *Ind. Eng. Chem. Res.,* **30,** 1239 (1991).

(H1) Hwang, S. T., and Kammermeyer, K. *Membranes in Separations.* New York: John Wiley & Sons, Inc., 1975.

(H2) Ho, W. S., and Sirkar, K. K. *Membrane Handbook.* New York: Van Nostrand Reinhold, 1992.

(K1) Kimura, S., and Sourirajan, S. *A.I.Ch.E. J.,* **13,** 497 (1967).

(K2) Kaup, E. C. *Chem. Eng.,* **80** (Apr. 2), 46 (1973).

(L1) Lacey, R. E. *Chem. Eng.,* **79** (Sept. 4), 57 (1972).

(M1) McCabe, W. L. *Ind. Eng. Chem.,* **21,** 112 (1929).

(M2) Michaels, A. S. *Chem. Eng. Progr.,* **64**(12), 31 (1968).

(M3) Merten, U. (ed.). *Desalination by Reverse Osmosis.* Cambridge, Mass.: The MIT Press, 1966.

(M4) Matson, S. L., Lobez, J., and Quinn, J. A. *Chem. Eng. Sci.,* **38,** 503 (1983).

(M5) McCabe, W. L., Smith, J. C., and Harriott, P. *Unit Operations of Chemical Engineering,* 5th ed. New York: McGraw-Hill Book Company, 1993.

(N1) Noble, R. D., and Stern, S. A. *Membrane Separations Technology: Principles and Applications.* Amsterdam: Elsevier Science, 1995.

(P1) Perry, R. H., and Green, D. *Perry's Chemical Engineers' Handbook,* 6th ed. New York: McGraw-Hill Book Company, 1984.

(P2) Pan, C. Y. *A.I.Ch.E. J.,* **29,** 545 (1983).

(P3) Permasep Permeators. *E. I. duPont Tech. Bull.,* 401, 403, 405 (1972).

(P4) Pan, C. Y., and Habgood, H. W. *Ind. Eng. Chem. Fund.,* **13,** 323 (1974).

(P5) Pan, C. Y., and Habgood, H. W. *Can. J. Chem. Eng.,* **56,** 197, 210 (1978).

(P6) Porter, M. C. (ed.). *Handbook of Industrial Membrane Technology.* Park Ridge, N.J.: Noyes Publications, 1990.

(P7) Perry, R. H., and Green, D. *Perry's Chemical Engineers' Handbook,* 7th ed. New York: McGraw-Hill Book Company, 1997.

(R1) Rousseau, R. W. (ed.). *Handbook of Separation Process Technology.* New York: John Wiley & Sons, Inc., 1987.

(S1) Stern, S. A., Sinclair, T. F., Gareis, P. J., Vahldieck, N. P., and Mohr, P. H. *Ind. Eng. Chem.,* **57,** 49 (1965).

(S2) Stannett, V. T., Koros, W. J., Paul, D. R., Lonsdale, H. K., and Baker, R. W. *Adv. Polym. Sci.,* **32,** 69 (1979).

(S3) Stoughten, R. W., and Lietzke, M. H., Jr. *Chem. Eng. Data,* **10,** 254 (1965).

(S4) Schroeder, E. D. *Water and Wastewater Treatment.* New York: McGraw-Hill Book Company, 1977.

(S5) Sourirajan, S. *Reverse Osmosis.* New York: Academic Press, Inc., 1970.

(S6) Stern, S. A., and Walawender, W. P. *Sep. Sci.,* **4,** 129 (1969).

(S7) Stookey, D. J., Patton, C. J., and Malcolm, G. L. *Chem. Eng. Progr.,* **82**(11), 36 (1986).

(W1) Weber, W. J., Jr. *Physicochemical Processes for Water Quality Control.* New York: Wiley-Interscience, 1972.

(W2) Ward, W. J., Browal, W. R., and Salemme, R. M. *J. Membr. Sci.,* **1,** 99 (1976).

(W3) Weller, S., and Steiner, W. A. *Chem. Eng. Progr.,* **46,** 585 (1950).

(W4) Weller, S., and Steiner, W. A. *J. Appl. Phys.,* **21,** 279 (1950).

(W5) Walawender, W. P., and Stern, S. A. *Sep. Sci.,* **7,** 553 (1972).

CHAPTER 14

Mechanical–Physical
Separation Processes

14.1 INTRODUCTION AND CLASSIFICATION OF MECHANICAL–PHYSICAL SEPARATION PROCESSES

14.1A Introduction

In Chapters 10 and 11, gas–liquid and vapor–liquid separation processes were considered. These separation processes depended on molecules diffusing or vaporizing from one distinct phase to another phase. In Chapter 12, liquid–liquid separation processes were discussed, in which the two liquid phases are quite different chemically, leading to separation on a molecular scale according to physical–chemical properties. Also in Chapter 12, we considered liquid–solid leaching, ion-exchange, and adsorption separation processes. Again, differences in the physical–chemical properties of the molecules lead to separation on a molecular scale. In Chapter 13, we discussed membrane separation processes, where the separation also depends on physical–chemical properties.

All the separation processes considered so far have been based upon physical–chemical differences in the molecules themselves and on mass transfer of the molecules. In this way individual molecules are separated into two phases because of these molecular differences. In the present chapter, a group of separation processes will be considered where the separation is not accomplished on a molecular scale nor is it due to the differences among the various molecules. The separation will be accomplished using mechanical–physical forces and not molecular or chemical forces and diffusion. These mechanical–physical forces will be acting on particles, liquids, or mixtures of particles and liquids themselves and not necessarily on the individual molecules.

These mechanical–physical forces include gravitational and centrifugal, actual mechanical, and kinetic forces arising from flow. Particles and/or fluid streams are separated because of the different effects produced on them by these forces.

14.1B Classification of Mechanical–Physical Separation Processes

These mechanical–physical separation processes are considered under the following classifications:

1. Filtration. The general problem of the separation of solid particles from liquids can be solved by using a wide variety of methods, depending on the type of solids, the proportion of solid to liquid in the mixture, viscosity of the solution, and other factors. In filtration, a pressure difference is set up that causes the fluid to flow through small holes in a screen or cloth which block the passage of the large solid particles; these, in turn, build up on the cloth as a porous cake.

2. Settling and sedimentation. In settling and sedimentation, the particles are separated from the fluid by gravitational forces acting on particles of various sizes and densities.

3. Centrifugal settling and sedimentation. In centrifugal separations, the particles are separated from the fluid by centrifugal forces acting on particles of various sizes and densities. Two general types of separation processes are used. In the first type of process, centrifugal settling or sedimentation occurs.

4. Centrifugal filtration. In the second type of centrifugal separation process, centrifugal filtration occurs, which is similar to ordinary filtration, where a bed or cake of solids builds up on a screen, but centrifugal force is used to cause the flow instead of a pressure difference.

5. Mechanical size reduction and separation. In mechanical size reduction, the solid particles are broken mechanically into smaller particles and separated according to size.

14.2 FILTRATION IN SOLID–LIQUID SEPARATION

14.2A Introduction

In filtration, suspended solid particles in a fluid of liquid or gas are physically or mechanically removed by using a porous medium that retains the particles as a separate phase or cake and passes the clear filtrate. Commercial filtrations cover a very wide range of applications. The fluid can be a gas or a liquid. The suspended solid particles can be very fine (in the micrometer range) or much larger, very rigid or plastic particles, spherical or very irregular in shape, aggregates of particles or individual particles. The valuable product may be the clear filtrate from the filtration or the solid cake. In some cases, complete removal of the solid particles is required, in other cases only partial removal.

The feed or slurry solution may carry a heavy load of solid particles or a very small amount. When the concentration is very low, the filters can operate for very long periods of time before the filter needs cleaning. Because of the wide diversity of filtration problems, a multitude of types of filters have been developed.

Industrial filtration equipment differs from laboratory filtration equipment only in the amount of material handled and in the necessity for low-cost operation. A typical laboratory filtration apparatus is shown in Fig. 14.2-1, which is similar to a Büchner funnel. The liquid is made to flow through the filter cloth or paper by a vacuum on the exit end. The slurry consists of the liquid and the suspended particles. The passage of the particles is blocked by the

slurry solution

FIGURE 14.2-1. *Simple laboratory filtration apparatus.*

small openings in the pores of the filter cloth. A support with relatively large holes is used to hold the filter cloth. The solid particles build up in the form of a porous filter cake as the filtration proceeds. This cake itself also acts as a filter for the suspended particles. As the cake builds up, resistance to flow also increases.

In section 14.2 the ordinary type of filtration will be considered, where a pressure difference is used to force the liquid through the filter cloth and the filter cake that builds up.

In Section 14.4E, centrifugal filtration will be discussed, where centrifugal force is used instead of a pressure difference. In many filtration applications, ordinary filters and centrifugal filters are often competitive and either type can be used.

14.2B Types of Filtration Equipment

1. Classification of filters.   There are a number of ways to classify types of filtration equipment; unfortunately, it is not possible to devise a single classification scheme that includes all types of filters. In one classification, filters are classified according to whether the desired product is the filter cake or the clarified filtrate or outlet liquid. In either case, the slurry can have a relatively large percentage of solids so that a cake is formed, or have just a trace of suspended particles.

Filters can also be classified by operating cycle. Filters can be operated as batch, where the cake is removed after a run, or continuous, where the cake is removed continuously. In another classification, filters can be of the gravity type, where the liquid simply flows by means of a hydrostatic head, or pressure or vacuum can be used to increase the flow rates. An important method of classification depends upon the mechanical arrangement of the filter media. The filter cloth can be in a series arrangement as flat plates in an enclosure, as individual leaves dipped in the slurry, or on rotating-type rolls in the slurry. In the following sections only the most important types of filters will be described. For more details, see references (B1, P1).

2. Bed filters.   The simplest type of filter is the bed filter shown schematically in Fig. 14.2-2. This type is useful mainly in cases where relatively small amounts of solids are to be removed from large amounts of water in clarifying the liquid. Often the bottom layer is composed of coarse pieces of gravel resting on a perforated or slotted plate. Above the gravel is fine sand, which acts as the actual filter medium. Water is introduced at the top onto a baffle which spreads the water out. The clarified liquid is drawn out at the bottom.

FIGURE 14.2-2. *Bed filter of solid particles.*

The filtration continues until the precipitate of filtered particles has clogged the sand so that the flow rate drops. Then the flow is stopped, and water is introduced in the reverse direction so that it flows upward, backwashing the bed and carrying the precipitated solid away. This apparatus can only be used on precipitates that do not adhere strongly to the sand and can be easily removed by backwashing. Open-tank filters are used in filtering municipal water supplies.

3. Plate-and-frame filter presses. One of the important types of filters is the plate-and-frame filter press, which is shown diagrammatically in Fig. 14.2-3a. These filters consist of plates and frames assembled alternately with a filter cloth over each side of the plates. The plates have channels cut in them so that clear filtrate liquid can drain down along each plate. The feed slurry is pumped into the press and flows through the duct into each of the open frames so that slurry fills the frames. The filtrate flows through the filter cloth and the solids build up as a cake on the frame side of the cloth. The filtrate flows between the filter cloth and the face of the plate through the channels to the outlet.

The filtration proceeds until the frames are completely filled with solids. In Fig. 14.2-3a all the discharge outlets go to a common header. In many cases the filter press will have a separate discharge to the open for each frame. Then visual inspection can be made to see if the filtrate is running clear. If one is running cloudy because of a break in the filter cloth or other factors, it can be shut off separately. When the frames are completely full, the frames and plates are separated and the cake removed. Then the filter is reassembled and the cycle is repeated.

If the cake is to be washed, the cake is left in the plates and through-washing is performed, as shown in Fig. 14.2-3b. In this press a separate channel is provided for the wash-water inlet. The wash water enters the inlet, which has ports opening behind the filter cloths at every other plate of the filter press. The wash water then flows through the filter cloth, through the entire cake (not half the cake as in filtration), through the filter cloth at the other side of the frames, and out the discharge channel. It should be noted that there are two kinds of plates in Fig. 14.2-3b: those having ducts to admit wash water behind the filter cloth, alternating with plates without such ducts.

The plate-and-frame presses suffer from the disadvantages common to batch processes. The cost of labor for removing the cakes and reassembling plus the cost of fixed charges for downtime can be an appreciable part of the total operating cost. Some newer types of plate-and-frame presses have duplicate sets of frames mounted on a rotating shaft. Half of the

filter cloth

slurry

filtrate

frame

cake

plate

(a)

filter cloth

washing plates

wash

cake

nonwashing plate

outlet wash

(b)

FIGURE 14.2-3. *Diagrams of plate-and-frame filter presses: (a) filtration of slurry with closed delivery, (b) through washing in a press with open delivery.*

frames are in use while the others are being cleaned, saving downtime and labor costs. Other advances in automation have been applied to these types of filters.

Filter presses are used in batch processes but cannot be employed for high-throughput processes. They are simple to operate, very versatile and flexible in operation, and can be used at high pressures, when necessary, if viscous solutions are being used or the filter cake has a high resistance.

4. Leaf filters. The filter press is useful for many purposes but is not economical for handling large quantities of sludge or for efficient washing with a small amount of wash water. The wash water often channels in the cake and large volumes of wash water may be needed. The leaf filter shown in Fig. 14.2-4 was developed for larger volumes of slurry and more efficient washing. Each leaf is a hollow wire framework covered by a sack of filter cloth.

A number of these leaves are hung in parallel in a closed tank. The slurry enters the tank and is forced under pressure through the filter cloth, where the cake deposits on the outside of the leaf. The filtrate flows inside the hollow framework and out a header. The wash liquid follows the same path as the slurry. Hence, the washing is more efficient than the through-washing in plate-and-frame filter presses. To remove the cake, the shell is opened. Sometimes air is blown in the reverse direction into the leaves to help in dislodging the cake. If the solids are not wanted, water jets can be used to simply wash away the cakes without opening the filter.

Leaf filters also suffer from the disadvantages of batch operation. They can be automated for the filtering, washing, and cleaning cycle. However, they are still cyclical and are used for batch processes and relatively modest throughput processes.

5. Continuous rotary filters. Plate-and-frame filters suffer from the disadvantages common to all batch processes and cannot be used for large-capacity processes. A number of continuous-type filters are available, as discussed below.

FIGURE 14.2-4. *Leaf filter.*

FIGURE 14.2-5. *Schematic of continuous rotary-drum filter.*

(a) Continuous rotary vacuum-drum filter. This filter, shown in Fig. 14.2-5, filters, washes, and discharges the cake in a continuous, repeating sequence. The drum is covered with a suitable filtering medium. The drum rotates and an automatic valve in the center serves to activate the filtering, drying, washing, and cake-discharge functions in the cycle. The filtrate leaves through the axle of the filter.

The automatic valve provides separate outlets for the filtrate and the wash liquid. Also, if needed, a connection for compressed-air blowback just before discharge can be used to help in cake removal by the knife scraper. The maximum pressure differential for the vacuum filter is only 1 atm. Hence, this type is not suitable for viscous liquids or for liquids that must be enclosed. If the drum is enclosed in a shell, pressures above atmospheric can be used; however, the cost of a pressure-type filter is about two times that of a vacuum-type rotary-drum filter (P2).

Modern, high-capacity processes use continuous filters. The important advantages are that the filters are continuous and automatic and labor costs are relatively low. However, the capital cost is relatively high.

(b) Continuous rotary disk filter. This filter consists of concentric vertical disks mounted on a horizontal rotating shaft. The filter operates on the same principle as the vacuum rotary-drum filter. Each disk is hollow and covered with a filter cloth and is partly submerged in the slurry. The cake is washed, dried, and scraped off when the disk is in the upper half of its rotation. Washing is less efficient than with the rotating-drum type.

(c) Continuous rotary horizontal filter. This type is a vacuum filter with the rotating annular filtering surface divided into sectors. As the horizontal filter rotates, it successively receives slurry, is washed, is dried, and the cake is scraped off. The washing efficiency is better than with the rotary-disk filter. This filter is widely used in ore-extraction processes, pulp washing, and other large-capacity processes.

14.2C Filter Media and Filter Aids

1. Filter media. The filter medium for industrial filtration must fulfill a number of requirements. First and foremost, it must remove the solids to be filtered from the slurry and give a clear filtrate. Also, the pores should not become plugged so that the rate of filtration becomes too slow. The filter medium must allow the filter cake to be removed easily and cleanly.

Obviously, it must have sufficient strength not to tear and must be chemically resistant to the solutions used.

Some widely used filter media are twill or duckweave heavy cloth, other types of woven heavy cloth, woolen cloth, glass cloth, paper, felted pads of cellulose, metal cloth, nylon cloth, dacron cloth, and other synthetic cloths. The ragged fibers of natural materials are more effective in removing fine particles than the smooth plastic or metal fibers. Sometimes the filtrate may come through somewhat cloudy at first before the first layers of particles, which help filter the subsequent slurry, are deposited. This filtrate can be recycled for refiltration.

2. Filter aids.   Certain filter aids may be used to aid filtration. These are often incompressible diatomaceous earth or kieselguhr, which is composed primarily of silica. Also used are wood cellulose and other inert porous solids.

These filter aids can be used in a number of ways. They can be used as a precoat before the slurry is filtered. This will prevent gelatinous-type solids from plugging the filter medium and also give a clearer filtrate. They can also be added to the slurry before filtration. This increases the porosity of the cake and reduces resistance of the cake during filtration. In a rotary filter, the filter aid may be applied as a precoat; subsequently, thin slices of this layer are sliced off with the cake.

The use of filter aids is usually limited to cases where the cake is discarded or where the precipitate can be separated chemically from the filter aid.

14.2D   Basic Theory of Filtration

1. Pressure drop of fluid through filter cake.   Figure 14.2-6 is a section through a filter cake and filter medium at a definite time t s from the start of the flow of filtrate. At this time the thickness of the cake is L m (ft). The filter cross-sectional area is A m^2 (ft^2), and the linear velocity of the filtrate in the L direction is v m/s (ft/s) based on the filter area A m^2.

The flow of the filtrate through the packed bed of cake can be described by an equation similar to Poiseuille's law, assuming laminar flow occurs in the filter channels. Equation (2.10-2) gives Poiseuille's equation for laminar flow in a straight tube, which can be written

$$-\frac{\Delta p}{L} = \frac{32\mu v}{D^2} \quad \text{(SI)}$$

$$-\frac{\Delta p}{L} = \frac{32\mu v}{g_c D^2} \quad \text{(English)}$$

(14.2-1)

where Δp is pressure drop in N/m^2 (lb$_f$/ft^2), v is open-tube velocity in m/s (ft/s), D is diameter in m (ft), L is length in m (ft), μ is viscosity in Pa · s or kg/m · s (lb$_m$/ft · s), and g_c is 32.174 lb$_m$ · ft/lb$_f$ · s^2.

For laminar flow in a packed bed of particles, the *Carman–Kozeny relation*, which is similar to Eq. (14.2-1) and to the Blake–Kozeny equation (3.1-17), has been shown to apply to filtration:

$$-\frac{\Delta p_c}{L} = \frac{k_1 \mu v (1 - \varepsilon)^2 S_0^2}{\varepsilon^3}$$

(14.2-2)

where k_1 is a constant and equals 4.17 for random particles of definite size and shape, μ is viscosity of filtrate in Pa · s (lb$_m$/ft · s), v is linear velocity based on filter area in m/s (ft/s), ε is void fraction or porosity of cake, L is thickness of cake in m (ft), S_0 is specific surface area of

FIGURE 14.2-6. *Section through a filter cake.*

particle in m² (ft²) of particle area per m³ (ft³) volume of solid particle, and Δp_c is pressure drop in the cake in N/m² (lb$_f$/ft²). For English units, the right-hand side of Eq. (14.2-2) is divided by g_c. The linear velocity is based on the empty cross-sectional area and is

$$v = \frac{dV/dt}{A} \qquad (14.2\text{-}3)$$

where A is filter area in m² (ft²) and V is total m³ (ft³) of filtrate collected up to time t s. The cake thickness L may be related to the volume of filtrate V by a material balance. If c_S is kg solids/m³ (lb$_m$/ft³) of filtrate, a material balance gives

$$L\,A(1 - \varepsilon)\rho_p = c_S(V + \varepsilon L\,A) \qquad (14.2\text{-}4)$$

where ρ_p is density of solid particles in the cake in kg/m³ (lb$_m$/ft³) solid. The final term of Eq. (14.2-4) is the volume of filtrate held in the cake. This is usually small and will be neglected.

Substituting Eq. (14.2-3) into (14.2-2) and using Eq. (14.2-4) to eliminate L, we obtain the final equation as

$$\frac{dV}{A\,dt} = \frac{-\Delta p_c}{\dfrac{k_1(1 - \varepsilon)S_0^2}{\rho_p \varepsilon^3}\dfrac{\mu c_S V}{A}} = \frac{-\Delta p_c}{\alpha \dfrac{\mu c_S V}{A}} \qquad (14.2\text{-}5)$$

where α is the specific cake resistance in m/kg(ft/lb$_m$), defined as

$$\alpha = \frac{k_1(1 - \varepsilon)S_0^2}{\rho_p \varepsilon^3} \qquad (14.2\text{-}6)$$

For the filter-medium resistance, we can write, by analogy with Eq. (14.2-5),

$$\frac{dV}{A\,dt} = \frac{-\Delta p_f}{\mu R_m} \qquad (14.2\text{-}7)$$

where R_m is the resistance of the filter medium to filtrate flow in m⁻¹ (ft⁻¹) and Δp_f is the pressure drop. When R_m is treated as an empirical constant, it includes the resistance to flow of the piping leads to and from the filter and the filter medium resistance.

Since the resistances of the cake and the filter medium are in series, Eqs. (14.2-5) and (14.2-7) can be combined, and become

$$\frac{dV}{A\,dt} = \frac{-\Delta p}{\mu\left(\dfrac{\alpha c_S V}{A} + R_m\right)} \tag{14.2-8}$$

where $\Delta p = \Delta p_c + \Delta p_f$. Sometimes Eq. (14.2-8) is modified as follows:

$$\frac{dV}{A\,dt} = \frac{-\Delta p}{\dfrac{\mu \alpha c_S}{A}(V + V_e)} \tag{14.2-9}$$

where V_e is a volume of filtrate necessary to build up a fictitious filter cake whose resistance is equal to R_m.

The volume of filtrate V can also be related to W, the kg of accumulated dry cake solids, as follows:

$$W = c_S V = \frac{\rho c_x}{1 - m c_x} V \tag{14.2-10}$$

where c_x is mass fraction of solids in the slurry, m is mass ratio of wet cake to dry cake, and ρ is density of filtrate in kg/m^3 (lb_m/ft^3).

2. Specific cake resistance. From Eq. (14.2-6) we see that the specific cake resistance is a function of void fraction ε and S_0. It is also a function of pressure, since pressure can affect ε. By conducting constant-pressure experiments at various pressure drops, the variation of α with Δp can be determined.

Alternatively, compression–permeability experiments can be performed. A filter cake at a low pressure drop and atm pressure is built up by gravity filtering in a cylinder with a porous bottom. A piston is loaded on top and the cake compressed to a given pressure. Then filtrate is fed to the cake and α is determined by a differential form of Eq. (14.2-9). This is then repeated for other compression pressures (G1).

If α is independent of $-\Delta p$, the sludge is incompressible. Usually, α increases with $-\Delta p$, since most cakes are somewhat compressible. An empirical equation often used is

$$\alpha = \alpha_0(-\Delta p)^s \tag{14.2-11}$$

where α_0 and s are empirical constants. The compressibility constant s is zero for incompressible sludges or cakes. The constant s usually falls between 0.1 to 0.8. Sometimes the following is used:

$$\alpha = \alpha_0'[1 + \beta(-\Delta p)^{s'}] \tag{14.2-12}$$

where α_0', β, and s' are empirical constants. Experimental data for various sludges are given by Grace (G1).

The data obtained from filtration experiments often do not have a high degree of reproducibility. The state of agglomeration of the particles in the slurry can vary and have an effect on the specific cake resistance.

14.2E   Filtration Equations for Constant-Pressure Filtration

1. Basic equations for filtration rate in batch process.   Often a filtration is done under conditions of constant pressure. Equation (14.2-8) can be inverted and rearranged to give

$$\frac{dt}{dV} = \frac{\mu \alpha c_S}{A^2(-\Delta p)}V + \frac{\mu}{A(-\Delta p)}R_m = K_p V + B \qquad (14.2\text{-}13)$$

where K_p is in s/m^6 (s/ft^6) and B in s/m^3 (s/ft^3):

$$K_p = \frac{\mu \alpha c_S}{A^2(-\Delta p)} \qquad \text{(SI)}$$
$$\qquad (14.2\text{-}14)$$
$$K_p = \frac{\mu \alpha c_S}{A^2(-\Delta p)g_c} \qquad \text{(English)}$$

$$B = \frac{\mu R_m}{A(-\Delta p)} \qquad \text{(SI)}$$
$$\qquad (14.2\text{-}15)$$
$$B = \frac{\mu R_m}{A(-\Delta p)g_c} \qquad \text{(English)}$$

For constant pressure, constant α, and incompressible cake, V and t are the only variables in Eq. (14.2-13). Integrating to obtain the time of filtration in t s,

$$\int_0^t dt = \int_0^V (K_p V + B)\, dV \qquad (14.2\text{-}16)$$

$$t = \frac{K_p}{2}V^2 + BV \qquad (14.2\text{-}17)$$

Dividing by V

$$\frac{t}{V} = \frac{K_p V}{2} + B \qquad (14.2\text{-}18)$$

where V is total volume of filtrate in m^3 (ft^3) collected to t s.

  To evaluate Eq. (14.2-17) it is necessary to know α and R_m. This can be done by using Eq. (14.2-18). Data for V collected at different times t are obtained. Then the experimental data are plotted as t/V versus V, as in Fig. 14.2-7. Often, the first point on the graph does not fall on the line and is omitted. The slope of the line is $K_p/2$ and the intercept B. Then, using Eqs. (14.2-14) and (14.2-15), values of α and R_m can be determined.

> ***EXAMPLE 14.2-1. Evaluation of Filtration Constants for Constant-Pressure Filtration***
> Data for the laboratory filtration of $CaCO_3$ slurry in water at 298.2 K (25°C) are reported as follows at a constant pressure $(-\Delta p)$ of 338 kN/m^2 (7060 lb_f/ft^2) (R1, R2, M1). The filter area of the plate-and-frame press was $A = 0.0439$ m^2 (0.473 ft^2) and the slurry concentration was $c_s = 23.47$ kg/m^3 (1.465 lb_m/ft^3). Calculate the constants α and R_m from the experimental data given, where t is time in s and V is filtrate volume collected in m^3.

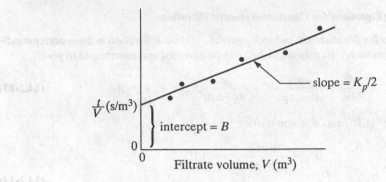

FIGURE 14.2-7. *Determination of constants in a constant-pressure filtration run.*

t	V	t	V	t	V
4.4	0.498×10^{-3}	34.7	2.498×10^{-3}	73.6	4.004×10^{-3}
9.5	1.000×10^{-3}	46.1	3.002×10^{-3}	89.4	4.502×10^{-3}
16.3	1.501×10^{-3}	59.0	3.506×10^{-3}	107.3	5.009×10^{-3}
24.6	2.000×10^{-3}				

Solution: First, the data are calculated as t/V and tabulated in Table 14.2-1. The data are plotted as t/V versus V in Fig. 14.2-8 and the intercept is determined as $B = 6400$ s/m^3 (181 s/ft^3) and the slope as $K_p/2 = 3.00 \times 10^6$ s/m^6. Hence, $K_p = 6.00 \times 10^6$ s/m^6 (4820 s/ft^6).

TABLE 14.2-1. *Values of t/V for Example 14.2-1*
(t = s, V = m^3)

t	$V \times 10^3$	$(t/V) \times 10^{-3}$
0	0	
4.4	0.498	8.84
9.5	1.000	9.50
16.3	1.501	10.86
24.6	2.000	12.30
34.7	2.498	13.89
46.1	3.002	15.36
59.0	3.506	16.83
73.6	4.004	18.38
89.4	4.502	19.86
107.3	5.009	21.42

FIGURE 14.2-8. *Determination of constants for Example 14.2-1.*

At 298.2 K the viscosity of water is 8.937×10^{-4} Pa·s $= 8.937 \times 10^{-4}$ kg/m·s. Substituting known values into Eq. (14.2-14) and solving,

$$K_p = 6.00 \times 10^6 = \frac{\mu \alpha c_S}{A^2(-\Delta p)} = \frac{(8.937 \times 10^{-4})(\alpha)(23.47)}{(0.0439)^2(338 \times 10^3)}$$

$$\alpha = 1.863 \times 10^{11} \, \text{m/kg} \, (2.77 \times 10^{11} \, \text{ft/lb}_m)$$

Substituting into Eq. (14.2-15) and solving,

$$B = 6400 = \frac{\mu R_m}{A(-\Delta p)} = \frac{(8.937 \times 10^{-4})(R_m)}{0.0439(338 \times 10^3)}$$

$$R_m = 10.63 \times 10^{10} \, \text{m}^{-1} \, (3.24 \times 10^{10} \, \text{ft}^{-1})$$

EXAMPLE 14.2-2. Time Required to Perform a Filtration

The same slurry used in Example 14.2-1 is to be filtered in a plate-and-frame press having 20 frames and 0.873 m² (9.4 ft²) area per frame. The same pressure will be used in constant-pressure filtration. Assuming the same filter-cake properties and filter cloth, calculate the time to recover 3.37 m³ (119 ft³) filtrate.

Solution: In Example 14.2-1, the area $A = 0.0439$ m², $K_p = 6.00 \times 10^6$ s/m⁶, and $B = 6400$ s/m³. Since the α and R_m will be the same as before, K_p can be corrected. From Eq. (14.2-14), K_p is proportional to $1/A^2$. The new area is $A = 0.873(20) = 17.46$ m² (188 ft²). The new K_p is

$$K_p = 6.00 \times 10^6(0.0439/17.46)^2 = 37.93 \, \text{s/m}^6 \, (0.03042 \, \text{s/ft}^6)$$

The new B is proportional to $1/A$ from Eq. (14.2-15):

$$B = (6400)\frac{0.0439}{17.46} = 16.10 \text{ s/m}^3 \ (0.456 \text{ s/ft}^3)$$

Substituting into Eq. (14.2-17),

$$t = \frac{K_p}{2}V^2 + BV = \frac{37.93}{2}(3.37)^2 + (16.10)(3.37) = 269.7 \text{ s}$$

Using English units,

$$t = \frac{K_p}{2}V^2 + BV = \frac{0.03042}{2}(119)^2 + (0.456)(119) = 269.7 \text{ s}$$

2. Equations for washing of filter cakes and total cycle time. The washing of a cake after the filtration cycle has been completed takes place by displacement of the filtrate and by diffusion. The amount of wash liquid should be sufficient to give the desired washing effect. To calculate washing rates, it is assumed that the conditions during washing are the same as those that existed at the end of the filtration. It is assumed that the cake structure is not affected when wash liquid replaces the slurry liquid in the cake.

In filters where the wash liquid follows a flow path similar to that during filtration, as in leaf filters, the final filtering rate gives the predicted washing rate. For constant-pressure filtration, using the same pressure in washing as in filtering, the final filtering rate is the reciprocal of Eq. (14.2-13):

$$\left(\frac{dV}{dt}\right)_f = \frac{1}{K_p V_f + B} \tag{14.2-19}$$

where $(dV/dt)_f$ = rate of washing in m³/s (ft³/s) and V_f is the total volume of filtrate for the entire period at the end of filtration in m³ (ft³).

For plate-and-frame filter presses, the wash liquid travels through a cake twice as thick and an area only half as large as in filtering, so the predicted washing rate is one-fourth of the final filtration rate:

$$\left(\frac{dV}{dt}\right)_f = \frac{1}{4}\frac{1}{K_p V_f + B} \tag{14.2-20}$$

In actual experience the washing rate may be less than predicted because of cake consolidation, channeling, and formation of cracks. Washing rates in a small plate-and-frame filter were found to be from 70 to 92% of that predicted (M1).

After washing is completed, additional time is needed to remove the cake, clean the filter, and reassemble the filter. The total filter-cycle time is the sum of the filtration time, plus the washing time, plus the cleaning time.

EXAMPLE 14.2-3. Rate of Washing and Total Filter-Cycle Time
At the end of the filtration cycle in Example 14.2-2, a total filtrate volume of 3.37 m³ is collected in a total time of 269.7 s. The cake is to be washed by through-washing in the plate-and-frame press using a volume of wash water equal to 10% of the filtrate volume. Calculate the time of washing and the total filter-cycle time if cleaning the filter takes 20 min.

Solution: For this filter, Eq. (14.2-20) holds. Substituting $K_p = 37.93$ s/m^6, $B = 16.10$ s/m^3, and $V_f = 3.37$ m^3, the washing rate is as follows:

$$\left(\frac{dV}{dt}\right)_f = \frac{1}{4}\frac{1}{(37.93)(3.37) + 16.10} = 1.737 \times 10^{-3} \text{ m}^3\text{/s } (0.0613 \text{ ft}^3\text{/s})$$

The time of washing is then as follows for 0.10(3.37), or 0.337 m^3 of wash water:

$$t = \frac{0.337 \text{ m}^3}{1.737 \times 10^{-3} \text{ m}^3\text{/s}} = 194.0 \text{ s}$$

The total filtration cycle is

$$\frac{269.7}{60} + \frac{194.0}{60} + 20 = 27.73 \text{ min}$$

3. Equations for continuous filtration. In a filter that is continuous in operation, such as a rotary-drum vacuum type, the feed, filtrate, and cake move at steady, continuous rates. In a rotary drum the pressure drop is held constant for the filtration. The cake formation involves a continual change in conditions. In continuous filtration, the resistance of the filter medium is generally negligible compared with the cake resistance. So in Eq. (14.2-13), $B = 0$.

Integrating Eq. (14.2-13), with $B = 0$,

$$\int_0^t dt = K_p \int_0^V V\,dV \qquad \text{(14.2-21)}$$

$$t = K_p\frac{V^2}{2} \qquad \text{(14.2-22)}$$

where t is the time required for formation of the cake. In a rotary-drum filter, the filter time t is less than the total cycle time t_c by

$$t = ft_c \qquad \text{(14.2-23)}$$

where f is the fraction of the cycle used for cake formation. In the rotary drum, f is the fraction submergence of the drum surface in the slurry.

Next, substituting Eq. (14.2-14) and Eq. (14.2-23) into (14.2-22) and rearranging,

$$\text{flow rate} = \frac{V}{At_c} = \left[\frac{2f(-\Delta p)}{t_c\mu\alpha c_S}\right]^{1/2} \qquad \text{(14.2-24)}$$

If the specific cake resistance varies with pressure, the constants in Eq. (14.2-11) are needed to predict the value of α to be used in Eq. (14.2-24). Experimental verification of Eq. (14.2-24) shows that the flow rate varies inversely with the square root of the viscosity and the cycle time (N1).

When short cycle times are used in continuous filtration and/or the filter medium resistance is relatively large, the filter resistance term B must be included, and Eq. (14.2-13) becomes

$$t = ft_c = K_p\frac{V^2}{2} + BV \qquad \text{(14.2-25)}$$

Then Eq. (14.2-25) becomes

$$\text{flow rate} = \frac{V}{At_c} = \frac{-R_m/t_c + [R_m^2/t_c^2 + 2c_s\alpha(-\Delta p)f/(\mu t_c)]^{1/2}}{\alpha c_s} \qquad (14.2\text{-}26)$$

EXAMPLE 14.2-4. Filtration in a Continuous Rotary-Drum Filter

A rotary-vacuum-drum filter having a 33% submergence of the drum in the slurry is to be used to filter a $CaCO_3$ slurry as given in Example 14.2-1 using a pressure drop of 67.0 kPa. The solids concentration in the slurry is $c_x = 0.191$ kg solid/kg slurry and the filter cake is such that the kg wet cake/kg dry cake = $m = 2.0$. The density and viscosity of the filtrate can be assumed as those of water at 298.2 K. Calculate the filter area needed to filter 0.778 kg slurry/s. The filter-cycle time is 250 s. The specific cake resistance can be represented by $\alpha = (4.37 \times 10^9)\,(-\Delta p)^{0.3}$, where $-\Delta p$ is in Pa and α in m/kg.

Solution: From Appendix A.2 for water, $\rho = 996.9$ kg/m^3, $\mu = 0.8937 \times 10^{-3}$ Pa·s. From Eq. (14.2-10),

$$c_S = \frac{\rho c_x}{1 - mc_x} = \frac{996.9(0.191)}{1 - (2.0)(0.191)} = 308.1 \text{ kg solids/m}^3 \text{ filtrate}$$

Solving for α, $\alpha = (4.37 \times 10^9)\,(67.0 \times 10^3)^{0.3} = 1.225 \times 10^{11}$ m/kg. To calculate the flow rate of the filtrate,

$$\frac{V}{t_c} = 0.778(c_x)/(c_s)$$

$$= \left(0.778\frac{\text{kg slurry}}{\text{s}}\right)\left(0.191\frac{\text{kg solid}}{\text{kg slurry}}\right) \Big/ \left(\frac{1}{308.1 \text{ kg solid/m}^3 \text{ filtrate}}\right)$$

$$= 4.823 \times 10^{-4} \text{ m}^3 \text{ filtrate/s}$$

Substituting into Eq. (14.2-24), neglecting and setting $B = 0$, and solving,

$$\frac{V}{At_c} = \frac{4.823 \times 10^{-4}}{A} = \left[\frac{2(0.33)(67.0 \times 10^3)}{250(0.8937 \times 10^{-3})(1.225 \times 10^{11})(308.1)}\right]^{1/2}$$

Hence, $A = 6.60$ m^2.

14.2F Filtration Equations for Constant-Rate Filtration

In some cases filtration runs are made under conditions of constant rate rather than constant pressure. This occurs if the slurry is fed to the filter by a positive-displacement pump. Equation (14.2-8) can be rearranged to give the following for a constant rate (dV/dt) m^3/s:

$$-\Delta p = \left(\frac{\mu\alpha c_S}{A^2}\frac{dV}{dt}\right)V + \left(\frac{\mu R_m}{A}\frac{dV}{dt}\right) = K_V V + C \qquad (14.2\text{-}27)$$

where

$$K_V = \left(\frac{\mu\alpha c_S}{A^2}\frac{dV}{dt}\right) \quad \text{(SI)}$$

$$\qquad (14.2\text{-}28)$$

$$K_V = \left(\frac{\mu\alpha c_S}{A^2 g_c}\frac{dV}{dt}\right) \quad \text{(English)}$$

$$C = \left(\frac{\mu R_m}{A}\frac{dV}{dt}\right)(\text{SI})$$

(14.2-29)

$$C = \left(\frac{\mu R_m}{A g_c}\frac{dV}{dt}\right)(\text{English})$$

K_V is in N/m^5 (lb$_f$/ft^5) and C is in N/m^2 (lb$_f$/ft^2).

Assuming that the cake is incompressible, K_V and C are constants characteristic of the slurry, cake, rate of filtrate flow, and so on. Hence, a plot of pressure, $-\Delta p$, versus the total volume of filtrate collected, V, gives a straight line for a constant rate dV/dt. The slope of the line is K_V and the intercept is C. The pressure increases as the cake thickness increases and the volume of filtrate collected increases.

The equations can also be rearranged in terms of $-\Delta p$ and time t as variables. At any moment during the filtration, the total volume V is related to the rate and total time t as follows:

$$V = t\frac{dV}{dt}$$

(14.2-30)

Substituting Eq. (14.2-30) into Eq. (14.2-27),

$$-\Delta p = \left[\frac{\mu\alpha c_S}{A^2}\left(\frac{dV}{dt}\right)^2\right]t + \left(\frac{\mu R_m}{A}\frac{dV}{dt}\right)$$

(14.2-31)

For the case where the specific cake resistance α is not constant but varies as in Eq. (14.2-11), this can be substituted for α in Eq. (14.2-27) to obtain a final equation.

14.3 SETTLING AND SEDIMENTATION IN PARTICLE–FLUID SEPARATION

14.3A Introduction

In filtration, the solid particles are removed from the slurry by forcing the fluid through a filter medium, which blocks the passage of the solid particles and allows the filtrate to pass through. In settling and sedimentation, the particles are separated from the fluid by gravitational forces acting on the particles.

Applications of settling and sedimentation include removal of solids from liquid sewage wastes, settling of crystals from the mother liquor, separation of liquid–liquid mixture from a solvent-extraction stage in a settler, settling of solid food particles from a liquid food, and settling of a slurry from a soybean leaching process. The particles can be solid particles or liquid drops. The fluid can be a liquid or gas and it may be at rest or in motion.

In some processes of settling and sedimentation, the purpose is to remove the particles from the fluid stream so that the fluid is free of particle contaminants. In other processes, the particles are recovered as the product, as in recovery of the dispersed phase in liquid–liquid extraction. In some cases the particles are suspended in fluids so that the particles can be separated into fractions differing in size or in density.

When a particle is at a sufficient distance from the walls of the container and from other particles so that its fall is not affected by them, the process is called *free settling*. Interference is less than 1% if the ratio of the particle diameter to the container diameter is less than 1:200 or if the particle concentration is less than 0.2 vol % in the solution. When the particles are crowded, they settle at a lower rate and the process is called *hindered settling*. The separation of a dilute slurry or suspension by gravity settling into a clear fluid and a slurry of higher solids content is called *sedimentation*.

14.3B Theory of Particle Movement Through a Fluid

1. Derivation of basic equations for rigid spheres. Whenever a particle is moving through a fluid, a number of forces will be acting on the particle. First, a density difference is needed between the particle and the fluid. An external force of gravity is needed to impart motion to the particle. If the densities of the fluid and particle are equal, the buoyant force on the particle will counterbalance the external force and the particle will not move relative to the fluid.

For a rigid particle moving in a fluid, there are three forces acting on the body: gravity acting downward, buoyant force acting upward, and resistance or drag force acting in opposite direction to the particle motion.

We will consider a particle of mass m kg falling at a velocity v m/s relative to the fluid. The density of the solid particle is ρ_p kg/m^3 solid and that of the liquid is ρ kg/m^3 liquid. The buoyant force F_b in N on the particle is

$$F_b = \frac{m\rho g}{\rho_p} = V_p \rho g \tag{14.3-1}$$

where m/ρ_p is the volume V_p in m^3 of the particle and g is the gravitational acceleration in m/s^2.

The gravitation or external force F_g in N on the particle is

$$F_g = mg \tag{14.3-2}$$

The drag force F_D on a body in N may be derived from the fact that, as in flow of fluids, the drag force or frictional resistance is proportional to the velocity head $v^2/2$ of the fluid displaced by the moving body. This must be multiplied by the density of the fluid and by a significant area A, such as the projected area of the particle. This was defined previously in Eq. (3.1-1):

$$F_D = C_D \frac{v^2}{2}\rho A \tag{14.3-3}$$

where the drag coefficient C_D is the proportionality constant and is dimensionless.

The resultant force on the body is then $F_g - F_b - F_D$. This resultant force must equal the force due to acceleration:

$$m\frac{dv}{dt} = F_g - F_b - F_D \tag{14.3-4}$$

Substituting Eqs. (14.3-1)–(14.3-3) into (14.3-4),

$$m\frac{dv}{dt} = mg - \frac{m\rho g}{\rho_p} - \frac{C_D v^2 \rho A}{2} \tag{14.3-5}$$

If we start from the moment the body is released from its position of rest, the falling of the body consists of two periods: the period of accelerated fall and the period of constant-velocity fall. The initial acceleration period is usually very short, on the order of a tenth of a second or so. Hence, the period of constant-velocity fall is the important one. The velocity is called the *free settling velocity* or *terminal velocity* v_t.

To solve for the terminal velocity in Eq. (14.3-5), $dv/dt = 0$ and the equation becomes

$$v_t = \sqrt{\frac{2g(\rho_p - \rho)m}{A\rho_p C_D \rho}} \tag{14.3-6}$$

For spherical particles $m = \pi D_p^3 \rho_p /6$ and $A = \pi D_p^2 /4$. Substituting these into Eq. (14.3-6), we obtain, for spherical particles,

$$v_t = \sqrt{\frac{4(\rho_p - \rho)g D_p}{3 C_D \rho}} \qquad \text{(14.3-7)}$$

where v_t is m/s (ft/s), ρ is kg/m^3 (lb$_m$/ft^3), g is 9.80665 m/s^2 (32.174 ft/s^2), and D_p is m (ft).

2. Drag coefficient for rigid spheres. The drag coefficient for rigid spheres has been shown to be a function of the Reynolds number $D_p v \rho / \mu$ of the sphere and is shown in Fig. 14.3-1. In the laminar-flow region, called the Stokes' law region for $N_{Re} < 1$, as discussed in Section 3.1B, the drag coefficient is

$$C_D = \frac{24}{D_p v \rho / \mu} = \frac{24}{N_{Re}} \qquad \text{(14.3-8)}$$

where μ is the viscosity of the liquid in Pa·s or kg/m·s (lb$_m$/ft·s). Substituting this into Eq. (14.3-7) for laminar flow,

$$v_t = \frac{g D_p^2 (\rho_p - \rho)}{18 \mu} \qquad \text{(14.3-9)}$$

For other shapes of particles, drag coefficients will differ from those given in Fig. 14.3-1, and data are given in Fig. 3.1-2 and elsewhere (B2, L2, P1). In the turbulent Newton's law region above a Reynolds number of about 1000 to 2.0×10^5, the drag coefficient is approximately constant at $C_D = 0.44$.

Solution of Eq. (14.3-7) is by trial and error when the particle diameter is known and the terminal velocity is to be obtained, because C_D also depends upon the velocity v_t.

If the particles are quite small, Brownian motion is present. Brownian motion is the random motion imparted to the particle by collisions between the molecules of the fluid sur-

FIGURE 14.3-1. Drag coefficient for a rigid sphere.

rounding the particle and the particle. This movement of the particles in random directions tends to suppress the effect of gravity, so settling of the particles may occur more slowly or not at all. At particle sizes of a few micrometers, the Brownian effect becomes appreciable, and at sizes of less than 0.1 μm, the effect predominates. For very small particles, application of centrifugal force helps reduce the effect of Brownian motion.

EXAMPLE 14.3-1. Settling Velocity of Oil Droplets

Oil droplets having a diameter of 20 μm (0.020 mm) are to be settled from air at temperature of 37.8°C (311 K) and 101.3 kPa pressure. The density of the oil is 900 kg/m³. Calculate the terminal settling velocity of the droplets.

Solution: The various knowns are $D_p = 2.0 \times 10^{-5}$ m and $\rho_p = 900$ kg/m³. From Appendix A.3, for air at 37.8°C, $\rho = 1.137$ kg/m³, $\mu = 1.90 \times 10^{-5}$ Pa·s. The droplet will be assumed to be a rigid sphere.

The solution is trial and error since the velocity is unknown. Hence, C_D cannot be directly determined. The Reynolds number is as follows:

$$N_{Re} = \frac{D_p v_t \rho}{\mu} = \frac{(2.0 \times 10^{-5})(v_t)(1.137)}{1.90 \times 10^{-5}} = 1.197 v_t \qquad \textbf{(14.3-10)}$$

For the first trial, assume that $v_t = 0.305$ m/s. Then $N_{Re} = 1.197(0.305) = 0.365$. Substituting into Eq. (14.3-7) and solving for C_D,

$$v_t = \sqrt{\frac{4(\rho_p - \rho)g D_p}{3 C_D \rho}} = \sqrt{\frac{4(900 - 1.137)(9.8066)(2.0 \times 10^{-5})}{(3) C_D (1.137)}}$$

$$C_D = \frac{0.2067}{v_t^2} \qquad \textbf{(14.3-11)}$$

Using $v_t = 0.305$ m/s, $C_D = 0.2067/(0.305)^2 = 2.22$.

Assuming that $v_t = 0.0305$ m/s, $N_{Re} = 0.0365$ from Eq. (14.3-10) and $C_D = 222$ from Eq. (14.3-11). For the third trial, assuming that $v_t = 0.00305$ m/s, $N_{Re} = 0.00365$ and $C_D = 22\,200$. These three values calculated for N_{Re} and C_D are plotted on a graph similar to Fig. 14.3-1 and shown in Fig. 14.3-2. It can be shown that the line through these points is a straight line. The intersection of this line and the drag-coefficient correlation line is the solution to the problem at $N_{Re} = 0.012$. The velocity can be calculated from the Reynolds number in Eq. (14.3-10):

$$N_{Re} = 0.012 = 1.197 v_t$$

$$v_t = 0.0100 \text{ m/s } (0.0328 \text{ ft/s})$$

The particle is in the Reynolds number range less than 1, which is the laminar Stokes' law region. Alternatively, the velocity can be calculated by substituting into Eq. (14.3-9):

$$v_t = \frac{9.8066(2.0 \times 10^{-5})^2(900 - 1.137)}{18(1.90 \times 10^{-5})} = 0.0103 \text{ m/s}$$

Note that Eq. (14.3-9) could not be used until it was determined that the particle fall was in the laminar region.

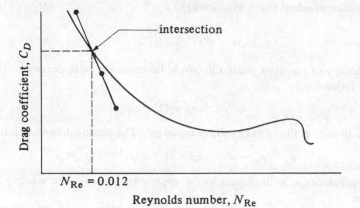

$$N_{Re} = 0.012$$

FIGURE 14.3-2. *Solution of Example 14.3-1 for settling velocity of a particle.*

For particles that are rigid but nonspherical, the drag depends upon the shape of the particle and the orientation of the particle with respect to its motion. Correlations of drag coefficients for particles of different shapes are given in a number of references (B2, C1, P1).

3. Drag coefficients for nonrigid spheres. When particles are nonrigid, internal circulation inside the particle and particle deformation can occur. Both of these effects affect the drag coefficient and terminal velocity. Drag coefficients for air bubbles rising in water are given in Perry and Green (P1), and for a Reynolds number less than about 50, the curve is the same as for rigid spheres in water.

For liquid drops in gases, the same drag relationship as for solid spherical particles is obtained up to a Reynolds number of about 100 (H1). Large drops will deform with an increase in drag. Small liquid drops in immiscible liquids behave like rigid spheres and the drag coefficient curve follows that for rigid spheres up to a Reynolds number of about 10. Above this and up to a Reynolds number of 500, the terminal velocity is greater than that for solids because of internal circulation in the drop.

14.3C Hindered Settling

For many cases of settling, a large number of particles are present, and the surrounding particles interfere with the motion of individual particles. The velocity gradients surrounding each particle are affected by the close presence of other particles. The particles settling in the liquid displace the liquid, and an appreciable upward velocity of the liquid is generated. Hence, the velocity of the liquid is appreciably greater with respect to the particle than with respect to the apparatus itself.

For such hindered flow, the settling velocity is less than would be calculated from Eq. (14.3-9) for Stokes' law. The true drag force is greater in the suspension because of the interference of the other particles. This higher effective viscosity of the mixture μ_m is equal to the actual viscosity of the liquid itself, μ, divided by an empirical correction factor, ψ_p, which depends upon ε, the volume fraction of the slurry mixture occupied by the liquid (S1):

$$\mu_m = \frac{\mu}{\psi_p} \tag{14.3-12}$$

where ψ_p is dimensionless and is as follows (S1):

$$\psi_p = \frac{1}{10^{1.82(1-\varepsilon)}} \qquad (14.3\text{-}13)$$

The density of the fluid phase effectively becomes the bulk density of the slurry ρ_m, which is as follows:

$$\rho_m = \varepsilon\rho + (1 - \varepsilon)\rho_p \qquad (14.3\text{-}14)$$

where ρ_m is density of slurry in kg solid + liquid/m^3. The density difference is now

$$\rho_p - \rho_m = \rho_p - [\varepsilon\rho + (1 - \varepsilon)\rho_p] = \varepsilon(\rho_p - \rho) \qquad (14.3\text{-}15)$$

The settling velocity, v_t, with respect to the apparatus is ε times the velocity calculated by Stokes' law.

Substituting mixture properties of μ_m from Eq. (14.3-12) for μ in Eq. (14.3-9), ($\rho_p - \rho_m$) from Eq. (14.3-15) for ($\rho_p - \rho$), and multiplying the result by ε for the relative-velocity effect, Eq. (14.3-9) becomes, for laminar settling,

$$v_t = \frac{gD_p^2(\rho_p - \rho)}{18\mu}(\varepsilon^2\psi_p) \qquad (14.3\text{-}16)$$

This is the velocity calculated from Eq. (14.3-9), multiplied by the correction factor ($\varepsilon^2\psi_p$).

The Reynolds number is then based on the velocity relative to the fluid and is

$$N_{Re} = \frac{D_p v_t \rho_m}{\mu_m \varepsilon} = \frac{D_p^3 g(\rho_p - \rho)\rho_m \varepsilon \psi_p^2}{18\mu^2} \qquad (14.3\text{-}17)$$

When the Reynolds number is less than 1, the settling is in the Stokes' law range. For Reynolds numbers above 1.0, see (P1). The effect of concentration is greater for nonspherical particles and angular particles (S1).

EXAMPLE 14.3-2. Hindered Settling of Glass Spheres

Calculate the settling velocity of glass spheres having a diameter of 1.554×10^{-4} m (5.10×10^{-4} ft) in water at 293.2 K (20°C). The slurry contains 60 wt % solids. The density of the glass spheres is $\rho_p = 2467$ kg/m^3 (154 lb$_m$/ft^3).

Solution: Density of water $\rho = 998$ kg/m^3 (62.3 lb$_m$/ft^3), and viscosity of water $\mu = 1.005 \times 10^{-3}$ Pa·s (6.72×10^{-4} lb$_m$/ft·s). To calculate the volume fraction ε of the liquid,

$$\varepsilon = \frac{40/998}{40/998 + 60/2467} = 0.622$$

The bulk density of the slurry ρ_m according to Eq. (14.3-14) is

$$\rho_m = \varepsilon\rho + (1 - \varepsilon)\rho_p = 0.622(998) + (1 - 0.622)(2467)$$

$$= 1553 \text{ kg/m}^3 \text{ (96.9 lb}_m/\text{ft}^3)$$

Substituting into Eq. (14.3-13),

$$\psi_p = \frac{1}{10^{1.82(1-\varepsilon)}} = \frac{1}{10^{1.82(1-0.622)}} = 0.205$$

Substituting into Eq. (14.3-16), using SI and English units,

$$v_t = \frac{9.807(1.554 \times 10^{-4})^2(2467 - 998)(0.622^2 \times 0.205)}{18(1.005 \times 10^{-3})}$$

$$= 1.525 \times 10^{-3} \text{ m/s}$$

$$v_t = \frac{32.174(5.1 \times 10^{-4})^2(154 - 62.3)(0.622^2 \times 0.205)}{18(6.72 \times 10^{-4})}$$

$$= 5.03 \times 10^{-3} \text{ ft/s}$$

The Reynolds number is obtained by substituting into Eq. (14.3-17):

$$N_{Re} = \frac{D_p v_t \rho_m}{\mu_m \varepsilon} = \frac{D_p v_t \rho_m}{(\mu/\psi_p)\varepsilon} = \frac{(1.554 \times 10^{-4})(1.525 \times 10^{-3})1553}{(1.005 \times 10^{-3}/0.205)0.622}$$

$$= 0.121$$

Hence, the settling is in the laminar range.

14.3D Wall Effect on Free Settling

When the diameter D_p of the particle becomes appreciable with respect to the diameter D_W of the container in which the settling is occurring, a retarding effect known as the *wall effect* is exerted on the particle. The terminal settling velocity is reduced. In the case of settling in the Stokes' law regime, the computed terminal velocity can be multiplied by the following to allow for the wall effect (Z1) for $D_p/D_W < 0.05$:

$$k_W = \frac{1}{1 + 2.1(D_p/D_W)} \tag{14.3-18}$$

For a completely turbulent regime, the correction factor is

$$k'_W = \frac{1 - (D_p/D_W)^2}{[1 + (D_p/D_W)^4]^{1/2}} \tag{14.3-19}$$

14.3E Differential Settling and Separation of Solids in Classification

1. Sink-and-float methods. Devices for the separation of solid particles into several fractions based upon their rates of flow or settling through fluids are known as *classifiers*. There are several separation methods for accomplishing this, namely, sink-and-float and differential settling. In the *sink-and-float method,* a liquid is used whose density is intermediate between that of the heavy or high-density material and that of the light-density material. In this liquid, the heavy particles will not float but settle out from the medium, while the light particles will float.

This method is independent of the sizes of the particles and depends only upon the relative densities of the two materials. This means liquids used must have densities greater than water, since most solids have high densities. Unfortunately, few such liquids exist that are cheap and noncorrosive. As a result, pseudoliquids are used, consisting of a suspension in water of very fine solid materials with high specific gravities, such as galena (specific gravity = 7.5) and magnetite (specific gravity = 5.17).

Hindered settling is used and the bulk density of the medium can be varied widely by varying the amount of the fine solid materials in the medium. Common applications of this technique are concentrating ore materials and cleaning coal. The fine solid materials in the medium are so small in diameter that their settling velocity is negligible, giving a relatively stable suspension.

2. Differential settling methods. The separation of solid particles into several size fractions based upon their settling velocities in a particular medium is called *differential settling* or *classification.* The density of the medium is less than that of either of the two substances to be separated.

In differential settling, both light and heavy materials settle through the medium. A disadvantage of this method if the light and heavy materials both have a range of particle sizes is that the smaller heavy particles settle at the same terminal velocity as the larger light particles.

Suppose that we consider two different materials: heavy-density material *A* (such as galena, with a specific gravity $\rho_A = 7.5$) and light-density material *B* (such as quartz, with a specific gravity $\rho_B = 2.65$). The terminal settling velocity of components *A* and *B*, from Eq. (14.3-7), can be written

$$v_{tA} = \left[\frac{4(\rho_{pA} - \rho)gD_{pA}}{3C_{DA}\rho} \right]^{1/2} \tag{14.3-20}$$

$$v_{tB} = \left[\frac{4(\rho_{pB} - \rho)gD_{pB}}{3C_{DB}\rho} \right]^{1/2} \tag{14.3-21}$$

For particles of equal settling velocities, $v_{tA} = v_{tB}$ and we obtain, by equating Eq. (14.3-20) to (14.3-21), canceling terms, and squaring both sides,

$$\frac{(\rho_{pA} - \rho)D_{pA}}{\rho C_{DA}} = \frac{(\rho_{pB} - \rho)D_{pB}}{\rho C_{DB}} \tag{14.3-22}$$

or

$$\frac{D_{pA}}{D_{pB}} = \frac{\rho_{pB} - \rho}{\rho_{pA} - \rho} \frac{C_{DA}}{C_{DB}} \tag{14.3-23}$$

For particles that are essentially spheres at very high Reynolds numbers in the turbulent Newton's law region, C_D is constant and $C_{DA} = C_{DB}$, giving

$$\frac{D_{pA}}{D_{pB}} = \left(\frac{\rho_{pB} - \rho}{\rho_{pA} - \rho} \right)^{1.0} \tag{14.3-24}$$

For laminar Stokes' law settling,

$$C_{DA} = \frac{24\mu}{D_{pA}v_{tA}\rho} \qquad C_{DB} = \frac{24\mu}{D_{pB}v_{tB}\rho} \tag{14.3-25}$$

Substituting Eq. (14.3-25) into (14.3-23) and rearranging for Stokes' law settling, where $v_{tA} = v_{tB}$,

$$\frac{D_{pA}}{D_{pB}} = \left(\frac{\rho_{pB} - \rho}{\rho_{pA} - \rho} \right)^{0.5} \tag{14.3-26}$$

For transition flow between laminar and turbulent flow,

$$\frac{D_{pA}}{D_{pB}} = \left(\frac{\rho_{pB} - \rho}{\rho_{pA} - \rho}\right)^n \qquad \text{where } \tfrac{1}{2} < n < 1 \qquad \text{(14.3-27)}$$

For particles settling in the turbulent range, Eq. (14.3-24) holds for equal settling velocities. For particles where $D_{pA} = D_{pB}$ and settling is in the turbulent Newton's law region, combining Eqs. (14.3-20) and (14.3-21),

$$\frac{v_{tA}}{v_{tB}} = \left(\frac{\rho_{pA} - \rho}{\rho_{pB} - \rho}\right)^{1/2} \qquad \text{(14.3-28)}$$

If both A and B particles are settling in the same medium, then Eqs. (14.3-24) and (14.3-28) can be used to make the plots given in Fig. 14.3-3 for the relation of velocity to diameter for A and B.

First, we consider a mixture of particles of materials A and B with a size range of D_{p1} to D_{p4} for both types of material. In the size range D_{p1} to D_{p2} in Fig. 14.3-3, a pure fraction of substance B can be obtained, since no particles of A settle as slowly. In the size range D_{p3} to D_{p4}, a pure fraction of A can be obtained, since no B particles settle as fast as the A particles in this size range. In the size range D_{p1} to D_{p3}, A particles settle as rapidly as B particles in the size range D_{p2} to D_{p4}, forming a mixed fraction of A and B.

Increasing the density ρ of the medium in Eq. (14.3-24), the numerator becomes smaller proportionally faster than the denominator, and the spread between D_{pA} and D_{pB} is increased. Somewhat similar curves are obtained in the Stokes' law region.

EXAMPLE 14.3-3. Separation of a Mixture of Silica and Galena

A mixture of silica (B) and galena (A) solid particles having a size range of 5.21×10^{-6} m to 2.50×10^{-5} m is to be separated by hydraulic classification using free settling conditions in water at 293.2 K (B1). The specific gravity of silica is 2.65 and that of galena is 7.5. Calculate the size range of the various fractions obtained in the settling. If the settling is in the laminar region, the drag coefficients will be reasonably close to that for spheres.

FIGURE 14.3-3. *Settling and separation of two materials A and B in Newton's law region.*

Solution: The particle-size range is $D_p = 5.21 \times 10^{-6}$ m to $D_p = 2.50 \times 10^{-5}$ m. Densities are $\rho_{pA} = 7.5(1000) = 7500$ kg/m³, $\rho_{pB} = 2.65(1000) = 2650$ kg/m³, $\rho = 998$ kg/m³ for water at 293.2 K (20°C). The water viscosity $\mu = 1.005 \times 10^{-3}$ Pa·s $= 1.005 \times 10^{-3}$ kg/m·s.

Assuming Stokes' law settling, Eq. (14.3-9) becomes as follows:

$$v_{tA} = \frac{gD_{pA}^2(\rho_{pA} - \rho)}{18\mu} \tag{14.3-29}$$

The largest Reynolds number occurs for the largest particle and the biggest density, where $D_{pA} = 2.50 \times 10^{-5}$ m and $\rho_{pA} = 7500$. Substituting into Eq. (14.3-29),

$$v_{tA} = \frac{9.807(2.50 \times 10^{-5})^2(7500 - 998)}{18(1.005 \times 10^{-3})} = 2.203 \times 10^{-3} \text{ m/s}$$

Substituting into the Reynolds number equation,

$$N_{Re} = \frac{D_{pA}v_{tA}\rho}{\mu}$$

$$= \frac{(2.50 \times 10^{-5})(2.203 \times 10^{-3})998}{1.005 \times 10^{-3}} = 0.0547 \tag{14.3-30}$$

Hence, the settling is in the Stokes' law region.

Referring to Fig. 14.3-3 and using the same nomenclature, the largest size is $D_{p4} = 2.50 \times 10^{-5}$ m. The smallest size is $D_{p1} = 5.21 \times 10^{-6}$ m. The pure fraction of A consists of $D_{pA4} = 2.50 \times 10^{-5}$ m to D_{pA3}. The particles, having diameters D_{pA3} and D_{pB4}, are related by having equal settling velocities in Eq. (14.3-26). Substituting $D_{pB4} = 2.50 \times 10^{-5}$ m into Eq. (14.3-26) and solving,

$$\frac{D_{pA3}}{2.50 \times 10^{-5}} = \left(\frac{2650 - 998}{7500 - 998}\right)^{1/2}$$

$$D_{pA3} = 1.260 \times 10^{-5} \text{ m}$$

The size range of pure B fraction is D_{pB2} to $D_{pB1} = 5.21 \times 10^{-6}$ m. The diameter D_{pB2} is related to $D_{pA1} = 5.21 \times 10^{-6}$ by Eq. (14.3-26) at equal settling velocities:

$$\frac{5.21 \times 10^{-6}}{D_{pB2}} = \left(\frac{2650 - 998}{7500 - 998}\right)^{1/2}$$

$$D_{pB2} = 1.033 \times 10^{-5} \text{ m}$$

The three fractions recovered are as follows:

1. The size range of the first fraction of pure A (galena) is as follows:

$$D_{pA3} = 1.260 \times 10^{-5} \text{ m} \quad \text{to} \quad D_{pA4} = 2.50 \times 10^{-5} \text{ m}$$

2. The mixed-fraction size range is as follows:

$$D_{pB2} = 1.033 \times 10^{-5} \text{ m} \quad \text{to} \quad D_{pB4} = 2.50 \times 10^{-5} \text{ m}$$

$$D_{pA1} = 5.21 \times 10^{-6} \text{ m} \quad \text{to} \quad D_{pA3} = 1.260 \times 10^{-5} \text{ m}$$

3. The size range of the third fraction of pure B (silica) is as follows:

$$D_{pB1} = 5.21 \times 10^{-6}\text{ m} \quad\text{to}\quad D_{pB2} = 1.033 \times 10^{-5}\text{ m}$$

14.3F Sedimentation and Thickening

1. Mechanisms of sedimentation. When a dilute slurry is settled by gravity into a clear fluid and a slurry of higher solids concentration, the process is called *sedimentation* or sometimes *thickening.* To illustrate the method for determining settling velocities and the mechanisms of settling, a batch settling test is carried out by placing a uniform concentration of the slurry in a graduated cylinder. At the start, as shown in Fig. 14.3-4a, all the particles settle by free settling in suspension zone B. The particles in zone B settle at a uniform rate at the start, and a clear liquid zone A appears in Fig. 14.3-4b. The height z drops at a constant rate. Also, zone D begins to appear, which contains the settled particles at the bottom. Zone C is a transition layer whose solids content varies from that in zone B to that in zone D. After further settling, zones B and C disappear, as shown in Fig. 14.3-4c. Then compression first appears; this moment is called the *critical point.* During compression, liquid is expelled upward from zone D and the thickness of zone D decreases.

2. Determination of settling velocity. In Fig. 14.3-4d the height z of the clear-liquid interface is plotted versus time. As shown, the velocity of settling, which is the slope of the line, is constant at first. The critical point is shown at point C. Since sludges vary greatly in their settling rates, experimental rates for each sludge are necessary. Kynch (K1) and Talmage and Fitch (T1) describe a method for predicting thickener sizes from the batch settling test.

The settling velocity v is determined by drawing a tangent to the curve in Fig. 14.3-4d at a given time t_1, with slope $-dz/dt = v_1$. At this point the height is z_1, and z_i is the intercept of the tangent to the curve. Then,

$$v_1 = \frac{z_i - z_1}{t_1 - 0} \tag{14.3-31}$$

FIGURE 14.3-4. *Batch sedimentation results: (a) original uniform suspension, (b) zones of settling after a given time, (c) compression of zone D after zones B and C disappear, (d) clear liquid interface height z versus time of settling.*

The concentration c_1 is, therefore, the average concentration of the suspension if z_i is the height of this slurry. This is calculated by

$$c_1 z_i = c_0 z_0 \quad \text{or} \quad c_1 = \left(\frac{z_0}{z_i}\right) c_0 \tag{14.3-32}$$

where c_0 is the original slurry concentration in kg/m^3 at z_0 height and $t = 0$. This is repeated for other times, and a plot of settling velocity versus concentration is made. Further details of this and other methods of designing the thickener are given elsewhere (C1, F1, F2, T1, P1). These and other methods in the literature are highly empirical and care should be exercised in their use.

14.3G Equipment for Settling and Sedimentation

1. Simple gravity settling tank. In Fig. 14.3-5a a simple gravity settler is shown for removing by settling a dispersed liquid phase from another phase. The velocity horizontally to the right must be slow enough to allow time for the smallest droplets to rise from the bottom to the interface or from the top down to the interface and coalesce.

In Fig. 14.3-5b a gravity settling chamber is shown schematically. Dust-laden air enters at one end of a large, boxlike chamber. Particles settle toward the floor at their terminal settling velocities. The air must remain in the chamber a sufficient length of time (residence time) so that the particles reach the floor of the chamber. Knowing the throughput of the air stream through the chamber and the chamber size, the residence time of the air in the chamber can be calculated. The vertical height of the chamber must be small enough that this height, divided by the settling velocity, gives a time less than the residence time of the air.

2. Equipment for classification. The simplest type of classifier is one in which a large tank is subdivided into several sections, as shown in Fig. 14.3-6. A liquid slurry feed enters the tank containing a size range of solid particles. The larger, faster-settling particles settle to the bottom close to the entrance and the slower-settling particles settle to the bottom close to the exit. The linear velocity of the entering feed decreases as a result of the enlargement of the cross-sectional area at the entrance. The vertical baffles in the tank allow for the collection of several fractions. The settling-velocity equations derived in this section hold.

FIGURE 14.3-5. *Gravity settling tanks: (a) settler for liquid–liquid dispersion, (b) dust-settling chambers.*

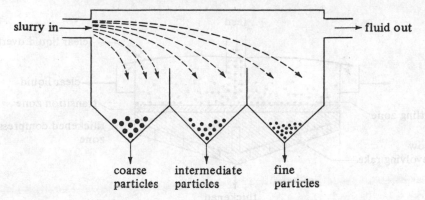

FIGURE 14.3-6. *Simple gravity settling classifier.*

3. Spitzkasten classifier. Another type of gravity settling chamber is the *Spitzkasten,* shown in Fig. 14.3-7, which consists of a series of conical vessels of increasing diameter in the direction of flow. The slurry enters the first vessel, where the largest and fastest-settling particles are separated. The overflow goes to the next vessel, where another separation occurs. This continues in the succeeding vessel or vessels. In each vessel the velocity of upflowing inlet water is controlled to give the desired size range for each vessel.

4. Sedimentation thickener. The separation of a dilute slurry by gravity settling into a clear fluid and a slurry of higher solids concentration is called *sedimentation.* Industrially, sedimentation operations are often carried out continuously in equipment called *thickeners.* A continuous thickener with a slowly revolving rake for removing the sludge or thickened slurry is shown in Fig. 14.3-8.

The slurry in Fig. 14.3-8 is fed at the center of the tank several feet below the surface of the liquid. Around the top edge of the tank is a clear-liquid-overflow outlet. The rake serves

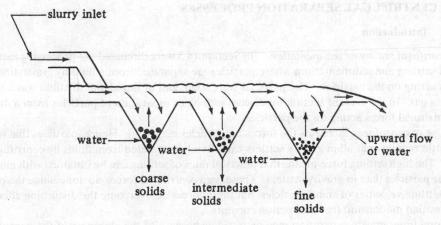

FIGURE 14.3-7. *Spitzkasten gravity settling chamber.*

feed

clear liquid overflow

clear liquid

transition zone

thickened compression zone

free settling zone

slow revolving rake

thickened sludge underflow

FIGURE 14.3-8. *Continuous thickener.*

to scrape the sludge toward the center of the bottom for removal. This gentle stirring aids in removing water from the sludge.

In the thickener the entering slurry spreads radially through the cross section of the thickener and the liquid flows upward and out the overflow. The solids settle in the upper zone by free settling. Below this dilute settling zone is the transition zone, in which the concentration of solids increases rapidly, and then the compression zone. A clear overflow can be obtained if the upward velocity of the fluid in the dilute zone is less than the minimal terminal settling velocity of the solids in this zone.

The settling rates are quite slow in the thickened zone, which consists of a compression of the solids with liquid being forced upward through the solids. This is an extreme case of hindered settling. Equation (14.3-16) may be used to estimate the settling velocities, but the results can be in considerable error because of agglomeration of particles. As a result, laboratory settling or sedimentation data must be used in the design of a thickener, as discussed previously in Section 14.3F.

14.4 CENTRIFUGAL SEPARATION PROCESSES

14.4A Introduction

1. Centrifugal settling or sedimentation. In Section 14.3 were discussed the processing methods of settling and sedimentation, where particles are separated from a fluid by gravitational forces acting on the particles. The particles were solid, gas, or liquid and the fluid was a liquid or a gas. In the present section we discuss settling or separation of particles from a fluid by centrifugal forces acting on the particles.

Use of centrifuges increases the forces on particles manyfold. Hence, particles that will not settle readily or at all in gravity settlers can often be separated from fluids by centrifugal force. The high settling force means that practical rates of settling can be obtained with much smaller particles than in gravity settlers. These high centrifugal forces do not change the relative settling velocities of small particles, but these forces do overcome the disturbing effects of Brownian motion and free convection currents.

Sometimes gravity separation may be too slow because of the closeness of the densities of the particles and the fluid, or because of association forces holding the components together, as in emulsions. An example in the dairy industry is the separation of cream from whole milk, giving skim milk. Gravity separation takes hours, while centrifugal separation is accomplished in minutes in a cream separator. Centrifugal settling or separation is employed in many food industries, such as breweries, vegetable-oil processing, fish-protein-concentrate processing, fruit juice processing to remove cellular materials, and so on. Centrifugal separation is also used in drying crystals and for separating emulsions into their constituent liquids or solid–liquid. The principles of centrifugal sedimentation are discussed in Sections 14.4B and 14.4C.

2. Centrifugal filtration. Centrifuges are also used in centrifugal filtration, where a centrifugal force is used instead of a pressure difference to cause the flow of slurry in a filter where a cake of solids builds up on a screen. The cake of granular solids from the slurry is deposited on a filter medium held in a rotating basket, washed, and then spun "dry." Centrifuges and ordinary filters are competitive in most solid–liquid separation problems. The principles of centrifugal filtration are discussed in Section 14.4E.

14.4B Forces Developed in Centrifugal Separation

1. Introduction. Centrifugal separators make use of the common principle that an object whirled about an axis or center point at a constant radial distance from the point is acted on by a force. The object being whirled about an axis is constantly changing direction and is thus accelerating, even though the rotational speed is constant. This centripetal force acts in a direction toward the center of rotation.

If the object being rotated is a cylindrical container, the contents of fluid and solids exert an equal and opposite force, called *centrifugal force,* outward to the walls of the container. This is the force that causes settling or sedimentation of particles through a layer of liquid or filtration of a liquid through a bed of filter cake held inside a perforated rotating chamber.

In Fig. 14.4-1a a cylindrical bowl is shown rotating, with a slurry feed of solid particles and liquid being admitted at the center. The feed enters and is immediately thrown outward to the walls of the container, as in Fig. 14.4-1b. The liquid and solids are now acted upon by

FIGURE 14.4-1. *Sketch of centrifugal separation: (a) initial slurry feed entering, (b) settling of solids from a liquid, (c) separation of two liquid fractions.*

the vertical gravitational force and the horizontal centrifugal force. The centrifugal force is usually so large that the force of gravity may be neglected. The liquid layer then assumes the equilibrium position, with the surface almost vertical. The particles settle horizontally outward and press against the vertical bowl wall.

In Fig. 14.4-1c two liquids having different densities are being separated by the centrifuge. The denser fluid will occupy the outer periphery, since the centrifugal force on it is greater.

2. Equations for centrifugal force. In circular motion the acceleration due to the centrifugal force is

$$a_e = r\omega^2 \tag{14.4-1}$$

where a_e is the acceleration from a centrifugal force in m/s^2 (ft/s^2), r is radial distance from the center of rotation in m (ft), and ω is angular velocity in rad/s.

The centrifugal force F_c in N (lb_f) acting on the particle is given by

$$F_c = ma_e = mr\omega^2 \quad \text{(SI)}$$

$$F_c = \frac{mr\omega^2}{g_c} \quad \text{(English)} \tag{14.4-2}$$

where $g_c = 32.174\ lb_m \cdot ft/lb_f \cdot s^2$.

Since $\omega = v/r$, where v is the tangential velocity of the particle in m/s (ft/s),

$$F_c = mr\left(\frac{v}{r}\right)^2 = \frac{mv^2}{r} \tag{14.4-3}$$

Often rotational speeds are given as N rev/min and

$$\omega = \frac{2\pi N}{60} \tag{14.4-4}$$

$$N = \frac{60v}{2\pi r} \tag{14.4-5}$$

Substituting Eq. (14.4-4) into Eq. (14.4-2),

$$F_c\ \text{newton} = mr\left(\frac{2\pi N}{60}\right)^2 = 0.01097 mrN^2 \quad \text{(SI)}$$

$$F_c\ lb_f = \frac{mr}{g_c}\left(\frac{2\pi N}{60}\right)^2 = 0.000341 mrN^2 \quad \text{(English)} \tag{14.4-6}$$

By Eq. (14.3-2), the gravitational force on a particle is

$$F_g = mg \tag{14.3-2}$$

where g is the acceleration of gravity and is $9.80665\ m/s^2$. In terms of gravitational force, the centrifugal force is as follows, by combining Eqs. (14.3-2), (14.4-2), and (14.4-3):

$$\frac{F_c}{F_g} = \frac{r\omega^2}{g} = \frac{v^2}{rg} = \frac{r}{g}\left(\frac{2\pi N}{60}\right)^2 = 0.001118 rN^2 \quad \text{(SI)}$$

$$\frac{F_c}{F_g} = 0.000341 rN^2 \quad \text{(English)} \tag{14.4-7}$$

Hence, the force developed in a centrifuge is $r\omega^2/g$ or v^2/rg times as large as the gravitational force. This is often expressed as equivalent to so many g forces.

EXAMPLE 14.4-1. *Force in a Centrifuge*
A centrifuge having a radius of the bowl of 0.1016 m (0.333 ft) is rotating at $N = 1000$ rev/min.
    (a) Calculate the centrifugal force developed in terms of gravity forces.
    (b) Compare this force to that for a bowl with a radius of 0.2032 m rotating
        at the same rev/min.

Solution: For part (a), $r = 0.1016$ m and $N = 1000$. Substituting into Eq. (14.4-7),

$$\frac{F_c}{F_g} = 0.001118\,rN^2 = 0.001118(0.1016)(1000)^2 \qquad \text{(SI)}$$

$$= 113.6 \text{ gravities or g's}$$

$$\frac{F_c}{F_g} = 0.000341(0.333)(1000)^2 = 113.6 \qquad \text{(English)}$$

For part (b), $r = 0.2032$ m. Substituting into Eq. (14.4-7),

$$\frac{F_c}{F_g} = 0.001118(0.2032)(1000)^2 = 227.2 \text{ gravities or g's}$$

14.4C Equations for Rates of Settling in Centrifuges

1. General equation for settling. If a centrifuge is used for sedimentation (removal of particles by settling), a particle of a given size can be removed from the liquid in the bowl if there is sufficient residence time of the particle in the bowl for the particle to reach the wall. For a particle moving radially at its terminal settling velocity, the diameter of the smallest particle which can be removed can be calculated.

In Fig. 14.4-2 a schematic of a tubular-bowl centrifuge is shown. The feed enters at the bottom, and it is assumed that all the liquid moves upward at a uniform velocity, carrying solid particles with it. The particle is assumed to be moving radially at its terminal settling velocity v_t. The trajectory or path of the particle is shown in Fig. 14.4-2. A particle of a given size is removed from the liquid if sufficient residence time is available for the particle to reach the wall of the bowl, where it is held. The length of the bowl is b m.

At the end of the residence time of the particle in the fluid, the particle is at a distance r_B m from the axis of rotation. If $r_B < r_2$, then the particle leaves the bowl with the fluid. If $r_B = r_2$, it is deposited on the wall of the bowl and effectively removed from the liquid.

For settling in the Stokes' law range, the terminal settling velocity at a radius r is obtained by substituting Eq. (14.4-1) for the acceleration g into Eq. (14.3-9):

$$v_t = \frac{\omega^2 r D_p^2(\rho_p - \rho)}{18\mu} \tag{14.4-8}$$

where v_t is settling velocity in the radial direction in m/s, D_p is particle diameter in m, ρ_p is particle density in kg/m^3, ρ is liquid density in kg/m^3, and μ is liquid viscosity in Pa·s. If hinliquid discharge

particle trajectory

feed flow

liquid surface

bowl wall

b

feed

r_1

r_B

r_2

FIGURE 14.4-2. *Particle settling in sedimenting tubular-bowl centrifuge.*

dered settling occurs, the right-hand side of Eq. (14.4-8) is multiplied by the factor $(\varepsilon^2 \psi_p)$ given in Eq. (14.3-16).

Since $v_t = dr/dt$, then Eq. (14.4-8) becomes

$$dt = \frac{18\mu}{\omega^2(\rho_p - \rho)D_p^2} \frac{dr}{r} \qquad (14.4\text{-}9)$$

Integrating between the limits $r = r_1$ at $t = 0$ and $r = r_2$ at $t = t_T$,

$$t_T = \frac{18\mu}{\omega^2(\rho_p - \rho)D_p^2} \ln \frac{r_2}{r_1} \qquad (14.4\text{-}10)$$

The residence time t_T is equal to the volume of liquid V m^3 in the bowl divided by the feed volumetric flow rate q in m^3/s. The volume $V = \pi b(r_2^2 - r_1^2)$. Substituting into Eq. (14.4-10) and solving for q,

$$q = \frac{\omega^2(\rho_p - \rho)D_p^2}{18\mu \ln(r_2/r_1)}(V) = \frac{\omega^2(\rho_p - \rho)D_p^2}{18\mu \ln(r_2/r_1)}[\pi b(r_2^2 - r_1^2)] \qquad (14.4\text{-}11)$$

Particles having diameters smaller than that calculated from Eq. (14.4-11) will not reach the wall of the bowl and will go out with the exit liquid. Larger particles will reach the wall and be removed from the liquid.

A cut point or critical diameter D_{pc} can be defined as the diameter of a particle that reaches half the distance between r_1 and r_2. This particle moves a distance of half the liquid layer or $(r_2 - r_1)/2$ during the time this particle is in the centrifuge. The integration is then between $r = (r_1 + r_2)/2$ at $t = 0$ and $r = r_2$ at $t = t_T$. Then we obtain

$$q_c = \frac{\omega^2(\rho_p - \rho)D_{pc}^2}{18\mu \ln[2r_2/(r_1 + r_2)]}(V) = \frac{\omega^2(\rho_p - \rho)D_{pc}}{18\mu \ln[2r_2/(r_1 + r_2)]}[\pi b(r_2^2 - r_1^2)] \quad \textbf{(14.4-12)}$$

At this flow rate q_c, particles with a diameter greater than D_{pc} will predominantly settle to the wall and most smaller particles will remain in the liquid.

2. *Special case for settling.* For the special case where the thickness of the liquid layer is small compared to the radius, Eq. (14.4-8) can be written for a constant $r \cong r_2$ and $D_p = D_{pc}$ as follows:

$$v_t = \frac{\omega^2 r_2 D_{pc}^2(\rho_p - \rho)}{18\mu} \quad \textbf{(14.4-13)}$$

The time of settling t_T is then as follows for the critical D_{pc} case:

$$t_T = \frac{V}{q_c} = \frac{(r_2 - r_1)/2}{v_t} \quad \textbf{(14.4-14)}$$

Substituting Eq. (14.4-13) into (14.4-14) and rearranging,

$$q_c = \frac{\omega^2 r_2 D_{pc}^2(\rho_p - \rho)V}{18\mu[(r_2 - r_1)/2]} \quad \textbf{(14.4-15)}$$

The volume V can be expressed as

$$V \cong 2\pi r_2(r_2 - r_1)b \quad \textbf{(14.4-16)}$$

Combining Eqs. (14.4-15) and (14.4-16),

$$q_c = \frac{2\pi b r_2^2 \omega^2 D_{pc}^2(\rho_p - \rho)}{9\mu} \quad \textbf{(14.4-17)}$$

The analysis above is somewhat simplified. The pattern of flow of the fluid is actually more complicated. These equations can also be used for liquid–liquid systems where droplets of liquid migrate according to the equations and coalesce in the other liquid phase.

EXAMPLE 14.4-2. Settling in a Centrifuge

A viscous solution containing particles with a density $\rho_p = 1461$ kg/m^3 is to be clarified by centrifugation. The solution density $\rho = 801$ kg/m^3 and its viscosity is 100 cp. The centrifuge has a bowl with $r_2 = 0.02225$ m, $r_1 = 0.00716$ m, and height $b = 0.1970$ m. Calculate the critical particle diameter of the largest particles in the exit stream if $N = 23\,000$ rev/min and the flow rate $q = 0.002832$ m^3/h.

Solution: Using Eq. (14.4-4),

$$\omega = \frac{2\pi N}{60} = \frac{2\pi(23\,000)}{60} = 2410 \text{ rad/s}$$

The bowl volume V is

$$V = \pi b(r_2^2 - r_1^2)$$
$$= \pi(0.1970)[(0.02225)^2 - (0.00716)^2] = 2.747 \times 10^{-4} \text{ m}^3$$

Viscosity $\mu = 100 \times 10^{-3} = 0.100$ Pa·s $= 0.100$ kg/m·s. The flow rate q_c is

$$q_c = \frac{0.002832}{3600} = 7.87 \times 10^{-7} \text{ m}^3/\text{s}$$

Substituting into Eq. (14.4-12) and solving for D_{pc},

$$q_c = 7.87 \times 10^{-7}$$

$$= \frac{(2410)^2(1461 - 801)D_{pc}^2(2.747 \times 10^{-4})}{18(0.100)\ln[2 \times 0.02225/(0.00716 + 0.02225)]}$$

$$D_{pc} = 0.746 \times 10^{-6} \text{ m} \quad \text{or} \quad 0.746 \; \mu\text{m}$$

Substituting into Eq. (14.4-13) to obtain v_t and then calculating the Reynolds number, the settling is in the Stokes' law range.

3. Sigma values and scale-up of centrifuges. A useful physical characteristic of a tubular-bowl centrifuge can be derived by multiplying and dividing Eq. (14.4-12) by $2g$ and then substituting Eq. (14.3-9) written for D_{pc} into Eq. (14.4-12) to obtain

$$q_c = 2\frac{(\rho_p - \rho)gD_{pc}^2}{18\mu}\frac{\omega^2 V}{2g\ln[2r_2/(r_1 + r_2)]} = 2v_t \cdot \Sigma \tag{14.4-18}$$

where v_t is the terminal settling velocity of the particle in a gravitational field and

$$\Sigma = \frac{\omega^2 V}{2g\ln[2r_2/(r_1 + r_2)]} = \frac{\omega^2[\pi b(r_2^2 - r_1^2)]}{2g\ln[2r_2/(r_1 + r_2)]} \tag{14.4-19}$$

where Σ is a physical characteristic of the centrifuge and not of the fluid–particle system being separated. Using Eq. (14.4-17) for the special case of settling for a thin layer,

$$\Sigma = \frac{\omega^2\pi b2r_2^2}{g} \tag{14.4-20}$$

The value of Σ is really the area in m^2 of a gravitational settler that will have the same sedimentation characteristics as the centrifuge for the same feed rate. To scale up from a laboratory test of q_1 and Σ_1 to q_2 (for $v_{t1} = v_{t2}$),

$$\frac{q_1}{\Sigma_1} = \frac{q_2}{\Sigma_2} \tag{14.4-21}$$

This scale-up procedure is dependable for centrifuges of similar type and geometry and if the centrifugal forces are within a factor of 2 from each other. If different configurations are involved, efficiency factors E should be used, where $q_1/\Sigma_1 E_1 = q_2/\Sigma_2 E_2$. These efficiencies must be determined experimentally, and values for different types of centrifuges are given elsewhere (F1, P1).

4. Separation of liquids in a centrifuge. Liquid–liquid separations in which the liquids are immiscible but finely dispersed as in an emulsion are common operations in the food and other industries. An example is the dairy industry, in which the emulsion of milk is separated into skim milk and cream. In these liquid–liquid separations, the position of the outlet overflow weir in the centrifuge is very important, not only in controlling the volumetric holdup V in the centrifuge but also in determining whether a separation is actually made.

FIGURE 14.4-3. *Tubular bowl centrifuge for separating two liquid phases.*

In Fig. 14.4-3, a tubular-bowl centrifuge is shown in which the centrifuge is separating two liquid phases, one a heavy liquid with density ρ_H kg/m^3 and the second a light liquid with density ρ_L. The distances shown are as follows: r_1 is radius to surface of light liquid layer, r_2 is radius to liquid–liquid interface, and r_4 is radius to surface of heavy liquid downstream.

To locate the interface, a balance must be made of the pressures in the two layers. The force on the fluid at distance r is, by Eq. (14.4-2),

$$F_c = mr\omega^2 \qquad \text{(14.4-2)}$$

The differential force across a thickness dr is

$$dF_c = dmr\omega^2 \qquad \text{(14.4-22)}$$

But,

$$dm = [(2\pi rb)dr]\rho \qquad \text{(14.4-23)}$$

where b is the height of the bowl in m and $(2\pi rb)\,dr$ is the volume of fluid. Substituting Eq. (14.4-23) in (14.4-22) and dividing both sides by the area $A = 2\pi rb$,

$$dP = \frac{dF_c}{A} = \omega^2 \rho r\, dr \qquad \text{(14.4-24)}$$

where P is pressure in N/m^2 (lb$_f$/ft^2).

Integrating Eq. (14.4-24) between r_1 and r_2,

$$P_2 - P_1 = \frac{\rho \omega^2}{2}(r_2^2 - r_1^2) \qquad \text{(14.4-25)}$$

Applying Eq. (14.4-25) to Fig. 14.4-3 and equating the pressure exerted by the light phase of thickness $r_2 - r_1$ to the pressure exerted by the heavy phase of thickness $r_2 - r_4$ at the liquid–liquid interface at r_2,

$$\frac{\rho_H \omega^2}{2}(r_2^2 - r_4^2) = \frac{\rho_L \omega^2}{2}(r_2^2 - r_1^2) \tag{14.4-26}$$

Solving for r_2^2, the interface position,

$$r_2^2 = \frac{\rho_H r_4^2 - \rho_L r_1^2}{\rho_H - \rho_L} \tag{14.4-27}$$

The interface at r_2 must be located at a radius smaller than r_3 in Fig. 14.4-3.

EXAMPLE 14.4-3. Location of Interface in Centrifuge

In a vegetable-oil-refining process, an aqueous phase is being separated from the oil phase in a centrifuge. The density of the oil is 919.5 kg/m^3 and that of the aqueous phase is 980.3 kg/m^3. The radius r_1 for overflow of the light liquid has been set at 10.160 mm and the outlet for the heavy liquid at 10.414 mm. Calculate the location of the interface in the centrifuge.

Solution: The densities are $\rho_L = 919.5$ and $\rho_H = 980.3$ kg/m^3. Substituting into Eq. (14.4-27) and solving for r_2,

$$r_2^2 = \frac{980.3(10.414)^2 - 919.5(10.160)^2}{980.3 - 919.5}$$

$$r_2 = 13.75 \text{ mm}$$

13.4D Centrifuge Equipment for Sedimentation

1. Tubular centrifuge. A schematic of a *tubular-bowl centrifuge* is shown in Fig. 14.4-3. The bowl is tall and has a narrow diameter, 100–150 mm. Such centrifuges, known as *supercentrifuges*, develop a force about 13 000 times the force of gravity. Some narrow centrifuges, having a diameter of 75 mm and very high speeds of 60 000 or so rev/min, are known as *ultracentrifuges*. These supercentrifuges are often used to separate liquid–liquid emulsions.

2. Disk bowl centrifuge. The *disk bowl centrifuge* shown in Fig. 14.4-4 is often used in liquid–liquid separations. The feed enters the actual compartment at the bottom and travels upward through vertically spaced feed holes, filling the spaces between the disks. The holes divide the vertical assembly into an inner section, where mostly light liquid is present, and an outer section, where mainly heavy liquid is present. This dividing line is similar to an interface in a tubular centrifuge.

The heavy liquid flows beneath the underside of a disk to the periphery of the bowl. The light liquid flows over the upper side of the disks and toward the inner outlet. Any small amount of heavy solids is thrown to the outer wall. Periodic cleaning is required to remove solids deposited. Disk bowl centrifuges are used in starch–gluten separation, concentration of rubber latex, and cream separation. Details are given elsewhere (P1, L1).

FIGURE 14.4-4. *Schematic of disk bowl centrifuge.*

14.4E Centrifugal Filtration

1. Theory for centrifugal filtration. Theoretical prediction of filtration rates in centrifugal filters have not been too successful. The filtration in centrifuges is more complicated than for ordinary filtration using pressure differences, since the area for flow and driving force increase with distance from the axis and the specific cake resistance may change markedly. Centrifuges for filtering are generally selected by scale-up from tests on a similar-type laboratory centrifuge using the slurry to be processed.

The theory of constant-pressure filtration discussed in Section 14.2E can be modified and used where centrifugal force causes the flow instead of impressed pressure difference. The equation will be derived for the case where a cake has already been deposited, as shown in Fig. 14.4-5. The inside radius of the basket is r_2, r_i is the inner radius of the face of the cake, and r_1 is the inner radius of the liquid surface. We will assume that the cake is nearly incompressible so that an average value of α can be used for the cake. Also, the flow is laminar. If we assume a thin cake in a large-diameter centrifuge, then the area A for flow is approximately constant. The velocity of the liquid is

$$v = \frac{q}{A} = \frac{dV}{A\,dt} \tag{14.4-28}$$

where q is the filtrate flow rate in m^3/s and v the velocity. Substituting Eq. (14.4-28) into (14.2-8),

$$-\Delta p = q\mu\left(\frac{m_c\alpha}{A^2} + \frac{R_m}{A}\right) \tag{14.4-29}$$

where $m_c = c_S V$, mass of cake in kg deposited on the filter.

For a hydraulic head of dz m, the pressure drop is

$$dp = \rho g\,dz \tag{14.4-30}$$

FIGURE 14.4-5. *Physical arrangement for centrifugal filtration.*

In a centrifugal field, g is replaced by $r\omega^2$ from Eq. (14.4-1) and dz by dr. Then,

$$dp = \rho r\omega^2\,dr \qquad (14.4\text{-}31)$$

Integrating between r_1 and r_2,

$$-\Delta p = \frac{\rho\omega^2(r_2^2 - r_1^2)}{2} \qquad (14.4\text{-}32)$$

Combining Eqs. (14.4-29) and (14.4-32) and solving for q,

$$q = \frac{\rho\omega^2(r_2^2 - r_1^2)}{2\mu\left(\dfrac{m_c\alpha}{A^2} + \dfrac{R_m}{A}\right)} \qquad (14.4\text{-}33)$$

For the case where the flow area A varies considerably with the radius, the following has been derived (G1):

$$q = \frac{\rho\omega^2(r_2^2 - r_1^2)}{2\mu\left(\dfrac{m_c\alpha}{\overline{A_L}\,\overline{A_a}} + \dfrac{R_m}{A_2}\right)} \qquad (14.4\text{-}34)$$

where $A_2 = 2\pi r_2 b$ (area of filter medium), $\overline{A_L} = 2\pi b(r_2 - r_i)/\ln(r_2/r_i)$ (logarithmic cake area), and $\overline{A_a} = (r_i + r_2)\pi b$ (arithmetic mean cake area). This equation holds for a cake of a given mass at a given time. It is not an integrated equation covering the whole filtration cycle.

2. Equipment for centrifugal filtration. In a centrifugal filter, slurry is fed continuously to a rotating basket which has a perforated wall and is covered with a filter cloth. The cake builds up on the surface of the filter medium to the desired thickness. Then, at the end of the filtration cycle, feed is stopped, and wash liquid is added or sprayed onto the cake. Then the wash liquid is stopped and the cake is spun as dry as possible. The motor is then shut off or slowed and the basked allowed to rotate while the solids are discharged by a scraper knife, so that the solids drop through an opening in the basket floor. Finally, the filter medium is rinsed clean to complete the cycle. Usually, the batch cycle is completely automated. Automatic batch centrifugals have basket sizes up to about 1.2 m in diameter and usually rotate below 4000 rpm.

Continuous centrifugal filters are available with capacities up to about 25 000 kg solids/h. Intermittently, the cake deposited on the filter medium is removed by being pushed toward the discharge end by a pusher, which then retreats, allowing the cake to build up once more. As the cake is being pushed, it passes through a wash region. The filtrate and wash liquid are kept separate by partitions in the collector. Details of different types of centrifugal filters are available (P1).

14.4F Gas–Solid Cyclone Separators

1. Introduction and equipment.   For separation of small solid particles or mist from gases, the most widely used type of equipment is the cyclone separator, shown in Fig. 14.4-6. The cyclone consists of a vertical cylinder with a conical bottom. The gas–solid particle mixture enters in a tangential inlet near the top. This gas–solid mixture enters in a rotating motion, and the vortex formed develops centrifugal force, which throws the particles radially toward the wall.

On entering, the air in the cyclone flows downward in a spiral or vortex adjacent to the wall. When the air reaches near the bottom of the cone, it spirals upward in a smaller spiral in the center of the cone and cylinder. Hence, a double vortex is present. The downward and upward spirals are in the same direction.

The particles are thrown toward the wall and fall downward, leaving out the bottom of the cone. A cyclone is a settling device in which the outward force on the particles at high tangential velocities is many times the force of gravity. Hence, cyclones accomplish much more effective separation than gravity settling chambers.

FIGURE 14.4-6.   *Gas–solid cyclone separator: (a) side view, (b) top view.*

The centrifugal force in a cyclone ranges from about 5 times gravity in large, low-velocity units to 2500 times gravity in small, high-resistance units. These devices are used often in many applications, such as in spray-drying of foods, where the dried particles are removed by cyclones; in cleaning dust-laden air; and in removing mist droplets from gases. Cyclones offer one of the least expensive means of gas–particle separation. They are generally applicable in removing particles over 5 μm in diameter from gases. For particles over 200 μm in size, gravity settling chambers are often used. Wet-scrubber cyclones are sometimes used, where water is sprayed inside, helping to remove the solids.

2. *Theory for cyclone separators.* It is assumed that particles on entering a cyclone quickly reach their terminal settling velocities. Particle sizes are usually so small that Stokes' law is considered valid. For centrifugal motion, the terminal radial velocity v_{tR} is given by Eq. (14.4-8), with v_{tR} being used for v_t:

$$v_{tR} = \frac{\omega^2 r D_p^2 (\rho_p - \rho)}{18\mu} \tag{14.4-35}$$

Since $\omega = v_{tan}/r$, where v_{tan} is tangential velocity of the particle at radius r, Eq. (14.4-35) becomes

$$v_{tR} = \frac{D_p^2 g(\rho_p - \rho)}{18\mu} \frac{v_{tan}^2}{gr} = v_t \frac{v_{tan}^2}{gr} \tag{14.4-36}$$

where v_t is the gravitational terminal settling velocity v_t in Eq. (14.3-9).

The higher the terminal velocity v_t, the greater the radial velocity v_{tR} and the easier it should be to "settle" the particle at the walls. However, the evaluation of the radial velocity is difficult, since it is a function of gravitational terminal velocity, tangential velocity, and position radially and axially in the cyclone. Hence, the following empirical equation is often used (S2):

$$v_{tR} = \frac{b_1 D_p^2 (\rho_p - \rho)}{18\mu r^n} \tag{14.4-37}$$

where b_1 and n are empirical constants.

3. *Efficiency of collection of cyclones.* Smaller particles have smaller settling velocities according to Eq. (14.4-37) and do not have time to reach the wall to be collected. Hence, they leave with the exit air in a cyclone. Larger particles are more readily collected. The efficiency of separation for a given particle diameter is defined as the mass fraction of the size particles that are collected.

A typical collection-efficiency plot for a cyclone shows that the efficiency rises rapidly with particle size. The cut diameter D_{pc} is the diameter for which one-half of the mass of the entering particles is retained.

14.5 MECHANICAL SIZE REDUCTION

14.5A Introduction

Many solid materials occur in sizes that are too large to be used and must be reduced. Often the solids are reduced in size so that the separation of various ingredients can be carried out. In general, the terms *crushing* and *grinding* are used to signify the subdividing of large solid particles into smaller particles.

In the food-processing industry, a large number of food products are subjected to size reduction. Roller mills are used to grind wheat and rye to flour and to grind corn. Soybeans are rolled, pressed, and ground to produce oil and flour. Hammer mills are often used to produce potato flour, tapioca, and other flours. Sugar is ground to a finer product.

Grinding operations are very extensive in the ore-processing and cement industries. Copper ores, nickel and cobalt ores, and iron ores, for example, are ground before chemical processing. Limestone, marble, gypsum, and dolomite are ground to use as fillers in paper, paint, and rubber. Raw materials for the cement industry, such as lime, alumina, and silica, are ground on a very large scale.

Solids may be reduced in size by a number of methods. *Compression* or *crushing* is generally used for reduction of hard solids to coarse sizes. *Impact* gives coarse, medium, or fine sizes. *Attrition* or *rubbing* yields fine products. *Cutting* is used to give definite sizes.

14.5B Particle-Size Measurement

The feed-to-size reduction processes and the product are defined in terms of the particle-size distribution. One common way to plot particle sizes is to plot particle diameter (sieve opening in screen) in mm or μm versus the cumulative percent retained at that size. (Openings for various screen sizes are given in Appendix A.5.) Such a plot was given on arithmetic probability paper in Fig. 12.12-2.

Often the plot is made, instead, as the cumulative amount as percent smaller than the stated size versus particle size, as shown in Fig. 14.5-1a. In Fig. 14.5-1b the same data are plotted as a particle-distribution curve. The ordinate is obtained by taking the slopes of the 5-μm intervals of Fig. 14.5-1a and converting to percent by weight per μm. Complete particle-size analysis is necessary for most comparisons and calculations.

FIGURE 14.5-1. *Particle-size-distribution curves: (a) cumulative percent versus particle size, (b) percent by weight per μm versus particle size. (From R. H. Perry and C. H. Chilton,* Chemical Engineers' Handbook, *5th ed. New York: McGraw-Hill Book Company, 1973. With permission.)*

14.5C Energy and Power Required in Size Reduction

1. Introduction. In size reduction of solids, feed materials of solid are reduced to a smaller size by mechanical action. The materials are fractured. The particles of feed are first distorted and strained by the action of the size-reduction machine. This work to strain the particles is first stored temporarily in the solid as strain energy. As additional force is added to the stressed particles, the strain energy exceeds a certain level, and the material fractures into smaller pieces.

When the material fractures, new surface area is created. Each new unit area of surface requires a certain amount of energy. Some of the energy added is used to create the new surface, but a large portion of it appears as heat. The energy required for fracture is a complicated function of the type of material, size, hardness, and other factors.

The magnitude of the mechanical force applied; the duration; the type of force, such as compression, shear, and impact; and other factors affect the extent and efficiency of the size-reduction process. The important factors in the size-reduction process are the amount of energy or power used and the particle size and new surface formed.

2. Power required in size reduction. The various theories or laws proposed for predicting power requirements for size reduction of solids do not apply well in practice. The most important ones will be discussed briefly. Part of the problem with the theories is estimating the theoretical amount of energy required to fracture and create new surface area. Approximate calculations give actual efficiencies of about 0.1 to 2%.

The theories derived depend upon the assumption that the energy E required to produce a change dX in a particle of size X is a power function of X:

$$\frac{dE}{dX} = -\frac{C}{X^n} \tag{14.5-1}$$

where X is size or diameter of particle in mm, and n and C are constants depending upon type and size of material and type of machine.

Rittinger proposed a law which states that the work in crushing is proportional to the new surface created. This leads to a value of $n = 2$ in Eq. (14.5-1), since area is proportional to length squared. Integrating Eq. (14.5-1),

$$E = \frac{C}{n-1}\left(\frac{1}{X_2^{n-1}} - \frac{1}{X_1^{n-1}}\right) \tag{14.5-2}$$

where X_1 is mean diameter of feed and X_2 is mean diameter of product. Since $n = 2$ for Rittinger's equation, we obtain

$$E = K_R\left(\frac{1}{X_2} - \frac{1}{X_1}\right) \tag{14.5-3}$$

where E is work to reduce a unit mass of feed from X_1 to X_2 and K_R is a constant. The law implies that the same amount of energy is needed to reduce a material from 100 mm to 50 mm as is needed to reduce the same material from 50 mm to 33.3 mm. It has been found experimentally that this law has some validity in grinding fine powders.

Kick assumed that the energy required to reduce a material in size was directly proportional to the size-reduction ratio. This implies $n = 1$ in Eq. (14.5-1), giving

$$E = C \ln \frac{X_1}{X_2} = K_K \log \frac{X_1}{X_2} \tag{14.5-4}$$

where K_K is a constant. This law implies that the same amount of energy is required to reduce a material from 100 mm to 50 mm as is needed to reduce the same material from 50 mm to 25 mm.

Recent data by Bond (B3) on correlating extensive experimental data suggest that the work required using a large-size feed is proportional to the square root of the surface/volume ratio of the product. This corresponds to $n = 1.5$ in Eq. (14.5-1), giving

$$E = K_B \frac{1}{\sqrt{X_2}} \qquad (14.5\text{-}5)$$

where K_B is a constant. To use Eq. (14.4-5), Bond proposed a work index E_i as the work in kW·h/ton required to reduce a unit weight from a very large size to 80% passing a 100-μm screen. Then the work E is the gross work required to reduce a unit weight of feed with 80% passing a diameter X_F μm to a product with 80% passing X_P μm.

Bond's final equation, in terms of English units, is

$$\frac{P}{T} = 1.46 E_i \left(\frac{1}{\sqrt{D_P}} - \frac{1}{\sqrt{D_F}} \right) \qquad (14.5\text{-}6)$$

where P is hp, T is feed rate in tons/min, D_F is size of feed in ft, and D_P is product size in ft. Typical values of E_i for various types of materials are given in Perry and Green (P1) and by Bond (B3). Some typical values are bauxite ($E_i = 9.45$), coal (11.37), potash salt (8.23), shale (16.4), and granite (14.39). These values should be multiplied by 1.34 for dry grinding.

EXAMPLE 14.5-1. Power to Crush Iron Ore by Bond's Theory

It is desired to crush 10 ton/h of iron ore hematite. The size of the feed is such that 80% passes a 3-in. (76.2-mm) screen and 80% of the product is to pass a $\frac{1}{8}$-in. (3.175-mm) screen. Calculate the gross power required. Use a work index E_i for iron ore hematite of 12.68 (P1).

Solution: The feed size is $D_F = \frac{3}{12} = 0.250$ ft (76.2 mm) and the product size is $D_P = \frac{1}{8}/12 = 0.0104$ ft (3.175 mm). The feed rate is $T = 10/60 = 0.167$ ton/min. Substituting into Eq. (14.5-6) and solving for P,

$$\frac{P}{0.167} = (1.46)(12.68) \left(\frac{1}{\sqrt{0.0104}} - \frac{1}{\sqrt{0.250}} \right)$$

$$P = 24.1 \text{ hp } (17.96 \text{ kW})$$

14.5D Equipment for Size Reduction

1. Introduction and classification. Size-reduction equipment may be classified according to the way the forces are applied as follows: between two surfaces, as in crushing and shearing; at one solid surface, as in impact; and by action of the surrounding medium, as in a colloid mill. A more practical classification is to divide the equipment into crushers, grinders, fine grinders, and cutters.

2. Jaw crushers. Equipment for coarse reduction of large amounts of solids consists of slow-speed machines called *crushers.* Several types are in common use. In the first type, a jaw crusher, the material is fed between two heavy jaws or flat plates. As shown in the *Dodge crusher* in Fig. 14.5-2a, one jaw is fixed and the other reciprocating and movable on a pivot where K_1 is a constant. This law implies that the same amount of energy is required to reduce a material from 100 mm to 50 mm as is needed to reduce the same material from 50 mm to 25 mm.

Rearranging Eq. (14.5-?) Kick concentrating... the work concentrated as heat... it is important to reduce power... the volume ratio of the product...

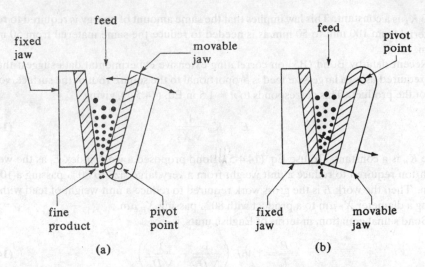

FIGURE 14.5-2. *Types of jaw crushers: (a) Dodge type, (b) Blake type.*

point at the bottom. The jaw swings back and forth, pivoting at the bottom of the V. The material is gradually worked down into a narrower space, being crushed as it moves.

The *Blake crusher* in Fig. 14.5-2b is more commonly used, where the pivot point is at the top of the movable jaw. The reduction ratios average about 8:1 in the Blake crusher. Jaw crushers are used mainly for primary crushing of hard materials and are usually followed by other types of crushers.

3. Gyratory crushers. The *gyratory crusher* shown in Fig. 14.5-3a has to a large extent taken over in the field of large hard-ore and mineral crushing applications. Basically it is like a mortar-and-pestle crusher. The movable crushing head is shaped like an inverted truncated cone and is inside a truncated cone casing. The crushing head rotates eccentrically and the material being crushed is trapped between the outer fixed cone and the inner gyrating cone.

4. Roll crushers. In Fig. 14.5-3b a typical smooth *roll crusher* is shown. The rolls are rotated toward each other at the same or different speeds. Wear of the rolls is a serious problem. The reduction ratio varies from about 4:1 to 2.5:1. Single rolls are often used, rotating against a fixed surface, and corrugated and toothed rolls are also used. Many food products that are not hard materials, such as flour, soybeans, and starch, are ground on rolls.

5. Hammer mill grinders. *Hammer mill devices* are used to reduce intermediate-sized material to small sizes or powder. Often the product from jaw and gyratory crushers is the feed to the hammer mill. In the hammer mill a high-speed rotor turns inside a cylindrical casing. Sets of hammers are attached to pivot points at the outside of the rotor. The feed enters the top of the casing and the particles are broken as they fall through the cylinder. The material is broken by the impact of the hammers and pulverized into powder between the hammers and casing. The powder then passes through a grate or screen at the discharge end.

6. Revolving grinding mills. For intermediate and fine reduction of materials, *revolving grinding mills* are often used. In such mills a cylindrical or conical shell rotating on a horizontal axis is charged with a grinding medium such as steel, flint, or porcelain balls, or with

feed

crushing head

fixed cone

feed

(a)

(b)

FIGURE 14.5-3. *Types of size-reduction equipment: (a) gyratory crusher, (b) roll crusher.*

steel rods. The size reduction is effected by the tumbling of the balls or rods on the material between them. In the revolving mill, the grinding elements are carried up the side of the shell and fall on the particles underneath. These mills may operate wet or dry.

Equipment for very fine grinding is highly specialized. In some cases two flat disks are used, where one or both disks rotate and grind the material caught between the disks (P1).

PROBLEMS

14.2-1. Constant-Pressure Filtration and Filtration Constants. Data for the filtration of $CaCO_3$ slurry in water at 298.2 K (25°C) are reported as follows (R1, R2, M1) at a constant pressure $(-\Delta p)$ of 46.2 kN/m² (6.70 psia). The area of the plate-and-frame press was 0.0439 m² (0.473 ft²) and the slurry concentration was 23.47 kg solid/m³ filtrate. Calculate the constants α and R_m. Data are given as t = time in s and V = volume of filtrate collected in m³.

$V \times 10^3$	t	$V \times 10^3$	t	$V \times 10^3$	t
0.5	17.3	1.5	72.0	2.5	152.0
1.0	41.3	2.0	108.3	3.0	201.7

Ans. $\alpha = 1.106 \times 10^{11}$ m/kg $(1.65 \times 10^{11}$ ft/lb$_m)$,
$R_m = 6.40 \times 10^{10}$ m^{-1} $(1.95 \times 10^{10}$ ft$^{-1})$

14.2-2. Filtration Constants for Constants-Pressure Filtration. Data for constant-pressure filtration at 194.4 kN/m² are reported for the same slurry and press as in Problem 14.2-1 as follows, where t is in s and V in m³:

$V \times 10^3$	t	$V \times 10^3$	t	$V \times 10^3$	t
0.5	6.3	2.5	51.7	4.5	134.0
1.0	14.0	3.0	69.0	5.0	160.0
1.5	24.2	3.5	88.8		
2.0	37.0	4.0	110.0		

Calculate the constants α and R_m.

Ans. $\alpha = 1.61 \times 10^{11}$ m/kg

14.2-3. Compressibility of Filter Cake. Use the data for specific cake resistance α from Example 14.2-1 and Problems 14.2-1 and 14.2-2 and determine the compressibility constant s in Eq. (14.2-11). Plot $\ln \alpha$ versus $\ln(-\Delta p)$ and determine the slope s.

14.2-4. Prediction of Filtration Time and Washing Time. The slurry used in Problem 14.2-1 is to be filtered in a plate-and-frame press having 30 frames and 0.873 m^2 area per frame. The same pressure, 46.2 kN/m^2, will be used in constant-pressure filtration. Assume the same filter-cake properties and filter cloth, and calculate the time to recover 2.26 m^3 of filtrate. At the end, using through-washing and 0.283 m^3 of wash water, calculate the time of washing and the total filter-cycle time if cleaning the press takes 30 min.

14.2-5. Constants in Constant-Pressure Filtration. McMillen and Webber (M2), using a filter press with an area of 0.0929 m^2, performed constant-pressure filtration at 34.5 kPa of a 13.9 wt % CaCO$_3$ solids in water slurry at 300 K. The mass ratio of wet cake to dry cake was 1.59. The dry-cake density was 1017 kg/m^3. The data obtained are as follows, where W = kg filtrate and t = time in s:

W	t	W	t	W	t
0.91	24	3.63	244	6.35	690
1.81	71	4.54	372	7.26	888
2.72	146	5.44	524	8.16	1188

Calculate the values of α and R_m.

14.2-6. Constant-Pressure Filtration and Washing in a Leaf Filter. An experimental filter press having an area of 0.0414 m^2 (R1) is used to filter an aqueous BaCO$_3$ slurry at a constant pressure of 267 kPa. The filtration equation obtained was

$$\frac{t}{V} = 10.25 \times 10^6 V + 3.4 \times 10^3$$

where t is in s and V in m^3.

(a) If the same slurry and conditions are used in a leaf press having an area of 6.97 m^2, how long will it take to obtain 1.00 m^3 of filtrate?

(b) After filtration, the cake is to be washed with 0.100 m^3 of water. Calculate the time of washing.

Ans. (a) $= 381.8$ s

14.2-7. Constant-Rate Filtration of Incompressible Cake. The filtration equation for filtration at a constant pressure of 38.7 psia (266.8 kPa) is

$$\frac{t}{V} = 6.10 \times 10^{-5} V + 0.01$$

where t is in s, $-\Delta p$ in psia, and V in liters. The specific resistance of the cake is independent of pressure. If the filtration is run at a constant rate of 10 liters/s, how long will it take to reach 50 psia?

14.2-8. Effect of Filter-Medium Resistance on Continuous Rotary-Drum Filter. Repeat Example 14.2-4 for the continuous rotary-drum vacuum filter but do not neglect the constant R_m, which is the filter-medium resistance to flow. Compare with results of Example 14.2-4.

Ans. $A = 7.78$ m^2

14.2-9. *Throughput in Continuous Rotary-Drum Filter.* A rotary-drum filter having an area of 2.20 m^2 is to be used to filter the CaCO$_3$ slurry given in Example 14.2-4. The drum has a 28% submergence and the filter-cycle time is 300 s. A pressure drop of 62.0 kN/m^2 is to be used. Calculate the slurry feed rate in kg slurry/s for the following cases:
   (a) Neglect the filter-medium resistance.
   (b) Do not neglect the value of B.

14.3-1. *Settling Velocity of a Coffee-Extract Particle.* Solid spherical particles of coffee extract (F1) from a dryer having a diameter of 400 μm are falling through air at a temperature of 422 K. The density of the particles is 1030 kg/m^3. Calculate the terminal settling velocity and the distance of fall in 5 s. The pressure is 101.32 kPa.

Ans. $v_t = 1.49$ m/s, 7.45 m fall

14.3-2. *Terminal Settling Velocity of Dust Particles.* Calculate the terminal settling velocity of dust particles having a diameter of 60 μm in air at 294.3 K and 101.32 kPa. The dust particles can be considered spherical, with a density of 1280 kg/m^3.

Ans. $v_t = 0.1372$ m/s

14.3-3. *Settling Velocity of Liquid Particles.* Oil droplets having a diameter of 200 μm are settling from still air at 294.3 K and 101.32 kPa. The density of the oil is 900 kg/m^3. A settling chamber is 0.457 m high. Calculate the terminal settling velocity. How long will it take the particles to settle? (*Note:* If the Reynolds number is above about 100, the equations and form-drag correlation for rigid spheres cannot be used.)

14.3-4. *Settling Velocity of Quartz Particles in Water.* Solid quartz particles having a diameter of 1000 μm are settling from water at 294.3 K. The density of the spherical particles is 2650 kg/m^3. Calculate the terminal settling velocity of these particles.

14.3-5. *Hindered Settling of Solid Particles.* Solid spherical particles having a diameter of 0.090 mm and a solid density of 2002 kg/m^3 are settling in a solution of water at 26.7°C. The volume fraction of the solids in the water is 0.45. Calculate the settling velocity and the Reynolds number.

14.3-6. *Settling of Quartz Particles in Hindered Settling.* Particles of quartz having a diameter of 0.127 mm and a specific gravity of 2.65 are settling in water at 293.2 K. The volume fraction of the particles in the slurry mixture of quartz and water is 0.25. Calculate the hindered settling velocity and the Reynolds number.

14.3-7. *Density Effect on Settling Velocity and Diameter.* Calculate the terminal settling velocity of a glass sphere 0.080 mm in diameter having a density of 2469 kg/m^3 in air at 300 K and 101.32 kPa. Also calculate the diameter of a sphalerite sphere having a specific gravity of 4.00 with the same terminal settling velocity.

14.3-8. *Differential Settling of Particles.* Repeat Example 14.3-3 for particles having a size range of 1.27×10^{-2} mm to 5.08×10^{-2} mm. Calculate the size range of the various fractions obtained using free settling conditions. Also calculate the value of the largest Reynolds number occurring.

14.3-9. *Separation by Settling.* A mixture of galena and silica particles has a size range of 0.075–0.65 mm and is to be separated by a rising stream of water at 293.2 K. Use specific gravities from Example 14.3-3.
   (a) To obtain an uncontaminated product of galena, what velocity of water flow is needed and what is the size range of the pure product?

(b) If another liquid, such as benzene, having a specific gravity of 0.85 and a viscosity of 6.50×10^{-4} Pa·s is used, what velocity is needed and what is the size range of the pure product?

14.3-10. *Separation by Sink-and-Float Method.* Quartz having a specific gravity of 2.65 and hematite having a specific gravity of 5.1 are present in a mixture of particles. It is desired to separate them by a sink-and-float method using a suspension of fine particles of ferrosilicon having a specific gravity of 6.7 in water. At what consistency in vol % ferrosilicon solids in water should the medium be maintained for the separation?

14.3-11. *Batch Settling and Sedimentation Velocities.* A batch settling test on a slurry gave the following results, where the height z in meters between the clear liquid and the suspended solids is given at time t hours:

t (h)	z (m)	t (h)	z (m)	t (h)	z (m)
0	0.360	1.75	0.150	12.0	0.102
0.50	0.285	3.00	0.125	20.0	0.090
1.00	0.211	5.00	0.113		

The original slurry concentration is 250 kg/m³ of slurry. Determine the velocities of settling and concentrations and make a plot of velocity versus concentration.

14.4-1. *Comparison of Forces in Centrifuges.* Two centrifuges rotate at the same peripheral velocity of 53.34 m/s. The first bowl has a radius of $r_1 = 76.2$ mm and the second $r_2 = 305$ mm. Calculate the rev/min and the centrifugal forces developed in each bowl.

> **Ans.** $N_1 = 6684$ rev/min, $N_2 = 1670$ rev/min, 3806 g's in bowl 1951 g's in bowl 2

14.4-2. *Forces in a Centrifuge.* A centrifuge bowl is spinning at a constant 2000 rev/min. What radius bowl is needed for the following?
(a) A force of 455 g's.
(b) A force four times that in part (a).

> **Ans.** (a) $r = 0.1017$ m

14.4-3. *Effect of Varying Centrifuge Dimensions and Speed.* Repeat Example 14.4-2 but with the following changes:
(a) Reduce the rev/min to 10 000 and double the outer-bowl radius r_2 to 0.0445 m, keeping $r_1 = 0.00716$ m.
(b) Keep all variables as in Example 14.4-2 but double the throughput.

> **Ans.** (b) $D_p = 1.747 \times 10^{-6}$ m

14.4-4. *Centrifuging to Remove Food Particles.* A dilute slurry contains small solid food particles having a diameter of 5×10^{-2} mm which are to be removed by centrifuging. The particle density is 1050 kg/m³ and the solution density is 1000 kg/m³. The viscosity of the liquid is 1.2×10^{-3} Pa·s. A centrifuge at 3000 rev/min is to be used. The bowl dimensions are $b = 100.1$ mm, $r_1 = 5.00$ mm, and $r_2 = 30.0$ mm. Calculate the expected flow rate in m³/s just to remove these particles.

14.4-5. *Effect of Oil Density on Interface Location.* Repeat Example 14.4-3, but for the case where the vegetable-oil density has been decreased to 914.7 kg/m³.

14.4-6. *Interface in Cream Separator.* A cream-separator centrifuge has an outlet discharge radius $r_1 = 50.8$ mm and outlet radius $r_4 = 76.2$ mm. The density of the skim milk is

1032 kg/m^3 and that of the cream is 865 kg/m^3 (E1). Calculate the radius of the interface neutral zone.

Ans. $r_2 = 150 \text{ mm}$

14.4-7. Scale-Up and Σ Values of Centrifuges. For the conditions given in Example 14.4-2, do as follows:
(a) Calculate the Σ value.
(b) A new centrifuge having the following dimensions is to be used: $r_2 = 0.0445$ m, $r_1 = 0.01432$ m, $b = 0.394$ m, and $N = 26\,000$ rev/min. Calculate the new Σ value and scale up the flow rate using the same solution.

Ans.   (a) $\Sigma = 196.3 \text{ m}^2$

14.4-8. Centrifugal Filtration Process. A batch centrifugal filter similar to Fig. 14.4-5 has a bowl height $b = 0.457$ m and $r_2 = 0.381$ m and operates at 33.33 rev/s at 25.0°C. The filtrate is essentially water. At a given time in the cycle, the slurry and cake formed have the following properties: $c_S = 60.0$ kg solids/m³ filtrate, $\varepsilon = 0.82$, $\rho_p = 2002$ kg solids/m³, cake thickness $= 0.152$ m, $\alpha = 6.38 \times 10^{10}$ m/kg, $R_m = 8.53 \times 10^{10}$ m⁻¹, $r_1 = 0.2032$ m. Calculate the rate of filtrate flow.

Ans. $q = 6.11 \times 10^{-4} \text{ m}^3/\text{s}$

14.5-1. Change in Power Requirements in Crushing. In crushing a certain ore, the feed is such that 80% is less than 50.8 mm in size, and the product size is such that 80% is less than 6.35 mm. The power required is 89.5 kW. What will be the power required using the same feed so that 80% is less than 3.18 mm? Use the Bond equation. (*Hint:* The work index E_i is unknown, but it can be determined using the original experimental data in terms of T. In the equation for the new size, the same unknowns appear. Dividing one equation by the other will eliminate these unknowns.)

Ans.   146.7 kW

14.5-2. Crushing of Phosphate Rock. It is desired to crush 100 ton/h of phosphate rock from a feed size where 80% is less than 4 in. to a product where 80% is less than $\frac{1}{8}$ in. The work index is 10.13 (P1).
(a) Calculate the power required.
(b) Calculate the power required to crush the product further to where 80% is less than 1000 μm.

REFERENCES

(B1)   BADGER, W. L., and BANCHERO, J. T. *Introduction to Chemical Engineering*. New York: McGraw-Hill Book Company, 1955.

(B2)   BECKER, H. A. *Can. J. Chem. Eng., 37*, 85 (1951).

(B3)   BOND, F. C. *Trans. A.I.M.E., 193*, 484 (1952).

(C1)   COULSON, J. M., and RICHARDSON, J. F. *Chemical Engineering*, Vol. 2, 3rd ed. New York: Pergamon Press, Inc., 1978.

(E1)   EARLE, R. L. *Unit Operations in Food Processing*. Oxford: Pergamon Press, Inc., 1966.

(F1)   FOUST, A. S., et al. *Principles of Unit Operations*, 2nd ed. New York: John Wiley & Sons, Inc., 1980.

(F2)   FITCH, B. *Ind. Eng. Chem., 58*(10), 18 (1966).

(G1)   GRACE, H. P. *Chem. Eng. Progr., 46*, 467 (1950); *49*, 303, 367, 427 (1953); *A.I.Ch.E. J., 2*, 307 (1956).

(H1)   HUGHES, R. R., and GILLILAND, E. R. *Chem. Eng. Progr., 48*, 497 (1952).

(K1)   KYNCH, G. J. *Trans. Faraday Soc., 48*, 166 (1952).

(L1) LARIAN, M. G. *Fundamentals of Chemical Engineering Operations*. Englewood Cliffs, N.J.: Prentice-Hall, Inc., 1958.

(L2) LAPPLE, C. E., and SHEPHERD, C. B. *Ind. Eng. Chem.*, **32,** 605 (1940).

(M1) MCCABE, W. L., and SMITH, J. C. *Unit Operations of Chemical Engineering*, 3rd ed. New York: McGraw-Hill Book Company, 1976.

(M2) MCMILLEN, E. L., and WEBBER, H. A. *Trans. A.I.Ch.E.*, **34,** 213 (1938).

(N1) NICKOLAUS, N., and DAHLSTROM, D. A. *Chem. Eng. Progr.*, **52**(3), 87M (1956).

(P1) PERRY, R. H., and GREEN, D. *Perry's Chemical Engineers' Handbook,* 6th ed. New York: McGraw-Hill Book Company, 1984.

(P2) PERRY, R. H., and CHILTON, C. H. *Chemical Engineers' Handbook,* 5th ed. New York: McGraw-Hill Book Company, 1973.

(R1) RUTH, B. F., and KEMPE, L. L. *Trans. A.I.Ch.E.*, **34,** 213 (1938).

(R2) RUTH, B. F. *Ind. Eng. Chem.,* **25,** 157 (1933).

(S1) STEINOUR, H. H. *Ind. Eng. Chem.,* **36,** 618, 840 (1944).

(S2) SHEPHERD, C. B., and LAPPLE, C. E. *Ind. Eng. Chem.,* **31,** 972 (1939); **32,** 1246 (1940).

(T1) TALMAGE, W. P., and FITCH, E. B. *Ind. Eng. Chem.,* **47**(1), 38 (1955).

(Z1) ZENZ, F. A., and OTHMER, D. F. *Fluidization and Fluid-Particle Systems.* New York: Reinhold Publishing Co., Inc., 1960.

Chapter 14   Mechanical–Physical Separation Processes

APPENDIX A.1

Fundamental Constants
and Conversion Factors

A.1-1 Gas Law Constant R

Numerical Value	Units
1.9872	g cal/g mol $\cdot$ K
1.9872	btu/lb mol $\cdot$ °R
82.057	cm^3 $\cdot$ atm/g mol $\cdot$ K
8314.34	J/kg mol $\cdot$ K
82.057 $\times$ 10^{-3}	m^3 $\cdot$ atm/kg mol $\cdot$ K
8314.34	kg $\cdot$ m^2/s^2 $\cdot$ kg mol $\cdot$ K
10.731	ft^3 $\cdot$ lb$_f$/in.^{2} $\cdot$ lb mol $\cdot$ °R
0.7302	ft^3 $\cdot$ atm/lb mol $\cdot$ °R
1545.3	ft $\cdot$ lb$_f$/lb mol $\cdot$ °R
8314.34	m^3 $\cdot$ Pa/kg mol $\cdot$ K

A.1-2 Volume and Density

1 g mol ideal gas at 0°C, 760 mm Hg = 22.4140 liters = 22 414 cm^3

1 lb mol ideal gas at 0°C, 760 mm Hg = 359.05 ft^3

1 kg mol ideal gas at 0°C, 760 mm Hg = 22.414 m^3

Density of dry air at 0°C, 760 mm Hg = 1.2929 g/liter
$\qquad\qquad\qquad\qquad\qquad\qquad\quad$ = 0.080711 lb$_m$/ft^3

Molecular weight of air = 28.97 lb$_m$/lb mol = 28.97 g/g mol

1 g/cm^3 = 62.43 lb$_m$/ft^3 = 1000 kg/m^3

1 g/cm^3 = 8.345 lb$_m$/U.S. gal

1 lb$_m$/ft^3 = 16.0185 kg/m^3

A.1-3   Length

1 in. = 2.540 cm

100 cm = 1 m (meter)

1 micron = 10^{-6} m = 10^{-4} cm = 10^{-3} mm = 1 μm (micrometer)

1 Å (angstrom) = 10^{-10} m = 10^{-4} μm

1 mile = 5280 ft

1 m = 3.2808 ft = 39.37 in.

A.1-4   Mass

1 lb_m = 453.59 g = 0.45359 kg

1 lb_m = 16 oz = 7000 grains

1 kg = 1000 g = 2.2046 lb_m

1 ton (short) = 2000 lb_m

1 ton (long) = 2240 lb_m

1 ton (metric) = 1000 kg

A.1-5   Standard Acceleration of Gravity

g = 9.80665 m/s^2

g = 980.665 cm/s^2

g = 32.174 ft/s^2

g_c (gravitational conversion factor) = 32.1740 $lb_m \cdot$ ft/$lb_f \cdot$ s^2

$\qquad\qquad\qquad\qquad\qquad\qquad\quad$ = 980.665 $g_m \cdot$ cm/$g_f \cdot$ s^2

A.1-6   Volume

1 L (liter) = 1000 cm^3	1 m^3 = 1000 L (liter)
1 in.^{3} = 16.387 cm^3	1 U.S. gal = 4 qt
1 ft^3 = 28.317 L (liter)	1 U.S. gal = 3.7854 L (liter)
1 ft^3 = 0.028317 m^3	1 U.S. gal = 3785.4 cm^3
1 ft^3 = 7.481 U.S. gal	1 British gal = 1.20094 U.S. gal
1 m^3 = 264.17 U.S. gal	1 m^3 = 35.313 ft^3

A.1-7   Force

1 g $\cdot$ cm/s^2 (dyn) = 10^{-5} kg $\cdot$ m/s^2 = 10^{-5} N (newton)

1 g $\cdot$ cm/s^2 = 7.2330 $\times$ 10^{-5} $lb_m \cdot$ ft/s^2 (poundal)

1 kg $\cdot$ m/s^2 = 1 N (newton)

1 lb_f = 4.4482 N

1 g $\cdot$ cm/s^2 = 2.2481 $\times$ 10^{-6} lb_f

A.1-8   Pressure

1 bar = 1 $\times$ 10^5 Pa (pascal) = 1 $\times$ 10^5 N/m^2

1 psia = 1 lb_f/in.^{2}

1 psia = 2.0360 in. Hg at 0°C

1 psia = 2.311 ft H$_2$O at 70°F

1 psia = 51.715 mm Hg at 0°C (ρ_{Hg} = 13.5955 g/cm^3)

1 atm = 14.696 psia = 1.01325 $\times$ 10^5 N/m^2 = 1.01325 bar

1 atm = 760 mm Hg at 0°C = 1.01325 $\times$ 10^5 Pa = 1.01325 $\times$ 10^2 kPa

1 atm = 29.921 in. Hg at 0°C
1 atm = 33.90 ft H_2O at 4°C
1 psia = 6.89476 × 10^4 g/cm · s^2
1 psia = 6.89476 × 10^4 dyn/cm^2
1 dyn/cm^2 = 2.0886 × 10^{-3} lb_f/ft^2
1 psia = 6.89476 × 10^3 N/m^2 = 6.89476 × 10^3 Pa
1 lb_f/ft^2 = 4.7880 × 10^2 dyn/cm^2 = 47.880 N/m^2
1 mm Hg (0°C) = 1.333224 × 10^2 N/m^2 = 0.1333224 kPa

A.1-9 Power

1 hp = 0.74570 kW   1 watt (W) = 14.340 cal/min
1 hp = 550 ft· lb_f/s   1 btu/h = 0.29307 W (watt)
1 hp = 0.7068 btu/s   1 J/s (joule/s) = 1 W

A.1-10 Heat, Energy, Work

1 J = 1 N · m = 1 kg · m^2/s^2
1 kg · m^2/s^2 = 1 J (joule) = 10^7 g · cm^2/s^2 (erg)
1 btu = 1055.06 J = 1.05506 kJ
1 btu = 252.16 cal (thermochemical)
1 kcal (thermochemical) = 1000 cal = 4.1840 kJ
1 cal (thermochemical) = 4.1840 J
1 cal (IT) = 4.1868 J
1 btu = 251.996 cal (IT)
1 btu = 778.17 ft · lb_f
1 hp · h = 0.7457 kW · h
1 hp · h = 2544.5 btu
1 ft · lb_f = 1.35582 J
1 ft · lb_f/lb_m = 2.9890 J/kg

A.1-11 Thermal Conductivity

1 btu/h · ft · °F = 4.1365 × 10^{-3} cal/s · cm · °C
1 btu/h · ft · °F = 1.73073 W/m · K

A.1-12 Heat-Transfer Coefficient

1 btu/h · ft^2 · °F = 1.3571 × 10^{-4} cal/s · cm^2 · °C
1 btu/h · ft^2 · °F = 5.6783 × 10^{-4} W/cm^2 · °C
1 btu/h · ft^2 · °F = 5.6783 W/m^2 · K
1 kcal/h · m^2 · °F = 0.2048 btu/h · ft^2 · °F

A.1-13 Viscosity

1 cp = 10^{-2} g/cm · s (poise)
1 cp = 2.4191 lb_m/ft · h
1 cp = 6.7197 × 10^{-4} lb_m/ft · s
1 cp = 10^{-3} Pa · s = 10^{-3} kg/m · s = 10^{-3} N · s/m^2
1 cp = 2.0886 × 10^{-5} lb_f · s/ft^2
1 Pa · s = 1 N · s/m^2 = 1 kg/m · s = 1000 cp = 0.67197 lb_m/ft · s

A.1-14 Diffusivity

$1 \text{ cm}^2/\text{s} = 3.875 \text{ ft}^2/\text{h}$ $1 \text{ m}^2/\text{s} = 3.875 \times 10^4 \text{ ft}^2/\text{h}$
$1 \text{ cm}^2/\text{s} = 10^{-4} \text{ m}^2/\text{s}$ $1 \text{ centistoke} = 10^{-2} \text{ cm}^2/\text{s}$
$1 \text{ m}^2/\text{h} = 10.764 \text{ ft}^2/\text{h}$

A.1-15 Mass Flux and Molar Flux

$1 \text{ g/s} \cdot \text{cm}^2 = 7.3734 \times 10^3 \text{ lb}_m/\text{h} \cdot \text{ft}^2$
$1 \text{ g mol/s} \cdot \text{cm}^2 = 7.3734 \times 10^3 \text{ lb mol/h} \cdot \text{ft}^2$
$1 \text{ g mol/s} \cdot \text{cm}^2 = 10 \text{ kg mol/s} \cdot \text{m}^2 = 1 \times 10^4 \text{ g mol/s} \cdot \text{m}^2$
$1 \text{ lb mol/h} \cdot \text{ft}^2 = 1.3562 \times 10^{-3} \text{ kg mol/s} \cdot \text{m}^2$

A.1-16 Heat Flux and Heat Flow

$1 \text{ btu/h} \cdot \text{ft}^2 = 3.1546 \text{ W/m}^2$
$1 \text{ btu/h} = 0.29307 \text{ W}$
$1 \text{ cal/h} = 1.1622 \times 10^{-3} \text{ W}$

A.1-17 Heat Capacity and Enthalpy

$1 \text{ btu/lb}_m \cdot {}^\circ\text{F} = 4.1868 \text{ kJ/kg} \cdot \text{K}$
$1 \text{ btu/lb}_m \cdot {}^\circ\text{F} = 1.000 \text{ cal/g} \cdot {}^\circ\text{C}$
$1 \text{ btu/lb}_m = 2326.0 \text{ J/kg}$
$1 \text{ ft} \cdot \text{lb}_f/\text{lb}_m = 2.9890 \text{ J/kg}$
$1 \text{ cal (IT)/g} \cdot {}^\circ\text{C} = 4.1868 \text{ kJ/kg} \cdot \text{K}$
$1 \text{ kcal/g mol} = 4.1840 \times 10^3 \text{ kJ/kg mol}$

A.1-18 Mass-Transfer Coefficient

$1 \, k_c \text{ cm/s} = 10^{-2} \text{ m/s}$
$1 \, k_c \text{ ft/h} = 8.4668 \times 10^{-5} \text{ m/s}$
$1 \, k_x \text{ g mol/s} \cdot \text{cm}^2 \cdot \text{mol frac} = 10 \text{ kg mol/s} \cdot \text{m}^2 \cdot \text{mol frac}$
$1 \, k_x \text{ g mol/s} \cdot \text{cm}^2 \cdot \text{mol frac} = 1 \times 10^4 \text{ g mol/s} \cdot \text{m}^2 \cdot \text{mol frac}$
$1 \, k_x \text{ lb mol/h} \cdot \text{ft}^2 \cdot \text{mol frac} = 1.3562 \times 10^{-3} \text{ kg mol/s} \cdot \text{m}^2 \cdot \text{mol frac}$
$1 \, k_x a \text{ lb mol/h} \cdot \text{ft}^3 \cdot \text{mol frac} = 4.449 \times 10^{-3} \text{ kg mol/s} \cdot \text{m}^3 \cdot \text{mol frac}$
$1 \, k_G \text{ kg mol/s} \cdot \text{m}^2 \cdot \text{atm} = 0.98692 \times 10^{-5} \text{ kg mol/s} \cdot \text{m}^2 \cdot \text{Pa}$
$1 \, k_G a \text{ kg mol/s} \cdot \text{m}^3 \cdot \text{atm} = 0.98692 \times 10^{-5} \text{ kg mol/s} \cdot \text{m}^3 \cdot \text{Pa}$

A.1-19 Temperature

$0{}^\circ\text{C} = 32{}^\circ\text{F}$ (freezing point of water)
$1.0 \text{ K} = 1.0{}^\circ\text{C} = 1.8{}^\circ\text{F} = 1.8{}^\circ\text{R}$ (Rankine)
${}^\circ\text{F} = 32 + 1.8 \, ({}^\circ\text{C})$
${}^\circ\text{C} = (1/1.8)({}^\circ\text{F} - 32)$
${}^\circ\text{R} = {}^\circ\text{F} + 459.67$
$\text{K} = {}^\circ\text{C} + 273.15$
$100{}^\circ\text{C} = 212{}^\circ\text{F} = 373.15 \text{ K} = 671.67{}^\circ\text{R}$
$0{}^\circ\text{C} = 32{}^\circ\text{F} = 273.15 \text{ K} = 491.67{}^\circ\text{R}$
$-273.15{}^\circ\text{C} = -459.67{}^\circ\text{F} = 0 \text{ K} = 0{}^\circ\text{R}$ (absolute zero)

APPENDIX A.2

Physical Properties
of Water

A.2-1 Latent Heat of Water at 273.15 K (0°C)

$$\text{Latent heat of fusion} = 1436.3 \text{ cal/g mol}$$
$$= 79.724 \text{ cal/g}$$
$$= 2585.3 \text{ btu/lb mol}$$
$$= 6013.4 \text{ kJ/kg mol}$$

Source: O. A. Hougen, K. M. Watson, and R. A. Ragatz, *Chemical Process Principles*, Part I, 2nd ed. New York: John Wiley & Sons, Inc., 1954.

Latent heat of vaporization at 298.15 K (25°C)

Pressure (mm Hg)	Latent Heat
23.75	44 020 kJ/kg mol, 10.514 kcal/g mol, 18 925 btu/lb mol
760	44 045 kJ/kg mol, 10.520 kcal/g mol, 18 936 btu/lb mol

Source: National Bureau of Standards, *Circular 500*.

A.2-2 Vapor Pressure of Water

Temperature		Vapor Pressure		Temperature		Vapor Pressure	
K	°C	kPa	mm Hg	K	°C	kPa	mm Hg
273.15	0	0.611	4.58	323.15	50	12.333	92.51
283.15	10	1.228	9.21	333.15	60	19.92	149.4
293.15	20	2.338	17.54	343.15	70	31.16	233.7
298.15	25	3.168	23.76	353.15	80	47.34	355.1
303.15	30	4.242	31.82	363.15	90	70.10	525.8
313.15	40	7.375	55.32	373.15	100	101.325	760.0

Source: Physikalish-technishe, Reichsansalt, Holborn, Scheel, and Henning, *Warmetabellen*. Brunswick, Germany: Friedrich Viewig and Son, 1909.

A.2-3 Density of Liquid Water

Temperature		Density		Temperature		Density	
K	°C	g/cm³	kg/m³	K	°C	g/cm³	kg/m³
273.15	0	0.99987	999.87	323.15	50	0.98807	988.07
277.15	4	1.00000	1000.00	333.15	60	0.98324	983.24
283.15	10	0.99973	999.73	343.15	70	0.97781	977.81
293.15	20	0.99823	998.23	353.15	80	0.97183	971.83
298.15	25	0.99708	997.08	363.15	90	0.96534	965.34
303.15	30	0.99568	995.68	373.15	100	0.95838	958.38
313.15	40	0.99225	992.25				

Source: R. H. Perry and C. H. Chilton, *Chemical Engineers' Handbook*, 5th ed. New York: McGraw-Hill Book Company, 1973. With permission.

A.2-4 Viscosity of Liquid Water

Temperature		Viscosity [(Pa·s)10³, (kg/m·s) 10³, or cp]	Temperature		Viscosity, [(Pa·s)10³, (kg/m·s) 10³, or cp]
K	°C		K	°C	
273.15	0	1.7921	323.15	50	0.5494
275.15	2	1.6728	325.15	52	0.5315
277.15	4	1.5674	327.15	54	0.5146
279.15	6	1.4728	329.15	56	0.4985
281.15	8	1.3860	331.15	58	0.4832
283.15	10	1.3077	333.15	60	0.4688
285.15	12	1.2363	335.15	62	0.4550
287.15	14	1.1709	337.15	64	0.4418
289.15	16	1.1111	339.15	66	0.4293
291.15	18	1.0559	341.15	68	0.4174
293.15	20	1.0050	343.15	70	0.4061
293.35	20.2	1.0000	345.15	72	0.3952
295.15	22	0.9579	347.15	74	0.3849
297.15	24	0.9142	349.15	76	0.3750
298.15	25	0.8937	351.15	78	0.3655
299.15	26	0.8737	353.15	80	0.3565
301.15	28	0.8360	355.15	82	0.3478
303.15	30	0.8007	357.15	84	0.3395
305.15	32	0.7679	359.15	86	0.3315
307.15	34	0.7371	361.15	88	0.3239
309.15	36	0.7085	363.15	90	0.3165
311.15	38	0.6814	365.15	92	0.3095
313.15	40	0.6560	367.15	94	0.3027
315.15	42	0.6321	369.15	96	0.2962
317.15	44	0.6097	371.15	98	0.2899
319.15	46	0.5883	373.15	100	0.2838
321.15	48	0.5683			

Source: Bingham, *Fluidity and Plasticity*. New York: McGraw-Hill Book Company, 1922. With permission.

A.2-5 Heat Capacity of Liquid Water at 101.325 kPa (1 Atm)

Temperature		Heat Capacity, c_p		Temperature		Heat Capacity, c_p	
°C	K	cal/g·°C	kJ/kg·K	°C	K	cal/g·°C	kJ/kg·K
0	273.15	1.0080	4.220	50	323.15	0.9992	4.183
10	283.15	1.0019	4.195	60	333.15	1.0001	4.187
20	293.15	0.9995	4.185	70	343.15	1.0013	4.192
25	298.15	0.9989	4.182	80	353.15	1.0029	4.199
30	303.15	0.9987	4.181	90	363.15	1.0050	4.208
40	313.15	0.9987	4.181	100	373.15	1.0076	4.219

Source: N. S. Osborne, H. F. Stimson, and D. C. Ginnings, *Bur. Standards J. Res.*, **23**, 197 (1939).

A.2-6 Thermal Conductivity of Liquid Water

Temperature			Thermal Conductivity	
°C	°F	K	btu/h·ft·°F	W/m·K
0	32	273.15	0.329	0.569
37.8	100	311.0	0.363	0.628
93.3	200	366.5	0.393	0.680
148.9	300	422.1	0.395	0.684
215.6	420	588.8	0.376	0.651
326.7	620	599.9	0.275	0.476

Source: D. L. Timrot and N. B. Vargaftik, *J. Tech. Phys. (U.S.S.R.)*, **10**, 1063 (1940); 6th International Conference on the Properties of Steam, Paris, 1964.

A.2-7 Vapor Pressure of Saturated Ice–Water Vapor and Heat of Sublimation

Temperature			Vapor Pressure			Heat of Sublimation	
K	°F	°C	kPa	psia	mm Hg	btu/lb$_m$	kJ/kg
273.2	32	0	6.107×10^{-1}	8.858×10^{-2}	4.581	1218.6	2834.5
266.5	20	−6.7	3.478×10^{-1}	5.045×10^{-2}	2.609	1219.3	2836.1
261.0	10	−12.2	2.128×10^{-1}	3.087×10^{-2}	1.596	1219.7	2837.0
255.4	0	−17.8	1.275×10^{-1}	1.849×10^{-2}	0.9562	1220.1	2838.0
249.9	−10	−23.3	7.411×10^{-2}	1.082×10^{-2}	0.5596	1220.3	2838.4
244.3	−20	−28.9	3.820×10^{-2}	6.181×10^{-3}	0.3197	1220.5	2838.9
238.8	−30	−34.4	2.372×10^{-2}	3.440×10^{-3}	0.1779	1220.5	2838.9
233.2	−40	−40.0	1.283×10^{-2}	1.861×10^{-3}	0.09624	1220.5	2838.9

Source: ASHRAE, *Handbook of Fundamentals*. New York: ASHRAE, 1972.

A.2-8 Heat Capacity of Ice

Temperature		c_p		Temperature		c_p	
°F	K	$btu/lb_m \cdot °F$	$kJ/kg \cdot K$	°F	K	$btu/lb_m \cdot °F$	$kJ/kg \cdot K$
32	273.15	0.500	2.093	−10	249.85	0.461	1.930
20	266.45	0.490	2.052	−20	244.25	0.452	1.892
10	260.95	0.481	2.014	−30	238.75	0.442	1.850
0	255.35	0.472	1.976	−40	233.15	0.433	1.813

Source: Adapted from ASHRAE, *Handbook of Fundamentals.* New York: ASHRAE, 1972.

A.2-9 Properties of Saturated Steam and Water (Steam Table), SI Units

Temper-ature (°C)	Vapor Pressure (kPa)	Specific Volume (m³/kg)		Enthalpy (kJ/kg)		Entropy (kJ/kg · K)	
		Liquid	Sat'd Vapor	Liquid	Sat'd Vapor	Liquid	Sat'd Vapor
0.01	0.6113	0.0010002	206.136	0.00	2501.4	0.0000	9.1562
3	0.7577	0.0010001	168.132	12.57	2506.9	0.0457	9.0773
6	0.9349	0.0010001	137.734	25.20	2512.4	0.0912	9.0003
9	1.1477	0.0010003	113.386	37.80	2517.9	0.1362	8.9253
12	1.4022	0.0010005	93.784	50.41	2523.4	0.1806	8.8524
15	1.7051	0.0010009	77.926	62.99	2528.9	0.2245	8.7814
18	2.0640	0.0010014	65.038	75.58	2534.4	0.2679	8.7123
21	2.487	0.0010020	54.514	88.14	2539.9	0.3109	8.6450
24	2.985	0.0010027	45.883	100.70	2545.4	0.3534	8.5794
25	3.169	0.0010029	43.360	104.89	2547.2	0.3674	8.5580
27	3.567	0.0010035	38.774	113.25	2550.8	0.3954	8.5156
30	4.246	0.0010043	32.894	125.79	2556.3	0.4369	8.4533
33	5.034	0.0010053	28.011	138.33	2561.7	0.4781	8.3927
36	5.947	0.0010063	23.940	150.86	2567.1	0.5188	8.3336
40	7.384	0.0010078	19.523	167.57	2574.3	0.5725	8.2570
45	9.593	0.0010099	15.258	188.45	2583.2	0.6387	8.1648
50	12.349	0.0010121	12.032	209.33	2592.1	0.7038	8.0763
55	15.758	0.0010146	9.568	230.23	2600.9	0.7679	7.9913
60	19.940	0.0010172	7.671	251.13	2609.6	0.8312	7.9096
65	25.03	0.0010199	6.197	272.06	2618.3	0.8935	7.8310
70	31.19	0.0010228	5.042	292.98	2626.8	0.9549	7.7553
75	38.58	0.0010259	4.131	313.93	2635.3	1.0155	7.6824
80	47.39	0.0010291	3.407	334.91	2643.7	1.0753	7.6122
85	57.83	0.0010325	2.828	355.90	2651.9	1.1343	7.5445
90	70.14	0.0010360	2.361	376.92	2660.1	1.1925	7.4791
95	84.55	0.0010397	1.9819	397.96	2668.1	1.2500	7.4159
100	101.35	0.0010435	1.6729	419.04	2676.1	1.3069	7.3549

Temperature (°C)	Vapor Pressure (kPa)	Specific Volume (m³/kg)		Enthalpy (kJ/kg)		Entropy (kJ/kg · K)	
		Liquid	Sat'd Vapor	Liquid	Sat'd Vapor	Liquid	Sat'd Vapor
105	120.82	0.0010475	1.4194	440.15	2683.8	1.3630	7.2958
110	143.27	0.0010516	1.2102	461.30	2691.5	1.4185	7.2387
115	169.06	0.0010559	1.0366	482.48	2699.0	1.4734	7.1833
120	198.53	0.0010603	0.8919	503.71	2706.3	1.5276	7.1296
125	232.1	0.0010649	0.7706	524.99	2713.5	1.5813	7.0775
130	270.1	0.0010697	0.6685	546.31	2720.5	1.6344	7.0269
135	313.0	0.0010746	0.5822	567.69	2727.3	1.6870	6.9777
140	316.3	0.0010797	0.5089	589.13	2733.9	1.7391	6.9299
145	415.4	0.0010850	0.4463	610.63	2740.3	1.7907	6.8833
150	475.8	0.0010905	0.3928	632.20	2746.5	1.8418	6.8379
155	543.1	0.0010961	0.3468	653.84	2752.4	1.8925	6.7935
160	617.8	0.0011020	0.3071	675.55	2758.1	1.9427	6.7502
165	700.5	0.0011080	0.2727	697.34	2763.5	1.9925	6.7078
170	791.7	0.0011143	0.2428	719.21	2768.7	2.0419	6.6663
175	892.0	0.0011207	0.2168	741.17	2773.6	2.0909	6.6256
180	1002.1	0.0011274	0.19405	763.22	2778.2	2.1396	6.5857
190	1254.4	0.0011414	0.15654	807.62	2786.4	2.2359	6.5079
200	1553.8	0.0011565	0.12736	852.45	2793.2	2.3309	6.4323
225	2548	0.0011992	0.07849	966.78	2803.3	2.5639	6.2503
250	3973	0.0012512	0.05013	1085.36	2801.5	2.7927	6.0730
275	5942	0.0013168	0.03279	1210.07	2785.0	3.0208	5.8938
300	8581	0.0010436	0.02167	1344.0	2749.0	3.2534	5.7045

Source: Abridged from J. H. Keenan, F. G. Keyes, P. G. Hill, and J. G. Moore, *Steam Tables—Metric Units.* New York: John Wiley & Sons, Inc.,.1969. Reprinted by permission of John Wiley & Sons, Inc.

A.2-9 Properties of Saturated Steam and Water (Steam Table), English Units

Temperature (°F)	Vapor Pressure (psia)	Specific Volume (ft³/lbₘ)		Enthalpy (btu/lbₘ)		Entropy (btu/lbₘ · °F)	
		Liquid	Sat'd Vapor	Liquid	Sat'd Vapor	Liquid	Sat'd Vapor
32.02	0.08866	0.016022	3302	0.00	1075.4	0.000	2.1869
35	0.09992	0.016021	2948	3.00	1076.7	0.00607	2.1764
40	0.12166	0.016020	2445	8.02	1078.9	0.01617	2.1592
45	0.14748	0.016021	2037	13.04	1081.1	0.02618	2.1423
50	0.17803	0.016024	1704.2	18.06	1083.3	0.03607	2.1259
55	0.2140	0.016029	1431.4	23.07	1085.5	0.04586	2.1099
60	0.2563	0.016035	1206.9	28.08	1087.7	0.05555	2.0943
65	0.3057	0.016042	1021.5	33.09	1089.9	0.06514	2.0791

A.2-9 English Units, *Continued*

Temper- ature (°F)	Vapor Pressure (psia)	·Specific Volume (ft³/lbₘ)		Enthalpy (btu/lbₘ)		Entropy (btu/lbₘ · °F)	
		Liquid	Sat'd Vapor	Liquid	Sat'd Vapor	Liquid	Sat'd Vapor
70	0.3622	0.016051	867.7	38.09	1092.0	0.07463	2.0642
75	0.4300	0.016061	739.7	43.09	1094.2	0.08402	2.0497
80	0.5073	0.016073	632.8	48.09	1096.4	0.09332	2.0356
85	0.5964	0.016085	543.1	53.08	1098.6	0.10252	2.0218
90	0.6988	0.016099	467.7	58.07	1100.7	0.11165	2.0083
95	0.8162	0.016114	404.0	63.06	1102.9	0.12068	1.9951
100	0.9503	0.016130	350.0	68.05	1105.0	0.12963	1.9822
110	1.2763	0.016166	265.1	78.02	1109.3	0.14730	1.9574
120	1.6945	0.016205	203.0	88.00	1113.5	0.16465	1.9336
130	2.225	0.016247	157.17	97.98	1117.8	0.18172	1.9109
140	2.892	0.016293	122.88	107.96	1121.9	0.19851	1.8892
150	3.722	0.016343	96.99	117.96	1126.1	0.21503	1.8684
160	4.745	0.016395	77.23	127.96	1130.1	0.23130	1.8484
170	5.996	0.016450	62.02	137.97	1134.2	0.24732	1.8293
180	7.515	0.016509	50.20	147.99	1138.2	0.26311	1.8109
190	9.343	0.016570	40.95	158.03	1142.1	0.27866	1.7932
200	11.529	0.016634	33.63	168.07	1145.9	0.29400	1.7762
210	14.125	0.016702	27.82	178.14	1149.7	0.30913	1.7599
212	14.698	0.016716	26.80	180.16	1150.5	0.31213	1.7567
220	17.188	0.016772	23.15	188.22	1153.5	0.32406	1.7441
230	20.78	0.016845	19.386	198.32	1157.1	0.33880	1.7289
240	24.97	0.016922	16.327	208.44	1160.7	0.35335	1.7143
250	29.82	0.017001	13.826	218.59	1164.2	0.36772	1.7001
260	35.42	0.017084	11.768	228.76	1167.6	0.38193	1.6864
270	41.85	0.017170	10.066	238.95	1170.9	0.39597	1.6731
280	49.18	0.017259	8.650	249.18	1174.1	0.40986	1.6602
290	57.33	0.017352	7.467	259.44	1177.2	0.42360	1.6477
300	66.98	0.017448	6.472	269.73	1180.2	0.43720	1.6356
310	77.64	0.017548	5.632	280.06	1183.0	0.45067	1.6238
320	89.60	0.017652	4.919	290.43	1185.8	0.46400	1.6123
330	103.00	0.017760	4.312	300.84	1188.4	0.47722	1.6010
340	117.93	0.017872	3.792	311.30	1190.8	0.49031	1.5901
350	134.53	0.017988	3.346	321.80	1193.1	0.50329	1.5793
360	152.92	0.018108	2.961	332.35	1195.2	0.51617	1.5688
370	173.23	0.018233	2.628	342.96	1197.2	0.52894	1.5585
380	195.60	0.018363	2.339	353.62	1199.0	0.54163	1.5483
390	220.2	0.018498	2.087	364.34	1200.6	0.55422	1.5383
400	247.1	0.018638	1.8661	375.12	1202.0	0.56672	1.5284
410	276.5	0.018784	1.6726	385.97	1203.1	0.57916	1.5187
450	422.1	0.019433	1.1011	430.2	1205.6	0.6282	1.4806

Source: Abridged from J. H. Keenan, F. G. Keyes, P. G. Hill, and J. G. Moore, *Steam Tables—English Units*. New York: John Wiley & Sons, Inc., 1969. Reprinted by permission of John Wiley & Sons, Inc.

A.2-10 Properties of Superheated Steam (Steam Table), SI Units (v, specific volume, m^3/kg; H, enthalpy, kJ/kg; s, entropy, kJ/kg · K)

Absolute Pressure, kPa (Sat. Temp., °C)		Temperature (°C)							
		100	150	200	250	300	360	420	500
10 (45.81)	v	17.196	19.512	21.825	24.136	26.445	29.216	31.986	35.679
	H	2687.5	2783.0	2879.5	2977.3	3076.5	3197.6	3320.9	3489.1
	s	8.4479	8.6882	8.9038	9.1002	9.2813	9.4821	9.6682	9.8978
50 (81.33)	v	3.418	3.889	4.356	4.820	5.284	5.839	6.394	7.134
	H	2682.5	2780.1	2877.7	2976.0	3075.5	3196.8	3320.4	3488.7
	s	7.6947	7.9401	8.1580	8.3556	8.5373	8.7385	8.9249	9.1546
75 (91.78)	v	2.270	2.587	2.900	3.211	3.520	3.891	4.262	4.755
	H	2679.4	2778.2	2876.5	2975.2	3074.9	3196.4	3320.0	3488.4
	s	7.5009	7.7496	7.9690	8.1673	8.3493	8.5508	8.7374	8.9672
100 (99.63)	v	1.6958	1.9364	2.172	2.406	2.639	2.917	3.195	3.565
	H	2672.2	2776.4	2875.3	2974.3	3074.3	3195.9	3319.6	3488.1
	s	7.3614	7.6134	7.8343	8.0333	8.2158	8.4175	8.6042	8.8342
150 (111.37)	v		1.2853	1.4443	1.6012	1.7570	1.9432	2.129	2.376
	H		2772.6	2872.9	2972.7	3073.1	3195.0	3318.9	3487.6
	s		7.4193	7.6433	7.8438	8.0720	8.2293	8.4163	8.6466
400 (143.63)	v		0.4708	0.5342	0.5951	0.6548	0.7257	0.7960	0.8893
	H		2752.8	2860.5	2964.2	3066.8	3190.3	3315.3	3484.9
	s		6.9299	7.1706	7.3789	7.5662	7.7712	7.9598	8.1913
700 (164.97)	v			0.2999	0.3363	0.3714	0.4126	0.4533	0.5070
	H			2844.8	2953.6	3059.1	3184.7	3310.9	3481.7
	s			6.8865	7.1053	7.2979	7.5063	7.6968	7.9299
1000 (179.91)	v			0.2060	0.2327	0.2579	0.2873	0.3162	0.3541
	H			2827.9	2942.6	3051.2	3178.9	3306.5	3478.5
	s			6.6940	6.9247	7.1229	7.3349	7.5275	7.7622
1500 (198.32)	v			0.13248	0.15195	0.16966	0.18988	0.2095	0.2352
	H			2796.8	2923.3	3037.6	3.1692	3299.1	3473.1
	s			6.4546	6.7090	6.9179	7.1363	7.3323	7.5698
2000 (212.42)	v			0.11144	0.12547	0.14113	0.15616	0.17568	
	H				2902.5	3023.5	3159.3	3291.6	3467.6
	s				6.5453	6.7664	6.9917	7.1915	7.4317
2500 (223.99)	v				0.08700	0.09890	0.11186	0.12414	0.13998
	H				2880.1	3008.8	3149.1	3284.0	3462.1
	s				6.4085	6.6438	6.8767	7.0803	7.3234
3000 (233.90)	v				0.07058	0.08114	0.09233	0.10279	0.11619
	H				2855.8	2993.5	3138.7	3276.3	3456.5
	s				6.2872	6.5390	6.7801	6.9878	7.2338

Source: Abridged from J. H. Keenan, F. G. Keyes, P. G. Hill, and J. G. Moore, *Steam Tables—Metric Units.* New York: John Wiley & Sons, Inc., 1969. Reprinted by permission of John Wiley & Sons, Inc.

A.2-10 Properties of Superheated Steam (Steam Table), English Units (v, specific volume, ft³/lb$_m$; H, enthalpy, btu/lb$_m$; s, entropy, btu/lb$_m \cdot$ °F)

Absolute Pressure, kPa (Sat. Temp., °F)		Temperature (°F)								
		200	300	400	500	600	700	800	900	1000
1.0 (101.70)	v	392.5	452.3	511.9	571.5	631.1	690.7	750.3	809.9	869.5
	H	1150.1	1195.7	1241.8	1288.5	1336.1	1384.5	1433.7	1483.8	1534.8
	s	2.0508	2.1150	2.1720	2.2235	2.2706	2.3142	2.3550	2.3932	2.4294
5.0 (162.21)	v	78.15	90.24	102.24	114.20	126.15	138.08	150.01	161.94	173.86
	H	1148.6	1194.8	1241.2	1288.2	1335.8	1384.3	1433.5	1483.7	1534.7
	s	1.8715	1.9367	1.9941	2.0458	2.0930	2.1367	2.1775	2.2158	2.2520
10.0 (193.19)	v	38.85	44.99	51.03	57.04	63.03	69.01	74.98	80.95	86.91
	H	1146.6	1193.7	1240.5	1287.7	1335.5	1384.0	1433.3	1483.5	1534.6
	s	1.7927	1.8592	1.9171	1.9690	2.0164	2.0601	2.1009	2.1393	2.1755
14.696 (211.99)	v		30.52	34.67	38.77	42.86	46.93	51.00	55.07	59.13
	H		1192.6	1239.9	1287.3	1335.2	1383.8	1433.1	1483.4	1534.5
	s		1.8157	1.8741	1.9263	1.9737	2.0175	2.0584	2.0967	2.1330
20.0 (227.96)	v		22.36	25.43	28.46	31.47	34.77	37.46	40.45	43.44
	H		1191.5	1239.2	1286.8	1334.8	1383.5	1432.9	1483.2	1534.3
	s		1.7805	1.8395	1.8919	1.9395	1.9834	2.0243	2.0627	2.0989
60.0 (292.73)	v		7.260	8.353	9.399	10.425	11.440	12.448	13.452	14.454
	H		1181.9	1233.5	1283.0	1332.1	1381.4	1431.2	1481.8	1533.2
	s		1.6496	1.7134	1.7678	1.8165	1.8609	1.9022	1.9408	1.9773
100.0 (327.86)	v		4.934	5.587	6.216	6.834	7.445	8.053	8.657
	H		1227.5	1279.1	1329.3	1379.2	1429.6	1480.5	1532.1
	s		1.6517	1.7085	1.7582	1.8033	1.8449	1.8838	1.9204
150.0 (358.48)	v		3.221	3.679	4.111	4.531	4.944	5.353	5.759
	H		1219.5	1274.1	1325.7	1376.6	1427.5	1478.8	1530.7
	s		1.5997	1.6598	1.7110	1.7568	1.7989	1.8381	1.8750
200.0 (381.86)	v		2.361	2.724	3.058	3.379	3.693	4.003	4.310
	H		1210.8	1268.8	1322.1	1373.8	1425.3	1477.1	1529.3
	s		1.5600	1.6239	1.6767	1.7234	1.7660	1.8055	1.8425
250.0 (401.04)	v		2.150	2.426	2.688	2.943	3.193	3.440
	H		1263.3	1318.3	1371.1	1423.2	1475.3	1527.9
	s		1.5948	1.6494	1.6970	1.7401	1.7799	1.8172
300.0 (417.43)	v		1.766	2.004	2.227	2.442	2.653	2.860
	H		1257.5	1314.5	1368.3	1421.0	1473.6	1526.5
	s		1.5701	1.6266	1.6751	1.7187	1.7589	1.7964
400 (444.70)	v		1.2843	1.4760	1.6503	1.8163	1.9776	2.136
	H		1245.2	1306.6	1362.5	1416.6	1470.1	1523.6
	s		1.5282	1.5892	1.6397	1.6884	1.7252	1.7632

Source: Abridged from J. H. Keenan, F. G. Keyes, P. G. Hill, and J. G. Moore, *Steam Tables—Metric Units.* New York: John Wiley & Sons, Inc., 1969. Reprinted by permission of John Wiley & Sons, Inc.

A.2-11 Heat-Transfer Properties of Liquid Water, SI Units

T (°C)	T (K)	ρ (kg/m³)	c_p (kJ/kg·K)	$\mu \times 10^3$ (Pa·s, or kg/m·s)	k (W/m·K)	N_{Pr}	$\beta \times 10^4$ (1/K)	$(g\beta\rho^2/\mu^2) \times 10^{-8}$ (1/K·m³)
0	273.2	999.6	4.229	1.786	0.5694	13.3	−0.630	
15.6	288.8	998.0	4.187	1.131	0.5884	8.07	1.44	10.93
26.7	299.9	996.4	4.183	0.860	0.6109	5.89	2.34	30.70
37.8	311.0	994.7	4.183	0.682	0.6283	4.51	3.24	68.0
65.6	338.8	981.9	4.187	0.432	0.6629	2.72	5.04	256.2
93.3	366.5	962.7	4.229	0.3066	0.6802	1.91	6.66	642
121.1	394.3	943.5	4.271	0.2381	0.6836	1.49	8.46	1300
148.9	422.1	917.9	4.312	0.1935	0.6836	1.22	10.08	2231
204.4	477.6	858.6	4.522	0.1384	0.6611	0.950	14.04	5308
260.0	533.2	784.9	4.982	0.1042	0.6040	0.859	19.8	11 030
315.6	588.8	679.2	6.322	0.0862	0.5071	1.07	31.5	19 260

A.2-11 Heat-Transfer Properties of Liquid Water, English Units

T (°F)	ρ $\left(\dfrac{lb_m}{ft^3}\right)$	c_p $\left(\dfrac{btu}{lb_m \cdot °F}\right)$	$\mu \times 10^3$ $\left(\dfrac{lb_m}{ft \cdot s}\right)$	k $\left(\dfrac{btu}{h \cdot ft \cdot °F}\right)$	N_{Pr}	$\beta \times 10^4$ (1/°R)	$(g\beta\rho^2/\mu^2) \times 10^{-6}$ (1/°R·ft³)
32	62.4	1.01	1.20	0.329	13.3	−0.350	
60	62.3	1.00	0.760	0.340	8.07	0.800	17.2
80	62.2	0.999	0.578	0.353	5.89	1.30	48.3
100	62.1	0.999	0.458	0.363	4.51	1.80	107
150	61.3	1.00	0.290	0.383	2.72	2.80	403
200	60.1	1.01	0.206	0.393	1.91	3.70	1010
250	58.9	1.02	0.160	0.395	1.49	4.70	2045
300	57.3	1.03	0.130	0.395	1.22	5.60	3510
400	53.6	1.08	0.0930	0.382	0.950	7.80	8350
500	49.0	1.19	0.0700	0.349	0.859	11.0	17 350
600	42.4	1.51	0.0579	0.293	1.07	17.5	30 300

A.2-12 Heat-Transfer Properties of Water Vapor (Steam) at 101.32 kPa (1 Atm Abs), SI Units

T (°C)	T (K)	ρ (kg/m³)	c_p (kJ/kg·K)	$\mu \times 10^5$ (Pa·s, or kg/m·s)	k (W/m·K)	N_{Pr}	$\beta \times 10^3$ (1/K)	$(g\beta\rho^2/\mu^2)$ (1/K·m³)
100.0	373.2	0.596	1.888	1.295	0.02510	0.96	2.68	0.557×10^8
148.9	422.1	0.525	1.909	1.488	0.02960	0.95	2.38	0.292×10^8
204.4	477.6	0.461	1.934	1.682	0.03462	0.94	2.09	0.154×10^8
260.0	533.2	0.413	1.968	1.883	0.03946	0.94	1.87	0.0883×10^8
315.6	588.8	0.373	1.997	2.113	0.04448	0.94	1.70	52.1×10^5
371.1	644.3	0.341	2.030	2.314	0.04985	0.93	1.55	33.1×10^5
426.7	699.9	0.314	2.068	2.529	0.05556	0.92	1.43	21.6×10^5

A.2-12 Heat-Transfer Properties of Water Vapor (Steam) at 101.32 kPa (1 Atm Abs), English Units

T (°F)	ρ $\left(\dfrac{lb_m}{ft^3}\right)$	c_p $\left(\dfrac{btu}{lb_m \cdot °F}\right)$	$\mu \times 10^5$ $\left(\dfrac{lb_m}{ft \cdot s}\right)$	k $\left(\dfrac{btu}{h \cdot ft \cdot °F}\right)$	N_{Pr}	$\beta \times 10^3$ (1/°R)	$(g\beta\rho^2/\mu^2)$ (1/°R·ft³)
212	0.0372	0.451	0.870	0.0145	0.96	1.49	0.877×10^6
300	0.0328	0.456	1.000	0.0171	0.95	1.32	0.459×10^6
400	0.0288	0.462	1.130	0.0200	0.94	1.16	0.243×10^6
500	0.0258	0.470	1.265	0.0228	0.94	1.04	0.139×10^6
600	0.0233	0.477	1.420	0.0257	0.94	0.943	82×10^3
700	0.0213	0.485	1.555	0.0288	0.93	0.862	52.1×10^3
800	0.0196	0.494	1.700	0.0321	0.92	0.794	34.0×10^3

Source: D. L. Timrot and N. B. Vargaftik, *J. Tech. Phys. (U.S.S.R.),* **10,** 1063 (1940); R. H. Perry and C. H. Chilton. *Chemical Engineers' Handbook,* 5th ed. New York: McGraw-Hill Book Company, 1973; J. H. Keenan, F. G. Keyes, P. G. Hill, and J. G. Moore, *Steam Tables.* New York: John Wiley & Sons, Inc., 1969; National Research Council, *International Critical Tables.* New York: McGraw-Hill Book Company, 1929; L. S. Marks, *Mechanical Engineers' Handbook,* 5th ed. New York: McGraw-Hill Book Company, 1951.

APPENDIX A.3

Physical Properties of Inorganic and Organic Compounds

A.3-1 Standard Heats of Formation at 298.15 K (25°C) and 101.325 kPa (1 Atm Abs), (c) = crystalline, (g) = gas, (l) = liquid

Compound	ΔH_f°		Compound	ΔH_f°	
	$(kJ/kg \, mol)10^{-3}$	kcal/g mol		$(kJ/kg \, mol)10^{-3}$	kcal/g mol
$NH_3(g)$	−46.19	−11.04	$CaCO_3(c)$	−1206.87	−288.45
$NO(g)$	+90.374	+21.600	$CaO(c)$	−635.5	−151.9
$H_2O(l)$	−285.840	−68.3174	$CO(g)$	−110.523	−26.4157
$H_2O(g)$	−241.826	−57.7979	$CO_2(g)$	−393.513	−94.0518
$HCN(g)$	+130.1	+31.1	$CH_4(g)$	−74.848	−17.889
$HCl(g)$	−92.312	−22.063	$C_2H_6(g)$	−84.667	−20.236
$H_2SO_4(l)$	−811.32	−193.91	$C_3H_8(g)$	−103.847	−24.820
$H_3PO_4(c)$	−1281.1	−306.2	$CH_3OH(l)$	−238.66	−57.04
$NaCl(c)$	−411.003	−98.232	$CH_3CH_3OH(l)$	−277.61	−66.35
$NH_4Cl(c)$	−315.39	−75.38			

Source: J. H. Perry and C. H. Chilton, *Chemical Engineers' Handbook*, 5th ed. New York: McGraw-Hill Book Company, 1973; and O. A. Hougen, K. M. Watson, and R. A. Ragatz, *Chemical Process Principles*, Part I, 2nd ed. New York: John Wiley & Sons, Inc., 1954.

A.3-2 **Standard Heats of Combustion at 298.15 K (25°C) and 101.325 kPa (1 Atm Abs)**
(g) = gas, (l) = liquid, (s) = solid

Compound	Combustion Reaction	ΔH_c° kcal/g mol	$(kJ/kg\ mol)10^{-3}$
C(s)	$C(s) + \frac{1}{2}O_2(g) \rightarrow CO(g)$	−26.4157	−110.523
CO(g)	$CO(g) + \frac{1}{2}O_2(g) \rightarrow CO_2(g)$	−67.6361	−282.989
C(s)	$C(s) + O_2(g) \rightarrow CO_2(g)$	−94.0518	−393.513
$H_2(g)$	$H_2(g) + \frac{1}{2}O_2(g) \rightarrow H_2O(l)$	−68.3174	−285.840
$H_2(g)$	$H_2(g) + \frac{1}{2}O_2(g) \rightarrow H_2O(g)$	−57.7979	−241.826
$CH_4(g)$	$CH_4(g) + 2O_2(g) \rightarrow CO_2(g) + 2H_2O(l)$	−212.798	−890.346
$C_2H_6(g)$	$C_2H_6(g) + \frac{7}{2}O_2(g) \rightarrow 2CO_2(g) + 3H_2O(l)$	−372.820	−1559.879
$C_3H_8(g)$	$C_3H_8(g) + 5O_2(g) \rightarrow 3CO_2(g) + 4H_2O(l)$	−530.605	−2220.051
d-Glucose (dextrose) $C_6H_{12}O_6(s)$	$C_6H_{12}O_6(s) + 6O_2(g) \rightarrow 6CO_2(g) + 6H_2O(l)$	−673	−2816
Lactose (anhydrous) $C_{12}H_{22}O_{11}(s)$	$C_{12}H_{22}O_{11}(s) + 12O_2(g) \rightarrow 12CO_2(g) + 11H_2O(l)$	−1350.1	−5648.8
Sucrose $C_{12}H_{22}O_{11}(s)$	$C_{12}H_{22}O_{11}(s) + 12O_2(g) \rightarrow 12CO_2(g) + 11H_2O(l)$	−1348.9	−5643.8

Source: R. H. Perry and C. H. Chilton, *Chemical Engineers' Handbook,* 5th ed. New York: McGraw-Hill Book Company, 1973; and O. A. Hougen, K. M. Watson, and R. A. Ragatz, *Chemical Process Principles, Part I,* 2nd ed. New York: John Wiley & Sons, Inc., 1954.

FIGURE A.3-1. *Mean molar heat capacities from 77°F (25°C) to t°F at constant pressure of 101.325 kPa (1 atm abs) (From O. A. Hougen, K. M. Watson, and R. A. Ragatz,* Chemical Process Principles, Part I, *2nd ed. New York: John Wiley & Sons, Inc., 1954. With permission.)*

A.3-3 Physical Properties of Air at 101.325 kPa (1 Atm Abs), SI Units

T (°C)	T (K)	ρ (kg/m³)	c_p (kJ/kg·K)	$\mu \times 10^5$ (Pa·s, or kg/m·s)	k (W/m·K)	N_{Pr}	$\beta \times 10^3$ (1/K)	$g\beta\rho^2/\mu^2$ (1/K·m³)
−17.8	255.4	1.379	1.0048	1.62	0.02250	0.720	3.92	2.79×10^8
0	273.2	1.293	1.0048	1.72	0.02423	0.715	3.65	2.04×10^8
10.0	283.2	1.246	1.0048	1.78	0.02492	0.713	3.53	1.72×10^8
37.8	311.0	1.137	1.0048	1.90	0.02700	0.705	3.22	1.12×10^8
65.6	338.8	1.043	1.0090	2.03	0.02925	0.702	2.95	0.775×10^8
93.3	366.5	0.964	1.0090	2.15	0.03115	0.694	2.74	0.534×10^8
121.1	394.3	0.895	1.0132	2.27	0.03323	0.692	2.54	0.386×10^8
148.9	422.1	0.838	1.0174	2.37	0.03531	0.689	2.38	0.289×10^8
176.7	449.9	0.785	1.0216	2.50	0.03721	0.687	2.21	0.214×10^8
204.4	477.6	0.740	1.0258	2.60	0.03894	0.686	2.09	0.168×10^8
232.2	505.4	0.700	1.0300	2.71	0.04084	0.684	1.98	0.130×10^8
260.0	533.2	0.662	1.0341	2.80	0.04258	0.680	1.87	0.104×10^8

Source: National Bureau of Standards, Circular 461C, 1947; 564, 1955; NBS–NACA, Tables of Thermal Properties of Gases, 1949; F. G. Keyes, Trans. A.S.M.E., 73, 590, 597 (1951); 74, 1303 (1952); D. D. Wagman, Selected Values of Chemical Thermodynamic Properties, Washington, D.C.: National Bureau of Standards, 1953.

A.3-3 Physical Properties of Air at 101.325 kPa (1 Atm Abs), English Units

T (°F)	ρ $\left(\dfrac{lb_m}{ft^3}\right)$	c_p $\left(\dfrac{btu}{lb_m \cdot °F}\right)$	μ (centipoise)	k $\left(\dfrac{btu}{h \cdot ft \cdot °F}\right)$	N_{Pr}	$\beta \times 10^3$ (1/°R)	$g\beta\rho^2/\mu^2$ (1/°R·ft³)
0	0.0861	0.240	0.0162	0.0130	0.720	2.18	4.39×10^6
32	0.0807	0.240	0.0172	0.0140	0.715	2.03	3.21×10^6
50	0.0778	0.240	0.0178	0.0144	0.713	1.96	2.70×10^6
100	0.0710	0.240	0.0190	0.0156	0.705	1.79	1.76×10^6
150	0.0651	0.241	0.0203	0.0169	0.702	1.64	1.22×10^6
200	0.0602	0.241	0.0215	0.0180	0.694	1.52	0.840×10^6
250	0.0559	0.242	0.0227	0.0192	0.692	1.41	0.607×10^6
300	0.0523	0.243	0.0237	0.0204	0.689	1.32	0.454×10^6
350	0.0490	0.244	0.0250	0.0215	0.687	1.23	0.336×10^6
400	0.0462	0.245	0.0260	0.0225	0.686	1.16	0.264×10^6
450	0.0437	0.246	0.0271	0.0236	0.674	1.10	0.204×10^6
500	0.0413	0.247	0.0280	0.0246	0.680	1.04	0.163×10^6

Source: National Bureau of Standards, Circular 461C, 1947; 564, 1955; NBS–NACA, Tables of Thermal Properties of Gases, 1949; F. G. Keyes, Trans. A.S.M.E., 73, 590, 597 (1951); 74, 1303 (1952); D. D. Wagman, Selected Values of Chemical Thermodynamic Properties. Washington, D.C.: National Bureau of Standards, 1953.

Viscosity of Gases at 101.325 kPa (1 Atm Abs) [Viscosity in (Pa · s) 10³, (kg/m · s) 10³, or cp]

Temperature							
K	°F	°C	H_2	O_2	N_2	CO	CO_2
255.4	0	−17.8	0.00800	0.0181	0.0158	0.0156	0.0128
273.2	32	0	0.00840	0.0192	0.0166	0.0165	0.0137
283.2	50	10.0	0.00862	0.0197	0.0171	0.0169	0.0141
311.0	100	37.8	0.00915	0.0213	0.0183	0.0183	0.0154
338.8	150	65.6	0.00960	0.0228	0.0196	0.0195	0.0167
366.5	200	93.3	0.0101	0.0241	0.0208	0.0208	0.0179
394.3	250	121.1	0.0106	0.0256	0.0220	0.0220	0.0191
422.1	300	148.9	0.0111	0.0267	0.0230	0.0231	0.0203
449.9	350	176.7	0.0115	0.0282	0.0240	0.0242	0.0215
477.6	400	204.4	0.0119	0.0293	0.0250	0.0251	0.0225
505.4	450	232.2	0.0124	0.0307	0.0260	0.0264	0.0236
533.2	500	260.0	0.0128	0.0315	0.0273	0.0276	0.0247

Source: National Bureau of Standards, *Circular* **461C**, 1947; **564,** 1955; NBS–NACA, *Tables of Thermal Properties of Gases,* 1949; F. G. Keyes, *Trans. A.S.M.E.,* **73,** 590, 597 (1951); **74,** 1303 (1952); D. D. Wagman, *Selected Values of Chemical Thermodynamic Properties.* Washington, D.C.: National Bureau of Standards, 1953.

A.3-5 Thermal Conductivity of Gases at 101.325 kPa (1 Atm Abs)

Temperature			H_2		O_2		N_2		CO		CO_2	
K	°C	°F	W/m·K	btu/ h·ft·°F	W/m·K	btu/ h·ft·°F	W/m·K	btu/ h·ft·°F	W/m·K	btu/ h·ft·°F	W/m·K	btu/ h·ft·°F
255.4	−17.8	0	0.1592	0.0920	0.0228	0.0132	0.0228	0.0132	0.0222	0.0128	0.0132	0.0076
273.2	0	32	0.1667	0.0963	0.0246	0.0142	0.0239	0.0138	0.0233	0.0135	0.0145	0.0084
283.2	10.0	50	0.1720	0.0994	0.0253	0.0146	0.0248	0.0143	0.0239	0.0138	0.0152	0.0088
311.0	37.8	100	0.1852	0.107	0.0277	0.0160	0.0267	0.0154	0.0260	0.0150	0.0173	0.0100
338.8	65.6	150	0.1990	0.115	0.0299	0.0173	0.0287	0.0166	0.0279	0.0161	0.0190	0.0110
366.5	93.3	200	0.2111	0.122	0.0320	0.0185	0.0303	0.0175	0.0296	0.0171	0.0216	0.0125
394.3	121.1	250	0.2233	0.129	0.0343	0.0198	0.0329	0.0190	0.0318	0.0184	0.0239	0.0138
422.1	148.9	300	0.2353	0.136	0.0363	0.0210	0.0348	0.0201	0.0338	0.0195	0.0260	0.0150
449.9	176.7	350	0.2458	0.142	0.0382	0.0221	0.0365	0.0211	0.0355	0.0205	0.0286	0.0165
477.6	204.4	400	0.2579	0.149	0.0398	0.0230	0.0382	0.0221	0.0369	0.0213	0.0308	0.0178
505.4	232.2	450	0.2683	0.155	0.0422	0.0244	0.0400	0.0231	0.0384	0.0222	0.0334	0.0193
533.2	260.0	500	0.2786	0.161	0.0438	0.0253	0.0419	0.0242	0.0407	0.0235	0.0355	0.0205

Source: National Bureau of Standards. *Circular* 461C, 1947: **564**, 1955; NBS–NACA, *Table of Thermal Properties of Gases*, 1949; F. G. Keyes, *Trans. A.S.M.E.*, **73**, 590, 597 (1951); **74**, 1303 (1952); D. D. Wagman, *Selected Values of Chemical Thermodynamic Properties*. Washington, D.C.: National Bureau of Standards, 1953.

A.3-6 Heat Capacity of Gases at Constant Pressure at 101.325 kPa (1 Atm Abs)

Temperature			H_2		O_2		N_2		CO		CO_2	
K	°C	°F	$\frac{kJ}{kg \cdot K}$	$\frac{btu}{lb_m \cdot °F}$	$\frac{kJ}{kg \cdot K}$	$\frac{btu}{lb_m \cdot °F}$	$\frac{kJ}{kg \cdot K}$	$\frac{btu}{lb_m \cdot °F}$	$\frac{kJ}{kg \cdot K}$	$\frac{btu}{lb_m \cdot °F}$	$\frac{kJ}{kg \cdot K}$	$\frac{btu}{lb_m \cdot °F}$
255.4	−17.8	0	14.07	3.36	0.909	0.217	1.034	0.247	1.034	0.247	0.800	0.191
273.2	0	32	14.19	3.39	0.913	0.218	1.038	0.248	1.038	0.248	0.816	0.195
283.2	10.0	50	14.19	3.39	0.917	0.219	1.038	0.248	1.038	0.248	0.825	0.197
311.0	37.8	100	14.32	3.42	0.921	0.220	1.038	0.248	1.043	0.249	0.854	0.204
338.8	65.6	150	14.36	3.43	0.925	0.221	1.038	0.248	1.043	0.249	0.883	0.211
366.5	93.3	200	14.40	3.44	0.929	0.222	1.043	0.249	1.047	0.250	0.904	0.216
394.3	121.1	250	14.44	3.45	0.938	0.224	1.043	0.249	1.047	0.250	0.929	0.222
422.1	148.9	300	14.49	3.46	0.946	0.226	1.047	0.250	1.051	0.251	0.950	0.227
449.9	176.7	350	14.49	3.46	0.955	0.228	1.047	0.250	1.055	0.252	0.976	0.233
477.6	204.4	400	14.49	3.46	0.963	0.230	1.051	0.251	1.059	0.253	0.996	0.238
505.4	232.2	450	14.52	3.47	0.971	0.232	1.055	0.252	1.063	0.254	1.017	0.243
533.2	260.0	500	14.52	3.47	0.976	0.233	1.059	0.253	1.068	0.255	1.030	0.246

Source: National Bureau of Standards, *Circular* **461C**, 1947; **564**, 1955; NBS–NACA, *Tables of Thermal Properties of Gases*, 1949; F. G. Keyes, *Trans. A.S.M.E.*, **73**, 590, 597 (1951); **74**, 1303 (1952); D. D. Wagman, *Selected Values of Chemical Thermodynamic Properties*. Washington, D.C.: National Bureau of Standards, 1953.

A.3-7 Prandtl Number of Gases at 101.325 kPa (1 Atm Abs)

Temperature			H_2	O_2	N_2	CO	CO_2
°C	°F	K					
−17.8	0	255.4	0.720	0.720	0.720	0.740	0.775
0	32	273.2	0.715	0.711	0.720	0.738	0.770
10.0	50	283.2	0.710	0.710	0.717	0.735	0.769
37.8	100	311.0	0.700	0.707	0.710	0.731	0.764
65.6	150	338.8	0.700	0.706	0.700	0.727	0.755
93.3	200	366.5	0.694	0.703	0.700	0.724	0.752
121.1	250	394.3	0.688	0.703	0.696	0.720	0.746
148.9	300	422.1	0.683	0.703	0.690	0.720	0.738
176.6	350	449.9	0.677	0.704	0.689	0.720	0.734
204.4	400	477.6	0.670	0.706	0.688	0.720	0.725
232.2	450	505.4	0.668	0.702	0.688	0.720	0.716
260.0	500	533.2	0.666	0.700	0.688	0.720	0.702

Source: National Bureau of Standards, *Circular* **461C,** 1947; **564,** 1955; NBS–NACA, *Tables of Thermal Properties of Gases,* 1949; F. G. Keyes, *Trans. A.S.M.E.,* **73,** 590, 597 (1951); **74,** 1303 (1952); D. D. Wagman, *Selected Values of Chemical Thermodynamic Properties.* Washington, D.C.: National Bureau of Standards, 1953.

Temperature
(°C)   (°F)

Viscosity
[(kg/m·s)10³ or cp]

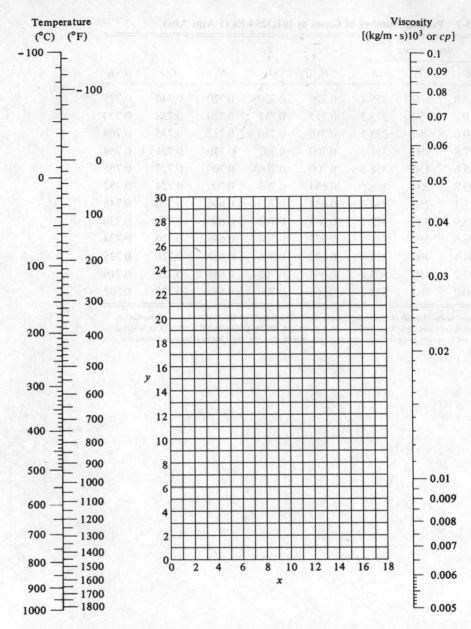

FIGURE A.3-2.   Viscosities of gases at 101.325 kPa (1 atm abs). (From R. H. Perry and C. H.
Chilton, Chemical Engineers' Handbook, 5th ed. New York: McGraw-Hill
Book Company, 1973. With permission.) See Table A.3-8 for coordinates for
use with Fig. A.3-2.

A.3-8 Viscosities of Gases (Coordinates for Use with Fig. A.3-2)

No.	Gas	X	Y	No.	Gas	X	Y
1	Acetic acid	7.7	14.3	29	Freon-113	11.3	14.0
2	Acetone	8.9	13.0	30	Helium	10.9	20.5
3	Acetylene	9.8	14.9	31	Hexane	8.6	11.8
4	Air	11.0	20.0	32	Hydrogen	11.2	12.4
5	Ammonia	8.4	16.0	33	$3H_2 + 1N_2$	11.2	17.2
6	Argon	10.5	22.4	34	Hydrogen bromide	8.8	20.9
7	Benzene	8.5	13.2	35	Hydrogen chloride	8.8	18.7
8	Bromine	8.9	19.2	36	Hydrogen cyanide	9.8	14.9
9	Butene	9.2	13.7	37	Hydrogen iodide	9.0	21.3
10	Butylene	8.9	13.0	38	Hydrogen sulfide	8.6	18.0
11	Carbon dioxide	9.5	18.7	39	Iodine	9.0	18.4
12	Carbon disulfide	8.0	16.0	40	Mercury	5.3	22.9
13	Carbon monoxide	11.0	20.0	41	Methane	9.9	15.5
14	Chlorine	9.0	18.4	42	Methyl alcohol	8.5	15.6
15	Chloroform	8.9	15.7	43	Nitric oxide	10.9	20.5
16	Cyanogen	9.2	15.2	44	Nitrogen	10.6	20.0
17	Cyclohexane	9.2	12.0	45	Nitrosyl chloride	8.0	17.6
18	Ethane	9.1	14.5	46	Nitrous oxide	8.8	19.0
19	Ethyl acetate	8.5	13.2	47	Oxygen	11.0	21.3
20	Ethyl alcohol	9.2	14.2	48	Pentane	7.0	12.8
21	Ethyl chloride	8.5	15.6	49	Propane	9.7	12.9
22	Ethyl ether	8.9	13.0	50	Propyl alcohol	8.4	13.4
23	Ethylene	9.5	15.1	51	Propylene	9.0	13.8
24	Fluorine	7.3	23.8	52	Sulfur dioxide	9.6	17.0
25	Freon-11	10.6	15.1	53	Toluene	8.6	12.4
26	Freon-12	11.1	16.0	54	2,3,3-Trimethylbutane	9.5	10.5
27	Freon-21	10.8	15.3	55	Water	8.0	16.0
28	Freon-22	10.1	17.0	56	Xenon	9.3	23.0

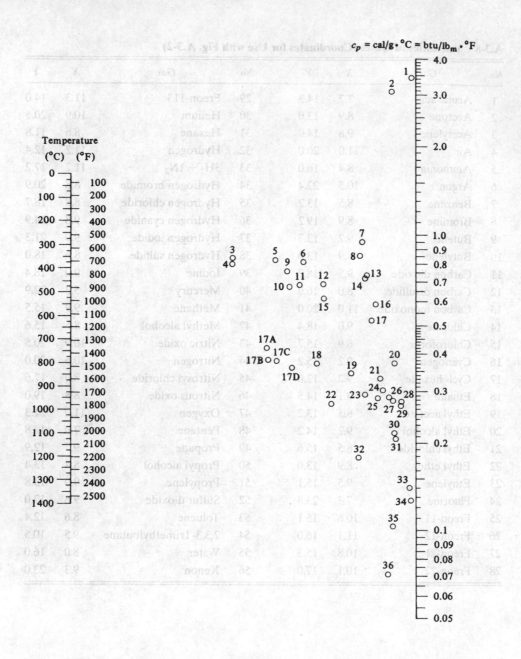

FIGURE A.3-3. *Heat capacity of gases at constant pressure at 101.325 kPa (1 atm abs). (From R. H. Perry and C. H. Chilton, Chemical Engineers' Handbook, 5th ed. New York: McGraw-Hill Book Company, 1973. With permission.) See Table A.3-9 for use with Fig. A.3-3.*

A.3-9 Heat Capacity of Gases at Constant Pressure (for Use with Fig. A.3-3)

No.	Gas	Range (°C)
10	Acetylene	0–200
15	Acetylene	200–400
16	Acetylene	400–1400
27	Air	0–1400
12	Ammonia	0–600
14	Ammonia	600–1400
18	Carbon dioxide	0–400
24	Carbon dioxide	400–1400
26	Carbon monoxide	0–1400
32	Chlorine	0–200
34	Chlorine	200–1400
3	Ethane	0–200
9	Ethane	200–600
8	Ethane	600–1400
4	Ethylene	0–200
11	Ethylene	200–600
13	Ethylene	600–1400
17B	Freon-11 (CCl_3F)	0–150
17C	Freon-21 ($CHCl_2F$)	0–150
17A	Freon-22 ($CHClF_2$)	0–150
17D	Freon-113 ($CCl_2F—CClF_2$)	0–150
1	Hydrogen	0–600
2	Hydrogen	600–1400
35	Hydrogen bromide	0–1400
30	Hydrogen chloride	0–1400
20	Hydrogen fluoride	0–1400
36	Hydrogen iodide	0–1400
19	Hydrogen sulfide	0–700
21	Hydrogen sulfide	700–1400
5	Methane	0–300
6	Methane	300–700
7	Methane	700–1400
25	Nitric oxide	0–700
28	Nitric oxide	700–1400
26	Nitrogen	0–1400
23	Oxygen	0–500
29	Oxygen	500–1400
33	Sulfur	300–1400
22	Sulfur dioxide	0–400
31	Sulfur dioxide	400–1400
17	Water	0–1400

A.3-10 Thermal Conductivities of Gases and Vapors at 101.325 kPa (1 Atm Abs); $k = W/m \cdot K$

Gas or Vapor	K	k	Gas or Vapor	K	k
Acetone[1]	273	0.0099	Ethane[5,6]	239	0.0149
	319	0.0130		273	0.0183
	373	0.0171		373	0.0303
	457	0.0254	Ethyl alcohol[1]	293	0.0154
Ammonia[2]	273	0.0218		373	0.0215
	373	0.0332	Ethyl ether[1]	273	0.0133
	473	0.0484		319	0.0171
Butane[3]	273	0.0135		373	0.0227
	373	0.0234	Ethylene[6]	273	0.0175
Carbon monoxide[2]	173	0.0152		323	0.0227
	273	0.0232		373	0.0279
	373	0.0305	n-Hexane[3]	273	0.0125
Chlorine[4]	273	0.00744		293	0.0138
			Sulfur dioxide[7]	273	0.0087
				373	0.0119

Source: (1) Moser, dissertation, Berlin, 1913; (2) F. G. Keyes, *Tech. Rept.* 37, Project Squid, Apr. 1, 1952; (3) W. B. Mann and B. G. Dickens, *Proc. Roy. Soc. (London).* **A134,** 77 (1931); (4) *International Critical Tables.* New York: McGraw-Hill Book Company, 1929; (5) T. H. Chilton and R. P. Genereaux, personal communication, 1946; (6) A. Eucken, *Physik, Z.,* **12,** 1101 (1911); **14.** 324 (1913); (7) B. G. Dickens, *Proc. Roy. Soc. (London),* **A143,** 517 (1934).

A.3-11 Heat Capacities of Liquids (c_p = kJ/kg · K)

Liquid	K	c_p	Liquid	K	c_p
Acetic acid	273	1.959	Hydrochloric acid (20 mol %)	273	2.43
	311	2.240		293	2.474
Acetone	273	2.119	Mercury	293	0.01390
	293	2.210	Methyl alcohol	293	2.512
Aniline	273	2.001		313	2.583
	323	2.181	Nitrobenzene	283	1.499
Benzene	293	1.700		303	1.419
	333	1.859		363	1.436
Butane	273	2.300	Sodium chloride (9.1 mol %)	293	3.39
i-Butyl alcohol	303	2.525		330	3.43
Ethyl alcohol	273	2.240	Sulfuric acid (100%)	293	1.403
	298	2.433	Toluene	273	1.616
Formic acid	273	1.825		323	1.763
	289	2.131	o-Xylene	303	1.721
Glycerol	288	2.324			
	305	2.412			

Source: N. A. Lange, *Handbook of Chemistry,* 10th ed. New York: McGraw-Hill Book Company, 1967; National Research Council, *International Critical Tables,* Vol. V. New York: McGraw-Hill Book Company, 1929; R. H. Perry and C. H. Chilton, *Chemical Engineers' Handbook,* 5th ed. New York: McGraw-Hill Book Company, 1973.

Temperature

(°C)   (°F)

200 ─┬─ 390
190 ─┼─ 380
     │   370
180 ─┼─ 360
     │   350
170 ─┼─ 340
     │   330
160 ─┼─ 320
     │   310
150 ─┼─ 300
     │   290
140 ─┼─ 280
     │   270
130 ─┼─ 260
120 ─┼─ 250
     │   240
110 ─┼─ 230
100 ─┼─ 220
     │   210
90 ─┼─ 200
    │   190
80 ─┼─ 180
    │   170
70 ─┼─ 160
    │   150
60 ─┼─ 140
    │   130
50 ─┼─ 120
    │   110
40 ─┼─ 100
30 ─┼─ 90
    │   80
20 ─┼─ 70
    │   60
10 ─┼─ 50
    │   40
0 ─┼─ 30
   │   20
-10 ─┼─ 10
     │   0
-20 ─┼─ -10
-30 ─┴─ -20

Viscosity

$[(kg/m \cdot s)10^3$ or $cp]$

FIGURE A.3-4.   *Viscosities of liquids. (From R. H. Perry and C. H. Chilton,* Chemical Engineers' Handbook, *5th ed. New York: McGraw-Hill Book Company, 1973. With permission.) See Table A.3-12 for use with Fig. A.3-4.*

A.3-12 Viscosities of Liquids (Coordinates for Use with Fig. A.3-4)

Liquid	X	Y	Liquid	X	Y
Acetaldehyde	15.2	4.8	Dibromomethane	12.7	15.8
Acetic acid, 100%	12.1	14.2	Dichloroethane	13.2	12.2
Acetic acid, 70%	9.5	17.0	Dichloromethane	14.6	8.9
Acetic anhydride	12.7	12.8	Diethyl ketone	13.5	9.2
Acetone, 100%	14.5	7.2	Diethyl oxalate	11.0	16.4
Acetone, 35%	7.9	15.0	Diethylene glycol	5.0	24.7
Acetonitrile	14.4	7.4	Diphenyl	12.0	18.3
Acrylic acid	12.3	13.9	Dipropyl ether	13.2	8.6
Allyl alcohol	10.2	14.3	Dipropyl oxalate	10.3	17.7
Allyl bromide	14.4	9.6	Ethyl acetate	13.7	9.1
Allyl iodide	14.0	11.7	Ethyl acrylate	12.7	10.4
Ammonia, 100%	12.6	2.0	Ethyl alcohol, 100%	10.5	13.8
Ammonia, 26%	10.1	13.9	Ethyl alcohol, 95%	9.8	14.3
Amyl acetate	11.8	12.5	Ethyl alcohol, 40%	6.5	16.6
Amyl alcohol	7.5	18.4	Ethyl benzene	13.2	11.5
Aniline	8.1	18.7	Ethyl bromide	14.5	8.1
Anisole	12.3	13.5	2-Ethyl butyl acrylate	11.2	14.0
Arsenic trichloride	13.9	14.5	Ethyl chloride	14.8	6.0
Benzene	12.5	10.9	Ethyl ether	14.5	5.3
Brine, CaCl₂, 25%	6.6	15.9	Ethyl formate	14.2	8.4
Brine, NaCl, 25%	10.2	16.6	2-Ethyl hexyl acrylate	9.0	15.0
Bromine	14.2	13.2	Ethyl iodide	14.7	10.3
Bromotoluene	20.0	15.9	Ethyl propionate	13.2	9.9
Butyl acetate	12.3	11.0	Ethyl propyl ether	14.0	7.0
Butyl acrylate	11.5	12.6	Ethyl sulfide	13.8	8.9
Butyl alcohol	8.6	17.2	Ethylene bromide	11.9	15.7
Butyric acid	12.1	15.3	Ethylene chloride	12.7	12.2
Carbon dioxide	11.6	0.3	Ethylene glycol	6.0	23.6
Carbon disulfide	16.1	7.5	Ethylidene chloride	14.1	8.7
Carbon tetrachloride	12.7	13.1	Fluorobenzene	13.7	10.4
Chlorobenzene	12.3	12.4	Formic acid	10.7	15.8
Chloroform	14.4	10.2	Freon-11	14.4	9.0
Chlorosulfonic acid	11.2	18.1	Freon-12	16.8	15.6
Chlorotoluene, ortho	13.0	13.3	Freon-21	15.7	7.5
Chlorotoluene, meta	13.3	12.5	Freon-22	17.2	4.7
Chlorotoluene, para	13.3	12.5	Freon-113	12.5	11.4
Cresol, meta	2.5	20.8	Glycerol, 100%	2.0	30.0
Cyclohexanol	2.9	24.3	Glycerol, 50%	6.9	19.6
Cyclohexane	9.8	12.9	Heptane	14.1	8.4

Appendix A.3   Physical Properties of Inorganic and Organic Compounds

Liquid	X	Y	Liquid	X	Y
Hexane	14.7	7.0	Pentane	14.9	5.2
Hydrochloric acid, 31.5%	13.0	16.6	Phenol	6.9	20.8
Iodobenzene	12.8	15.9	Phosphorus tribromide	13.8	16.7
Isobutyl alcohol	7.1	18.0	Phosphorus trichloride	16.2	10.9
Isobutyric acid	12.2	14.4	Propionic acid	12.8	13.8
Isopropyl alcohol	8.2	16.0	Propyl acetate	13.1	10.3
Isopropyl bromide	14.1	9.2	Propyl alcohol	9.1	16.5
Isopropyl chloride	13.9	7.1	Propyl bromide	14.5	9.6
Isopropyl iodide	13.7	11.2	Propyl chloride	14.4	7.5
Kerosene	10.2	16.9	Propyl formate	13.1	9.7
Linseed oil, raw	7.5	27.2	Propyl iodide	14.1	11.6
Mercury	18.4	16.4	Sodium	16.4	13.9
Methanol, 100%	12.4	10.5	Sodium hydroxide, 50%	3.2	25.8
Methanol, 90%	12.3	11.8	Stannic chloride	13.5	12.8
Methanol, 40%	7.8	15.5	Succinonitrile	10.1	20.8
Methyl acetate	14.2	8.2	Sulfur dioxide	15.2	7.1
Methyl acrylate	13.0	9.5	Sulfuric acid, 110%	7.2	27.4
Methyl *i*-butyrate	12.3	9.7	Sulfuric acid, 100%	8.0	25.1
Methyl *n*-butyrate	13.2	10.3	Sulfuric acid, 98%	7.0	24.8
Methyl chloride	15.0	3.8	Sulfuric acid, 60%	10.2	21.3
Methyl ethyl ketone	13.9	8.6	Sulfuryl chloride	15.2	12.4
Methyl formate	14.2	7.5	Tetrachloroethane	11.9	15.7
Methyl iodide	14.3	9.3	Thiophene	13.2	11.0
Methyl propionate	13.5	9.0	Titanium tetrachloride	14.4	12.3
Methyl propyl ketone	14.3	9.5	Toluene	13.7	10.4
Methyl sulfide	15.3	6.4	Trichloroethylene	14.8	10.5
Naphthalene	7.9	18.1	Triethylene glycol	4.7	24.8
Nitric acid, 95%	12.8	13.8	Turpentine	11.5	14.9
Nitric acid, 60%	10.8	17.0	Vinyl acetate	14.0	8.8
Nitrobenzene	10.6	16.2	Vinyl toluene	13.4	12.0
Nitrogen dioxide	12.9	8.6	Water	10.2	13.0
Nitrotoluene	11.0	17.0	Xylene, ortho	13.5	12.1
Octane	13.7	10.0	Xylene, meta	13.9	10.6
Octyl alcohol	6.6	21.1	Xylene, para	13.9	10.9
Pentachloroethane	10.9	17.3			

$$c_p = \text{cal/g} \cdot {}^\circ C = \text{btu/lb}_m \cdot {}^\circ F$$

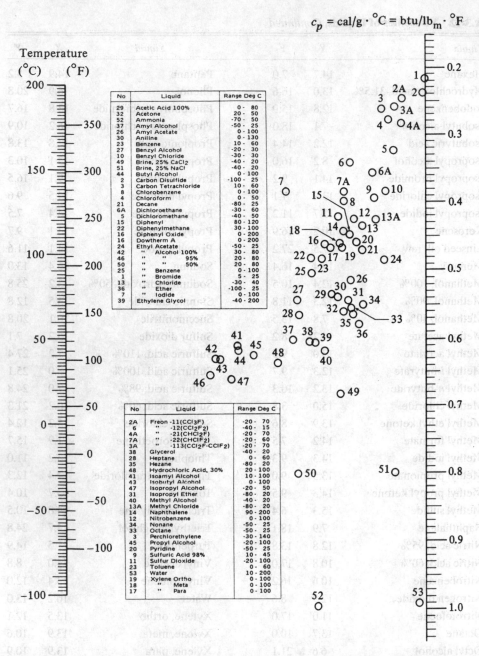

FIGURE A.3-5. *Heat capacity of liquids. (From R. H. Perry and C. H. Chilton,* Chemical Engineers' Handbook, *5th ed. New York: McGraw-Hill Book Company, 1973. With permission.)*

A.3-13 Thermal Conductivities of Liquids ($k = W/m \cdot K$)*

Liquid	K	k	Liquid	K	k
Acetic acid			Ethylene glycol	273	0.265
100%	293	0.171	Glycerol, 100%	293	0.284
50%	293	0.346	n-Hexane	303	0.138
Ammonia	243–258	0.502		333	0.135
n-Amyl alcohol	303	0.163	Kerosene	293	0.149
	373	0.154		348	0.140
Benzene	303	0.159	Methyl alcohol		
	333	0.151	100%	293	0.215
Carbon tetrachloride	273	0.185	60%	293	0.329
	341	0.163	20%	293	0.492
n-Decane	303	0.147	100%	323	0.197
	333	0.144	n-Octane	303	0.144
Ethyl acetate	293	0.175		333	0.140
Ethyl alcohol			NaCl brine		
100%	293	0.182	25%	303	0.571
60%	293	0.305	12.5%	303	0.589
20%	293	0.486	Sulfuric acid		
100%	323	0.151	90%	303	0.364
			60%	303	0.433
			Vaseline	332	0.183

*A linear variation with temperature may be assumed between the temperature limits given.

Source: R. H. Perry and C. H. Chilton, *Chemical Engineers' Handbook*, 5th ed. New York: McGraw-Hill Book Company, 1973. With permission.

A.3-14 Heat Capacities of Solids ($c_p = kJ/kg \cdot K$)

Solid	K	c_p	Solid	K	c_p
Alumina	373	0.84	Benzoic acid	293	1.243
	1773	1.147	Camphene	308	1.591
Asbestos		1.05	Caprylic acid	271	2.629
Asphalt		0.92	Dextrin	273	1.218
Brick, fireclay	373	0.829	Formic acid	273	1.800
	1773	1.248	Glycerol	273	1.382
Cement, portland		0.779	Lactose	293	1.202
Clay		0.938	Oxalic acid	323	1.612
Concrete		0.63	Tartaric acid	309	1.202
Corkboard	303	0.167	Urea	293	1.340
Glass		0.84			
Magnesia	373	0.980			
	1773	0.787			
Oak		2.39			
Pine, yellow	298	2.81			
Porcelain	293–373	0.775			
Rubber, vulcanized		2.01			
Steel		0.50			
Wool		1.361			

Source: R. H. Perry and C. H. Chilton, *Chemical Engineers' Handbook*, 5th ed. New York: McGraw-Hill Book Company, 1973; National Research Council, *International Critical Tables*, Vol. V. New York: McGraw-Hill Book Company, 1929; L. S. Marks, *Mechanical Engineers' Handbook*, 5th ed. New York: McGraw-Hill Book Company, 1951; F. Kreith, *Principles of Heat Transfer*, 2nd ed. Scranton, Pa.: International Textbook Co., 1965.

A.3-15 Thermal Conductivities of Building and Insulating Materials

Material	ρ $\left(\dfrac{kg}{m^3}\right)$	t^* (°C)	$k(W/m \cdot K)$		
Asbestos	577		0.151 (0°C)	0.168 (37.8°C)	0.190 (93.3°C)
Asbestos sheets	889	51	0.166		
Brick, building		20	0.69		
Brick, fireclay			1.00 (200°C)	1.47 (600°C)	1.64 (1000°C)
Clay soil, 4% H_2O	1666	4.5	0.57		
Concrete, 1:4 dry			0.762		
Corkboard	160.2	30	0.0433		
Cotton	80.1		0.055 (0°C)	0.061 (37.8°C)	0.068 (93.3°C)
Felt, wool	330	30	0.052		
Fiber insulation board	237	21	0.048		
Glass, window			0.52–1.06		
Glass fiber	64.1	30	0.0310 (−6.7°C)	0.0414 (37.8°C)	0.0549 (93.3°C)
Ice	921	0	2.25		
Magnesia, 85%	271		0.068 (37.8°C)	0.071 (93.3°C)	0.080 (204.4°C)
	208		0.059 (37.8°C)	0.062 (93.3°C)	0.066 (148.9°C)
Oak, across grain	825	15	0.208		
Pine, across grain	545	15	0.151		
Paper			0.130		
Polystyrene board	16		0.040		
Polyurethane sprayed foam	24–40		0.023–0.026		
Rock wool	192		0.0317 (−6.7°C)	0.0391 (37.8°C)	0.0486 (93.3°C)
	128		0.0296 (−6.7°C)	0.0395 (37.8°C)	0.0518 (93.3°C)
Rubber, hard	1198	0	0.151		
Sand soil					
4% H_2O	1826	4.5	1.51		
10% H_2O	1922	4.5	2.16		
Sandstone	2243	40	1.83		
Snow	559	0	0.47		
Wool	110.5	30	0.036		

*Room temperature when none is noted.

Source: L. S. Marks, *Mechanical Engineers' Handbook,* 5th ed. New York: McGraw-Hill Book Company, 1951; W. H. McAdams, *Heat Transmission,* 3rd ed. New York: McGraw-Hill Book Company, 1954; F. H. Norton, *Refractories.* New York: McGraw-Hill Book Company, 1949; National Research Council, *International Critical Tables.* New York: McGraw-Hill Book Company, 1929; M. S. Kersten, *Univ. Minn. Eng. Ex. Sta., Bull. 28,* June 1949; R. H. Heilman, *Ind. Eng. Chem.,* **28,** 782 (1936).

A.3-16 Thermal Conductivities, Densities, and Heat Capacities of Metals

Material	t ($°C$)	ρ $\left(\dfrac{kg}{m^3}\right)$	c_p $\left(\dfrac{kJ}{kg \cdot K}\right)$	$k(W/m \cdot K)$		
Aluminum	20	2707	0.896	202 (0°C) 230 (300°C)	206 (100°C)	215 (200°C)
Brass (70–30)	20	8522	0.385	97 (0°C)	104 (100°C)	109 (200°C)
Cast iron	20	7593	0.465	55 (0°C)	52 (100°C)	48 (200°C)
Copper	20	8954	0.383	388 (0°C)	377 (100°C)	372 (200°C)
Lead	20	11 370	0.130	35 (0°C)	33 (100°C)	31 (200°C)
Steel 1%C	20	7801	0.473	45.3 (18°C) 43 (300°C)	45 (100°C)	45 (200°C)
308 stainless	20	7849	0.461	15.2 (100°C)	21.6 (500°C)	
304 stainless	0	7817	0.461	13.8 (0°C)	16.3 (100°C)	18.9 (300°C)
Tin	20	7304	0.227	62 (0°C)	59 (100°C)	57 (200°C)

Source: L. S. Marks, *Mechanical Engineers' Handbook,* 5th ed. New York: McGraw-Hill Book Company, 1951; E. R. G. Eckert and R. M. Drake, *Heat and Mass Transfer,* 2nd ed. New York: McGraw-Hill Book Company, 1959; R. H. Perry and C. H. Chilton, *Chemical Engineers' Handbook,* 5th ed. New York: McGraw-Hill Book Company, 1973; National Research Council, *International Critical Tables.* New York: McGraw-Hill Book Company, 1929.

A.3-17 Normal Total Emmissivities of Surfaces

Surface	K	ε	Surface	K	ε
Aluminum			Lead, unoxidized	400	0.057
highly oxidized	366	0.20	Nickel, polished	373	0.072
highly polished	500	0.039	Nickel oxide	922	0.59
	850	0.057	Oak, planed	294	0.90
Aluminum oxide	550	0.63	Paint		
Asbestos board	296	0.96	aluminum	373	0.52
Brass, highly	520	0.028	oil (16 different, all colors)	373	0.92–0.96
polished	630	0.031	Paper	292	0.924
Chromium, polished	373	0.075	Roofing paper	294	0.91
Copper			Rubber (hard, glossy)	296	0.94
oxidized	298	0.78	Steel		
polished	390	0.023	oxidized at 867 K	472	0.79
Glass, smooth	295	0.94	polished stainless	373	0.074
Iron			304 stainless	489	0.44
oxidized	373	0.74	Water	273	0.95
tin-plated	373	0.07		373	0.963
Iron oxide	772	0.85			

Source: R. H. Perry and C. H. Chilton, *Chemical Engineers' Handbook,* 5th ed. New York: McGraw-Hill Book Company, 1973; W. H. McAdams, *Heat Transmission,* 3rd ed. New York: McGraw-Hill Book Company, 1954; E. Schmidt, *Gesundh.-Ing. Beiheft,* **20,** Reihe 1, 1 (1927).

A.3-18 Henry's Law Constants for Gases in Water ($H \times 10^{-4}$)*

| T | | | | | | | | | | | |
K	°C	CO_2	CO	C_2H_6	C_2H_4	He	H_2	H_2S	CH_4	N_2	O_2
273.2	0	0.0728	3.52	1.26	0.552	12.9	5.79	0.0268	2.24	5.29	2.55
283.2	10	0.104	4.42	1.89	0.768	12.6	6.36	0.0367	2.97	6.68	3.27
293.2	20	0.142	5.36	2.63	1.02	12.5	6.83	0.0483	3.76	8.04	4.01
303.2	30	0.186	6.20	3.42	1.27	12.4	7.29	0.0609	4.49	9.24	4.75
313.2	40	0.233	6.96	4.23		12.1	7.51	0.0745	5.20	10.4	5.35

*$p_A = Hx_A$, p_A = partial pressure of A in gas in atm, x_A = mole fraction of A in liquid, H = Henry's law constant in atm/mole frac.

Source: National Research Council, *International Critical Tables,* Vol. III. New York: McGraw-Hill Book Company, 1929.

A.3-19 Equilibrium Data for SO₂–Water System

Mole Fraction SO₂ in Liquid, x_A	Partial Pressure of SO₂ in Vapor, p_A (mm Hg)		Mole Fraction SO₂ in Vapor, y_A; $P = 1$ Atm	
	20°C (293 K)	30°C (303 K)	20°C	30°C
0	0	0	0	0
0.0000562	0.5	0.6	0.000658	0.000790
0.0001403	1.2	1.7	0.00158	0.00223
0.000280	3.2	4.7	0.00421	0.00619
0.000422	5.8	8.1	0.00763	0.01065
0.000564	8.5	11.8	0.01120	0.0155
0.000842	14.1	19.7	0.01855	0.0259
0.001403	26.0	36	0.0342	0.0473
0.001965	39.0	52	0.0513	0.0685
0.00279	59	79	0.0775	0.1040
0.00420	92	125	0.121	0.1645
0.00698	161	216	0.212	0.284
0.01385	336	452	0.443	0.594
0.0206	517	688	0.682	0.905
0.0273	698		0.917	

Source: T. K. Sherwood, *Ind. Eng. Chem.,* **17,** 745 (1925).

A.3-20 Equilibrium Data for Methanol–Water System

Mole Fraction Methanol in Liquid, x_A	Partial Pressure of Methanol in Vapor, p_A (mm Hg)	
	39.9°C (313.1°K)	59.4°C (332.6 K)
0	0	0
0.05	25.0	50
0.10	46.0	102
0.15	66.5	151

Source: National Research Council, *International Critical Tables,* Vol. III. New York: McGraw-Hill Book Company, 1929.

A.3-21 Equilibrium Data for Acetone–Water System at 20°C (293 K)

Mole Fraction Acetone in Liquid, x_A	Partial Pressure of Acetone in Vapor, p_A (mm Hg)
0	0
0.0333	30.0
0.0720	62.8
0.117	85.4
0.171	103

Source: T. K. Sherwood, *Absorption and Extraction.* New York: McGraw-Hill Book Company, 1937. With permission.

A.3-22 Equilibrium Data for Ammonia–Water System

Mole Fraction NH_3 in Liquid, x_A	Partial Pressure of NH_3 in Vapor, p_A (mm Hg)		Mole Fraction NH_3 in Vapor, y_A; $P = 1$ Atm	
	20°C (293 K)	30°C (303 K)	20°C	30°C
0	0	0	0	0
0.0126		11.5		0.0151
0.0167		15.3		0.0201
0.0208	12	19.3	0.0158	0.0254
0.0258	15	24.4	0.0197	0.0321
0.0309	18.2	29.6	0.0239	0.0390
0.0405	24.9	40.1	0.0328	0.0527
0.0503	31.7	51.0	0.0416	0.0671
0.0737	50.0	79.7	0.0657	0.105
0.0960	69.6	110	0.0915	0.145
0.137	114	179	0.150	0.235
0.175	166	260	0.218	0.342
0.210	227	352	0.298	0.463
0.241	298	454	0.392	0.597
0.297	470	719	0.618	0.945

Source: J. H. Perry, *Chemical Engineers' Handbook,* 4th ed. New York: McGraw-Hill Book Company, 1963. With permission.

A.3-23 Equilibrium Data for Ethanol–Water System at 101.325 kPa (1 Atm)*

Temperature		Vapor–Liquid Equilibria, Mass Fraction Ethanol	
°C	°F	x_A	y_A
100.0	212	0	0
98.1	208.5	0.020	0.192
95.2	203.4	0.050	0.377
91.8	197.2	0.100	0.527
87.3	189.2	0.200	0.656
84.7	184.5	0.300	0.713
83.2	181.7	0.400	0.746
82.0	179.6	0.500	0.771
81.0	177.8	0.600	0.794
80.1	176.2	0.700	0.822
79.1	174.3	0.800	0.858
78.3	173.0	0.900	0.912
78.2	172.8	0.940	0.942
78.1	172.7	0.960	0.959
78.2	172.8	0.980	0.978
78.3	173.0	1.00	1.00

Mass Fraction	Temperature		Enthalpy (btu/lb$_m$) of mixture		Enthalpy (kJ/kg) of mixture	
	°C	°F	Liquid	Vapor	Liquid	Vapor
0	100.0	212	180.1	1150	418.9	2675
0.1	91.8	197.2	159.8	1082	371.7	2517
0.3	84.7	184.5	135.0	943	314.0	2193
0.5	82.0	179.6	122.9	804	285.9	1870
0.7	80.1	176.2	111.1	664	258.4	1544
0.9	78.3	173.0	96.6	526	224.7	1223
1.0	78.3	173.0	89.0	457.5	207.0	1064

*Reference state for enthalpy is pure liquid at 273 K or 0°C.

Source: Data from L. W. Cornell and R. E. Montonna, *Ind. Eng. Chem.,* **25,** 1331 (1933); and W. A. Noyes and R. R. Warfel, *J. Am. Chem. Soc.,* **23,** 463 (1901), as given by G. G. Brown, *Unit Operations.* New York: John Wiley & Sons, Inc., 1950. With permission.

A.3-24 Acetic Acid–Water–Isopropyl Ether System, Liquid–Liquid Equilibria at 293 K or 20°C

Water Layer (wt %)			Isopropyl Ether Layer (wt %)		
Acetic Acid	Water	Isopropyl Ether	Acetic Acid	Water	Isopropyl Ether
0	98.8	1.2	0	0.6	99.4
0.69	98.1	1.2	0.18	0.5	99.3
1.41	97.1	1.5	0.37	0.7	98.9
2.89	95.5	1.6	0.79	0.8	98.4
6.42	91.7	1.9	1.93	1.0	97.1
13.30	84.4	2.3	4.82	1.9	93.3
25.50	71.1	3.4	11.40	3.9	84.7
36.70	58.9	4.4	21.60	6.9	71.5
44.30	45.1	10.6	31.10	10.8	58.1
46.40	37.1	16.5	36.20	15.1	48.7

Source: Trans. A.I.Ch.E., **36**, 601, 628 (1940). With permission.

A.3-25 Liquid–Liquid Equilibrium Data for Acetone–Water–Methyl Isobutyl Ketone (MIK) System at 298–299 K or 25–26°C

Composition Data (wt %)			Acetone Distribution Data (wt %)	
MIK	Acetone	Water	Water Phase	MIK Phase
98.0	0	2.00	2.5	4.5
93.2	4.6	2.33	5.5	10.0
77.3	18.95	3.86	7.5	13.5
71.0	24.4	4.66	10.0	17.5
65.5	28.9	5.53	12.5	21.3
54.7	37.6	7.82	15.5	25.5
46.2	43.2	10.7	17.5	28.2
12.4	42.7	45.0	20.0	31.2
5.01	30.9	64.2	22.5	34.0
3.23	20.9	75.8	25.0	36.5
2.12	3.73	94.2	26.0	37.5
2.20	0	97.8		

Source: Reprinted with permission from D. F. Othmer, R. E. White, and E. Trueger, *Ind. Eng. Chem.*, **33**, 1240 (1941). Copyright by the American Chemical Society.

APPENDIX A.4

Physical Properties of Foods and Biological Materials

A.4-1 Heat Capacities of Foods (Average c_p 273–373 K or 0–100°C)

Material	H_2O (wt %)	c_p (kJ/kg · K)
Apples	75–85	3.73–4.02
Apple sauce		4.02*
Asparagus		
Fresh	93	3.94†
Frozen	93	2.01‡
Bacon, lean	51	3.43
Banana purée		3.66§
Beef, lean	72	3.43
Bread, white	44–45	2.72–2.85
Butter	15	2.30¶
Cantaloupe	92.7	3.94†
Carrot	88.2	3.81–3.94
Cheese, Swiss	55	2.68†
Corn, sweet		
Fresh		3.32†
Frozen		1.77‡
Cream, 45–60% fat	57–73	3.06–3.27
Cucumber	97	4.10
Eggs		
Fresh		3.18†
Frozen		1.68‡

Material	H_2O (wt %)	c_p (kJ/kg · K)
Egg yolk	4.00	2.81
Fish, cod		
Fresh	70	3.18
Frozen	70	1.72‡
Flour	12–13.5	1.80–1.88
Ice	100	1.958‖
Ice cream		
Fresh	58–66	3.27†
Frozen	58–66	1.88‡
Lamb	70	3.18*
Macaroni	12.5–13.5	1.84–1.88
Milk, cows'		
Whole	87.5	3.85
Skim	91	3.98–4.02
Olive oil		2.01**
Oranges		
Fresh	87.2	3.77†
Frozen	87.2	1.93‡
Peas, air-dried	14	1.84
Peas, green		
Fresh	74.3	3.31†
Frozen	74.3	1.76‡
Pea soup		4.10
Plums	75–78	3.52
Pork		
Fresh	60	2.85†
Frozen	60	1.34‡
Potatoes	75	3.52
Poultry		
Fresh	74	3.31†
Frozen	74	1.55‡
Sardines	57.4	3.01
Sausage, franks		
Fresh	60	3.60†
Frozen	60	2.35‡
String beans		
Fresh	88.9	3.81†
Frozen	88.9	1.97‡
Tomatoes	95	3.98†

A.4-1 *Continued*

Material	H_2O (wt %)	c_p (kJ/kg·K)
Veal	63	3.22
Water	100	4.185**

*32.8°C.   ¶4.4°C.
† Above freezing. || −20°C.
‡ Below freezing.   **20°C.
§24.4°C.

Source: W. O. Ordinanz, *Food Ind.,* **18,** 101 (1946); G. A. Reidy, Department of Food Science. Michigan State University, 1968; S. E. Charm, *The Fundamentals of Food Engineering,* 2nd ed. Westport, Conn.: Avi Publishing Co., Inc., 1971; R. L. Earle, *Unit Operations in Food Processing.* Oxford: Pergamon Press, Inc., 1966; ASHRAE, *Handbook of Fundamentals.* New York: ASHRAE, 1972, 1967; H. C. Mannheim, M. P. Steinberg, and A. I. Nelson, *Food Technol.,* **9,** 556 (1955).

A.4-2   Thermal Conductivities, Densities, and Viscosities of Foods

Material	H_2O (wt %)	Temperature (K)	k (W/m·K)	ρ (kg/m³)	μ [(Pa·s)10³, or cp]
Apple juice	87.4	293.2	0.559		
Apple sauce		295.7	0.692		
Apple	85.6	275.2–309.2	0.393		
Beef, lean	78.8	308.2	0.458		
Beef, fat			0.19		
Butter	15	277.6	0.197	998	
Cantaloupe			0.571		
Egg					
white		309.2	0.577		
yolk		306.2	0.338		
Fish					
Fresh		273.2	0.431		
Frozen		263.2	1.22		
Flour, wheat	8.8		0.450		
Honey	12.6	275.4	0.50		
Ice	100	273.2	2.25		
	100	253.2	2.42		
Lamb	71	278.8	0.415		
Milk					
Whole		293.2		1030	2.12
Skim		274.7	0.538		

Material	H_2O (wt %)	Temperature (K)	k (W/m·K)	ρ (kg/m³)	$[(Pa \cdot s)10^3,$ or cp] μ
		298.2		1041	1.4
Oil					
Cod liver		298.2		924	
Corn		288.2		921	
Olive		293.2	0.168	919	84
Peanut		277.1	0.168		
Soybean		303.2		919	40
Oranges	61.2	303.5	0.431		
Pears		281.9	0.595		
Pork, lean					
Fresh	74	275.4	0.460		
Frozen		258.2	1.109		
Potatoes					
Raw			0.554		
Frozen		260.4	1.09	977	
Salmon					
Fresh	67	277.1	0.50		
Frozen	67	248.2	1.30		
Sucrose solution	80	294.3		1073	1.92
Turkey					
Fresh	74	276.0	0.502		
Frozen		248.2	1.675		
Veal					
Fresh	75	335.4	0.485		
Frozen	75	263.6	1.30		
Water	100	293.2	0.602		
	100	273.2	0.569		

Source: R. C. Weast, *Handbook of Chemistry and Physics,* 48th ed. Cleveland: Chemical Rubber Co., Inc., 1967; C. P. Lentz, *Food Technol.,* **15,** 243 (1961); G. A. Reidy, Department of Food Science, Michigan State University, 1968; S. E. Charm, *The Fundamentals of Food Engineering,* 2nd ed. Westport, Conn.: Avi Publishing Co., Inc., 1971; R. Earle, *Unit Operations in Food Processing.* Oxford: Pergamon Press, 1966; R. H. Perry and C. H. Chilton, *Chemical Engineers' Handbook,* 5th ed. New York: McGraw-Hill Book Company, 1973; V. E. Sweat, *J. Food Sci.,* **39,** 1080 (1974).

APPENDIX A.5

Properties of Pipes, Tubes, and Screens

A.5-1 Dimensions of Standard Steel Pipe

Nominal Pipe Size (in.)	Outside Diameter in.	Outside Diameter mm	Schedule Number	Wall Thickness in.	Wall Thickness mm	Inside Diameter in.	Inside Diameter mm	Inside Cross-Sectional Area ft²	Inside Cross-Sectional Area $m^2 \times 10^4$
$\frac{1}{8}$	0.405	10.29	40	0.068	1.73	0.269	6.83	0.00040	0.3664
			80	0.095	2.41	0.215	5.46	0.00025	0.2341
$\frac{1}{4}$	0.540	13.72	40	0.088	2.24	0.364	9.25	0.00072	0.6720
			80	0.119	3.02	0.302	7.67	0.00050	0.4620
$\frac{3}{8}$	0.675	17.15	40	0.091	2.31	0.493	12.52	0.00133	1.231
			80	0.126	3.20	0.423	10.74	0.00098	0.9059
$\frac{1}{2}$	0.840	21.34	40	0.109	2.77	0.622	15.80	0.00211	1.961
			80	0.147	3.73	0.546	13.87	0.00163	1.511
$\frac{3}{4}$	1.050	26.67	40	0.113	2.87	0.824	20.93	0.00371	3.441
			80	0.154	3.91	0.742	18.85	0.00300	2.791
1	1.315	33.40	40	0.133	3.38	1.049	26.64	0.00600	5.574
			80	0.179	4.45	0.957	24.31	0.00499	4.641
$1\frac{1}{4}$	1.660	42.16	40	0.140	3.56	1.380	35.05	0.01040	9.648
			80	0.191	4.85	1.278	32.46	0.00891	8.275
$1\frac{1}{2}$	1.900	48.26	40	0.145	3.68	1.610	40.89	0.01414	13.13
			80	0.200	5.08	1.500	38.10	0.01225	11.40
2	2.375	60.33	40	0.154	3.91	2.067	52.50	0.02330	21.65
			80	0.218	5.54	1.939	49.25	0.02050	19.05
$2\frac{1}{2}$	2.875	73.03	40	0.203	5.16	2.469	62.71	0.03322	30.89
			80	0.276	7.01	2.323	59.00	0.02942	27.30
3	3.500	88.90	40	0.216	5.49	3.068	77.92	0.05130	47.69
			80	0.300	7.62	2.900	73.66	0.04587	42.61
$3\frac{1}{2}$	4.000	101.6	40	0.226	5.74	3.548	90.12	0.06870	63.79
			80	0.318	8.08	3.364	85.45	0.06170	57.35

Nominal Pipe Size (in.)	Outside Diameter		Schedule Number	Wall Thickness		Inside Diameter		Inside Cross-Sectional Area	
	in.	mm		in.	mm	in.	mm	ft^2	$m^2 \times 10^4$
4	4.500	114.3	40	0.237	6.02	4.026	102.3	0.08840	82.19
			80	0.337	8.56	3.826	97.18	0.07986	74.17
5	5.563	141.3	40	0.258	6.55	5.047	128.2	0.1390	129.1
			80	0.375	9.53	4.813	122.3	0.1263	117.5
6	6.625	168.3	40	0.280	7.11	6.065	154.1	0.2006	186.5
			80	0.432	10.97	5.761	146.3	0.1810	168.1
8	8.625	219.1	40	0.322	8.18	7.981	202.7	0.3474	322.7
			80	0.500	12.70	7.625	193.7	0.3171	294.7

A.5-2 Dimensions of Heat-Exchanger Tubes

Outside Diameter		BWG Number	Wall Thickness		Inside Diameter		Inside Cross-Sectional Area	
in.	mm		in.	mm	in.	mm	ft^2	$m^2 \times 10^4$
$\frac{5}{8}$	15.88	12	0.109	2.77	0.407	10.33	0.000903	0.8381
		14	0.083	2.11	0.459	11.66	0.00115	1.068
		16	0.065	1.65	0.495	12.57	0.00134	1.241
		18	0.049	1.25	0.527	13.39	0.00151	1.408
$\frac{3}{4}$	19.05	12	0.109	2.77	0.532	13.51	0.00154	1.434
		14	0.083	2.11	0.584	14.83	0.00186	1.727
		16	0.065	1.65	0.620	15.75	0.00210	1.948
		18	0.049	1.25	0.652	16.56	0.00232	2.154
$\frac{7}{8}$	22.23	12	0.109	2.77	0.657	16.69	0.00235	2.188
		14	0.083	2.11	0.709	18.01	0.00274	2.548
		16	0.065	1.65	0.745	18.92	0.00303	2.811
		18	0.049	1.25	0.777	19.74	0.00329	3.060
1	25.40	10	0.134	3.40	0.732	18.59	0.00292	2.714
		12	0.109	2.77	0.782	19.86	0.00334	3.098
		14	0.083	2.11	0.834	21.18	0.00379	3.523
		16	0.065	1.65	0.870	22.10	0.00413	3.836
$1\frac{1}{4}$	31.75	10	0.134	3.40	0.982	24.94	0.00526	4.885
		12	0.109	2.77	1.032	26.21	0.00581	5.395
		14	0.083	2.11	1.084	27.53	0.00641	5.953
		16	0.065	1.65	1.120	28.45	0.00684	6.357
$1\frac{1}{2}$	38.10	10	0.134	3.40	1.232	31.29	0.00828	7.690
		12	0.109	2.77	1.282	32.56	0.00896	8.326
		14	0.083	2.11	1.334	33.88	0.00971	9.015
2	50.80	10	0.134	3.40	1.732	43.99	0.0164	15.20
		12	0.109	2.77	1.782	45.26	0.0173	16.09

A.5-3 Tyler Standard Screen Scale

Mesh	Sieve Clear Opening		Nominal Wire Diameter	
	in.	mm	mm	in.
1.050 in.	1.050	26.67	3.76	0.148
0.833 in	0.833	22.43	3.43	0.135
0.742 in.	0.742	18.85	3.43	0.135
0.624 in	0.624	15.85	3.05	0.120
0.525 in.	0.525	13.33	2.67	0.105
0.441 in.	0.441	11.20	2.67	0.105
0.371 in.	0.371	9.423	2.34	0.092
$2\frac{1}{2}$ mesh	0.312	7.925	2.24	0.088
3 mesh	0.263	6.680	1.78	0.070
$3\frac{1}{2}$ mesh	0.221	5.613	1.65	0.065
4 mesh	0.185	4.699	1.65	0.065
5 mesh	0.156	3.962	1.12	0.044
6 mesh	0.131	3.327	0.914	0.036
7 mesh	0.110	2.794	0.833	0.0328
8 mesh	0.093	2.362	0.813	0.032
9 mesh	0.078	1.981	0.838	0.033
10 mesh	0.065	1.651	0.889	0.035
12 mesh	0.055	1.397	0.711	0.028
14 mesh	0.046	1.168	0.635	0.025
16 mesh	0.0390	0.991	0.597	0.0235
20 mesh	0.0328	0.833	0.437	0.0172
24 mesh	0.0276	0.701	0.358	0.0141
28 mesh	0.0232	0.589	0.318	0.0125
32 mesh	0.0195	0.495	0.300	0.0118
35 mesh	0.0164	0.417	0.310	0.0122
42 mesh	0.0138	0.351	0.254	0.0100
48 mesh	0.0116	0.295	0.234	0.0092
60 mesh	0.0097	0.246	0.178	0.0070
65 mesh	0.0082	0.208	0.183	0.0072
80 mesh	0.0069	0.175	0.142	0.0056
100 mesh	0.0058	0.147	0.107	0.0042
115 mesh	0.0049	0.124	0.097	0.0038
150 mesh	0.0041	0.104	0.066	0.0026
170 mesh	0.0035	0.088	0.061	0.0024
200 mesh	0.0029	0.074	0.053	0.0021
250 mesh	0.0025	0.063	0.044	0.0017
270 mesh	0.0021	0.053	0.037	0.0015
325 mesh	0.0017	0.044	0.030	0.0012
400 mesh	0.0015	0.037	0.025	0.0010

Notation

SI units are given first (followed by English and/or cgs units).

a	shape factor, dimensionless
a	particle radius, m (ft)
a	area, m^2 (ft^2); also m^2 area/m^3 volume bed or packing (ft^2/ft^3)
a_e	acceleration from centrifugal force, m/s^2 (ft/s^2)
a_v	specific surface area of particle, m^{-1} (ft^{-1})
A	cross-sectional area, m^2 (ft^2, cm^2); also area, m^2 (ft^2)
A	absorption factor $= L/mV$, dimensionless; also filter area, m^2 (ft^2)
A_m	membrane area, cm^2, m^2 (ft^2)
A_w	solvent permeability constant, kg/s $\cdot$ m^2 $\cdot$ atm
A_s	solute permeability constant, m/s (ft/h)
b	length, m (ft, cm)
B	length of side in structured packing, cm (in.)
B	flow rate of dry solid, kg/h (lb_m/h); also filtration constant, s/m^3 (s/ft^3)
B	physical property of membrane, atm^{-1}
B^o	nucleation rate, number of nuclei/h $\cdot$ L
c	concentration, kg/m^3, kg mol/m^3 (lb_m/ft^3, g mol/cm^3)
c	concentration of absorbate in fluid, kg/m^3 (lb_m/ft^3)
c_A	concentration of A, kg mol/m^3 (lb mol/ft^3, g mol/cm^3)
c_b	break-point concentration, kg/m^3 (lb_m/ft^3)
c_g	concentration of solute in gel, kg solute/m^3 (lb_m/ft^3, g/cm^3)
c_s	concentration of solute at surface of membrane, kg solute/m^3 (lb_m/ft^3, g/cm^3)
c_S	concentration of A in solid, kg mol A/m^3 (lb_m/ft^3, g mol/cm^3)
c_S	concentration of solids in slurry, kg/m^3 (lb_m/ft^3)
c_S	humid heat, kJ/kg dry air $\cdot$ K (btu/lb_m dry air $\cdot$ °F)
c_x	concentration of solids in slurry, mass frac
c_p	heat capacity at constant pressure, J/kg $\cdot$ K, kJ/kg $\cdot$ K, kJ/kg mol $\cdot$ K (btu/lb_m $\cdot$ °F, cal/g $\cdot$ °C)
c_{w2}	concentration of solvent in permeate, kg solvent/m^3
c'_A	deviation of concentration from mean concentration $\bar{c}_A$, kg mol/m^3
c_p	concentration of P, kg P/m^3
c_v	heat capacity at constant volume, J/kg $\cdot$ K
C	filtration constant, N/m^2 (lb_f/ft^2); also, number of components
C	fluid heat capacity, W/K (btu/h $\cdot$ °F)

C	height of bottom of agitator above tank bottom, m (ft)
C	total concentration in liquid solution, equiv/L
C_p	pitot tube coefficient, dimensionless
C_D	drag coefficient, dimensionless
C_v, C_o, C_n	Venturi coefficient, orifice coefficient, flow nozzle coefficient, dimensionless
d_p	packing diameter, mm (in.)
d_o	hole diameter, ft
D	molecular diffusivity, m^2/s (ft^2/h, cm^2/s); also diameter, m (ft)
D	decimal reduction time, min; also distillate flow rate, kg/h, kg mol/h (lb$_m$/h)
D_{AB}	molecular diffusivity, m^2/s (ft^2/h, cm^2/s)
D_{AB}^o	molecular diffusivity in dilute solution, cm^2/s (ft^2/h)
D_p	particle diameter, m (ft)
D_{KA}	Knudsen diffusivity m^2/s (ft^2/h, cm^2/s)
D_{NA}	transition-region diffusivity, m^2/s (ft^2/h, cm^2/s)
$D_{A\,\text{eff}}$	effective diffusivity, m^2/s (ft^2/h, cm^2/s)
$D_{p,m}$	effective mean diameter for mixture, m (ft)
D_a	diameter of agitator, m (ft)
D_t	diameter of tank, m (ft)
D_{pc}	critical diameter, m (ft)
D_{AP}	diffusivity of A in protein solution, m^2/s
D_+	molecular diffusivity of cation, cm^2/s
D_-	molecular diffusivity of anion, cm^2/s
E	height of element in structured packing, cm (in.)
E	activation energy, J/kg mol (cal/g mol)
E	energy for size reduction, kW · h/ton; also tray efficiency, dimensionless
E	total energy, J/kg (ft · lb$_f$/lb$_m$)
E	fraction unaccomplished change, dimensionless
E	emitted radiation energy, W/m^2 (btu/h · ft^2)
E	axial dispersion coefficient, m^2/s (ft^2/h)
$E_{B\lambda}$	monochromatic emissive power, W/m^3 (btu/h · ft^3)
E_o	fraction or % tray efficiency
f	fraction of feed vaporized; also cycle fraction, dimensionless
f	Fanning friction factor, dimensionless
f_p	relative mass-transfer coefficient, dimensionless
f_t	mixing factor, dimensionless
F	number of degrees of freedom
F	frictional loss, J/kg (ft · lb$_f$/lb$_m$)
F	flow rate, kg/h, kg mol/h (lb$_m$/h)
F	force, N (lb$_f$, dyn)
F_T	correction factor for temperature difference, dimensionless
F_0	process time at 121.1°C(250°F), min
F_p	packing factor, m^{-1}(ft^{-1})
$\mathscr{F}_{12}$	geometric view factor for gray surfaces, dimensionless
F_{12}	geometric view factor, dimensionless
g	standard acceleration of gravity (see Appendix A.1)
g_c	gravitional conversion factor (see Appendix A.1)
G	mass velocity $= v\rho$, kg/s · m^2, kg/h · m^2 (lb$_m$/h · ft^2)

G	growth constant, mm/h
G'	mass velocity $= v'\rho$, kg/s $\cdot$ m^2, kg/h $\cdot$ m^2 (lb$_m$/h $\cdot$ ft^2)
G	irradiation on a body, W/m^2 (btu/h $\cdot$ ft^2)
h	constant spacing in x for Simpson's rule
h	head, J/kg (ft $\cdot$ lb$_f$/lb$_m$); also height of fluid, m (ft)
h	heat-transfer coefficient, W/m^2 $\cdot$ K (btu/h $\cdot$ ft^2 $\cdot$ °F)
h	enthalpy of liquid, J/kg, kJ/kg, kJ/kg mol (btu/lb$_m$)
h	height of triangle in structured packing, cm (in.)
h_{fg}	latent heat of vaporization, J/kg, kJ/kg (btu/lb$_m$)
h_c	contact resistance coefficient, W/m^2 $\cdot$ K (btu/h $\cdot$ ft^2 $\cdot$ °F)
H	distance, m (ft)
H	Henry's law constant, atm/mol frac
H	head, J/kg (ft $\cdot$ lb$_f$/lb$_m$); also height of fluid, m (ft)
H	enthalpy, J/kg, kJ/kg, kJ/kg mol (btu/lb$_m$); also enthalpy kJ/kg dry air (btu/lb$_m$ dry air)
H	humidity, kg water vapor/kg dry air (lb water vapor/lb dry air)
H	enthalpy of vapor, J/kg, kJ/kg, kJ/kg mol (btu/lb$_m$)
H	equilibrium relation, kg mol/m^3 $\cdot$ atm
H	bed length, m (ft); also effective length of spindle, m (ft)
H	height of packing, m (ft)
H'	enthalpy, kJ/kg dry solid (btu/lb$_m$); also enthalpy, kJ/kg dry air (btu/lb$_m$ dry air)
H_B	length of bed used up to break point, m (ft)
H_G, H_L, H_y, H_{oy} $H_{OG}, H_{OL}, H_x, H_{ox}$	height of transfer unit, m (ft)
H_P, H_R	percentage humidity, percentage relative humidity, respectively
H_T	total bed length, m (ft)
H_{UNB}	length of unused bed, m (ft)
HETS	height of equilibrium stage, m (ft)
HETP	height equivalent of packed tower equal to one theoretical plate, m (ft)
i	unit vector along x axis
I	intensity of turbulence, dimensionless; also current, amp
I_B	radiation intensity of black body, W/m^2 $\cdot$ sr (btu/h $\cdot$ ft^2 $\cdot$ sr)
I_λ	intensity of radiation, W/m^2 (btu/h $\cdot$ ft^2)
j	unit vector along y axis
J	width of baffle, m (ft)
j_A	mass flux of A relative to mass average velocity, kg/s $\cdot$ m^2
j_A^*	mass flux of A relative to molar average velocity, kg/s $\cdot$ m^2
J_A	molar flux of A relative to mass average velocity, kg mol/s $\cdot$ m^2
$\boldsymbol{J}_A^*$	molar flux vector of A relative to molar average velocity, kg mol/s $\cdot$ m^2 (lb mol/h $\cdot$ ft^2, g mol/s $\cdot$ cm^2)
J_D, J_H	mass-transfer and heat-transfer factors, dimensionless
$\boldsymbol{k}$	unit vector along z axis
k, k'	reaction velocity constant, h^{-1}, min^{-1}, or s^{-1}
k	thermal conductivity, W/m $\cdot$ K (btu/h $\cdot$ ft $\cdot$ °F)
k	reaction velocity constant, h^{-1}, min^{-1}, or s^{-1}
k_1'	first-order heterogeneous reaction velocity constant, m/s (cm/s)
$k_c', k_c, k_G, k_x, \ldots$	mass-transfer coefficient, kg mol/s $\cdot$ m^2 $\cdot$ conc diff (lb mol/h $\cdot$ ft^2 $\cdot$ conc diff, g mol/s $\cdot$ cm^2 $\cdot$ conc diff); kg mol/s $\cdot$ m^2 $\cdot$ Pa, kg mol/s $\cdot$ m^2 $\cdot$ atm (lb mol/h $\cdot$ ft^2 $\cdot$ atm). (See Table 7.2-1.)

k_c	mass-transfer coefficient, m/s (ft/ h, cm/s)
k_c^o	mass transfer coefficient defined by Eq. (7.2-23), m/s (ft/h, cm/s)
$k_G a, k_x a, k_y a, \ldots$	volumetric mass-transfer coefficient, kg mol/s $\cdot$ m^3 $\cdot$ conc diff (lb mol/ h $\cdot$ ft^3 $\cdot$ conc diff, g mol/s $\cdot$ cm^3 $\cdot$ conc diff); kg mol/s $\cdot$ m^3 $\cdot$ Pa
k_s	surface reaction coefficient, kg mol/s $\cdot$ m^2 $\cdot$ mol frac
k_w, k_w'	wall constants, dimensionless
K_y', K_x'	overall mass-transfer coefficient, kg mol/s $\cdot$ m^2 $\cdot$ mol frac (lb mol/ h $\cdot$ ft^2 $\cdot$ mol frac, g mol/s $\cdot$ cm^2 $\cdot$ mol frac)
K	consistency index, N $\cdot$ s^n/m^2 (lb$_f$ $\cdot$ s^n/ft^2)
K	overall mass transfer coefficient in crystallization, kg mol/s $\cdot$ m^2 $\cdot$ mol frac
K_v	constant in allowable vapor velocity equation, ft/s
K	relative molar selectivity coefficient, dimensionless
K_{AB}	equilibrium constant for exchange of ions A and B
K_1	constant in Eq. (3.1-39), m/s (ft/s)
K', K_s	equilibrium distribution coefficient, dimensionless
K'	consistency index, N $\cdot$ s$^{n'}$/m^2 (lb$_f$ $\cdot$ s$^{n'}$/ft^2)
K	equilibrium distribution coefficient, dimensionless
K_p	filtration constant, s/m^6 (s/ft^6)
K_V	filtration constant, N/m^5 (lb$_f$/ft^5)
K_c, K_{ex}, K_f	contraction, expansion, fitting loss coefficient, dimensionless
L	length, m (ft); also amount, kg, kg mol (lb$_m$); also kg/h $\cdot$ m^2
L	liquid flow rate, kg/h, kg mol/h (lb$_m$/h)
L	crystal size, mm
L	residue or reject flow rate, cm^3 (STP)/s, m^3/s (ft^3/h)
L	Prandtl mixing length, m (ft)
L	mean beam length, m (ft)
L_a	average crystal size, mm
L_d	predominant crystal size, mm
L_f	feed flow rate, cm^3 (STP)/s, m^3/s (ft^3/h)
L_S	dry solid weight, kg dry solid (lb$_m$ dry solid)
L'	flow rate, kg inert/h, kg mol inert/h (lb$_m$ inert/h)
m, m', m''	slope of equilibrium line, dimensionless
m	flow rate, kg/s, kg/h (lb$_m$/s)
m	dimensionless ratio $= k/hx_1$; also, position m
m	parameter in Table 7.1-1, dimensionless; also position parameter
m	ratio, kg wet cake/kg dry cake (lb wet cake/lb dry cake)
M	molecular weight, kg/kg mol (lb$_m$/lb mol)
M	total mass, kg (lb$_m$); also parameter $= (\Delta x)^2/\alpha \Delta t$, dimensionless
M	modulus $= (\Delta x)^2/D_{AB} \Delta t$, dimensionless
M	flow rate, kg/h, kg mol/h (lb$_m$/h)
M	amount of adsorbent, kg(lb$_m$)
M_L	average molecular weight of liquid
n	number of theoretical stages
n	number of crystals/(L $\cdot$ mm)
n	exponent, dimensionless; also flow behavior index, dimensionless
n'	slope of line for power-law fluid, dimensionless
n	position parameter; also dimensionless ratio $= x/x_1$
n	total amount, kg mol (lb mol, g mol)
n^o	zero-size population density, number/(L $\cdot$ mm)

n_A	flux of A relative to stationary coordinates, kg/s $\cdot$ m^2
n_+	valence of cation
n_-	valence of anion
N	rpm or rps; also number of radiation shields
N	parameter $= h\,\Delta x/k$, dimensionless; also number of viable organisms, dimensionless
N	total flux relative to stationary coordinates, kg mol/s $\cdot$ m^2 (lb mol/ h $\cdot$ ft^2, g mol/s $\cdot$ cm^2)
N	modulus $= k_c\Delta x/D_{AB}$, dimensionless; also number of stages
N	number of crystals/L
N	concentration of solid B, kg solid B/kg solution (lb solid B/lb solution)
N	number of equal temperature subdivisions, dimensionless
N_T	number of tubes in parallel
N_s	solute flux, kg/s $\cdot$ m^2 (lb$_m$/h $\cdot$ ft^2)
N_w	solvent flux, kg solvent/s $\cdot$ m^2 (lb$_m$/h $\cdot$ ft^2)
$\overline{N}_{n,m}$	residual defined by Eq. (6.6-3), kg mol/m^3 (lb mol/ft^3)
N_A	molar flux vector of A relative to stationary coordinates, kg mol/s $\cdot$ m^2 (lb mol/h $\cdot$ ft^2, g mol/s $\cdot$ cm^2)
$\overline{N}_A$	mass transfer of A relative to stationary coordinates, kg mol/s (lb mol/h, g mol/s)
(NPSH)	net positive suction head, m (ft)
N_G, N_L, N_{OG}, N_{OL}	number of transfer units, dimensionless
N_{Gr}	Grashof number defined in Eq. (4.7-4), dimensionless
N_{Bi}	Biot number $= hx_1/k$, dimensionless
N_{Gz}	Graetz number defined in Eq. (4.12-3), dimensionless
$N_{Gr,\delta}$	Grashof number defined in Eq. (4.7-5), dimensionless
N_{Ma}	Mach number defined by Eq. (2.11-15), dimensionless
N_{Pe}	Peclet number $= N_{Re}N_{Pr}$, dimensionless
$N_{Nu,\delta}$	Nusselt number $= h\delta/k$, dimensionless
N_{Fr}	Froude number $= v^2/gL$, dimensionless
N_{Kn}	Knudsen number $= \lambda/2\bar{r}$, dimensionless
N_{Nu}	Nusselt number $= hL/k$, dimensionless
$N_{Nu,x}$	Nusselt number $= h_x x/k$, dimensionless
N_{Pr}	Prandtl number $= c_p\mu/k$, dimensionless
N_{Re}	Reynolds number $= Dv\rho/\mu$, dimensionless
N'_{Re}	Reynolds number $= D_a^2 N\rho/\mu$, dimensionless
$N_{Re,gen}$	Reynolds number defined by Eq. (3.5-11), dimensionless
$N_{Re,L}$	Reynolds number $= Lv_\infty\rho/\mu$, dimensionless
$N_{Re,x}$	Reynolds number $= xv_\infty\rho/\mu$, dimensionless
$N'_{Re,n}$	Reynolds number defined by Eq. (3.5-39) dimensionless
$N_{Re,p}$	Reynolds number defined by Eq. (3.1-15), dimensionless
$N_{Re,mf}$	Reynolds number at minimum fluidization defined by Eq. (3.1-35), dimensionless
N_{Eu}	Euler number $= p/\rho v^2$, dimensionless
N_{Sc}	Schmidt number $= \mu/\rho D_{AB}$, dimensionless
N_{Sh}	Sherwood number $= k'_c D/D_{AB}$, dimensionless
N_P	power number defined by Eq. (3.4-2), dimensionless
N_Q	flow number, dimensionless
N_{St}	Stanton number $= k'_c/v$, dimensionless
NTU	number of transfer units, dimensionless

O	flow rate, kg/h, kg mol/h (lb_m/h)
p	pressure, N/m^2, Pa (lb_f/ft^2, atm, psia, mm Hg)
p_{vp}	vapor pressure of fluid, N/m^2 (lb_f/ft^2)
p_A	partial pressure of A, N/m^2, Pa (lb_f/ft^2, atm, psia, mm Hg)
p_s	pressure at STP, Pa
p_{BM}	log mean inert partial pressure of B in Eq. (6.2-21), N/m^2, Pa (lb_f/ft^2, atm, psia, mm Hg)
p_h	total pressure in high-pressure side (feed), cm Hg, Pa (atm)
p_l	total pressure in low-pressure side (permeate) cm Hg, Pa (atm)
p_M	permeance in solid, m/s (ft/h)
P	parameter in Eq. (5.5-12), dimensionless
P	total pressure, N/m^2, Pa (lb_f/ft^2, atm, mm H)
P	power, W (ft · lb_f/s, hp)
P	flow rate, kg/h, kg/min; also number of phases at equilibrium
$\boldsymbol{P}$	momentum vector, kg · m/s (lb_m · ft/s)
P_A	vapor pressure of pure A, N/m^2, Pa (lb_f/ft^2, atm, psia, mm Hg)
P'_A	permeability of A, cm^3 (STP) · cm/s · cm^2 · cm Hg
P'_A/t	permeance of A, cm^3 (STP)/s · cm^2 · cm Hg, m^3 (STP)/s · m^2 · Pa
P_w	solvent membrane permeability, kg solvent/s · m · atm (lb_m/h · ft · atm)
P_M	permeability, m^3(STP)/(s · m^2 C.S. · atm/m)
q	heat-transfer rate, W (btu/h); also net energy added to system, W (btu/h); also J (btu)
q	flow rate, m^3/s (ft^3/s)
$\boldsymbol{q}$	heat flux vector, W/m^2 (btu/h · ft^2)
$\dot{q}$	rate of heat generation, W/m^3 (btu/h · ft^3)
q	feed condition defined by Eq. (11.4-12)
q'	flow rate in Darcy's law, cm^3/s
q	kg adsorbate/kg adsorbent (lb_m/lb_m)
q_c	condenser duty, kJ/h, kW (btu/h)
$\bar{q}_{n,m}$	residual defined by Eq. (4.5-11), K (°F)
q_R	reboiler duty, kJ/h, kW (btu/h)
q_{AR}	concentration of A in bulk bed volume, equiv/L volume
Q	total concentration of A and B in bulk bed volume, equiv/L volume
Q	outflow in crystallizer, L/h
Q	circulation rate, m^3/s (ft^3/h)
Q	amount absorbed, kg mol/m^2; also heat loss, W (btu/h); also heat absorbed, J/kg (btu/lb_m, ft · lb_f/lb_m)
r	radius, m (ft)
r	ratio of pressures, p_l/p_h
r_A	rate of generation, kg A/s · m^3 ($lb_m A$/h · ft^3)
r_H	hydraulic radius, m (ft)
$(r_2)_{cr}$	critical value of radius, m (ft)
R	rate of drying, kg/h · m^2 (lb_m/h · ft^2)
R	solute rejection, dimensionless
R	scaleup ratio, dimensionless
R	radius, m (ft); also resistance, K/W (h · °F/btu)
R	parameter in Eq. (5.5-12), dimensionless; also resistance, ohms
R	gas constant (see Appendix A.1); also reflux ratio = L_n/D, dimensionless

R_A	rate of generation, kg mol $A/s \cdot m^3$ (lb mol $A/h \cdot ft'$)
R_b	radius of spindle, m (ft)
R_c	radius of outer cylinder, m (ft)
R_c	contact resistance, K/W (h · °F/btu)
R_g	gel layer resistance, s · m² · atm/kg
R_m	resistance of filter medium, $m^{-1}(ft^{-1})$
R_m	membrane resistance, m²/kg
R_c	cake resistance, m²/kg
R_i	rate of generation of i, kg/s (lb$_m$/h)
R_x	x component of force, N (lb$_f$, dyn)
s	compressibility constant, dimensionless
s	mean surface renewal factors, s^{-1}
S	conduction shape factor, m (ft)
S	solubility of a gas, m³ solute(STP)/m³ solid · atm [cc solute(STP)/cc solid · atm]
S	distance between centers, m (ft); also steam flow rate, kg/h, kg mol/h (lb$_m$/h)
S	volume of feed solution, m³ (ft³)
S	cross-sectional area of tower, m² (ft²); also stripping factor, $1/A$
S	length of side in structured packing, cm (in.)
S_0	specific surface area, m²/m³ volume (ft²/ft³ volume)
S_p	surface area of particle, m² (ft²)
t	fin thickness, m (ft)
t	time, s, min, or h
t	temperature, K, °C (°F)
t	membrane thickness, cm, m (ft)
t_b	break-point time, h
t_t	time equivalent to total capacity, h
t_T	mixing time, s
t_u	time equivalent to usable capacity up to break-point time, h
T	tray spacing, m (ft)
T	torque, kg · m²/s²
T	temperature. K, °C (°F, °R); also feed rate, ton/min
T_S	temperature at STP, K
T'	deviation of temperature from mean temperature $\overline{T}$, K (°F)
$\overline{u}$	average velocity, m/s (ft/s)
U	overall heat-transfer coefficient, W/m² · K (btu/h · ft² · °F)
U	internal energy, J/kg (btu/lb$_m$)
v	velocity, m/s (ft/s)
v	velocity vector, m/s (ft/s)
v_A	velocity of A relative to stationary coordinates, m/s (ft/s, cm/s)
v_{Ad}	diffusion velocity of A relative to molar average velocity, m/s (ft/s, cm/s)
v_p	volume of particle, mm³/particle
v'_{mb}	minimum bubbling velocity, m/s (ft/s)
v_M	molar average velocity of stream relative to stationary coordinates, m/s (ft/s, cm/s)
v_H	humid volume, m³/kg dry air (ft³/lb$_m$ dry air)
v_t	terminal settling velocity, m/s (ft/s)
v^+	dimensionless velocity defined by Eq. (3.10-34)

v^*	velocity defined by Eq. (3.10-42), dimensionless
v'_x	deviation of velocity in x direction from mean velocity $\bar{v}_x$, m/s (ft/s)
v'	superficial velocity based on cross section of empty tube, m/s (ft/s, cm/s)
v'_{mf}	velocity at minimum fluidization, m/s (ft/s)
v'_t	terminal settling velocity, m/s (ft/s)
V_A	solute molar volume, m^3/kg mol
V	flow rate, kg/h, kg mol/h, m^3/s (lb$_m$/h, ft^3/s)
V	volume, m^3 (ft^3, cm^3); also specific volume, m^3/kg (ft^3/lb$_m$)
V	volume of crystallizer, L
V	velocity, m/s (ft/s); also total amount, kg, kg mol (lb$_m$)
V	flow rate of permeate, cm^3 (STP)/s, m^3/s (ft^3/h)
V_p	outlet permeate flow rate, m^3 (STP)/s, m^3/s (ft^3/h)
V'	inert flow rate, kg/h, kg/s, kg mol/h (lb$_m$/h)
V_C, V_D	superficial velocities of continuous and dispersed phase, ft/h
w_A	mass fraction of A
$\dot{W}$	work done on surroundings, W (ft · lb$_f$/s)
W	free water, kg (lb$_m$)
$\dot{W}_s$	mechanical shaft work done on surroundings, W (ft · lb$_f$/s)
W	flow rate, kg/h, kg mol/h (lb$_m$/h)
W	work done on surroundings, J/kg(ft · lb$_f$/lb$_m$)
W	weight of wet solid, kg (lb$_m$)
W	height or width, m (ft); also power, W (hp); also mass dry cake, kg (lb$_m$)
W	width of paddle, m (ft)
W_S	mechanical shaft work done on surroundings, J/kg(ft · lb$_f$/lb$_m$)
W_p	shaft work delivered to pump, J/kg(ft · lb$_f$/lb$_m$)
$(1 - W_f)$	cumulative wt fraction
x	distance in x direction, m (ft)
x	mass fraction or mole fraction; also fraction remaining of original free moisture
x_A	mass fraction of A, mole fraction of A, dimensionless
x'_B	inert mole ratio, mol B/mol inert
x_f	mole fraction of A in feed, dimensionless
x_o	mole fraction of A in reject, dimensionless
x_{oM}	mole fraction of minimum reject concentration, dimensionless
x_{BM}	log mean mole fraction of inert or stagnant B given in Eq. (6.3-4)
$(1 - x_A)_{\cdot M}$	log mean inert mole fraction defined by Eq. (10.4-27)
$(1 - x_A)_{iM}$	log mean inert mole fraction defined by Eq. (10.4-7)
X	particle size, m (ft); also parameter $= \alpha t/x_1^2$, dimensionless
X	parameter $= Dt/x^2$, dimensionless; also free moisture, kg water/kg dry solid (lb water/lb dry solid)
y	distance in y direction, m (ft); also mole fraction
y'	mole fraction in permeate at interface, dimensionlesss
y_A	mass fraction of A or mole fraction of A; also kg A/kg solution (lb A/lb solution)
y_{BM}	log mean mole fraction of inert or stagnant B given in Eq. (7.2-11)
y^+	dimensionless number defined by Eq. (3.10-35)
y_p	mole fraction of A in permeate, dimensionless
$(y - y_i)_M$	log mean driving force defined by Eq. (10.6-27)

$(1 - y_A)_{iM}$	log mean inert mole fraction defined by Eq. (10.4-6)

$(1 - y_A)_{iM}$ log mean inert mole fraction defined by Eq. (10.4-6)

$(y - y^*)_M$ log mean driving force defined by Eq. (10.6-28)

Y temperature ratio defined by Eq. (4.10-2), dimensionless

Y fraction of unaccomplished change in Table 5.3-1 or Eq. (4.9-3)

Y expansion correction factor defined in Eqs. (3.2-9) and (3.2-11)

z distance in z direction, m (ft); also tower height, m (ft)

z temperature range for 10:1 change in D_T, °C (°F)

Z height, m (ft); also temperature ratio in Eq. (4.9-2)

Greek letters

α correction factor = 1.0, turbulent flow and $\frac{1}{2}$, laminar flow

α absorptivity, dimensionless; also flux ratio = $1 + N_B/N_A$

α thermal diffusivity $- k/\rho c_p$, m²/s (ft²/h, cm²/s)

α, α_{AB} relative volatility of A with respect to B, dimensionless

α specific cake resistance, m/kg (ft/lb$_m$)

α angle, rad

α kinetic-energy velocity correction factor, dimensionless

α^* ideal separation factor = P'_A/P'_B, dimensionless

α_G gas absorptivity, dimensionless

α_T eddy thermal diffusivity, m²/s (ft²/h)

β concentration polarization, ratio of salt concentration at membrane surface to the salt concentration in bulk feed stream, dimensionless

β momentum velocity correction factor, dimensionless

β volumetric coefficient of expansion, 1/K (1/°R)

β ratio D_2/D_1 of diameters, dimensionless

γ viscosity coefficient, N·s$^{n'}$/m² (lb$_m$/ft·s$^{2-n'}$)

γ ratio of heat capacities = c_p/c_v, dimensionless

Γ flow rate, kg/s·m (lb$_m$/h·ft)

Γ concentration of property, amount of property/m³

δ molecular diffusivity, m²/s

δ boundary-layer thickness, m (ft); also distance, m (ft)

δ constant in Eq. (4.12-2), dimensionless

δ_f film thickness for film theory, m (ft)

Δ difference; also difference operating-point flow rate, kg/h(lb$_m$/h)

ΔL growth of crystals, mm

ΔT_a arithmetic temperature drop, K, °C(°F)

ΔT_{1m} log mean temperature driving force, K, °C(°F)

ΔH enthalpy change, J/kg, kJ/kg, kJ/kg mol(btu/lb$_m$, btu/lb mol)

∇ design criterion for sterilization, dimensionless

Δp pressure drop, N/m², Pa (lb$_f$/ft²)

ε roughness parameter, m (ft); or void fraction, dimensionless

ε emissivity, dimensionless; also volume fraction, dimensionless

ε_M mass eddy diffusivity m²/s (ft²/h, cm²/s)

ε heat-exchanger effectiveness, dimensionless

ε void fraction of packing, dimensionless

ε_G gas emissivity, dimensionless

ε_t momentum eddy diffusivity, m²/s (ft²/s)

ε_{mf} void fraction at minimum fluidization, dimensionless

η_f fin efficiency, dimensionless

η_t turbulent eddy viscosity, Pa·s, kg/m·s (lb$_m$/ft·s)

η	efficiency, dimensionless
θ	angle, rad
θ	parameter in Eq. (11.7-19)
θ	cut or fraction of feed permeated, dimensionless
θ^*	fraction permeated up to a value of $x = 1 - L/L_f$, dimensionless
λ	wavelength, m (ft)
λ	latent heat, J/kg, kJ/kg (btu/lb$_m$); also mean free path, m (ft)
λ_+	limiting ionic conductance in water of cation, (A/cm^2)(V/cm) (g equiv/cm^2)
λ_-	limiting ionic conductance in water of anion, (A/cm^2)(V/cm) (g equiv/cm^2)
λ_{Ab}	latent heat of A at normal boiling point, J/kg, kJ/kg mol (btu/lb$_m$)
μ	viscosity, Pa · s, kg/m · s, N · s/m^2 (lb$_m$/ft · s, lb$_m$/ft · h, cp)
μ_a	apparent viscosity, Pa · s, kg/m · s (lb$_m$/ft · s)
ν	momentum diffusivity μ/ρ, m^2/s (ft^2/s, cm^2/s)
ν	kinematic viscosity, centistokes
π_1	dimensionless group, dimensionless
π	osmotic pressure, Pa, N/m^2 (lb$_f$/ft^2, atm)
ρ	crystal density, g/mm^3
ρ	density, kg/m^3 (lb$_m$/ft^3); also reflectivity, dimensionless
σ	interfacial tension of liquid, dyn/cm
σ	constant, 5.676×10^{-8} W/m^2 · K^4 (0.1714×10^{-8} btu/h · ft^2 · °R^4); also collision diameter, Å
Σ	sigma value for centrifuge, m^2 (ft^2)
τ_{zx}	flux of x-directed momentum in z direction, (kg · m/s)/s · m^2 or N/m^2 (lb$_f$/ft^2, dyn/cm^2)
τ	shear stress, N/m^2 (lb$_f$/ft^2, dyn/cm^2)
τ	holdup time, h
τ	tortuosity, dimensionless
ϕ	velocity potential, m^2/s (ft^2/h)
ϕ	angle, rad; also association parameter, dimensionless
ϕ	osmotic coefficient, dimensionless
ϕ_S	shape factor of particle, dimensionless
Ψ_z	flux of property, amount of property/s · m^2
ψ	correction factor, dimensionless
ψ	stream function, m^2/s (ft^2/h)
ψ_p	parameter defined by Eq. (14.3-13), dimensionless
ω	angular velocity, rad/s
ω	solid angle, sr
$\Omega_{D,AB}$	collision integral, dimensionless

Index

Comminution (*see* Mechanical size reduction)
Compressible flow of gases
adiabatic conditions, 110
basic differential equation, 107–108
isothermal conditions, 108–109
Mach number for, 110
maximum flow conditions, 109
Compressors
equations for, 151–153
equipment, 151
Concentration units, 9
Condensation
derivation of equation for, 287–291
mechanisms of, 287
outside horizontal cylinders, 291
outside vertical surfaces, 287–289
Condensers for evaporation
calculation methods, 550–551
direct-contact type, 550–551
surface type, 550
Conduction heat transfer (*see also* Unsteady-state heat transfer)
combined conduction and convection, 249–250
contact resistance at interface, 255–256
critical thickness of insulation, 253–254
in cylinders, 242–243, 246–247
effect of variable thermal conductivity, 241–242
equations for
in cylindrical coordinates, 397
in rectangular coordinates, 397
in spherical coordinates, 397
Fourier's law, 46, 235–238, 397
graphical curvilinear square method, 256–257
with heat generation, 251–253
in hollow sphere, 244
through materials in parallel, 248
mechanism of, 236
shape factors in, 257–259
steady-state in two dimensions
Laplace equation, 338
numerical method, 338–344
with other boundary conditions, 342–344
through a wall, 241–242
through walls in series, 244–246
Continuity equation

for binary mixture, 491–493
for boundary layer, 211–213
for pure fluid, 54–57, 183, 185–188
Control volume, 55–57
Convection heat transfer (*see also* Heat transfer coefficients; Natural convection)
general discussion of, 237, 240–241, 249–250
physical mechanism of, 259–260
Convective heat transfer coefficients (*see* Heat transfer coefficients)
Convective mass transfer coefficients (*see* Mass transfer coefficients)
Conversion factors, 955–958
Cooling towers (*see* Humidification processes)
Coriolis flow meter, 143
Coriolis force, 193
Countercurrent processes (*see* Absorption; Distillation; Leaching; Liquid-liquid extraction; Stage processes)
Creeping flow, 208–209
Critical diameter, 936–937
Critical moisture content, 578
Critical thickness of insulation, 253–254
Crushing and grinding (*see* Mechanical size reduction)
Crystallization (*see also* Crystallizers)
crystal geometry, 817–818
crystal particle-size distribution, 825–826
crystal size effect on solubility, 823–824
heat balances, 820–821
heat of solution, 820–821
mass transfer in, 824–825
material balances, 818–819
McCabe ΔL law, 825
models for, 826–829
nucleation theories, 823–824, 828
rate of crystal growth, 824–825
solubility (phase equilibria), 528, 818
supersaturation, 821–824
Crystallizers (*see also* Crystallization)
circulating-liquid evaporator-crystallizer, 822–823
circulating-magma vacuum crystallizer, 822–823
classification of, 821–822

transition, 502–503

Diffusivity (momentum), 403–404, 410–411

Diffusivity (thermal), 358, 403–404, 411

Dilitant fluids, 170

Dimensional analysis
    Buckingham pi theorem, 222–224, 335–337, 511–512
    in differential equations, 221–222
    in heat transfer, 335–337
    in mass transfer, 511–512
    in momentum transfer, 221–224

Dimensional homogeneity, 7

Disk, drag coefficient for, 123–124

Distillation (*see also* Multicomponent distillation: Vapor-liquid equilibrium)
    constant molal overflow, 707
    direct steam injection, 720–722
    enriching operating line, 708–709
    enriching tower, 720
    enthalpy-concentration method
        benzene-toluene data, 734
        construction of plot for, 732–734
        enriching equations, 734–736
        equilibrium data, 734, 990
        example of, 736–740
        stripping equations, 736
    equilibrium or flash, 744–745
    feed condition and location, 710–712, 750
    Fenske equation, 716, 745
    introduction and process flow, 700, 706–707
    McCabe-Thiele method, 706–724
    packed towers, 655–661
    partial condensers, 723–724
    Ponchon-Savarit method, 740
    reflux ratio
        minimum, 716–717, 748–749
        operating, 717
        total, 715–716, 745
    relative volatility, 701, 742
    sidestream, 722–723
    simple batch or differential, 702–703
    simple steam, 705
    single stage contact, 699
    stripping operating line, 709–710
    stripping tower, 718–719
    tower flooding velocity and diameter, 729–730

tray efficiencies
    introduction, 724
    Murphree, 725–727
    overall, 724–725
    point, 725–726
    relationship between efficiencies, 726
    types of trays, 654–655

Distribution coefficient, in mass transfer, 462–463, 508–509

Dodge crusher, 947–948

Drag coefficient
    definition of, 122–124, 221
    for disk, 123–124
    for flat plate, 121–122, 211–213
    form drag, 121–122, 209
    for long cylinder, 123–124
    skin drag, 121
    for sphere, 122–124, 208–209, 920–923, 925

Dryers (*see also* Drying)
    continuous tunnel, 561
    drum, 562–563
    fixed bed, 597–599
    grain, 563–564
    rotary, 562
    spray, 563
    tray, 560, 601–602
    vacuum shelf, 561

Drying (*see also* Dryers)
    air recirculation in, 604–605
    of biological materials, 573–574
    bound moisture, 575
    capillary movement theory, 579–580, 593–595
    through circulation, 597–599
    constant-drying conditions
        constant-rate period, 578, 580–585
        effect of air velocity, 584
        effect of humidity, 584–585
        effect of solid thickness, 585
        effect of temperature, 585
        falling-rate period, 578–580, 585–587
        prediction for constant-rate period, 581–585
        rate-of-drying curve, 576–578
        time for, 580–581
    continuous countercurrent, 605–607
    critical moisture, 578
    effect of shrinkage, 580
    equilibrium moisture, 573–575

Drying (*continued*)
  experimental methods, 575–576
  free moisture, 575
  freeze drying, 607–610
  heat balance in dryers, 601–603
  introduction to, 559–560
  liquid diffusion theory, 579, 592–595
  in packed beds, 597–599
  in trays with varying air conditions, 601–602
  unbound moisture, 575
Dühring lines, 537–538

E

Electric motor efficiency, 145
Emissivity
  definition of, 302–303, 308–309
  values of, 987
Energy balances
  for boundary layer, 399–402
  in compressible flow, 107–110
  differential, 394–397
  mechanical, 67–72
  overall, 60–65
English system of units, 6–7
Enthalpy, 19, 61
Enthalpy of air-water vapor mixtures, 567, 649–650
Enthalpy-concentration diagram
  in distillation, 731–734
  in evaporation, 539–540
Enthalpy-concentration method (*see* Distillation)
Equilibrium or flash distillation, 701–702
Equilibrium moisture, 572–575
Equivalent diameter
  in fluid flow, 104–105
  in heat transfer, 264
Erbar-Maddox correlation, 749
Euler equations, 204
Euler number, 222
Evaporation (*see also* Evaporators)
  of biological materials, 527–528
  boiling point rise in, 537–539
  capacity in multiple-effect, 542
  Dühring lines, 537–538
  effects of processing variables on, 527–528, 537

enthalpy-concentration charts for, 539–540
heat transfer coefficients for, 533–534
methods of operation
  backward-feed multiple-effect, 533
  forward-feed multiple-effect, 532–533
  parallel-feed multiple-effect, 533
  single-effect, 531–532
multiple-effect calculations, 541–544
single-effect calculations, 534–536
steam economy, 532
temperature drops in, 543–544
vapor recompression
  mechanical recompression, 553–554
  thermal recompression, 554
Evaporators (*see also* Evaporation)
  agitated film, 531
  condensers for, 550–551
  falling-film, 530–531
  forced-circulation, 531
  horizontal-tube natural circulation, 529
  long-tube vertical, 529–530
  open kettle, 529
  short-tube, 529
  vertical-type natural circulation, 529
Extraction (*see* Leaching; Liquid-liquid extraction)

F

Falling film
  diffusion in, 477–478
  shell momentum balance, 86–88
Fans, 149
Fenske equation, 716, 745
Fermentation, mass transfer in, 487–489
Fick's law (*see* Diffusion)
Film temperature, 272
Film theory, 470–472
Filter aids, 910
Filter media, 909–910
Filters (*see also* Filtration)
  bed. 905–906
  classification of, 905
  continuous rotary, 908–909
  leaf, 908
  plate-and-frame, 906–908

Osmotic pressure, 884–885
Overall energy balance (*see* Energy
  balances)

P

Packed beds
  Darcy's law for flow in, 130
  drying in, 597–599
  heat transfer coefficients for, 276, 484,
    599
  mass transfer coefficients for, 484–485
  tortuosity in, 446, 505
  pressure drop in
    laminar flow, 125–127, 130
    turbulent flow, 127–128
  shape factors for particles, 129
  surface area in, 125, 485, 599
Packed towers, 645, 655–657, 784
Packing, 655–657
Particle-size measurement
  in crystallization, 825–826
  in mechanical size reduction, 945
  standard screens for, 998
Pasteurization, 617–618
Penetration theory, 478, 516
Permeability of solids, 442–443, 840–841,
    845
Permeance, 842, 847
Phase rule, 627, 696, 705, 777
Physical properties of compounds, 959–
    995
Pipes
  dimensions of, 996–997
  schedule number of, 88–89, 996
  size selection of, 106
Pitot tube meter, 136–137
Planck's law, 307
Pohlhausen boundary layer relation, 401
Poiseuille equation (*see* Hagen-Poiseuille
    equation)
Porous solids
  effective diffusivity of, 445, 505
  introduction to, 440, 445–446, 499–500
  Knudsen diffusion in, 500–501
  molecular diffusion in, 464, 445–446,
    501
  transition diffusion in, 502–506
Potential energy, 61
Potential flow, 204–208

Prandtl analogy, 475
Prandtl mixing length (*see* Turbulent flow)
Prandtl number
  definition of, 260
  of gases 2nd liquids, 967–968, 971, 975
Pressure
  conversion factors for, 956–957
  devices to measure, 39–42
  heat and, 38–39
  units of, 9
Pressure drop (*see also* Fluid friction)
  in compressible flow, 96–97, 107–110
  in laminar flow, 90–93
  in packed beds, 125–130
  in pipes, 90–100
  in turbulent flow, 93–95
Pseudoplastic fluids, 169–170
Psychometric ratio, 572
Pumps
  affinity laws for, 147
  centrifugal, 144–149
  developed head of, 147–148
  efficiency of, 147–148
  NPSH (*see* Suction lift of pumps)
  positive displacement, 149
  power requirements for, 147–148
  suction lift of, 145–146

R

Radiation heat transfer
  in absorbing gases, 320–322
  absorptivity, 301–302
  black body, 301–302
  combined radiation and convection,
    303–305
  effect on temperature measurement,
    305–306
  emissivity, 302, 308–309, 987
  gray body, 303, 309–311
  introduction to, 237, 301–302
  Kirchoff's law, 302, 308–309
  Planck's law for emissive power, 307
  shields, 306, 311–312
  Stefan-Boltzmann law, 303, 306
  to small object, 303
  view factors
    between black bodies, 309–318
    general equation for, 312–315
    between gray bodies, 318–320

Triangular coordinates, 777–779
Tubes (see Circular pipes and tubes)
Turbine and paddle flow meter, 143
Turboblowers, 151
Turbulence, 213–214
Turbulent flow (see also Boundary layers)
  boundary layer separation in, 122, 210–211
  boundary layer theory for
    heat transfer, 399–402
    mass transfer, 512–514
    momentum transfer, 211–212, 218–221
  deviating velocities in, 213–214
  discussion of, 51–52, 213–214
  on flat plate, 209–213, 218–221
  maximum velocity in, 89–90
  Prandtl mixing length
    in heat transfer, 403–404
    in mass transfer, 515
    in momentum transfer, 215–216
  Reynolds number for, 52–53
  in tubes, 52–53, 89–90, 93
  turbulent shear in, 215
  turbulent diffusion in, 411
  velocity profile in, 89–90, 216–220
Two-dimensional conduction, 256–259
Tyler standard screens, 998

U

Ultrafiltration
  comparison to reverse osmosis, 892
  concentration polarization in, 893–894
  equipment for, 893
  introduction to, 892–893
  membranes for, 893
  processing variables in, 895–896
  theory of, 893–895
Unbound moisture, 575
Underwood, minimum reflux ratio, 748–749
Units
  cgs system, 6
  and dimensions, 7
  English system, 6–7
  SI system, 5–6
  table of, 955–958
Universal velocity distribution, 216–218

Unsteady-state diffusion (see also Numerical methods)
  analytical equations for flat plate, 461–462
  basic equation for, 459–461
  charts for various geometries, 463
  and chemical reaction, 495–497
  in leaching, 804–805
  mass and heat transfer parameters for, 463–464
  in three directions, 465–466
Unsteady-state heat transfer (conduction)
    (see also Numerical methods)
  analytical equations for, 357–359
  average temperature for, 376–377
  in biological materials, 389–393
  in cylinder, 370–371
  derivation of equation for, 235–236, 357–359
  to flat plate, 365–368
  heat and mass transfer parameters for, 366, 463–464
  lumped capacity method for, 359–361
  method for negligible internal resistance, 359–361
  in semiinfinite solid, 363–364
  in sphere, 371–374
  in three directions, 372–373, 375

V

Valve trays, 654
Vapor-liquid equilibrium
  azeotropic mixtures, 698
  benzene-toluene, 696–698
  boiling point diagrams, 696–697
  calculations using Raoult's law, 697–698
  enthalpy-concentration, 731–734
  ethanol-water, 990
  n-heptane-ethylbenzene, 753
  n-heptane-n-octane, 754
  n-hexane-n-octane, 751
  multicomponent, 742–743
  n-pentane-n-heptane, 703–704
  phase rule, 648, 696, 705
  water-benzene, 753
  water-ethylaniline, 752

About the Author

Christie John Geankoplis is Professor of Chemical Engineering and Materials Science at the University of Minnesota. He received his B.S. at the University of Minnesota and his M.S. and Ph.D. in Chemical Engineering at the University of Pennsylvania. He has been teaching and doing research for over 40 years.

His research interests are in mass transfer, biochemical engineering, and separation processes and he has published extensively in these fields. Professor Geankoplis has also published a textbook entitled *Mass Transport Phenomena*. He is the author of four editions of *Transport Processes and Separation Process Principles*.

Professor Geankoplis was employed as a chemical engineer in the process industry for several years. He has served as a consultant for many years for General Mills Chemicals, Inc. He has consulted with many varied industries in the areas of ore extraction, biochemical processes, nuclear reactors, distillation, extraction, absorption, adhesives, fermentation, mass transfer, and emulsions.

He is a member of the American Chemical Society and the American Institute of Chemical Engineers. He also is a Licensed Professional Engineer in Ohio and Pennsylvania. His interests are travel, reading ancient and medieval history, and playing tennis.